EMISSION CONTROL SERVICE & REPAIR DOMESTIC CARS

1983 SUPPLEMENT

National Service Data
Manuals For The Automotive Professional

Published By:
MITCHELL MANUALS, INC.
A Cordura Company
P.O. BOX 26260
SAN DIEGO, CALIFORNIA 92126

ISBN 0-8470-7633-4

ACKNOWLEDGEMENT

Mitchell Manuals thanks the automotive and equipment manufacturers, distributors, dealers and the entire automotive industry for their fine cooperation and assistance which makes the publication of this manual possible.

PUBLISHED BY

MITCHELL MANUALS, INC.
9889 Willow Creek Road
P.O. Box 26260
San Diego, California 92126

a subsidiary of
CORDURA PUBLICATIONS, INC.
C.L. Kobrin, President
John Opelt, Senior Vice President of Finance & Administration
Malcolm Ferrier, Senior Vice President of Technology
Robert W. Ladd, Vice President of Manufacturing

For Subscription Information:
CALL TOLL FREE 800 - 854-7030. In California CALL COLLECT 619 - 578-8770. Or WRITE: P.O. Box 26260, San Diego, CA 92126

ISBN 0-8470-7633-4

INTRODUCTION

The 1983 Domestic Emission Control Service and Repair Manual covers 1983 domestic passenger cars. Nearly 100 well-researched articles written by our staff of automotive experts provide you with the necessary information to service emission control systems (including the new computers) on 1983 vehicles.

Clear and simple step-by-step procedures on all emission systems, controls and components as well as valuable information on testing and repair of these systems, will make your job easier and more precise. Detailed illustrations and diagrams provide accurate visual explanations of complex systems.

SECTION DESCRIPTIONS

EMISSION CONTROL APPLICATIONS

These pages list the emission control system applications, according to manufacturer, model and engine. At the bottom of each page you will find an explanation of abbreviations used in the charts.

TUNE-UP SPECIFICATIONS

You will find these Tune-Up specification charts are your quick reference to important engine tune-up settings for 1983 domestic passenger vehicles. They are arranged alphabetically by manufacturer.

DISTRIBUTOR SPECIFICATIONS

These pages offer a complete listing of all distributor applications, according to manufacturer and distributor number. Immediately following the application charts are several pages of vital distributor operation specifications, according to distributor make and number.

CRANKCASE VENTILATION

Crankcase ventilation systems are used on every vehicle manufactured, and whether the system is an internal type or has an external PCV valve and tubing, this section describes each system and how and when service is required.

FUEL EVAPORATION

Control of raw fuel vapors is another important, nearly universal emission control for domestic vehicles. This section describes each system in detail, and includes diagrams of the systems for each vehicle.

EXHAUST EMISSION SYSTEMS

Each manufacturer, model and engine application requires a different combination of systems to meet Clean Air Standards. This section explains major systems and their components, testing procedures, trouble shooting and adjustment. The section is arranged by manufacturer and includes full information on the new computerized engine control systems.

FUEL SYSTEMS

All carburetors and fuel injection systems for gasoline and diesel engines are described fully within this section. Full description, operation, testing, and all specifications are included within each individual article. This section is arranged alphabetically by system manufacturer.

LATEST CHANGES

This is a very important section for keeping you up to date on important emission control tune-up information direct from the factory. Any revised procedure, modification or specification change which we received just before publication time is included in this section. Do not overlook these important articles.

EMISSION CONTROL SERVICE AND REPAIR

CONTENTS

EXHAUST EMISSION SYSTEMS (Cont.)

Emission Standards & Tune-Ups

MANUFACTURING STANDARDS

Federal and state governments have established air quality standards during the past 20 years. Automobile manufacturers design their vehicles to conform to standards where the vehicle will be sold. These standards cover carbon monoxide (CO), hydrocarbons (HC) and oxides of nitrogen (NOx).

Federal and California standards which must be met by manufacturers are specified in units easily measured in a testing laboratory. Since 1970, these standards have been in "grams per mile". This means no vehicle, whether 2-cylinder or V8, may emit more than a set weight (in grams) of pollutants for each mile it travels. Since large engines burn more fuel per mile than smaller ones, they must be "cleaner" per gallon burned if they are to meet these standards.

When manufacturers certify vehicles, the cars are placed on a dynamometer and the exhaust gases are collected in a bag. After the vehicle runs for a specified time, the gases are analyzed and weighed. Engines and emission systems are designed so the weight of emissions will be less than the specified grams per mile.

Infra-red exhaust analyzers are commonly used in automotive test stations. They use a test probe placed in the exhaust stream, and measure the percentage of CO in the exhaust gas, or parts per million of HC. These are not the same units used by the manufacturer when the car is certified. (NOx emissions can be measured only in a laboratory.)

TUNE-UP STANDARDS

When a tune-up is performed, the mechanic must have specifications to use when adjusting the vehicle. The first few years of emission-regulated vehicles were adjusted using carbon monoxide percentage or hydrocarbon parts per million. These are the units measured by an exhaust gas analyzer.

In the past few years, manufacturers have made their vehicles much cleaner (measured in grams per mile). The CO% and HC ppm have become very low, especially when measured AFTER a catalytic converter. It has become hard to accurately measure the effect of turning the idle mixture screws.

One solution to this problem requires the use of artifically-enriched propane adjustments. The added propane boosts the emissions by a known amount, and makes the effect of turning the mixture screws easily measureable. However, CO and HC can only be accurately measured while the propane is being added.

As computer-controlled systems were developed, it became possible to have the vehicle adjust its own mixture throughout the entire engine operating range, not just at idle. These "feedback" systems use oxygen sensors to measure how much unburned oxygen is left in the exhaust. The computer can then determine when the air/fuel mixture is too rich or too lean, and correct it as necessary. Even if a mechanic incorrectly adjusts the mixture, most computers can compensate enough so the vehicle will still run clean. In fact, the newest cars burn fuel so completely that changes in the pollutant levels after the catalytic converter are hard to measure accurately.

New vehicles are now adjusted by measuring the percentage of time that the computer-controlled system is adding fuel versus the time fuel is shut off. The mechanic checks this percentage with a dwell meter (normally used to measure the time a set of points is open/closed), then adjusts the fuel system until the percentage is correct.

Although many shops have exhaust gas analyzers which measure tailpipe emissions, manufacturers do not use CO or HC specifications for tuning. These specifications would be neither useful or possible for adjusting new vehicles. This manual provides procedures and specifications given by the manufacturers and does not list CO or HC specifications.

STATE TEST STANDARDS

Some states have established standards for testing used vehicles to see if they are still running clean. Generally speaking, these standards are given in CO% and HC ppm. They can be checked with an exhaust gas analyzer. Typical standards for newer cars would be less than 2.0% CO (non-catalyst) or 0.5% CO (with catalyst) and less than 200 ppm of HC. If vehicle emissions are below these levels, the vehicle passes inspection. The important thing to remember is that these specifications are NOT to be used for TUNING. They are only for testing to see if the vehicle is functioning properly. If it isn't, it must be tuned using the manufacturer's procedures and specifications, then tested again.

Test standards change each year and vary from state to state, and even by county within each state. It is not possible to provide an accurate and up-to-date list in this manual. Specifications can be obtained from your local county or state government. Remember that these standards are ONLY for test purposes. The manufacturer's adjustment procedures and specifications MUST be used when actually tuning a vehicle.

EMISSION CONTROL APPLICATION TABLES 1983 MODELS

1983 Emission Control Application

AMERICAN MOTORS

1983 AMERICAN MOTORS

Engine	Emission Control Systems & Devices	Remarks
1.4L (85") 4-Cyl. Alliance Calif.	AWD, CPS, CPV, CTS, CTSWH, EEC, EGR, EGRS, ISC, MAFTS,	[1] — Auto. Trans. only. [2] — Man. Trans. only.
1.4L (85") 4-Cyl. Alliance Federal	ACV, CAT, CTS, CTTS, EEC, ICM, OXS, PCV, RV, MAP, OXS, PCV, TPS [1], TPSW, WOTSW	
2.5L (151") 4-Cyl. Eagle Calif.	CAT, CTO, CTSW, DCLV, DCTO, DIDV, EGR, EGR-TVS, EEC, OXS, PCV, TAC, TAC-CV, TAC-DV, TAC-TVS, TES, VS	
2.5L (151") 4-Cyl. Eagle Federal	CAT, CTO, DCTO, DIDV, EEC, EGR, EGR-TVS, PCV, TAC, TAC-CV, TAC-DV, TAC-TVS	
4.2L (258") 6-Cyl. Eagle Calif.	ACV, ASS, CAT, CoV, CTSW, DCLV [2], EEC, EGR, EGR-TVS, KS, OXS, PACV, PAI, PCV, PCVS, TAC, TAC-DV, TES, VS	
4.2L (258") 6-Cyl. Eagle Federal	ACV, ASS, CAT, CTSW, CoV, EEC, EGR, EGR-DCTO, EGR-TVS, KS, OXS, PACV, PAI, PCV, PCVS, TAC, TAC-CV, TAC-DV, TAC-TVS, TES, VS	
4.2L (258") 6-Cyl. Concord & Spirit (All)	ACV, ASS, CAT, CoV, CTO, CTSW, DCLV [2], EEC, EGR, EGR-TVS, KS, OXS, PACV, PAI, PCV, PCVS, TAC, TAC-CV, TAC-DV, TES, VS	

ACV - Air Control Valve
AI - Air Injection
ASS - Air Switching Solenoid
AWD - Air Warming Device
CAT - Catalytic Converter
CoV - Control Valve
CPS - Canister Purge Solenoid
CPV - Canister Purge Valve
CTO - Coolant Temp. Override
CTS - Coolant Temp. Sensor
CTSW - Coolant Temp. Switch
CTSWH - Closed Throttle Switch
CTTS - Coolant Temp. Thermo Switch
DCLV - Deceleration Valve
DCTO - Dual Coolant Temp. Override
DIDV - Dual Ign. Delay Valve
EEC - Evap. Emission Control
EGR - Ex. Gas Recirculation
EGRS - EGR Solenoid
EGR-TVS - EGR Thermal Vac. Sw.
ICM - Ignition Control Module
ISC - Idle Speed Control Motor
KS - Knock Sensor
MAFTS - Manifold Air/Fuel Temp. Sens.
MAP - Manifold Absolute Press. Sens.
OXS - Oxygen Sensor
PACV - Pulse Air Check Valve
PAI - Pulse Air Injection
PCV - Pos. Crankcase Ventilation
PCVS - PCV Solenoid
RV - Rollover Valve
TAC - Thermostatic Air Cleaner
TAC-CV - TAC Check Valve
TAC-DV - TAC Delay Valve
TAC-TVS - TAC Therm. Vac. Sw.
TES - Thermal Elec. Switch
TPS - Throttle Position Sensor
TPSW - Throttle Position Switch
VS - Vacuum Switch
WOTS - Wide Open Throttle Switch

1983 Emission Control Application

CHRYSLER CORP.

1983 CHRYSLER CORP.

Engine	Emission Control Systems & Devices	Remarks
1.6L (98") 4-Cyl. 2-Bbl.	AICV, AIS, ASRV, CAT, CBVV, CCEGR, CCEVS, CTS, CVSCC, ECS, EGR, ESC, OS, PCV, PVCS, PVFFC, RVSV, TAC	
1.7L (104") 4-Cyl. 2-Bbl.	AICV, AIS, ASRV, CAT, CBVV, CCEGR, CCEVS, CTS, CVSCC, ECS, EGR, ESC, OS, PCV, PVCS, PVFFC, RVSV, TAC	
2.2L (135") 4-Cyl. 2-Bbl.	AICV, AIS, ASRV, CAT, CBVV, CCEGR, CCEVS, CTS, CVSCC, ECS, EGR, ESC, OS, PCV, PVCS, PVFFC, RVSV, TAC	
2.2L (135") 4-Cyl. EFI	AICV, AIS, ASRV, CAT, CCEGR, CCEVS, CPS, CTS, ECS, EGR, EGR-SOL, ESC, MAP, OS, PCV, PVCS, PVFFC, RVSV, TAC, TPS, VSS	
2.6L (156") 4-Cyl. 2-Bbl.	ASRV, CAT, CBVV, CCEGR, CCEVS, CTS, CVSCC, ECS, EGR, EIS, OS, PAF, PCV, PVCS, PVFFC, RVSV, SEGR, TAC	
3.7L (225") 6-Cyl. 1-Bbl.	AICV, AIS, ASRV, CAT, CTS, CVSCO, ECS, EFC, EGR, EGR-SOL, EGR-TDS, ESC, ETC, OS, OSAC, PCV, PVFFC, RVSV, TAC, VVCS	
5.2L (318") V8 4-Bbl.	AICV, AIS, ASRV, CAT, CTS, CVSCO, ECS, EGR, EGR-SOL, EGR-TDS, ESC, OS, OSAC, PCV, PVFFC, RVSV, TAC, VVCS	
5.2L (318") V8 EFI	AICV, AIS, AS, ASRV, CAT, CCEGR, CPS, CPCV, CTS, CVSCO, ECS, EFC, EGR, EGR-SOL, EGR-TDS, ESC, ETC, OS, OSAC, PCV, PVFFC, RVSV, TAC, VSS, VVCS	

AICV - Air Injection Check Valve
AIS - Air Injection System
AS - Airflow Sensor
ASRV - Air Switching Relief Valve
CAT - Catalytic Converter
CBVV - Carburetor Bowl Vent Valve
CCEGR - Coolant Controlled Exhaust Gas Recirculation
CCEVS - Coolant Controlled Engine Vacuum Switch
CPCV - Canister Purge Control Valve
CPS - Canister Purge Solenoid
CTS - Coolant Temperature Switch or Charge Temperature Switch
CVSCC - Coolant Vacuum Switch Cold Closed
CVSCO - Coolant Vacuum Switch Cold Open
ECS - Evaporative Control System
EFC - Electronic Feedback Carburetor
EGR - Exhaust Gas Recirculation
EIS - Electronic Ignition System
ESC - Electronic Spark Control
ETC - Electronic Throttle Control
MAP - Manifold Absolute Pressure Sensor
OS - Oxygen Sensor
OSAC - Orifice Spark Advance Control
PAF - Pulse Air Feeder
PCV - Positive Crankcase Ventilation
PVCS - Ported Vacuum Control System
PVFFC - Pressure/Vacuum Fuel Filler Cap
RVSV - Rollover/Vapor Separator Valve
SEGR - Sub-Exhaust Gas Recirculation Valve
SOL - Solenoid
TAC - Thermostatic Air Cleaner
TDS - Time Delay Solenoid
TPS - Throttle Position Sensor
VSS - Vehicle Speed Sensor
VVCS - Venturi Vacuum Control System

1983 Emission Control Application

FORD MOTOR CO.

1983 FORD MOTOR CO.

Engine	Emission Control Systems & Devices	Remarks
1.6L (98") 4-Cyl. Carbureted	ACCWM, ACDV, ACV, AIR, ANTBV, Bi-MET, CAT, EGR, FVEC, ISC, PCV, SV-CBV, SOL-V, TVS, TVV, VCV, VCS, VDV, VOTM	[1] — Information incomplete from manufacturer. [2] — Pulse air on Fed. Auto. Trans.
1.6L (98") 4-Cyl. EFI	ACDV, Bi-MET, CAT, EGR, FVEC, OXY, PA, PCOV, PCV, SOL-V, VCV, VDV, VCS, VRes, VRest,	
2.3L (140") 4-Cyl. Carbureted	ABV, ACCWM, ACDV, ACV, AIR[2], Bi-MET, CAT, DVTW, EGR, FVEC, LCV, PCOV, PCV, SOL-V, TVS, TVV, VCV, VCKV, VDV, VRest, VOTM	
2.3L (140") 4-Cyl. Tempo & Topaz	ACCWM, ACDV, ACV, AIR, Bi-MET, CAT, EGR, EGRC, EGRV, FVEC, MAP, OXY, PCOV, PCV, SV-CBV, TAB, TAD, TK, TVV, VCKV, VRes	
2.3L (140") 4-Cyl. EFI Turbo [1]	AIR, CAT, EGR, EGRC, FVEC, ISC, MAP, OXY, PCV,	
3.3L (200") 6-Cyl.	ABV, ACCWM, ACDV, AIR, Bi-MET, CAT, EGR, FVEC, LCV, PCOV, PCV, SA-FV, SOL-V, VCKV, VCV, VDV, VOTM, VRV, VRest	
3.8L (232") V6	ABV, ACCWM, ACDV, ACV, AIR, BiMET, CAT, EGR, FVEC, ITVS, LCV, PCOV, PCV, SV-CBV, TVS, TVV, VCKV, VCV, VDV, VRDV, VRes,	
5.0L (302") V8 Carbureted	ACCWM, ACDV, ACV, AIR, Bi-MET, CAT, EGR, HCV, HICV, PCOV, PCV, SV-CBV, SOL-V, TVS, VCKV, VCS, VCV, VDV, VRest	
5.0L (302") V8 Central Fuel Injection	ACCWM, ACDV, ACV, AIR, Bi-MET, BMAP, CAT, EGR, FVEC, HCV, PCOV, PCV, SOL-V, VCKC, VOTM, VRes, VRest	
5.8L (351"W) V8 [1]	AIR, Bi-MET, CAT, EGR, FVEC, OXY, PCV, VRes	

ABV — Air Bypass Valve
ACCWM — Air Cleaner Cold Weather Modulator
ACDV — Air Cleaner Diverter Valve
ACV — Air Control Valve
AIR — AIR Pump
ANTBV — Anti-Backfire Valve
Bi-MET — Air Cleaner Temp. Sensor
BMAP — Barometric Manifold Absolute Pressure Sensor
CAT — Catalytic Converter
DVTW — 2-Way Vac. Delay Valve
EGR — Exhaust Gas Recirculation
EGRC — EGR Control Solenoid
EGRV — EGR Vent Solenoid
FVEC — Fuel Vapor Emission Control
HCV — Heat Control Valve
HICV — Hot Idle Compensator Valve
ISC — Idle Speed Control
ITVS — Ign. Timing Vac. Switch
LCV — Load Control Valve
MAP — Manifold Absolute Pressure Sensor
PA — Pulse Air
PCOV — Purge Control Valve
PCV — Positive Crankcase Ventilation
OXY — Oxygen Sensor
SA-FV — Separator Assembly-Fuel Vacuum
SOL-V — Solenoid Valve
SV-CBV — Carburetor Bowl Vent Solenoid
TAB — Thermactor Air Bypass
TAD — Thermactor Air Diverter
TK — Throttle Kicker
TVS — Temp. Vacuum Switch
TVV — Thermal Vent Valve
VCKV — Vacuum Check Valve
VCS — Vacuum Control Switch
VCV — Vacuum Control Valve
VCV — Vacuum Check Valve
VDV — Vacuum Delay Valve
VOTM — Vacuum Operated Throttle Modulator
VRes — Vacuum Reservoir
VRest — Vacuum Restrictor
VRV — Vacuum Regulator Valve
VVV — Vacuum Vent Valve

1983 Emission Control Application

GENERAL MOTORS

1983 BUICK

Engine	Emission Control Systems & Devices	Remarks
1.8L (112") 4-Cyl. TBI	ATS, BPEGR, CAN, CCC, CAT, MAP, OXS, PAIR, PCV, TAC	
2.0L (122") 4-Cyl. TBI	ATS, BPEGR, CAN, CAT, CCC, CP, DV [1], EGRCS, MAP, OXS, PAIR, PAS, PCV, PSV, PV, TAC, VP [1]	
2.5L (151") 4-Cyl. TBI	ATS, CAT, CCC, CTS, EGR, MAP, OXS, PCV	
2.8L (173") V6 2-Bbl.	AIR, AMgV, ATS, BPEGR, CAN, CAT, CCC, CKV [1], CP, CanCV, DV, EGR, EGRCS, OXS, PCV, TVS [1], TAC, VSens	[1] — Some Applications
3.0L (181") V6 2-Bbl.	ACV, AIR, ASV, ATS, BPEGR, CAN, CanCV, CAT, CCC, CKV, DV, EFE [2], MAP, OXS, PCV, TAC, TAS, TVS	[2] — Century
3.8L (231") V6 Turbo	ACV, AIR, ATS, ASV, BPEGR, CAN, CanCV, CAT, CCC, CKV, DV [1], EGRCS, EGR-VRV, MAP, OXS, PCV, TAC, WSTGT ACT, TVS [1]	
3.8L (231") V6 2-Bbl.	ACV, AIR, ATS, ASV [1], BPEGR, CAN, CanCV, CAT, CCC, CKV, DV, EFE [1], EGRCS, EGR-VRV [1], MAP, OXS, PCV, TAC, TVS	
4.1L (250") V6 2-Bbl.	ACV, AIR, ATS, ASV, BPEGR, CAN, CanCV, CAT, CCC, CKV, DV, EFE, EFE VSV, EGR VSV, MAP, OXS, PCV, TAC, TVS [1], VP [1]	
4.3L (262") V6 Diesel	EGR, EPR [1], VRV, VP	
5.0L (307") V8 4-Bbl.	AIR, BPEGR, CAN, CanCV, CAT, CCC, CP, DPS, EAC, EAS, EFE, EFE TVS, EGRCS, OXS, PCV, TAC, TVS	
5.7L (350") V8 Diesel	EGR, EGR-VS, VRV, VP	

ACV — AIR Control Valve
ASV — AIR Switching Valve
AIR — Air Injection Reactor
AMgV — Air Management Valve
ATS — Air Temperature Sensor
ASV — AIR Switching Valve
BPEGR — Back Pressure EGR
CAN — Charcoal Canister
CanCV — Canister Check Valve
CAT — Catalytic Converter
CCC — Computer Command Control
CKV — Check Valve
CP — Canister Purge
DV — Deceleration Valve
EFE — Early Fuel Evaporation
EGR — Exhaust Gas Recirculation
EGRCS — EGR Control Solenoid
EPR — Exhaust Pressure Regulator
MAP — Manifold Pressure Sensor
OXS — Oxygen Sensor
PAIR — Pulse Air Injector
PAS — Pulse Air Solenoid
PCV — Positive Crankcase Ventilation
PSV — Pulse Air Shutoff Valve
PV — Pulse Air Valve
TAC — Thermostatic Air Cleaner
TBI — Throttle Body Injection
TVS — Thermal Vacuum Switch
VP — Vacuum Pump
VRV — Vacuum Regulator Valve
VS — Vacuum Switch
VSens — Vacuum Sensor
VSV — Vacuum Solenoid Valve
WSTGT ACT — Wastegate Actuator

1983 Emission Control Application

GENERAL MOTORS

1983 CADILLAC

Engine	Emission Control Systems & Devices	Remarks
2.0L (122") 4-Cyl. TBI	ATS, BPEGR, CAN, CAT, CCC, CP, DV [1], EGRCS, MAP, PAIR, PAS, OXS, PCV, PSV, PV, TAC, VP [1]	[1] — Some Applications
4.1L (250") V8 DFI	AIR, AMgV, BPEGR, CAN, CAT, CP, EFE, EGRCS, OXS, PCV, TAC, TVS, VP	
5.7L (350") V8 Diesel	EGR, EGR-VS, VRV, VP	
6.0L (368") V8 4-Bbl.	AIR, ACV, ASV, ATS, CAT, CCC, EFE, EFE-TVS, EGR, EGR-TVS, EGR-TVV, EVS, OXS, PCV, TAC, TVS	
6.0L (368") V8 DFI	AIR, AMgV, BPEGR, CAN, CAT, CP, EFE, EFE-TVS, EGRCS, OXS, PCV, TAC, VP	

AIR — Air Injection Reactor
ACV — AIR Control Valve
AMgV — Air Management Valve
ASV — AIR Solenoid Valve
ATS — Air Temperature Sensor
BPEGR — Back Pressure EGR
CAN — Charcoal Canister
CAT — Catalytic Converter
CP — Canister Purge
DFI — Digital Fuel Injection
DV — Deceleration Valve
EFE — Early Fuel Evaporation
EGR — Exhaust Gas Recirculation
EGRCS — EGR Control Solenoid
EVS — Economy Vacuum Switch
MAP — Manifold Pressure Sensor
OXS — Oxygen Sensor
PAIR — Pulse Air Injector
PAS — Pulse Air Solenoid
PCV — Positive Crankcase Ventilation
PSV — Pulse Air Shutoff Valve
PV — Pulse Air Valve
TAC — Thermostatic Air Cleaner
TVS — Thermal Vacuum Switch
TVV — Thermal Vacuum Valve
VP — Vacuum Pump
VRV — Vacuum Regulator Valve
VS — Vacuum Switch

1983 Emission Control Application

GENERAL MOTORS

1983 CHEVROLET

Engine	Emission Control Systems & Devices	Remarks
1.6L (98") 4-Cyl. 2-Bbl.	AIR, AMgV, ATS, BPEGR, CAN, CanCV, CAT, CCC, DV, OXS, PCV, SEC ACT, SSC ACT [1], SSC SOL [1], TAC, TCS [1], TVS, VB, VCV [1], VL-DV, VRV, VSV [1], VSS [1]	
1.8L (110") 4-Cyl. Diesel	FIA, PCV, VP, VSV	
2.0L (122") 4-Cyl. TBI	ATS, BPEGR, CAN, CAT, CCC, CP, DV [1], EGRCS, MAP, OXS, PAIR, PAS, PCV, PSV, PV, TAC, VP [1]	[1] — Some Applications
2.5L (151") 4-Cyl. TBI	ATS, CAT, CCC, CTS, EGR, MAP, OXS, PCV	
2.8L (173") V6 2-Bbl.	AIR, AMgV, ATS, BPEGR, CAT, CAN, CCC, CP, CKV [1], CanCV, DV, EGR, EGRCS, OXS, PCV, TVS [1], TAC, VSens	
3.8L (229") V6 2-Bbl.	AIR, AMgV, ATS, BPEGR, CAN, CanCV, CAT, CCC, EFE TVS, EFE, EGRCS, OXS, PCV, TAC, TVS, VSens	
3.8L (231") V6 2-Bbl.	ACV, AIR, ATS, ASV [1], BPEGR, CAN, CanCV, CAT, CCC, CKV, DV, EFE [1], EGRCS, EGR-VRV [1], MAP, OXS, PCV, TAC, TVS	
4.3L (262") V6 Diesel	EGR, EPR [1], VRV, VP	
5.0L (305") V8 4-Bbl.	AIR, AMgV, ATS, BPEGR, CAN, CanCV, CAT, CCC, EFE, EFE TVS, EGRCS, OXS, PCV, TAC, TVS, VSens	
5.0L (305") V8 CFI	AIR, AMgV, ATS, BPEGR, CAN, CAT, CCC, CP EGRCS, MAP, OXS, PCV, TAC	
5.7L (350") V8 4-Bbl	AIR, ATS, AMgV, BPEGR, CAN, CanCV, CAT, CCC, EFE, EFE-TVS, EGRCS, OXS, PCV, TAC, TVS, VSens	
5.7L (350") V8 CFI [2]	AIR, AMgV, ATS, BPEGR, CAN, CAT, CCC, CP, EGRCS, MAP, OXS, PCV, TAC, VM	[2] — 1984 Corvette
5.7L (350") V8 Diesel	EGR, EGR-VS, VRV, VP	

ACV — AIR Control Valve
AIR — Air Injector Reactor
AMgV — Air Management Valve
ATS — Air Temperature Sensor
BPEGR — Back Pressure Exhaust Gas Recycle
CAN — Charcoal Canister
CanCV — Canister Control Valve
CAT — Catalytic Converter
CCC — Computer Command Control
CFI — Cross Fire Injection
CKV — Check Valve
CP — Canister Purge
DV — Deceleration Valve
EFE — Early Fuel Evaporation
EGR — Exhaust Gas Recirculation
EGRCS — EGR Control Solenoid
EPR — Exhaust Pressure Regulator
FIA — Fast Idle Actuator
MAP — Manifold Pressure Sensor
OXS — Oxygen Sensor
PAIR — Pulse Air Injector
PAS — Pulse Air Solenoid
PCV — Positive Crankcase Ventilation
PSV — Pulse Air Shutoff Valve
PV — Pulse Air Valve
SEC ACT — Secondary Actuator
SSC ACT — Stepped Speed Control Actuator
SSC SOL — Stepped Speed Control Solenoid
TAC — Thermostatic Air Cleaner
TBI — Throttle Body Injection
TCS — Transmission Converter Switch
TVS — Thermal Vacuum Switch
VB — Vacuum Break
VCV — Vacuum Control Valve
VL-DV — Vacuum Delay Valve
VP — Vacuum Pump
VRV — Vacuum Regulator Valve
VS — Vacuum Switch
VSens — Vacuum Sensor
VSV — Vacuum Solenoid Valve
VSS — Vacuum Switching Solenoid

1983 Emission Control Application

GENERAL MOTORS

1983 OLDSMOBILE

Engine	Emission Control Systems & Devices	Remarks
1.8L (112") 4-Cyl. TBI	ATS, BPEGR, CAN, CCC, CAT, MAP, OXS, PAIR, PCV, TAC	
2.0L (122") 4-Cyl. TBI	ATS, BPEGR, CAN, CAT, CCC, CP, DV [1], EGRCS, MAP, PAIR, PAS, OXS, PCV, PSV, PV, TAC, VP [1]	[1] — Some Applications
2.5L (151") 4-Cyl. TBI	ATS, CAT, CCC, CTS, EGR, MAP, OXS, PCV	
2.8L (173") V6 2-Bbl.	AIR, ATS, AMgV, BPEGR, CAT, CAN, CCC, CP, CanCV, DV, EGRCS, OXS, PCV, TAC, VSens	
3.0L (181") V6 2-Bbl.	ACV, AIR, ASV, ATS, BPEGR, CAN, CanCV, CAT, CCC, CKV, DV, EFE [2], MAP, OXS, PCV, TAC, TAS, TVS	[2] — Ciera
3.8L (231") V6 2-Bbl.	ACV, AIR, ATS, ASV [1], BPEGR, CAN, CanCV, CAT, CCC, CKV, DV, EFE [1], EGRCS, EGR-VRV [1], MAP, OXS, PCV, TAC, TVS	
4.1L (250") V6 2-Bbl.	ACV, AIR, ATS, ASV, GPEGR, CAN, CanCV, CAT, CCC, CKV, DV, EFE, EFE VSV, EGR VSV, MAP, OXS, PCV, TAC, TVS [1], VP [1]	
4.3L (262") V6 Diesel	EGR, EPR [1], VRV, VP	
5.0L (307") V8 4-Bbl.	AIR, BPEGR, CAN, CanCV, CAT, CCC, CP, DPS, EAC, EAS, EFE, EFE TVS, EGRCS, OXS, PCV, TAC, TVS	
5.7L (350") V8 Diesel	EGR, EGR-VS, VRV, VP	

ACV — AIR Control Valve
AIR — Air Injection Reactor
AMgV — Air Management Valve
ASV — AIR Switching Valve
ATS — Air Temperature Sensor
BPEGR — Back Pressure EGR
CAN — Charcoal Canister
CanCV — Canister Control Valve
CAT — Catalytic Converter
CCC — Computer Command Control
CKV — Check Valve
CP — Canister Purge
CTS — Coolant Temperature Sensor
DV — Deceleration Valve
EFE — Early Fuel Evaporation
EGR — Exhaust Gas Recirculation
EGRCS — EGR Control Solenoid
EPR — Exhaust Pressure Regulator
MAP — Manifold Pressure Sensor
OXS — Oxygen Sensor
PAIR — Pulse Air Injector
PAS — Pulse Air Solenoid
PCV — Positive Crankcase Ventilation
PSV — Pulse Air Shutoff Valve
PV — Pulse Air Valve
TAC — Thermostatic Air Cleaner
TBI — Throttle Body Injection
TVS — Thermal Vacuum Switch
VP — Vacuum Pump
VRV — Vacuum Regulator Valve
VS — Vacuum Switch
VSens — Vacuum Sensor
VSV — Vacuum Solenoid Valve

1983 Emission Control Application

GENERAL MOTORS

1983 PONTIAC

Engine	Emission Control Systems & Devices	Remarks
1.6L (98") 4-Cyl. 2-Bbl.	AIR, AMgV, ATS, BPEGR, CAN, CanCV, CAT, CCC, DV, OXS, PCV, SEC ACT, SSC ACT [1], SSC SOL [1], TAC, TCS [1], TVS, VB, VCV [1], VL-DV, VP, VRV, VSV [1], VSS [1]	
1.8L (112") 4-Cyl. TBI	ATS, BPEGR, CAN, CCC, CAT, MAP, OXS, PAIR, PCV, TAC	
2.0L (122") 4-Cyl. TBI	ATS, BPEGR, CAN, CAT, CCC, CP, DV [1], EGRCS, MAP, PAIR, PAS, OXS, PCV, PSV, PV, TAC, VP [1]	[1] — Some Applications
2.5L (151") 4-Cyl. TBI	ATS, CAT, CCC, CTS, EGR, MAP, OXS, PCV	
2.8L (173") V6 2-Bbl.	AIR, ATS, AMgV, BPEGR, CAT, CAN, CCC, CP, CanCV, DV, EGR, EGRCS, OXS, PCV, TAC, VSens	
3.8L (231") V6 2-Bbl.	ACV, AIR, ATS, ASV [1], BPEGR, CAN, CanCV, CAT, CCC, CKV, DV, EFE [1], EGRCS, EGR-VRV [1], MAP, OXS, PCV, TAC, TVS	
4.3L (262") V6 Diesel	EGR, EPR, VRV, VP	
5.0L (305") V8 4-Bbl.	AIR, AMgV, ATS, BPEGR, CAN, CanCV, CAT, CCC, EFE, EFE TVS, EGRCS, OXS, PCV, TAC, TVS, VSens	
5.0L (305") V8 CFI	AIR, AMgV, ATS, BPEGR, CAN, CAT, CCC, CP, EGRCS, MAP, OXS, PCV, TAC	
5.7L (350") V8 Diesel	EGR, EGR-VS, VRV, VP	

ACV — AIR Control Valve
AIR — Air Injector Reactor
AMgV — Air Management Valve
ASV — AIR Switching Valve
ATS — Air Temperature Sensor
BPEGR — Back Pressure Exhaust Gas Recycle
CAN — Charcoal Canister
CanCV — Canister Control Valve
CAT — Catalytic Converter
CCC — Computer Command Control
CFI — Cross Fire Injection
CKV — Check Valve
CP — Canister Purge
DV — Deceleration Valve
EFE — Early Fuel Evaporation
EGR — Exhaust Gas Recirculation
EGRCS — EGR Control Solenoid
EPR — Exhaust Pressure Regulator
MAP — Manifold Pressure Sensor
OXS — Oxygen Sensor
PAIR — Pulse Air Injector
PAS — Pulse Air Solenoid
PCV — Positive Crankcase Ventilation
PSV — Pulse Air Shutoff Valve
PV — Pulse Air Valve
SEC ACT — Secondary Actuator
SSC ACT — Stepped Speed Control Actuator
SSC SOL — Stepped Speed Control Solenoid
TAC — Thermostatic Air Cleaner
TBI — Throttle Body Injection
TCS — Transmission Converter Switch
TVS — Thermal Vacuum Switch
VB — Vacuum Break
VCV — Vacuum Control Valve
VL-DV — Vacuum Delay Valve
VP — Vacuum Pump
VSens — Vacuum Sensor
VRV — Vacuum Regulator Valve
VS — Vacuum Pump
VSV — Vacuum Solenoid Valve
VSS — Vacuum Switching Solenoid

QUICK-CHECK TUNE-UP SPECIFICATIONS 1983

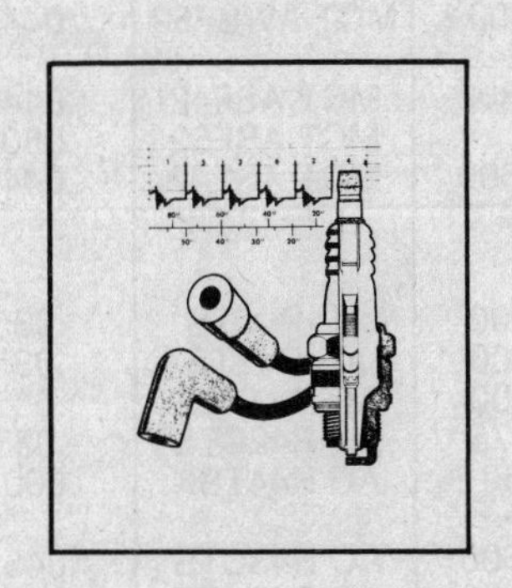

1983 Passenger Car Tune-Up

TUNE-UP SPECIFICATIONS

ENGINE	IGNITION TIMING *		SPARK PLUGS		FUEL SYSTEM	No.
	Man. Trans.	Auto. Trans.	Type	Gap In. (mm)	Make & Type	
AMERICAN MOTORS						
1.4L (85") 4-Cyl.	[1]	[1]	AC R45XLS	.032 (.8)	AMC TBI	1
1.4L (85") 4-Cyl.	[1]	[1]	AC R45XLS	.032 (.8)	Bosch AFC	2
2.5L (151") 4-Cyl.						
California	12 @ 900 [3]	12 @ 700 [3]	AC R44TSX	.060 (1.5)	Rochester E2SE	3
Federal	10 @ 900 [3]	10 @ 700 [3]	AC R44TSX	.060 (1.5)	Rochester 2SE	4
4.2L (258") 6-Cyl.						
Federal	6 @ 1600	6 @ 1600	CH RFN14LY	.035 (.9)	Carter BBD	5
California	6 @ 1600	6 @ 1600	CH RFN14LY	.035 (.9)	Carter BBD	6
High Alt.	13 @ 1600	13 @ 1600	CH RFN14LY	.035 (.9)	Carter BBD	7
CHRYSLER CORP.						
1.6L (97") 4-Cyl.	12 @ 850	.....	CH RN12Y	.035 (.9)	Holley 6520	8
1.7L (105") 4-Cyl.	20 @ 850	12 @ 850	CH RN12Y	.035 (.9)	Holley 6520	9
2.2L (135") 4-Cyl.						
Federal	10 @ 775	10 @ 900 [5]	CH RN12Y	.035 (.9)	Holley 6520 [2 6]	10
Calif.	10 @ 775	10 @ 900	CH RN12Y	.035 (.9)	Holley 6520 [2]	11
High Alt.	6 @ 850	6 @ 850	CH RN12Y	.035 (.9)	Holley 6520 [2]	12
2.6L (156") 4-Cyl.	7 @ 800	7 @ 800	CH RN12Y	.040 (1.0)	Mikuni	13
3.7L (225") 6-Cyl.	.....	16 @ 750	CH RBL16Y	.035 (.9)	Holley 6145	14
5.2L (318") V8						
2-Bbl.	.....	16 @ 700	CH RN12Y	.035 (.9)	Carter BBD	15
4-Bbl.	.....	16 @ 700	CH RN12Y	.035 (.9)	Carter Thermo-Quad	16
EFI	.....	12 @ 580	CH RN12Y	.035 (.9)	Chrysler EFI	17
FORD MOTOR CO.						
1.6L (98") 4-Cyl.						
2-Bbl.	8 @ 800	10 @ 800	MCT AWSF34	.044 (1.1)	Motorcraft 740	18
2-Bbl. High Output	14 @ 800 [1]	14 @ 800	MCT AWSF34 [2]	.044 (1.1)	Motorcraft 740	19
EFI	10 @ 800	10 @ 750	MCT AWSF24	.044 (1.1)	Ford EFI	20
2.3L (140") 4-Cyl.						
1-Bbl. HSC	[5]	[5]	MCT AWSF62	.044 (1.1)	Holley 6149	21
1-Bbl.	9 @ 700	9 @ 700	MCT AWSF44	.044 (1.1)	Carter YFA	22
EFI-Turbo	[5]	[5]	MCT ASWF32	.034 (.9)	Ford EFI	23
3.3L (200") 6-Cyl.	10 @ 900 [6]	10 @ 900 [6]	MCT BSF92	.050 (1.3)	Holley 1946	24
3.8L (232") V6	10 @ 800 [9]	10 @ 800 [9]	MCT AWSF52	.044 (1.1)	Motorcraft 2150	25
5.0L (302") V8						
4-Bbl.	10 @ 800	10 @ 800	MCT ASF42	.044 (1.1)	Holley 4180-C	26
EFI	.....	[4]	MCT ASF52	.050 (1.3)	Ford EFI	27
5.8L (351") V8	.....	12 @ 600	MCT ASF42	.044 (1.1)	Motorcraft 7200VV	28
GENERAL MOTORS						
1.6L (98") 4-Cyl.						
Federal	8 @ 800 [1]	6 @ 700	AC R42TS	.035 (.9)	Holley 6510-C	29
Calif.	6 @ 800	6 @ 700	AC R42TS	.035 (.9)	Holley 6510-C	30
1.8L (112") 4-Cyl.	8 @ 800	8 @ 800	AC R44XLS	.035 (.9)	GM Model 300 TBI	31
2.0L (122") 4-Cyl.	0 @ 875	0 @ 875	AC R42CTS	.035 (.9)	GM Model 500 TBI	32
2.5L (151") 4-Cyl.	8 @ 850 [5]	8 @ 750 [6]	AC R44TSX	.060 (1.5)	GM Model 300 TBI	33
2.8L (173") V6						
VIN X & 1	10 @ 800	10 @ 600	AC R43CTS	.045 (1.1)	Rochester E2SE	34
VIN L & Z	10 @ 800	10 @ 600	AC R42CTS	.045 (1.1)	Rochester E2SE	35
3.0L (181") V6	15 @ 725	15 @ 725	AC R44TSB	.080 (2.0)	Rochester E2ME	36
3.8L (229") V6	.....	0 @ 1200	AC R45TS	.045 (1.1)	Rochester E2ME	37
3.8L (231") V6						
2-Bbl.	.....	15 @ 450	AC R45TS8	.080 (2.0)	Rochester E2ME	38
4-Bbl. Turbo	.....	15 @ 450	AC R45TS8	.080 (2.0)	Rochester E4ME	39
4.1L (252") V6	.....	15 @ 470	AC R45TS8	.080 (2.0)	Rochester E4ME	40
4.1L (250") V8	.....	10 @ 450	AC R43NTS6	.060 (1.5)	GM Model 200 DFI	41
5.0L (305") V8						
4-Bbl.	6 @ 700	6 @ 500	AC R45TS	.045 (1.1)	Rochester E4ME	42
EFI	.....	6 @ 475	AC R45TS	.045 (1.1)	GM Model 400 TBI	43
5.0L (307") V8	.....	20 @ 1100	AC R46SX	.080 (2.0)	Rochester E4ME	44
5.7L (350") V8	[11]	[11]	AC R45TS	.045 (1.1)	GM Model 400 TBI	45
6.0L (368") V8						
4-Bbl.	.....	10 @ 450	AC R45NSX	.060 (1.5)	Rochester E4ME	46
DFI	.....	10 @ 450	AC R45NSX	.060 (1.5)	GM Model 200 DFI	47

SPARK PLUGS: AC — AC Delco; **CH** — Champion; **MCT** — Motorcraft.
FUEL INJECTION: DFI — Digital Fuel Injection; **EFI** — Electronic Fuel Injection; **TBI** — Throttle Body Injection.

TUNE-UP SPECIFICATIONS (Cont.)

No.	HOT IDLE •		FAST IDLE †			REMARKS
	Man. Trans.	Auto. Trans.	M/T RPM	Cam Step	A/T RPM	
1	3600 [2]	3600 [2]	[1]	[1]	[1]	1 — Non-adjustable.
2	650	650	[1]	[1]	[1]	2 — With ISC plunger fully extended.
3	650	550	2500	High	2700	3 — Solenoid on, without A/C. With A/C, turn solenoid and A/C off.
4	650	550	2500	High	2700	4 — Eagle is 530-670.
5	580-720 [4]	480-620 [5]	1700	2nd	1850	5 — Eagle is 430-570.
6	580-720	480-620	1700	2nd	1850	
7	630-770	580-720	1700	2nd	1850	
8	850 [1]	.....	1400	1st	.....	1 — High altitude models are 900.
9	850	.....	1400	1st	.....	2 — Fuel injected models use Chrysler TBI.
10	775	900	1400 [3] [7]	1st	1500 [3]	3 — Adjustment not possible on TBI.
11	775	900	1400 [3]	1st	1600 [3] [4]	4 — Rampage and Scamp are 1500.
12	900	850	1350 [3]	1st	1275 [3]	5 — Rampage and Scamp are 10 @ 775.
13	800 [8]	800 [8]	[9]	.....	[9]	6 — Fed. Rampage and Scamp use Holley 5220.
14	.....	725	.....	2nd	2000	7 — Rampage and Scamp are 1300.
15	.....	700	.....	2nd	1400	8 — 900 with A/C on.
16	.....	700	.....	2nd	1400	9 — Non-adjustable.
17	.....	700	.....	.....	[9]	
18	800/1200	720/750	2150	2nd	2400	1 — High Alt. man. trans. is 10 @ 800.
19	900/1500	720/750 [3]	2400	2nd	2400	2 — High Alt. man. trans. uses AWSF32.
20	800	750	[4]	[4]	[4]	3 — High Alt. ISC off is 820.
21	800	800	[5]	[5]	[5]	4 — Non-adjustable.
22	850	800	1800	Kickdown	2600 [6]	5 — Check Decal for specification.
23	[5]	[5]	[5]	[5]	[5]	6 — Calif. is 2000.
24	600 [8]	600 [8]	2000 [9]	2nd	2000 [9]	7 — High Alt. is 12 @ 900.
25	550	550	2150	High	2150	8 — Calif. & High Alt. are 550.
26	700	700	2400	High	2400	9 — LTD and Marquis are 2200 Fed. and 2100 Calif.
27	.....	550	.....	High	2200	
28	.....	700/600	.....	2nd	1650	
29	800 [2]	700 [3]	2500	High	2500	1 — 4-Speed with A/C is 6 @ 800. 5-Speed is 8 @ 950.
30	800 [3]	700 [3]	2500	High	2500	2 — 5-Speed is 950. Solenoid ISS RPM 1150.
31	775-825	675-725	[4]	.....	[4]	3 — Solenoid ISS RPM is 875.
32	625-675	625-675	[4]	.....	[4]	4 — Non-adjustable.
33	750-800	475-525	[4]	.....	[4]	5 — VIN 2 is 8 @ 900.
34	775/1100 [7]	600/750	2500 [8]	High	2500	6 — VIN 2 is 8 @ 650.
35	800/1100	725/850	2600	High	2700	7 — VIN 1 is 800/1000.
36	500/1300	500/1300	2400 [9]	High	2400 [9]	8 — VIN 1 is 2600.
37	.....	475/850	.....	High	2200	9 — Calif. models are 2300.
38	.....	450/900	.....	High	2200 [10]	10 — FWD models are 2100.
39	.....	450/900	.....	High	2200	11 — Information not available.
40	.....	470/900	.....	High	2200 [10]	
41	.....	450	.....	.....	[4]	
42	700/800	500/650	1800	High	2200	
43	.....	475	.....	.....	[4]	
44	.....	550/725	.....	High	2200	
45	[11]	[11]	[11]	[11]	[11]	
46	.....	450	.....	High	[11]	
47	.....	450	.....	.....	[4]	

* — All specifications are Before Top Dead Center (BTDC); Auto. Trans. in "D" unless otherwise noted.
• — When idle solenoid is used, lower RPM is with solenoid disconnected, higher RPM is with solenoid connected.
† — All specifications are with transmission in Neutral unless otherwise noted.

1983 Distributor Applications

ALL MANUFACTURERS

CHRYSLER CORP.

CHRYSLER, DODGE & PLYMOUTH

Application	Part No.
1.6L 4-Cyl.	5213366
1.7L 4-Cyl.	5206945
2.2L 4-Cyl.	5206975
2.6L 4-Cyl.	
Federal	4243707
Calif.	4243694
3.7L 6-Cyl.	4145751
5.2L 2-Bbl. V8	4145753
5.2L 4-Bbl. V8	4145753
5.2L EFI V8	4091140

DELCO-REMY

AMERICAN MOTORS

Application	Part No.
2.5L 4-Cyl.	
Federal	1110598
Calif.	1103527

BUICK

Application	Part No.
1.8L 4-Cyl. (VIN O)	1103514
2.0L 4-Cyl. (VIN P)	1103515
2.5L 4-Cyl. (VIN R)	1103513
2.8L V6 (VIN X)	1103519
2.8L V6 (VIN Z)	1103519
3.0L V6 (VIN E)	1103470
3.8L V6 (VIN A)	1103470
3.8L V6 (VIN 8)	1103470
4.1L V6 (VIN 4)	1103470
5.0L V8 (VIN Y)	1103457

CADILLAC

Application	Part No.
2.0L 4-Cyl. (VIN P)	1103515
4.1L V8 (VIN 8)	
Deville & Fleetwood	1103540
All Other Models	1103541
6.0L V8 (VIN 6)	1103415
6.0L V8 (VIN 9)	1103455

CHEVROLET

Application	Part No.
1.6L 4-Cyl. (VIN C)	
Man. Trans.	
4-Speed	1103504
5-Speed	1103505
Auto. Trans.	1103506
2.0L 4-Cyl. (VIN P)	1103515
2.5L 4-Cyl. (VIN R)	1103513
2.5L 4-Cyl. (VIN 2)	1103513
2.8L V6 (VIN L)	1103519
2.8L V6 (VIN X)	1103519

DELCO-REMY (Cont.)

CHEVROLET (Cont.)

Application	Part No.
2.8L V6 (VIN Z)	1103519
2.8L V6 (VIN 1)	1103519
3.8L V6 (VIN A)	1103470
3.8L V6 (VIN 9)	1110584
5.0L V8 (VIN H)	1103460
5.0L V8 (VIN S)	1103539
5.7L V8 (VIN 8)	1103538

OLDSMOBILE

Application	Part No.
1.8L 4-Cyl. (VIN O)	1103514
2.0L 4-Cyl. (VIN P)	1103515
2.5L 4-Cyl. (VIN R)	1103513
2.8L V6 (VIN X)	1103519
2.8L V6 (VIN Z)	1103519
3.0L V6 (VIN E)	1103470
3.8L V6 (VIN A)	1103470
4.1L V6 (VIN 4)	1103457
5.0L V8 (VIN Y)	1103457

PONTIAC

Application	Part No.
1.6L 4-Cyl. (VIN C)	
Man. Trans.	
4-Speed	1103504
5-Speed	1103505
Auto. Trans.	1103506
1.8L 4-Cyl. (VIN O)	1103514
2.0L 4-Cyl. (VIN P)	1103515
2.5L 4-Cyl. (VIN R)	1103513
2.5L 4-Cyl. (VIN 2)	1103513
2.8L V6 (VIN L)	1103519
2.8L V6 (VIN X)	1103519
2.8L V6 (VIN Z)	1103519
2.8L V6 (VIN 1)	1103519
3.8L V6 (VIN A)	1103470
5.0L V8 (VIN H)	1103539
5.0L V8 (VIN S)	1103519

DUCELLIER

AMERICAN MOTORS

Application	Part No.
1.4L 4-Cyl.	
With Right Angle Cap	77 00 707 304
With Standard Cap	77 00 707 070

MOTORCRAFT

AMERICAN MOTORS

Application	Part No.
4.2L 6-Cyl.	3242409

ALL MANUFACTURERS (Cont.)

MOTORCRAFT (Cont.)

FORD, LINCOLN & MERCURY

Application	[1] Part No.
1.6L 2-Bbl. 4-Cyl.	
Federal	
Man. Trans.	
With Fuel Ecomony Pkg.	E3EE-NA
Without Fuel Economy Pkg.	E3EE-PA
Auto. Trans.	E3EE-HA
Calif.	
Man. Trans.	E3EE-PA
Auto. Trans.	E3EE-HA
1.6L High Output 2-Bbl. 4-Cyl.	
Federal & Calif	
Auto. Trans.	E3EE-RA
High Alt.	
Man. Trans.	E3EE-DA
Auto. Trans.	E3EE-RA
1.6L EFI 4-Cyl.	[2]
2.3L 4-Cyl.	
1-Bbl. Std.	E3ZE-DA
1-Bbl. HSC	[2]
EFI-Turbo	[2]
3.3L 6-Cyl.	
Fairmont & Zephyr	
Federal & Calif.	E2BE-CA
High Alt.	E1BE-EA
LTD & Marquis	
Federal	E3AE-EA
Calif.	E3AE-CA
3.8L V6	
Federal	
Capri & Mustang	E3ZE-FA
Cougar, LTD, Marquis & T-Bird with AOT Trans.	E2SE-DA
Cougar & T-Bird with C5 Trans.	E3ZE-FA
Calif.	
Capri & Mustang	E3SE-BA
Cougar, LTD, Marquis & T-Bird with AOT Trans.	E3SE-DA
Cougar & T-Bird with C5 Trans.	E3ZE-FA
High Alt.	
Capri & Mustang	E3ZE-CA
Cougar, LTD, Marquis & T-Bird	E3AE-DA
5.0L 4-Bbl. V8	
Capri & Mustang with 5-Spd. Trans.	E3ZE-HA
All Others	[2]
5.0L EFI V8	[2]
5.8L V8	E2AE-EA

[1] — Basic part number is 12127.
[2] — Information not available from manufacturer.

1983 Distributor Specifications

ALL MANUFACTURERS

CHRYSLER CORP. DISTRIBUTOR ADVANCE SPECIFICATIONS
FOR DISTRIBUTOR RPM AND DEGREES, DIVIDE SPECIFICATIONS BY 2

Distributor Part No.	Rot.[1]	Automatic Advance (Engine Degrees & RPM)						Vacuum Advance (Engine Deg. & In. of Hg)			
		Deg.	RPM	Deg.	RPM	Deg.	RPM	Deg.	In. Hg	Deg.	In. Hg
4243694	C	0	1200	12	2800	20	6000	0	5.1	15	11.8
4243707	C	0	1200	12	2800	20	6000	0	3.1	20	11.8

[1] — C (Clockwise), CC (Counterclockwise) as viewed from rotor end.

DELCO-REMY (AMERICAN MOTORS) DISTRIBUTOR ADVANCE SPECIFICATIONS
FOR DISTRIBUTOR RPM AND DEGREES, DIVIDE SPECIFICATIONS BY 2

Distributor Part No.	Rot.[1]	Automatic Advance (Engine Degrees & RPM)						Vacuum Advance (Engine Deg. & In. of Hg)			
		Deg.	RPM	Deg.	RPM	Deg.	RPM	Deg.	In. Hg	Deg.	In. Hg
1103527	CC	0-4	1600	6-10	2600	12-18	4000	0	3.0-4.7	10	9.5-11.8
1110598	CC	0-4	1600	4-10	2400	12-16	4000	0	1.8-3.6	10	7.1-8.9

[1] — C (Clockwise), CC (Counterclockwise) as viewed from rotor end.

DELCO-REMY (GENERAL MOTORS) DISTRIBUTOR ADVANCE SPECIFICATIONS

NOTE: General Motors distributors in 1983 do not have centrifugal or vacuum advance units. All advance is controlled by the Computer Command Control system's electronic control module or by the distributor's HEI module. The advance data programmed into the ECM is not available from the manufacturer.

DUCELLIER (AMERICAN MOTORS) DISTRIBUTOR ADVANCE SPECIFICATIONS

NOTE: 1983 Ducellier distributors do not contain centrifugal or vacuum advance mechanisms. All advance is controlled by the electronic control module. The advance data programmed into the electronic control module is not available from the maufacturer.

MOTORCRAFT (FORD) DISTRIBUTOR ADVANCE SPECIFICATIONS

Distributor Part Number (Basic Part No. is 12127)	Rot.[1]	Initial Ignition Timing (Degrees BTDC)	Total Advance @ 2500 Engine RPM (Including Initial Advance)	
			Hose Disconnected [2] (Degrees BTDC)	Hose Connected [2] (Degrees BTDC)
E1BE-EA	C	12	19-23	36-46
E2AE-EA	CC	12	17-22	48-59
E2BE-CA	C	10	16-21	33-44
E2SE-DA	CC	12	17-21	38-48
E3AE-CA	C	10	17-21	31-40
E3AE-DA	CC	12	17-22	38-49
E3AE-EA	C	10	13-18	38-49
E3EE-DA	C	10	17-22	35-45
E3EE-HA	C	10	14-19	43-54
E3EE-NA	C	8	14-19	41-53
E3EE-PA	C	8	14-19	31-42
E3EE-RA [3]	C	14	19-23	40-50
E3SE-BA	CC	8	15-19	32-42
E3SE-DA	CC	10	15-19	36-46
E3ZE-CA	CC	18	23-36	49-57
E3ZE-DA	C	9	7-11	24-34
E3ZE-FA [4]	CC	10	15-21	38-51
E3ZE-HA	CC	10	17-22	35-46

[1] — C (Clockwise), CC (Counterclockwise) as viewed from rotor end.
[2] — Part throttle advance at distributor diaphragm. If hose is disconnected, plug hose.
[3] — High altitude models are 12° initial timing, 21-25° disconnected, and 42-52° connected.
[4] — Mustang convertible is 12° initial timing, 17-23° disconnected, and 40-53° connected.

1983 Distributor Specifications

ALL MANUFACTURERS

MOTORCRAFT (AMERICAN MOTORS) DISTRIBUTOR ADVANCE SPECIFICATIONS
FOR DISTRIBUTOR RPM AND DEGREES, DIVIDE SPECIFICATIONS BY 2

Distributor Part No.	Rot.[1]	Automatic Advance (Engine Degrees & RPM)						Vacuum Advance (Engine Deg. & In. of Hg)			
		Deg.	RPM	Deg.	RPM	Deg.	RPM	Deg.	In. Hg	Deg.	In. Hg
3243409	C	0	1000	12	2200	10	4400	13	10	23	20

[1] — C (Clockwise), CC (Counterclockwise) as viewed from rotor end.

1983 Engine Identification

AMERICAN MOTORS

ENGINE CODE EXPLANATION

Engines for AMC vehicles can be identified by a code letter found on the Vehicle Identification Number (VIN) plate located on upper left instrument panel. The fourth character of the VIN number represents the cubic inch displacement and fuel system type. In addition, Concord, Eagle and Spirit engines can also be identified by the build code plate located on the engine.

AMERICAN MOTORS ENGINE CODES

Model	VIN Code	Engine
4-Cylinder		
Alliance	D	[1] 1.4L TBI
Alliance	E	[2] 1.4L MPI
Concord, Eagle & Spirit	B	2.5L 2-Bbl.
6-Cylinder		
Concord, Eagle & Spirit	C	4.2L 2-Bbl.

[1] — Throttle Body Fuel Injection
[2] — Multi-Point Fuel Injection

ENGINE CODE PLATE IDENTIFICATION

4-Cylinder Eagle

The two character engine identification code is stamped into front top left corner of block.

6-Cylinder

Located on machined pad on right side of block between No. 2 and No. 3 spark plugs. Numbers indicate year, month and day of production. Letter "C" indicates 6-cylinder engine with 2-barrel carburetor.

EAGLE 4-CYLINDER ENGINE CODES

Application	Code
Federal	
Auto. Trans.	KT
Man. Trans.	CC
California	
Auto. Trans.	KZ
Man. Trans.	KY

Fig. 1: Concord, Eagle & Spirit Engine Code Locations

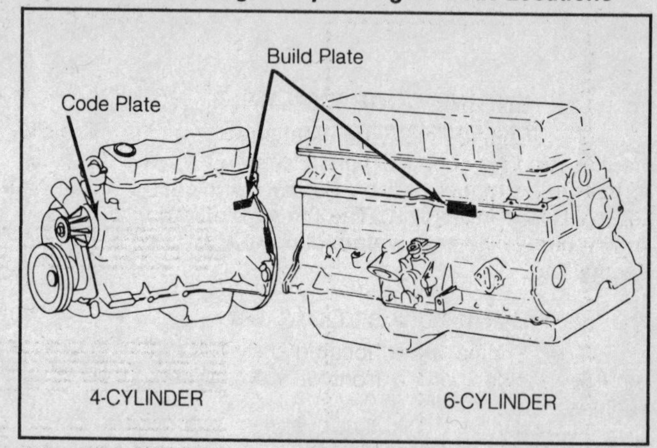

CHRYSLER CORP.

ENGINE CODE EXPLANATION

The 8th character of the Vehicle Identification Number (VIN) located on engine and upper left side of instrument panel, identifies engine displacement and fuel system type. Engine can also be identified by engine identification number.

CHRYSLER CORP. ENGINE CODES

Model	VIN Code	Engine
4-Cylinder		
Horizon, Omni, Rampage & Scamp	A	1.6L 2-Bbl.
Horizon, Omni, Rampage & Scamp	B	1.7L 2-Bbl.
Aries, E Class, Horizon, New Yorker (FWD), LeBaron, Omni, Rampage, Scamp, 400, 600	C	2.2L 2-Bbl.
E Class, New Yorker (FWD), 600	D	2.2L EFI
Aries, E Class, LeBaron, New Yorker (FWD), 400, 600	G	2.6L 2-Bbl.
6-Cylinder		
Cordoba, Diplomat, Gran Fury, Mirada, New Yorker (RWD)	H	3.7L 1-Bbl.

CHRYSLER CORP. ENGINE CODES (Cont.)

Model	VIN Code	Engine
Cordoba, Diplomat, Gran Fury, Mirada, New Yorker (RWD)	J	[1] 3.7L 1-Bbl.
V8		
Cordoba, Diplomat, Gran Fury, Mirada, New Yorker (RWD)	P	5.2L 2-Bbl.
Cordoba, Diplomat, Gran Fury, Mirada, New Yorker (RWD)	R	5.2L 4-Bbl.
Cordoba, Diplomat, Gran Fury, Mirada, New Yorker (RWD)	S	[1] 5.2L 4-Bbl.
Imperial	N	5.2L EFI

[1] — Heavy Duty Engines.

ENGINE IDENTIFICATION NUMBER

The first number indicates model year, the 2nd indicates manufacturing plant and following 3 numbers indicate cubic inch displacement.

4-Cylinder Engines

Number appears on left side of engine just above and behind fuel pump on 1.6L engine. Number is on rear face of engine block, above transaxle on 1.7L and

1983 Engine Identification

CHRYSLER CORP. (Cont.)

2.2L engines. On 2.6L engines, number is on left side of engine block, between core plug and rear face of block (radiator side).

6-Cylinder Engine

Number is located on a pad on right side of engine block, below No. 6 spark plug.

V8 Engine

Number is located on a pad on right side of engine block, just to rear of engine mount.

ENGINE SERIAL NUMBER

4-Cylinder Engines

Serial number for parts purposes is located above fuel pump on 1.7L engine. On 2.2L engine, it is found just below engine identification number on rear face of engine block. On 2.6L engine, it is on right front side of engine block near exhaust manifold.

6-Cylinder Engine

Number is on right side of engine block below No. 1 spark plug.

V8 Engine

Number is on left front corner of engine block, below cylinder head.

FORD MOTOR CO.

ENGINE CODE EXPLANATION

Engine may be identified by the Vehicle Identification Number (VIN) plate located on upper left side of instrument panel and on Safety Certification Decal on left front door face panel. The 8th digit of VIN will give the engine code. The same information will also be located on Engine Tag.

ENGINE TAG LOCATION

Engine tag is located on front of timing cover on 1.6L engines, or on front of valve cover on all other engines.

FORD MOTOR CO. ENGINE CODES

Model	VIN Code	Engine
Escort, EXP, LN7, Lynx	2	1.6L 2-Bbl.
Escort, EXP, LN7, Lynx	4	[1] 1.6L 2-Bbl.
Escort, EXP, LN7, Lynx	5	1.6L EFI
Capri, Fairmont, LTD, Marquis, Mustang, Zephyr	R	2.3L 2-Bbl.
Capri, Cougar, Mustang, Thunderbird	W	2.3L Turbo
Tempo, Topaz	R	2.3L 1-Bbl.
Fairmont, LTD, Marquis, Zephyr	X	3.3L 1-Bbl.
Capri, Cougar, LTD, Marquis, Mustang, Thunderbird	3	3.8L 2-Bbl.
Continental	3	3.8L CFI
Capri, Continental, Crown Victoria, Grand Marquis, Mark VI, Mustang, Town Car	F	[2] 5.0L 2-Bbl.
Crown Victoria	G	[3] 5.8L 2-Bbl.

[1] — High Output engine.
[2] — High Output engine on Capri & Mustang.
[3] — Police vehicles only.

GENERAL MOTORS

ENGINE CODE & DIVISION USAGE

1.6L 4-CYLINDER (VIN C)

Used by Chevrolet and Pontiac. Code is located on lower right portion of block near oil pan-to-block mating surface.

1.8L DIESEL 4-CYLINDER (VIN D)

Used by Chevrolet and Pontiac. Code is located at rear left side of cylinder block, below exhaust manifold.

1.8L 4-CYLINDER (VIN 0)

Used by Buick, Oldsmobile and Pontiac. Code is located at left rear of engine block near flywheel housing.

2.0L 4-CYLINDER (VIN P)

Used by Buick, Cadillac, Chevrolet, Oldsmobile and Pontiac. Code is located at right front of engine block above water pump housing,

2.5L 4-CYLINDER (VIN R)

Used by Buick, Chevrolet, Oldsmobile and Pontiac. Code is located at right front of block below cylinder head or on left rear of block above oil pan.

2.5L 4-CYLINDER (VIN 2)

Used by Chevrolet and Pontiac. Code is located at left rear of block on flywheel housing just above starter motor.

2.8L V6 (VIN L)

Used by Chevrolet and Pontiac. Code is located on block near water pump housing.

2.8L V6 (VIN X)

Used by Buick, Chevrolet, Oldsmobile and Pontiac. Code is located at front of engine block near cylinder head-to-block mating surface.

1983 Engine Identification

GENERAL MOTORS (Cont.)

2.8L V6 (VIN Z)

Used by Buick, Chevrolet, Oldsmobile and Pontiac. Code is located at front of engine block near cylinder head-to-block mating surface.

2.8L V6 (VIN 1)

Used by Chevrolet and Pontiac. Code is located on block near water pump housing.

3.0L V6 (VIN E)

Used by Buick and Oldsmobile. Code is located on pad at left rear of engine block, near starter.

3.8L V6 (VIN A)

Used by Buick, Chevrolet, Oldsmobile and Pontiac. Code is located at lower left of engine block.

3.8L V6 TURBO (VIN 8)

Used by Buick. Code is located at lower left rear side of engine block.

3.8L V6 (VIN 9)

Used by Chevrolet. Code is located at left rear of block on flywheel housing just above starter motor.

4.1L V6 (VIN 4)

Used by Buick and Oldsmobile. Code is located at left rear of engine block near flywheel housing.

4.1L V8 DFI (VIN 8)

Used by Cadillac. Code is located on plate at left rear of engine block

4.3L V6 DIESEL (VIN T)

Used by Buick, Chevrolet, Oldsmobile and Pontiac. Code is located on pad at right front of engine.

4.3L V6 (VIN V)

Used by Buick, Chevrolet and Oldsmobile. Code is located at left front of engine block.

5.0L V8 (VIN H)

Used by Chevrolet and Pontiac. Code is located at right front of engine block below cylinder head.

5.0L V8 (VIN S)

Used by Chevrolet and Pontiac. Code is located at right front of engine block below cylinder head.

5.0L V8 (VIN Y)

Used by Buick and Oldsmobile. Code is located at left front of engine block below cylinder head.

5.0L (VIN 9)

Used by Oldsmobile. Code located at left front of engine block below cylinder head.

5.7L V8 DIESEL (VIN N)

Used by Buick, Cadillac, Chevrolet, Oldsmobile and Pontiac. Code is located at left front of engine block.

5.7L V8 (VIN 8)

Used by Chevrolet. Code is located at right front of engine below cylinder head.

6.0L V8 (VIN 6)

Used by Cadillac. Code is located at left rear of engine block.

6.0L V8 DFI (VIN 9)

Used by Cadillac. Code is located at left rear of engine block.

1983 GENERAL MOTORS ENGINE CODES

Engine (VIN Code)	Engine Codes
1.6L 4-Cyl. (VIN C)	DAB, DWA, DWB, DWC, DWD, DWF, DWH, DWJ, DWK, DWM, DWN, DWR, DWS, DWT, DWU, DWW, DWX, DWY, DZA, DZC, DZD, DZJ, DZK, DZR, DZS, DZW, DZX, D8A, D8C, D8D
1.8L Diesel 4-Cyl. (VIN D)	[1]
1.8L 4-Cyl. (VIN 0)	YLL, YLM
2.0L 4-Cyl. (VIN P)	DSA, DSB, DSC, DSD, DSF, DSH, DSJ, DSK, DSM, DSN, DSR, DSS, DST, DSU, DSW, DSX, DSY, DSZ, DJM, DJN, DJR, DJS, DJT, DJU, DJW, DJX, DJY, DMN, DMR, DMS, DMT, DMW, DMU, DMX, DMY, DMZ,
2.5L 4-Cyl. (VIN R)	YAA, YAL, YAP, 3J, 3K, 3L 3M, 3P, 3S
2.5L 4-Cyl. (VIN 2)	YMM, YMT
2.8L V6 (VIN L)	[1]
2.8L V6 (VIN X)	CAY, CAZ, CBA, CBB, CBC, CBD, CBF, CBH, CBJ, CBK, CMC, CMF, CMH, CMJ, CMM, CMS, C7N, C7R, C7S, C7T, C7U, C7W, DCA, DCB, DCC, DCD, DCF, DCH, DCJ, DCK, DCM, DCN, DCR, DCS, DCT, DCV, DCW, DCX, D2A, D2B, D2C, D2D, D2F, D2H, D2J, D2K, D2M, D2N, D2R, D2S,
2.8L V6 (VIN Z)	DFA, DFB, DFC, DFD, DFF, DFH, DTA, DTB, DTC, DTJ, DTK
2.8L V6 (VIN 1)	DAA, DAB, DAC, DAD, DAF, DAJ, DAK, D6A, D6B, D6C, D6D
3.0L V6 (VIN E)	RA, RB, RC
3.8L V6 (VIN A)	ND, NG, NH, NJ, NL
3.8L V6 (VIN 8)	NB, NC, NK
3.8L V6 (VIN 9)	DBA, DBB, DBC
4.1L V6 (VIN 4)	SA, SB, SC, SD, SF, SG, SH
4.1L V8 (VIN 8)	HLA, HMA, HNA, HOA, HPA, HQA, HRA
4.3L V6 (VIN T)	UAC, UAH, UAL, ULJ, ULK, ULL, ULM, ULN, ULP
4.3L V6 (VIN V)	UKA, UKB, UKC, UKJ, UKK, UAA, UAD, VAJ
5.0L V8 (VIN H)	DDB, DDC, DDD, DDF, DDH, DDJ, DDK, DDN, DGN, DSC, D5B, D5C, D5F, D5H
5.0L V8 (VIN S)	DDA, DUA
5.0L V8 (VIN Y)	TAA, TAB, TAC, TAD, TAF, TAK, TAM, TAW, TAX, TAY, TAZ, TBA, TBB, TKA, TKB, TKD, TKH, TKK, TKL, TKM, TKN, TKP, TKS, TKT, TKY
5.0L V8 (VIN 9)	[1]
5.7L V8 (VIN N)	VAB, VAC, VAD, VAK, VAL, VAM, VAN, VAP, VAS, VAU, VAW, VAX, VAY, VAZ, VBA, VBB, VBC, VBP, VBU, VBW, VKB, VKC, VKD, VKK, VKL, VKR, VKS, VKT, VKZ, VLA, VLB, VLP, VLS, VLT, VLW
5.7L V8 (VIN 8)	[1]
6.0L V8 (VIN 6)	HBA
6.0L V8 (VIN 9)	LFA, LRA

[1] — Codes not available from manufacturer.

1983 Engine Identification

GENERAL MOTORS (Cont.)

Fig. 2: General Motors Engine Code Locations

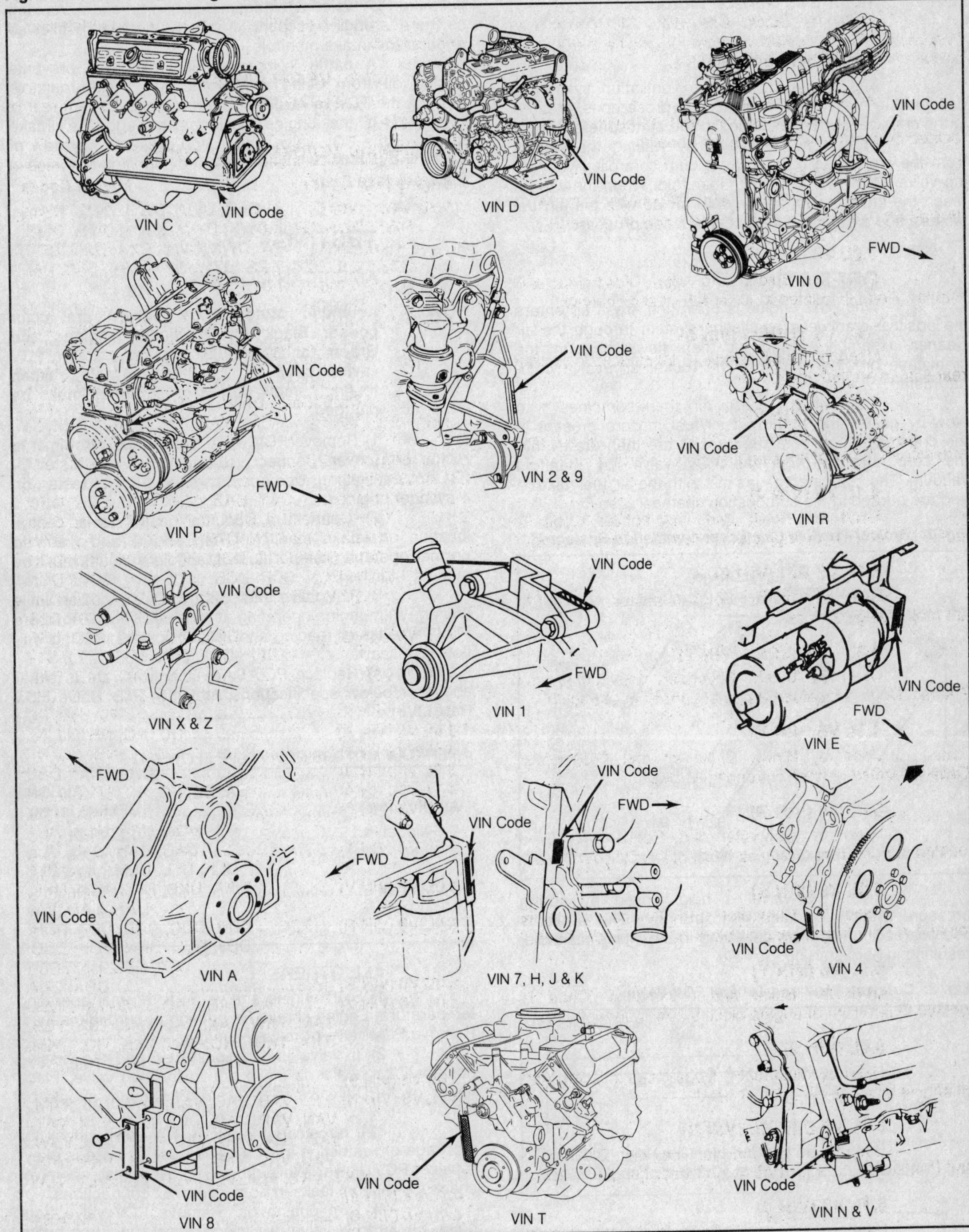

1983 Crankcase Ventilation

POSITIVE CRANKCASE VENTILATION (PCV) SYSTEM

American Motors, Chrysler Corp., Ford Motor Co., General Motors

DESCRIPTION

The positive crankcase ventilation system is designed to prevent contaminating hydrocarbons, created in the crankcase, from escaping to the atmosphere.

This is accomplished by routing the vapors from the crankcase through a vacuum controlled ventilating valve (PCV) into the intake manifold. When the vapors reach the intake manifold they are mixed with the air/fuel mixture and are burned in the combustion process.

OPERATION

When the engine is operating, fresh air enters the positive crankcase ventilation system through the air cleaner assembly. Fresh air then flows through the crankcase breather and into the rocker arm/valve compartment.

The entering fresh air then combines with blow-by gases and unburned air/fuel mixture present in the crankcase. The combined gases are then drawn into the carburetor, through the PCV valve, by manifold vacuum. The combined gases mix with the air/fuel mixture and are burned in the combustion chamber. *See Fig. 1.*

Fig. 1: Typical Positive Crankcase Ventilation System

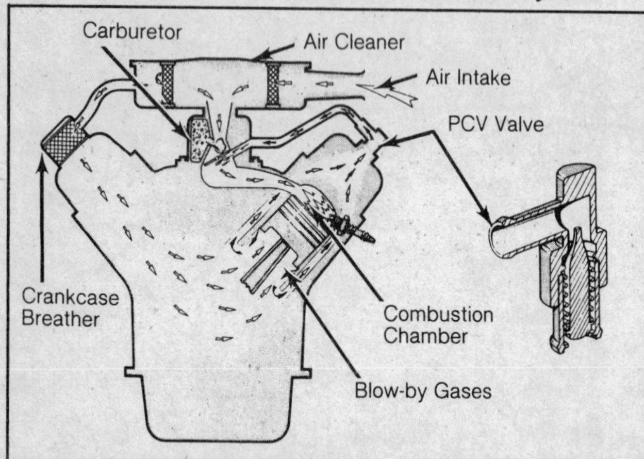

The PCV valve is held closed by spring pressure when the engine is not running. This prevents hydrocarbon fumes from collecting in the intake manifold, resulting in hard starting. *See Fig. 2.*

Fig. 2: Cutaway View of a Typical PCV Valve

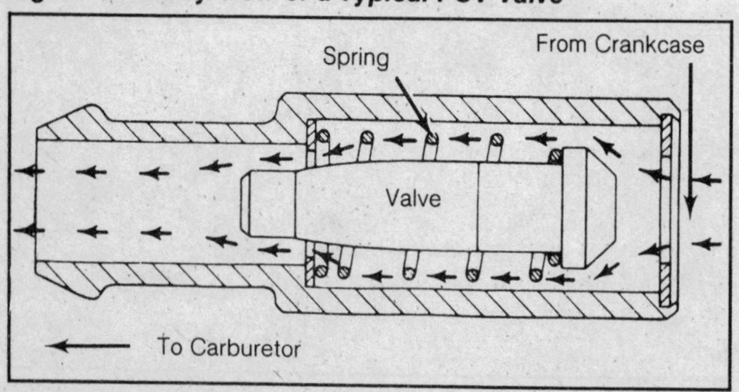

When the engine is started, manifold vacuum pulls the PCV valve open against spring pressure. As long as there is engine vacuum, crankcase fumes are allowed to enter the intake manifold.

A baffle in the rocker arm cover prevents engine oil from being drawn into the intake manifold through the PCV valve.

If the engine backfires through the intake manifold, the PCV valve closes and prevents any flow of gases through it. This is to prevent the ignition of fumes in the crankcase.

TESTING

AMERICAN MOTORS

NOTE: **American Motors PCV valves are color coded: Black for 4-cylinder engines and Green for 6-cylinder engines. Green PCV vavles have a "T" fitting at inlet. When testing, small port of "T" fitting must be plugged.**

1) Remove PCV valve from rubber grommet in rocker arm cover. Connect valve to PCV valve tester (J-2311 or equivalent). Use adapter, supplied with tester, on 4-cylinder engines.

2) Connect a vacuum gauge to a central location on intake manifold. Start engine and warm to normal operating temperature. Manifold vacuum must be at least 14 in. Hg.

3) PCV valve must be in vertical position while testing. With engine operating at curb idle speed, compare PCV valve tester reading and vacuum gauge reading with flow rate chart.

4) Replace PCV valve if airflow rate is either above or below specifications shown in PCV Valve Flow Rate chart.

AMERICAN MOTORS PCV VALVE FLOW RATE

Application	Airflow CFM @ In. Hg
4-Cylinder	1.22-2.21 @ 3
	.77-1.66 @ 6
	.69-1.13 @ 15
6-Cylinder	1.5-2.5 @ 3
	.9-2.0 @ 6
	0-.2 @ 15

ALL OTHERS

1) Start engine and warm to normal operating temperature. Engine should be running at curb idle speed. Remove PCV valve from its mounting.

2) If valve is functioning properly, a hissing noise will be heard as air is drawn through valve. Place finger over PCV valve inlet. A strong vacuum should be felt.

3) If no vacuum is felt at PCV valve, check for blockage or restriction in PCV valve hose. If hose is okay, replace PCV valve. While finger is over inlet of valve, check for vacuum leaks in hose and at all connections.

4) Turn engine off. Remove PCV valve from hose. Shake PCV valve. A clicking noise should be heard

POSITIVE CRANKCASE VENTILATION (PCV) (Cont.)

when shaking valve, indicating valve is free. If no clicking noise is heard, replace PCV valve.

SERVICE PROCEDURES

An engine may idle slow or rough due to a clogged PCV valve or system. Never adjust idle speeds without first checking the entire PCV system.

CAUTION: **If a PCV system component becomes clogged, all crankcase ventilation will stop and serious engine damage could occur.**

Although the following manufacturers' service procedures give specific service intervals, it is recommended that the PCV system be serviced more frequently if vehicle is operated under severe conditions (extreme dust, prolonged idling, trailer hauling or short trips in cold weather).

AMERICAN MOTORS

PCV Valve

Replace PCV valve every 30,000 miles. Cleaning may be required between valve replacement intervals if vehicle is operated under severe operating conditions.

Air Inlet Filter

Filter is located in a retainer in air cleaner assembly. Remove retainer and remove filter. Use kerosene to clean filter. Filter should be cleaned every 30,000 miles on all vehicles except those equipped with a 4-cylinder engine and an automatic transmission. On vehicles with a 4-cylinder engine and an automatic transmission, filter should be replaced every 30,000 miles.

CHRYSLER CORP.

PCV Valve

Inspect PCV valve every 15,000 miles and replace every 30,000 miles. DO NOT attempt to clean valve.

Filter Element

Remove and clean filter element every 52,500 miles. After cleaning filter element, filter should be soaked in SAE 30W engine oil before it is reinstalled.

FORD MOTOR CO.

PCV Valve

If PCV valve is clogged or defective, replace valve. DO NOT attempt to clean valve. Replace PCV valve every 30,000 miles on front wheel drive vehicles or every 52,500 miles on rear wheel drive vehicles.

Filter Element

Replace filter element every 30,000 miles on front wheel drive vehicles or every 52,500 miles on rear wheel drive vehicles. Periodic cleaning of filter between replacement intervals may be required if vehicle is operated under severe operating conditions.

GENERAL MOTORS

PCV Valve

Remove PCV valve from intake manifold or rocker arm cover and replace every 30,000 miles. DO NOT attempt to clean valve.

Filter Element

Filter element should be replaced every 30,000 miles. On vehicles equipped with diesel engines, filter element should be cleaned every 15,000 miles.

1983 Fuel Evaporation Control

AMERICAN MOTORS FUEL VAPOR CONTROL SYSTEM

DESCRIPTION & OPERATION

The Fuel Vapor Control system prevents raw fuel vapors from escaping into the atmosphere. Fuel vapors from the fuel tank and carburetor bowl (if equipped) are collected in a charcoal filled canister.

The fuel vapors are then metered into the intake manifold where they are mixed with the air/fuel mixture and burned in the combustion chamber. The system incorporates the following components:

FUEL TANK FILLER CAP

The filler cap incorporates a 2-way relief valve which is normally closed to the atmosphere. The relief valve is calibrated to open only when a pressure of more than .8 psi or a vacuum of more than .1 in. Hg occurs.

When pressure or vacuum is relieved, the valve returns to its normally closed position. It is normal to occasionally encounter an air pressure release when removing the filler cap.

CHARCOAL CANISTER

The charcoal canister is filled with granules of activated charcoal. Fuel vapors entering the canister are adsorbed into the surface of the granules.

All models except Alliance use canisters with a staged dual purge feature. Two inlets are provided, one for tank vapors and another for carburetor bowl vapors. The outlet is connected to intake manifold vacuum. The fouth port on the canister is connected to the carburetor or injection pump spark port.

Fig. 1: Charcoal Canister & Vacuum Hose Connections

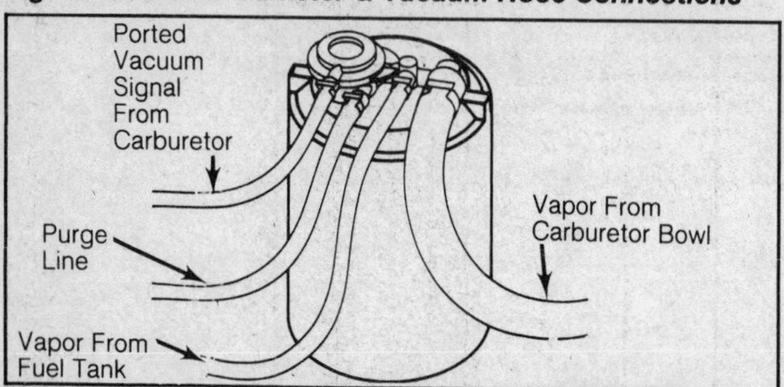

Concord, Eagle and Spirit shown, Alliance is similar.

When the engine is running, manifold vacuum draws fresh air through the inlet filter in the canister. The fresh air entering the canister purges the stored vapors.

When ported vacuum increases (increased throttle opening), the secondary purge circuit is opened. This causes the canister to be purged at a much greater rate. A replaceable air filter is installed in the bottom of the canister.

Alliance models are equipped with a vacuum operated canister purge solenoid.

ROLLOVER CHECK VALVE

The rollover check valve prevents fuel flow from the fuel tank in the event of vehicle rollover. The check valve consists of a plunger and a stainless steel ball.

When the check valve is inverted, the ball presses the plunger against its seat. A properly functioning valve will sustain 3 psi of air pressure on the inlet side when the valve is inverted.

CARBURETOR EXTERNAL BOWL VENT

All Models Except Alliance

The carburetor external bowl vent provides and outlet for fuel vapors when the engine is not running. If a vent were not provided, raw fuel vapors would enter the atmosphere. Some vapors would also enter the intake manifold, making hot restarts difficult.

When the engine is running, the fuel bowl must be vented to the inside of the air cleaner for proper fuel flow. This is accomplished by automatically closing the bowl vent with manifold vacuum.

Fig. 2: Schematic of Fuel Vapor Control System Used on Concord, Eagle & Spirit

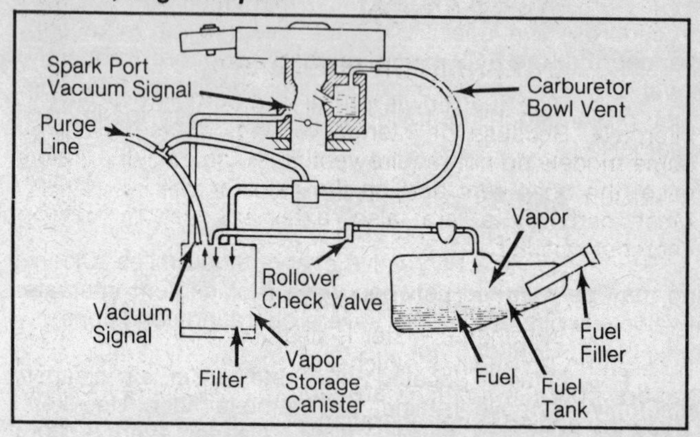

Fig. 3: Schematic of Fuel Vapor Control System Used on Alliance Models

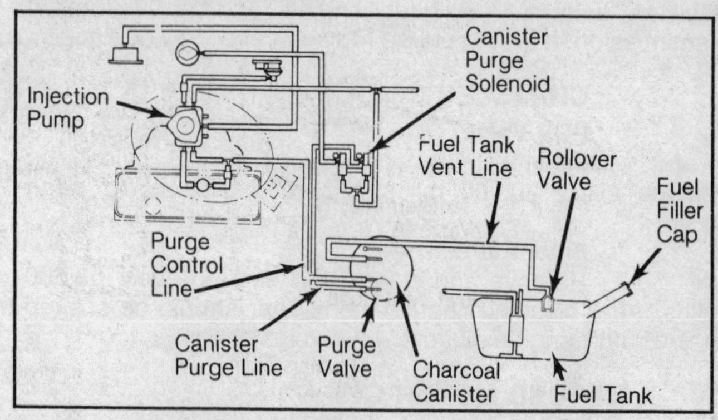

FUEL RETURN SYSTEM

All vehicles equipped with 6-cylinder engines use a fuel return system. This system reduces the possibility of high temperature fuel vapor problems. This system consists of a line connected to a nipple on the fuel filter and to a nipple on the fuel tank sending unit.

During normal operation, a small portion of fuel is returned to fuel tank. When underhood temperatures are high, vaporized fuel is returned to fuel tank instead of passing through carburetor. A check valve prevents fuel from feeding back through return line.

MAINTENANCE

Inspect check valve, hoses, connections and canister every 30,000 miles and replace as necessary. Replace fuel filter every 12,500 miles. Replace charcoal canister filter every 30,000 miles.

1983 Fuel Evaporation Control

CHRYSLER CORP. EVAPORATION CONTROL SYSTEM

DESCRIPTION

The purpose of the Evaporation Control System is to prevent gasoline vapors (hydrocarbons), from the fuel tank and carburetor, from entering the atmosphere.

When fuel evaporates in the fuel tank or in the carburetor float chamber, the vapors pass through vent hoses to a charcoal canister.

The vapors are stored in the canister until they are drawn into the intake manifold after the engine begins to run. *See Figs. 1 and 2.*

OPERATION

CARBURETOR FUEL BOWL

The fuel bowls on all carburetors are vented internally. Because of internal venting of the fuel bowl, some models do not require venting to the canister. In this case, the bowl vent port on the canister will be capped. Most carburetors are also externally vented to the charcoal canister.

CHARCOAL CANISTER

An open canister is used on all models except 3.7L and 5.2L engines which use a sealed canister. Fuel vapors from the fuel tank are stored in activated charcoal while the engine is not operating.

When the engine is operating, vapor is purged from the charcoal canister into the engine where it is burned with the air/fuel mixture.

FUEL TANK FILLER CAP

Relief valves in the fuel tank filler cap operate to prevent excessive pressure or vacuum in the fuel tank. The proper replacement cap must be used if the original cap is lost or damaged.

CAUT:ON: Remove the fuel tank filler cap prior to removing or repairing fuel lines.

ROLLOVER/VAPOR SEPARATOR

All models are equipped with a rollover/vapor separator valve to prevent fuel leakage if the vehicle is accidentally rolled over. This valve is located on top of the fuel tank.

MAINTENANCE

The only service that is required is to check the filter located on the bottom of the charcoal canister every 30,000 miles.

Replacement is only required if the vehicle is frequently driven in dusty areas or the filter is dirty or clogged. All hoses should be inspected periodically and replaced if cracked or leaking.

Fig. 1: Evaporation Control System for 2.6L Engine

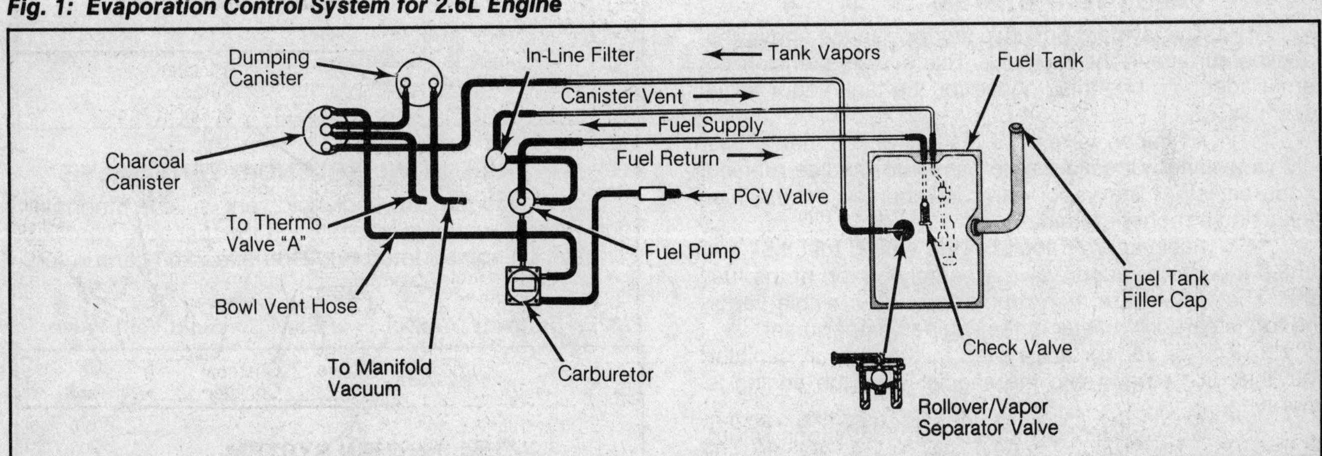

Fig. 2: Evaporation Control System for All Engines Except 2.6L

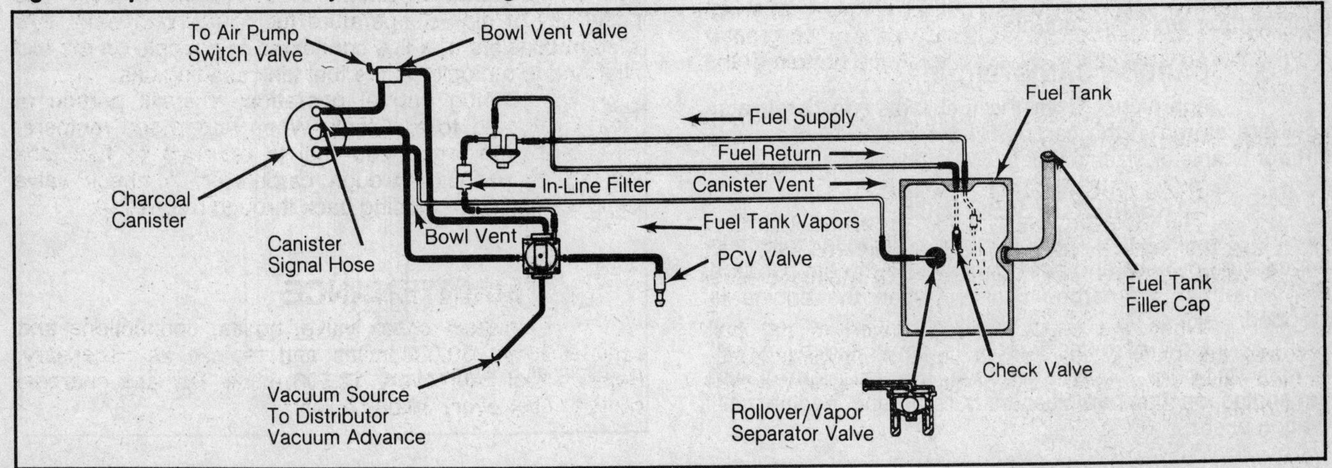

1983 Fuel Evaporation Control

FORD MOTOR CO. FUEL VAPOR EMISSION CONTROL

DESCRIPTION

This system is designed to prevent fuel vapors (hydrocarbons), from the fuel tank and carburetor, from being emitted into the atmosphere.

The system consists of a sealed fuel tank, pressure/vacuum relief fuel cap, fuel tank vapor valve, vapor tube and hoses, and a carbon canister.

Systems are also equipped with a purge control valve, solenoid vent valve, purge regulator valve, thermactor idle vacuum valve (TIV), thermal vent valve and external bowl vent solenoid.

NOTE: **Not all of these components are used on any one system. Component usage depends on the calibration of the complete vehicle.**

OPERATION

FILL CONTROL/VENT SYSTEM

Fill limiting is accomplished through the configuration of the fill neck and/or internal vent lines within the fill neck and tank. The vent system is designed to permit air space in 10-12 percent of the tank when the tank is filled to capacity.

The air space provides for thermal expansion of fuel as well as being an aid to the in tank vapor vent system.

VAPOR VENT SYSTEM

This system provides a vapor space above the gasoline surface in the fuel tank. This area is sufficient to permit adequate breathing space for the tank vapor valve assembly.

All vapor valves use a small orifice that allows only vapor and not solid fuel to pass into the line running to the canister. The vapor valve is mounted on the fuel tank using a rubber grommet.

Fuel vapors trapped in the sealed fuel tank are vented though the vapor valve assembly on top of the fuel tank. The vapors are then routed through a single vapor line to the carbon canister in the engine compartment.

The vapors are stored in the carbon canister until they are purged into the engine while the engine is operating.

On vehicles equipped with fuel/vapor return lines, vapor generated in the fuel supply line is continuously vented back to the fuel tank. This venting prevents engine surging from fuel enrichment and assists in hydrocarbon emission control.

CARBON CANISTER

Fuel vapor from the fuel tank and carburetor bowl are stored in the carbon-filled canister. There are 2 different canister sizes used: 925ML and 1400ML.

CARBURETOR VENTING

Fuel vapors which might otherwise collect in the carburetor bowl and pass directly into the atmosphere are vented to the carbon canister when the engine is stopped.

Flow of these vapors is controlled by a fuel bowl vent valve or a fuel bowl thermal vent valve, depending on the particluar carburetor and engine calibration used.

When the engine is started, the vapors will be drawn into the engine for burning. The time at which the vapors are drawn into the engine will depend on the operating mode of the engine when the purging system is most efficient.

PURGE CONTROL VALVE

The purge control valve is in line with the carbon canister. The purge control valve controls the flow of fuel vapors into and out of the carbon canister.

Fig. 1: Purge Control Valve & Carbon Canister

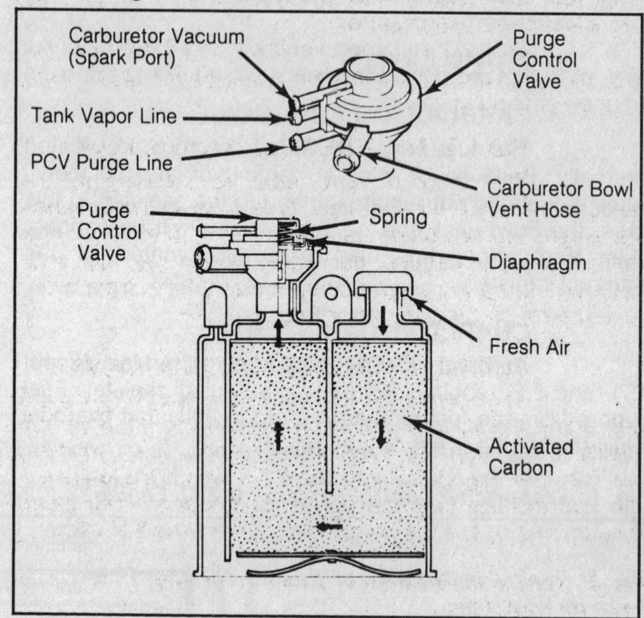

FUEL BOWL SOLENOID VENT VALVE

The fuel bowl solenoid vent valve is a normally open valve. This valve is located in the fuel bowl vent line. It is used on some Motorcraft 2150 and 7200 carburetors.

Fig. 2: Cutaway View of Fuel Bowl Solenoid Vent Valve

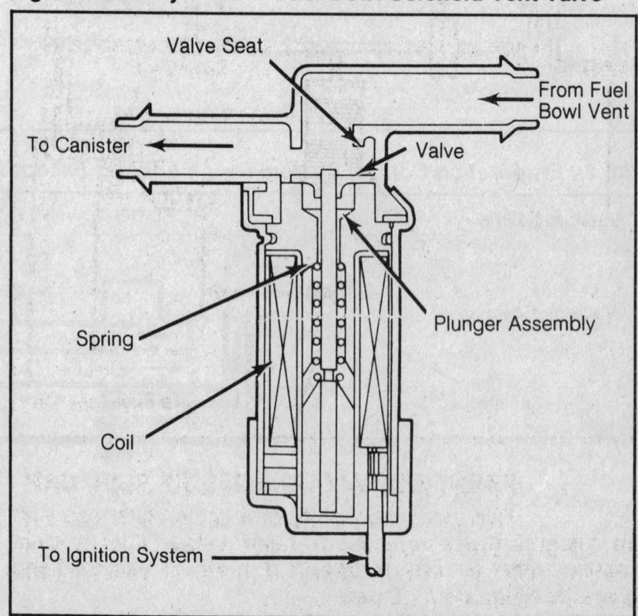

FORD MOTOR CO. FUEL VAPOR EMISSION CONTROL (Cont.)

The 7200 carburetor is also equipped with a built-in fuel bowl vent valve.

The solenoid vent valve closes off the fuel bowl vent line when the engine is running. When the ignition switch is turned off, the solenoid vent valve returns to the normally open postion.

If a lean fuel mixture is suspected as the cause of a problem, inspect either the solenoid vent valve or the fuel bowl vent valve for proper closing during engine operation.

If the valve opens, allowing purge vacuum to effect fuel bowl balanced air pressure, the carburetor will give a leaner air/fuel mixture.

On EEC equipped vehicles with 7200 carburetors, the opposite condition (rich mixture) will result from an open or leaking valve.

FUEL BOWL THERMAL VENT VALVE

The thermal vent valve is inserted in the carburetor-to-canister vent line. This valve is closed when the engine compartment temperature is cold. This prevents fuel tank vapors, generated when the fuel tank heats up before the engine compartment does, from being vented through the carburetor fuel bowl.

THERMACTOR IDLE VACUUM VALVE

The thermactor idle vacuum valve (TIV) is used with some evaporative emission systems to improve idle quality at hot start. To overcome this poor idle condition, the TIV valve bleeds air into the PCV tube. This leans the idle fuel mixture until the purge valve opens. The same vacuum that opens the purge valve closes the TIV valve.

Fig. 3: Typical Installation of Thermactor Idle Vacuum Vent Valve

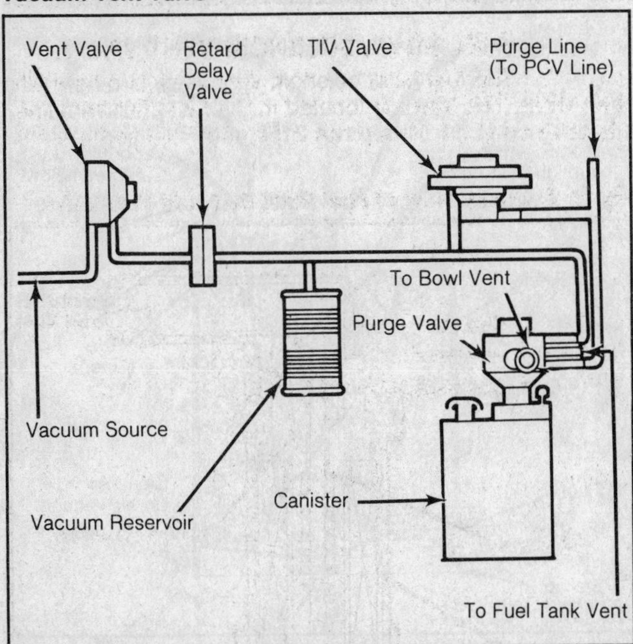

PRESSURE/VACUUM RELIEF FUEL CAP

This system consists of a sealed filler cap with an integral pressure/vacuum relief valve. Fuel system vacuum relief is provide after 1.0 in Hg of vacuum, and pressure relief after 1.8 psi.

Under Normal conditions, the fill cap allows air to enter the fuel tank as fuel is used while preventing vapors from escaping.

FUEL VAPOR RETURN SYSTEM

This system consists of a vapor return line from the fuel pump to the fuel return outlet of the fuel sender. This reduces the amount of fuel vapor entering the carburetor.

AIR CLEANER ASSEMBLY

On some models, an auxiliary fuel bowl vent tube runs to the air cleaner. An air filter installed on the air cleaner end of the fuel bowl vent tube keeps dirt out of the carburetor fuel bowl.

MAINTENANCE

No scheduled maintenance is required. All hoses and connections should be checked periodically for cracks, leaks or other damage and replaced as necessary.

1983 Fuel Evaporation Control

GENERAL MOTORS EVAPORATIVE CONTROL SYSTEM

DESCRIPTION

Carbon storage is the basic method of evaporative control on all General Motors vehicles. This reduces the amount of gasoline vapor emissions (hydrocarbons).

Fuel vapors are stored in the carbon canister until they can be drawn into the engine for burning during the combustion process. This system burns fuel vapors in the engine rather than venting vapors into the atmosphere.

The fuel tank and the carburetor fuel bowl are vented through a hose into a canister containing activated carbon. The carbon adsorbs the fuel vapors when the engine is not operating. When the engine is started, fuel vapors are drawn from the canister into the engine.

Carbon canisters can be of either open or closed design. The open design draws fresh air from the filter in the bottom of the canister. The closed design draws fresh air from the air cleaner.

Some models use an electric solenoid or a thermostatically controlled vacuum valve, combined with ported vacuum, to control the canister purge function.

Fig. 1: Cutaway View of Basic 2-Tube Vapor Canister

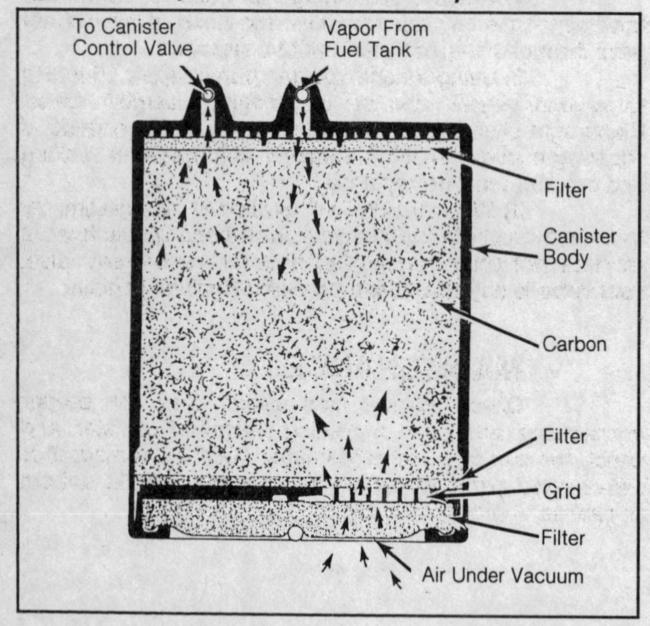

OPERATION

BASIC 2-TUBE CANISTER

Gasoline vapors from the fuel tank flow into the canister and are adsorbed by the carbon. The canister is purged when the engine is running above idle speeds.

A timed vacuum source is applied to the canister to draw fresh air through the bottom of the canister. The fresh air mixes with the fuel vapors and are drawn into the intake manifold to be burned in the engine.

Some models are equipped with a second canister purge hose. This hose is connected to a canister control valve (CCV). The CCV is then connected to the carburetor bowl vent line.

This allows the carburetor bowl to be vented to the canister, through the CCV, when the engine is not running. These vapors are then drawn into the intake manifold once the engine is started.

NOTE: **There are several variations of the basic 2-tube canister. A canister may be equipped with one or more of the following variations.**

Canister with Center Cone

The center cone on the canister is a separator wall inside the canister. This wall surrounds the fuel tank vapor inlet.

The wall prevents driveability problems by keeping fuel tank vapors from traveling directly into the intake manifold when the engine is operating at off idle speeds.

This causes fuel tank vapors to be forced into the canister before being drawn into the engine.

3-Tube Canister

This variation provides venting of the carburetor fuel bowl as well as the fuel tank. Fuel vapors in the float bowl are drawn through a hose to the third tube on the canister.

These vapors are then adsorbed in the canister and purged to the intake mainfold when the engine is started.

Vapor Vent Valve Canister

This variation of the 3-tube canister prevents venting of the carburetor bowl when the engine is operating. The vapor vent valve is a spring controlled diaphragm valve. When the engine is running the valve is closed.

This prevents vapors from the carburetor float bowl from being drawn into the canister. When the engine is turned off, spring pressure opens the valve. This allows vapors from the float bowl to be vented to the canister.

Fig. 2: Cutaway View of Carbon Canister with Vapor Vent Valve

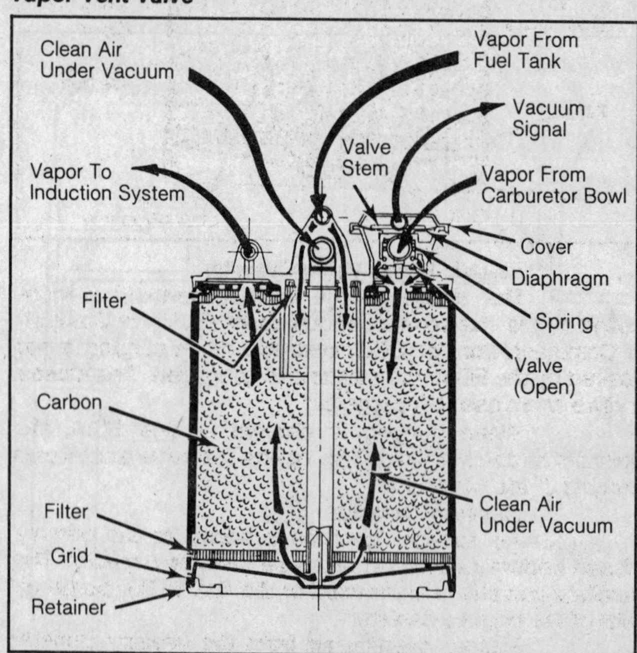

Closed Bottom Canister

The closed bottom canister keeps water from entering the bottom of the canister. If water enters the bottom of the canister, it could freeze and restrict purging air flow.

On these canisters, fresh air is drawn from the clean side of the air cleaner assembly. The air cleaner is

GENERAL MOTORS EVAPORATIVE CONTROL SYSTEM (Cont.)

equipped with a activated carbon filter. This filter is to adsorb any fuel vapors that may escape from the purge air inlet on the canister.

Purge Valve Canister

The purge valve is a spring controlled valve which is normally closed. This valve prevents or allows purging of the canister.

When the engine is off or idling, the valve is closed. This prevents canister purging. When the engine is running above idle speed, manifold vacuum pulls the valve open. This allows the canister to be purged.

Fig. 3: Cutaway View of Carbon Canister with Purge Control Valve & Vapor Vent Valve

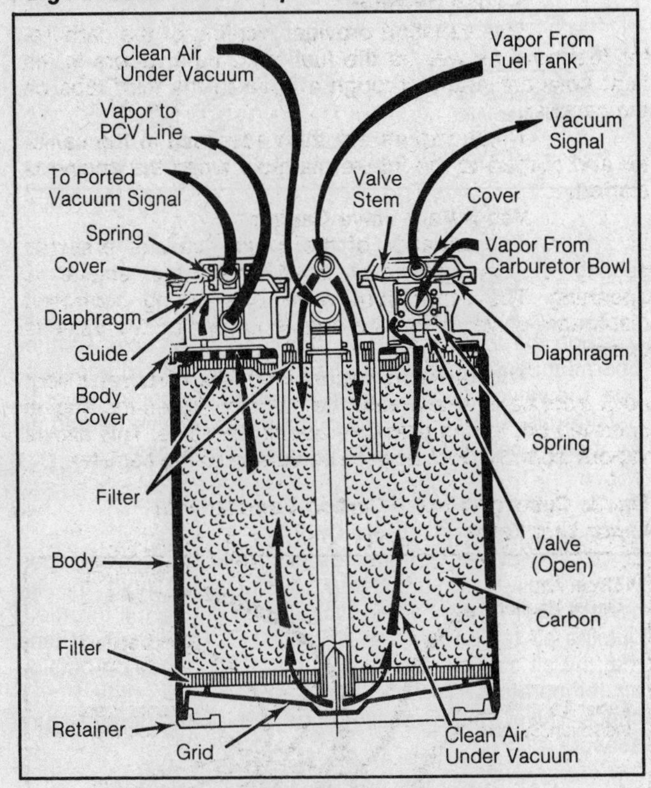

Electric Purge Valve Canister

The electric purge control solenoid is controlled by the electronic control module (ECM) on Computer Command Control (CCC) systems. When purging is not desired by the ECM, the solenoid is energized. This closes a valve and closes off purge air.

When purging is desired by the ECM, the solenoid is de-energized. This opens the valve and allows purging of the canister.

Auxiliary Canister

An auxiliary canister is added to the primary closed bottom canister to increase canister capacity. The auxiliary canister is connected in the line to the purge air inlet of the primary canister.

Vapors overflowing from the primary canister are stored in the auxiliary canister. During purging, the excess vapors are routed to the intake manifold for burning in the engine.

CANISTER CONTROL VALVE

There are 2 types of canister control valves:

The first type of valve performs the same function as the vapor vent valve.

The second type of valve performs the function of both the vapor vent valve and the purge valve. When the engine is running, manifold vacuum from the PCV system pulls the lower diaphragm upward. This shuts off venting of the carburetor float bowl.

When the engine is running, control vacuum pulls the upper diaphragm upward. This allows purging of the canister through the PCV system.

FUEL TANK PRESSURE CONTROL VALVE

The fuel tank pressure control valve is a spring controlled valve. When the engine is running, vacuum is applied to the valve and the valve is opened. This allows vapors from the fuel tank to vent to the canister.

When the engine is not running, the valve closes. This causes the fuel tank vapors to be vented through the restriction in the valve. This restriction is to retain most of the fuel tank vapors in the fuel tank.

TESTING

1) Install a short length of hose on carburetor bowl vent tube of canister. Blow into hose. If air will not pass through hose, canister must be replaced.

2) Using a hand vacuum pump, apply 15 in. Hg to vacuum signal tube on diaphragm assembly cover. Diaphragm should hold vacuum for at least 20 seconds. If diaphragm does not hold vacuum, diaphragm is leaking and canister must be replaced.

3) With vacuum still applied to diaphragm, try to blow through carburetor bowl vent hose on canister. If air does not enter the canister past the vapor vent valve, vent valve is not functioning properly. Replace canister.

MAINTENANCE

Check all fuel and vapor lines for proper connections and correct routing. Remove canister and check for cracks or other damage. Replace damaged or deteriorated parts as necessary. Replace filter in bottom of canister if dirty or clogged.

1983 Exhaust Emission Systems

THERMOSTATIC AIR CLEANERS — ALL MODELS

DESCRIPTION

All passenger cars are equipped with a system for preheating the air entering the carburetor or fuel injection unit.

This device maintains incoming air temperature at a point where the carburetor or fuel injection unit can be calibrated much leaner to reduce hydrocarbon (HC) emissions. This also improves warm-up operations and reduces carburetor icing.

This system consists of an air cleaner assembly, integral air control door, vacuum control temperature sensor, vacuum motor(s) or thermostatic spring, heat shroud (on exhaust manifold), heated air tube and vacuum hoses.

Some models also use additional controls such as vacuum traps, cold weather modulators, vacuum check valves and vacuum delay valves.

Fig. 1: Exploded View of Thermostatic Air Cleaner Assembly

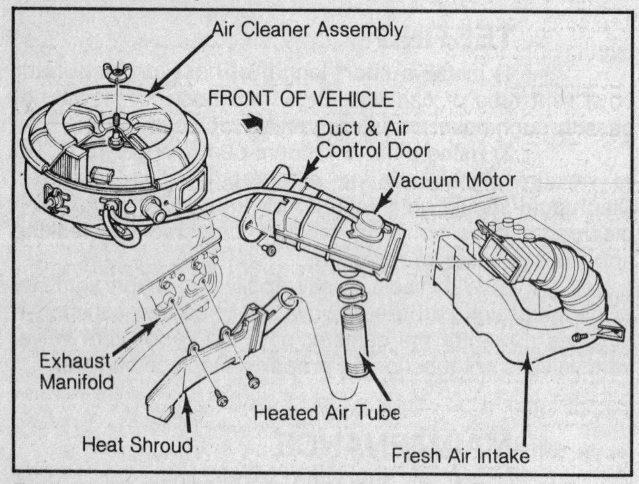

Ford models shown, other models are similar.

OPERATION

When the temperature of the air entering the air cleaner is less than the calibrated temperature of the temperature sensor, the sensor closes. This allows engine vacuum to operate the vacuum motor.

When engine vacuum is applied to the vacuum motor, the door closes off outside air. Air is then drawn into the air cleaner from around the exhaust manifold.

As air inside the air cleaner warms, the temperature sensor begins to close. This gradually bleeds off vacuum to the vacuum motor. As vacuum to the vacuum motor decreases, the air control door begins to open.

As the air control door opens, outside air is allowed to enter the air cleaner assembly. When the air entering the air cleaner reaches a predetermined temperature, the air control door opens completely. This completely closes off air from around the exhaust manifold.

On American Motors vehicles equipped with 4.2L 6-cylinder engines, a vacuum motor controlled trap door is also used. This door is designed to close when the engine is not running. This prevents fuel vapors from escaping into the atmosphere when the engine is not running.

Fig. 2: Thermostatic Air Cleaner Assembly with Temperature Sensor & Vacuum Motor

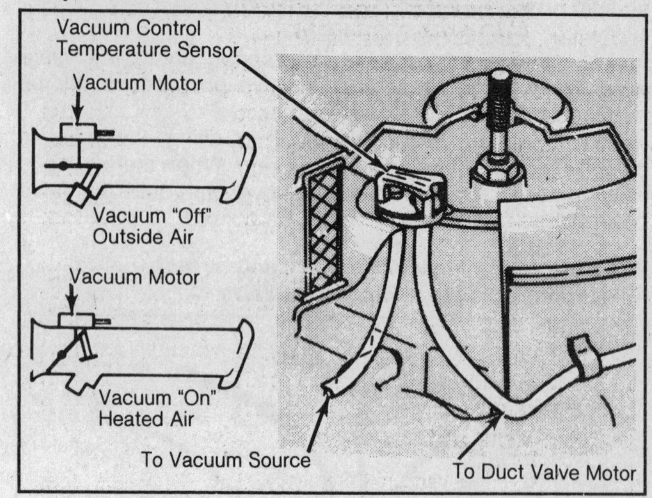

VACUUM CHECK VALVE & DELAY VALVE

A vacuum check valve and/or delay valve is used on the thermostatic air cleaner. During cold weather operation, and when engine is under full or hard acceleration, the valve will postpone opening of the control door to outside air. The engine will continue to receive heated air for a short period of time to improve driveability.

VACUUM TRAP

General Motors Only

Some General Motors vehicles are equipped with a built-in vacuum trap, designed to hold the air control door in the heated air position during full throttle if outside air temperature is below 70°F. The length of time that the air control door is held closed depends on outside air temperature. The vacuum trap can be identified by a check valve in the small orifice leg of the temperature sensor.

Fig. 3: Thermostatic Air Cleaner Assembly Showing Air Flow into Carburetor

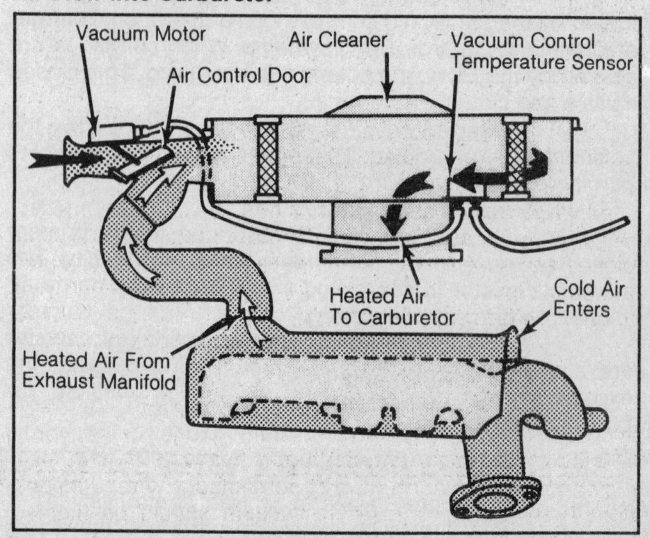

THERMOSTATIC AIR CLEANERS — ALL MODELS (Cont.)

COLD WEATHER MODULATOR

Ford Motor Co. Only

Some Ford Motor Co. vehicles have a vacuum modulator located in the air cleaner. During engine operations in cold weather, it prevents the air cleaner duct door from opening to non-heated intake air. When available outside air is above 55°F (13°C), the cold weather modulator does not operate.

Fig. 4: Ford Motor Co. Cold Weather Modulator

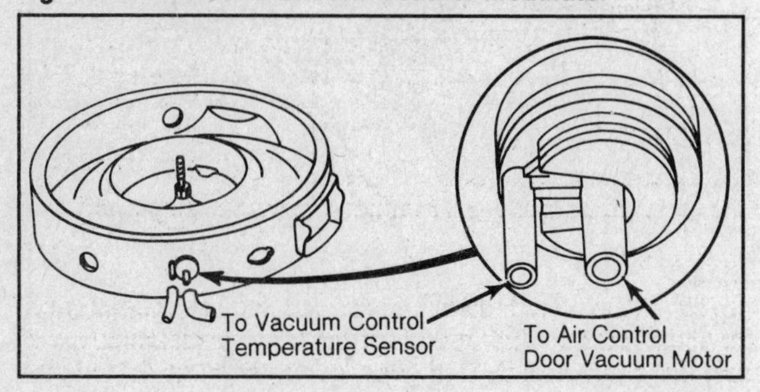

TESTING

NOTE: See Specifications tables for correct specifications when performing the following tests.

VACUUM CONTROL TEMPERATURE SENSOR SPECIFICATIONS

Application	Heated Air Temp. °F (°C)	Fresh Air Temp. °F (°C)
American Motors	40 (4)	55 (13)
Chrysler Corp.		
1.6L, 1.7L & 2.2L	65 (18)	90 (32)
2.6L	84 (29)	113 (45)
3.7L & 5.2L	50 (10)	100 (38)
Ford Motor Co.		
Sensor Color Code		
Brown	75 (24)	75 (24)
Black or Pink	75 (24)	90 (32)
Blue, Yellow or Green	75 (24)	105 (41)
General Motors		
Buick	70 (21)	162 (72)
Cadillac	77 (25)	123 (50)
Chevrolet		
Cavalier & Corvette	86 (30)	131 (55)
Chevette	80 (27)	100 (38)
All Other Models	77 (25)	123 (50)
Oldsmobile	77 (25)	123 (50)
Pontiac	77 (25)	123 (50)

VACUUM CONTROL TEMPERATURE SENSOR

American Motors

1) Disconnect vacuum hoses from sensor. Connect vacuum pump and vacuum gauge to sensor. Make sure that sensor temperature is below 40°F (4°C).

2) Apply 14 in. Hg to sensor. With sensor temperature below 40°F (4°C), vacuum should be maintained. Heat sensor to above 55°F (13°C).

3) Air bleed valve should open and vacuum should decrease to zero. Replace sensor if it does not meet specifications.

All Other Models

1) Tape a thermometer close to the vacuum control temperature sensor located inside the air cleaner. Leave wing nuts off top of air cleaner so that top can be quickly removed to read thermometer during test.

2) With engine cold, temperature below vacuum control temperature sensor specifications, check air control door in air cleaner. It should be in fully open position (open to outside air).

3) Start engine. As soon as engine starts, door should move to full heated air position (closed to outside air). Watch air control door.

4) When door reaches fully open position, quickly remove air cleaner top and read thermometer. Compare thermometer reading with specifications.

5) If reading is not to specifications, perform vacuum motor test. If vacuum motor is okay replace sensor.

VACUUM MOTOR TEST

1) Remove air cleaner from vehicle. Disconnect vacuum hose from vacuum motor. Apply 20 in. Hg vacuum to motor and pinch off hose.

2) Vacuum should not leak down more than 10 in. Hg in 5 minutes. If vacuum motor does leak down, replace it.

3) Connect a vacuum pump to vacuum motor. Apply specified amount of vacuum to vacuum motor to open or close heated air door. If door does not open or close at specified vacuum, replace vacuum motor.

AIR CONTROL DOOR OPENING/CLOSING VACUUM

Application	Vacuum In. Hg
American Motors	4
Chrysler Corp.	
1.6L, 1.7L, 2.2L & 2.6L	2-4
3.7L & 5.2L	5.5
Ford Motor Co.	[1]
General Motors	7

[1] — Information not available from manufacturer.

VACUUM MOTOR TRAP DOOR TEST

American Motors 4.2L Only

1) Remove air cleaner cover and note position of trap door. It should be closed. Remove trap door vacuum hose at intake manifold and connect a vacuum pump.

2) Apply 2-4 in. Hg to trap door. Trap door should open. If door does not open, apply vacuum directly to vacuum motor. If trap door does not open, check for binding and/or distortion and adjust as necessary.

3) Replace vacuum motor if trap door swings freely. If trap door opened when vacuum was directly applied to vacuum motor, check vacuum hose for restrictions or leaks.

4) If vacuum hose is not defective, remove reverse delay valve and retest. If door now opens, test reverse delay valve for proper operation.

5) Reverse delay valve provides approximately 100 seconds of delay before allowing trap door to

THERMOSTATIC AIR CLEANERS — ALL MODELS (Cont.)

completely close. To test, remove vacuum hose from Yellow end of valve and apply 2-4 in. Hg to valve.

6) Note time for atmospheric pressure to pass through valve and eliminate vacuum. If time required to eliminate vacuum is less than 4 seconds or more than 13 seconds, replace reverse delay valve.

NOTE: If reverse delay valve is replaced, make sure that Yellow end of valve faces vacuum motor.

COLD WEATHER MODULATOR

Ford Motor Co. Only

1) Connect a vacuum gauge to vacuum supply side of modulator. Connect an auxiliary vacuum pump to vacuum motor side of modulator. Apply 16 in. Hg of vacuum with auxiliary vacuum pump.

2) When modulator holds vacuum, it should not leak down to less than 5 in. Hg. If is does, replace modulator. If modulator temperature is above leak down temperature and it holds vacuum, replace modulator.

COLD WEATHER MODULATOR SPECIFICATIONS

Modulator Color/Type	Holds Vacuum @ °F (°C)	Leaks Vacuum @ °F (°C)
Brown/ Normally Open	5 (-15)	40 (4)
Purple/ Normally Open	30 (-1)	60 (16)
Red/ Normally Closed	40 (4)	80 (27)
White/ Normally Open	40 (4)	80 (27)

CATALYTIC CONVERTERS — ALL MODELS

DESCRIPTION & OPERATION

CATALYTIC CONVERTERS

The catalytic converter(s) is installed in the exhaust system in front of the muffler so that all exhaust gases must pass through it. The converter is a stainless steel, muffler shaped, device that reduces exhaust emissions.

There are 2 types of catalytic converters, oxidation and 3-way converters. The oxidation type converter contains material that is coated with platinum and palladium. This catalyst reduces hydrocarbons (HC) and carbon monoxide (CO).

The 3-way converters contain material coated with platinum, palladium and rhodium. This catalyst reduces hydrocarbons (HC), carbon monoxide (CO) and oxides of nitrogen (NOx).

Fig. 1: Cutaway View of Dual-Bed Catalytic Converter

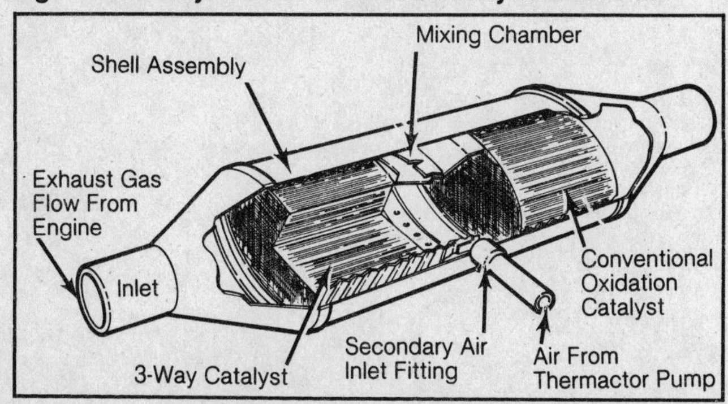

The catalyst may be one of 2 types: a honeycomb-type block that is non-serviceable, or small ceramic beads that can be removed and replaced on some models.

Use only unleaded fuel on vehicles equipped with a catalytic converter. If leaded fuel is used, the Tetra Ethyl Lead in the fuel will coat the palladium, platinum and rhodium. If this coating effect takes place, the converter is useless. If this happens, the converter must be replaced.

The 3-way catalytic converter is used in conjunction with the conventional oxidation catalytic converter. All models with the oxygen sensor/feedback carburetor system use this type of converter.

American Motors, Chrysler Corp. and Ford Motor Co. use 2 separate converters while General Motors uses only 1 converter.

On some Ford Motor Co. models, the first converter in the exhaust system is a light off catalyst converter. This is a single bed converter designed to control exhaust emissions during engine warm-up, when the main converter is not at a temperature required for maximum efficiency.

On all other models, the first converter (3-way) in the exhaust system reduces hydrocarbons (HC) and carbon monoxide (CO), but mainly oxides of nitrogen (NOx). The second converter (oxidation type) reduces, with extra air from the AIR pump, hydrocarbons (HC) and carbon monoxide (CO) only.

HEAT SHIELDS

The combustion reaction, which is furthered by the converter, releases additional heat into the exhuast system. Temperatures in the catalytic converter can reach 1600°F (871°C) under normal conditions.

Special heat shields are used to protect the underbody and under-vehicle components from this extreme heat.

SERVICE PROCEDURES

MAINTENANCE

There is no scheduled maintenance of the catalytic converter since it is designed to last the lifetime of the vehicle. However, on American Motors vehicles equipped with converters that are filled with catalyst coated beads (all models except Alliance), bead removal and replacement is possible.

SHELL REPLACEMENT

General Motors Only

1) Remove bottom cover by making a shallow cut close to the bottom outside edge. *See Fig. 2.* A shallow cut is required to avoid damage to inner shell.

Fig. 2: Removal of Catalytic Converter Bottom Cover

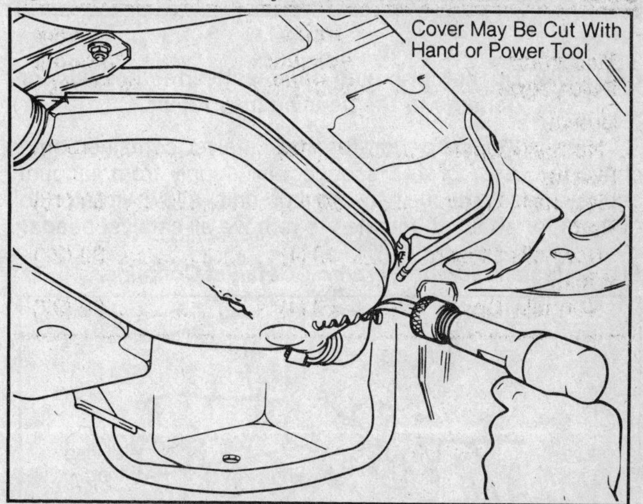

Bottom cover can be replaced on General Motors vehicles only.

2) Remove insulation and check inner shell for damage. If damage to inner shell is found, the entire catalytic converter must be replaced.

3) If no damage is found, position new insulation into replacement cover. Apply a heat resistant sealer around edge of cover, using extra sealer at front and rear of pipe openings.

4) Install replacement cover on converter and position retaining channel along edges. Complete installation by attaching clamps, provided with replacement cover, to both ends of converter.

CATALYST REPLACEMENT

American Motors (Except Alliance)

1) Raise vehicle on hoist. Attach vacuum aspirator device (J-25077) to exhaust pipe. *See Fig. 3.* Attach air supply to air hose fitting on vacuum pump. Apply enough air pressure (minimum 80 psi) to hold catalyst beads in place.

2) Drive a small chisel between fill plug and converter housing, making sure not to damage housing. Continue driving small chisel into plug until plug is deformed enough to be removed with pliers.

CATALYTIC CONVERTERS — ALL MODELS (Cont.)

Fig. 3: Attaching Vacuum Aspirator to Tailpipe

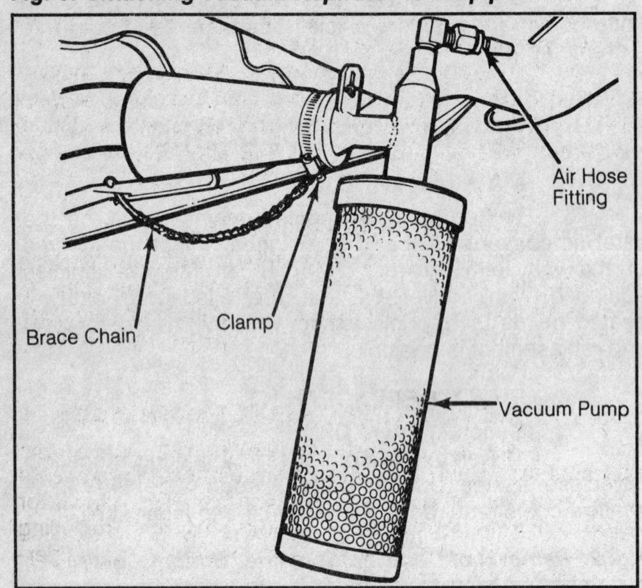

CAUTION: Do not pry plug from converter housing or damage to the housing may result.

3) Clamp vibrator and catalyst container onto converter. *See Fig. 4*. Disconnect air supply from vacuum aspirator and attach it to vibrator unit. Allow vibrator to operate for about 10 minutes to remove all catalyst beads.

Fig. 4: Installation of Vibrator & Catalyst Container

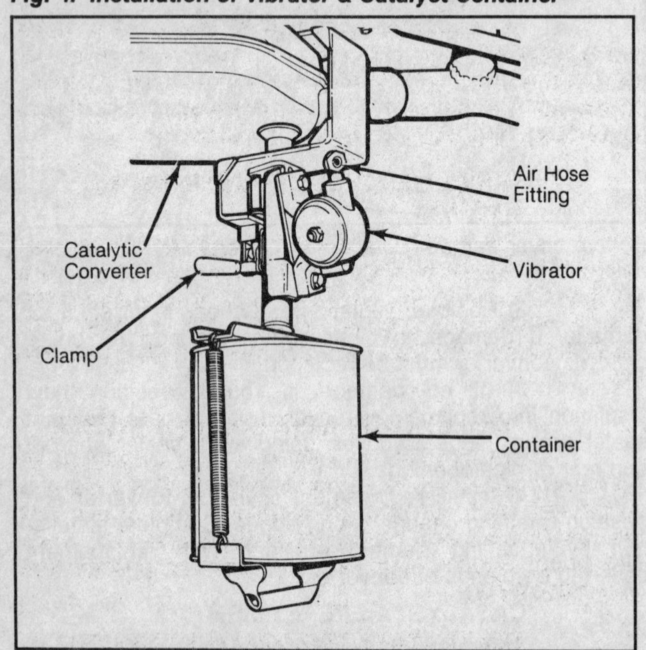

4) When all catalyst material is removed, disconnect air supply and remove container from converter. Discard catalyst beads. Fill container with approved replacement catalyst beads. Install a fill tube fixture to vibrator device.

5) Attach air supply to both vibrator and aspirator. With container attached to fill tube, catalyst will begin to move into converter.

6) When catalyst stops flowing, disconnect air supply to vibrator and note level of catalyst. It should be even with the fill plug. Add more catalyst if required.

NOTE: If any beads exit through the tailpipe during refilling of the converter, the converter is defective and must be replaced.

7) Apply a anti-seize compound to fill plug. Install plug and tighten. If equipped with a press type fill plug, install a "bridge-and-bolt" type service plug and tighten to 28 ft. lbs. (38 N.m).

AMERICAN MOTORS SYSTEMS & TUNE-UP PROCEDURES

DESCRIPTION

Several emission control systems are used on American Motors vehicles. System usage varies depending on model, engine and transmission.

SINGLE AIR INJECTION SYSTEM

The single air injection system is used on all Federal models equipped with 2.5L 4-cylinder engines and manual transmissions. This system is used to inject air into each exhaust port to assist in more complete burning of the combustion mixture. System air pressure is regulated by a diverter valve located between the air pump and exhaust manifold.

NOTE: The 1.4L 4-cylinder engine is not equipped with an air injection system.

DUAL AIR INJECTION SYSTEM

The dual air injection system is used on all 6-cylinder engines. This system is used to inject air into the exhaust ports and the catalytic converter.

The system is regulated by the Computerized Emission Control system, through a number of controlling solenoids and valves, for more complete burning of the combustion mixutre.

EXHAUST GAS RECIRCULATION (EGR)

The EGR system consists of a diaphragm actuated EGR valve, back-pressure sensor on some models, thermal vacuum switch (TVS), coolant temperature override (CTO) switch and connecting vacuum hoses.

The EGR system introduces metered amounts of exhaust gas into the combustion chamber. This lowers peak combustion chamber temperatures and reduces oxides of nitrogen (NOx) emissions.

COMPUTER CONTROLLED CATALYTIC CONVERTER (C-4)

The C-4 system is used on some 2.5L 4-cylinder engines. The C-4 system closely controls air/fuel ratio through a feedback system. The feedback portion of the system is signaled by an oxygen sensor in the exhaust system.

The major components of this system include an exhaust gas oxygen sensor, an electronic control module, a special electronically controlled air/fuel ratio carburetor and a catalytic converter.

COMPUTERIZED EMISSION CONTROL (CEC) SYSTEM

1.4L 4-Cylinder

The 1.4L CEC system is used on Federal models only. The major function of this system is to reduce exhaust emissions by controlling air/fuel ratio, ignition timing, idle speed and emission control devices.

The major components of this system are the electronic control unit (ECU), oxygen sensor, manifold air temperature sensor (MAT), coolant temperature sensor (CTS), manifold absolute pressure sensor (MAP), wide open throttle switch (WOT) and throttle position sensor (TPS).

2.5L 4-Cylinder & 4.2L 6-Cylinder

The CEC system is used on some 2.5L 4-cylinder engines and on all 4.2L 6-cylinder engines. The CEC system closely controls air/fuel ratio through a feedback system. The feedback system is signaled by an oxygen sensor in the exhaust system.

The major components of this system include an exhaust gas oxygen sensor, vacuum switches, temperature switches, a micro computer unit (MCU) and a special carburetor with a stepper motor that controls the air/fuel mixture.

CATALYTIC CONVERTER

All models are equipped with a catalytic converter to control exhaust emissions. Some 2.5L 4-cylinder engines are equipped with an additional monolithic-type converter. For additional information, see Catalytic Converter article.

THERMOSTATIC AIR CLEANER (TAC)

All models are equipped with a vacuum operated air cleaner system for controlling temperature of air entering the carburetor or injection unit. This allows for more accurate combustion control, thereby reducing exhaust emissions. For additional information, see Thermostatic Air Cleaners article.

POSITIVE CRANKCASE VENTILATION (PCV)

The PCV system controls crankcase vapors by drawing them into the engine to be burned with the air/fuel mixture during the combustion process. For additional information, see Positive Crankcase Ventilation article.

EVAPORATIVE EMISSION CONTROL SYSTEM

A closed fuel system is incorporated to route fuel vapors into the air cleaner to be burned with the air/fuel mixture. This prevents fuel vapors from escaping to the atmosphere. For additional information, see American Motors Fuel Vapor Control System article.

DUCELLIER ELECTRONIC IGNITION SYSTEM

The Ducellier Electronic Ignition system is used on all 1.4L 4-cylinder engines. The system consists of a computer, a distributor, an ignition coil, a vacuum sensor and a crankshaft position sensor. The ignition coil, vacuum sensor and computer are mounted as an assembly.

HIGH ENERGY IGNITION (HEI) SYSTEM

The HEI ignition system is used on all 2.5L 4-cylinder engines. The HEI system consists of a battery, a distributor which contains an electronic control unit and the ignition coil, and conventional distributor cap, wires and plugs. System also uses conventional primary and secondary wiring.

SOLID STATE IGNITION (SSI) SYSTEM

The SSI ignition system is used on all 6-cylinder engines. The SSI system consists of a solid state distributor, an electronic control unit, an ignition coil and conventional distributor cap, rotor, plug wires and spark plugs. The system is also equipped with a primary resistance wire and a by-pass wire.

AMERICAN MOTORS SYSTEMS & TUNE-UP PROCEDURES (Cont.)

TUNE-UP SERVICE PROCEDURES

In addition to servicing of the individual emission systems, it is important that all ignition timing and carburetor adjustments are properly set.

Due to late changes and corrections, always refer to the Engine Tune-Up Decal in the engine compartment before performing tune-up procedures. In the event that specifications in this manual and decal specifications differ, always use the decal specifications.

IGNITION TIMING

NOTE: 2.5L and 4.2L engines are equipped with a magnetic probe timing socket for use with special electronic timing equipment. Refer to the equipment manufacturers instructions for procedures. Do not use the probe location to check ignition timing with a conventional timing light.

1.4L Engine

Initial ignition timing is controlled by the ignition module and is not adjustable.

Fig. 1: 1.4L Firing Order & Distributor Location

Timing is not adjustable on 1.4L engine.

Fig. 2: 2.5L Firing Order & Timing Marks

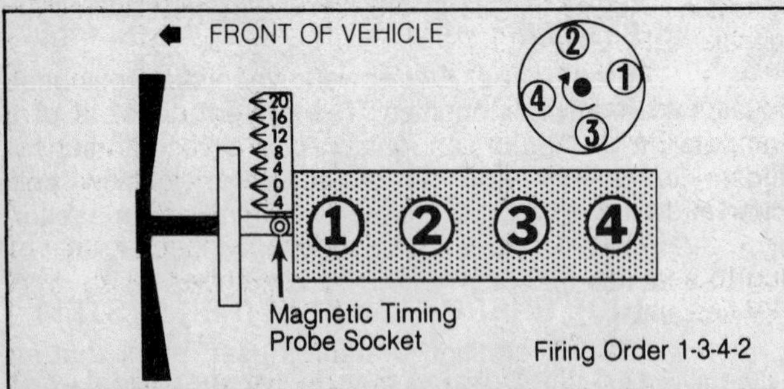

Fig. 3: 4.2L Firing Order & Timing Marks

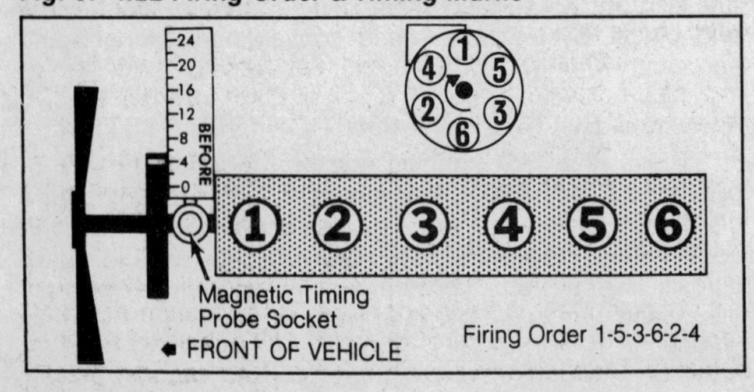

2.5L & 4.2L Engines

Check and/or adjust ignition timing with engine at normal operating temperature, distributor vacuum advance hose disconnected (if equipped) and engine running at specified RPM.

IGNITION TIMING SPECIFICATIONS

Application	[1] Degrees BTDC @ RPM
1.4L	[2]
2.5L	
Federal	
Man. Trans.	10 @ 800-1000
Auto. Trans.	10 @ 600-800
Calif.	
Man. Trans.	12 @ 800-1000
Auto. Trans.	12 @ 600-800
4.2L	
Federal & Calif.	6 @ 1600
High Alt.	13 @ 1600

[1] — On non A/C models, set with solenoid activated. On A/C models, set with A/C switch OFF and solenoid deactivated.

[2] — Initial timing is not adjustable on this engine.

HOT (SLOW) IDLE RPM

1.4L AFC Engine

1) Start engine and allow it to reach normal operating temperature. Connect positive lead of tachometer to diagnostic connector pin D1-1. Connect negative lead of tachometer to diagnostic connector pin D1-3.

NOTE: Diagnostic connector is located in engine compartment on right fenderwell. For pin location, see AMC Alliance Computerized Engine Control System article.

Fig. 4: 1.4L AFC Curb Idle Adjusting Screw Location

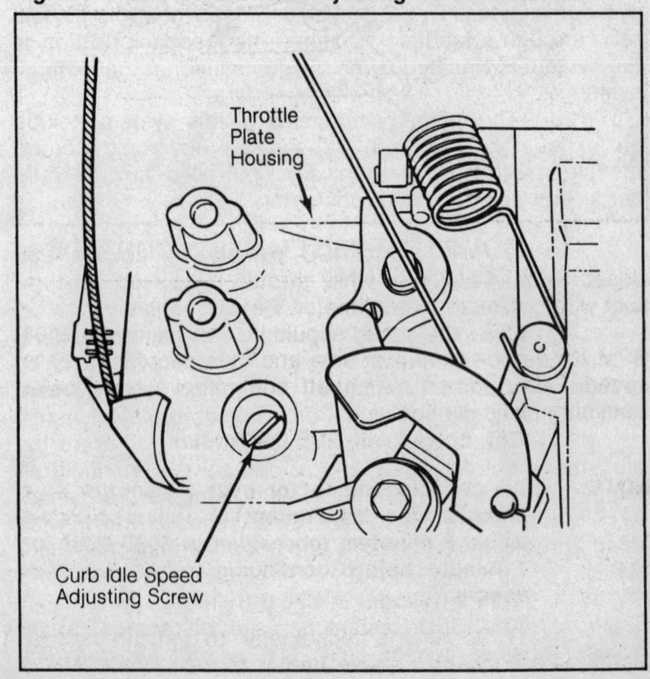

AMERICAN MOTORS SYSTEMS & TUNE-UP PROCEDURES (Cont.)

2) Turn all accessories off. Wait for electric cooling fan to come on and then turn off. Adjust throttle plate by-pass screw to obtain specified idle speed. *See Fig. 4*. Remove tachometer leads from diagnostic connector.

1.4L TBI Engine

NOTE: **Adjustment of the Idle Speed Control (ISC) motor plunger is only necessary to set the initial position of the plunger when the ISC motor has been replaced.**

1) Remove air filter assembly. Start engine and allow it to reach normal operating temperature. Turn air conditioner off.

2) Connect negative lead of tachometer to diagnostic connector pin D1-3. Connect positive lead of tachometer to diagnostic connector pin D1-1. Turn ignition switch off. ISC plunger should move to fully extended position.

3) With ISC plunger fully extended, remove wire connector from ISC motor. Restart engine. Engine idle speed should be 3300-3700 RPM. If idle speed is not correct, turn hex head of ISC plunger to obtain 3500 RPM. *See Fig. 5*.

Fig. 5: 1.4L TBI Idle Speed Control Motor Adjustment

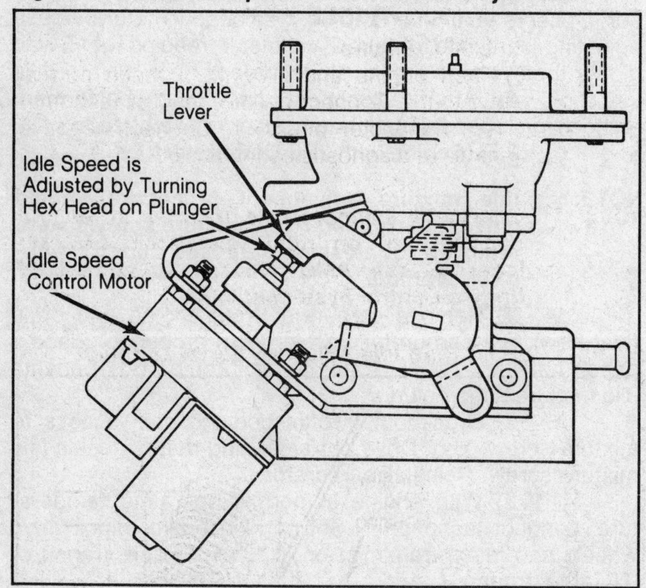

4) Fully retract ISC plunger by holding the closed throttle switch in while throttle is opened. Reconnect wire connector to ISC motor. Restart engine.

5) Engine speed should be approximately 3500 RPM for a short period of time and then decrease to idle speed. Turn ignition switch off and remove tachometer from diagnostic connector.

2.5L Engine with 2SE Carburetor

NOTE: **Do not idle engine for over 3 minutes at a time. If idle adjustment is not completed within 3 minutes, run engine at 2000 RPM for 1 minute before continuing; repeat as necessary.**

1) Connect a tachometer to ignition coil or pigtail wire connector above heater blower motor. Make sure that ignition timing is properly set.

2) Disconnect deceleration valve and canister purge hoses, then plug hoses. Remove air cleaner. Disconnect air conditioning compressor clutch wiring connector.

3) If vehicle is equipped with A/C, adjust idle speed screw to obtain specified RPM. Turn A/C on and open throttle momentarily to make sure solenoid is fully extended. Adjust solenoid idle speed screw to obtain specified RPM. Turn A/C off.

4) If vehicle is not equipped with A/C, adjust solenoid idle speed screw with solenoid energized to obtain specified RPM. Disconnect solenoid wire connector and adjust idle speed to slow idle RPM.

2.5L Engine with E2SE Carburetor

1) Connect a tachometer to ignition coil or pigtail wire connector above heater blower motor. Make sure that ignition timing is properly set.

2) Disconnect deceleration valve and canister purge hoses, then plug hoses. Remove air cleaner. Disconnect air conditioning compressor clutch wiring connector.

3) Insert dwell meter positive probe into terminal marked 7 and negative probe into terminal marked 14 of diagnostic connector. Turn meter switch to the 6-Cyl. scale.

NOTE: **The electronic fuel control system must be in the closed-loop mode during idle speed adjustment. When engine is at normal operating temperature, fuel control system should be in the closed-loop mode of operation.**

4) Dwell meter should oscillate between the 10° to 50° range with a maximum 15° needle movement. If idle speed adjustment is necessary, remove carburetor and knock out hardened steel plug covering idle screw. Reinstall carburetor and proceed to the next step.

5) If vehicle is equipped with A/C, adjust idle speed screw to obtain specified RPM. Turn A/C on and open throttle momentarily to make sure solenoid is fully extended. Adjust solenoid idle speed screw to obtain specified RPM. Turn A/C off.

6) If vehicle does not have A/C, adjust solenoid idle speed screw with solenoid energized to obtain specified RPM. Disconnect solenoid wire connector and adjust idle speed screw to obtain specified slow idle speed RPM.

7) Reconnect solenoid wire connector. Install plug to seal idle speed screw or fill idle speed cavity with RTV sealant.

4.2L Engine

1) Connect tachometer to negative terminal of ignition coil. Start engine and allow it to reach normal operating temperature. Intake manifold heater and carburetor choke must both be off.

2) Block drive wheels, set parking brake firmly, and place transmission in Neutral (man. trans.) or "D" (auto. trans.).

3) Disconnect and plug vacuum hose from Sole-Vac vacuum actuator. Disconect wire connector from holding solenoid. Adjust idle speed adjusting screw to obtain specified curb idle speed.

4) Apply vacuum to vacuum actuator until throttle positioner is fully extended. Turn vacuum actuator adjustment screw on throttle lever until specified RPM is obtained. Disconnect vacuum source from vacuum actuator.

AMERICAN MOTORS SYSTEMS & TUNE-UP PROCEDURES (Cont.)

5) If vehicle is equipped with A/C, disconnect Sole-Vac wire connector and turn A/C on. Connect a jumper wire from battery positive terminal to Sole-Vac throttle positioner. Open throttle by hand and allow solenoid plunger to extend.

6) If Sole-Vac throttle positioner is activated and idle speed is not to specifications, adjust Sole-Vac adjusting screw to obtain specified RPM. Disconnect jumper wire and reconnect Sole-Vac wire connector. Disconnect tachometer and reconnect vacuum hose to vacuum actuator.

HOT (SLOW) IDLE SPEED RPM

Application	Man. Trans.	Auto. Trans.
1.4L		
AFC	650	650
TBI	[1] 3600	[1] 3600
2.5L		
With A/C		
Solenoid & A/C On	1250	900
Solenoid & A/C Off	650	550
Without A/C		
Solenoid On	900	700
Solenoid Off	650	550
4.2L		
Concord & Spirit		
Federal & Calif.	580-720	480-620
High Alt.	630-770	580-720
Eagle		
Federal	530-670	430-570
Calif.	580-720	480-620
High. Alt.	630-770	580-720

[1] — With ISC plunger fully extended.

SOLE-VAC ADJUSTMENT SPEED (RPM)

Application	Holding Solenoid Energized	Vacuum Actuator Energized
4.2L		
Federal & Calif.		
Man. Trans.	700-800	900-1000
Auto. Trans.	600-700	800-900
High Alt.		
Man. Trans.		
Concord & Spirit	900-1000	950-1050
Eagle	700-800	950-1050
Auto. Trans.	700-800	800-900

IDLE MIXTURE ADJUSTMENT

1.4L Engine

NOTE: **No idle mixture adjustments are required on 1.4L TBI engine. On 1.4L AFC, airflow meter by-pass adjustment should only be performed after engine overhaul or airflow meter replacement.**

1) Make sure that idle speed is properly adjusted. Remove tamper resistant cap to gain access to airflow meter by-pass adjustment screw. *See Fig. 6.*

Fig. 6: 1.4L AFC Airflow Meter By-Pass Screw Location

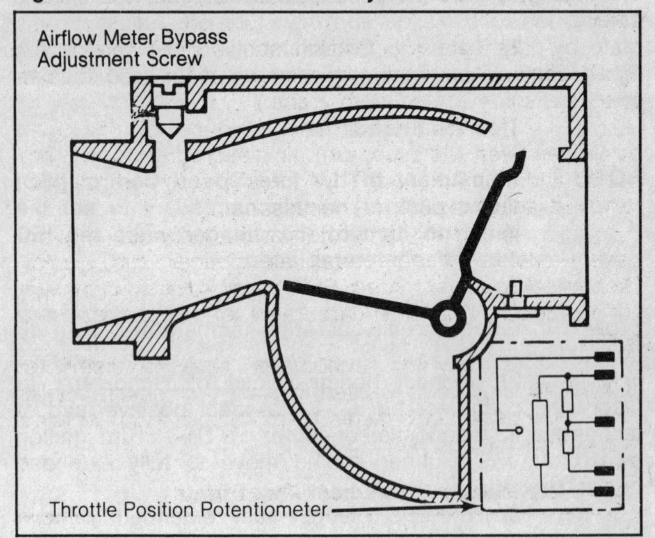

2) Disconect wire connector from oxygen sensor. Connect voltmeter to diagnostic connector pins D2-2 and D2-7. Record voltmeter reading. Voltage should be 6-7 volts.

3) Reconnect wire connector to oxygen sensor. Observe voltmeter reading. Use airflow meter by-pass adjusting screw to obtain a voltmeter reading of .5 volt higher than voltage previously recorded.

4) After adjustment has been performed, recheck idle speed. Install new tamper resistant cap.

2.5L Engine with 2SE Carburetor

NOTE: **Idle mixture adjustment procedure should only be performed if idle mixture screws were removed for cleaning purposes during carburetor overhaul.**

1) Remove carburetor from engine and drain float bowl. Set carburetor upside down on bench. Place a punch between 2 locator points on throttle body beneath idle mixture screw plug.

2) Break out throttle body to gain access to mixture screw plug. Drive out steel plug that conceals idle mixture screw. Reinstall carburetor.

3) With engine at normal operating temperature, connect tachometer. Set parking brake, block drive wheels and place transmission in Neutral (man. trans.) or "D" (auto. trans.).

4) Turn mixture screw lean (clockwise) until drop in RPM is noted.

5) Turn idle mixture screw rich (counterclockwise) until highest possible RPM is reached. Do not turn mixture screw any further than the point at which highest RPM is reached.

6) Slowly turn mixture screw clockwise until idle drops 100 RPM from idle speed noted in previous step.

7) If idle speed is not within 20 RPM of specified curb idle, readjust curb idle speed as necessary and repeat steps **4)**, **5)** and **6)**.

2.5L Engine with E2SE Carburetor

1) Disconnect negative battery cable. Remove carburetor from vehicle. Place a punch between 2 locator points in throttle body beneath idle mixture screw plug. Break out throttle body to gain access to idle mixture screw plug. Drive out steel plug that conceals idle mixture screw.

2) Turn idle mixture screw clockwise until it lightly seats. Now back out mixture screw 2 1/2 turns (man. trans.) or 3 turns (auto. trans.).

3) If plug in air horn covering idle air bleed screw has been removed, turn air bleed screw until lightly seated and then back out 1 1/4 turns. If plug has not been removed, adjustment is not necessary.

4) Install carburetor and reconnect negative battery cable. Do not install air cleaner and gasket. Disconnect bowl vent hose, EGR valve hose, and canister purge vacuum hoses at carburetor and plug carburetor ports.

5) Connect tachometer lead to distributor tachometer connector located in vicinity of heater blower motor. Connect dwell meter to mixture control solenoid test wire connector. *See Fig. 7.*

Fig. 7: Idle Mixture Adjustment Preparation

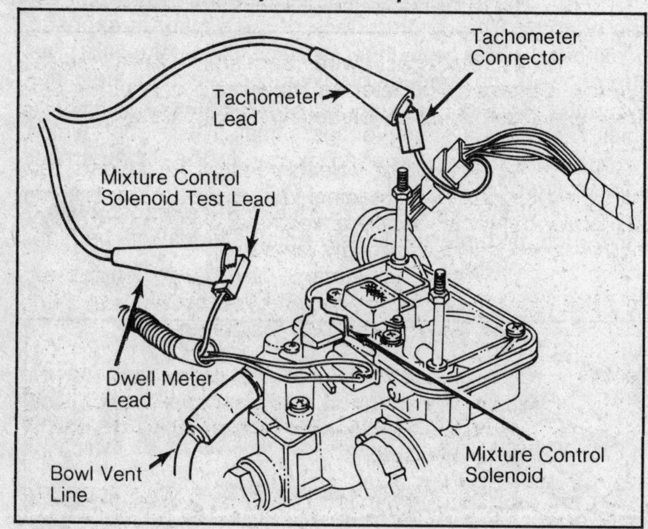

This applies to models with E2SE carburetor only.

6) Place transmission in Neutral (man. trans.) or "P" (auto. trans.) and set parking brake. Start engine and set idle to 700 RPM.

7) Adjust idle mixture screw until an average dwell meter reading of 25° is reached. If dwell is too low, slowly turn mixture screw clockwise. Allow time for dwell to stabilize after each adjustment.

8) Disconnect wire connector at mixture control solenoid while watching tachometer. Tachometer reading should change at least 50 RPM. If idle does not change enough, check idle air bleed circuit for leaks or restrictions. Reconnect mixture control solenoid wire.

9) Connect bowl vent hose, EGR valve hose, canister purge vacuum hoses and reset curb idle to specified range. Disconnect tachometer and dwell meter. Install plug or fill with RTV sealant. Install air cleaner and gasket.

4.2L Engine

1) It is necessary to remove carburetor to gain access to dowel pins covering idle mixture screws. Remove dowel pins and reinstall carburetor.

2) Place transmission in Neutral (man. trans.) or "D" (auto. trans.), block drive wheels, set parking brake firmly, and connect tachometer to engine. Start engine and wait until it reaches normal operating temperature.

NOTE: **Curb idle speed must be set to specification before continuing.**

3) Turn idle mixture screws leaner (clockwise) until a drop of 50 RPM is noted. Now turn idle mixture screws richer (counterclockwise) until highest RPM is reached.

4) As a final adjustment, turn idle mixture adjustment screws leaner (clockwise) until idle speed drops 50 RPM. If this RPM is not within 30 RPM specified curb idle, readjust curb idle speed and repeat steps **3)** and **4)**.

COLD (FAST) IDLE RPM

NOTE: **No fast idle adjustment is necessary or possible on models equipped with 1.4L engines.**

2.5L Engine

Prepare vehicle for adjustment as instructed by the Emission Label on the vehicle. Place fast idle screw on highest step of fast idle cam and turn fast idle screw to obtain specified RPM.

4.2L Engine

1) Adjust fast idle speed with engine at normal operating temperature and EGR disconnected.

2) Place fast idle adjusting screw in contact with second step and against shoulder of fast idle cam. Turn fast idle adjusting screw to obtain specified fast idle speed.

FAST IDLE SPEED (RPM)

Application	Man. Trans.	Auto. Trans.
2.5L	2500	2700
4.2L	1600-1800	1750-1950

EMISSION MAINTENANCE REMINDER LIGHT RESET

The emission maintenance lamp illuminates after 1000 hours of engine operation. This is to indicate required service of the oxygen sensor. After performing the required service, the emission maintenance E-Cell timer must be replaced.

Replace the E-Cell timer by removing its printed circuit. The printed circuit is located in an encloser within the wiring harness leading to the feedback system microprocessor.

1983 Exhaust Emission Systems

AMC ALLIANCE COMPUTERIZED ENGINE CONTROLS

Federal Models Only

NOTE: **Information on this system is also covered in the FUEL SYSTEMS Section. Additional diagnostic information that relates strictly to the fuel portion of this system can be found in the AMC THROTTLE BODY FUEL INJECTION article.**

DESCRIPTION

The computerized engine control system used on federal Alliance models is built around a microprocessor based computer. The major task of this system is to reduce emissions by controlling air/fuel ratio, ignition, idle speed and emission control devices. In order to carry out this task it is necessary to monitor several engine conditions.

These engine conditions are monitored by a system of sensors that input information into the computer. The computer processes this information to get an accurate picture of engine operation. The computer is then able to control the engine for optimum performance and minimum emissions

OPERATION

The Alliance engine control system is divided into 6 sub-systems: Electronic Control Unit, Sensors and Switches, Fuel Control, Emission Control, Idle Speed Control, and Ignition Advance Control.

ELECTRONIC CONTROL UNIT (ECU)

The ECU is located below the glove box near the fuse panel. It receives information from the various engine sensors to determine engine operating conditions at any particular moment. The ECU responds to these signals by sending a control signal to the fuel injector, fuel pump, ignition control module, idle speed motor, EGR solenoid, and canister purge solenoid.

SENSORS & SWITCHES

Oxygen (O_2) Sensor

The amount of oxygen in exhaust gases varies according to the air/fuel ratio of the intake charge. The oxygen sensor detects this content and transmits a low voltage signal to the ECU.

The oxygen sensor is located in the exhaust pipe adaptor. The outer surface of the sensor is exposed to exhaust gases, the inner surface to outside air. The difference in the amount of oxygen contacting the inner and outer surfaces of the sensor creates a pressure, which results in a small voltage signal. This signal, which is a measure of the unburned oxygen in the exhaust gas, is transmitted to the ECU.

If the amount of oxygen in the exhaust system is low (rich mixture), the sensor voltage signal will be high.

Fig. 1: AMC Alliance Engine Control System Components

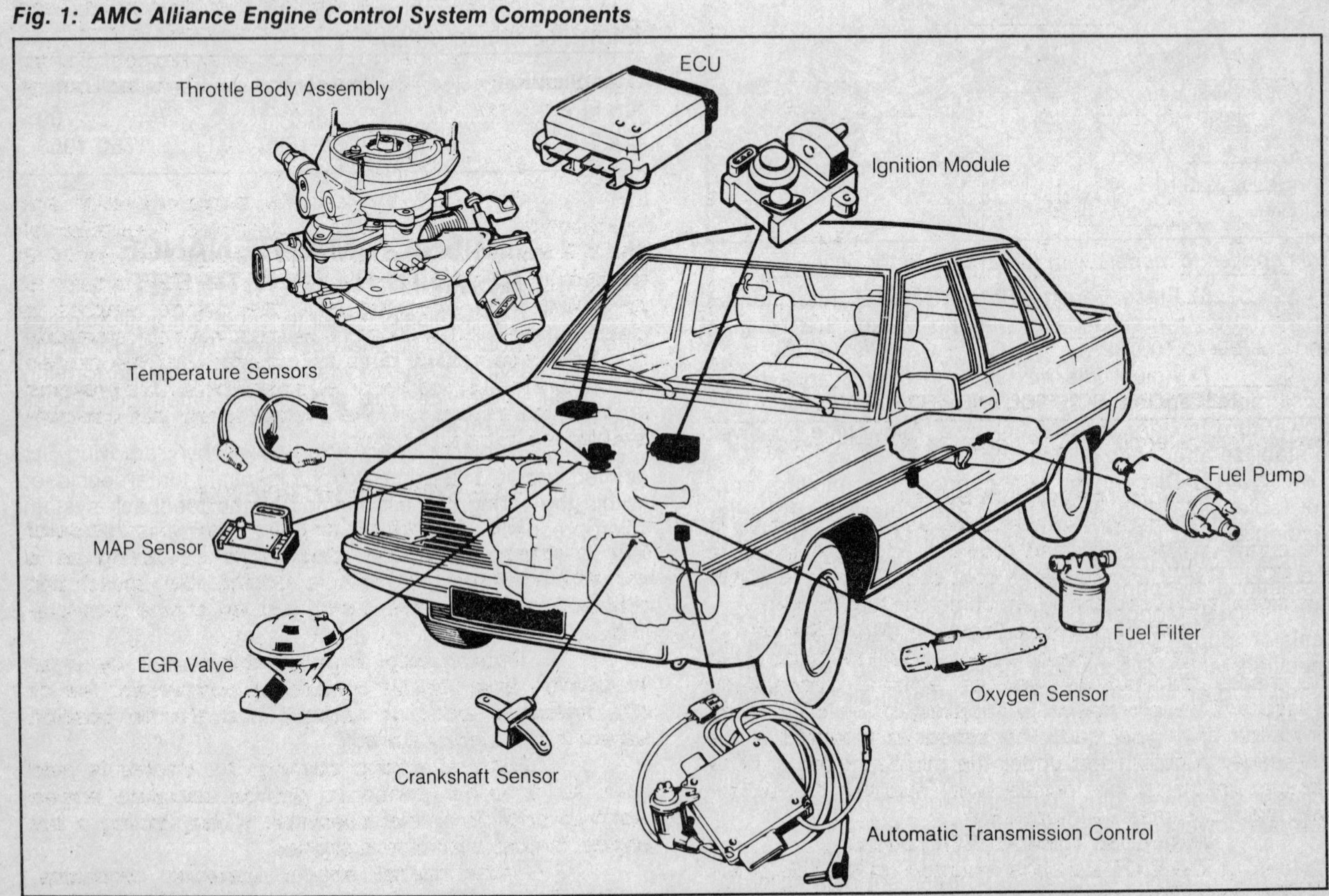

The closed throttle and wide open throttle switches, throttle position sensor and idle speed control motor are all located on the throttle body assembly.

AMC ALLIANCE COMPUTERIZED ENGINE CONTROLS (Cont.)

If the mixture is lean, the oxygen sensor will generate a low voltage signal.

Manifold Air Temperature (MAT) Sensor

The MAT sensor is installed in the intake manifold in front of an intake port. This sensor provides a voltage signal to the ECU representing the temperature of the air/fuel mixture in the intake manifold.

Fig. 2: ECU Input Signals and Output Controls

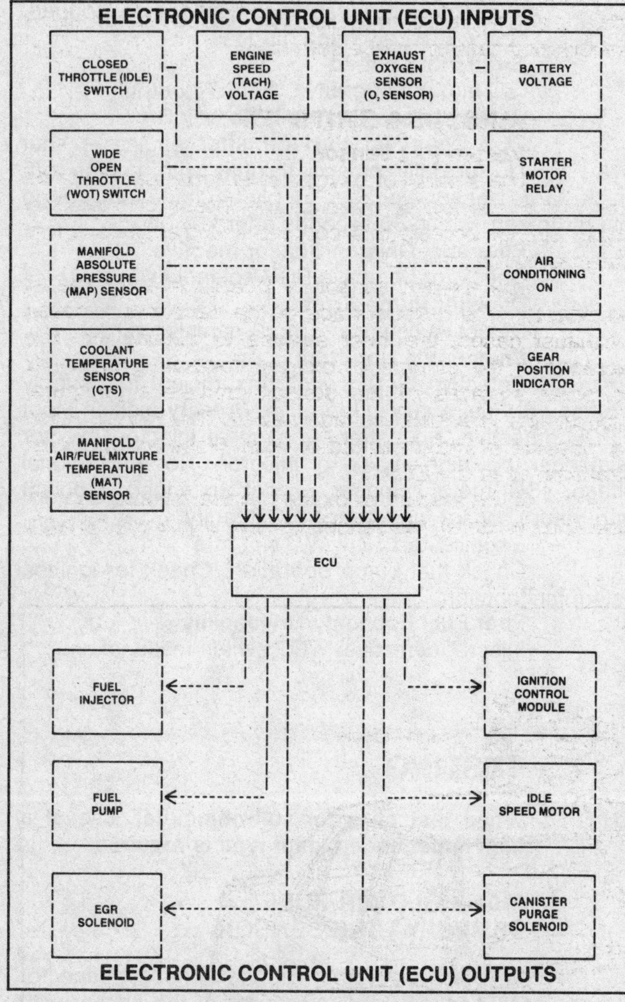

Sensor input determines ECU signals to output devices.

Coolant Temperature Sensor

The coolant temperature sensor is installed in the engine water jacket and provides a voltage signal to the ECU. The ECU determines cold engine operation from this signal and responds by enriching the fuel mixture.

Manifold Absolute Pressure (MAP) Sensor

The MAP sensor detects absolute pressure in the intake manifold as well as ambient atmospheric pressure. This information is supplied to the ECU as an indication of engine load. The sensor is mounted in the passenger compartment under the middle of the dash. A vacuum line from the throttle body supplies the sensor with manifold pressure information.

Wide Open Throttle (WOT) Switch

The WOT switch is mounted on the side of the throttle body. The switch provides a voltage signal to the ECU under wide open throttle conditions. The ECU responds to this signal by increasing the amount of fuel delivered by the injector.

Closed Throttle (Idle) Switch

This switch is integral with the idle speed control motor and provides a voltage signal to the ECU which increases or decreases the throttle stop angle in response to engine operating conditions.

Throttle Position Sensor (TPS)

The TPS is a variable resistor mounted on the throttle body and connected to the throttle shaft. It is found on vehicles with automatic transaxles only. Movement of the throttle cable causes the throttle shaft to rotate (opening or closing the throttle). The sensor detects this movement and provides the ECU with an appropriate voltage signal. The ECU uses this signal to determine engine operating conditions for the automatic transmission control system.

FUEL CONTROL

An electric fuel pump, located in the gas tank, supplies fuel to the throttle body. The fuel pump is switched on and off by the ECU. A fuel injector is mounted in the throttle body such that fuel is injected into the incoming air flow.

When electric current is supplied to the injector, the armature and pintle assembly move a short distance against a spring, opening a small orifice at the end of the injector. Fuel supplied to the injector is forced around the pintle valve and through this opening, resulting in a fine spray of fuel.

Since fuel pressure at the injector is kept constant, the volume of fuel injected is dependent only on the length of time that the injector is energized. During engine start-up, the injector delivers an extra amount of fuel to aid in starting.

EMISSION CONTROL

Both EGR and canister purge operation are regulated by the engine control computer. Regulation of these 2 systems is accomplished through the use of 2 electrically operated vacuum valves. The EGR system is prevented from operating until the engine reaches a predetermined temperature. This improves cold driveability. The canister purge does not operate until the oxygen sensor warms up and becomes operational. This prevents an over-rich mixture until the oxygen sensor can compensate for the extra fuel vapor.

IDLE SPEED CONTROL (ISC)

The ISC motor is an electrically driven actuator that changes the throttle stop angle by acting as a movable idle stop. It controls engine idle speed and maintains a smooth idle during sudden engine deceleration.

Throttle stop angle is determined by input information from the air conditioner compressor (on or off), transaxle (park or neutral), and throttle position sensor (wide open or closed).

For cold engine starting, the throttle is held open for a longer period to provide adequate engine warm-up prior to normal operation. When starting a hot engine, throttle open time is shorter.

Under normal engine operating conditions, engine idle is maintained at a pre-programmed RPM which may vary slightly due to engine operating conditions.

AMC ALLIANCE COMPUTERIZED ENGINE CONTROLS (Cont.)

Under certain engine deceleration conditions, the throttle is held slightly open.

IGNITION ADVANCE CONTROL

Under certain engine operating conditions, the predetermined ignition advance curve is modified. This is accomplished through 2 switching circuits that connect the ECU and the ignition control module.

DIAGNOSIS

PRELIMINARY CHECKS

The following systems and components must be in good condition and operating properly before assuming an engine control system malfunction.

- All support systems and wiring.
- Battery connections and specific gravity.
- Electrical connections on components and sensors.
- Emission control devices.
- Ignition system.
- Vacuum hoses.

SYSTEM DIAGNOSIS

The Alliance engine control system is equipped with a self-diagnostic capacity. When a failure occurs within the system, a trouble code is stored in the ECU.

To recall trouble codes, install a test light between pins 2 and 4 of diagnostic connector D2. Push the WOT switch lever on the throttle body to wide open position and close the ISC motor plunger (activates closed throttle switch). Turn the ignition switch on and observe the test bulb.

The ECU test bulb will light for a moment, then go out. This should always occur, regardless of whether or not any trouble codes are stored, to indicate that the ECU is functional.

The bulb will then indicate all stored trouble codes as a series of brief flashes (flash, flash for code 2, flash, flash, flash, for code 3, etc.). If multiple trouble codes are stored in the ECU, the first code stored is indicated first, followed by a short pause, and any remaining codes. After a longer pause, the cycle repeats. Each trouble code indicates the malfunction of a specific sensor or sensors. Note codes.

Some injection system difficulties or abnormalities may occur without setting a trouble code. If this happens, refer to specific problem descriptions listed after trouble code references.

Code 1

Check MAT sensor resistance.

Code 2

Check coolant temperature sensor resistance and replace if needed. Check MAT sensor.

Code 3

Check WOT switch, closed throttle switch and associated wiring harness.

Code 4

Simultaneous closed throttle switch and MAP sensor failure. Check and replace as needed.

Code 5

Simultaneous WOT switch and MAP sensor failure. Check and replace as needed.

Code 6

Check oxygen sensor operation. Check for correct fuel pressure.

No Test Bulb Flash

Check battery voltage to ECU with key on. Check ECU ground. Simultaneous WOT and coolant temperature switch contact, check both switches. No battery voltage to test bulb. Defective test bulb. Battery voltage less than 11.5 Volts.

Continuous Fuel Pump Operation

Check fuel pump relay for short to ground.

Poor Idle When Started Cold

ISC motor not extending when engine stopped. Check ISC motor, ECU or wiring harness.

Erratic Idle Speed

ISC motor inoperative. No ECU output.

Battery Loses Charge With Key Off

ECU does not turn off after engine is shut down. Check for fully closed throttle with engine off. Check MAP sensor voltage supply. Voltage should go from 5V to zero within 30 seconds after key off.

Poor Idle, Oxygen Sensor Inactive

Check for defective EGR solenoid valve.

Canister Purge Erratic

Defective solenoid. Check canister purge.

Engine Will Not Start

Defective WOT switch. Insufficient fuel supply or pressure. Fuel pump inoperative. Primary ignition input to ECU defective. No battery voltage at injector. Injector resistance too high. Leaking injector. No start signal voltage. ISC motor plunger is not extended. Coolant temperature sensor inoperative. ECU faulty.

Engine Starts But Will Not Idle

Check fuel pump operation. Check for ignition system malfunction.

Poor Fuel Economy/Driveability

Injector defective. WOT switch malfunction.

TESTING

NOTE: **When test calls for volt-ohmmeter, use of a high impedence digital type is required.**

MANIFOLD AIR/FUEL TEMPERATURE SENSOR

1) Disconnect the wiring harness connector from the MAT sensor. Test resistance of the sensor with an ohmmeter. Resistance ranges from 300 ohms to 300,000 ohms (10,000 ohms at room temperature). Replace sensor if outside of specified range.

2) Test resistance of the wiring harness between pin 13 of ECU harness connector J2 and the sensor connector, and between pin 11 of connector J2 and sensor connector. See *Fig. 6* for connector identification. Repair harness if resistance is greater than 1 ohm.

COOLANT TEMPERATURE SENSOR

1) Disconnect wiring harness from sensor. Disconnect the wiring harness connector. Test resistance of sensor. If resistance is not 300-300,000 ohms (10,000 ohms at room temperature), replace the sensor.

2) Test resistance of the wiring harness between pin 14 of ECU connector J2 and the sensor connector. Test resistance between pin 11 of connector J2 and sensor connector. Repair wiring harness if any open circuit is found.

AMC ALLIANCE COMPUTERIZED ENGINE CONTROLS (Cont.)

WIDE OPEN THROTTLE (WOT) SWITCH

1) Disconnect the wiring harness from the WOT switch and test resistance while opening and closing switch manually. When switch is closed, resistance should be infinite. A low resistance should be indicated at the wide open position. Test switch operation several times. Replace switch if defective. Reconnect wiring harness.

2) With ignition switch ON, test for WOT switch voltage between pin 6 and pin 7 (ground) of diagnostic connector D2. Voltage should be 0 with switch in wide open position and greater than 2 volts in any other position.

3) If voltage is always zero, test for short circuit to ground in the wiring harness or switch. Check for open circuit between pin 19 of ECU connector J2 and the switch connector. Repair or replace as needed.

4) If voltage is always greater than 2 volts, test for an open wire or connector between the switch and ground. Repair as needed.

CLOSED THROTTLE SWITCH

NOTE: **It is important that all testing be done with the idle speed control motor plunger in the fully extended position, as it would be after a normal engine shut down. If it is necessary to extend the motor plunger to test the switch, an ISC motor failure can be suspected. Refer to ISC motor test.**

1) With ignition ON, test switch voltage at diagnostic connector D2 between pin 13 and pin 7 (ground). Voltage should be close to zero at closed throttle and greater than 2 volts off closed throttle position.

2) If the voltage is always zero, test for a short circuit to ground in the wiring harness or switch. Test for an open circuit between pin 20 of ECU connector J2 and throttle switch.

3) If voltage is always more than 2 volts, test for an open circuit in the wiring harness between the ECU and switch connector. Check for open circuit between the switch connector and ground. Repair or replace wiring harness as needed.

MANIFOLD ABSOLUTE PRESSURE SENSOR

1) Test MAP sensor output voltage at MAP sensor connector pin B (as marked on sensor body) with the ignition switch ON and the engine OFF. Output voltage should be 4.0-5.0 volts.

NOTE: **Voltage should drop 0.5-1.5 volts with hot engine, at idle.**

2) Test pin 12 of ECU connector J2 for 4.0-5.0 volts to verify wiring harness condition.

3) Check for MAP sensor supply voltage of 4.5-5.5 volts at sensor connector, pin C, with ignition ON. Similar voltage should be present at pin 2 of ECU connector J2. Repair or replace wiring harness if required. Test for sensor ground between pin 13 of ECU connector J2 and pin A of sensor connector.

4) Check for ground from pin 13 of ECU connector J2 to pin F of connector J1. If an open circuit is indicated, check for a good sensor ground on the flywheel housing near the starter motor.

5) If ground is good, the ECU must be replaced. Before replacing ECU, check to see if pin 13 of ECU connector J2 is shorted to 12 volts. If so, correct the condition before replacing ECU.

OXYGEN SENSOR

1) Test continuity of harness between O_2 sensor connector and pin 9 of ECU harness connector J2. Ensure that the wiring harness is not shorted to ground. Repair or replace as necessary.

2) Test continuity between sensor ground (exhaust manifold) and pin 13 of ECU connector J2. Repair harness if needed.

3) Check sensor operation by driving vehicle with a test lamp (no. 158 bulb) connected between pins 2 and 4 of diagnostic connector D2.

4) Bulb lighted at start is normal operation for test circuit. If the bulb does not light after warm up, the O_2 sensor is functioning normally. If the bulb stays lit or lights after the engine warms up, replace the O_2 sensor.

5) Before installing new sensor, check for system failures which may have caused O_2 sensor malfunction. System failures which can affect O_2 sensor are: EGR solenoid control, canister purge control, PCV system, secondary ignition circuit and fuel delivery system.

EGR & CANISTER PURGE SOLENOIDS

Disconnect solenoid valve from harness. Connect solenoid coil to 12 volts. Check to see that valve opens and closes. If valve does not open and close as voltage is applied and removed, replacement is required. If valve operates properly, but did not work when connected to system, check wiring back to ECU and check ECU.

IDLE SPEED CONTROL (ISC) MOTOR

Disconnect ISC motor from wiring harness. Connect 12 volts positive to terminal D on ISC motor and ground to terminal C. ISC plunger should extend. Extending plunger also verifies that motor is not jammed in the retract position. If motor does not operate as specified, replacement is required.

ELECTRONIC CONTROL UNIT

1) If all components have been checked and/or repaired, but a system failure or problem still exists, the ECU may be at fault. However, it is extremely important to note that the ECU is a very reliable unit and must always be the final component replaced if a doubt exists concerning the cause of an injection system failure.

2) The only way to confirm an ECU malfunction is to take the unit to an AMC/Renault dealer and have it tested. This is the only sure way to avoid replacing a good ECU.

REMOVAL & INSTALLATION

THROTTLE POSITION SENSOR

Removal & Installation

Disconnect wire connector from sensor and remove the 2 torx head retaining screws. Remove the

AMC ALLIANCE COMPUTERIZED ENGINE CONTROLS (Cont.)

throttle position sensor from the throttle shaft lever. Reverse removal procedures to install.

IDLE SPEED CONTROL MOTOR

Removal & Installation

Disconnect the throttle return spring and ISC motor wiring connector. Remove the motor-to-bracket retaining nuts (3). Separate the motor from the bracket. To install motor, reverse removal procedures.

ELECTRONIC CONTROL UNIT

Removal & Installation

Locate ECU in passenger compartment, below glove box. Remove retaining screws and mounting bracket. Remove the ECU and disconnect wire harness. Reverse removal procedure to install.

OXYGEN SENSOR

Removal

Disconnect the wire connector from sensor and unscrew sensor from exhaust pipe adaptor. Clean threads in adaptor.

Installation

1) Apply anti-seize compound to sensor threads. DO NOT allow compound to adhere to any other part of the sensor. Hand start the sensor into place and tighten to 20-25 ft. lbs. (27-34 N.m). Check that the wire terminal ends are properly seated in the connector. Connect wire.

2) Do not push the rubber boot over the sensor body lower than 1/2" above the base of the sensor. If the sensor wire should break, the sensor must be replaced. These wires cannot be spliced or otherwise repaired.

ADJUSTMENTS

NOTE: **The following adjustment procedures should not be necessary during normal vehicle operation or maintainence. Adjustment of the listed components should only be required when a faulty component is replaced with a new one.**

IDLE SPEED CONTROL MOTOR

1) With air cleaner removed, air conditioner off (if equipped) and engine at normal operating temperature, connect a tachometer to terminals 1 (+) and 3 (-) of the small diagnostic connecter (D1). *See Fig. 3.* Turn ignition off and observe ISC motor plunger. The plunger should move to fully extended position.

2) Disconnect the ISC motor wire connector and start the engine. Idle speed should be 3300-3700 RPM. If not, turn adjusting nut on plunger until correct idle is obtained. *See Fig. 4.*

3) Hold the closed throttle switch plunger all the way in while opening the throttle. Release the throttle. The throttle lever should not make contact with the plunger. If contact is made, inspect throttle linkage and/or cable for binding or damage. Repair as needed.

4) Reconnect the ISC motor wire connector and turn ignition off for 10 seconds. Motor should move to fully extended position. Start the engine. Engine should idle at 3300-3700 RPM for a short time and then fall to normal idle. Turn off engine and remove tachometer.

Fig. 3: TBI System Diagnostic Connector Location With Terminal Identification

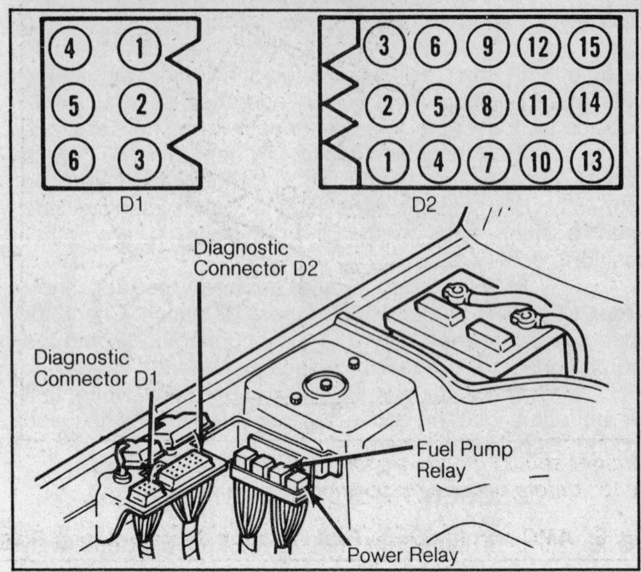

Diagnostic connectors and relays are mounted on a common bracket, just in front of the shock tower.

5) When final adjustments to the ISC motor have been made, apply a thread sealer to adjustment screw threads to prevent movement. Install air cleaner. Since step **3)** may set a trouble code, remove the negative battery cable for 10 seconds to clear ECU memory.

Fig. 4: Idle Speed Control and WOT Switch Adjustment

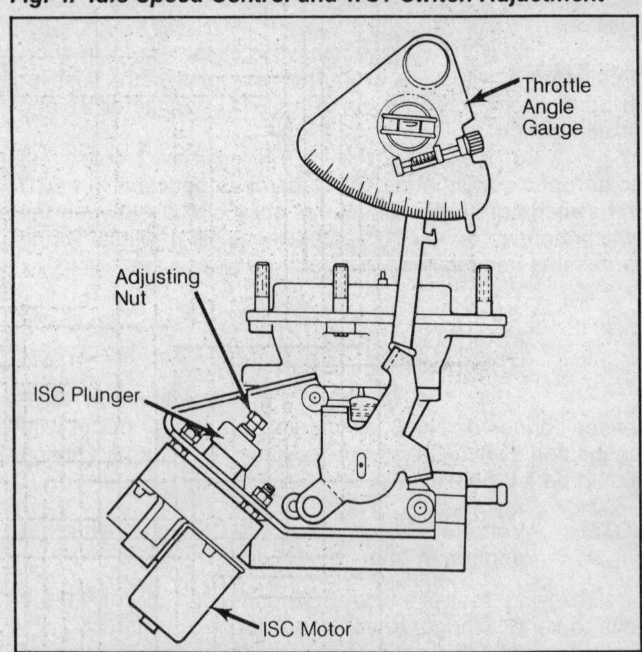

Use a throttle angle gauge to set WOT switch at 15° before wide open throttle.

WIDE OPEN THROTTLE SWITCH

1) Remove the throttle body assembly from the engine and loosen the WOT switch retaining screws (2). Hold throttle in wide open position and attach a throttle angle gauge to the flat surface of the lever. *See Fig. 4.*

AMC ALLIANCE COMPUTERIZED ENGINE CONTROLS (Cont.)

Fig. 5: Wide Open Throttle Switch

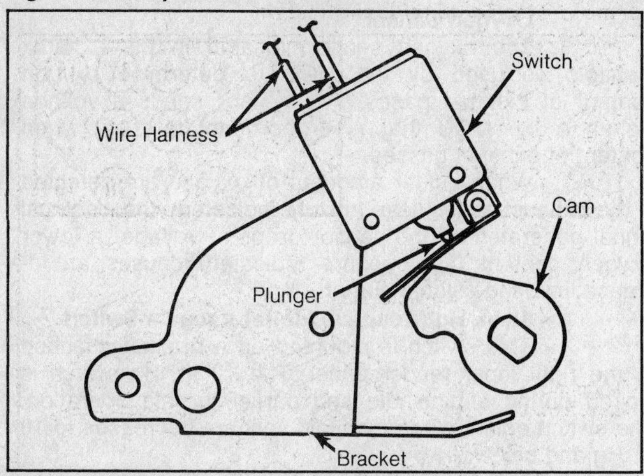

Plunger should be just closed with throttle at 15° before wide open position.

2) Rotate scale to align the 15 degree mark with the pointer. Level the gauge. Rotate scale to align zero with the pointer and close the throttle enough to center the bubble. This positions the throttle at 15° before wide open.

3) Adjust the WOT switch lever on the throttle cam so that the plunger is just closed. Tighten the retaining screws and remove the gauge.

Fig. 6: AMC Throttle Body Fuel Injection System Wiring Diagram

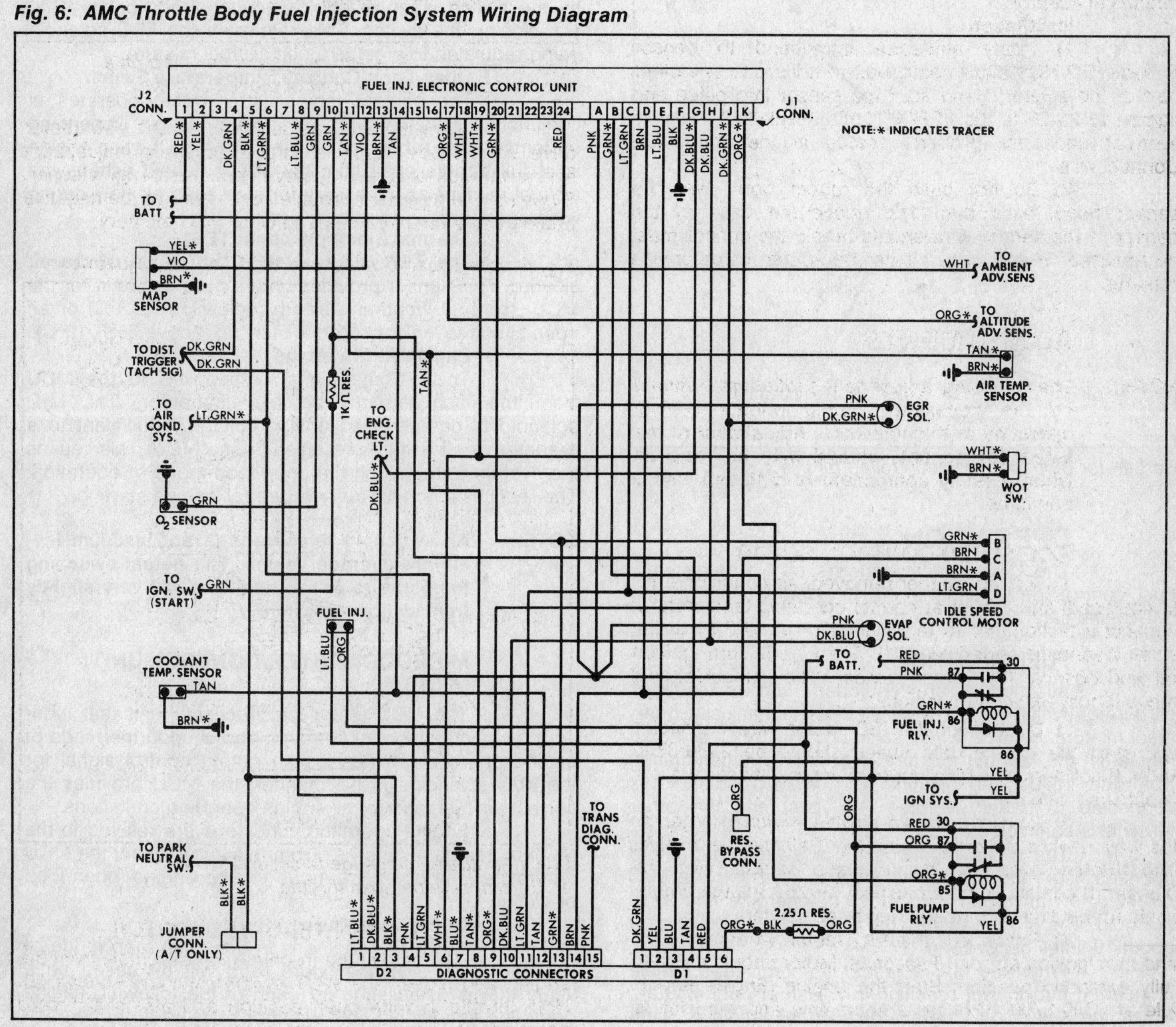

AMC 4-CYL. COMPUTERIZED EMISSION CONTROLS

Eagle (Calif. Only)

DESCRIPTION

The Computerized Emission Control (CEC) system is an electronically controlled system that closely controls air/fuel ratio. This close control of the air/fuel ratio is needed to lower exhaust emissions while maintaining good fuel economy and performance.

The primary objective of the CEC system is to maintain the ideal air/fuel mixture ratio of 14.7:1 under all operating conditions. When the ideal air/fuel ratio is maintained, the catalytic converter can effectively control nitrogen oxides (NOx), hydrocarbons (HC) and carbon monoxide (CO).

Fig. 1: American Motors 4-Cyl. CEC System

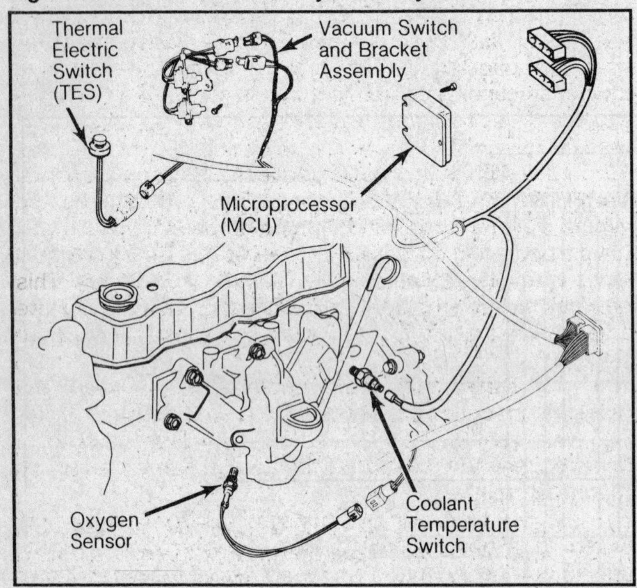

Carburetor (not shown) is controlled by this system.

OPERATION

The CEC system consists of 4 sub-systems: Fuel control, data sensors, Microcomputer Control Unit (MCU) and catalytic converter.

FUEL CONTROL

All models are equipped with a feedback carburetor which contains an electro-mechanically operated mixture control (M/C) solenoid. The M/C solenoid regulates the air/fuel mixture according to commands from the MCU. One terminal of the M/C solenoid is connected to battery voltage (12 volts) and the other terminal is connected to the MCU.

The MCU functions as a switch that either provides a ground for current flow to energize the M/C solenoid or an open circuit to de-energize the M/C solenoid. The MCU switches the M/C solenoid on and off about 10 times per second.

When the M/C solenoid is energized, a needle is inserted into the jet resulting in a lean air/fuel mixture. When the solenoid is de-energized, the needle is withdrawn from the jet resulting in a rich air/fuel mixture.

DATA SENSORS

Oxygen Sensor

The oxygen sensor, located in the exhaust manifold, is used by the MCU to determine oxygen content of exhaust gases. The sensor sends a voltage signal to the MCU that is proportional to the oxygen content of exhaust gasses.

When higher amounts of oxygen are detected in the exhaust gases (lean mixture indicated), the electrical signal generated by the sensor drops in voltage. A lower oxygen content (rich mixture indicated) causes an increase in voltage signal output.

10 in. Hg (Adaptive Mode) Vacuum Switch

This switch is mounted on a bracket attached to the right inner fender panel. The 10 in. Hg switch is closed during engine idle and partial throttle operation. The switch opens when manifold vacuum decreases to 10 in. Hg and below.

4 in. Hg (Wide Open Throttle) Vacuum Switch

The 4 in. Hg vacuum switch is used to sense a full throttle condition. A full throttle condition is detected by the switch when manifold vacuum drops below 4 in. Hg, closing the switch. This results in the M/C solenoid being regulated to provide a rich air/fuel mixture.

Open Loop Coolant Temperature Switch

The coolant temperature switch operates in conjunction with the 4 in. Hg vacuum switch. Depending on temperature (above or below 100°F/38°C) when engine is at full throttle operation, the M/C solenoid richens the air/fuel mixture as necessary for increased air flow during wide open throttle operation.

Thermal Electric Switch (TES)

The TES is attached to the inside of the air cleaner. This sensor provides both a ground circuit for the MCU, for cold weather start-up (below 55°F/13°C) or an open circuit to indicate normal start-up (above 65°F/18°C).

Engine RPM Voltage

This voltage signal is supplied to the MCU from the tach terminal on the distributor. The M/C solenoid is de-energized until a voltage, equivalent to a predetermined RPM, is received by the MCU. This causes the system to remain in the open loop mode of operation. The result is a rich air/fuel mixture for engine starting.

NOTE: **All switching temperatures and vacuum levels are average values. The actual switching temperature or vacuum level will vary slightly from switch to switch.**

MICROCOMPUTER CONTROL UNIT (MCU)

The MCU is a microprocessor unit that monitors oxygen sensor voltage and, based upon the mode of engine operation, generates an output control signal for the M/C solenoid. In this manner, the MCU provides the correct air/fuel ratio for all engine operating conditions.

Engine operating conditions are relayed to the MCU by the data sensors. From this information, the MCU determines the operating mode for the engine (open loop or closed loop).

Open Loop Mode

When the engine is in the open loop mode of operation, the air/fuel mixture ratio will be based on a value that is established for each of the following engine operating conditions: cold weather start-up and operation (below 55°F/13°C), cold engine at or near WOT operation (below 100°F/38°C & below 4 in. Hg), warm engine at or near WOT operation (above 100°F/38°C & below 4 in. Hg), adaptive operation (at idle speed, accelerating from idle speed, or decelerating to idle speed).

Closed Loop Mode

This mode of operation occurs when none of the open loop engine operating conditions exist. In this mode, the MCU regulates the M/C solenoid to adjust the air/fuel mixture according to voltage signals from the oxygen sensor.

The oxygen sensor only measures oxygen content in the exhaust. Because of this, air leakage anywhere between the carburetor and the oxygen sensor can cause incorrect operation during the closed loop mode.

Closed loop operation is characterized by constant variation of the air/fuel mixture. This is because the MCU is forced to constantly make small changes in order to maintain an optimum air/fuel mixture ratio.

CATALYTIC CONVERTER

A 3-way catalytic converter and a conventional oxidizing catalyst are combined to form a dual bed converter. The dual bed converter has the ability to convert the following gases:

- Carbon monoxide (CO) and hydrocarbons (HC) to water vapor (H_2O)and carbon dioxide (CO_2).
- Nitrogen oxide (NOx) and carbon monoxide (CO) to nitrogen (N_2) and carbon dioxide (CO_2).

REMOVAL & INSTALLATION

OXYGEN SENSOR

Removal & Installation

Disconnect wire connector from oxygen sensor. Remove sensor from exhaust manifold using sensor wrench (J-29533). Clean threads in manifold. Coat threads of replacement sensor with anti-seize compound. Install new sensor in exhaust manifold and tighten to 20-25 ft. lbs. (27-34 N.m). Reconnect wire connector.

MIXTURE CONTROL UNIT

Removal & Installation

The MCU is located behind the right front kick panel. Remove MCU mounting bolts and disconnect wiring harness connector. Do not bend connector pins when removing. Reconnect harness to MCU and replace mounting bolts.

MIXTURE CONTROL SOLENOID

Removal & Installation

Remove air cleaner and disconnect solenoid harness connector. Remove retaining screws and remove solenoid from carburetor. Coat rubber seal, on end of solenoid stem, with silicone grease or light engine oil prior to reinsertion. Using a new gasket, replace solenoid. Reconnect wiring harness and replace air cleaner.

DIAGNOSIS & TESTING

The CEC system should be considered as a possible source of trouble for engine performance, fuel economy and exhaust emission problems only after normal tests and inspections are performed. Normal tests and inspections are those that would apply to a vehicle without the CEC system (ignition system, carburetor, etc.).

The steps listed in the following charts will provide a systematic evaluation of each component that could cause a malfunction. After completing a repair, repeat the test to ensure that the malfunction has been corrected.

TESTING INFORMATION

The following tools will be needed to perform the diagnostic tests: Dwell meter, digital volt-ohmmeter, tachometer, vacuum gauge and jumper wire.

NOTE: **Although most dwell meters should be acceptable, if one causes a change in engine operation when connected to the test location, it should not be used.**

To determine air/fuel mixture the dwell meter should be set on the 6-cylinder scale and connected to a pigtail wire test connector leading from the mixture control solenoid or diagnostic connector pin 14. When the dwell meter is connected, do not allow the connector terminal to contact any engine component that is connected to engine ground. This includes hoses that may be electrically conductive.

With a normally operating engine, at partial throttle, the dwell will be between 10 and 50 degrees and will be varying. Varying means the pointer continually moves back and forth across the scale. The amount it varies is not important, only the fact that it does vary. This indicates closed loop operation, indicating that the mixture is being varied according to the oxygen sensor being input to the MCU.

During idle, WOT, and/or cold operation, the mixture is predetermined by the MCU so the meter pointer will vary only slightly. This is open loop operation, indicating that the oxygen sensor output has no effect on on air/fuel mixture.

If there is any question as to whether the system is in open or closed loop operation, richening or leaning out the air/fuel mixture will cause the dwell meter reading to vary more during closed loop operation.

NOTE: **The "System Operational Test" should also be performed after all repairs on the CEC system have been completed.**

Fig. 2: Diagnostic Connector Pin Location

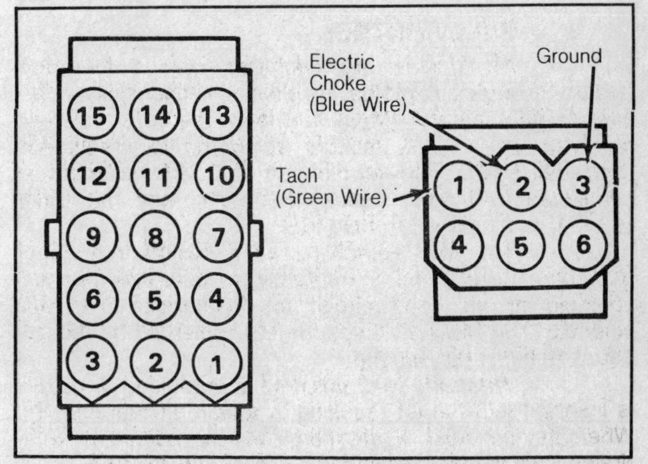

Connect meter to these terminals as directed by test charts.

AMC 4-CYL. COMPUTERIZED EMISSION CONTROLS (Cont.)

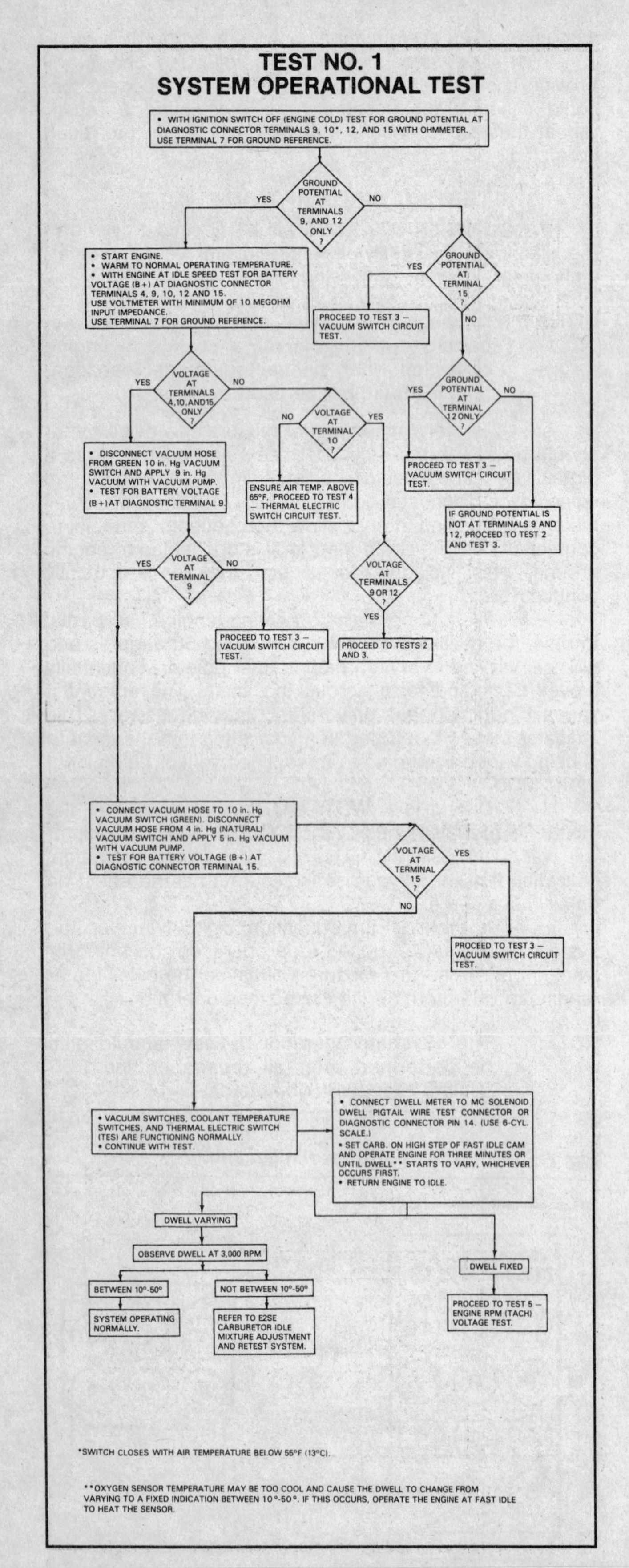

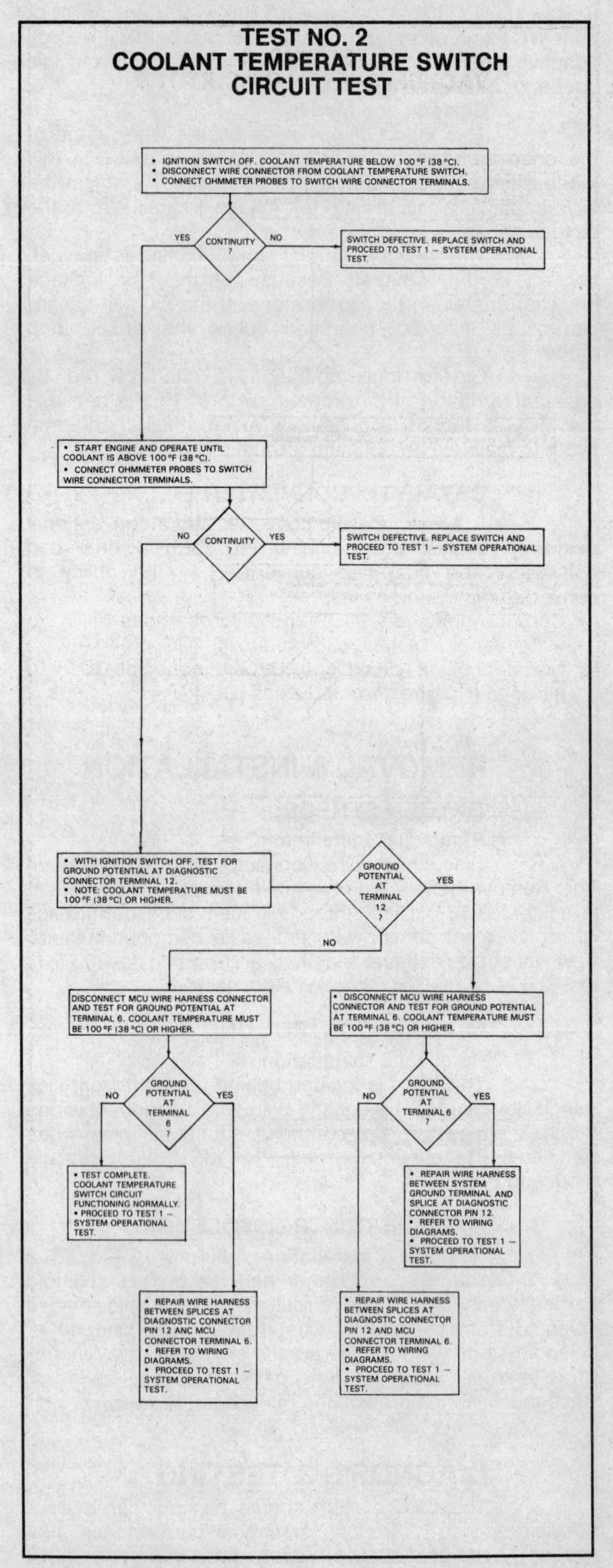

AMC 4-CYL. COMPUTERIZED EMISSION CONTROLS (Cont.)

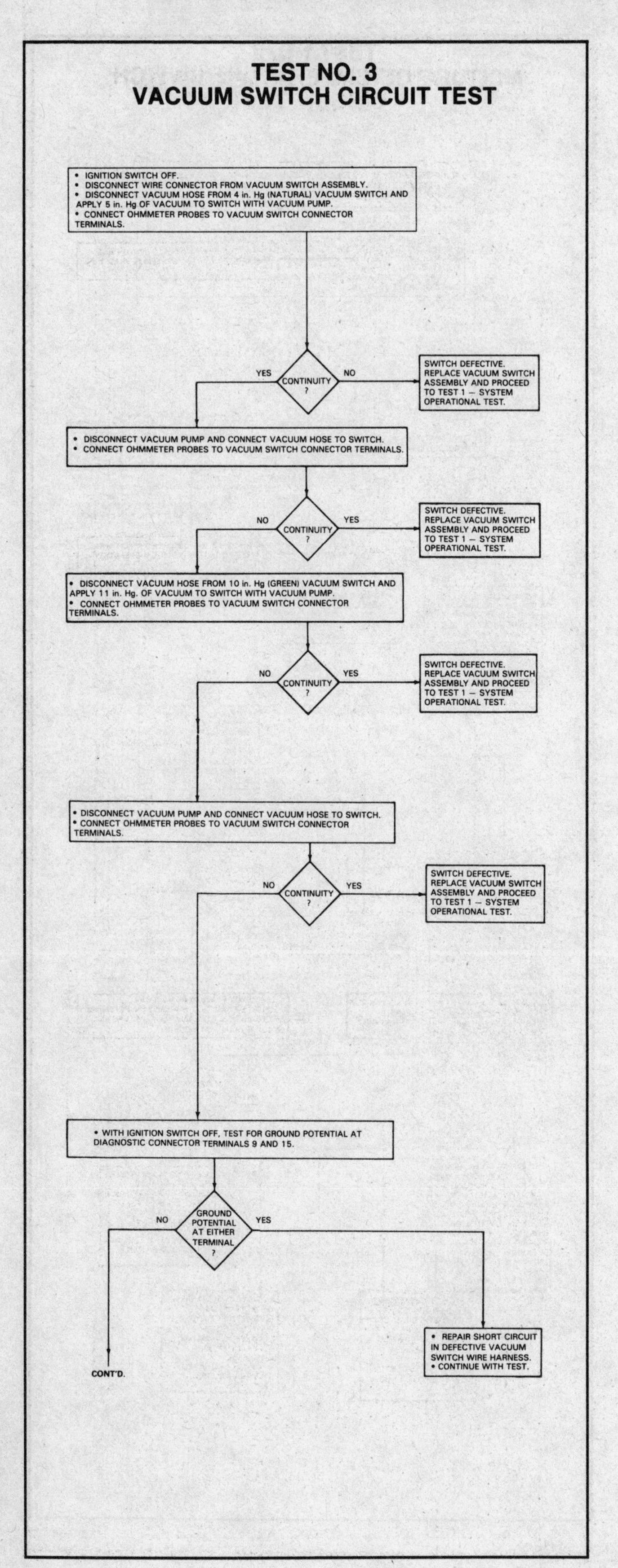

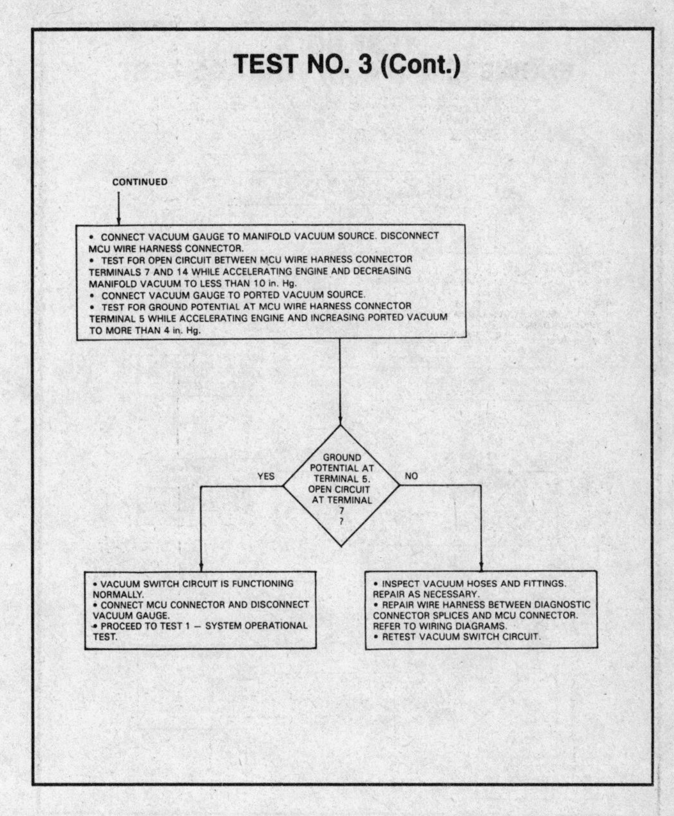

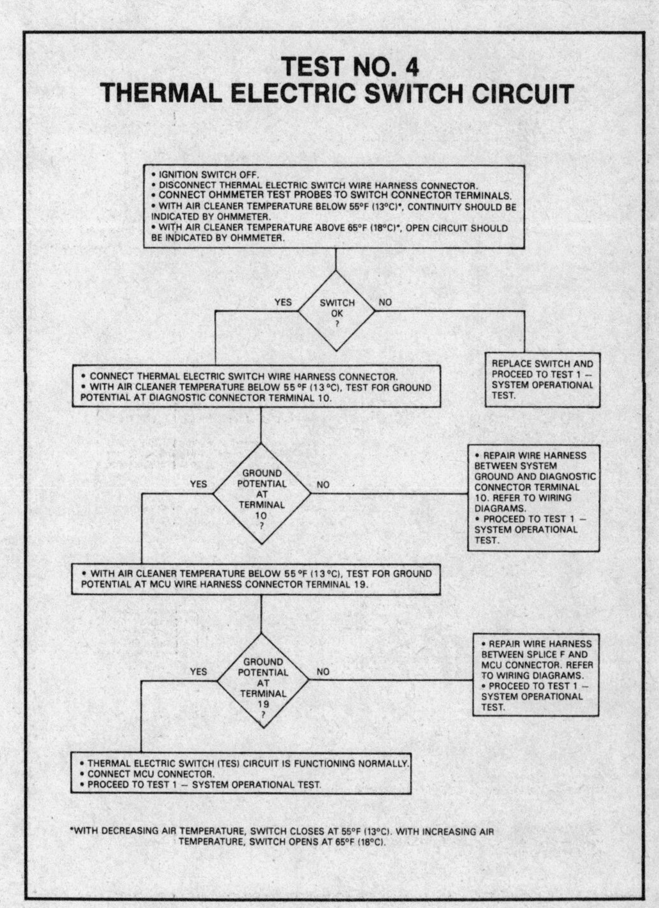

AMC 4-CYL. COMPUTERIZED EMISSION CONTROLS (Cont.)

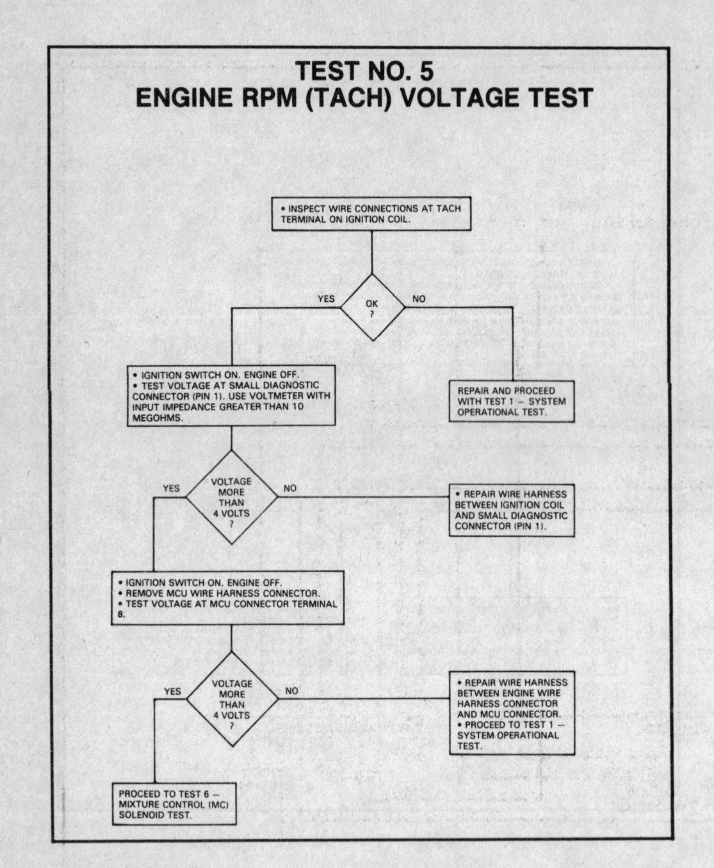

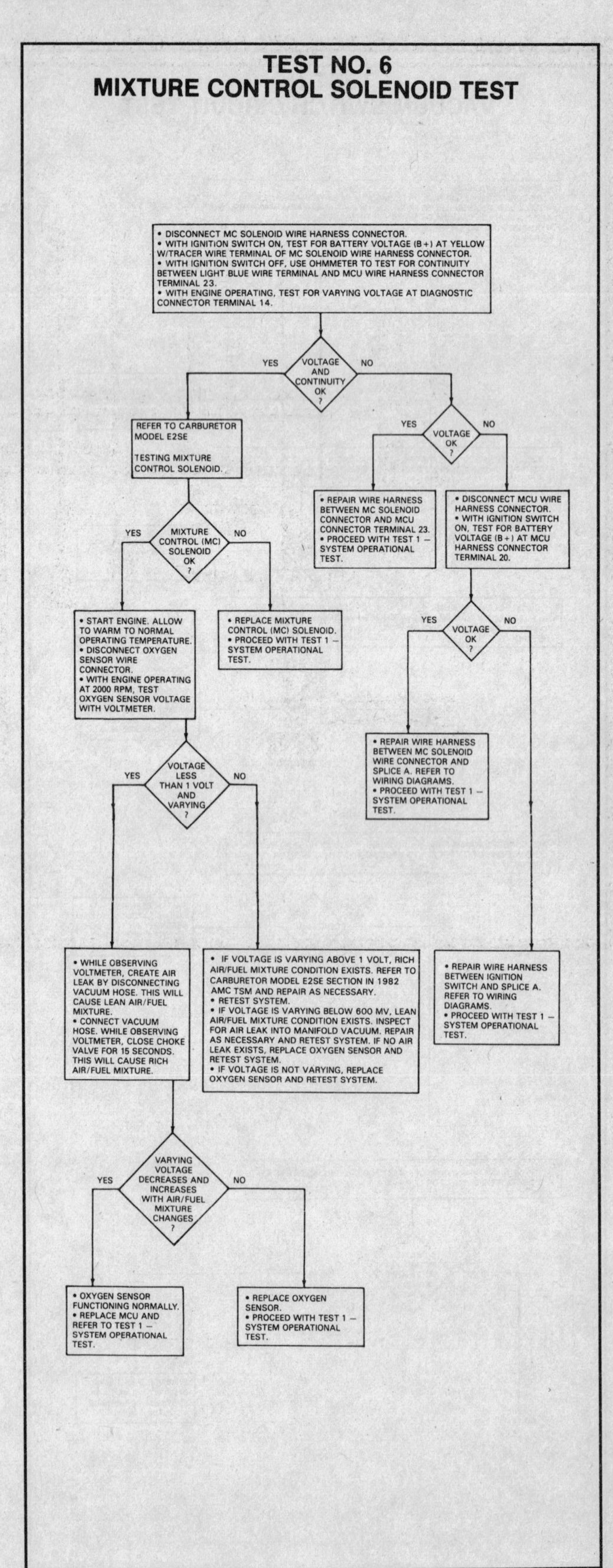

AMC 4-CYL. COMPUTERIZED EMISSION CONTROLS (Cont.)

Fig. 3: American Motors 4-Cyl. CEC System Wiring Diagram

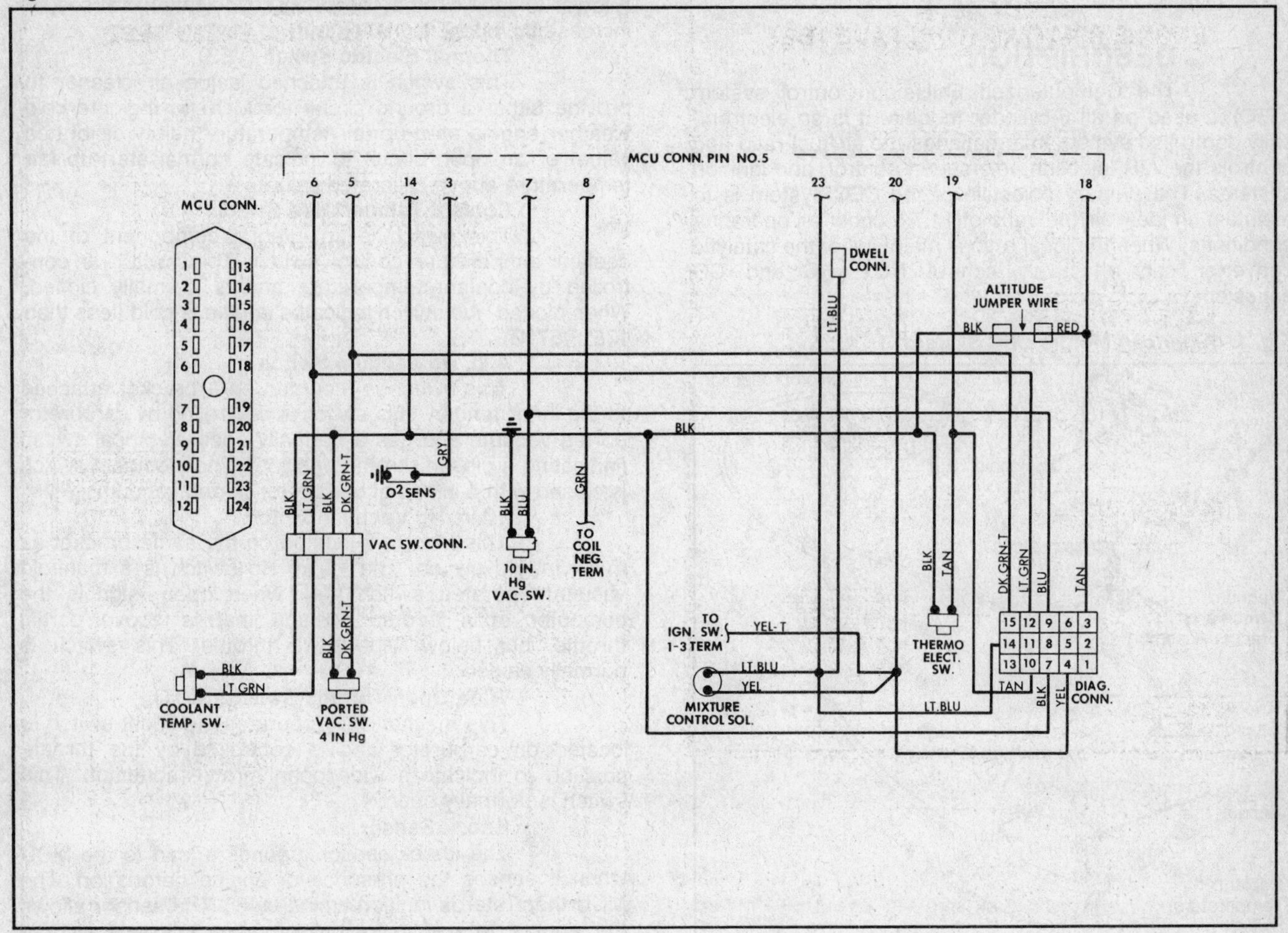

1983 Exhaust Emission Systems

AMC 6-CYL. COMPUTERIZED EMISSION CONTROLS

All Models

DESCRIPTION

The Computerized Emission Control system (CEC) is used on all 6-cylinder models. It is an electronically controlled system that manages the air/fuel ratio and controls the AIR injection, idle speed control, and ignition systems. The primary objective of the CEC system is to maintain an ideal air/fuel ratio of 14.7:1 under all operating conditions. When the ideal ratio is maintained, the catalytic converter can effectively control NOx, HC and CO emissions.

Fig. 1: American Motors CEC System

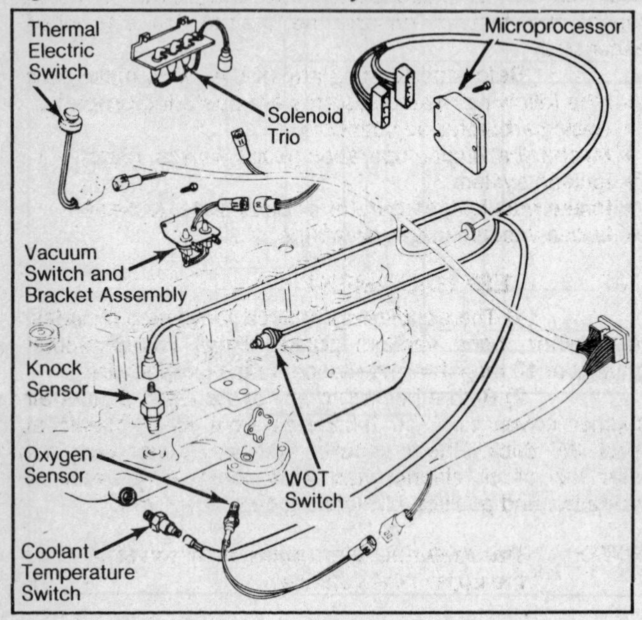

Carburetor (not shown) is controlled by this system.

OPERATION

The CEC system consists of 7 sub-systems: fuel control, data sensors, Microcomputer Control Unit (MCU), catalytic converter, idle speed control, air injection control, and ignition advance control.

FUEL CONTROL

All models are equipped with feedback carburetors which contain an electronically operated stepper motor. The stepper motor controls metering pins which vary the size of idle and main air bleed orifices in carburetor body. The stepper motor moves the pins in and out of the orifices in steps, in response to signals received from MCU. The motor has a range of 100 steps, but normally operates in the middle of its range.

When the metering pins are stepped into the orifices, the air/fuel mixture becomes richer. When the pins are stepped out of the orifices, the mixture becomes leaner.

DATA SENSORS

Oxygen Sensor

The oxygen sensor is located in the exhaust manifold to measure oxygen content of exhaust gases. As more oxygen is sensed (lean mixture indication), the electrical signal generated by the sensor drops in voltage. A lower oxygen content (rich mixture indication) causes an increase in voltage signal output.

Thermal Electric Switch (TES)

This switch is attached inside air cleaner to provide either a ground circuit for MCU to indicate cold weather engine start-up (air temperature below calibrated value) or an open circuit to indicate normal start-up (air temperature above calibrated value).

Coolant Temperature Switch

This switch is an integral component of the coolant temperature control switch. This switch is controlled by coolant temperature and is normally closed. When closed, the switch indicates engine is cold (less than 135°F/57°C).

4 in. Hg Vacuum Switch

This switch is mounted on a bracket attached to the inner fender. This switch is controlled by carburetor ported vacuum and has a normally open electrical switch (indicating a closed throttle position). The electrical switch is closed with 4 in. Hg of carburetor ported vacuum.

10 in. Hg Vacuum Switch

This switch is located on the same bracket as the 4 in. Hg switch. The 10 in. Hg switch is a manifold vacuum operated switch that, when open, signals the computer of a throttle position that is above partial throttle, but below wide open throttle. This switch is normally closed.

Wide Open Throttle Switch (WOT)

This mechanically operated electrical switch is located on carburetor and is controlled by the throttle position to indicate a wide open throttle condition. This switch is normally open.

Knock Sensor

The knock sensor grounds a lead to the MCU when it senses the presence of engine detonation. The MCU then retards ignition timing by 6°. The sensor allows the engine to run maximum possible advance without danger of piston damage due to detonation.

Engine RPM Voltage

This voltage is supplied from the tach terminal on the distributor. Until a voltage equal to a predetermined RPM is received by the MCU, the system remains in open loop mode of operation. The result is a fixed rich air/fuel mixture for engine starting.

Timer

This timer is activated whenever system is operating in open loop 2 mode (wide open throttle). This timer remains active for a preset period of time. If a "lean limit" condition (altitude jumper wire installed) occurs, the timer becomes inoperative. The timer has multi-function abilities; in addition to OL2 mode, it is used as a WOT timer and start-up timer.

MICROCOMPUTER CONTROL UNIT

The MCU is located in passenger compartment, behind right-hand kick panel. The MCU monitors the CEC system data sensors and, based upon mode of operation, generates an output control signal to the stepper motor mounted in carburetor. The MCU allows the following 3 modes of operation:

Initialization

This function occurs when ignition switch is turned on. This sets initial air bleed metering rod position by signaling the stepper motor to drive them first to a full rich position (fully toward front of vehicle) and then, by a pre-programmed number of steps, in lean direction

AMC 6-CYL. COMPUTERIZED EMISSION CONTROLS (Cont.)

(toward rear of vehicle). This serves as a starting point of mixture control operation.

Open Loop

In this mode, the MCU determines the air/fuel mixture based upon engine operation rather than oxygen sensor input signals. There are 5 open loop modes of operation and each has a specific metering pin position. However, because more than one condition may exist at any time, the MCU is programmed with a priority ranking for each operation. The MCU complies with the highest priority. The open loop priorities (listed from highest to lowest) are as follows: Cold Weather Start-Up, Open Loop 2 (Wide Open Throttle), Open Loop 4 (Low Manifold Vacuum), Open Loop 3 (Low Ported Vacuum), Open Loop 1 (Cold Engine Operation).

NOTE: With each engine start-up, a start-up timer is activated. During this interval, if engine operating condition would otherwise trigger normal closed loop operation, OL1 mode is selected.

Closed Loop

When all input data and engine operation meet programmed criteria (when OL1, OL2, OL3, OL4 and cold start modes are not selected and start-up timer has deactivated), the CEC system goes into closed loop operation. In this mode, oxygen sensor input signals are accepted by MCU to determine proper air/fuel mixture based upon oxygen content of exhaust gases. Air injection is routed "downstream" during this mode for partial or wide open throttle conditions and both "upstream" and "downstream" for all other throttle positions.

NOTE: Closed loop operation is characterized by constant movement of the metering pins. The MCU is constantly making small corrections in air/fuel ratio in an attempt to create the ideal air/fuel ratio.

CATALYTIC CONVERTER

Proper emission control is accomplished with the special catalytic converter used with the CEC system. All models, except Federal Eagle models, use a dual bed monolithic-type converter with "downstream" air injection. The injection of air between the 2 beds allows more complete oxidation of HC and CO in the closed loop mode. Federal Eagle models are equipped with a pellet-type converter. In order for these converters to be effective, precise control of the oxygen content of exhaust gases entering the converter is necessary; thus the need for the oxygen sensor, MCU and feedback carburetor.

IDLE SPEED CONTROL

The idle speed control system is operated by vacuum signals and the MCU. The idle speed system raises and/or maintains the engine idle whenever high electrical loads or air conditioning compressor loads are present. The idle speed control system consists of a sole-vac (throttle positioner), an idle vacuum switching solenoid, and an idle speed relay.

AIR INJECTION CONTROL

The air injection system is switched from upstream to downstream injection (or both) by the MCU. Two electrically operated vacuum valves supply operating vacuum to the upstream air injection valve and the downstream air injection valve. This allows the MCU to control catalyst operation and thereby reduce exhaust emissions.

IGNITION ADVANCE CONTROL

A vacuum operated electrical switch is used to electronically retard the ignition timing advance during certain phases of engine operation.

TESTING

The steps listed in the following charts will provide a systematic evaluation of each component that could cause the malfunction. After completing a repair, repeat the test to ensure the malfunction has been eliminated.

Before performing any of the tests, make sure that the following related systems are operating properly:

- Basic carburetor adjustments.
- Mechanical engine operation (plugs, valves, rings).
- Ignition system.
- Intake manifold, carburetor or base plate gaskets.
- Loose vacuum hoses or fittings.

TEST EQUIPMENT

1) The equipment required for testing includes: tachometer, hand vacuum pump, digital volt-ohmmeter (minimum 10 megohm impedance) and a jumper wire.

2) Before beginning any of the tests, a clear air cleaner cover must be fabricated from clear plastic at least .25" thick. This is secured with air cleaner wing nut after top of air cleaner has been removed to observe operation and position of metering pins. *See Fig. 2.*

NOTE: The metering pins operate in tandem. Only the upper pin is visible.

Fig. 2: Air Cleaner Cover Dimensions

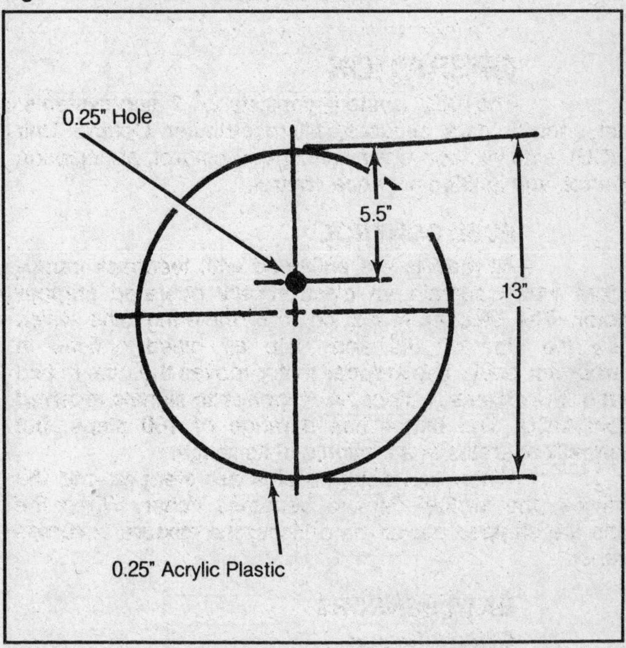

Fabricate cover to allow observation of metering pins.

AMC 6-CYL. COMPUTERIZED EMISSION CONTROLS (Cont.)

SYSTEM TEST CHARTS

Chart No.	Test
No. 1	Operational test.
No. 2	Initialization test.
No. 3	Open loop switch test.
No. 4	Closed loop operational test.
No. 5	Electronic ignition retard test.
No. 6	Oxygen sensor and closed loop test.
No. 7	"Downstream" solenoid test.
No. 8	"Upstream" solenoid test.
No. 9	Idle speed control system test.
No. 10	Sole-Vac vacuum switching solenoid test.
No. 11	Sole-Vac idle speed relay test.
No. 12	Basic engine test.

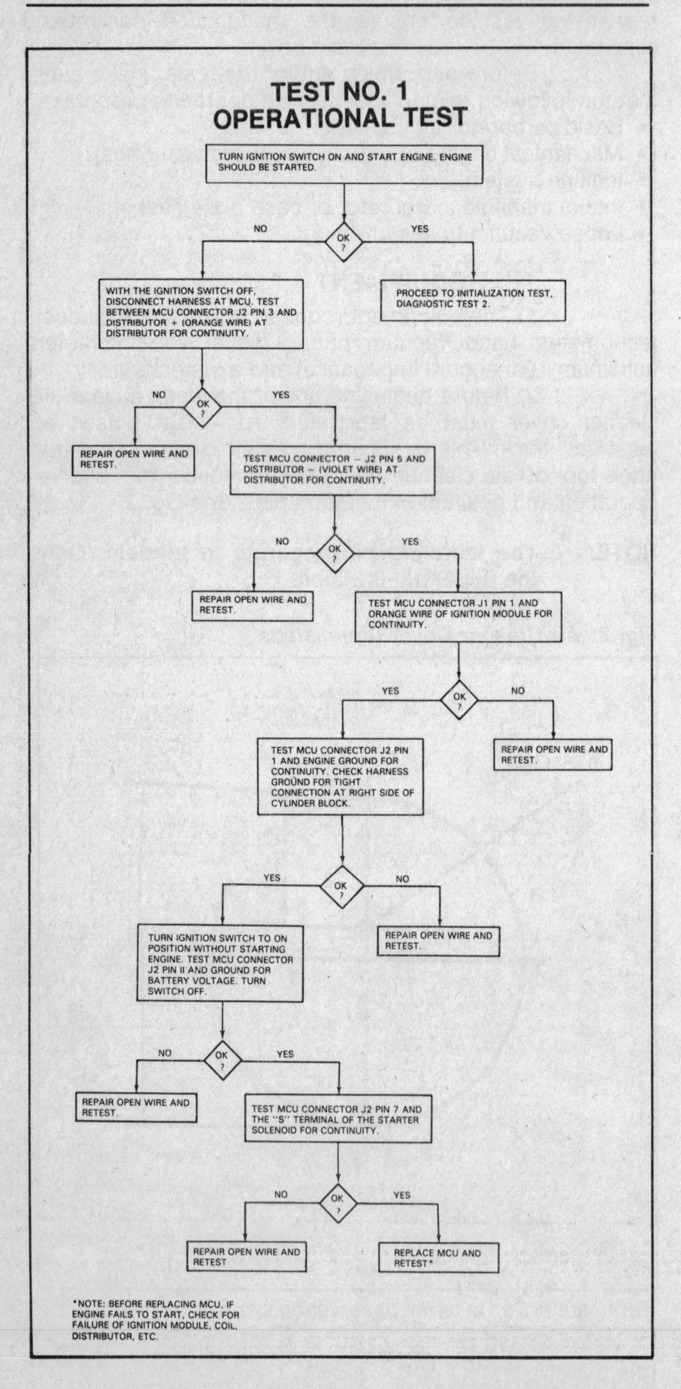

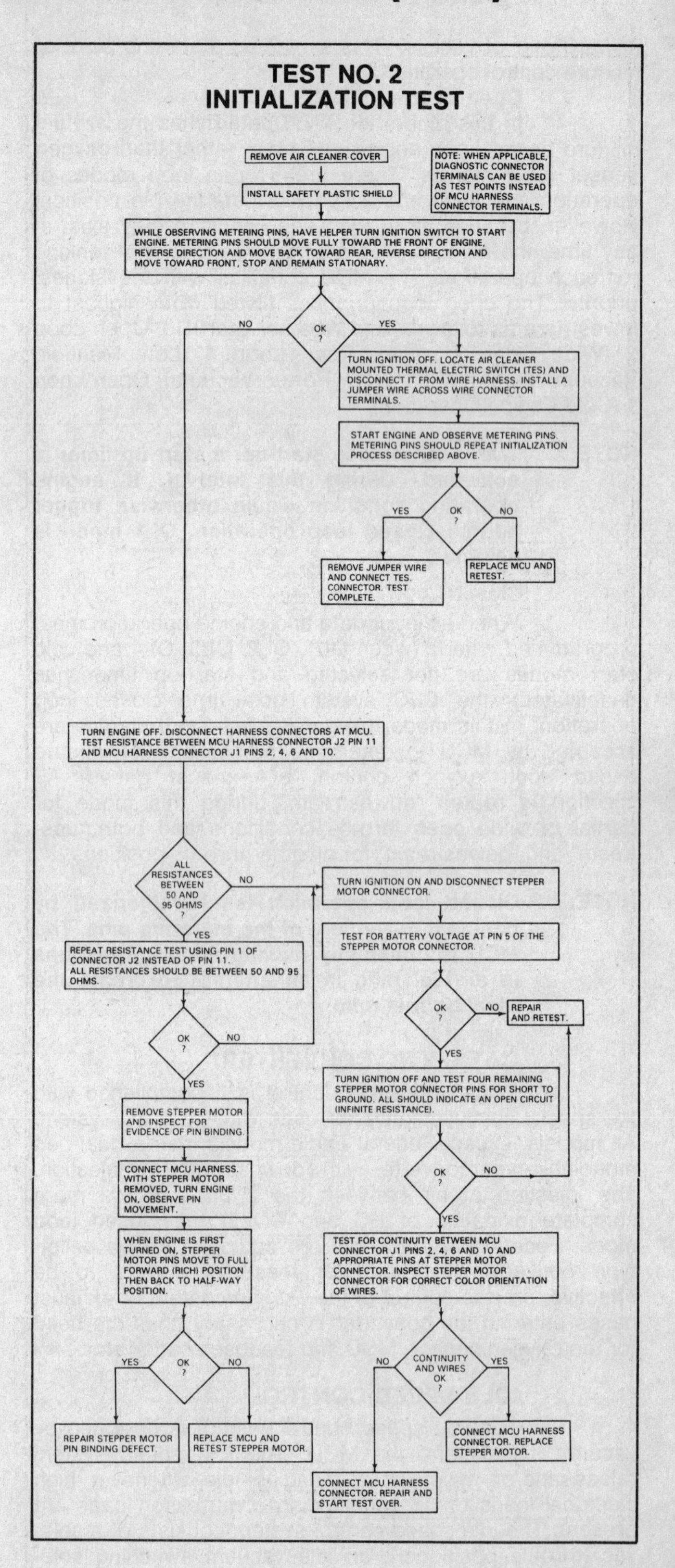

AMC 6-CYL. COMPUTERIZED EMISSION CONTROLS (Cont.)

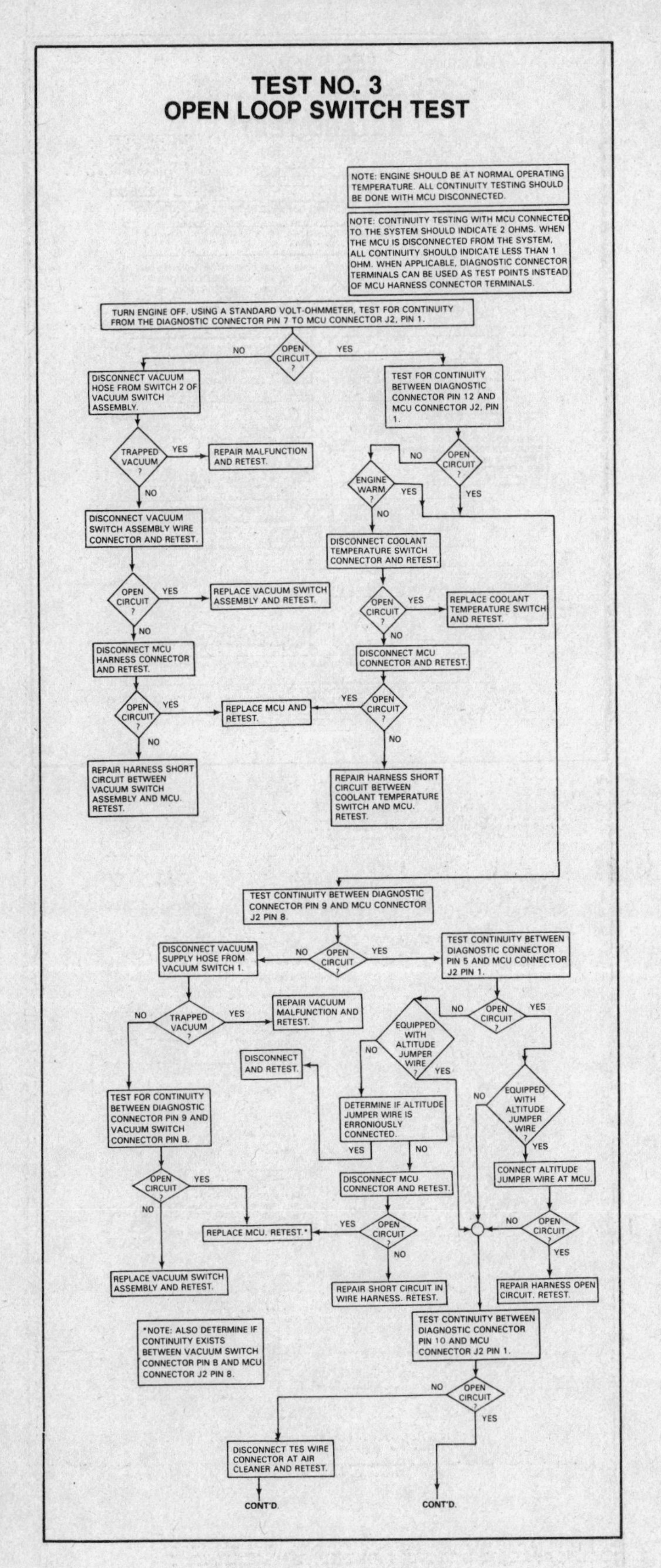

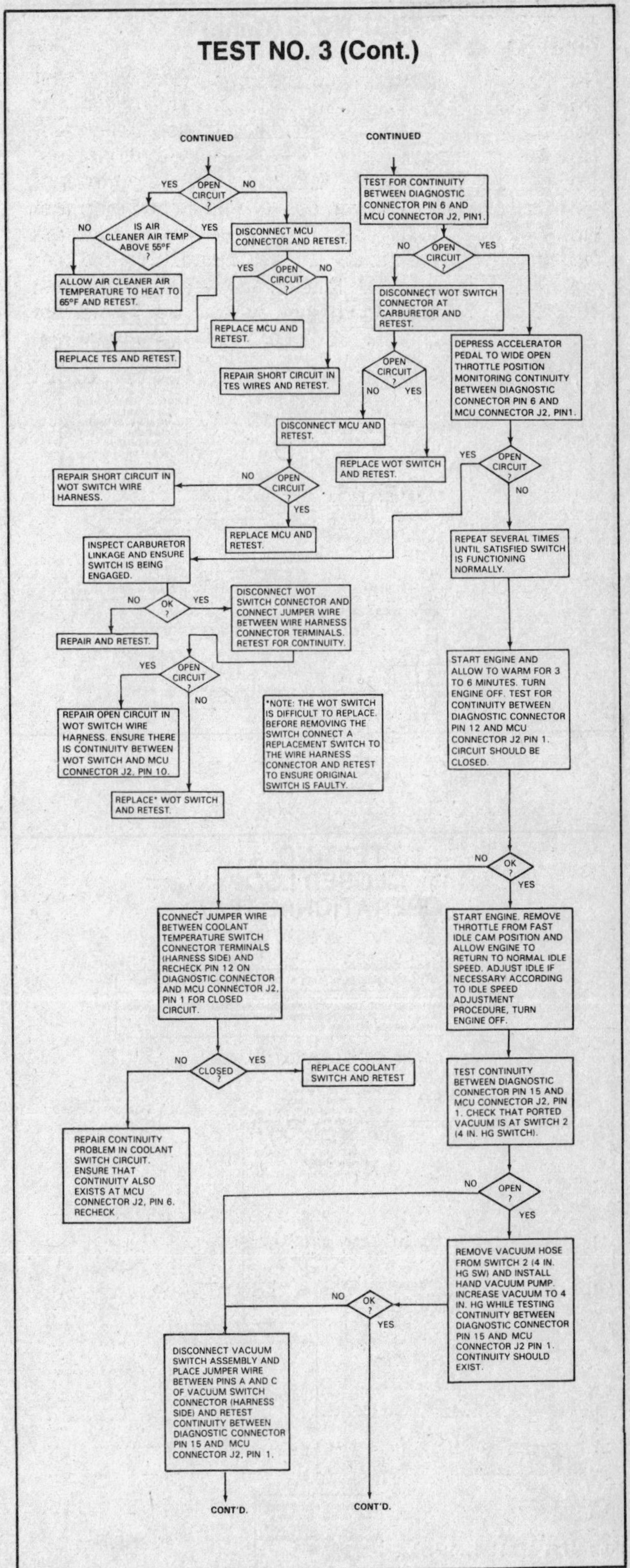

AMC 6-CYL. COMPUTERIZED EMISSION CONTROLS (Cont.)

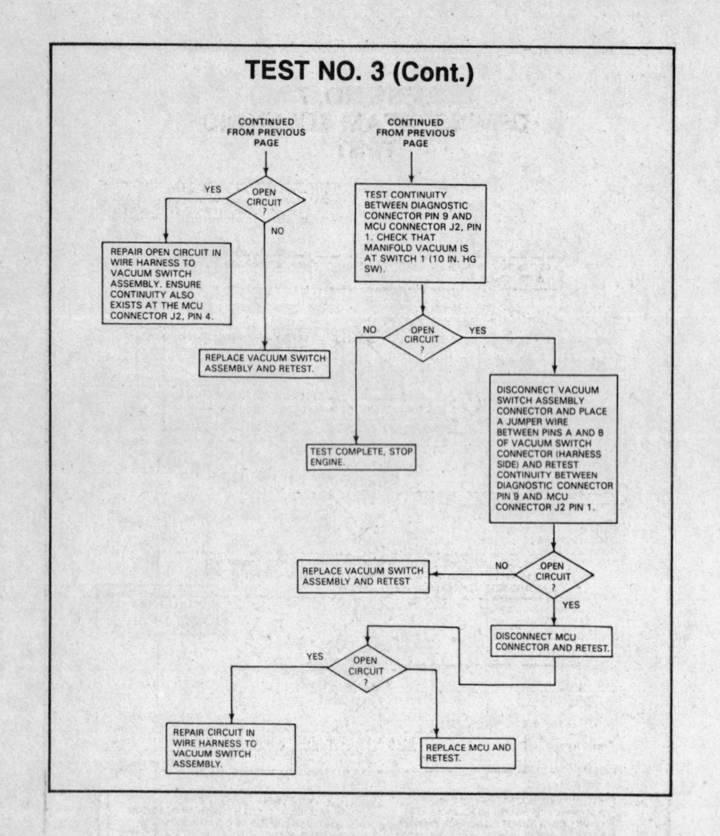

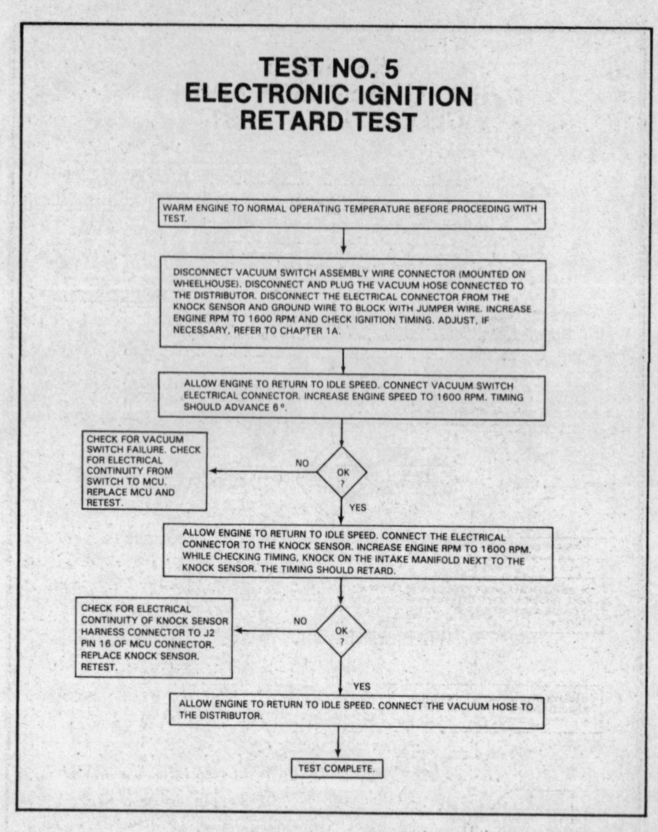

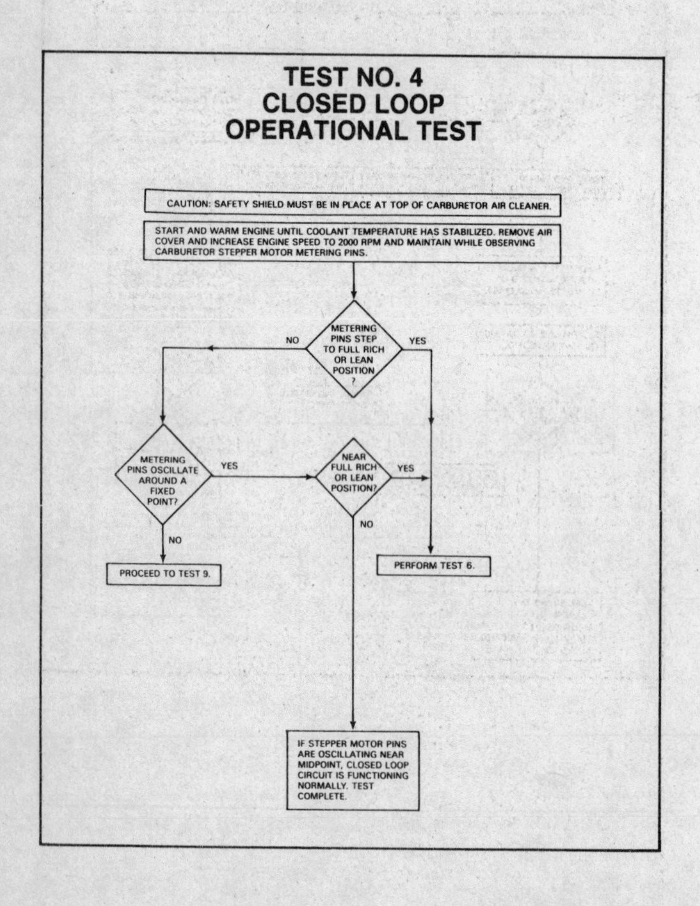

AMC 6-CYL. COMPUTERIZED EMISSION CONTROLS (Cont.)

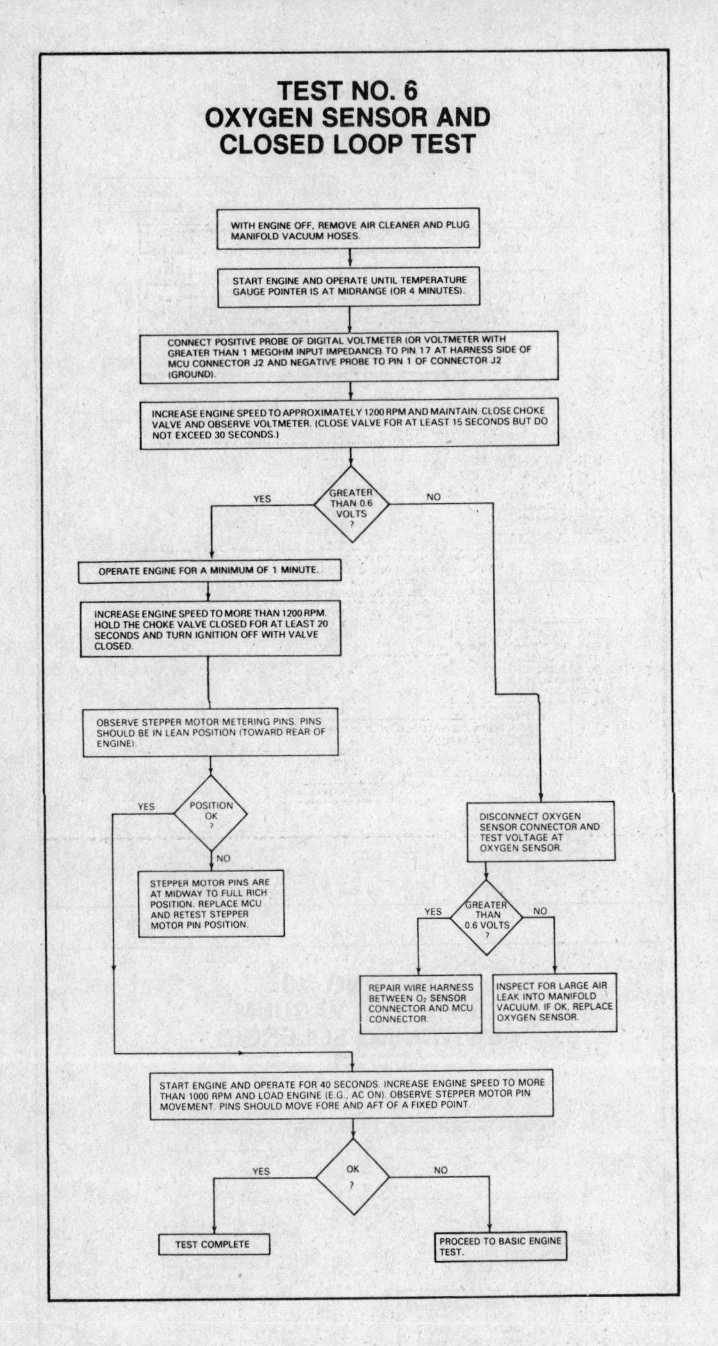

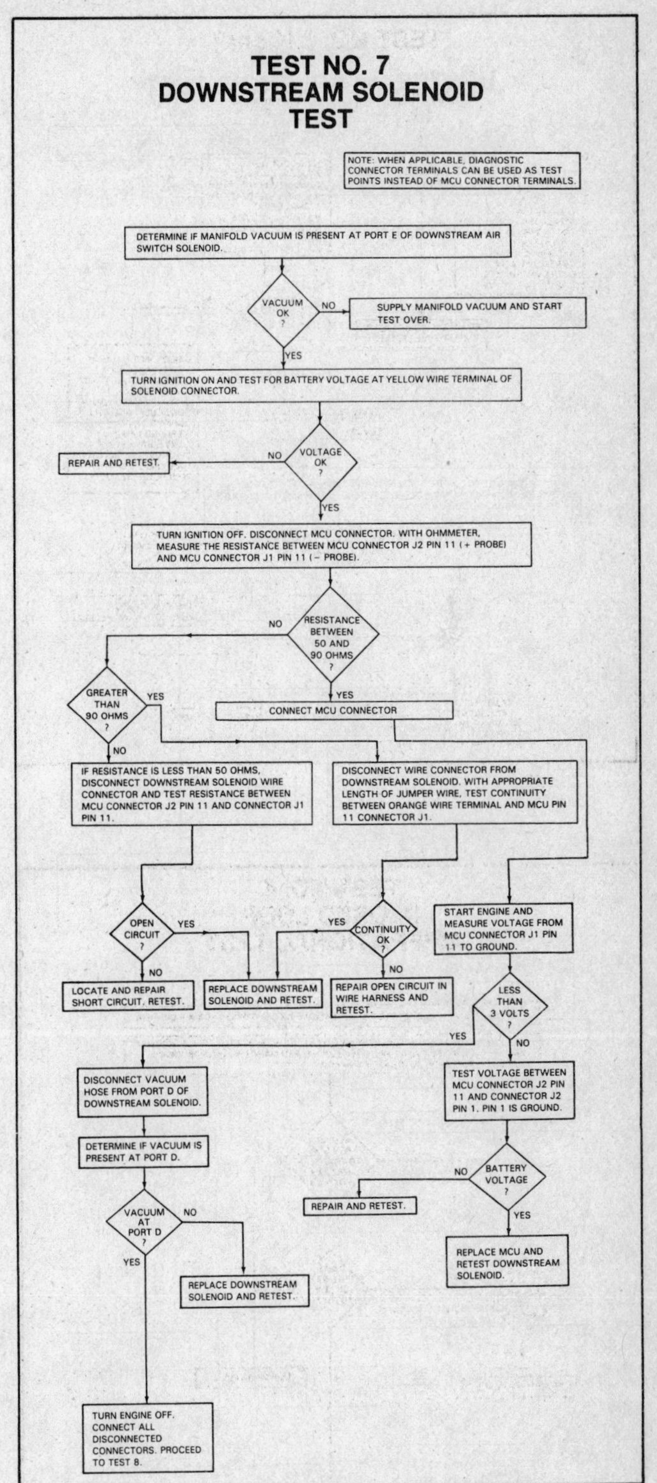

AMC 6-CYL. COMPUTERIZED EMISSION CONTROLS (Cont.)

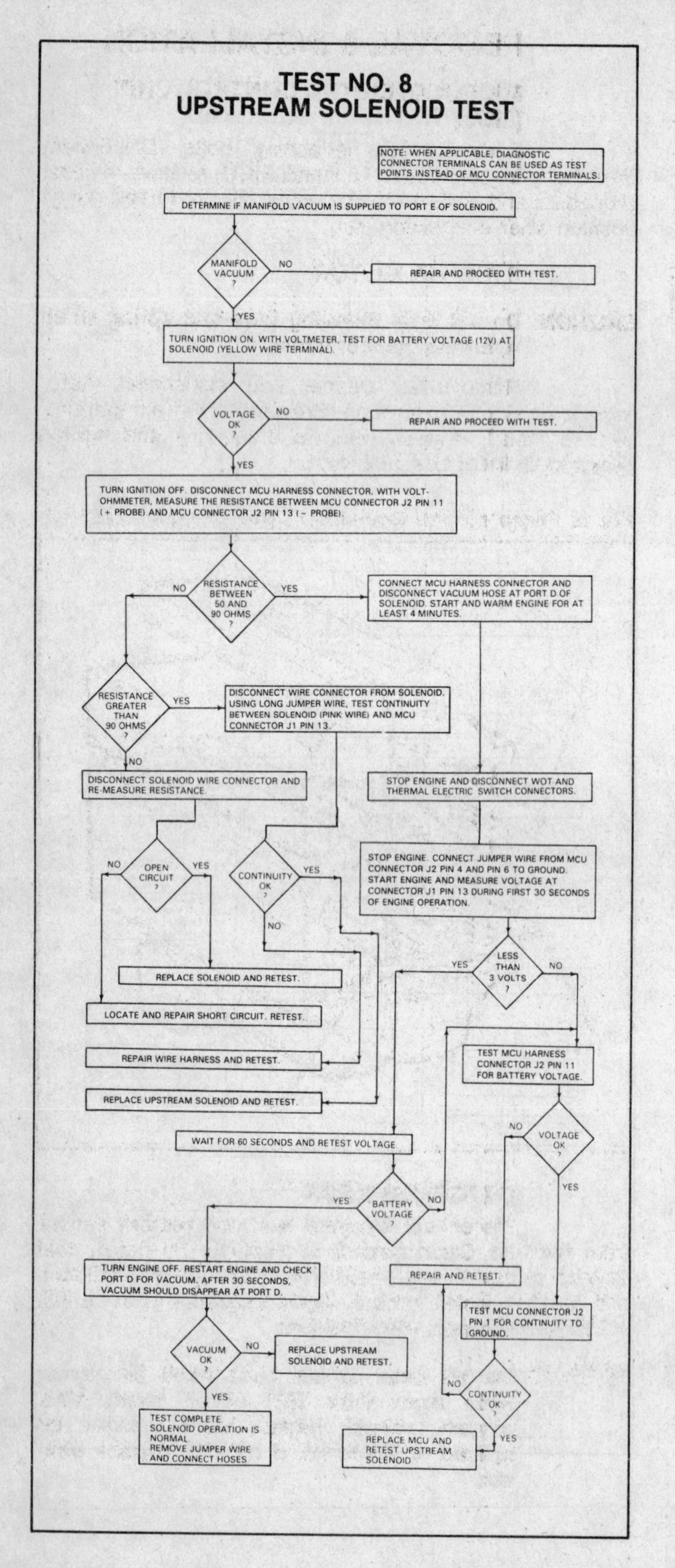

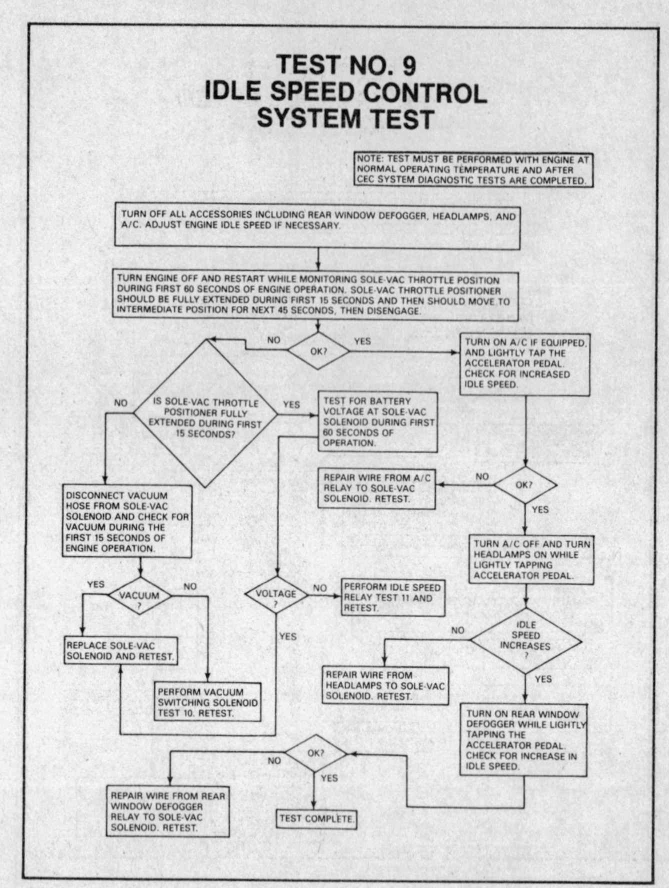

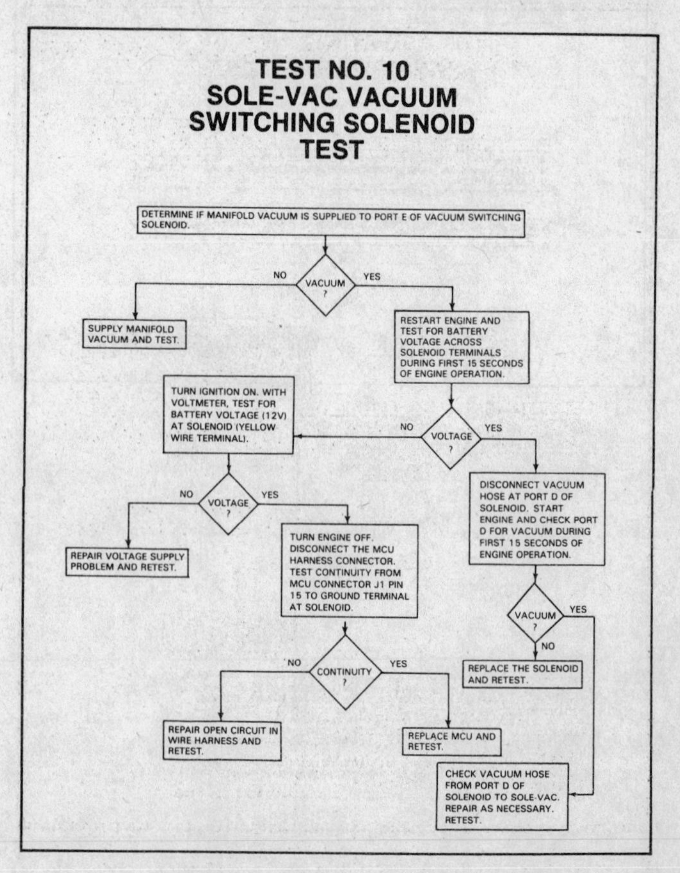

AMC 6-CYL. COMPUTERIZED EMISSION CONTROLS (Cont.)

TEST NO. 11
SOLE-VAC IDLE SPEED RELAY TEST

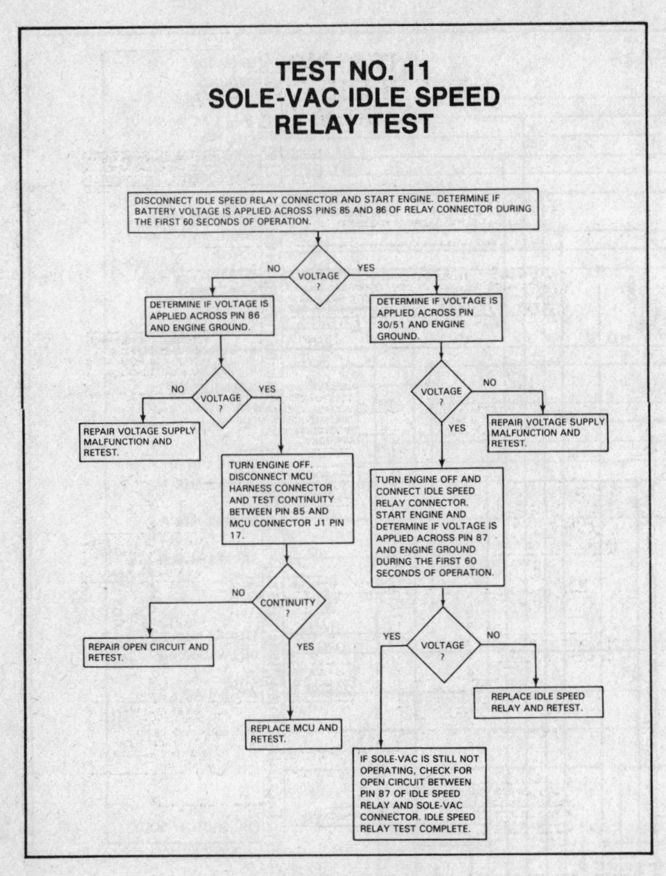

TEST NO. 12
BASIC ENGINE TEST

IF THE RESULTS OF DIAGNOSTIC TESTS 1 THROUGH 6 INDICATE THAT THE CEC SYSTEM IS FUNCTIONING NORMALLY AND ENGINE PERFORMANCE REMAINS INADEQUATE, PERFORM THE FOLLOWING TEST.

DETERMINE WHICH DIRECTION, RICH OR LEAN, THAT STEPPER MOTOR METERING PINS CONSISTENTLY MOVE TOWARD.

RICH ?

NO

YES

- INSPECT FOR AIR LEAKS AT INTAKE MANIFOLD AND CARBURETOR GASKETS. INSPECT FOR FAULTY VACUUM HOSES OR FITTINGS. REPAIR SOURCE OF AIR LEAKS AND RETEST.
- CHECK FOR EXHAUST LEAKS AT OR NEAR O_2 SENSOR. REPAIR AND RETEST.

LEAN ?

NO

YES

IF METERING PINS VARY CONSISTENTLY WITHIN MIDRANGE, OPERATION IS NORMAL. TEST COMPLETE.

CHECK FOR FAULTY SPARK PLUG(S); MISADJUSTED IGNITION TIMING; AND MALFUNCTIONING IGNITION ADVANCE MECHANISMS.

OK ?

YES

NO

ADJUST AND/OR REPLACE COMPONENTS AS NECESSARY. RETEST.

- CHECK CARBURETOR IDLE SPEED ADJUSTMENT AND CHOKE ADJUSTMENT. CHECK OPERATION OF CHOKE LINKAGE. ENSURE HOSES AND WIRES ARE NOT INTERFERRING WITH OR RESTRICTING CARBURETOR LINKAGE. REPAIR AS NECESSARY AND RETEST.
- INSPECT HEATED AIR TUBE FOR PROPER CONNECTION AT AIR CLEANER AND EXHAUST MANIFOLD HEAT STOVE. REPAIR AS NECESSARY AND RETEST.
- INSPECT EGR VALVE FOR CORRECT INSTALLATION AND PROPER OPERATION. REPAIR AS NECESSARY AND RETEST.
- INSPECT PCV VALVE FOR PROPER OPERATION. REPAIR AS NECESSARY AND RETEST.
- INSPECT VAPOR CANISTER FOR PROPER "PURGE" OPERATION AND CONDITION OF HOSES. REPAIR AS NECESSARY AND RETEST.

REMOVAL & INSTALLATION

MICROCOMPUTER CONTROL UNIT (MCU)

Remove MCU attaching bolts. Disconnect electrical plug connector. To install MCU, reverse removal procedure and ensure terminal ends are not forced out of position when connecting plug.

STEPPER MOTOR

CAUTION: Do not drop metering pins and spring when removing stepper motor.

Remove air cleaner and disconnect motor connector. Remove retaining screw and unit from carburetor. To install, reverse removal procedure and tighten screw to 25 INCH Lbs. (2.8 N.m).

Fig. 3: Stepper Motor Connector Terminal Identification

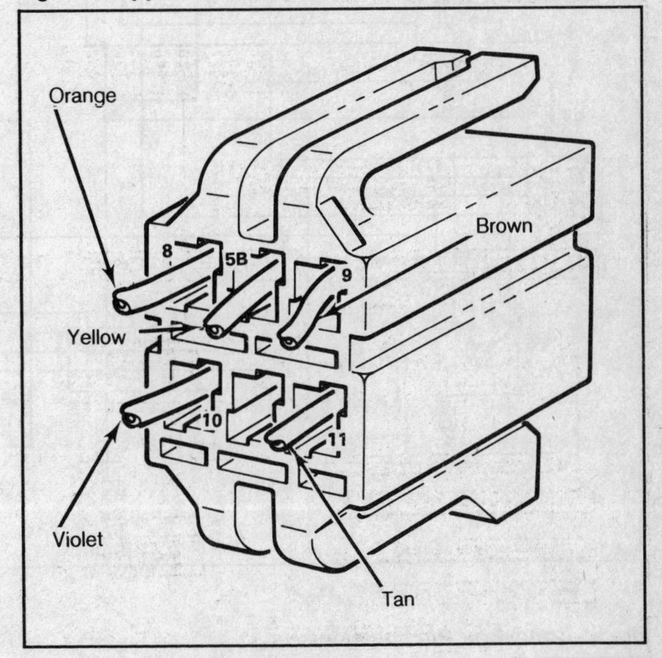

OXYGEN SENSOR

Disconnect electrical lead and remove sensor from manifold. Clean threads of manifold. To install, coat threads of new oxygen sensor with anti-seize compound and carefully install sensor. Tighten sensors to 31 ft. lbs. (42 N.m). Reconnect electrical lead.

NOTE: Do not push rubber boot down on sensor body more than 1/2" above base. Also, oxygen sensor pigtail wires cannot be spliced or soldered. If broken, replace sensor.

AMC 6-CYL. COMPUTERIZED EMISSION CONTROLS (Cont.)

Fig. 4: American Motors 6-Cyl. CEC System Wiring Diagram

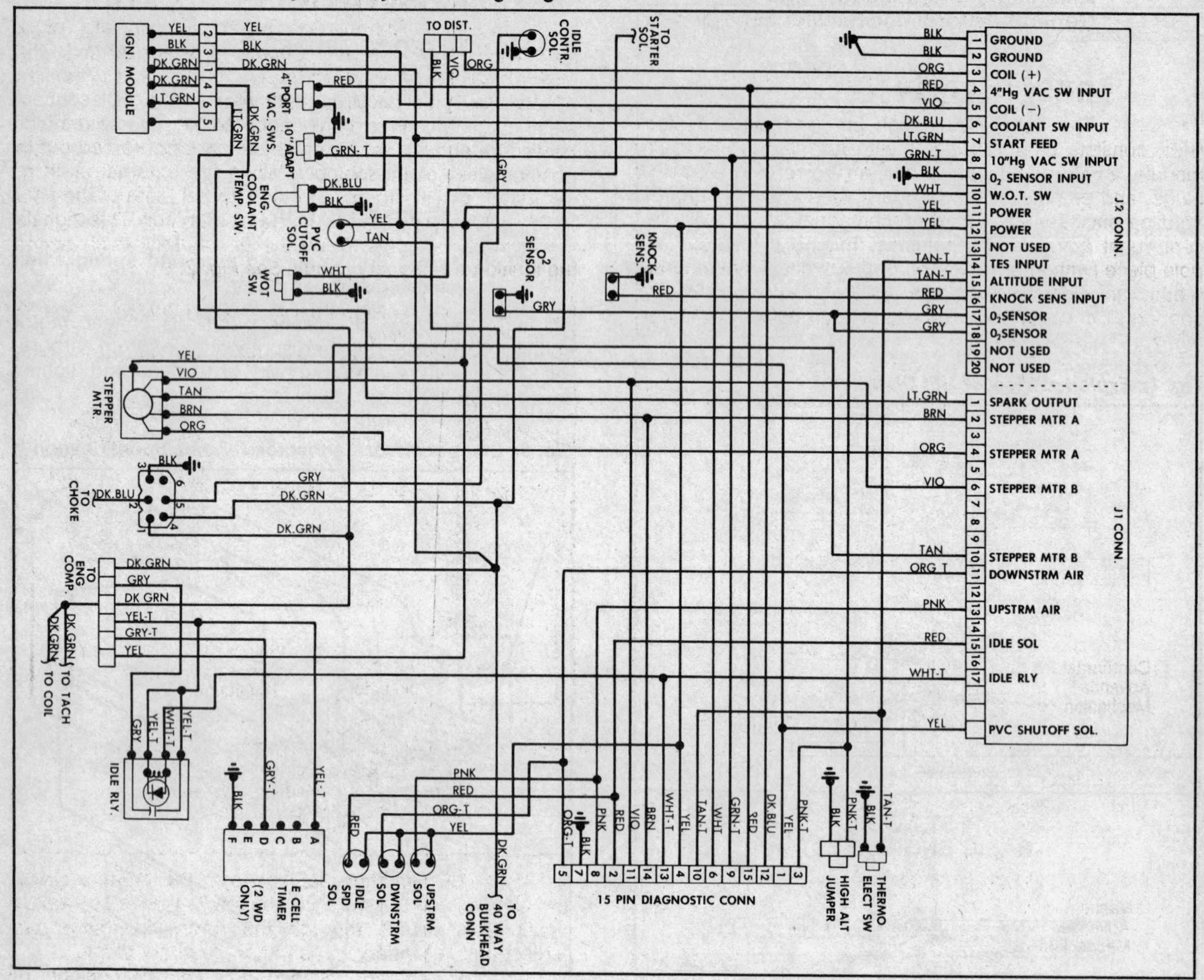

Fig. 5: Connector Pin Locations

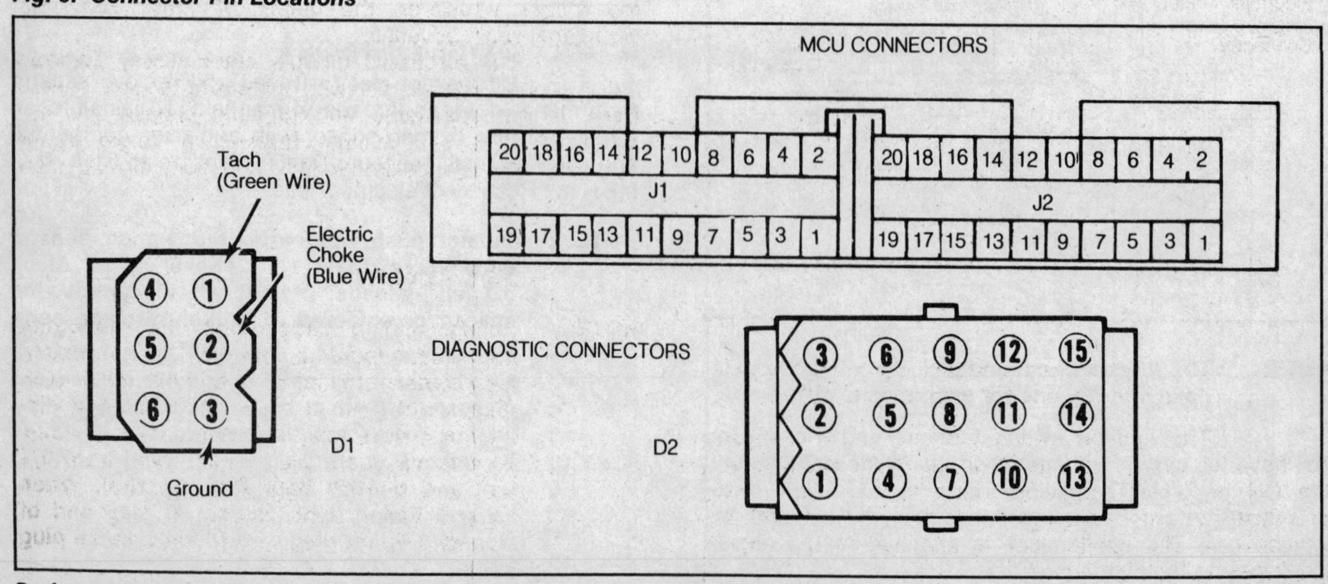

Perform tests on circuits as required by connecting meter to appropriate connector pins.

DELCO-REMY HIGH ENERGY IGNITION

American Motors Models with 2.5L & General Motors Models with Federal 1.6L

DESCRIPTION

The Delco-Remy High Energy Ignition System (HEI) consists of a distributor with an integral electronic module, a battery, an ignition coil, an ignition switch, spark plugs, and primary and secondary wiring. The distributor housing encloses the following components: Vacuum and centrifugal advance mechanisms, magnetic pick-up coil, pole piece (with internal teeth), trigger wheel (with external teeth), an electronic module (with built-in radio noise suppression capacitor), rotor and distributor shaft. *See Fig. 1.*

Fig. 1: Exploded View of HEI Distributor

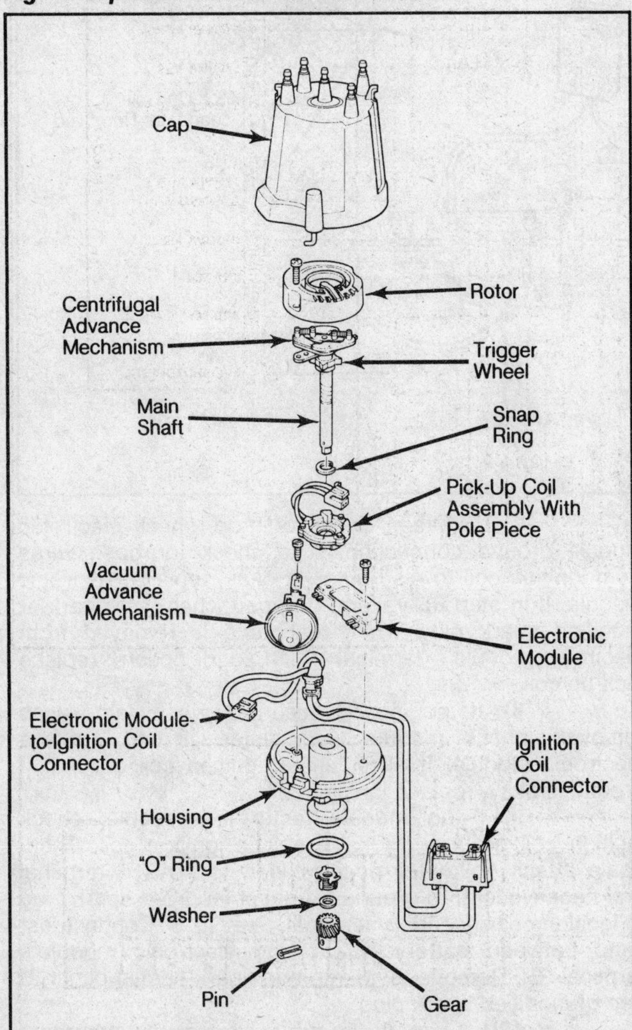

NOTE: **The trigger wheel and pick-up coil piece each have 4 teeth, one for each engine cylinder.**

The ignition switch terminal and the ignition coil have full battery voltage when the ignition switch is in the "ON" or "START" position. There is no ballast resistor or resistance wire between the ignition switch and the ignition coil. The ignition coil is attached to the engine block next to the distributor.

OPERATION

The pick-up coil assembly consists of a permanent magnet, a pole piece and a pick-up coil. The pick-up coil assembly is stationary, unless it is advanced or retarded by the vacuum diaphragm

The timer core mounted on the distributor shaft, rotates with the shaft inside the pole piece portion of the pick-up coil assembly. When the external teeth of the trigger wheel line up with the internal teeth of the pole piece, a voltage is induced in the pick-up coil. This signals the electronic module inside the distributor, which opens the ignition coil primary circuit. *See Fig. 2.*

Fig. 2: Delco-Remy High Energy Ignition System Basic Wiring Diagram

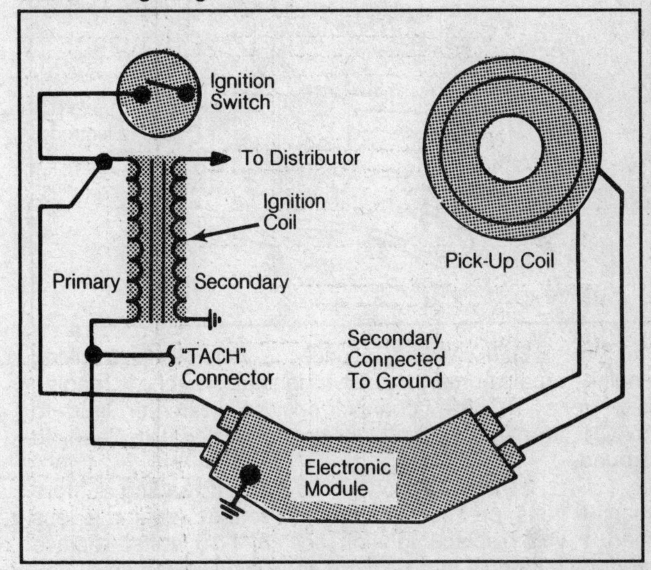

Current then decreases in the primary circuit and high voltage is induced in the ignition coil's secondary circuit. This travels through the rotor, distributor cap contact and secondary wires to fire the spark plugs.

A vacuum advance unit adjusts position of pick-up coil and pole piece, providing vacuum spark advance. Conventional centrifugal advance weights shift the trigger wheel on the distributor shaft, providing centrifugal spark advance.

The electronic module automatically controls dwell period, extending it with increased engine speed. Dwell is not adjustable and periodic checks are not necessary. The HEI system features a longer spark duration, which is desirable for firing lean air/fuel mixtures.

TESTING

NOTE: **During testing procedures, the following precautions must be observed. Do not ground tachometer terminal of distributor connector. Disconnect ignition switch connector at distributor before making compression checks. To remove spark plug wires, twist boot 1/2 turn and pull on boot (not on wire). When using a timing light connect at plug end of number 1 spark plug wire (do not pierce plug boot).**

1983 Exhaust Emission Systems

DELCO-REMY HIGH ENERGY IGNITION (Cont.)

Check that wiring connector is properly attached to connector at side of distributor cap and that spark plug wires are properly connected at both ends before continuing with test procedures.

SYSTEM VOLTAGE CHECK WITH MODIFIED SPARK PLUG

1) Using spark tester or modified spark plug (side electrode cut off), check for spark at each spark plug. *See Fig. 3.* If spark occurs, check fuel system and spark plugs. If no spark occurs, check voltage at ignition coil terminal "B+" while cranking engine.

Fig. 3: Modifying Spark Plug for Testing

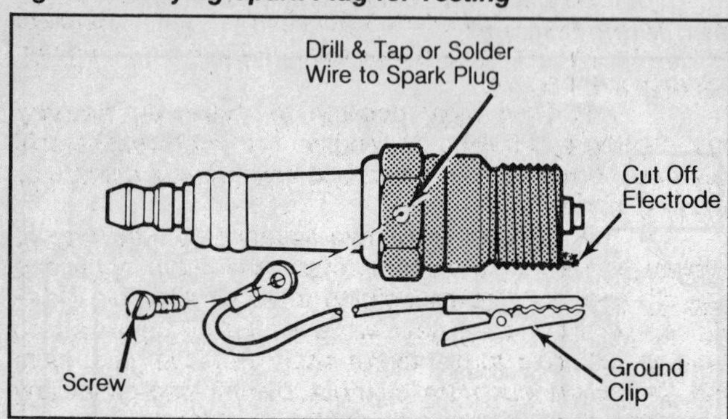

2) If reading is under 7 volts while cranking engine, repair primary circuit to ignition switch. If reading is 7 volts or more, connect positive voltmeter lead to "TACH" terminal of ignition coil and negative lead to ground.

3) Turn ignition switch "ON". If reading is more than 10 volts, proceed to step **5)**. If voltage reading is less than 1 volt, replace ignition coil. If 1-10 volts, replace electronic module in distributor and proceed to step **4)**.

4) Again check for spark as described in step **1)**. If spark occurs, system is operating properly. If no spark occurs, replace ignition coil as it is also defective.

5) If in step **3)**, the reading was more than 10 volts, attach modified spark plug again to coil secondary terminal. *See Fig. 4*. Leave wires between distributor and ignition coil connected. Crank engine and check for spark at modified spark plug. If spark occurs, inspect distributor cap for water, cracks or other damage. If okay, replace rotor.

Fig. 4: Checking Distributor Operation

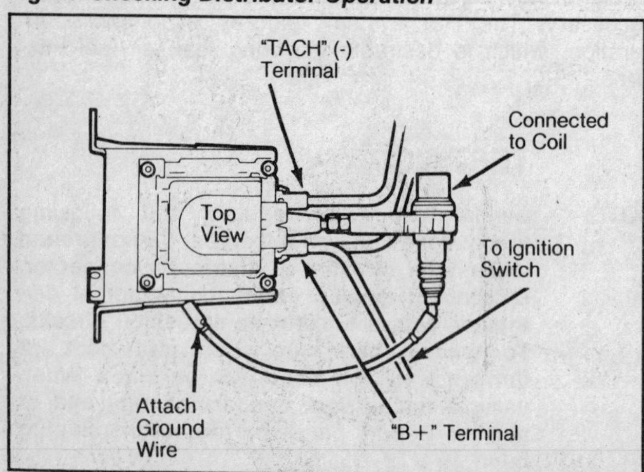

6) If in step **5)**, no spark occurred, remove pick-up coil leads from electronic module. Turn ignition switch "ON". Connect positive voltmeter lead to ignition coil "TACH" terminal and negative lead to ground. Watch voltmeter as test lamp is connected from battery power to electronic module's terminal "P" for 5 seconds. *See Fig. 5*.

Fig. 5: Testing Electronic Module

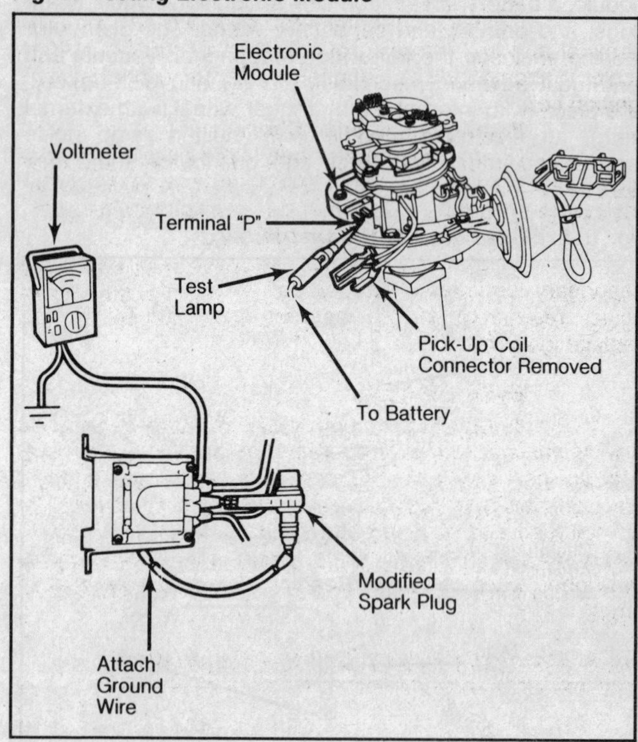

7) If voltage does not drop, check electronic module ground connection. Also check for open wires from ignition coil to distributor. If okay, replace electronic module. If in step **6)**, voltage dropped, check for spark at modified spark plug when test lamp is removed from electronic module's terminal "P". If spark occurs, replace pick-up coil.

8) If no spark occurred when lamp was removed, check module with tester. If bad, replace electronic module. If okay, check ignition coil ground. If ground is okay, replace ignition coil.

9) If no module tester is available, check ignition coil ground. If okay, replace ignition coil. Then, again attach voltmeter positive lead to "TACH" terminal and negative lead to ground. Connect modified spark plug to ignition coil secondary terminal. *See Fig. 5*. Connect test lamp between battery power and electronic module's terminal "P". Remove test lamp and spark should occur at gap of modified spark plug.

10) If spark occurs, system is operating properly. If no spark occurs, reinstall original ignition coil and replace electronic module.

INTERMITTENT PROBLEMS

1) Attach modified spark plug, in turn, to 2 different spark plug wires and crank engine. If no spark, repeat previous test, System Voltage Check with Modified Spark Plug.

2) If spark occurs from one or both wires, check pick-up coil resistance for 500-1500 ohms. If not to

DELCO-REMY HIGH ENERGY IGNITION (Cont.)

specifications, replace pick-up coil. If okay, check for dwell increase from a high to low RPM.

3) If dwell increases, check fuel system, spark plug wires, distributor cap and spark plugs. If no increase occurs, replace electronic module.

IGNITION COIL

Short Check

Connect an ohmmeter between coil positive terminal and coil frame (ground). With ohmmeter in high scale, it should indicate infinite resistance. If not, replace ignition coil.

Primary Resistance Check

Connect ohmmeter between positive and negative terminals of ignition coil. With ohmmeter in low scale, resistance should be 0-1 ohm. If not, replace ignition coil.

Secondary Resistance Check

Connect ohmmeter between negative and secondary terminals of ignition coil. With ohmmeter in low scale, resistance should be less than infinite. If not, replace ignition coil.

PICK-UP COIL

1) Connect vacuum pump to vacuum advance unit. If vacuum unit is inoperative, replace unit. Remove pick-up coil connector (Green and White wires) from electronic module. Connect ohmmeter leads to either pick-up coil lead and to distributor housing. *See "A" in Fig. 6.* Set ohmmeter in middle scale. Operate vacuum advance throughout vacuum range. Reading should be infinite at all times.

Fig. 6: Distributor Pick-Up Coil Test Connections

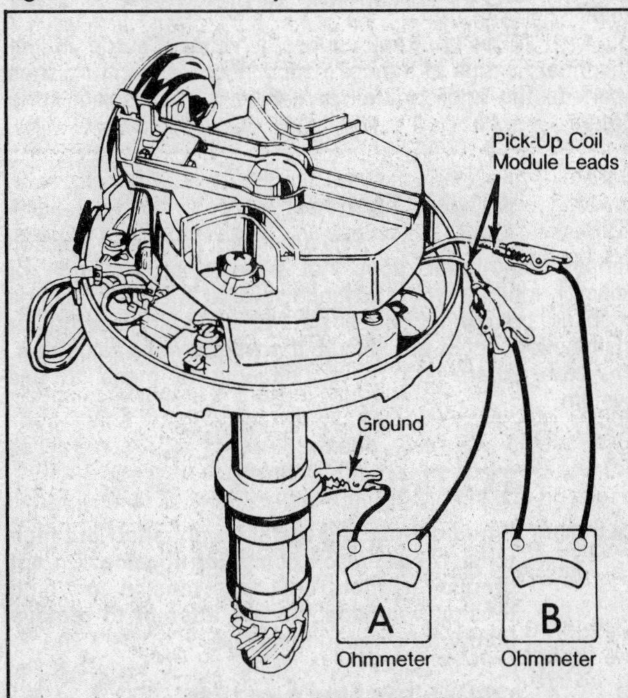

2) Connect ohmmeter leads to pick-up coil leads (Green and White wires shown in *"B" of Fig. 6*). Again use middle scale of ohmmeter. Operate vacuum advance throughout vacuum range. Ohmmeter should read 500-1500 ohms in all advance positions. If either reading is not to specifications, replace pick-up coil.

ELECTRONIC MODULE

If engine still does not run or operation is still rough after all preceding tests are completed, replace the electronic module.

OVERHAUL

NOTE: **When distributor is removed from 1.6L engine, the fuel pump and fuel pump rod MUST be removed first.**

DISASSEMBLY

1) Disconnect wiring harness from distributor cap. Disconnect coil connectors from cap. Remove distributor cap and disconnect vacuum hose from vacuum advance mechanism.

2) Mark rotor position to distributor housing and distributor housing to engine for later reassembly reference. Remove hold-down bolt and remove distributor housing from engine.

3) Remove rotor, two advance springs, weight retainer and advance weights. Mark distributor shaft and gear so they may be assembled in same position. Drive out roll pin from drive gear while supporting gear so no damage will occur to distributor shaft. Remove gear, shim and tanged washer from distributor shaft and clean any burrs from shaft. Remove distributor shaft from housing.

NOTE: **Do not attempt to service shaft bushings in housing.**

4) Remove 2 attaching screws holding module to housing and position module so pick-up coil leads can be removed. Remove electronic module. Remove snap ring from housing and lift out pick-up coil assembly. Remove 2 attaching screws and lift out vacuum advance mechanism.

REASSEMBLY

Reverse disassembly procedures while noting the following: Ensure that there is special silicone lubricant between module and distributor housing to provide heat transfer for electronic module cooling. After installation of distributor shaft, rotate to check for even clearance between external trigger wheel teeth and internal pole piece teeth.

Fig. 7: Internal Components of HEI Distributor

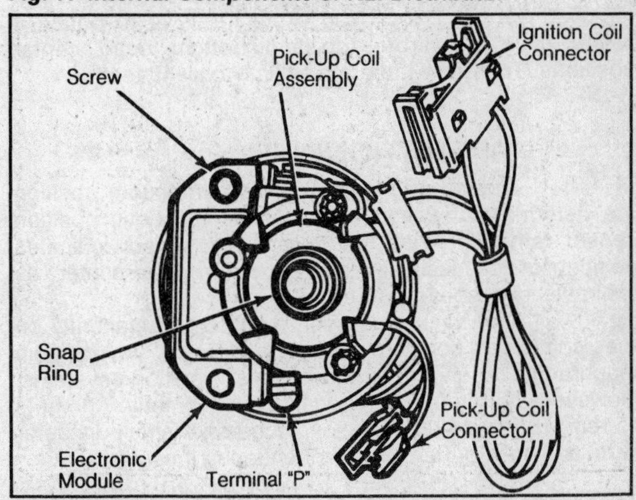

DUCELLIER ELECTRONIC IGNITION

American Motors Alliance

DESCRIPTION

The electronic ignition system used by American Motors in the Alliance includes a computer, distributor, ignition coil, vacuum sensor and a crankshaft position sensor. *See Fig. 1*. The ignition coil, which is part of the computer assembly, may be replaced separately if it is determined to be defective.

Fig. 1: Wiring Diagram of Ducellier Electronic Ignition System

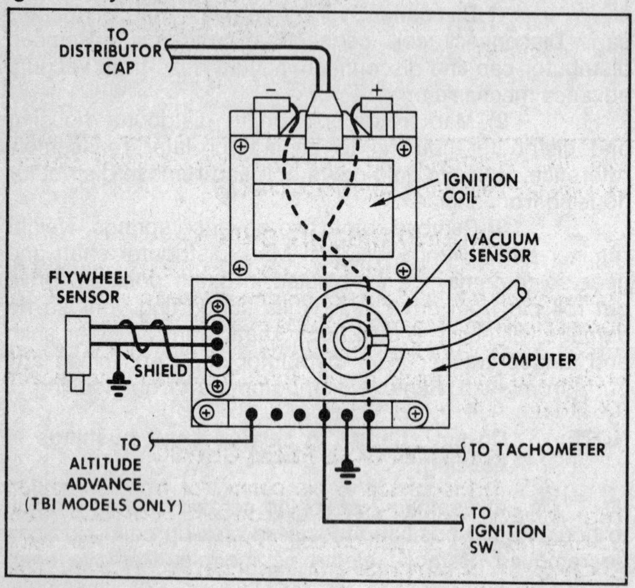

This system used on American Motors Alliance models.

As engine speed and crankshaft position are determined by the preset magnetic position sensor, the distributor's only function is to distribute the spark to the correct spark plug at the proper time.

The vacuum sensor, which cannot be removed from the computer housing, supplies the computer with engine load conditions. Vehicles with throttle body fuel injection have a calibrated orifice in the hose between the vacuum sensor and the vacuum pipe.

The flywheel has 44 evenly spaced teeth around its circumference. Two of these teeth have been removed 90° before top dead center and two have been removed 90° after top dead center. This is to obtain a timing mark 90° from top and bottom dead center positions. Therefore there are actually only 40 teeth.

OPERATION

Engine speed and crankshaft (piston) position are determined by the non-adjustable magnetic position sensor rather than the distributor. This sensor indicates position of top dead center and bottom dead center, as well as engine speed.

The vacuum sensor, mounted permanently on the computer housing, appears identical to vacuum diaphragms found on conventional ignition systems. However, the internal components differ greatly. Attempts to remove the vacuum sensor will break a small diameter wire leading into the computer, rendering it useless.

As the engine operates and the crankshaft flywheel turns, information is received by the computer indicating engine speed and crankshaft position. The vacuum sensor informs the computer of engine load conditions. *See Fig. 2*.

Fig. 2: Relationship of Computer and Ignition Coil

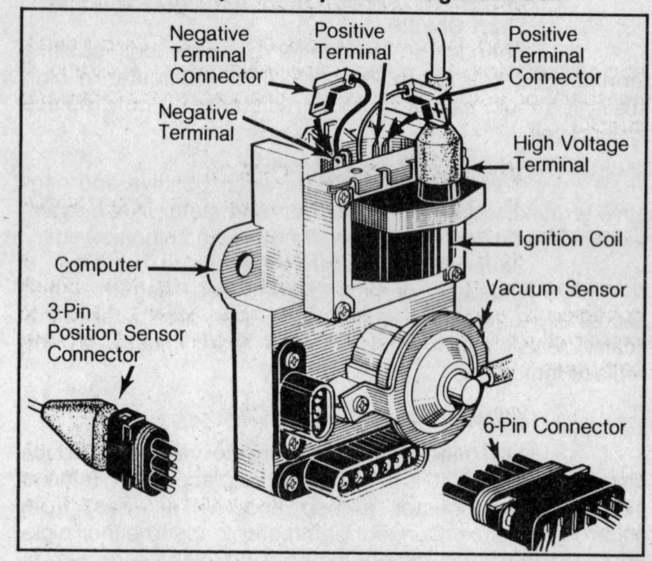

Vacuum sensor cannot be removed from computer.

The computer then interprets the information received, and sets the ignition advance ratio. The computer then opens and closes the primary circuit of the ignition coil, causing a build-up and collapse of the coil's magnetic field.

This in turn, causes a voltage surge in the secondary circuit of the coil. The distributor then furnishes spark to the appropriate spark plug in the correct firing order.

ADJUSTMENT

There is no adjustment of magnetic position sensor. Distributor does not have a pick-up coil or reluctor. Ignition timing advance valve at idle speed can be checked, but cannot be adjusted. Checking for a computer malfunction would be difficult, if advance were adjustable. Therefore, there are no adjustments to made to this system.

TESTING

CAUTION: When conducting tests, do not short out high tension current on computer housing. Do not ground ignition coil low tension or high tension windings. Do not attempt to remove computer's vacuum sensor.

VISUAL SYSTEM CHECKS

Check spark plugs, spark plug wires, distributor cap and rotor, and ignition coil high tension wire. Also check condition of harness connectors attached to computer. Repeatedly disconnect and reconnect these connectors. Clean terminals if necessary. Always do this before replacing any component.

DUCELLIER ELECTRONIC IGNITION (Cont.)

SYSTEM HIGH VOLTAGE CHECK

1) Disconnect coil high voltage wire from distributor cap. Hold wire approximately 3/4" from cylinder block. Crank engine, but do not start it.

CAUTION: Never ground high voltage wire against computer, as permanent damage will result.

2) If good spark results, check carburetion, engine mechanical condition, and initial advance setting. If no spark or poor spark results, proceed to the following checks.

VACUUM SENSOR CHECK

1) Stabilize engine speed at 3000 RPM. Disconnect vacuum hose from vacuum sensor.

2) If engine speed drops, vacuum sensor is operating properly. If engine speed does not drop, check condition of vacuum hose. If it is bad, replace hose and repeat check again. If hose condition was good, replace computer.

COIL VOLTAGE CHECK

1) Turn ignition switch "ON", but do not start engine. Connect voltmeter positive lead to coil positive terminal. *See Fig. 3*. Coil connectors should be on terminals.

Fig. 3: Checking Voltage at Positive Coil Terminal

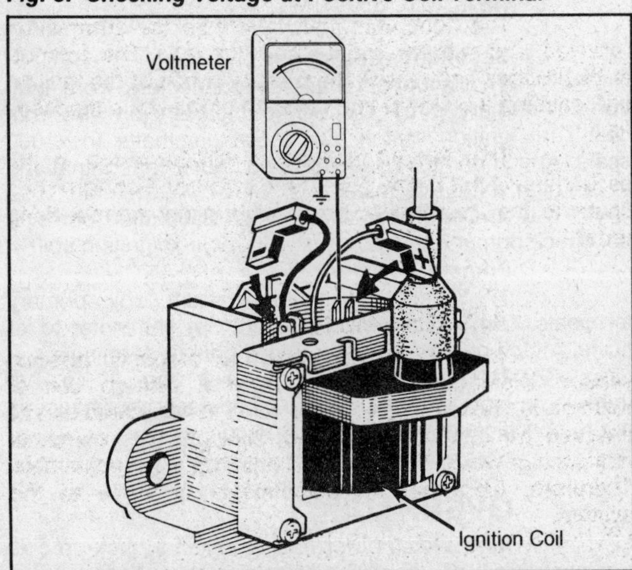

This is a preliminary check to determine system condition.

2) Connect negative lead to vehicle ground. Reading should be at least 9.5 volts. If good, proceed to Position Sensor Check. If less than 9.5 volts are read, proceed with next check.

POWER SUPPLY CHECK

1) Disconnect 6-pin connector from computer. Turn ignition switch "ON". Connect voltmeter positive lead to pin "D" of harness connector. *See Fig. 4*. Connect negative lead to vehicle ground.

2) Crank engine, but do not start it. Reading again should be 9.5 volts or more. If so, proceed to next check. If not, check battery voltage, recharge battery, check lead wires from module to ignition switch.

Fig. 4: Computer and Harness Connector Test Terminals

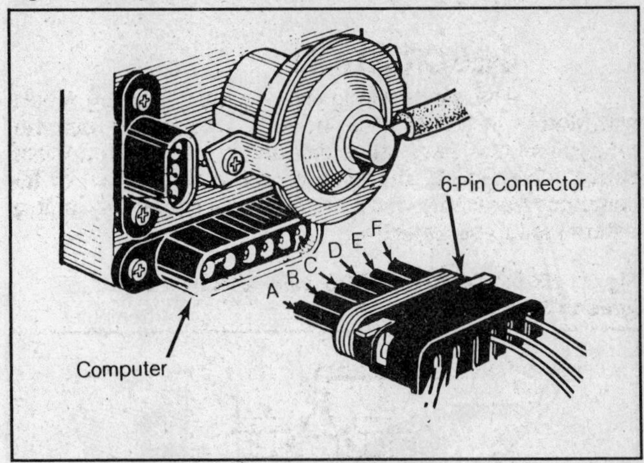

Use this illustration for power supply, ground circuit, ignition coil feed, and connector checks.

GROUND CIRCUIT CHECK

1) Disconnect 6-pin connector from computer. Turn ignition "OFF". Connect ohmmeter leads to pin "E" of harness connector and to vehicle ground. *See Fig. 4*.

2) Reading should be 0 (zero) ohms. If so, proceed to next check. If not, check computer ground wire for breaks, cuts or corrosion.

IGNITION COIL FEED CHECK

1) Disconnect 6-pin connector from computer. Turn ignition switch "OFF". Disconnect connector from positive terminal of ignition coil. Connect ohmmeter leads to cavity "D" of computer and to connector removed from positive coil terminal. *See Fig. 4*.

2) A reading of 0 (zero) ohms should be indicated. If so, proceed to next check. If not, replace computer.

6-PIN CONNECTOR CHECK

1) Connect 6-pin connector to computer. *See Fig. 4*. Turn ignition switch "ON". Connect voltmeter positive lead to cavity "D" of computer. Attach negative lead to ground.

2) A reading of at least 9.5 volts should be indicated. If so, proceed to next check. If not, slightly shake or wiggle connector assembly. If problem continues, replace 6-pin connector.

NOTE: Testing has already established that you have power to the 6-pin connector, as well as, continuity between terminal 11 of computer and connector for ignition coil positive terminal. If there is no voltage at positive connector terminal, the 6-pin connector must be at fault.

POSITION SENSOR CHECK

1) Disconnect 3-pin connector from computer. *See Fig. 5*. Turn ignition switch "OFF". Attach ohmmeter leads to terminals "B" and "C" of 3-pin harness connector.

2) Resistance should read 100-200 ohms. If so, proceed to next check. If not, replace magnetic position sensor.

DUCELLIER ELECTRONIC IGNITION (Cont.)

Fig. 5: Connector Terminals for Magnetic Position Sensor

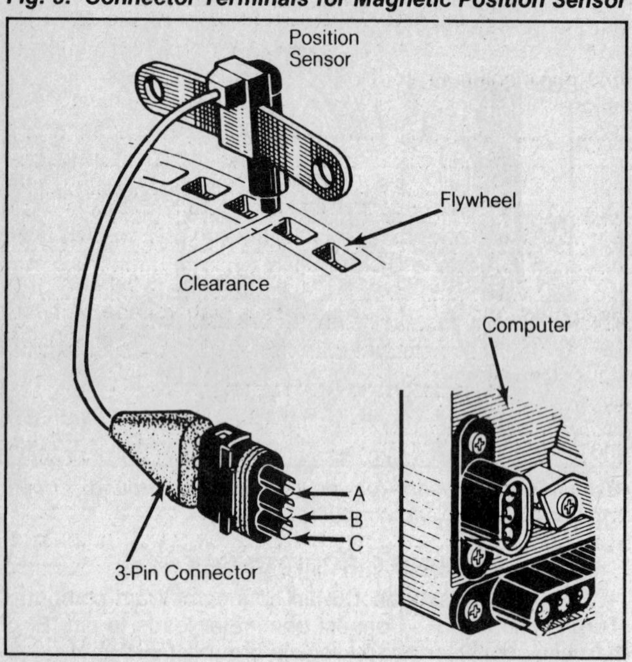

Use this illustration for position sensor, sensor insulation, and position sensor clearance checks.

SENSOR INSULATION CHECK

1) Disconnect 3-pin connector. *See Fig. 5.* Turn ignition switch "OFF". Connect ohmmeter leads to terminals "A" and "C".

2) An infinite reading should be indicated. If so, proceed to next check. If not, replace magnetic position sensor.

NOTE: **In case of infinite readings, be sure that the ohmmeter probe is properly inserted to touch bottom of terminal.**

POSITION SENSOR CLEARANCE CHECK

1) Using a plastic feeler gauge, check clearance between flywheel and magnetic position sensor. *See Fig. 5.*

2) Clearance should be .02-.06" (.5-1.5 mm). If so, proceed to next check. If not, replace sensor.

COMPUTER CHECK

1) Be sure all connectors are attached to computer. Disconnect harness connectors from coil primary terminals. Install 12-volt test lamp between 2 connectors just removed. *See Fig. 6.*

2) Crank engine. At cranking speed, lamp should flicker. If so, proceed to next check. If not, replace computer.

Fig. 6: Test Lamp Hookup for Checking Computer

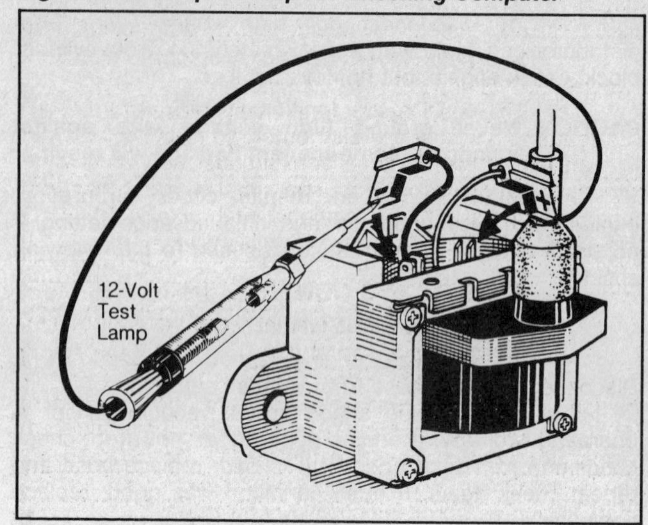

Attach 12-volt lamp to disconnected coil primary leads.

IGNITION COIL RESISTANCE CHECK

CAUTION: **When resistance checks are complete, be sure wires are reattached to proper terminals. Red wire goes on positive terminal. Black wire goes on negative terminal.**

Secondary Resistance

1) Disconnect harness connectors from ignition coil primary wires. Disconnect high tension wire from coil. Turn ignition switch "OFF". Set ohmmeter to x1000 scale. Attach ohmmeter leads to coil positive terminal and to coil high voltage terminal.

2) Ohmmeter should read 2500-5500 ohms. If so, check primary resistance. If not, replace ignition coil.

Primary Resistance

1) Remove connectors from coil primary terminals. Turn ignition switch "OFF". Set ohmmeter to x1 scale. Attach ohmmeter leads to coil primary terminals.

2) Reading should be .4-.8 ohm. If so, but there is no high voltage, replace computer. If resistance is not to specification, replace ignition coil.

OVERHAUL

As the distributor has no reluctor, pick-up coil, nor centrifugal or vacuum advance, overhaul procedures are simple. Remove distributor cap and rotor. Remove pin from drive gear. Check shaft for burrs, and remove shaft from housing. Reassemble in reverse order.

MOTORCRAFT SOLID STATE IGNITION

American Motors Models with 4.2L

DESCRIPTION

The Solid State Ignition system, often called SSI, features a solid state distributor, an electronic control unit, an ignition coil, and a conventional distributor cap, rotor, spark plug wires and spark plugs. Other components include the battery, ignition switch, starter solenoid, primary resistance wires and a by-pass wire.

ELECTRONIC CONTROL UNIT

There are 6 wires leading from the control unit, 2 to one connector and 4 to another. The White wire and Red wire leading from one 2-wire connector are for ignition feed circuits (White wire for cranking and Red wire for after engine is running). The control unit uses the Dark Green wire to turn power to the ignition coil off and on. The Light Green wire supplies a compensated ignition spark timing signal to electronic control module from the Micro Computer Unit (MCU). The Black wire supplies the distributor ground circuit.

DISTRIBUTOR

Components are divided into 3 groups, the pick-up coil (sensor) and trigger wheel, the spark advance and the cap and rotor. The trigger wheel, which has 6 teeth (one for each cylinder), rotates with the distributor shaft. The pick-up coil is a coil of fine wire mounted around a permanent magnet. There are no contacting surfaces between the trigger wheel and pick-up coil. Dwell is not adjustable and is controlled electronically. Centrifugal advance is controlled by engine speed, vacuum spark advance by carburetor ported vacuum supplied to the distributor's vacuum unit. Distributor cap and rotor are of conventional design.

IGNITION COIL

Coils are oil-filled, sealed and contain a primary and secondary circuit. As in any system, the coil's basic function is to convert battery voltage applied to the primary circuit into high secondary voltage for firing the spark plugs. The coil has positive and negative primary terminals and a single secondary terminal. A special coil connector slides over the primary terminals.

RESISTANCE WIRE

A wire with 1.3-1.4 ohms resistance is provided in the Red wire (engine running) circuit to supply less than battery voltage to the coil. This resistance wire is by-passed during starting so that full battery voltage may be applied to the coil. The by-pass is accomplished through the "I" terminal of the starter solenoid.

SYSTEM PROTECTION

The electronic control unit has built-in reverse polarity and transient voltage protection. However, damage to the system can occur if proper testing procedures are not followed.

OPERATION

The electronic control unit and ignition coil are turned on whenever the ignition switch is in the "START" or "ON" position. When the engine begins turning the distributor shaft, the trigger wheel rotates with it. As each tooth passes the pick-up coil, it interrupts the magnetic field around the pick-up coil. This continual build-up and collapse of the magnetic field provides a signal to the MCU.

The MCU receives the pick-up coil signals, along with other engine sensor signals, and sends a compensated spark timing signal to the electronic control unit. The electronic control unit then turns off current flow to the ignition coil primary circuit.

The collapse of the magnetic field in the ignition coil primary circuit induces a high voltage surge in the secondary circuit. This causes current to flow from the coil to the distributor, rotor, cap and spark plug wires.

Ignition timing is constantly changed by the control unit, the Micro Computer Unit (MCU), and vacuum and centrifugal advance mechanisms according to engine operation.

SOLID STATE IGNITION SYSTEM NOTES

NOTE: **When disconnecting wire from spark plug or distributor cap, twist rubber boot slightly to loosen. Grasp boot (not wire) and pull off with steady, even force.**

NOTE: **When disconnecting control unit connectors, pull apart with firm, straight pull. Do not attempt to pry apart with screwdriver. When connecting, press together firmly to overcome hydraulic pressure caused by the silicone dielectric compound. If connector locking tabs weaken or break off, it is unnecessary to replace connector. Just press firmly together and bind with electrical tape or a harness tie strap. This should assure a good connection.**

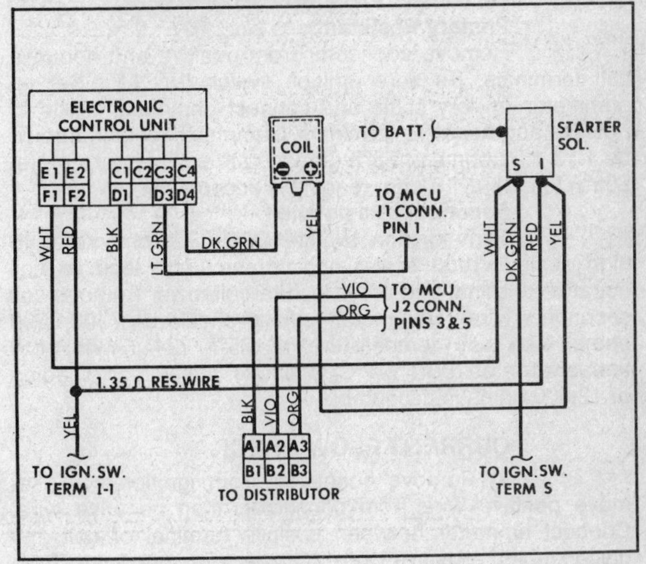

Fig. 1: American Motors (Motorcraft) Solid State Ignition System Wiring Diagram

MOTORCRAFT SOLID STATE IGNITION (Cont.)

TESTING

SECONDARY SPARK VOLTAGE

CAUTION: **When checking secondary voltage, do not remove spark plug wires from No. 1 or No. 5 spark plugs, as this could damage pick-up coil.**

NOTE: **On vehicles with catalytic converter, do not run engine for more than 30 seconds with a spark plug wire removed,**

1) Disconnect ignition coil high tension wire from center tower of distributor cap. Using insulated pliers, hold wire terminal approximately 1/2" from engine block or intake manifold.

2) Rotate engine with starter motor and check for spark at gap to ground. If no spark occurs, check coil primary and secondary resistance and proceed to High Tension Wire Resistance. If spark occurs, reconnect coil wire to distributor center tower. Remove wire from one spark plug.

3) Hold spark plug wire approximately 1/2" from cylinder head while cranking engine. Observe spark at gap. If spark occurs, ignition system is not at fault. Check other systems such as fuel and ignition timing. If no spark occurs, check for defective rotor, distributor cap or spark plug wires.

HIGH TENSION WIRE RESISTANCE

Coil-to-Distributor Wire Resistance

Using an ohmmeter, check resistance of coil-to-distributor wire. Resistance should be 10,000 ohms maximum.

Spark Plug Wire Resistance

Check spark plug wire resistance, using an ohmmeter. For used wires, resistance should not exceed 5000 ohms per INCH with spark plug wire connected to distributor cap and check made through internal cap terminal. For NEW wires, resistance reading should be less than 7000 ohms per FOOT.

IGNITION COIL RESISTANCE

Primary Resistance

Remove connector from positive and negative coil terminals. Be sure ignition switch if "OFF". Set an ohmmeter on low scale and connect ohmmeter leads to positive and negative terminals. Ohmmeter reading should be 1.13-1.23 ohms at 75°F (24°C). With coil temperature at 200°F (94°C), a 1.5 ohm reading is acceptable.

Secondary Resistance

Turn ignition switch "OFF". Set ohmmeter to high scale (x1000 scale) and connect one lead to coil negative terminal and other lead to coil tower (remove coil secondary wire). Ohmmeter reading should be 7700-9300 ohms with coil temperature at 75°F (24°). With coil temperature at 200°F (94°C) or above, a maximum reading of 12,000 ohms is acceptable.

CURRENT FLOW CHECK

1) Remove connector from ignition coil. Remove positive wire from connector, then negative wire. Connect ammeter between positive terminal of coil and disconnected positive wire. Connect jumper wire from negative terminal to good ground.

2) Turn ignition switch "ON". Current flow should be approximately 7 amps., but should not exceed 7.6 amps. If more than 7.6 amps., replace ignition coil.

3) With ammeter still connected to coil positive terminal, remove jumper wire from negative terminal. Connect coil Green wire to negative terminal. Current flow should be approximately 4 amps. If less than 3.5 amps, check for poor connection in 4-wire and 3-wire connectors or for poor ground at distributor ground screw.

4) If current flow is greater than 5 amps., the control unit is defective and must be replaced. Start engine. Normal current flow with engine running is 2.0-2.4 amps. If outside of specifications, replace control unit.

Fig. 2: Solid State Ignition Connectors

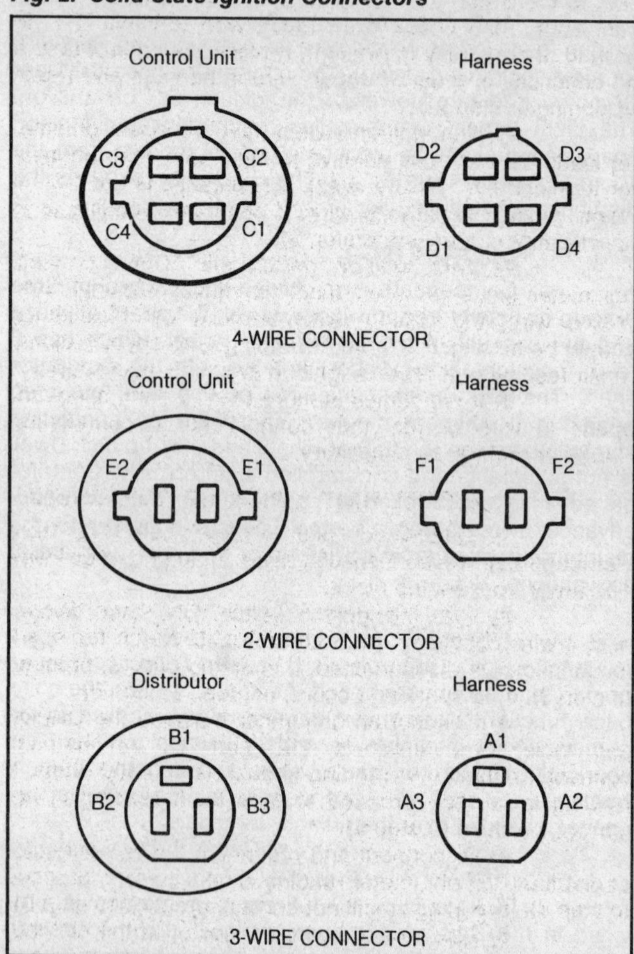

Figure shows terminal location in connectors.

COIL PRIMARY CIRCUIT CHECK

1) Connect a voltmeter to coil positive terminal and ground. Turn ignition switch to "ON" position. Reading should be 5.5-6.5 volts. If voltage is too high (battery voltage), proceed to step **4)**. If voltage is too low (below 5.5 volts), disconnect capacitor lead. If voltage is now correct, replace capacitor. If voltage is still low, proceed to step **7)**.

2) If voltage was 5.5-6.5 volts in step **1)**, turn ignition switch to "START" position. Voltage should be the same as battery cranking voltage. If correct, check other systems (fuel, mechanical, etc.) for problems. If voltage is not correct, proceed to step **3)**.

MOTORCRAFT SOLID STATE IGNITION (Cont.)

3) Check wire connected to starter solenoid "I" terminal for shorts or opens. If wire is okay, check for defective starter solenoid. Replace solenoid if necessary.

4) With ignition switch in "ON" position and voltmeter still connected to coil positive terminal, disconnect wire connected to starter solenoid "I" terminal. If voltage drops to 5.5-6.5 volts, replace starter solenoid.

5) If voltage remains high, connect a jumper wire from coil negative terminal to ground. If voltage drops to 5.5-6.5 volt range, proceed to step **6)**. If voltage does not drop, resistance wire is defective. Replace resistance wire and retest, beginning with step **2)**.

6) With ignition switch "OFF", connect an ohmmeter lead to the coil negative terminal and the other lead to the Green wire terminal "D4" of the 4-wire harness connector. Also check from Black wire terminal "D1" to ground. If continuity is present, replace the control unit. If no continuity is present, repair wire in harness and retest beginning at step **2)**.

7) With ignition switch "OFF", connect ohmmeter leads between coil positive terminal and dash connector terminal "FW" (Yellow wire). If resistance is not 1.3-1.4 ohms, replace resistance wire. If ohmmeter reading is to specifications, proceed to step **8)**.

8) With ignition switch still "OFF", connect ohmmeter leads between dash connector terminal "FW" (Yellow wire) and ignition switch terminal "L1". Resistance should be less than .1 ohm. If reading is to specifications, repair feed wire or replace ignition switch as necessary.

9) If resistance is more than .1 ohm, check for opens in wire or for poor connections at connectors. Repair or replace as necessary.

CONTROL UNIT & PICK-UP COIL CHECK

1) Disconnect high tension coil wire from distributor cap. Using insulated pliers, hold end of coil wire 1/2" away from engine block.

2) Turn the ignition switch "ON", then disconnect 4-wire connector from control unit. Watch for spark as connector is disconnected. If sparking occurs, proceed to step **3)**. If no sparking occurs, proceed to step **6)**.

3) Connect an ohmmeter between the Orange and Violet wire terminals "D2" and "D3" of harness connector. Ohmmeter reading should be 400-800 ohms. If reading is correct, proceed to step **8)**. If reading is not correct, proceed to step **4)**.

4) Disconnect and reconnect 3-wire connector at distributor. If ohmmeter reading is now correct, proceed to step **8)**. If reading is still not correct, proceed to step **5)**.

5) Disconnect 3-wire connector at the distributor and connect ohmmeter leads between the Orange and Violet wire terminals "B2" and "B3" of distributor connector. If reading is now 400-800 ohms, repair or replace harness between 3-wire and 4-wire connectors. If reading is still not to specifications, replace pick-up coil assembly in distributor.

6) Connect ohmmeter leads to battery negative terminal (ground) and Black wire terminal "D1" in harness connector. Ohmmeter reading should be nearly 0 (less than .002 ohms).

7) If ohmmeter reading is okay, proceed to step **3)**. If reading is above specification, check for source of bad ground (ground cable resistance, distributor-to-engine block resistance or ground screw in distributor to Black wire terminal "D1").

8) With voltmeter connected to harness side of 4-wire connector Orange and Violet wire terminals "D2" and "D3", crank engine. Voltmeter reading should fluctuate. If no voltage fluctuation occurs, check for defective trigger wheel, distributor shaft not turning, or missing trigger wheel retaining pin (shaft turning but not trigger wheel).

CONTROL UNIT POWER FEED CHECK

NOTE: Before making this check, always check ignition coil primary circuit first.

1) Disconnect 2-wire connector (Red and White wires) at control unit. Connect negative voltmeter lead to ground and positive lead to Red wire harness connector terminal "F2". Turn ignition switch "ON". Voltage reading should be within .2 volts of battery voltage. If reading is correct, replace control unit and proceed to step **3)**.

2) If reading is not correct, locate and repair cause of voltage reduction (corroded connectors, defective ignition switch, etc.). If connectors are repaired and there is spark at coil wire, start engine. If connectors are repaired and there is no spark at coil wire, replace control unit.

3) Turn ignition switch "OFF", connect 2-wire connector and disconnect 4-wire connector. Connect an ammeter to Black wire terminal "C1" of control unit connector and to ground. Turn ignition switch "ON". Reading should be 0.9-1.1 amps. If reading is higher or lower than specified, replace the control unit.

Fig. 3: Exploded View of AMC Solid State Distributor

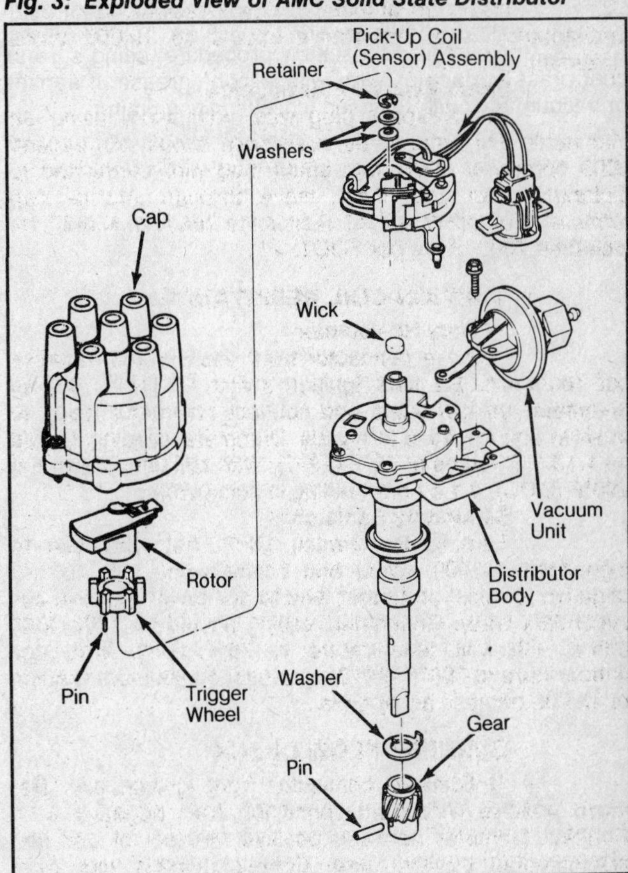

MOTORCRAFT SOLID STATE IGNITION (Cont.)

CENTRIFUGAL ADVANCE TEST

Disconnect and plug hose at vacuum advance unit. Connect timing light to No. 1 spark wire and connect tachometer to coil negative terminal. Start engine and note timing with engine idling. Slowly increase engine speed to 2000 RPM. Timing should advance smoothly as engine speed increases. See appropriate DISTRIBUTOR SPECIFICATIONS article in this section.

VACUUM ADVANCE TEST

Disconnect and plug vacuum hose at vacuum advance unit. Connect an auxiliary vacuum supply to vacuum advance unit. Connect a timing light and tachometer to engine. With engine at idle, check and note timing. Slowly increase engine speed to 2000 RPM. With vacuum applied, ignition timing should advance sooner than with centrifugal advance alone. See appropriate DISTRIBUTOR SPECIFICATIONS article in this section.

OVERHAUL

DISTRIBUTOR

Disassembly

1) Remove distributor cap and rotor. Using a gear puller, remove trigger wheel (two screwdrivers can be used to pry trigger wheel upward). Remove pin.

2) Remove pick-up coil retainer and washers from pivot pin on base plate. Remove pick-up coil plate screws. Lift pick-up coil assembly from distributor. Vacuum unit need not be removed unless replacement is necessary.

Reassembly

Reverse disassembly procedure, being sure to coat brass surface of rotor with silicone grease. If sensor or vacuum unit was replaced, check ignition timing.

AMERICAN MOTORS AIR INJECTION SYSTEMS

Concord, Eagle, Spirit

NOTE: **Alliance models are not equipped with an air injection system**

DESCRIPTION

There are 2 air injection systems used on AMC vehicles. A single air injection system is used with all Federal Spirit and Concord models equipped with 4-cylinder engines and manual transmissions. The dual air injection system is used on all models equipped with a 6-cylinder engine.

The systems add a controlled amount of air to exhaust gases in the exhaust ports. This causes oxidation of gases and reduction of carbon monoxide and hydrocarbon emissions. In addition to this, the dual systems adds air at the dual-bed catalytic converter.

The single stage system consists of a belt driven air pump, diverter (by-pass) valve, air injection manifold, check valve and connecting hoses.

In addition to these components the dual system contains an air switch valve, "downstream" air injection tube, and in conjunction with the CEC (Computerized Emission Control), a reverse delay valve, coolant temperature override valve, 2-way delay valve, diverter solenoid and upstream solenoid.

OPERATION

Fresh air is drawn into the air pump through a filter fan. The air is compressed in the pump and then discharged from the pump to the diverter valve. The diverter valve then directs the air to the air distribution system or dumps it through a by-pass port.

Air pressure in this system is maintained at approximately 5 psi by a relief valve incorporated in the diverter valve.

Air from the diverter valve is directed through the air injection mounted check valve. At each exhaust port, a hollow fitting carries air into the exhaust manifold. The air mixes with hot exhaust gases and causes a further burning of the mixture. This reduces hydrocarbon (HC) and carbon monoxide (CO) emissions.

Fig. 1: Single Air Injection System

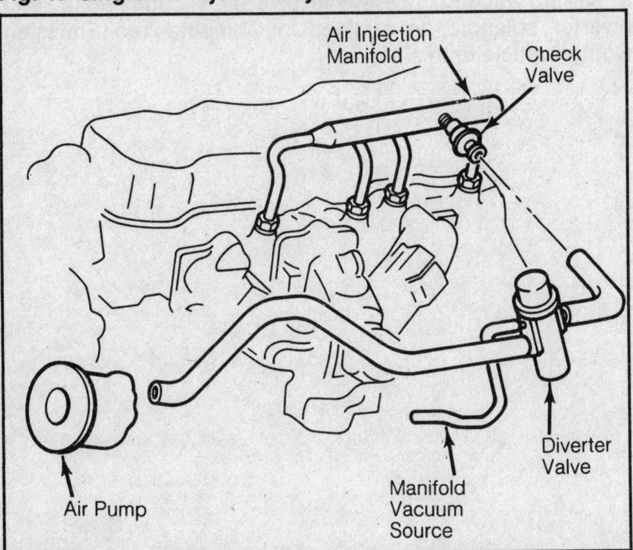

AIR PUMP

Air pump is belt driven and mounted on front of engine with power take-off at crankshaft pulley. Intake air passes through a centrifugal filter at front of pump. Air is delivered to injection manifold(s) by a rubber hose, through a diverter valve and tubing.

NOTE: **The internal components of the pump are not serviceable. The air pump is serviceable only by replacement. Do not remove rear housing cover for any reason.**

DIVERTER VALVE

This valve momentarily diverts air pump output from the exhaust manifold during rapid deceleration when intake manifold vacuum exceeds 20 in. Hg. Diverter also operates when pump output exceeds 5 psi.

AIR INJECTION MANIFOLD

The air injection manifold distributes air from the pump to each of the injection tubes. A check valve prevents reverse flow of exhaust gases in case of pump or belt failure. Air injection manifold distribution tubes are connected directly to the exhaust manifold.

COOLANT TEMPERATURE OVERRIDE VALVE

Dual System Only

The coolant temperature override (CTO) valve controls the manifold vacuum signal. Manifold vacuum should be present at air control valve when coolant temperature is less than 100°F on 4-cylinder engines and 115°F on 6-cylinder engines. No vacuum should be

Fig. 2: Dual Air Injection System

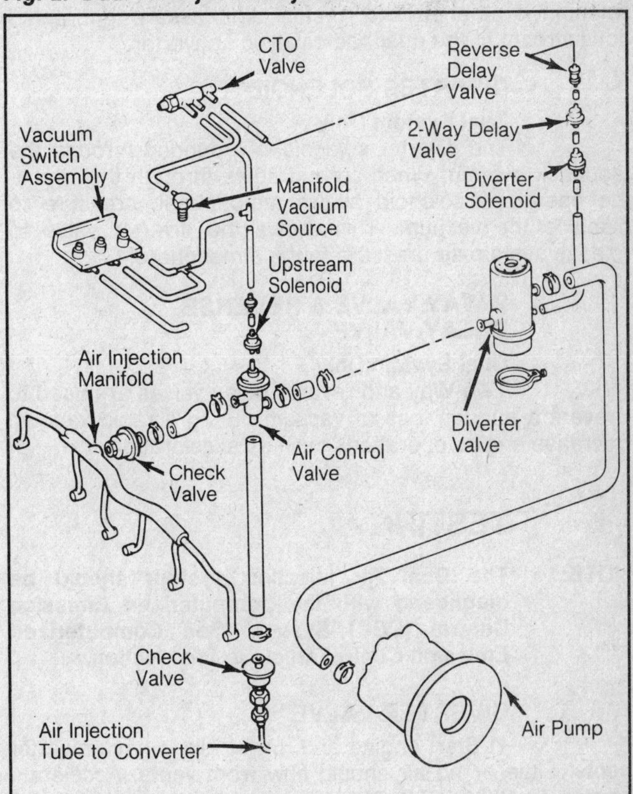

AMERICAN MOTORS AIR INJECTION SYSTEMS (Cont.)

present when coolant temperature is above these specifications. The CTO is connected to the air valve with a vacuum hose.

UPSTREAM AIR INPUT HOSES

The upstream air input hoses direct air up to the air injection manifold.

DOWNSTREAM AIR INPUT HOSES

These hoses direct air down to the dual-bed catalytic converter.

AIR CONTROL VALVE

Dual System Only

This valve is located between the diverter valve and the air injection manifold. Air control valve directs air pressure "upstream" (into air injection manifold) when no vacuum is applied to the valve and "downstream" (into the dual-bed catalytic converter) when vacuum is applied to the valve.

AIR BY-PASS CIRCUIT

Dual System Only

The controlling vacuum is regulated by the diverter solenoid, the open loop 3 vacuum switch feedback system, 2-way delay valves and reverse delay valves.

UPSTREAM SOLENOID

Dual System Only

Upstream solenoid controls the air control valve vacuum. When the solenoid is energized it opens air control valve vacuum to the atmosphere. This causes the air control valve to direct system air pressure to upstream air input hoses and air injection manifold. When the solenoid is de-energized, system air pressure is directed downstream to the dual-bed catalytic converter.

DIVERTER SOLENOID

Dual System Only

The diverter solenoid is grounded through the feedback system. When current flows through the circuit, the energized solenoid allows atmospheric pressure to displace the vacuum. This allows the diverter valve to release system air pressure to the atmosphere.

2-WAY VALVE & REVERSE DELAY VALVE

Dual System Only

Two-Way and reverse delay valves are used to prevent a sudden loss of vacuum during a rapid vacuum decrease engine operations such as acceleration.

TESTING

NOTE: **The Dual Air Injection system should be diagnosed with the Computerized Emission Control (CEC) System. See Computerized Emission Control article in this section.**

DIVERTER VALVE

1) Start engine and run at idle. Check diverter vents. Little or no air should flow from vents. Accelerate engine to 2000-3000 RPM and rapidly close throttle. A strong flow of air should pass from diverter vents for 5 seconds.

2) Slowly accelerate engine. Between 2500 and 3500 RPM air should begin to flow from diverter vents. Replace diverter valve if defective. Valve is not serviceable and must be replaced as an assembly.

CHECK VALVE

1) Disconnect air supply hose at check valve. With engine running above idle speed, listen and feel for exhaust leakage at check valve.

2) If valve leaks excessively, replace as a complete assembly.

AIR BY-PASS CIRCUIT

1) Disconnect air hoses from ports "A" and "B" of air control valve. Start engine and warm to normal operating temperature. Turn engine off.

NOTE: **Port "A" is connected to air injection manifold and port "B" is connected to catalytic converter pipe.**

2) Restart engine and increase engine speed to 1500 RPM. Air should exhaust from port "A" of the air control valve for approximately 30 seconds, then exhaust from port "B".

3) If no air exhausts, inspect base of diverter valve for air. If air is being exhausted, increase engine speed to 1500 RPM and determine if vacuum is being applied to diverter valve.

4) If vacuum is present, replace diverter valve and retest. If no vacuum is present, test diverter solenoid as outlined in Computerized Emission Control article in this section.

5) If air is not being exhausted from base of diverter valve, inspect air pump for proper operation. If air exhaust from air control valve is normal, depress accelerator to floor, return engine to idle and check base of diverter valve for air exhaust. If air is exhausted, circuit is okay.

6) If no air is exhausted, check diverter valve vacuum hose for vacuum. If no vacuum is present, replace diverter valve.

7) If after replacement of diverter valve, there is still no vacuum present in diverter vacuum hose, test diverter solenoid as outlined in Computerized Emission Control article in this section.

1983 Exhaust Emission Systems

AMERICAN MOTORS EXHAUST GAS RECIRCULATION

All Models Except Calif. Alliance

DESCRIPTION

The exhaust gas recirculation (EGR) system is designed to lower burning temperatures of gases in the combustion chambers, thereby reducing formations of oxides of nitrogen (NOx).

Metered amounts of exhaust gas dilutes the air/fuel mixture, thus lowering combustion temperatures. The EGR system used on the 1.4L engine consists of a diaphragm actuated EGR valve, an EGR valve solenoid and connecting vacuum hoses.

The EGR system used on the 2.5L and 4.2L engines consists of a diaphragm actuated EGR valve, coolant temperature override (CTO) valve, a thermal vacuum switch (TVS), connecting vacuum hoses and a forward delay valve on some 2.5L 4-cylinder engines.

EGR VALVE

The EGR valve is mounted on a spacer plate beneath the carburetor on 2.5L engines and on the side of the intake manifold on 1.4L and 4.2L engines. Two types of EGR valves are used.

EGR Valve without Back-Pressure Sensor

This type of EGR valve is used on 1.4L and 2.5L 4-cylinder engines. This valve is held in its normally closed position by spring pressure. When enough vacuum is applied, the EGR valve opens allowing exhaust gas recirculation.

EGR Valve with Back-Pressure Sensor

This type of EGR valve is used on some 2.5L engines and on all 4.2L engines. An EGR valve and back-pressure transducer are combined into one unit.

Exhaust gas exerts pressure (back-pressure) inside the exhaust manifold when the engine is running. This pressure is conducted through the hollow pintle stem into the control diaphragm chamber of the EGR valve.

Fig. 1: EGR System Layout for 2.5L 4-Cylinder Engine

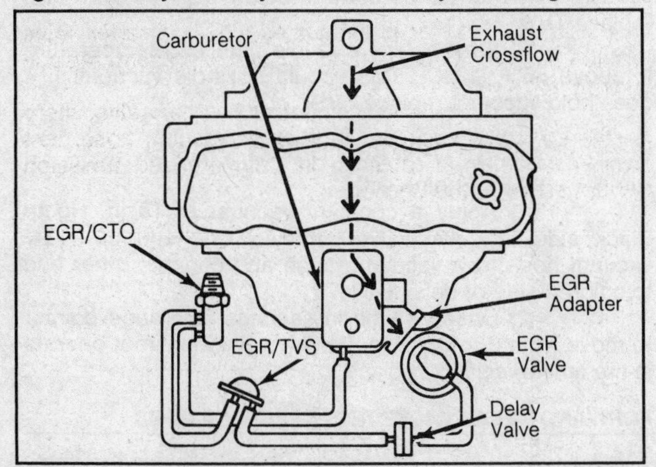

If this pressure is great enough to overcome control of spring pressure, the control diaphragm is moved out against the bleed valve. Full vacuum is now applied to the power diaphragm and the pintle moves, opening the EGR port.

If back-pressure drops enough, the control diaphragm moves away from the bleed valve. The power diaphragm relaxes and closes the EGR port causing exhaust gas recirculation to stop.

On some models, the EGR valve is mounted on a restrictor plate (thin stainless steel plate between manifold and EGR valve gaskets). These plates are stamped with a calibration identificaton number. If the restrictor plate is replaced, use a restrictor with the same calibration number.

COOLANT TEMPERATURE OVERRIDE SWITCH

2.5L 4-Cylinder

The coolant temperature override (CTO) valve is located in a coolant passage at the right rear side of the cylinder head. A single function valve is used on all 2.5L 4-cylinder engines.

The inner port "S" is connected by a vacuum hose to ported vacuum at the carburetor. The outer port "E" is connected by a vacuum hose to the thermal vacuum switch (TVS).

There is no vacuum applied to the EGR valve until coolant temperature reaches 100°F (38°C).

4.2L 6-Cylinder

The coolant temperature override (CTO) valve is located at the left front side of the intake manifold. The dual function valve is also used for distributor vacuum advance control.

The outer port "4" is connected by a vacuum hose to ported vacuum at the carburetor. The inner port "5" is connected by a vacuum hose to the thermal vacuum switch (TVS). Operating temperature of the CTO valve is above 115°F (46°C).

THERMAL VACUUM SWITCH (TVS)

2.5L & 4.2L Engines Only

This switch is located in the air cleaner and acts as an on-off switch for the EGR system. It is controlled by ambient temperature in the air cleaner. This switch controls the vacuum passage between the CTO valve and the EGR valve. When temperature of the TVS is below 40-55°F (4-13°C), it limits the passage of vacuum. This delays EGR operation and improves cold driveability.

Fig. 2: EGR System Layout for 4.2L 6-Cylinder Engine

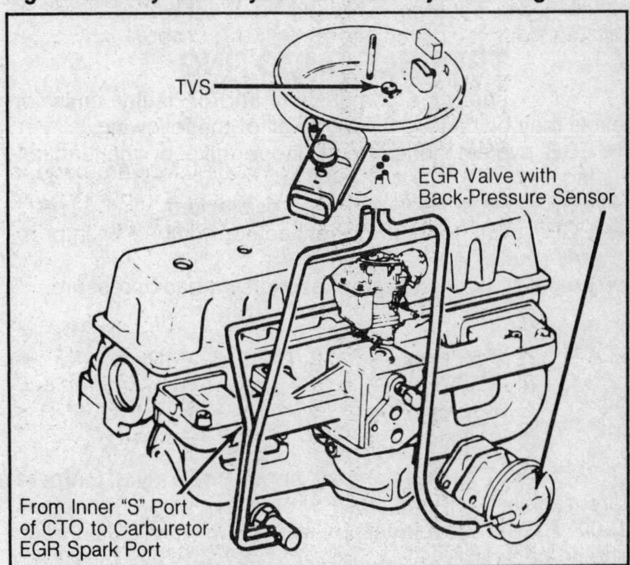

AMERICAN MOTORS EXHAUST GAS RECIRCULATION (Cont.)

EGR FORWARD DELAY VALVE

2.5L Engine Only

The EGR forward delay valve is used on some 2.5L 4-cylinder engines. It is located between the TVS and the EGR valve. *See Fig. 1*. Its purpose is to modify the initial vacuum signal applied to the EGR valve by delaying full vacuum force. A gradual vacuum is applied to the EGR valve, avoiding sudden application of the EGR system. The Black side of valve should be installed toward the EGR vacuum source.

Fig. 3: Cutaway View of EGR Valve & Back-Pressure Sensor

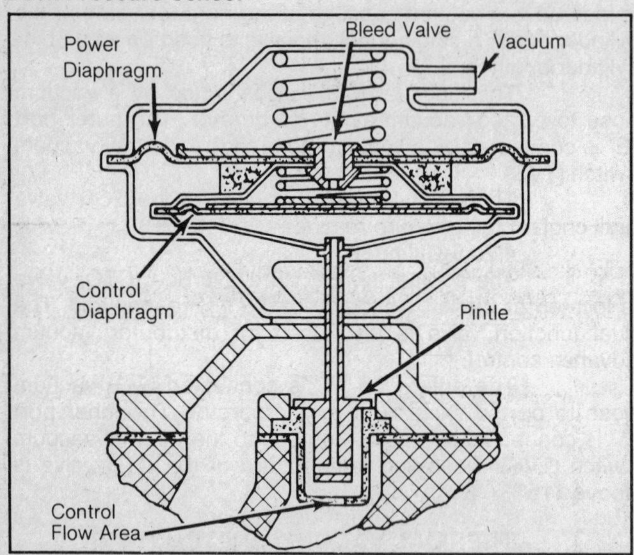

This type of EGR valve is used on all engines except 1.4L.

MAINTENANCE

Inspect the EGR system every 30,000 miles. The EGR system should be inspected for proper operation, carbon deposits and leaking vacuum hoses. Clean and/or repair system as necessary. Also check for proper vacuum hose routing.

TROUBLE SHOOTING

Improper combustion and/or faulty emission levels may be caused by any or all of the following:

- EGR system components inoperative or malfunctioning.
- EGR exhaust ports restricted or blocked.
- EGR vacuum hoses disconnected, crimped or improperly routed.
- Leaks in exhaust system decreasing back pressure.

TESTING

EGR VALVE

Opening Test

1) With engine at normal operating temperature, rapidly open and close throttle (rev engine to at least 1500 RPM). Movement of the EGR valve diaphragm should be seen.

2) If the diaphragm does not move, probable causes are a faulty vacuum signal to EGR valve, a defective EGR diaphragm, a defective back-pressure sensor diaphragm or a vacuum leak.

Closing Test

1) With engine operating at normal operating temperature, manually depress EGR valve diaphragm. This should cause an immediate drop in engine speed.

2) If engine speed does not drop, passage between EGR valve and manifold may be plugged. If engine idles rough and is not effected by depressing the diaphragm, fault is in hoses or EGR valve.

3) If engine idles properly but there is no change in engine speed when valve is depressed, exhaust gases are not reaching the combustion chamber. There is probably a plugged passage between the EGR valve and the intake manifold.

COOLANT TEMPERATURE OVERRIDE (CTO) VALVE

2.5L & 4.2L Engines Only

1) Coolant temperature must be below 90°F (32°C) on 2.5L 4-cylinder engines and below 105°F (41°C) on 4.2L 6-cylinder engines. Check for vacuum leaks and proper hose routing.

2) Disconnect vacuum hose from TVS and connect hose to vacuum gauge. Operate engine at 1500 RPM. No vacuum should be indicated. If vacuum is indicated, replace CTO valve.

3) Idle engine until coolant temperature is at least 100°F (38°C) on 2.5L 4-cylinder engines or 115°F (46°C) on 4.2L 6-cylinder engines. Accelerate engine to 1500 RPM. Carburetor ported vacuum should be indicated on vacuum gauge. If not, replace CTO valve.

THERMAL VACUUM SWITCH (TVS)

2.5L & 4.2L Engines Only

1) Cool air cleaner to less than 40°F (4°C). Detach vacuum lines from TVS and connect external vacuum souce to inner port of TVS.

2) Apply vacuum to TVS. TVS should hold vacuum when its temperature is below 40°F (4°C). If not, replace TVS.

3) Start engine and idle until TVS temperature is above 55°F (13°C). TVS should not hold vacuum. If it does hold vacuum, replace TVS.

EGR FORWARD DELAY VALVE

2.5L Engine Only

1) Apply a constant vacuum of 10 in. Hg to Black side of delay valve. Connect one end of a 24" vacuum hose to a vacuum gauge and connect other end to colored side of delay valve.

2) Observe time in seconds for gauge pointer to move from 0 to 8 in. Hg. If delay valve does not operate in the time specified, replace it.

FORWARD DELAY VALVE TEST SPECIFICATIONS

Valve Color	Minimum Time in Seconds	Maximum Time in Seconds
Black/Gray	10	12
Black/Brown	20	24
Black/White	64	77
Black/Yellow	100	120
Black/Purple	4	5
Black/Green	200	240
Black/Orange	2	3

AMERICAN MOTORS VACUUM DIAGRAMS

Fig. 1: 1.4L 4-Cylinder Federal — Alliance

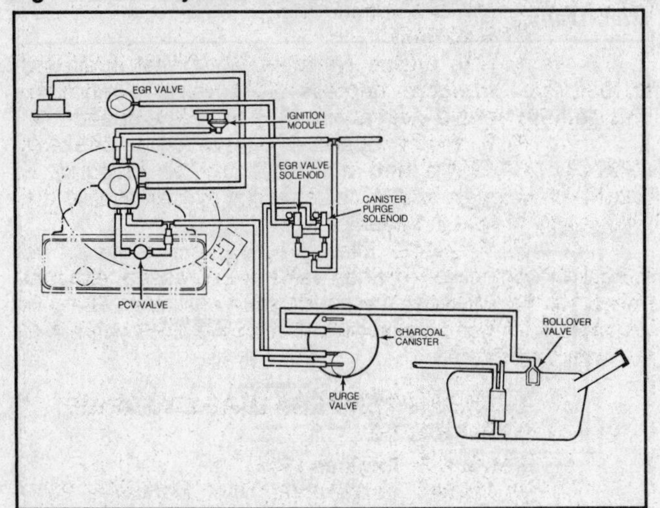

Fig. 2: 1.4L 4-Cylinder Calif. — Alliance

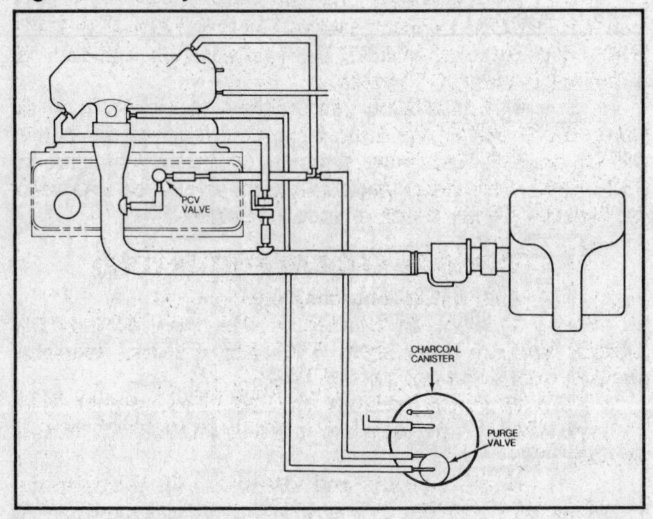

Fig. 3: 2.5L 4-Cylinder Federal — Eagle
Man. Trans. with A/C

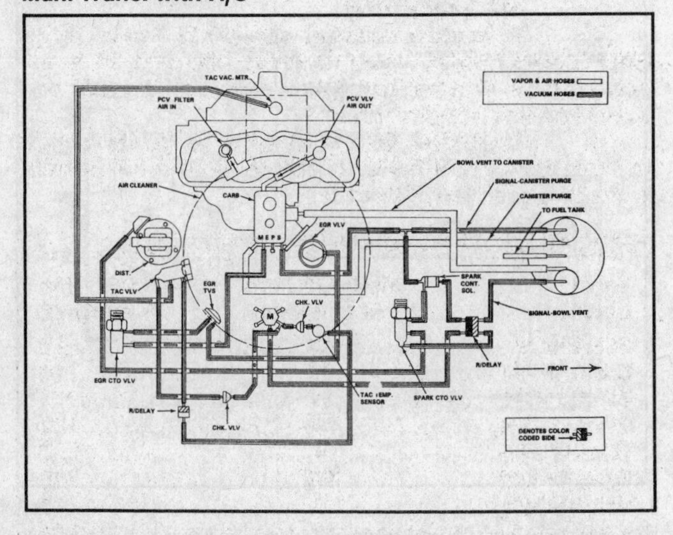

Fig. 4: 2.5L 4-Cylinder Federal — Eagle
Man. Trans. without A/C

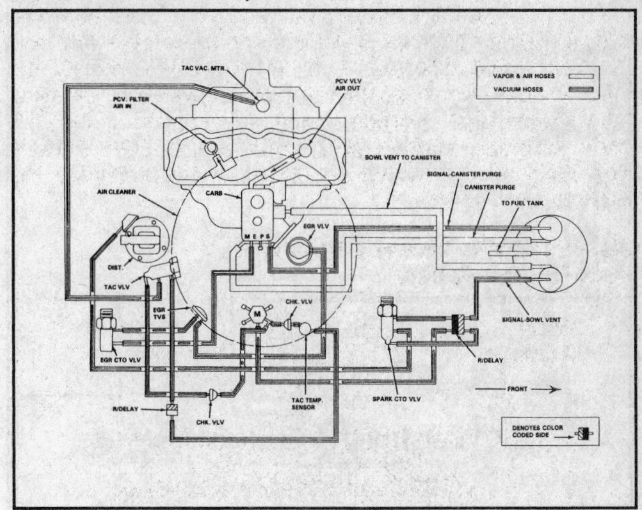

Fig. 5: 2.5L 4-Cylinder Federal — Eagle
Man. Trans. & Auto. Trans. with & without A/C

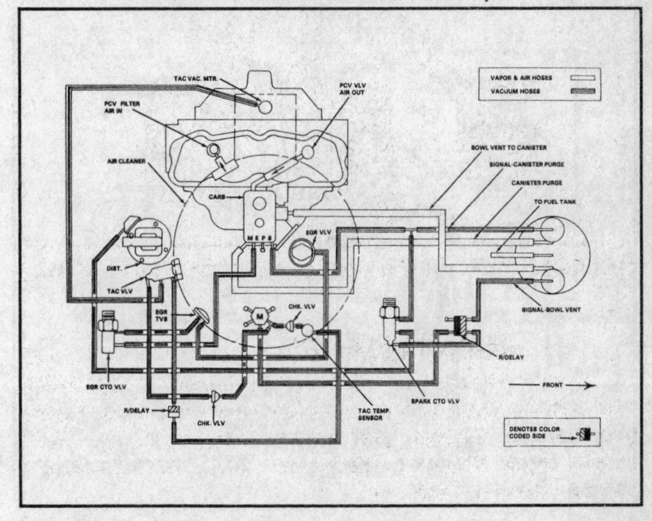

Fig. 6: 2.5L 4-Cylinder Calif. — Eagle
Man. Trans. with A/C

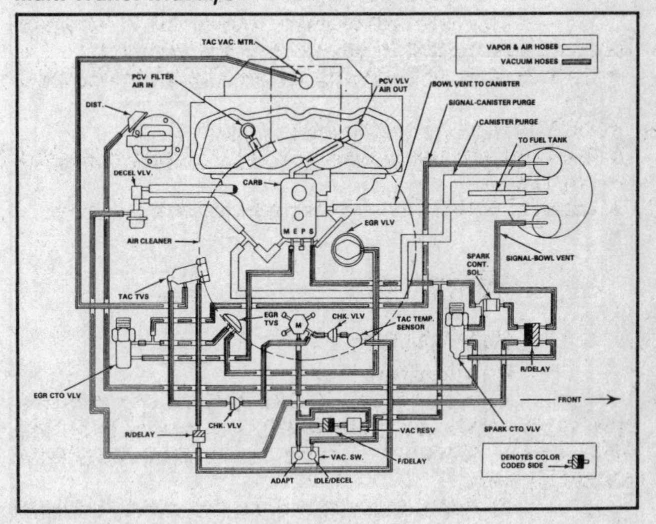

1983 Exhaust Emission Systems

AMERICAN MOTORS VACUUM DIAGRAMS (Cont.)

***Fig. 7:* 2.5L 4-Cylinder Calif. — Eagle Man. Trans. without A/C**

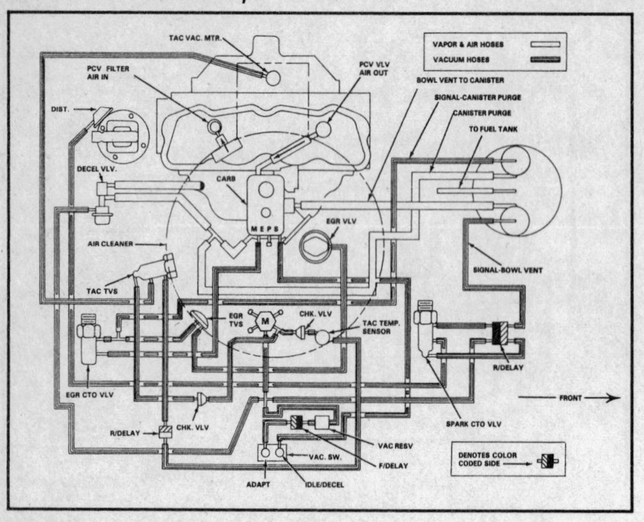

***Fig. 8:* 2.5L 4-Cylinder Calif. — Eagle Auto. Trans. with A/C**

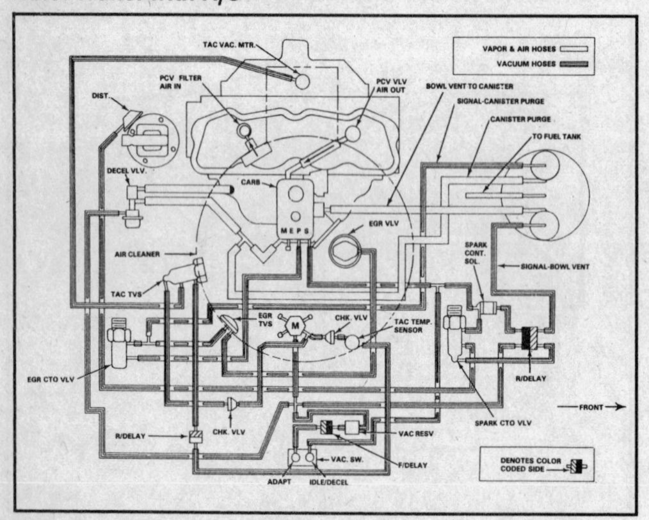

***Fig. 9:* 2.5L 4-Cylinder Calif. — Eagle Auto. Trans without A/C**

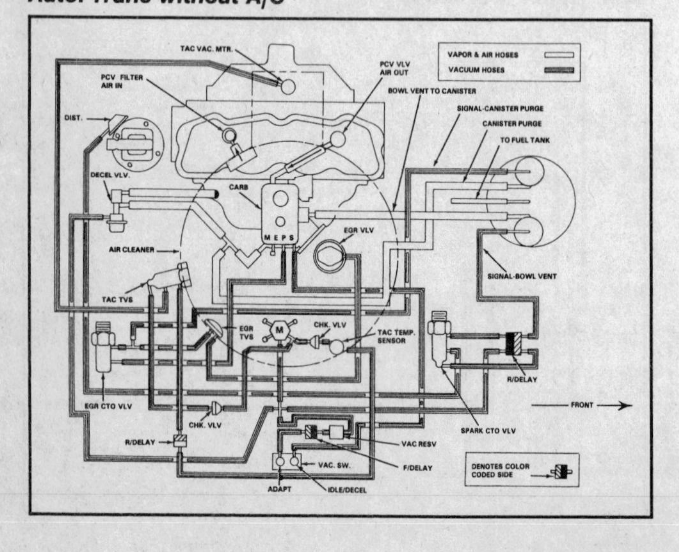

***Fig. 10:* 4.2L 6-Cylinder Federal — Concord & Spirit Man. Trans.**

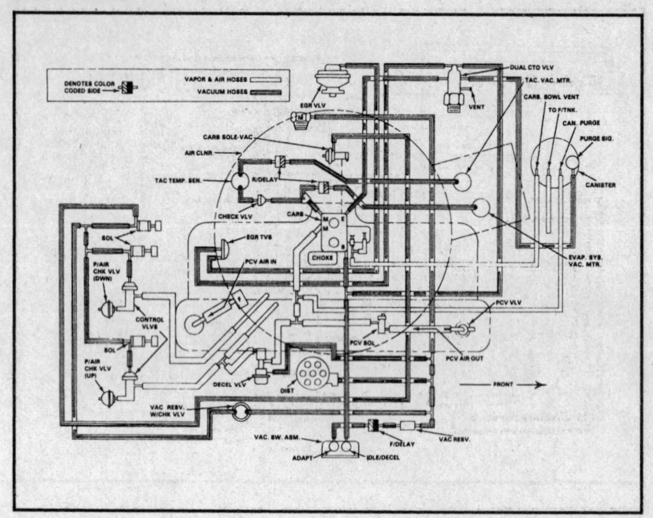

***Fig. 11:* 4.2L 6-Cylinder Federal — Concord & Spirit Auto. Trans.**

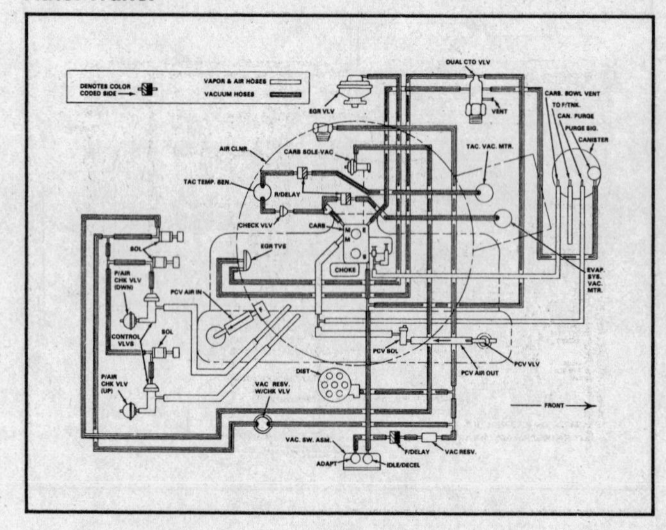

***Fig. 12:* 4.2L 6-Cylinder Federal — Eagle**

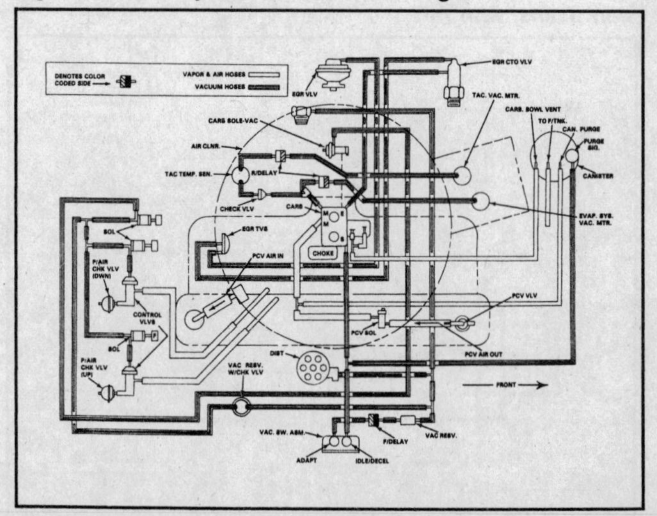

AMERICAN MOTORS VACUUM DIAGRAMS (Cont.)

Fig. 13: 4.2L 6-Cylinder Calif. — Concord, Eagle & Spirit Man. Trans.

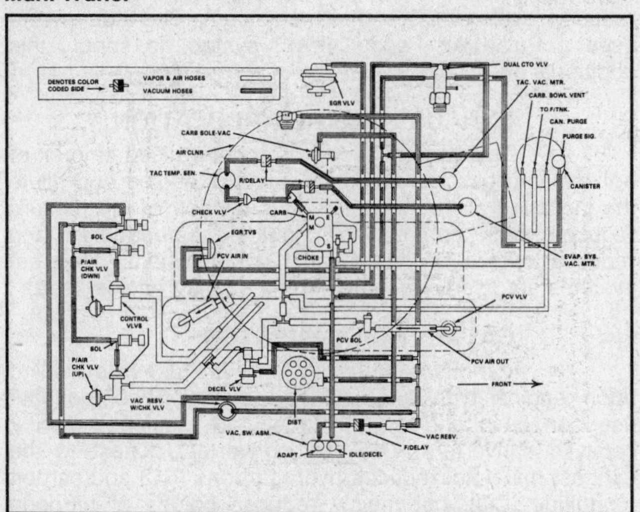

Fig. 14: 4.2L 6-Cylinder Calif. — Concord, Eagle & Spirit Auto. Trans.

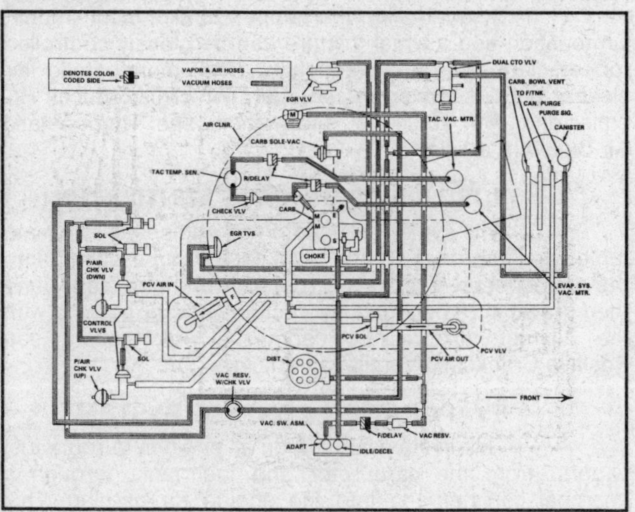

1983 Exhaust Emission Systems

CHRYSLER CORP. SYSTEMS & TUNE-UP PROCEDURES

DESCRIPTION

Control of exhaust emissions is accomplished by a combination of engine modifications and special control components. Component usage varies depending on engine and transmission combinations.

ELECTRONIC FUEL CONTROL

This system is used on all engines except 2.2L EFI, 2.6L and 5.2L EFI. This system is an electronically controlled system that closely controls air/fuel ratio and ignition timing.

The Spark Control Computer (SCC) is the heart of the system. This computer provides the capability of igniting a lean air/fuel mixture close to the ideal ratio of 14.7:1. Different sub-systems are used on front and rear wheel drive models.

COMBUSTION CONTROL COMPUTER (CCC)

This system is used only on vehicles equipped with the 5.2L EFI engine. This system controls the electronic fuel injection system, ignition timing, idle speed, air injection switching and fuel evaporation purging.

The CCC is capable of self-calibration to compensate for changes in altitude or atmospheric pressure. It can also shut down the fuel supply pump if the engine stalls or will not start after prolonged cranking.

MITSUBISHI ELECTRONIC IGNITION SYSTEM

The Mitsubishi electronic ignition system is used on the 2.6L engine only. This system consists of a battery, ignition switch, ignition coil, IC ignitor (electronic control unit), spark plug and spark plug wires.

The IC ignitor is built into the distributor. Spark timing is controlled by the IC ignitor, a centrifugal advance mechanism and a vacuum advance mechanism.

HALL EFFECT ELECTRONIC SPARK CONTROL

This system is used on 1.6L, 1.7L and 2.2L engines. This system uses a Hall Effect distributor and a Spark Control Computer (SCC). The SCC determines the exact instant when ignition is required.

Ignition timing is controlled by the SCC based on input from the vacuum transducer, an engine coolant temperature sensor, carburetor switch and an oxygen sensor.

ELECTRONIC SPARK CONTROL

The electronic spark control (ESC) system is used on all 3.7L and 5.2L engines. This system is governed by the spark control computer (SCC). The computer determines the exact instant when ignition is required.

The SCC determines the point at which ignition is required using input from up to 7 engine sensors, a special carburetor and a dual pick-up distributor (single pick-up on 5.2L EFI engines).

The ESC system is designed to burn a lean air/fuel mixture with a minimum of emissions.

AIR INJECTION SYSTEM

This system adds a controlled amount of fresh air to the exhaust gases at the exhaust manifold or downstream at the catalytic converter. This aids in complete oxidation of the exhaust gases. This results in reduced levels of CO and HC emissions. The 2.6L engine uses a Pulse Air Feeder (PAF) system to supply this additional air.

EXHAUST GAS RECIRCULATION

This system allows a predetermined amount of hot exhaust gas to recirculate into the engine and dilute the incoming air/fuel mixture. This dilution of the mixture reduces peak combustion chamber temperatures and reduces oxides of nitrogen (NOx) emissions. Different systems are used depending on the type of engine used.

CATALYTIC CONVERTER

Various exhaust systems are used depending upon engine type and required emission components used on each engine. All models are equipped with 2 catalytic converters. The first converter, closest to the exhaust manifold, reduces hydrocarbons (HC) and carbon monoxide (CO), but mainly reduces oxides of nitrogen (NOx). The second converter reduces HC and CO only.

THERMOSTATIC AIR CLEANER

By controlling the temperature of incoming air, combustion and air/fuel mixture can be closely controlled for efficient emission reduction. The thermostatic air cleaner permits leaner engine operation. This reduces HC emissions. For additional information, see Thermostatic Air Cleaners article.

POSITIVE CRANKCASE VENTILATION

This system is used on all engines to eliminate fumes and vapors, from the crankcase, from escaping into the atmosphere. Vapors are routed to the air cleaner and then drawn into the combustion chambers for burning with the air/fuel mixture. For additional information, see Positive Crankcase Ventilation article.

EVAPORATION CONTROL SYSTEM

This system is used on all engines to route fuel vapors, from the carburetor and fuel tank, through a charcoal canister and into the engine for burning. This closed system prevents fuel vapors from venting to the atmosphere. For additional information, see Chrysler Corp. Evaporation Control System article.

TUNE-UP SERVICE PROCEDURES

In addition to servicing of the individual emission systems, it is important that all ignition timing and carburetor adjustments are properly set.

Due to late changes and corrections, always refer to the Engine Tune-Up Decal in the engine compartment before performing tune-up procedures. In the event that specifications in this manual and decal specifications differ, always use the decal specifications.

IGNITION TIMING

CAUTION: Timing light connections should be made using proper adapters. Do not puncture cables, boots or nipples with test probes.

CHRYSLER CORP. SYSTEMS & TUNE-UP PROCEDURES (Cont.)

1) If a magnetic probe timing light is being used, refer to equipment manufacturers instructions for proper hookup. If a conventional timing light is being used, connect a timing light to number 1 cylinder.

2) Connect a tachometer to engine. Start engine and warm to normal operating temperature. Momentarily open throttle to ensure that linkage does not bind and that idle speed screw is against its stop.

3) If vehicle is equipped with a carburetor switch, connect a jumper wire between switch and ground. Disconnect and plug vacuum line at Spark Control Computer.

4) Make sure that engine is operating at curb idle RPM. If not, adjust using appropriate procedures under Hot (Slow) Idle RPM. Check timing. If timing is within 2° of specified timing, do not adjust.

5) If timing is not correct, loosen distributor hold down bolt and turn distributor housing until specified timing is reached. Recheck timing after distributor hold down bolt has been tightened.

NOTE: **On all engines except 1.6L, magnetic probe timing socket is located at 10° ATDC. This socket is only for use with special electronic timing equipment. Do not use this socket when checking timing with a conventional timing light.**

IGNITION TIMING SPECIFICATIONS (DEGREES BTDC @ RPM)

Application	Man. Trans.	Auto. Trans.
1.6L	12 @ 850	.....
1.7L		
Federal	20 @ 850	12 @ 850
Calif.	20 @ 850	.....
2.2L		
Federal		
Rampage & Scamp	10 @ 775	10 @ 775
All Others	10 @ 775	10 @ 900
Calif.	10 @ 775	10 @ 900
High Alt.	6 @ 850	6 @ 850
2.6L	7 @ 800	7 @ 800
3.7L	.....	16 @ 750
5.2L		
2-Bbl. & 4-Bbl.	.....	16 @ 700
EFI	.....	12 @ 580

Fig. 1: 1.6L Firing Order & Timing Marks

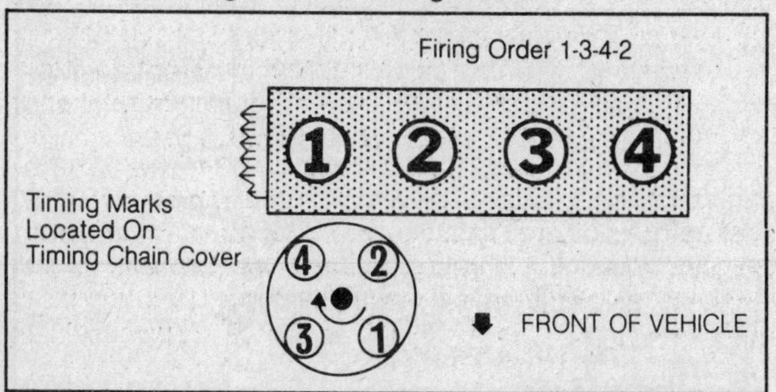

Fig. 2: 1.7L & 2.2L Firing Order & Timing Marks

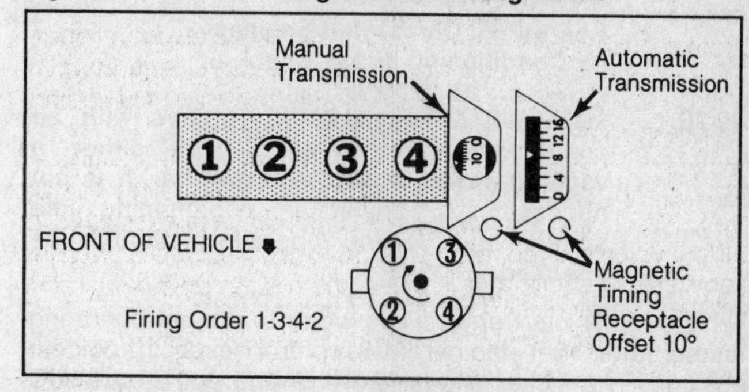

Fig. 3: 2.6L Firing Order & Timing Marks

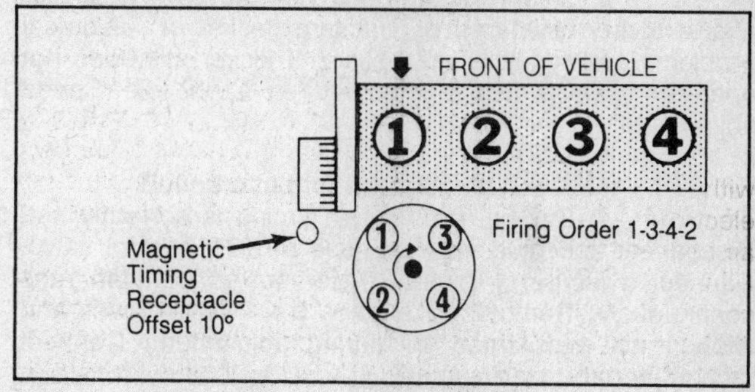

Fig. 4: 3.7L Firing Order & Timing Marks

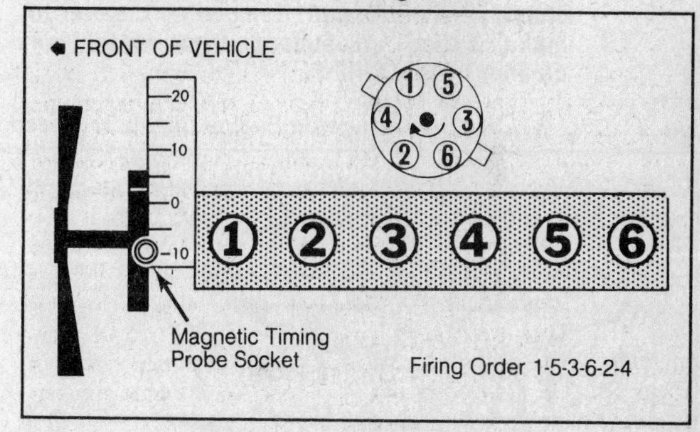

Fig. 5: 5.2L Firing Order & Timing Marks

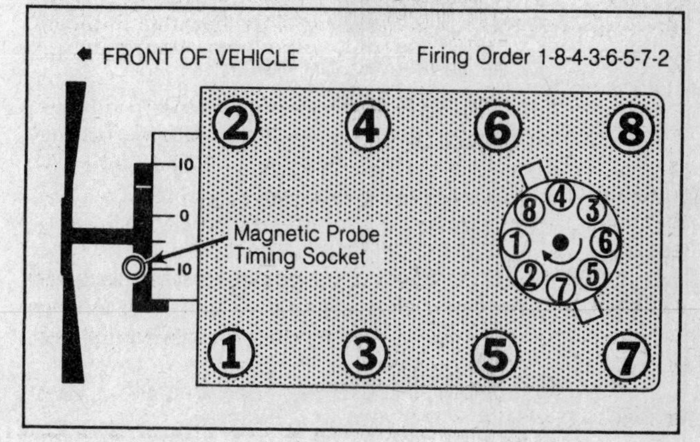

CHRYSLER CORP. SYSTEMS & TUNE-UP PROCEDURES (Cont.)

HOT (SLOW) IDLE RPM

1.6L & 2.2L Carbureted Engines
Air Conditioning Kicker Check

NOTE: 1.6L and 2.2L carbureted engines with air conditioning are equipped with either a vacuum kicker or a solenoid kicker. It is not necessary to adjust air conditioning idle speed, but kicker operation should be checked.

1) Start engine and warm to normal operating temperature. Set temperature control lever in coldest position. The kicker should move in and out as the A/C compressor clutch cycles on and off.

2) If the kicker does not move in and out, check kicker system for vacuum leaks or electrical problems and repair as necessary. If kicker still does not operate, replace kicker. Proceed to Curb Idle Speed adjustment.

1.7L Engine
Air Conditioning Solenoid Idle Speed

1) Ensure that ignition timing is correctly set. Disconnect and plug vacuum hose at EGR control valve. Connect a jumper wire to radiator fan so that fan runs continuously. Remove PCV valve from valve cover and allow it to draw fresh air during adjustment. Connect tachometer and start engine.

NOTE: Air cleaner must be installed when speed checks are performed. Remove air cleaner to make speed adjustment, then install air cleaner to check RPM.

2) Turn A/C on and set blower to low speed. Open throttle slightly to energize solenoid. Remove adjusting screw and spring from top of A/C solenoid. Insert a 1/8" Allen wrench into solenoid and adjust solenoid to obtain specified curb idle speed. *See Fig. 6.*

Fig. 6: 1.7L Air Conditioning Solenoid Idle Speed Adjusting Location

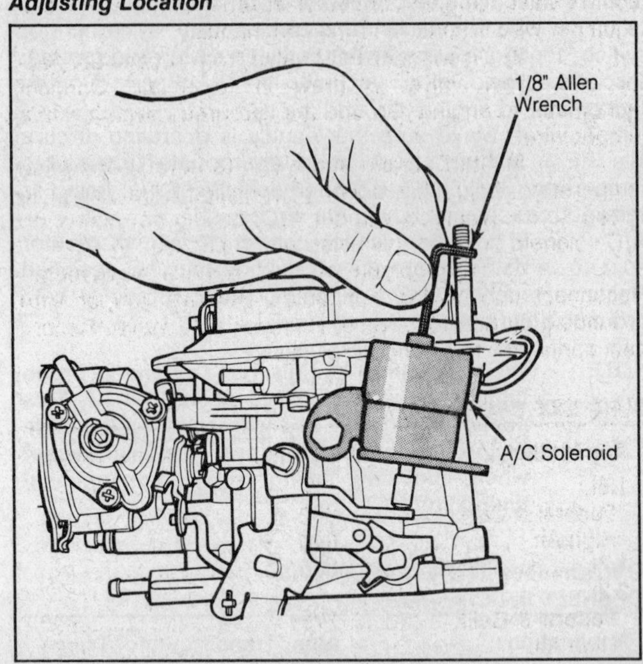

Fig. 7: 1.6L, 1.7L & 2.2L Carbureted Engine Curb Idle Speed Adjustment Locations

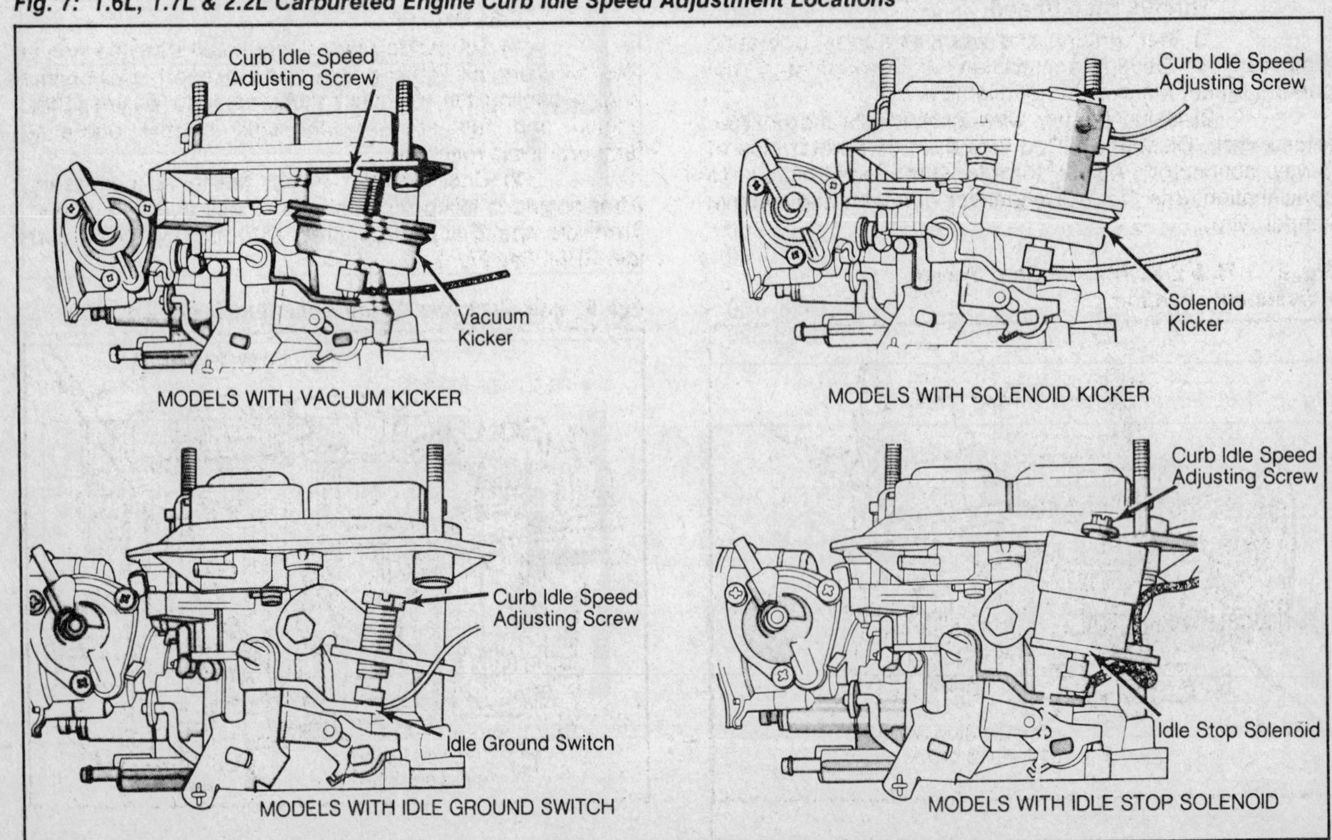

CHRYSLER CORP. SYSTEMS & TUNE-UP PROCEDURES (Cont.)

3) With idle speed adjusted, reinstall adjusting screw and spring on solenoid. Turn off A/C and proceed to Curb Idle Speed adjustment.

1.6L, 1.7L & 2.2L Carbureted Engines
Curb Idle Speed

1) Ensure that ignition timing is properly adjusted. Disconnect and plug vacuum hose at the EGR control valve. Unplug connector at radiator fan and install a jumper wire so that fan runs continuously.

2) Disconnect PCV valve from rubber connector and allow valve to draw in fresh air. Connect tachometer to engine. Ground the carburetor switch with a jumper wire.

3) Start engine and warm to normal operating temperature. Adjust idle speed to specified RPM using idle speed screw (vehicles without A/C) or idle set screw on A/C solenoid or kicker (vehicles with A/C). *See Fig. 7*.

4) Turn engine off and remove tachometer. Reconnect cooling fan connector. Remove jumper wire grounding carburetor switch. Reinstall PCV valve. Reconnect connector to EGR control valve.

CURB IDLE SPEED (RPM)

Application	Man. Trans.	Auto. Trans.
1.6L		
Federal & Calif.	850	.....
High Alt.	900	.....
1.7L	850	.....
2.2L		
Federal & Calif.	775	900
High Alt.	900	850

1.7L & 2.2L Carbureted Engines Only
Throttle Stop Speed

1) Start engine and warm to normal operating temperature. Place transmission in Neutral and set parking brake. Make sure headlights are off.

2) Using jumper wire, ground idle stop carburetor switch. Disconnect Red wire from carburetor side of 6-way connector. Adjust throttle stop speed screw to specification. *See Fig. 8*. Reconnect Red wire and remove jumper wire.

Fig. 8: 1.7L & 2.2L Throttle Stop Speed Adjustment Location

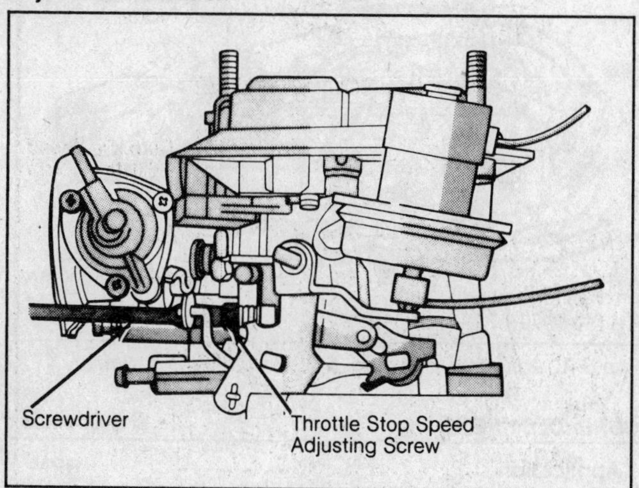

THROTTLE STOP SPEED

Application	RPM
1.7L & 2.2L	700

2.2L TBI Engine

NOTE: **Before adjusting curb idle, AIS motor operation, EGR vacuum leaks, ignition timing and coolant temperature sensor operation must be checked.**

1) Connect tachometer to engine. Start engine and warm to normal operating temperature. Turn all accessories off. Turn engine off and install a jumper wire to make cooling fan run continuously.

2) Disconnect 6-way throttle body connector. Remove automatic idle speed (AIS) wire (Brown/White) from connector and reconnect connector to throttle body.

3) Place transmission in "P" or "N" and start engine. Apply 12 volts to AIS wire. This should pull AIS motor fully closed and idle speed should drop.

4) Apply parking brake and place transmission in "D". Adjust throttle body idle stop to obtain specified RPM using idle stop adjusting tool (C-4804).

5) Turn engine off. Reinstall AIS wire in 6-way connector. Restart engine and allow idle to stabilize. AIS wire connected RPM should be as specified.

CURB IDLE SPEED (RPM)

Application	AIS Disconnected	AIS Connnected
2.2L TBI	650-675	600-800

2.6L Engine

1) Set parking brake and place transmission in Neutral. Turn all lights and accessories off. Disconnect engine cooling fan. Connect tachometer to engine. Start engine and run at fast idle until normal operating temperature is reached.

2) Check and/or adjust timing as necessary. After engine is idling for 1 minute, check curb idle speed. Turn idle speed adjusting screw to obtain specified curb idle RPM. *See Fig. 9*.

Fig. 9: 2.6L Curb Idle Speed Adjusting Screw Location

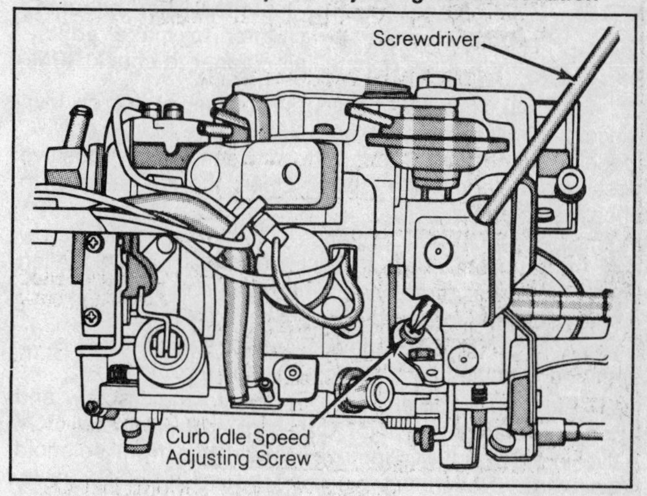

CHRYSLER CORP. SYSTEMS & TUNE-UP PROCEDURES (Cont.)

3) After adjusting curb idle, turn air A/C compressor clutch on. With compressor running, adjust A/C On RPM to specified RPM, by turning idle up adjusting screw. *See Fig. 10.*

Fig. 10: 2.6L Idle-Up Adjusting Screw Location

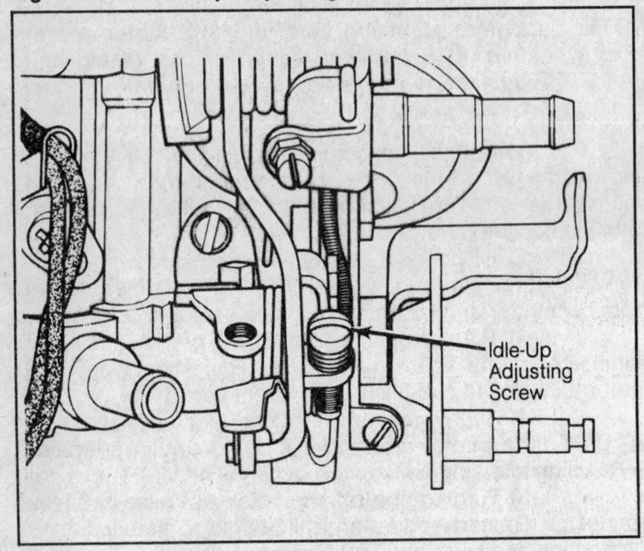

4) Turn engine off, disconnect tachometer and reconnect engine cooling fan.

CURD IDLE SPEED

Application	Curb Idle RPM	A/C On RPM
2.6L	800	900

3.7L & 5.2L Carbureted Engines
Solenoid Idle Stop Speed

1) Ensure that ignition timing is correctly set. Disconnect and plug vacuum hose at EGR valve. Remove PCV valve from valve cover and allow it to draw fresh air during adjustment.

2) Plug 3/16" diameter control hose at carbon canister. Connect tachometer to engine. Start engine and warm to normal operating temperature.

NOTE: **Air cleaner must be installed when checking RPM. Remove air cleaner to make adjustment, then reinstall air cleaner to check RPM.**

3) Turn A/C on and set blower motor on low. Disconnect A/C compressor clutch wire. On non-A/C models, connect a jumper wire between battery positive post and solenoid lead wire. Open throttle slightly to energize solenoid.

4) On 3.7L engines, remove solenoid screw and spring from rear of solenoid. Insert a 1/8" Allen wrench into rear of solenoid and adjust solenoid to obtain correct solenoid idle stop speed. *See Fig. 11.*

5) On 5.2L engines, adjust solenoid idle stop speed to specified RPM using screw on throttle lever.

6) On all engines, replace solenoid screw and spring on rear of solenoid. Turn engine off. Reinstall PCV valve in valve cover. Remove jumper wire from solenoid feed wire. Reconnect vacuum hose to EGR valve. Reconnect wire to A/C compressor clutch. Remove all test equipment.

Fig. 11: Adjusting Solenoid Idle Stop Speed on 3.7L Engine

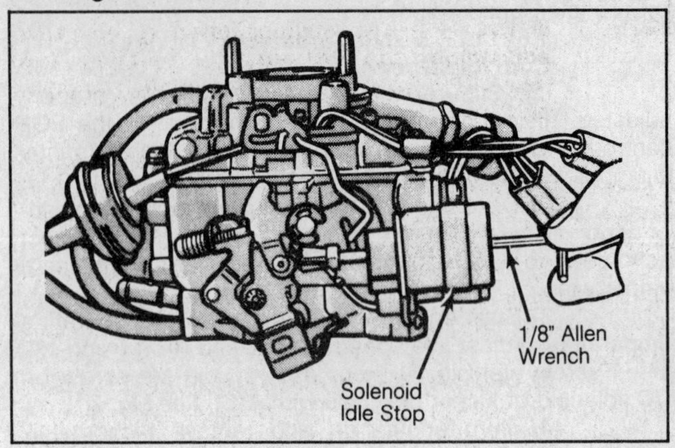

SOLENOID IDLE STOP SPEED

Application	RPM
3.7L Engine	900
5.2L 2-Bbl. & 4-Bbl.	850

3.7L & 5.2L Carbureted Engines
Curb Idle Speed

1) Ensure that ignition timing is correctly set. Disconnect and plug vacuum hose at EGR valve. Remove PCV valve from valve cover and allow valve to draw fresh air.

2) Connect tachometer to engine. Connect a jumper wire between carburetor switch and ground. Start engine and warm to normal operating temperature.

3) Disconnect the oxygen sensor lead and ground the harness connector. Disconnect and plug vacuum line leading to Spark Control Computer (SCC). Apply 16 in. Hg vacuum to vacuum transducer on SCC.

4) Run engine for 2 minutes to allow the effect of disconnecting oxygen sensor to take place. Adjust idle speed to specified RPM by turning idle set screw on rear of solenoid idle stop. *See Fig. 12.*

Fig. 12: Curb Idle & Fast Idle Adjusting Screw Locations

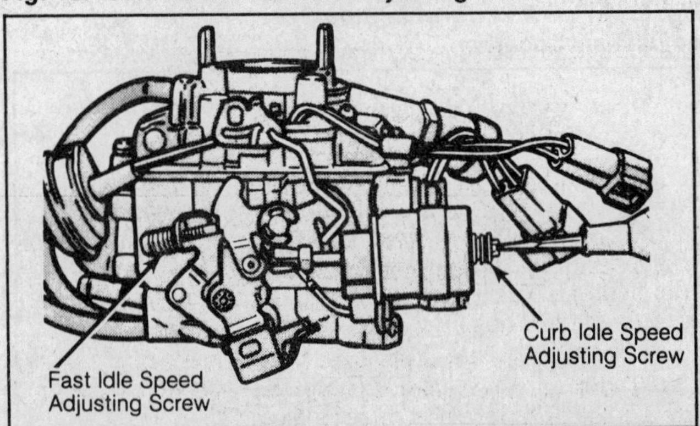

The 3.7L adjustment shown, 5.2L adjustment is similar.

CURB IDLE SPEED

Application	RPM
3.7L Engine	725
5.2L 2-Bbl. & 4-Bbl.	700

CHRYSLER CORP. SYSTEMS & TUNE-UP PROCEDURES (Cont.)

5.2L EFI Engine
Throttle Position Potentiometer (TPP)

NOTE: If the TPP has malfunctioned or requires adjustment, the TPP must be replaced. The new TPP comes with a new mounting bracket and 2 break-off screws.

1) Connect EFI tester to vehicle. Place toggle switch on EFI tester in EFI position. Turn rotary switch to throttle position setting. Turn ignition switch to "Run" position.

2) Move EFI toggle switch to manual position. Move automatic idle speed (AIS) control toggle switch to down position and hold it there until AIS motor stops running.

3) Depress ASD by-pass button on EFI tester and read TPP voltage. Adjust TPP position as necessary to obtain specified voltage reading. Tighten TPP screws until screw heads break off.

THROTTLE POSITION POTENTIOMETER VOLTAGE

Application	Voltage
5.2L EFI	4-5 Volts

5.2L EFI Engine
Automatic Idle Speed (AIS) Motor

1) Connect EFI tester diagnostic aid to AIS motor. Connect tachometer pick-up of EFI tester to number 1 spark plug wire. Connect EFI tester battery leads to battery. Place toggle switch on diagnostic aid in normal operation position.

2) Start engine and warm to normal operating temperature. Move toggle switch on diagnostic aid to manual position. Depress AIS control switch on EFI tester until engine speed no longer decreases.

3) Set parking brake and place transmission in "D". Adjust AIS motor curb idle speed to specified RPM by turning screw on end of AIS motor linkage. Remove all test equipment.

AIS MOTOR CURB IDLE SPEED

Application	RPM
5.2L EFI	530-630

IDLE MIXTURE SCREW PLUG REMOVAL

1.6L, 1.7L & 2.2L Engines

1) Remove air cleaner crossover. Remove canister purge and air pump diverter valve vacuum hoses from carburetor. Locate and center punch a mark 1/4" from end of mixture screw housing. Punch mark should be at 10:00 o'clock position. *See Fig. 13.*

2) Drill through outer section of housing using a 3/16" drill bit. Concealment plug should drop out. If not, use a small drift punch to remove plug.

CAUTION: Do not allow drift to contact mixture screw.

3) Reinstall vacuum hoses and air cleaner crossover. Perform propane idle mixture adjustment and reinstall plug.

Fig. 13: 1.6L, 1.7L & 2.2L Mixture Screw Plug Removal

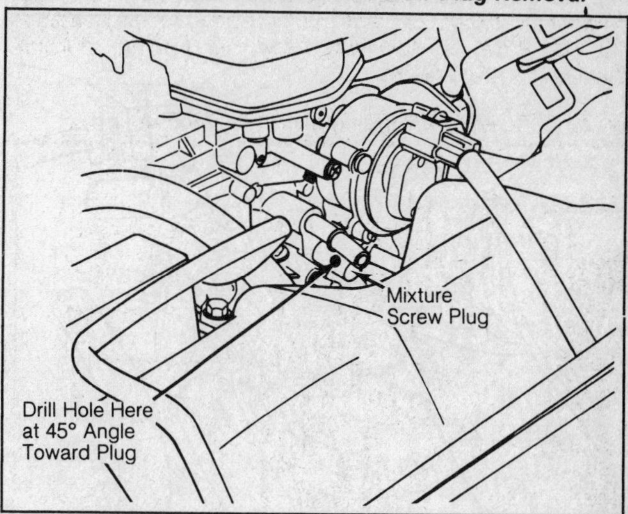

2.6L Engine

1) Remove carburetor from engine. Position carburetor in a soft jawed vise. Using a 3/32" drill bit, drill a hole at a 45° angle behind the mixture screw plug. *See Fig. 14.* Enlarge hole with 1/8" drill bit.

2) Using a narrow pin punch, drive mixture screw plug from carburetor base. Reinstall carburetor on engine using a new flange gasket.

Fig. 14: 2.6L Mikuni Mixture Screw Plug Removal

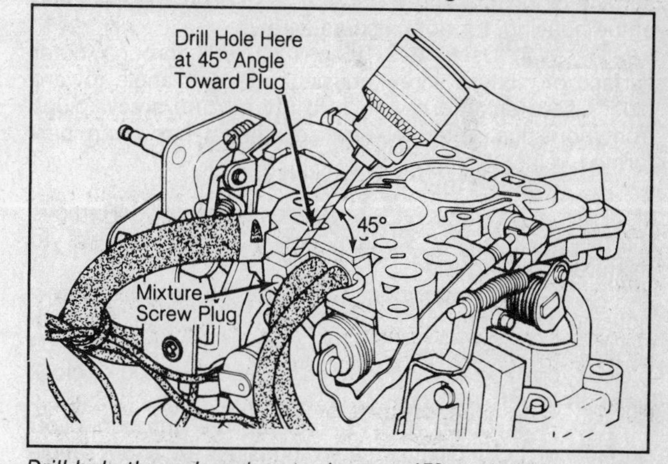

Drill hole through carburetor base at 45° angle behind plug.

3.7L Engine

1) Remove air cleaner assembly. Remove canister purge and air pump diverter valve vacuum hoses from carburetor. Locate and center punch a mark 1/4" from end of mixture screw housing. Punch mark should be indexed at 2:00 o'clock position. *See Fig. 15.*

2) Drill through outer section of housing using a 3/16" drill bit. Concealment plug should drop out. If not, use a small drift punch to remove plug.

CAUTION: Do not allow drift to contact mixture screw.

3) Reinstall vacuum hoses and air cleaner assembly. Perform idle mixture RPM adjustment and reinstall plug.

CHRYSLER CORP. SYSTEMS & TUNE-UP PROCEDURES (Cont.)

Fig. 15: 3.7L Mixture Screw Plug Removal

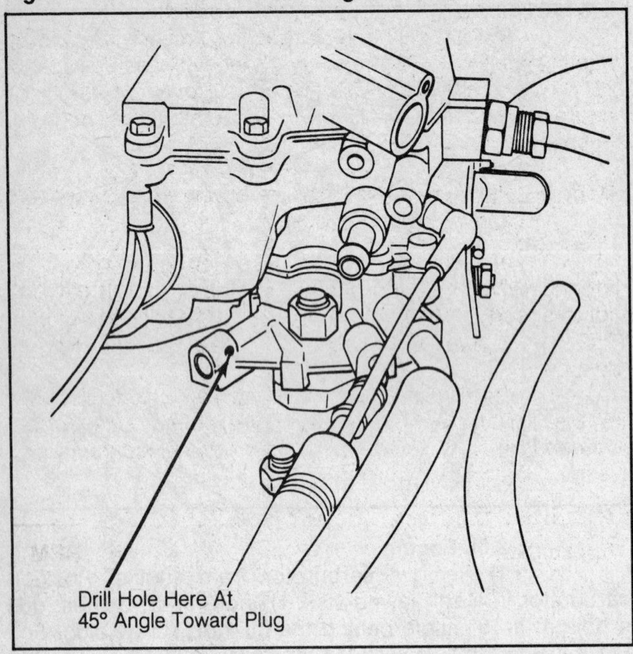

5.2L 2-Bbl. Engine

1) Remove air cleaner assembly. Remove throttle linkage and vacuum hoses to gain access to mixture screw housings. Center punch a mark on side surface of mixture screw housing, 5/16" from the front end of the housing, for both mixture screws.

2) Using a 3/16" drill bit, drill through outer surface of mixture screw housings at a 90° angle toward plug. Use a small drift punch to pry mixture screw plugs from housings. After mixture adjustment has been performed, reinstall plugs.

5.2L 4-Bbl. Engine

1) Remove air cleaner assembly. Remove throttle linkage and vacuum hoses to gain access to mixture screw housings.

2) Center punch a mark on mixture screw housing 1/4" from the front end of the housing, for both mixture screws. Center punch mark should be at 10:00 o'clock position on right housing and at 2:00 o'clock position on left housing.

3) Using a 3/16" drill bit, drill through outer surface of both mixture screw housings at a 90° angle toward plug. Use a small drift punch to pry mixture screw plug from housing. After mixture adjustment has been performed, reinstall plug.

IDLE MIXTURE ADJUSTMENT

NOTE: **No idle mixture adjustment is necessary or possible on 2.2L EFI and 5.2L EFI engines.**

1.6L, 1.7L & 2.2L Carbureted Engines

1) Set parking brake and place transmission in Neutral. Turn all lights and accessories off. Connect tachometer to engine. Start engine and warm to normal operating temperature.

2) Disconnect and plug vacuum connector at EGR control valve. Disconnect vacuum hose from heated air door at 3-way connector. Connect supply hose from propane bottle to 3-way connector.

3) Make sure that both valves on propane bottle are fully closed. Position propane bottle in upright and safe position. Disconnect connector at cooling fan and install a jumper wire so that fan will run continuously.

4) Remove PCV valve from valve cover so that valve can draw fresh air. Connect a jumper wire between carburetor switch and ground.

5) Open main valve on propane bottle. With air cleaner installed, slowly open propane metering valve until maximum engine RPM is reached. Carefully adjust metering valve to obtain a steady maximum RPM.

6) Turn main valve off and allow engine speed to stabilize. Adjust curb idle to specified RPM using mixture adjusting screw. Readjust curb idle to specified RPM, if necessary.

7) Turn main valve back on and note maximum RPM reading. If propane enriched RPM is not within 25 RPM of specified RPM, repeat steps **5)** through **7)** until proper propane idle RPM is obtained.

8) Turn both propane bottle valves off. Remove all test equipment and reconnect all vacuum lines. Remove all jumper wires and reconnect all connectors. On 1.7L engines, it is necessary to readjust curb idle speed after mixture procedures are complete.

1.6L, 1.7L & 2.2L PROPANE ENRICHED IDLE SPEED

Application	Propane Idle RPM
1.6L	
Federal & Calif.	1050
High Alt.	900
1.7L	950
2.2L	
Federal	
Man. Trans.	850
Auto. Trans.	975
Calif.	
Man. Trans.	
Rampage & Scamp	850
All Others	875
Auto. Trans.	
Rampage & Scamp	975
All Others	1000
High Alt.	
Man. Trans.	975
Auto. Trans.	900

2.6L Engine

1) Place transmission in Neutral. Turn all lights and accessories off. Disconnect engine cooling fan. Connect a tachometer to engine.

2) Start engine and warm to normal operating temperature. Make sure that ignition timing is correctly set. Disconnect air hose running between pulse air feeder and air cleaner. Plug hose to prevent any secondary air flow into pulse air feeder.

3) Insert infra-red exhaust gas analyzer probe into tailpipe. Set idle mixture CO level and curb idle speed to specifications, by simultaneously turning curb idle speed adjusting and mixture adjusting screws.

4) Remove plug from air hose and reconnect it to air cleaner. Install new plug into carburetor to seal mixture screw.

CHRYSLER CORP. SYSTEMS & TUNE-UP PROCEDURES (Cont.)

2.6L IDLE MIXTURE CO LEVEL

Application	CO%
2.6L	.5

3.7L Engine

1) Place transmission in Neutral. Turn all accessories off. Connect tachometer to engine. Remove exhaust manifold heat shield for access to oxygen sensor. Start engine and warm to normal operating temperature. Disconnect and plug hose at EGR control valve.

2) Connect a jumper wire between carburetor switch and ground. Disconnect vacuum supply hose from diaphragm at "T" fitting. Connect propane supply hose in its place. Remove PCV valve from valve cover and allow it to draw under hood air. Disconnect and plug 3/16" control hose at canister.

3) Disconnect the oxygen sensor lead and ground the harness connector. Disconnect and plug vacuum line leading to Spark Control Computer (SCC). Connect an auxiliary vacuum source to SCC and apply 16 in. Hg of vacuum. Run engine for 2 minutes to allow the effect of disconnecting oxygen sensor to take place.

4) Open main propane valve. Slowly open propane metering valve until maximum RPM is reached. Adjust idle speed screw on rear of solenoid to obtain propane RPM. Recheck propane flow and reset propane RPM if necessary.

5) Turn propane off and allow idle speed to stabilize. With air cleaner installed, adjust idle mixture screw carefully until curb idle speed is obtained. Pause between adjustments to allow idle to stabilize.

6) Turn propane on and observe maximum RPM. If more than 25 RPM from propane speed, repeat adjustment procedure.

7) Turn engine off and remove all test equipment. Reconnect hoses and wiring to original locations, then install new concealment plug in carburetor. Recheck solenoid idle stop speed, curb idle and fast idle; adjust if necessary.

5.2L Carbureted Engines

1) Set parking brake and place transmission in "N". Turn all lights and accessories off. Connect a tachometer to engine.

2) Start engine and warm to normal operating temperature. Disconnect and plug vacuum hose at EGR valve. Connect jumper wire between carburetor switch and ground.

3) On models with 2-barrel carburetors, disconnect vacuum hose at heated air door sensor at carburetor. Connect propane supply hose to heated air door sensor.

4) On models with 4-barrel carburetors, remove bowl vent vacuum hose from nipple on carburetor. Install a "T" fitting between vacuum hose and nipple. Connect propane supply hose to "T" fitting.

5) On all models, place propane bottle in upright position. Remove PCV valve from valve cover and allow it to draw fresh air. Disconnect and plug 3/16" diameter control hose at canister.

6) Disconnect engine harness lead from oxygen sensor and ground harness lead. Disconnect and plug hose to vacuum transducer on the Spark Control Computer (SCC). Connect and auxiliary vacuum source to transducer and apply 16 in. Hg of vacuum.

7) Allow engine to operate for 2 minutes to allow effect of disconnecting oxygen sensor to take place. Open propane main valve. Slowly open propane metering valve until maximum engine speed is obtained.

8) With propane still flowing, adjust idle speed adjusting screw on solenoid to obtain specified propane RPM. Turn main propane valve off. Slowly adjust both mixture screws in equal amounts to obtain specified curb idle speed.

NOTE: **Pause between mixture screw adjustments to allow idle to stabilize.**

9) Turn main propane valve on. Adjust propane metering valve to obtain highest engine speed. If highest engine speed is not within 25 RPM of specified propane RPM, repeat steps **7)** and **8)** until proper propane RPM is obtained.

10) Remove all plugs and reconnect all vacuum hoses. Remove all test equipment. Remove all jumper wires and reconnect all wires to their original locations.

3.7L & 5.2L PROPANE ENRICHED IDLE SPEED

Application	RPM
3.7L	835
5.2L	
2-Bbl.	760
4-Bbl.	775

COLD (FAST) IDLE RPM

NOTE: **No fast idle speed adjustment is possible on 2.2L TBI, 2.6L and 5.2L EFI engines.**

1.6L, 1.7L & 2.2L Carbureted Engines

1) Disconnect connector from radiator cooling fan and connect a jumper wire to fan so that it will run continuously. Remove PCV valve from valve cover and allow it to draw fresh air.

2) Disconnect and plug vacuum connector at EGR control valve. Connect tachometer to engine. Using a jumper wire, ground carburetor switch.

3) On all models except Federal Rampage and Scamp with 2.2L engine, disconnect O_2 system test connector on left fender shield near shock tower.

Fig. 16: 1.6L, 1.7L & 2.2L Fast Idle Speed Adjusting Screw Location

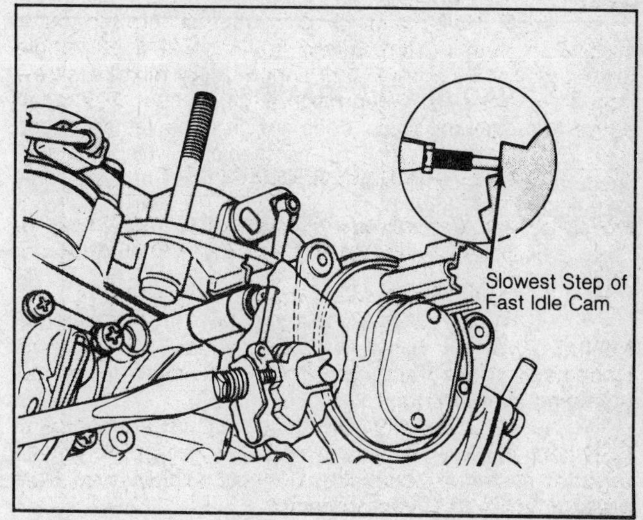

CHRYSLER CORP. SYSTEMS & TUNE-UP PROCEDURES (Cont.)

4) On all models, start engine and warm to normal operating temperature. Open throttle slightly and place fast idle adjusting screw on slowest step of fast idle cam. *See Fig. 16*.

5) Adjust fast idle speed to specified RPM using fast idle adjusting screw. Turn engine off and remove tachometer. Unplug and reconnect vacuum connector. Remove jumper wires and reconnect all connectors.

3.7L & 5.2L Engines

1) Ensure that ignition timing is properly set. Disconnect and plug vacuum hose at EGR valve. Connect a jumper wire between carburetor switch and ground.

2) Disconnect and plug 3/16" control hose at canister. Remove PCV valve from valve cover and allow it to draw fresh air. Connect tachometer to engine. Start engine and warm to normal operating temperature.

3) Disconnect engine harness lead from oxygen sensor and ground harness lead. Allow engine to operate for about 2 minutes to allow effect of disconnecting oxygen sensor to take place.

4) Open throttle slightly and place fast idle adjusting screw on second highest step of fast idle cam. With choke fully open, adjust fast idle speed to specified RPM by using fast idle speed adjusting screw. *See Fig. 12*.

5) Reconnect all disconnected wires and vacuum hoses to their original locations. When all wires and vacuum hoses are reconnected, idle speed may change; DO NOT readjust.

FAST IDLE SPEED (RPM)

Application	Man. Trans.	Auto. Trans.
1.6L	1400	.....
1.7L	1400	.....
2.2L		
Rampage & Scamp		
Federal	1300	1500
Calif.	1400	1500
High Alt.	1350	1275
All Others		
Federal	1400	1500
Calif.	1400	1600
High Alt.	1350	1275
3.7L	.....	2000
5.2L	.....	1400

VACUUM DIAGRAMS

Chrysler Corp. does not produce vacuum hose routing decals for any of its vehicles. Replacement vacuum hoses come as a complete harness and can only be installed in one way.

CHRYSLER CORP. ELECTRONIC FUEL CONTROL

All Front Wheel Drive Models (Exc. 2.2L EFI & 2.6L)

DESCRIPTION

The Electronic Fuel Control system (EFC) is used on all 1.6L, 1.7L and 2.2L engines with front wheel drive. EFC is an electronically controlled system that closely controls air/fuel ratio and ignition timing. The Spark Control Computer (SCC) is the heart of the system.

This computer provides the capability of igniting a lean air/fuel mixture according to different modes of engine operation; plus, during closed loop operation, the computer maintains the air/fuel mixture close to the ideal ratio of 14.7:1.

OPERATION

The EFC system consists of 6 sub-systems: fuel control, spark control, throttle control, data sensors, Spark Control Computer (SCC) and catalytic converter.

FUEL CONTROL

All models are equipped with feedback carburetors which contain an electrically operated duty cycle solenoid. This solenoid meters the main fuel system of carburetor and operates in parallel with the conventional fixed main metering jets. The computer controls the operation of the solenoid in response to signals received from data sensors. *See Fig. 1.*

Fig. 1: Sectional View of Feedback Carburetor With Duty Cycle Solenoid

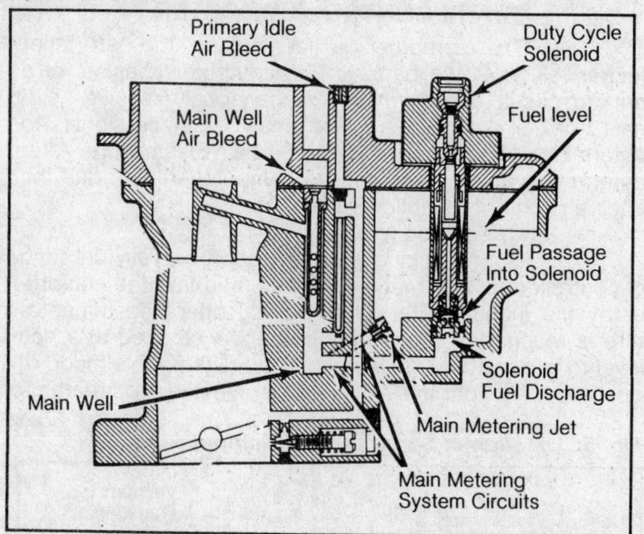

When the solenoid is de-energized by the computer, the solenoid valve spring pushes upward through main system fuel valve. When de-energized, the solenoid main metering orifice is fully uncovered, providing the richest mixture for any given air flow.

When the solenoid is energized by the computer, the solenoid main metering orifice is fully sealed. This solenoid position offers the leanest mixture within the carburetor for any given air flow.

The main system fuel may be regulated between richest and leanest mixture conditions by controlling the amount of time that the solenoid is energized and de-energized. The computer controls the duration of time that the solenoid is energized in comparison to total time of solenoid operation and in response to engine operating conditions and/or oxygen sensor signals. In this manner, the ideal air/fuel ratio can be constantly maintained.

SPARK CONTROL

Spark control allows the computer to determine the exact instant that ignition is required, then signals ignition coil to produce electrical impulses which fire the spark plugs. The computer eliminates the need for either vacuum advance units or centrifugal advance weights. Spark control operates in one of the following modes:

Start Mode

During cranking, an electrical signal from the distributor is fed into the computer, which causes the computer to fire the spark plugs at a fixed amount of advance.

Run Mode

Once the engine starts and is operating normally, the timing will be controlled by the computer, based upon information received by the data sensors.

Spark timing and dwell cannot be adjusted in the run mode. If the computer fails, the system will go into the start mode. This enables the vehicle to be driven in for repair; but performance and fuel economy will be poor. If the start mode fails, the engine will not start or run.

The amount of spark advance is determined by engine speed and engine vacuum, based on the following conditions:

Advance From Vacuum

Advance based upon engine vacuum is allowed by the computer when the carburetor switch is open. The amount of advance is programmed into the computer and is proportionate to the amount of vacuum and engine RPM.

Advance From Speed

Advance based upon engine speed (RPM) is allowed by the computer when the carburetor switch is open and advance from vacuum is not changing. This advance from speed is programmed into the computer, controlled by engine RPM and will build at a slow rate. If carburetor switch closes, advance from speed will be cancelled.

THROTTLE CONTROL

The throttle control system is used to maintain or raise engine speed for certain conditions. The conditions when engine speed is raised are during A/C or heated rear window (EBL — electrically heated backlight) operation, or during timer operation. There are 2 timers used in this system. When the engine is started, one of the timers provides a 2 second delay, during which engine speed is raised. Also, when the throttle is closed, another timer prevents the throttle from closing all the way immediately.

DATA SENSORS

Hall Effect Pick-Up Assembly

This device is located in the distributor to supply a basic timing signal to the computer. From this signal, the computer can determine engine speed (RPM), when each piston is coming up on its compression stroke or when engine is in the start mode. *See Fig. 2.*

CHRYSLER CORP. ELECTRONIC FUEL CONTROL (Cont.)

Fig. 2: Location of Hall Effect Pick-up Assembly in Distributor

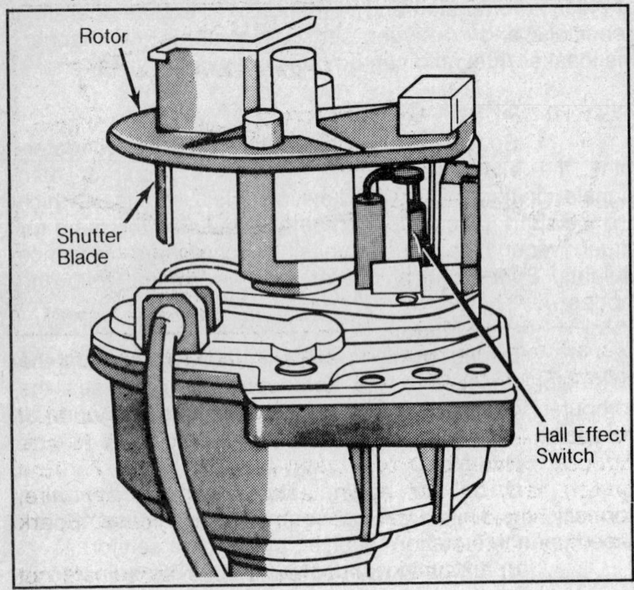

Coolant Switch

The switch is located on the thermostat housing and supply a signal to the computer when engine coolant temperature reaches a predetermined temperature.

This information is required to prevent air/fuel ratio from changing until engine reaches normal operating temperature. The computer also controls the amount of spark advance with a cold engine. *See Fig. 3.*

Fig. 3: Location of Coolant Switch

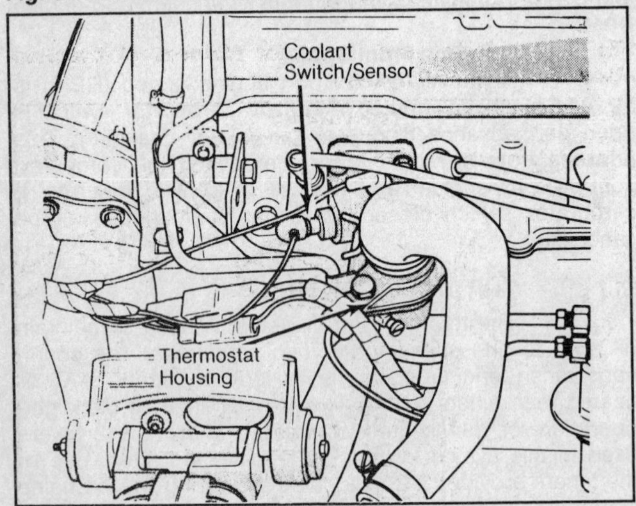

Vacuum Transducer

The vacuum transducer is mounted on the computer and provides the computer with a signal of the amount of engine vacuum. Engine vacuum is used by the computer to determine how much to advance or retard ignition timing and to change air/fuel mixture.

Carburetor Switch

This switch is located on the end of the idle stop to signal the computer when the engine is at idle. When the carburetor switch contacts the throttle lever ground, there will be a cancellation of spark advance and idle control of the air/fuel mixture. *See Fig. 4.*

Fig. 4: Location of Carburetor Switch

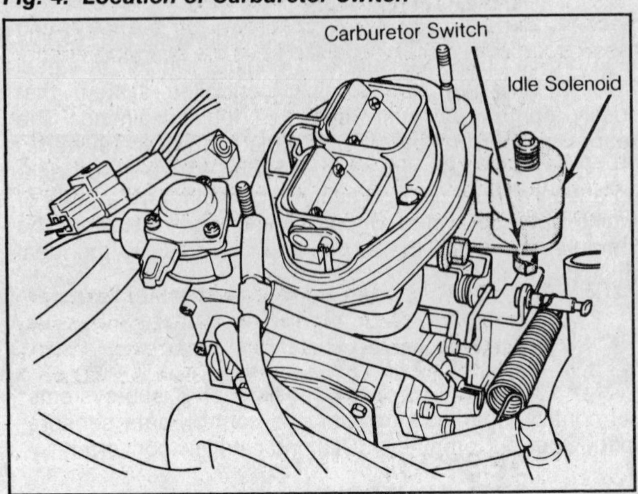

Oxygen Sensor

This sensor is located in the exhaust manifold to signal the computer of oxygen content of exhaust gases. The voltage output of the oxygen sensor is proportional to oxygen content of exhaust gases. The computer will adjust the air/fuel mixture (vary the time of the duty cycle solenoid) to a level which will maintain operating efficiency of the 3-way catalyst system and engine.

SPARK CONTROL COMPUTER

The computer is located on the left inner fenderwell, near the battery. The computer consists of a printed circuit board which simultaneously receives signals from all data sensors and analyzes these signals to determine correct ignition timing and air/fuel mixture. After determining spark advance, the computer will operate the engine in one of the following modes:

Open Loop Mode

During cold engine operation, the air/fuel ratio is controlled by information programmed into the computer by the manufacturer. Until normal operating temperature is reached, the air/fuel mixture will be fixed at a rich level to allow proper engine warm-up. During this mode of operation, air from the AIR pump is injected "upstream" in

Fig. 5: Location of Spark Control Computer

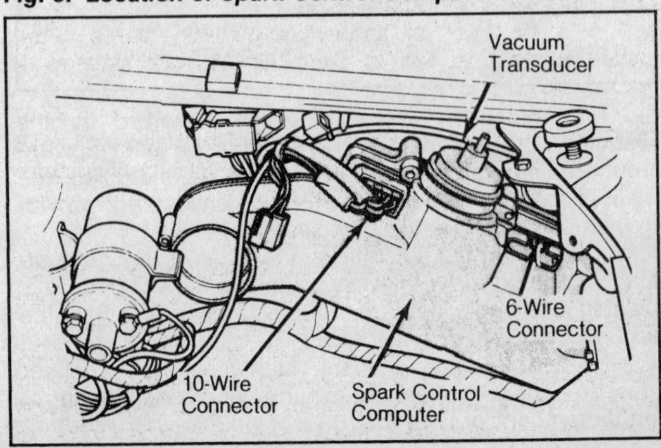

CHRYSLER CORP. ELECTRONIC FUEL CONTROL (Cont.)

the exhaust manifold to assist in heating up the oxygen sensor.

Closed Loop Mode

Once normal engine operating temperature is reached, the air/fuel ratio is controlled by the computer based upon information received from the oxygen sensor.

CATALYTIC CONVERTER

Proper emission control is accomplished with the special catalytic converter system used with the EFC system. All models use a front converter with air injection line and second (main) converter placed behind the front one.

NOTE: **Similarities exist between external characteristics of each converter system. However, extreme care must be exercised during replacement of converters due to internal design differences.**

TESTING

A malfunction in the EFC system may result in engine surge, hesitation, rough idle and/or poor fuel economy. Before making any tests, check all vacuum and electrical wiring for proper routing and connections, and check for exhaust and intake manifold leaks. If these are in order, testing may begin.

NOTE: **The Spark Control Computer controls ignition timing as well as air/fuel mixture. Before testing EFC system, perform spark control test.**

ELECTRONIC SPARK CONTROL SYSTEM TESTS

Ignition System Starting Test

1) Remove coil wire from distributor cap. Hold end of wire ¼" away from good engine ground. Have assistant crank engine, while you watch for spark at secondary wire. Spark should be constant and bright blue.

2) If there is a good spark, continue cranking engine while slowly moving secondary wire away from ground. Look for arcing at coil tower. If arcing occurs, replace coil. If spark is weak or not constant, or if there is no spark, proceed to "Failure to Start Test".

3) If spark is good and there is no arcing at the coil tower, secondary voltage is satisfactory. Make sure it is reaching spark plugs by checking distributor rotor, cap, spark plug wires and spark plugs.

4) If all of these components check okay, ignition system is not at fault. Check fuel system or mechanical engine damage.

CAUTION: **Perform "Ignition System Starting Test" first. Failure to do so may result in lost diagnostic time or incorrect results.**

Failure To Start Test

1) Measure and record battery voltage. Check battery specific gravity, which must be 1.220 (temperature corrected) to deliver proper voltage to ignition system.

2) Remove coil secondary wire from distributor cap and hold ¼" from a good ground. Prepare a special jumper wire assembly as shown in *Fig. 6.* With ignition switch on, momentarily touch special jumper wire to

Fig. 6: Special Jumper Wire Assembly for Grounding Coil Negative Terminal

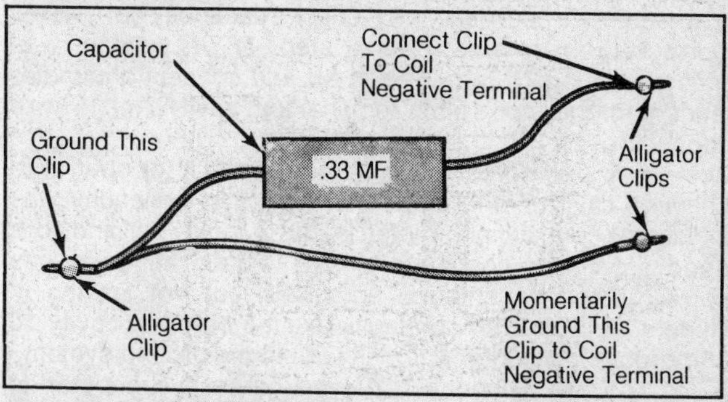

ground and coil negative terminal. A spark should be obtained at secondary wire.

3) If spark was obtained, proceed to step **6)**. If no spark resulted, turn ignition off and disconnect 10-wire harness connector from computer. *See Fig. 7.* Turn ignition back on and again, using special jumper wire, connect negative terminal momentarily to ground. Spark should be obtained.

4) If spark was obtained, but engine will not start, computer output is shorted. Replace computer. If no spark resulted in step **3)**, connect positive lead of voltmeter to coil positive terminal and negative lead to a good ground. Reading should be within 1 volt of battery voltage. If not, check wiring between battery and coil positive terminal.

5) If correct voltage was recorded in step **4)**, measure voltage between ground and coil negative terminal. Again, it should be within 1 volt of battery voltage. Replace ignition coil if there is either no voltage present, or if voltage is present but no spark results when shorting negative coil terminal.

Fig. 7: Distributor and Computer Harness Connectors Used in Testing ESA System

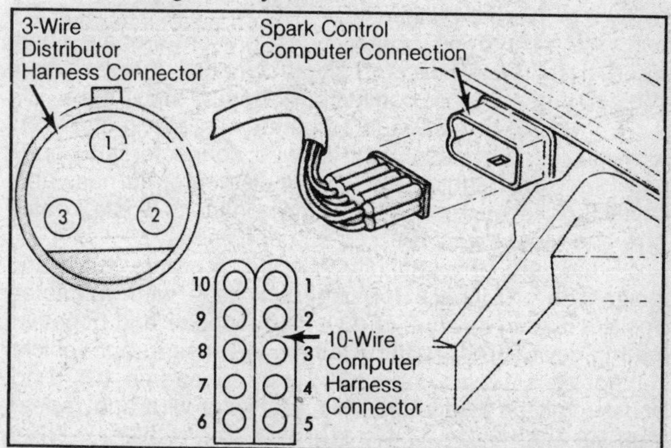

6) If no spark was obtained in step **2)** or if in step **5)** voltage was obtained but engine would not start, hold carburetor switch open with a thin cardboard insulator. Measure voltage between carburetor switch and ground. Reading should be at least 5 volts. If so, proceed to step **10)**.

7) If voltage was not at least 5 volts in step **6)**, turn ignition off and disconnect 10-wire harness connector from computer. Turn ignition on. Connect positive lead of voltmeter to cavity 2 of connector and negative lead to ground. Reading should be within 1 volt of battery voltage.

CHRYSLER CORP. ELECTRONIC FUEL CONTROL (Cont.)

8) If no battery voltage is present, check wire from battery to ignition switch to cavity 2. Use an ohmmeter if necessary to check continuity of wires. Correct problem and repeat step **7)**. If voltage was present in step **7)**, turn ignition off and connect ohmmeter leads to carburetor switch terminal and cavity 7 of 10-wire connector.

9) If no continuity is found, check for open wire between cavity 7 and carburetor switch. If continuity was indicated, connect ohmmeter leads to cavity 10 and to a good ground. If continuity exists, replace computer, as correct power is entering computer, but not leaving it. Repeat step **6)**. If no continuity existed between cavity 10 and ground, check for an open wire in the ground system.

10) Reconnect 10-wire harness connector to computer. Turn ignition on and hold secondary coil wire ¼" from a good ground. Disconnect 3-wire distributor connector from distributor. Attach jumper wire between cavities 2 and 3 of harness connector. A good spark should jump from coil wire to ground.

11) If spark resulted, but engine will not start, replace Hall Effect Pick-Up. Before replacing, however, always be sure rotor shutterblades are grounded. Connect 1 ohmmeter lead to a good ground and touch other lead to shutter blade. *See Fig. 2.* If no continuity, push down on rotor to seat against shaft. If still no continuity, replace rotor. If shutterblade is grounded, then proceed to replace Hall Effect Pick-Up.

12) If no spark resulted in step **10)**, connect voltmeter positive lead to distributor harness connector cavity 1 and negative lead to ground. Reading should be within 1 volt of battery voltage. If no battery voltage is present, proceed to step **15)**. If voltage was correct, turn ignition off and disconnect 10-wire harness connector from computer.

13) Connect ohmmeter leads between cavity 2 (Black/Light Blue wires) of distributor harness connector and cavity 9 of 10-wire connector. Then connect leads to cavity 3 (Gray wire) of distributor harness connector and cavity 5 of 10-wire connector.

14) If no continuity is present, repair open wires. If continuity exists, replace computer (power going into computer, but not coming out). Repeat step **10)**.

15) If there was no battery voltage in step **12)**, turn ignition off, disconnect 10-wire connector and connect ohmmeter leads to cavity 1 of distributor harness and cavity 3 of 10-wire connector. If no continuity exists, repair wire and repeat step **10)**.

16) If continuity existed in step **15)**, turn ignition on and check for battery voltage with voltmeter positive lead in cavity 2 of 10-wire connector and negative lead in cavity 10. If battery voltage is present, but vehicle will not start, replace computer and repeat step **10)**. If no battery voltage is present, check ground wire and repeat step **10)**.

Spark Control Computer Spark Test

1) Warm engine to normal operating temperature. Disconnect carburetor switch or unground it. Be sure coolant temperature switch/sensor is connected and working properly.

2) Remove and plug vacuum hose at vacuum transducer. Connect an auxiliary vacuum supply to vacuum transducer and apply 16 in. Hg. Increase engine speed to 2000 RPM and wait 1 minute before checking specifications. Advance specifications are in addition to basic advance. *See Spark Advance Test Specifications table.*

NOTE: On some systems with an accumulator (timer), the specified time must be reached with the carburetor switch ungrounded before checking for specified spark advance schedule.

3) If computer fails to obtain settings, replace computer.

SPARK ADVANCE TEST SPECIFICATIONS [1]

Application	Computer Part No.	Advance [2]
1.6L	5213641	19-27°
1.7L	5213438	26-34°
2.2L		
Rampage/Scamp		
Fed.	5213691	24-32°
Calif.		
Man. Trans.	5213834	24-32°
Auto. Trans.	5213832	24-32°
High Alt.	5213840	30-38°
All Others		
Fed.		
Man. Trans.	5213834	24-32°
Auto. Trans.	5213832	24-32°
Calif.		
Man. Trans.	5213838	27-35°
Auto. Trans.	5213836	30-38°
High Alt.	5213840	30-38°

[1] — Engine speed of 2000 RPM and 16 in. Hg vacuum applied.

[2] — All readings ±4°. If amount of advance differs from control label, use label as accurate listing.

ELECTRONIC THROTTLE CONTROL SYSTEM TEST

1) Connect a tachometer to engine. Start and run engine until it reaches normal operating temperature. Depress accelerator, then release accelerator pedal. Engine speed should not immediately return immediately to idle. On vehicles equipped with A/C or heated rear window (EBL — electrically heated backlight), a slight increase in idle speed should be observed while A/C or EBL are turned on.

2) Turning off either device will return idle speed to normal. As the A/C clutch cycles on and off, the throttle kicker solenoid (solekicker) plunger should extend and retract. If plunger does not move with clutch cycling, or after engine starts, or when the EBL is turned on, check the kicker system for vacuum leaks. If engine speed does not increase as specified, disconnect the 3-way connector at carburetor.

3) Connect ohmmeter leads from ground to solenoid terminal that was connected to black wire. Resistance should be 20-100 ohms. If not, replace solenoid. Reconnect solenoid. Start vehicle and immediately (before 2 second time delay times out) measure voltage across vacuun solenoid terminals.

4) Voltage should be within 2 volts of charging system voltage. If not, replace computer. Turn on A/C or

CHRYSLER CORP. ELECTRONIC FUEL CONTROL (Cont.)

EBL after time delay has timed out. Charging voltage should once again be present at solenoid.

ELECTRONIC FUEL CONTROL SYSTEM TESTS

NOTE: **The "Spark Control Computer Spark Test" should be made prior to beginning any test on EFC system. The following tests MUST be performed in the sequence given.**

Air Switching System Diagnosis (Vacuum Supply)

1) Remove vacuum hose for air switching/diverter valve and connect a vacuum gauge to hose. Set parking brake. Start engine and observe gauge reading.

2) On a cold engine, engine vacuum should be present until engine coolant temperature reaches 125-150°F (52-66°C). When temperature is reached, vacuum should drop to zero. If no vacuum is present on gauge, check the vacuum supply and Coolant Controlled Engine Vacuum Switch (CCEVS).

3) On a warm engine, no vacuum should be present. If vacuum is present, check Coolant Controlled Engine Vacuum Switch (CCEVS).

Air Switching System Diagnosis (Air Switching Valve)

1) Remove air supply hose from air switching valve. Remove vacuum hose from valve and install an auxiliary vacuum supply.

2) Set parking brake. Start engine. Air should blow out of side port. Apply vacuum to valve. Air should blow out bottom port. If valve does not operate as described, replace valve.

Coolant Switch Test

1) Turn ignition off and disconnect wire connector from switch. Connect one ohmmeter lead to a good ground and the other lead to switch terminal.

2) A cold engine should show continuity. If not, replace switch. A hot engine should show no continuity. If so replace switch.

Carburetor Duty Cycle Solenoid Test

1) Remove and plug vacuum hose at vacuum transducer. Connect a tachometer. Connect an auxiliary vacuum supply to vacuum transducer and apply 16 in. Hg. Set parking brake and start engine. Allow engine to reach normal operating temperature. DO NOT ground carburetor switch. Run engine at 2000 RPM.

2) On air conditioned models only, disconnect idle solenoid connector. On all models, disconnect Green wire from duty cycle solenoid. Average engine speed should increase at least 50 RPM.

3) Reconnect solenoid connector. Engine speed should slowly return to 2000 RPM. Disconnect the 12-pin connector at the computer. Connect a ground to harness connector pin 15. Engine speed should decrease at least 50 RPM. If engine speed does not change as outlined, service carburetor (check for air leaks).

Electronic Fuel Control Computer Test

1) Connect a tachometer and set parking brake. Start engine, warm to normal operating temperature and maintain engine speed of 2000 RPM. DO NOT ground carburetor switch. Connect a voltmeter to duty cycle solenoid output wire going to carburetor (Green wire).

NOTE: **Do not separate the connector from the wiring harness.**

2) Disconnect electrical connector at oxygen sensor and connect a jumper wire to the harness end. Connect the other end of the jumper wire to a good ground. Engine speed should increase at least 50 RPM and voltmeter should indicate more than 10 volts.

3) Hold the jumper wire with one hand and with the other hand, touch the battery positive terminal with the jumper wire. Engine speed should decrease at least 50 RPM and voltmeter should indicate less than 5 volts. If computer fails both tests, replace it. Reconnect oxygen sensor.

CAUTION: **Before performing the next test, the fuel control computer must be operating properly.**

Oxygen Sensor Test

1) Set parking brake and connect tachometer. Run engine at 2000 RPM and connect voltmeter to carburetor-to-computer output wire (Green). DO NOT ground carburetor switch. Hold choke blade closed. During the next 10 seconds, the voltage should decrease to 5 volts or less and maintain that level. If engine does not respond, proceed to step **2)**.

2) Disconnect PCV system. During the next 10 seconds, voltage should increase to 10 volts or greater and maintain that level until vacuum hose is reconnected. If sensor fails both tests, replace it. Reconnect all hoses and wires.

NOTE: **This test should not be performed for more than 90 seconds.**

NOTE: **Be sure basic timing and hot curb idle speed are set to specifications before performing these tests.**

Carburetor Switch Test

1) Turn ignition off and disconnect 10-wire connector from computer. With throttle completely closed, check continuity with ohmmeter leads connected to cavity 7 and ground.

NOTE: **Grounding carburetor switch eliminates spark advance on most systems.**

2) If no continuity is read, check wire from cavity 7 to carburetor switch terminal. Also check carburetor switch for proper operation.

3) Open throttle and check for continuity from cavity 7 to ground. There should be no continuity. If readings are not as described, replace carburetor switch.

NOTE: **After performing carburetor switch test, perform tests on the spark control system and fuel control system.**

REMOVAL & INSTALLATION

SPARK CONTROL COMPUTER

Removal & Installation

1) Remove battery. Disconnect 10-wire and 6-wire connectors from computer. Remove outside air duct from computer. Disconnect vacuum hose from vacuum transducer.

CHRYSLER CORP. ELECTRONIC FUEL CONTROL (Cont.)

NOTE: Do not remove grease from harness connectors or connector cavities in the computer. The grease is used in order to prevent moisture from corroding the terminals. If there is not at least ½" of grease on bottom of computer connector cavities, apply a liberal amount of Mopar multi-purpose grease No. 2932524 (or equivalent) over entire end of connector plug before reinstalling.

2) Remove 3 mounting screws that hold computer to fenderwell and remove computer. To install, reverse removal procedure.

NOTE: Computer is not serviceable. Do not attempt disassembly for any reason. If vacuum transducer is defective, entire computer must be replaced.

COOLANT SWITCH

Removal & Installation

Disconnect electrical connector and remove switch. To install, coat with anti-seize compound and reverse removal procedure.

HALL EFFECT PICK-UP ASSEMBLY

NOTE: Replacement of Hall Effect Pick-Up Assembly requires overhaul of distributor.

CARBURETOR SWITCH

Removal & Installation

Remove bracket and idle solenoid assembly from carburetor. Disconnect electrical connector. To install, reverse removal procedure and adjust if necessary.

DUTY CYCLE SOLENOID

Removal

1) Remove 2 duty cycle solenoid retaining screws and gently lift solenoid from air horn. Remove anti-rattle spring, 2 retaining screws and idle solenoid from carburetor.

2) Remove 2 wide-open throttle cut-out switch mounting screws (if equipped). Mark location for proper assembly. Remove harness mounting screws and open retaining clip. Remove wires from connector and thread through clip.

Installation

1) Install idle solenoid and anti-rattle spring. Install wide-open throttle cut-out switch (if equipped). Adjust switch so air conditioning clutch circuit is open in throttle position of 10° before wide-open throttle.

2) Install new duty cycle solenoid gasket on air horn and install new "O" ring on duty cycle solenoid tip. Lightly lubricate solenoid with petroleum jelly and carefully install solenoid into carburetor. Install and tighten mounting screws. Route wiring through clamp and connect to harness. Install and tighten harness mounting screw.

OXYGEN SENSOR

Removal

Disconnect battery cable and remove air cleaner. Disconnect electrical lead at sensor. Remove sensor.

Installation

Coat threads of new sensor with nickel-based anti-seize compound. Do not use graphite or other compounds. Start sensor by hand, then tighten to 35 ft. lbs. (47 N.m). Install air cleaner and connect battery cable.

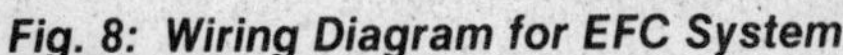

Fig. 8: Wiring Diagram for EFC System

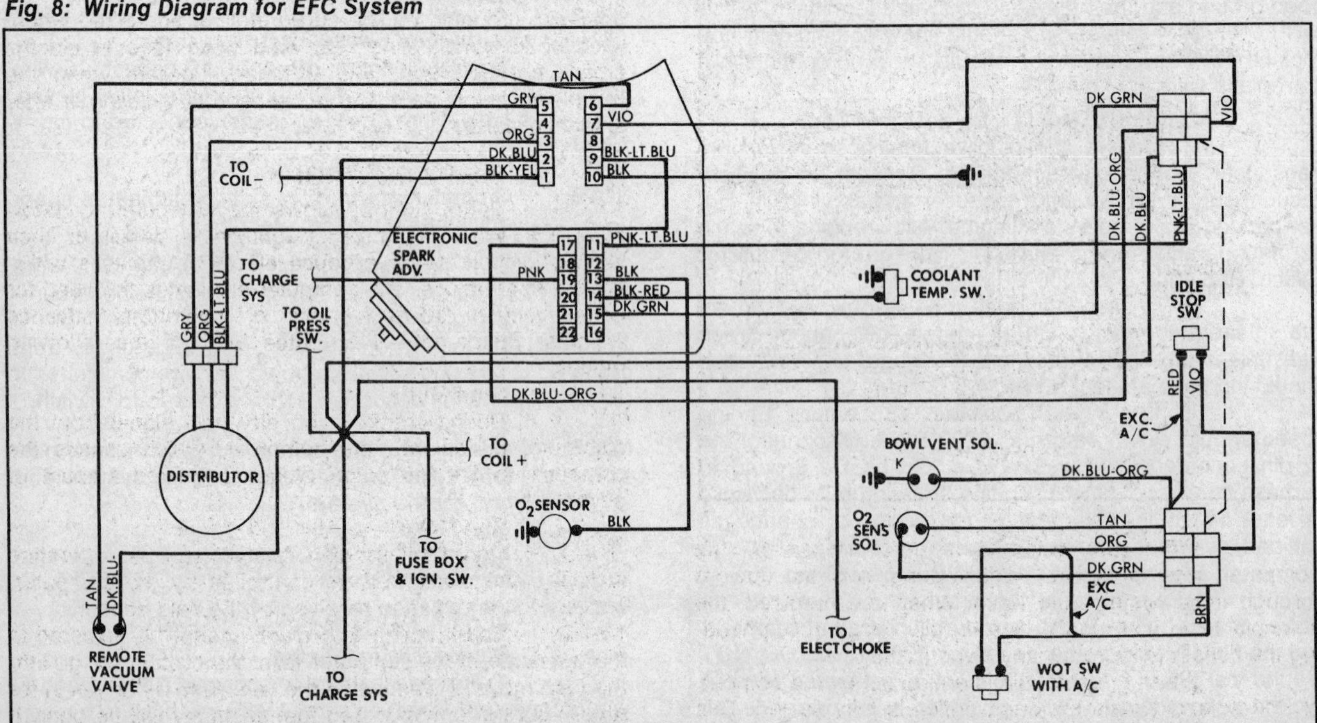

CHRYSLER CORP. ELECTRONIC FUEL CONTROL

All RWD Models (Exc. Imperial)

DESCRIPTION

The Electronic Fuel Control (EFC) system is used on all rear wheel drive cars except Imperial. EFC is an electronically controlled system that closely manages air/fuel ratio and ignition timing.

The Spark Control Computer (SCC) is the heart of the system. This computer provides the capability of igniting a lean air/fuel mixture according to different modes of engine operation; plus, during closed loop operation, the computer maintains the air/fuel mixture close to the ideal ratio of 14.7:1.

OPERATION

The EFC system consists of the following subsystems: fuel control, electronic throttle control, spark control, data sensors. Spark Control Computer (SCC), electronic exhaust gas recirculation (EGR), electronic air switching and catalytic converter.

FUEL CONTROL

All models are equipped with feedback carburetors which contain an electronically operated duty cycle solenoid. This solenoid meters the main fuel system of the carburetor and operates in parallel with the conventional fixed main metering jets. The computer controls the operation of the solenoid with electrical signals, in response to input from data sensors. *See Fig. 1.*

Fig. 1: Sectional View of Thermo-Quad Feedback Carburetor With Duty Cycle Solenoid

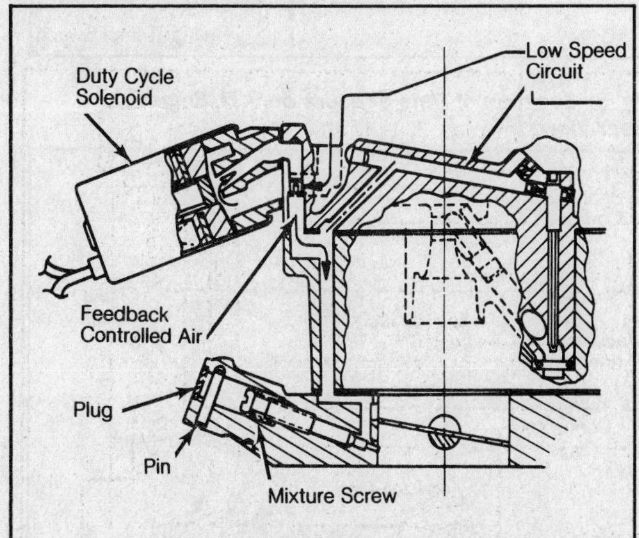

When the solenoid is de-energized by the computer, the solenoid valve spring pushes upward through main system fuel valve. When de-energized, the solenoid main metering orifice is fully uncovered, providing the richest mixture for any given air flow.

When the solenoid is energized by the computer, the solenoid main metering orifice is fully sealed. This solenoid position offers the leanest mixture within the carburetor for any given air flow.

Fig. 2: Sectional View of Holley 6145 Feedback Carburetor With Duty Cycle Solenoid

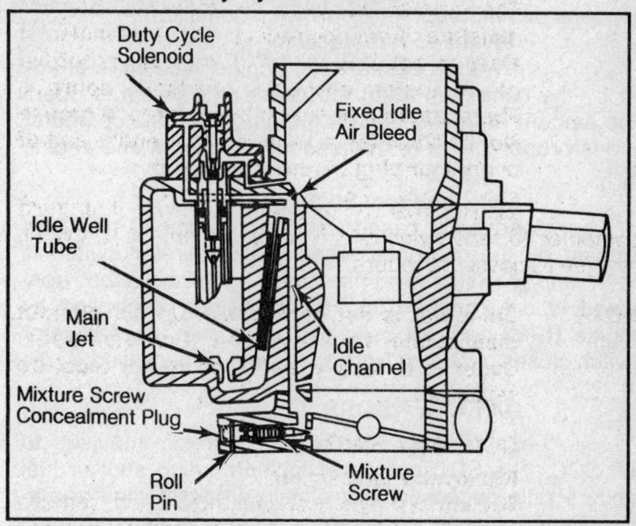

Main system fuel may be regulated between richest and leanest mixture conditions by controlling the amount of time that the solenoid is energized and de-energized. The computer controls the duration of time that solenoid is energized in comparison to total time of solenoid operation.

This duration of time is determined by engine operating conditions and/or oxygen sensor signals. In this manner, the ideal air/fuel ratio can be constantly maintained.

ELECTRONIC THROTTLE CONTROL

The Electronic Throttle Control system and 2 electric timers are incorporated within the SCC. A solenoid, mounted on the carburetor, is energized whenever the air conditioning, rear window defogger or electric timers are activated. The 2 timers operate when the throttle is closed, providing a 2 second time delay, or after engine is started.

SPARK CONTROL

Spark Control allows the computer to determine the exact instant that ignition is required; then signals ignition coil to produce electrical impulses which fire the spark plugs. The computer eliminates the need for either vacuum advance units or centrifugal advance weights. Spark control operates in 1 of the following modes:

Start Mode

During cranking, an electrical signal from the distributor is fed into the computer, which causes the computer to fire the spark plugs at a fixed amount of advance.

Run Mode

Once the engine starts and is operating normally, the timing will be controlled by the computer, based upon information received by the data sensors.

Spark timing and dwell cannot be adjusted in the run mode. If the computer fails, the system will go into the start mode. This enables the vehicle to be driven in for repair; but performance and fuel economy will be poor. If the start mode fails, the engine will not start or run.

CHRYSLER CORP. ELECTRONIC FUEL CONTROL (Cont.)

The amount of spark advance is determined by engine speed and engine vacuum. However, where it happens depends upon the following conditions:

Advance From Vacuum

Advance based upon engine vacuum is allowed by the computer when the carburetor switch is open. The amount of advance is programmed into the computer and is proportionate to the amount of vacuum and engine RPM.

Advance From Speed

Advance based upon engine speed (RPM) is allowed by the computer when the carburetor switch is open and vacuum level is steady. This advance from speed is programmed into the computer, controlled by engine RPM, and will build at a slow rate. If carburetor switch closes, advance from speed will be cancelled.

DATA SENSORS

Each sensor furnishes electronic impulses to the SCC. The SCC computes ignition timing and air/fuel mixture ratio necessary to maintain proper engine operation. The function of each sensor is closely related to each of the other sensors. Operation of each sensor is as follows:

Magnetic Pick-Up Assembly

The magnetic pick-up assembly consists of 2 pick-up coils: start pick-up coil and run pick-up coil. Both are located in the distributor and operate as follows:

- **Start Pick-Up Coil** — Supplies a signal to SCC which will cause the spark plugs to fire at a fixed amount of advance during cranking only. This coil is permanently positioned in distributor and the amount of advance will be determined by distributor position. *See Fig. 3.*
- **Run Pick-Up Coil** — Once engine begins to run, the start pick-up coil signal is by-passed and the run pick-up coil supplies advance information to SCC. The SCC then modifies advance to reflect engine operating conditions reported by other sensors. *See Fig. 3.*

Fig. 3: Location of Magnetic Pick-Up Assembly

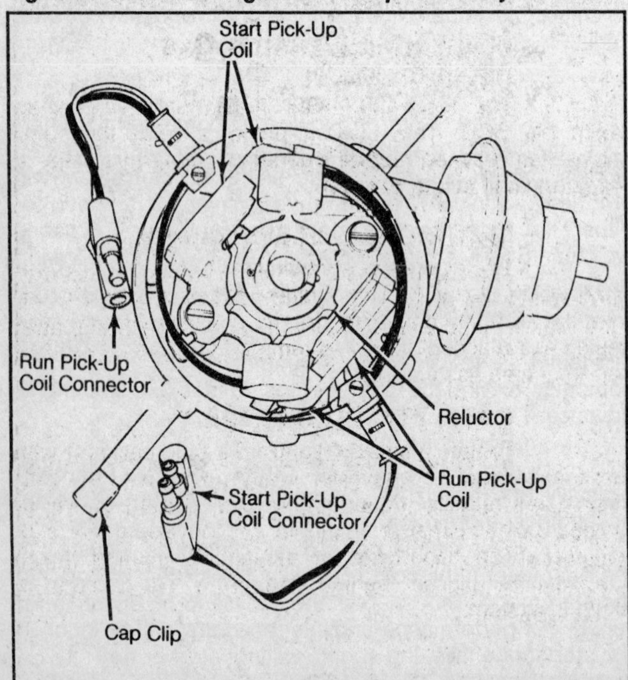

NOTE: **See Figs. 4, 5 and 6 for location of data sensors.**

Coolant Temperature Sensor/Switch

The coolant sensor/switch informs the SCC when the engine has reached normal operating temperature, preventing any changes until such temperature is reached so that proper adjustment can be made to the air/fuel ratio. The coolant sensor/switch also controls amount of ignition timing advance or retard when the engine is cold.

Fig. 4: Location of Data Sensors on 3.7L Engines

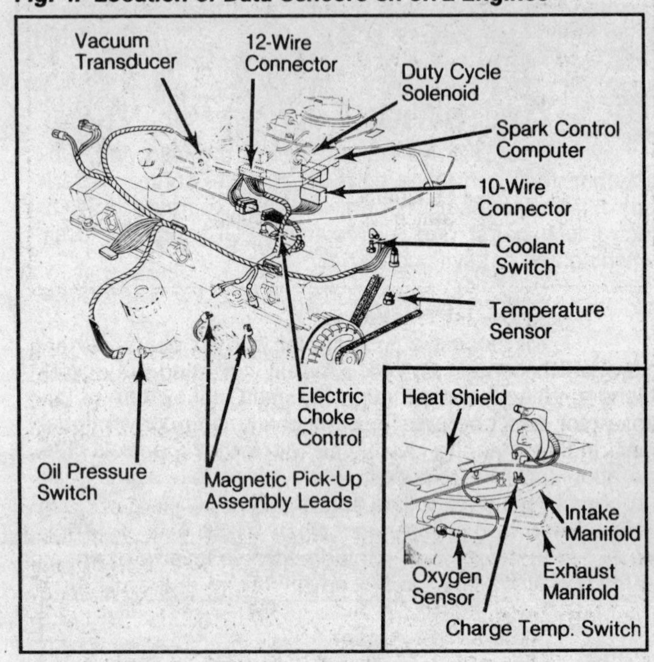

Fig. 5: Location of Data Sensors on 5.2L Engine (Rear View)

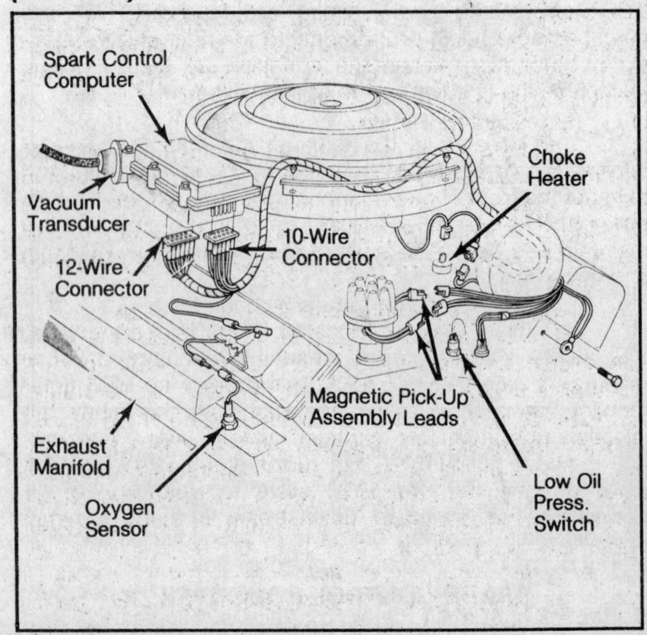

CHRYSLER CORP. ELECTRONIC FUEL CONTROL (Cont.)

Fig. 6: Location of Data Sensors on 5.2L Engine (Front View)

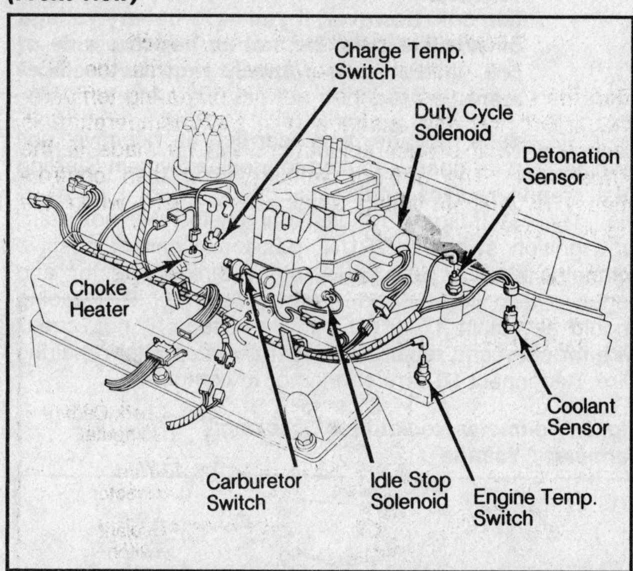

Vacuum Transducer

This sensor is mounted on the computer and provides the computer with a signal indicating the amount of engine vacuum. Engine vacuum is used by the computer to determine how much to advance or retard ignition timing and to change air/fuel mixture.

Carburetor Switch

Located on the end of idle stop, the carburetor switch informs the computer when the engine is at idle. When carburetor switch contacts throttle lever ground, the computer will cancel spark advance and prevent air/fuel ratio from being adjusted.

Detonation Sensor

Used only on the 5.2L engine, this sensor is mounted in the intake manifold and sends a low voltage signal to the SCC whenever engine knock is detected. The SCC then retards ignition timing a maximum of 11°, the actual amount being proportional to strength and frequency of detonation. When the condition no longer exists, ignition timing is advanced to original value.

Oxygen Sensor

Located in the exhaust manifold, this sensor informs the computer of the amount of oxygen present in exhaust gases. The amount is proportional to mixture strength. The computer adjusts air/fuel ratio so that it will maintain operating efficiency of the 3-way catalyst system and the engine.

Charge Temperature Switch

This sensor is located in the intake manifold. The switch will be closed when intake charge (air/fuel mixture) is below 60°F (16°C). This permits no EGR timer function, no EGR valve operation and switches air injection upstream into exhaust system. When temperature is above 60°F (16°C), the switch opens, allowing EGR timer to time out, the EGR valve to operate and air injection to be switched downstream into the exhaust system.

SPARK CONTROL COMPUTER

The computer is mounted on the air cleaner housing and consists of a printed circuit board which

Fig. 7: Internal View of Spark Control Computer

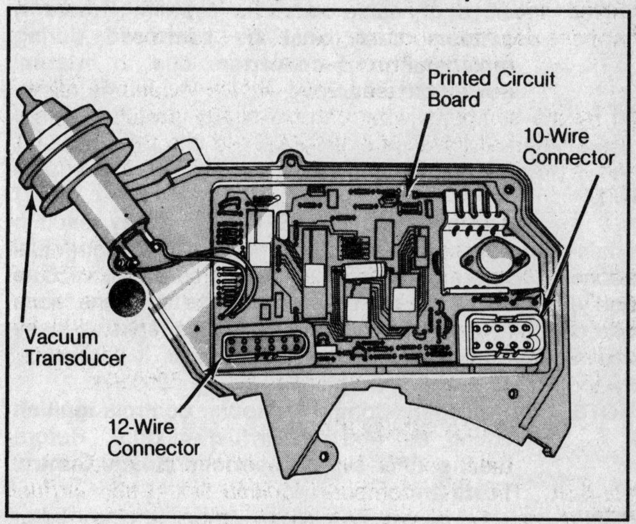

simultaneously receives signals from all data sensors and analyzes these signals to determine spark advance and air/fuel mixture. Incorporated within the computer are the electronics for the throttle control, EGR and air switching systems. After determining spark advance, the computer will operate the engine in one of the following modes:

Open Loop Mode

During cold engine operation, the air/fuel ratio is controlled by information programmed into the computer by the manufacturer. Until normal operating temperature is reached, the air/fuel mixture will be fixed at a rich level to allow proper engine warm-up. During this mode of operation, air from the air pump is injected "upstream" in the exhaust manifold to assist in heating-up the oxygen sensor.

Closed Loop Mode

Once normal engine operating temperature is achieved, the air/fuel ratio is controlled by the computer based upon information received from the oxygen sensor.

ELECTRONIC EXHAUST GAS RECIRCULATION

The electronic EGR system is incorporated within the SCC. This system prevents EGR flow until engine has reached normal operating temperture (after a predetermined length of time).

ELECTRONIC AIR SWITCHING

The electronic air switching system is incorporated within the SCC. This system directs the flow of air from the air pump either "upstream" or "downstream" after engine has reached operating temperature and a specified period of time has elapsed.

CATALYTIC CONVERTER

Proper emission control is accomplished with the special catalytic converter system used with the EFC system. All models are equipped with a front converter located below exhaust manifold (2 converters on 5.2L engines; 1 on each side of engine). A second (main) converter is placed behind the front converter(s) in exhaust system.

CHRYSLER CORP. ELECTRONIC FUEL CONTROL (Cont.)

NOTE: Similarities exist between external characteristics of each converter system. However, extreme care must be exercised during replacement of converters due to internal design differences.

TESTING

A malfunction in the EFC system may result in engine surge, hesitation, rough idle and/or poor fuel economy. Before performing any tests, check all vacuum and electrical wiring for proper routing and connections and check for exhaust and intake manifold leaks. If these are in order, proceed with testing.

NOTE: The Spark Control Computer controls ignition timing as well as air/fuel mixture. Before testing EFC system, perform Spark Control Tests first.

ELECTRONIC SPARK CONTROL SYSTEM TESTS

Ignition System Starting Test

1) Measure and record battery voltage. Check battery specific gravity, which must be 1.220 (temperature corrected) to deliver proper voltage to ignition system.

2) Turn ignition on and remove coil wire from distributor cap. Hold end of wire ¼" from a good engine ground. Intermittently jump coil negative terminal to ground, while watching for spark at coil wire. If there is a spark, it must be constant and bright blue.

3) If there is a good spark, continue cranking engine while slowly moving secondary wire away from ground. Look for arcing at coil tower. If arcing occurs, replace coil. If spark is weak or not constant, or if there is no spark, proceed to "Failure to Start Test".

4) If spark is good and there is no arcing at coil tower, secondary voltage is satisfactory. Make sure it is reaching spark plugs by checking distributor rotor, cap, spark plug wires and spark plugs.

5) If all of these components check okay, ignition system is not at fault. Check fuel system or mechanical engine damage.

CAUTION: Perform "Ignition System Starting Test" first. Failure to do so may result in lost diagnostic time or incorrect test results.

Failure to Start Test

1) Turn ignition switch off and disconnect 10-wire connector from SCC. Repeat Ignition System Starting Test, step **2)**. If spark results, replace computer.

2) If no spark is obtained, check voltage at coil positive terminal. With ignition switch on, connect positive voltmeter lead to coil positive terminal and negative lead to a good ground. Reading should be within 1 volt of battery voltage. If not, check wiring between battery and coil positive terminal.

3) If voltage at positive coil terminal was correct, connect positive voltmeter lead to coil negative terminal and negative lead to a good ground. Again, voltage should be within 1 volt of battery voltage. If not, replace ignition coil.

NOTE: You may wish to check coil primary and secondary resistance before replacing ignition coil. However, if you have battery voltage on positive side, but not on negative side of coil, ignition coil normally requires replacement.

4) If voltage was correct at negative coil terminal, but no spark resulted in Ignition System Starting Test, step **2)**, replace ignition coil.

5) If spark results, but engine will not start, turn ignition switch to "RUN" position. Connect positive voltmeter lead to terminal 1 of 10-wire connector and negative lead to a good ground. *See Fig. 8.* Reading should be within 1 volt of battery voltage. If not, check wire for open and repair it. Repeat this step after repairing wire. Reconnect 10-wire connector to computer.

Fig. 8: Voltmeter Hookup for Checking Terminal 1 Voltage

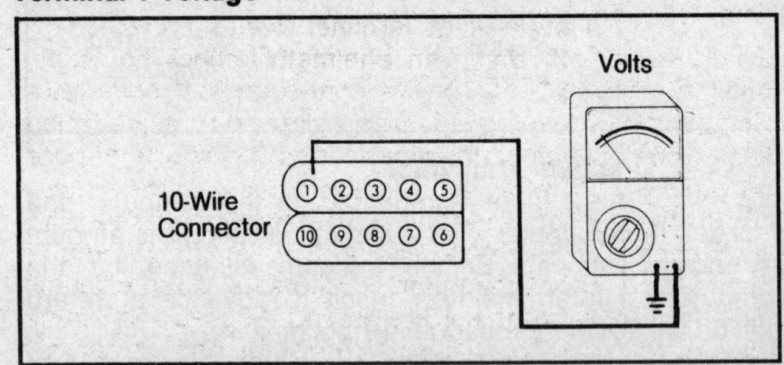

Fig. 9: Checking Voltage at Carburetor Switch

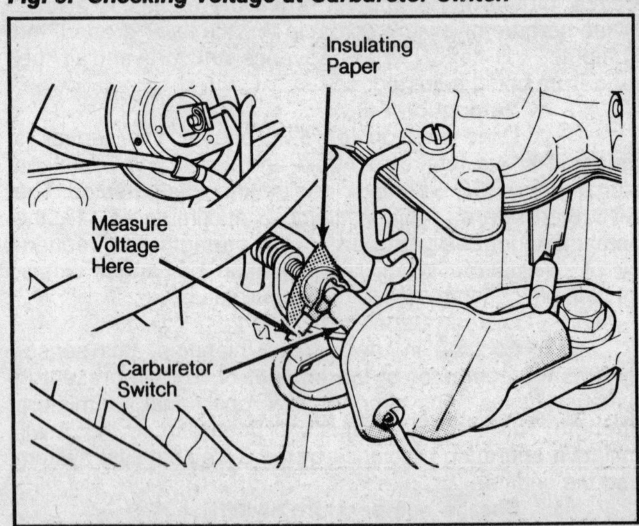

6) If battery voltage was recorded in step **5)**, place a thin insulator (thin piece of cardboard) between curb idle adjusting screw and carburetor switch or make sure screw does not touch switch. *See Fig. 9.* Connect negative lead of voltmeter to a good ground. Turn ignition switch to "RUN" position and touch positive voltmeter lead to carburetor switch terminal. Reading should be approximately 5 volts. If so, proceed to step **9)**.

7) If voltage was not at least 5 volts, turn ignition switch off. Disconnect 10-wire connector from computer. Turn ignition switch back to "RUN" position. Connect positive voltmeter lead to terminal 2 of 10-wire

CHRYSLER CORP. ELECTRONIC FUEL CONTROL (Cont.)

connector and negative lead to ground. *See Fig. 10.* Voltage reading should again be within 1 volt of battery voltage. If not, check wiring between terminal 2 and ignition switch for opens, shorts or poor connections.

Fig. 10: Voltmeter Hookup for Checking Terminal 2 Voltage

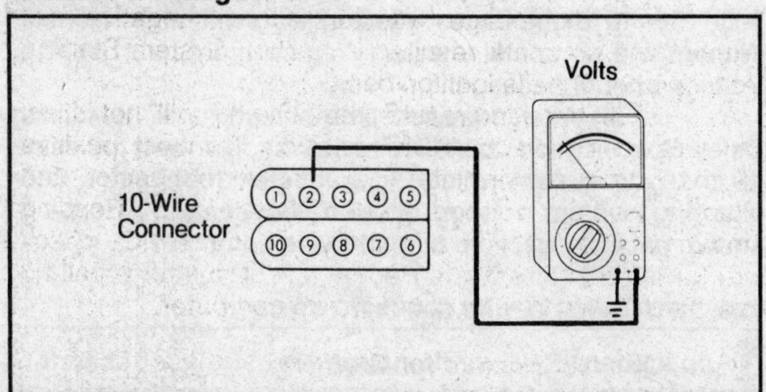

8) If voltage at terminal 2 was correct, turn ignition switch off. Using an ohmmeter, check continuity between terminal 7 of 10-wire connector and carburetor switch terminal. *See Fig. 11.* Continuity should exist. If not, check wire between connections for opens, shorts or poor connections. If continuity is present, use an ohmmeter with leads attached to terminal 10 and engine ground to check continuity of ground circuit. *See Fig. 12.* If there is continuity, replace computer. If there is no continuity, check wire from terminal 10 to ground. Recheck continuity between terminal 7 of 10-wire connector and carburetor switch. Try to start engine. If engine fails to start, proceed to next step.

Fig. 11: Ohmmeter Hookup for Checking Carburetor Switch Wiring Harness

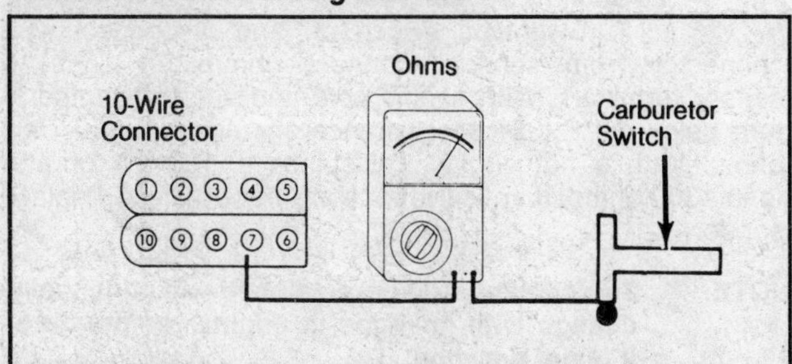

Fig. 12: Ohmmeter Hookup for Checking Computer Ground Circuit

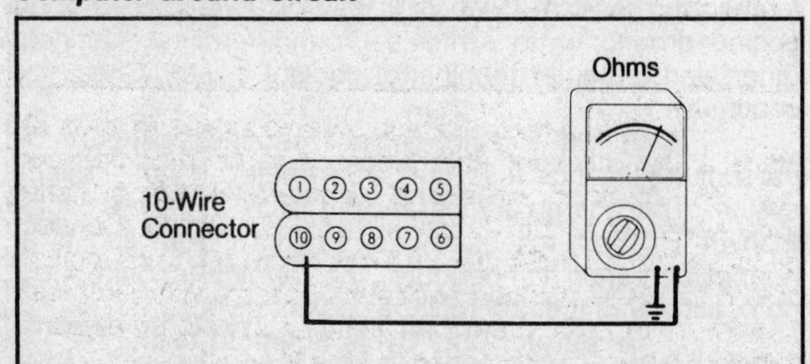

9) Turn ignition switch off. Attach ohmmeter leads to terminals 5 and 9 of 10-wire harness connector to check run pick-up coil resistance and to terminals 3 and 9 to check start pick-up coil resistance. *See Fig. 13.*

Fig. 13: Ohmmeter Hookup for Checking Pick-Up Coil Resistance

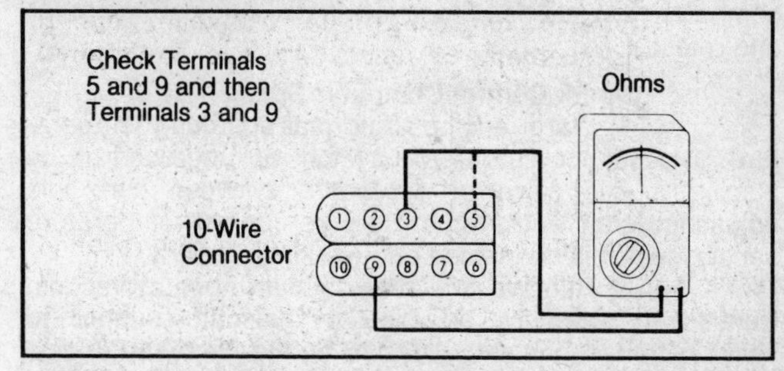

Resistance should be 150-900 ohms. If so, proceed to step **11)**.

10) If not, disconnect distributor connectors and attach ohmmeter leads to run pick-up coil leads and then to start pick-up coil leads coming from distributor. If resistance is now okay, wiring harness is defective. If resistance is still not 150-900 ohms, replace pick-up coils, as necessary.

11) Next, connect one lead of an ohmmeter to engine ground and touch other lead to each terminal of leads coming from 2 distributor pick-up coils. There should be no continuity. If continuity is indicated, replace pick-up coil.

12) Remove distributor cap and rotor and check reluctor-to-pick-up coil(s) air gap. Air gap for single pick-up coil distributor should be .006" (.15 mm). On dual pick-up distributors, air gap should be .006" (.15 mm) for start pick-up coil and .012" (.30 mm) for run pick-up coil. If not to specification, adjust gap using a non-magnetic feeler gauge. *See Fig. 14.*

Fig. 14: Checking Distributor Pick-Up Air Gap

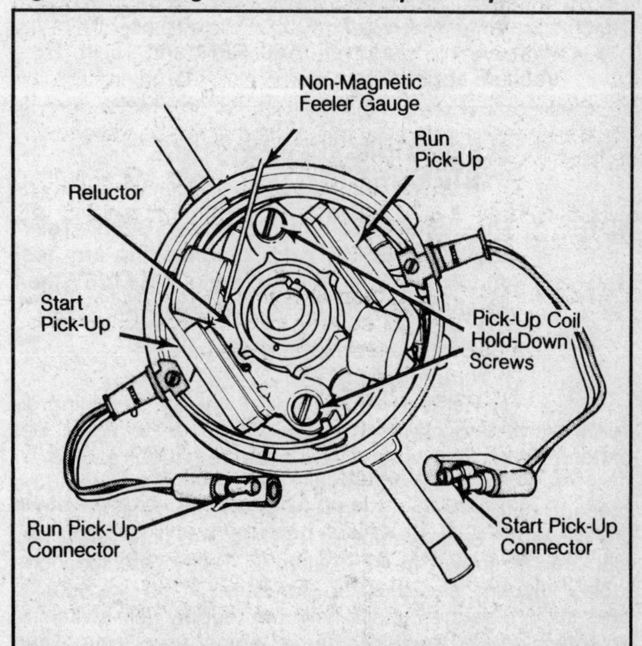

NOTE: **To adjust gap, loosen pick-up coil hold-down screws, move pick-up coil against feeler gauge, resting against reluctor tooth. Tighten hold-down screw, remove feeler gauge and recheck gap.**

CHRYSLER CORP. ELECTRONIC FUEL CONTROL (Cont.)

13) Install distributor cap and reinstall all wiring. If engine fails to start, replace spark control computer. If it still fails to start, install original computer and retest.

Spark Control Computer Spark Test

1) Warm engine to normal operating temperature. Disconnect carburetor switch or unground it by placing a thin piece of cardboard between curb idle adjusting screw and switch. Be sure coolant temperature sensor/switch is connected and working properly.

2) Remove and plug vacuum hose at vacuum transducer. Connect an auxiliary vacuum supply to vacuum transducer and apply 16 in. Hg. Increase engine speed to 1500 RPM and wait 1 minute before checking specifications. Advance specifications are in addition to basic advance. *See Spark Advance Test Specifications table.*

3) If computer fails to obtain settings, replace computer.

NOTE: The 3.7L engine is equipped with an accumulator (timer). The carburetor switch MUST be ungrounded for 30 seconds before checking specified spark advance schedule.

SPARK ADVANCE TEST SPECIFICATIONS

Application	Computer No.	Spark Advance [1]
3.7L		
Fed.	4289058	10-18°
Calif.	4289061	4-12°
5.2L		
Fed.		
2-Bbl.	4289063	26-34°
4-Bbl.	4145996	14-22°
Calif.	4289065	26-34°

[1] — With engine speed at 1500 RPM and 16 in. Hg Vacuum applied.

ELECTRONIC FUEL CONTROL SYSTEM TESTS

NOTE: The "Spark Control Computer Spark Test" should be tested prior to beginning any test on EFC system. The following test MUST then be performed in the sequence given.

Air Switching System Diagnosis (Vacuum Supply)

1) Remove vacuum hose for air switching/diverter valve and connect a vacuum gauge to hose. Set parking brake. Start engine and observe gauge reading.

2) On a cold engine, engine vacuum should be present until engine coolant temperature reaches 60°F (16°C). When temperature is reached and time delay has elapsed as shown in Air Switching Delay Specifications table, vacuum should drop to zero. If no vacuum is present on gauge, check vacuum supply air switching solenoid, coolant switch, charge temperature switch and computer wiring and connections. If all check okay, computer may be defective, preventing air switching function. Proceed to step **4)**.

3) On a warm engine, vacuum should be present for the specified time shown in the Air Switching Delay Specifications table after engine starts, then drop to zero. If there is no vacuum, check vacuum supply, air switching solenoid, coolant switch, charge temperature switch and computer wiring and connections. If all check okay, computer may be defective, preventing air switching function. Proceed to step **4)**.

4) If no vacuum was recorded in step **2)** and **3)** and all components are operating properly, connect a voltmeter to Light Green wire on air switching solenoid. With engine at normal operating temperature, start engine. Voltage should be less than 1 volt.

5) After specified time shown in Air Switching Delay Specifications table, voltmeter should read the same as charging system voltage. If voltmeter does not register charging system voltage or charging system voltage is shown prior to specified time, replace computer.

AIR SWITCHING DELAY SPECIFICATIONS

Application	Computer No.	Delay (Seconds)
3.7L		
Fed.	4289058	60
Calif.	4289061	60
5.2L		
Fed.		
2-Bbl.	4289063	0
4-Bbl.	4145996	0
Calif.	4289065	0

Air Switching Diagnosis (Air Switching Valve)

1) Remove air supply hose from air switching valve. Remove vacuum hose from valve and install an auxiliary vacuum supply.

2) Set parking brake. Start engine. Air should blow out of side port. Apply vacuum to valve. Air should blow out bottom port.

Coolant Sensor Test

Turn ignition switch off and disconnect wire connector from sensor. Connect ohmmeter leads to sensor terminals. With engine cold and ambient temperature below 90°F (32°C), resistance should read 500-1000 ohms. With a hot engine, resistance should be greater than 1300 ohms. If specifications are not obtained, replace sensor.

NOTE: The coolant sensor resistance will continually change with changes in engine temperature. It is not a switch.

Charge Temperature & Coolant Switch

1) Turn ignition off and disconnect wire from temperature switch. Connect 1 lead of ohmmeter to good engine ground or to switch's ground terminal. Connect other lead to center terminal of coolant switch. Check for continuity.

2) On a cold engine, continuity should be present (resistance less than 100 ohms). If not, replace switch. The charge temperature switch must be cooler than 60°F (16°C) to obtain this reading. On an engine at normal operating temperature, the terminal should show no continuity. If it does, replace coolant switch.

Carburetor Duty Cycle Solenoid Test

1) Remove and plug vacuum hose at vacuum transducer. Connect a tachometer. Connect an auxiliary vacuum supply to vacuum transducer and apply 16 in. Hg. Set parking brake and start engine. Allow engine to reach normal operating temperature. DO NOT ground carburetor switch. Run engine at 1500 RPM.

CHRYSLER CORP. ELECTRONIC FUEL CONTROL (Cont.)

NOTE: After any hot start, maintain 1500 RPM for at least 2 minutes before proceeding with test.

2) Disconnect duty cycle solenoid connector at solenoid. Average engine speed should increase a minimum of 50 RPM. Reconnect solenoid connector. Engine speed should slowly return to 1500 RPM.

3) Disconnect 12-pin connector at computer. Connect a ground to harness connector pin 11. Engine speed should decrease a minimum of 50 RPM. If engine speed does not change as outlined, service carburetor (check for air leaks).

Electronic Fuel Control Computer Test

1) Connect a tachometer and set parking brake. Start engine, warm to normal operating temperature and maintain engine speed of 1500 RPM. DO NOT ground carburetor switch. Connect a voltmeter to duty cycle solenoid output wire going to carburetor (Green wire).

NOTE: Do not separate the solenoid connector from the wiring harness.

2) Disconnect electrical connector at oxygen sensor and connect a jumper to a good ground. Engine speed should increase at least 50 RPM and voltmeter should indicate more than 9 volts.

3) Hold the jumper wire with 1 hand and with the other hand, touch the battery positive terminal with the jumper wire. Engine speed should decrease at least 50 RPM and voltmeter should indicate less than 3 volts. If computer fails both tests, replace it. Reconnect oxygen sensor harness.

CAUTION: Before performing the next test, the fuel control computer must be operating properly.

Oxygen Sensor Test

1) Set parking brake and connect tachometer. Run engine at 1500 RPM and connect voltmeter to carburetor-to-computer output wire (Green). DO NOT ground carburetor switch. Hold choke blade closed. During the next 10 seconds, the voltage should decrease to 3 volts or less and maintain that level. If engine does not respond, proceeed to step **2)**.

2) Disconnect PCV system. During the next 10 seconds, the voltage should increase to 9 volts or greater and maintain that level until vacuum hose is reconnected. If sensor fails both tests, replace it. Reconnect all hoses and wires.

NOTE: This test should not be performed for more than 90 seconds.

POOR PERFORMANCE TESTS

NOTE: Be sure basic timing and hot curb idle speed are set to specifications before performing these tests.

Carburetor Switch Test

1) Turn ignition off and disconnect 10-wire connector from computer. With throttle completely closed, check continuity with ohmmeter leads connected to cavity 7 and ground.

NOTE: Grounding carburetor switch eliminates all spark advance on systems.

2) If no continuity is read, check wire from cavity 7 to carburetor switch terminal. Also check carburetor switch for proper operation.

3) Open throttle and again check for continuity from cavity 7 to ground. There should be none.

NOTE: After performing carburetor switch test, perform tests on the spark control system and fuel control system.

ELECTRONIC THROTTLE CONTROL SYSTEM TEST

1) Connect a tachometer to engine. Start and run engine until normal operating temperature is obtained. On vehicle without air conditioning, depress and release accelerator. An RPM higher than curb idle speed should be seen for specified time shown in EGR and Throttle Control Specifications table.

2) On vehicles equipped with air conditioning or rear window defogger, turning on the air conditioner or defogger and depressing accelerator for a moment should give an RPM higher than curb idle speed. Turning off the air conditioner or rear window defogger will result in normal idle speed.

NOTE: The air conditioning clutch will cycle on and off as it is running. DO NOT mistake this for electronic throttle control operation.

3) On all vehicles, if speed increases do not occur as outlined above, turn engine off and disconnect 3-wire connector at carburetor (idle stop solenoid and duty cycle solenoid). Using an ohmmeter, check the resistance of the solenoid by measuring from the 3-wire connector containing the Black wire to ground. Resistance should be 15-35 ohms. If not, replace idle stop solenoid.

4) On vehicles without air conditioning or rear window defogger, start vehicle and before specified time has elapsed, measure voltage at Black wire of 3-wire connector. Voltmeter reading should equal charging system voltage. If voltmeter reading does not equal charging system voltage, replace the Gray starter timer on 3.7L Federal models. On all other models, replace the computer.

5) On air conditioned vehicles, start engine and turn on air conditioner. Measure voltage at Black wire of 3-wire connector. Voltmeter reading should equal charging system voltage AFTER specified time has elapsed. If not, check wiring back to instrument panel for an open circuit.

ELECTRONIC EGR SYSTEM TEST

NOTE: The engine temperature sensors must be working properly before performing this test.

1) With the engine temperature cold and ignition switch off, connect a voltmeter between Gray wire on EGR solenoid and ground. Start engine. Voltage should read less than 1 volt. This reading should be maintained until normal operating temperature is reached and specified time has elapsed as shown in EGR and Throttle Control Specifications table.

2) After normal operating temperature is reached and specified time has elapsed, voltmeter should register charging system voltage. If readings are not obtained as outlined, replace EGR solenoid and repeat

CHRYSLER CORP. ELECTRONIC FUEL CONTROL (Cont.)

test. If the voltmeter indicates charging system voltage before specified time elapses, replace computer.

NOTE: **If an engine is restarted while still at normal operating temperature, the voltmeter reading should register 1 volt for the specified time, then register charging system voltage.**

EGR & THROTTLE CONTROL SPECIFICATIONS

Application	Computer No.	Delay (Seconds)
3.7L		
Fed.	4289058	65
Calif.	4289061	65
5.2L		
Fed.		
2-Bbl.	4289063	60
4-Bbl.	4145996	60
Calif.	4289065	60

ELECTRONIC AIR SWITCHING TESTS

NOTE: **Follow the test procedure for Air Switching System Diagnosis (Vacuum Supply and Air Switching Valve) described in ELECTRONIC FUEL CONTROL SYSTEM TESTS.**

DETONATION SENSOR TEST

NOTE: **This test applies to 5.2L engines only.**

1) Connect a variable timing light to engine. Start engine and run it on second highest step of fast idle cam (about 1200 RPM). Connect an auxiliary vacuum supply of 16 in. Hg vacuum.

2) Using a small wrench, tap lightly on manifold, near the sensor. With timing light, look for a decrease in spark advance. The amount of timing decrease should be in proportion to the strength and frequency of the tapping. Maximum decrease in timing should be 11°. Turn engine off and remove timing light.

REMOVAL & INSTALLATION

SPARK CONTROL COMPUTER

NOTE: **Do not remove grease from either harness connectors or connector cavities in computer. The grease is used in order to prevent moisture from corroding the terminals. If there is not at least ½" of grease on bottom of computer connector cavities, apply a liberal amount of Mopar multipurpose grease No. 2932524 (or equivalent) over entire end of plug before reinstalling.**

Removal & Installation

Remove negative battery terminal. Disconnect 10-wire and 12-wire connectors from computer. Remove vacuum hose from vacuum transducer. Remove mounting screws from inside air cleaner and remove computer. To install, reverse removal procedure.

Fig. 15: Wiring Diagram for 3.7L and 5.2L EFC System

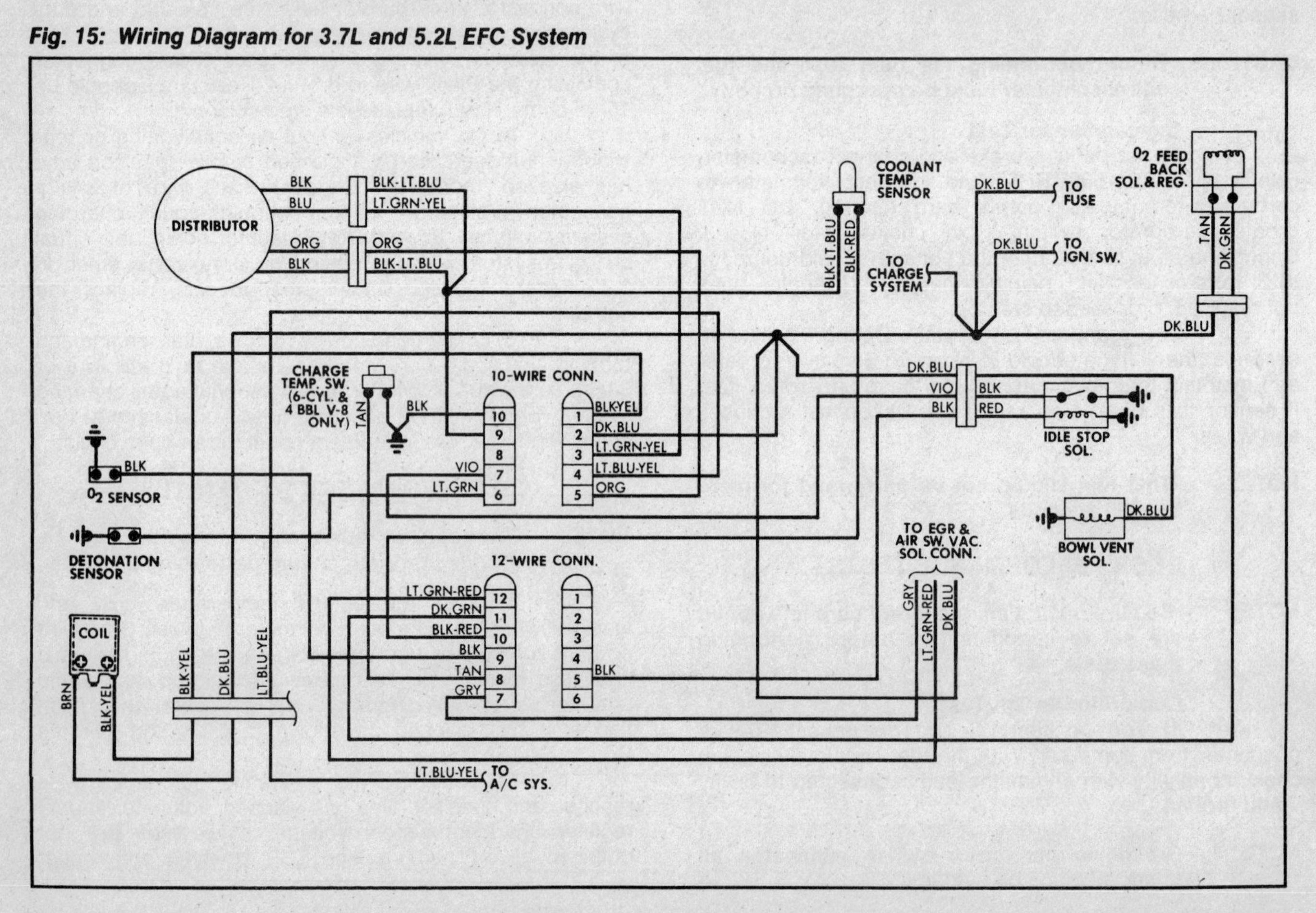

CHRYSLER CORP. ELECTRONIC FUEL CONTROL (Cont.)

NOTE: Computer is not serviceable. Do not attempt to take it apart for any reason. Also, if the vacuum transducer becomes defective, entire computer must be replaced.

CARBURETOR SWITCH

Removal & Installation

Remove bracket and switch assembly from carburetor. Disconnect electrical connector. To install, reverse removal procedure and adjust if necessary.

DUTY CYCLE SOLENOID

Removal & Installation

Disconnect electrical connector. Remove retaining screws, duty cycle solenoid and gasket. To install, reverse removal procedure.

OXYGEN SENSOR

Removal & Installation

Disconnect battery cable and electrical lead at sensor. Remove sensor. To install, coat threads of new sensor with nickel-based anti-seize compound. Do not use graphite or other compounds. Hand-start sensor, then tighten to 35 ft. lb. (48 N.m). Connect electrical connector and battery cable.

CHRYSLER CORP. 2.2L EFI ENGINE CONTROL SYSTEM

All Models With 2.2L EFI

NOTE: Information on this system is also covered in the FUEL SYSTEMS Section. Additional diagnostic information that relates strictly to the fuel portion of this system can be found in the CHRYSLER CORP. THROTTLE BODY FUEL INJECTION article.

DESCRIPTION

The computerized engine control system used on 2.2L fuel injected engines controls 3 areas of engine operation. These areas are the fuel system, the ignition system, and the emission control system. In order to control these systems, several engine and vehicle operating conditions must be monitred.

The engine conditions that need to be monitored include: manifold pressure, throttle position, engine temperature, manifold air temperature, exhaust gas oxygen content, and engine speed. Vehicle conditions monitored include vehicle speed and the status (off or on) of several vehicle systems that affect engine load.

The engine control computer consists of 2 separate modules. The logic module processes all sensor inputs and controls all low power output devices. The logic module also controls the power module. The power module controls the injector, ignition coil, and the auto shutdown relay.

OPERATION

The computerized engine control system consists of 6 sub-systems: computer, sensors and switches, fuel control, ignition, emission control, and air conditioning compressor cut out.

COMPUTER

The computer is divided into 2 modules. The logic module contains the operating software and performs the calculations and adjustments necessary for engine operation. This half of the computer is located inside the passenger compartment behind the right front kick panel.

The logic module is a microprocessor based digital computer. This module receives input signals from various switches, sensors, and other components. Using these signals, the microprocessor computes the fuel injector pulse width, spark advance, ignition coil dwell, automatic idle speed actuation, canister purge, and EGR control solenoid cycles.

The logic module also contains a diagnostic circuit to test input and output circuits. The diagnostic circuit will store information about any malfunctions as they occur for readout prior to service.

The second part of the computer is the power module. The power module contains the power supply and the control circuits for the fuel injector, the ignition system, and the automatic shutdown relay.

Fig. 1: Schematic Diagram of Computer, Input Sensors and Output Devices

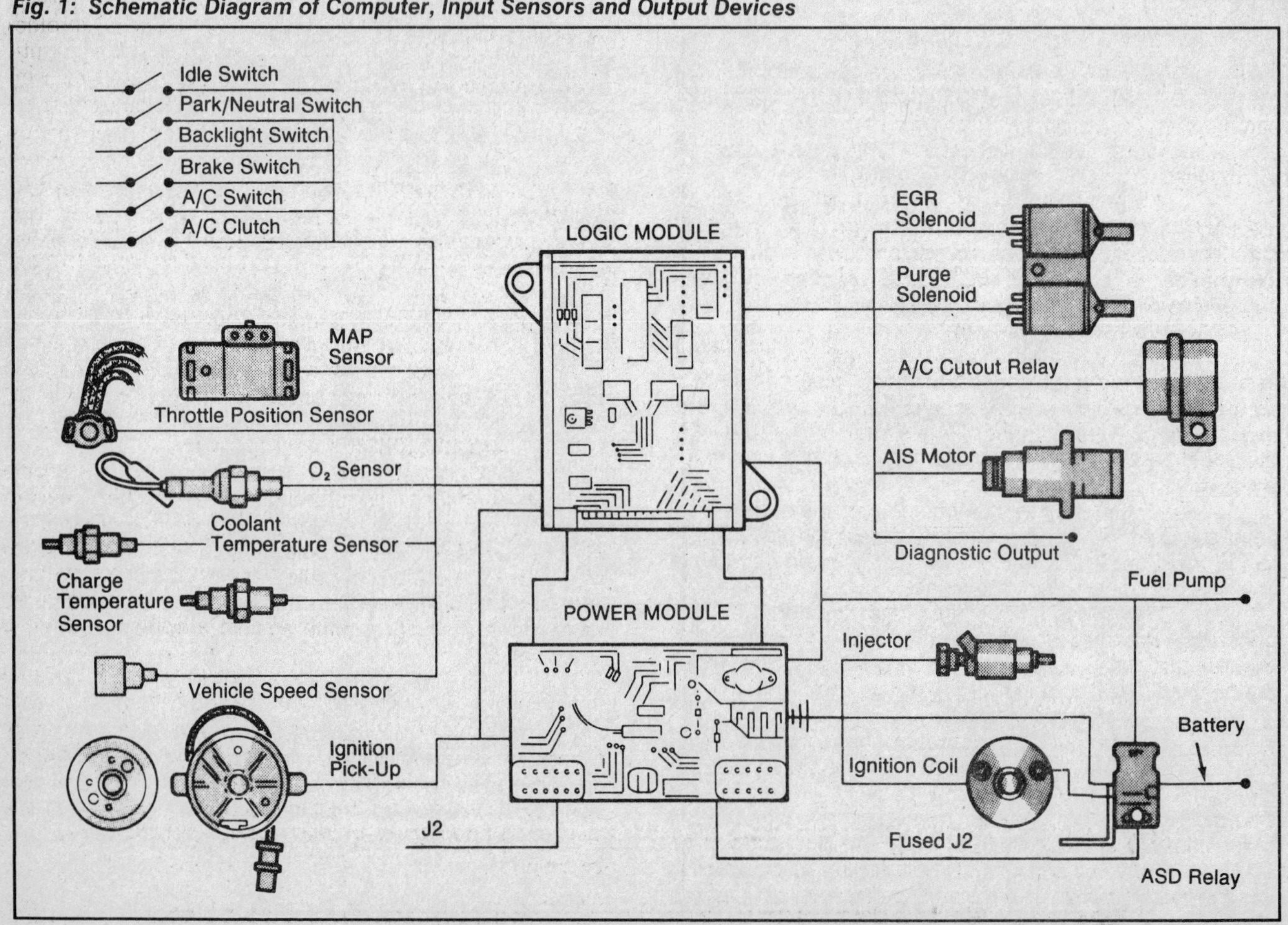

CHRYSLER CORP. 2.2L EFI ENGINE CONTROL SYSTEM (Cont.)

The power module is located in the engine compartment because the high current draw of the devices being controlled can cause electrical noise which must be isolated from the logic module. The power module is controlled by the logic module.

Fig. 2: Location of Logic Module, Sensor and Relay

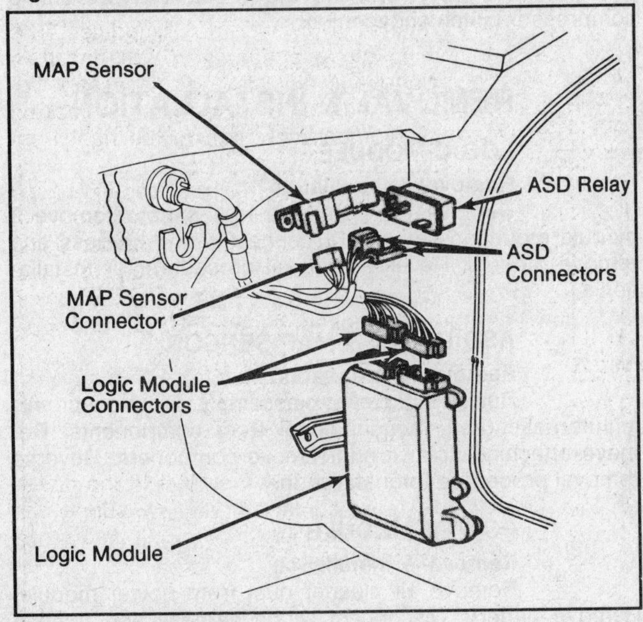

SENSORS & SWITCHES

Manifold Absolute Pressure (MAP) Sensor

The MAP sensor is located in the passenger compartment, just above the logic module. The MAP sensor monitors manifold vacuum. This is acomplished via a vacuum line fron the throttle body to the sensor.

The sensor supplies the logic module with an electrical signal which keeps the module informed of manifold vacuum conditions and barometrc pressure. This information is combined with data supplied by other sensors to determine correct air/fuel ratio.

Oxygen (O_2) Sensor

The O_2 sensor is screwed into the top of the exhaust manifold, just ahead of the tail-pipe connection, so that it is exposed to exhaust gas flow. Its function is to monitor the oxygen content of the exhaust, and to supply the logic module with a voltage signal which is directly proportional to this content.

If the oxygen content of the exhaust is high (lean air/fuel mixture), the voltage signal from the sensor to the logic module is low. As oxygen content decreases (mixture becomes richer), the signal voltage increases.

In this manner, the logic module is kept constantly informed of air/fuel ratio. It can then alter fuel injector "on" time, in response to these signals, to obtain the best air/fuel ratio under any given condition.

Temperature Sensors

There are 2 temperature sensors utilized in this system. One, the Coolant Temperature Sensor, measures temperature of engine coolant. The other, the Charge Temperature Sensor, measures the temperature of the incoming air/fuel mixture.

The coolant temperature sensor is mounted in the thermostat housing to monitor engine coolant (operating) temperature. It supplies the logic module with a voltage signal which varies with coolant temperature. The charge temperature sensor, mounted in the intake manifold, supplies the logic module with information on the temperature of the incoming air/fuel mixture.

Information provided by these 2 sensors allows the logic module to demand slightly richer air/fuel mixtures and higher idle speeds during cold engine operation. Lastly, if the coolant temperature switch should malfunction, information supplied by the charge temperature sensor is sufficient to determine engine operating temperature and engine warm-up cycles until the coolant temperature sensor can be repaired or replaced.

Throttle Position Sensor (TPS)

The TPS is a variable resistor which is operated by the movement of the throttle shaft. It is mounted on the throttle body and senses the angle of throttle blade opening.

A voltage signal is produced by the sensor which varies with this angle. This signal is transmitted to the logic module where it is used to adjust air/fuel ratio during acceleration, deceleration, idle, and wide open throttle conditions.

Engine Switches

Several switches provide operating information to the logic module. These include the idle, neutral safety, electric backlight, air conditioning, air conditioning clutch, and brake light switches. If one or more of these switches is sensed as being in the "on" position, the logic module signals the AIS to increase idle speed to a specific RPM.

With the air conditioning on and the throttle blade above a specific angle, the wide open throttle cutout relay prevents the air conditioning clutch from engaging until the throttle blade angle is reduced.

FUEL CONTROL

Fuel Supply

An electric fuel pump is located in the fuel tank as an integral part of the fuel gauge sending unit. This pump supplies fuel, at 36 psi (2.5 kg/cm²) pressure, to the throttle body assembly.

Power to the fuel pump is supplied by the power module via the Automatic Shut-Down (ASD) relay. The power module is supplied with an operating signal from the distributor. If this signal is not received, the ASD relay is not activated and power to the fuel pump is cut off.

Fuel Injector

The fuel injector is mounted in the throttle body so that fuel from the injector is directed into the incoming air stream. While power to the injector is supplied by the power module, it is controlled by indirect signal from the logic module. When electric current is supplied to the injector, an integral armature and pintle valve move a short distance against a spring, opening a small orifice.

Fuel supplied to the injector is forced around the pintle valve and through this opening, resulting in a fine spray of fuel in the shape of a hollow cone. Whereas a constant pressure drop is maintained across the injector (by the pressure regulator), the length of time that this opening is maintained (injector "on" time) determines the amount of fuel entering the engine and, therefore, the air/fuel ratio.

CHRYSLER CORP. 2.2L EFI ENGINE CONTROL SYSTEM (Cont.)

Fig. 3: Cross-Sectional View of Fuel Injector

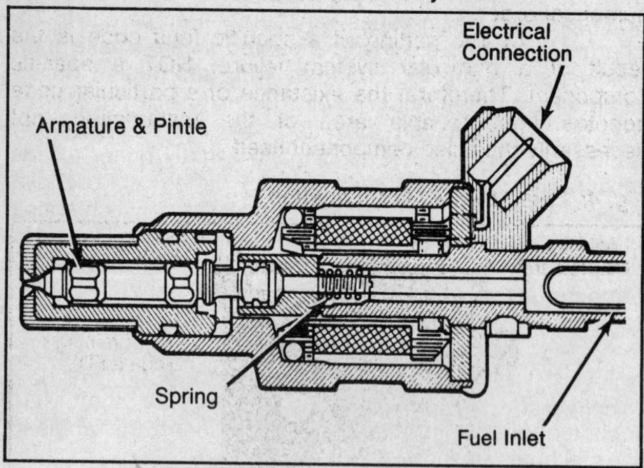

Automatic Idle Speed Motor (AIS)

The AIS is mounted on the throttle body assembly and is controlled by electrical signal from the logic module. The logic module uses sensor input to determine optimum engine idle speed for any idle condition.

The AIS is then adjusted to allow a specific amount of air through an air bypass on the back of the throttle body. This bypass is enlarged or restricted as an increase or decrease in engine idle speed is required to meet varying engine operating conditions.

This results in a change in air/fuel ratio, which alters the oxygen content of the exhaust gases as detected by the O_2 sensor. The logic module then changes the amount of fuel introduced into the intake charge to maintain an ideal air/fuel ratio.

IGNITION

The pick-up coil in the distributor feeds a signal to the power module and the logic module. Spark advance, dwell and timing are computed in the logic module. The logic module sends a signal back to the power module where the coil ground is switched off and on to create an ignition secondary pulse.

EMISSION CONTROL

Exhaust Gas Recirculation Solenoid

The EGR solenoid is operated by the logic module. When engine temperature is below 70°F (21°C), the logic module energizes the solenoid by completing the ground circuit. This closes the solenoid valve and prevents ported vacuum from reaching the EGR valve. When the predetermined temperature is reached, the logic module will break the ground circuit, which opens the valve allowing vacuum to reach the EGR valve. The solenoid valve is also closed, preventing EGR operation, during idle and wide open throttle operation.

Purge Solenoid

The purge solenoid operates in a manner similar to the EGR solenoid. Whe engine temperature is below 160°F (71°C), the logic module completes the ground circuit for the purge solenoid. This closes the solenoid valve, preventing vacuum from reaching the charcoal canister valve. When this temperature is reached, the logic module breaks the ground circuit allowing vacuum to reach the canister purge valve so that fuel vapors may be purged from the canister.

A/C COMPRESSOR CUT OUT

The air conditioning cut out relay is wired in series with the cycling clutch switch and low pressure cut out switch. This relay is normally closed during engine operation. When the logic module senses a wide open throttle condition through the throttle position sensor, it energizes the relay, opening the circuit and preventing compressor clutch engagement.

REMOVAL & INSTALLATION

LOGIC MODULE

Removal & Installation

Remove the right side kick panel. Remove 2 module mounting screws. Disconnect wiring harness and remove module. Reverse removal procedure for installation.

ASD RELAY & MAP SENSOR

Removal & Installation

Remove glove box assembly. Disconnect wiring harness (and vacuum hose) from components. Remove attaching screws and remove component. Reverse removal procedure for installation.

POWER MODULE

Removal & Installation

Remove air cleaner duct from power module. Remove battery. Disconnect wiring harness and remove attaching screws. Remove module from vehicle. Reverse removal procedure for installation.

OXYGEN SENSOR

Removal & Installation

The oxygen sensor is located in the exhaust manifold. Use of a special wrench (C-4589) may aid in removal of the sensor. The threads in the exhaust manifold must be cleaned with a 18 mm x 1.5 x 6E tap prior to reinsertion of the sensor. If the old sensor is being reinstalled, the threads on the sensor must be coated with anti-seize compound. The sensor should be tightened to 20 ft. lbs. (27 N.m).

TESTING & DIAGNOSIS

PRELIMINARY CHECKS

Most driveability problems in the engine control system result from faulty or poor wiring, or loose and/or leaking hose connections. To avoid unnecessary component testing, a visual check should be performed before beginning trouble shooting procedures to help spot these common faults. A preliminary visual check should include:

- Air ducts to air cleaner and from air cleaner to throttle body.
- Electrical connections at all components. Clean, tight and unbroken.

Check vacuum lines for secure, leak-free connections in these areas:

- Throttle body (2 front, 2 rear).
- EGR and purge solenoids (located on a common bracket at right rear corner of engine compartment).
- Vapor canister.

CHRYSLER CORP. 2.2L EFI ENGINE CONTROL SYSTEM (Cont.)

- PCV valve to intake manifold vacuum port.
- Back pressure transducer.
- MAP sensor.

Ensure that the following electrical connectors are securely attached:

- 21-way connectors (2) at logic module (Black connector to Black socket, Tan connector to Tan socket).
- 3-way connector at MAP sensor.
- 3-way and 1-way connectors at ASD Relay.
- 12-way and 10-way connectors at power module.
- 3-way connector at EGR and purge solenoids.
- 2-way connector at speed sensor (located in line with speedometer cable).
- 2-way connector at charge temperature sensor.
- 6-way connector at AIS motor and TPS (and ground wire to manifold).
- 2-way connector at fuel injector.
- O_2 connector.
- 2-way connector at coolant temperature sensor.
- 3-way connector at distributor.

SYSTEM DIAGNOSIS

The self-diagnostic capabilities of this system, if properly utilized, can greatly simplify testing.

If, at any time, the logic module receives an incorrect signal or no signal from either the Coolant Temperature Sensor, MAP sensor or TPS, a Power Loss Lamp on the instrument panel is illuminated. This lamp acts as a warning device to inform the operator that a malfunction in the system has occured and immediate service is required.

When certain malfunctions occur, the logic module enters the "Limp In Mode". In this mode, the logic module attempts to compensate for the failure of the particular component by substituting information from other sources. Ideally, this will allow the vehicle to be operated until proper repairs can be made.

If the Power Loss Lamp comes on, or if certain driveability or engine performance difficulties exist, the probable source of these difficulties may be determined by entering "On Board Diagnosis" and recording the fault codes as they are displayed.

Once these codes are known, refer to the fault codes listing to determine the questionable circuit. Then use the wiring diagram and connector identification charts to locate testing points for each circuit. With the ignition on, the wire(s) in question should read as specified under Wire Function in tables. Test circuits and repair or replace as needed.

ENTERING ON-BOARD DIAGNOSIS

1) Attach the Chrysler Diagnostic Readout Tool (C-4805) to self-test connector. The connector is located in the engine compartment near the right side strut tower. If this test box is not available, codes may be read off of the flashing light emitting diode (LED) on the logic module.

2) Start engine (if possible). Move transmission shift lever through all positions, ending in Park. Turn A/C switch on, then off (if present).

3) Stop the engine and, without starting it again, turn the key on, off, on, off and on. Record fault codes as displayed on Diagnostic Readout, or by counting flashes of the LED.

4) Codes displayed by the LED are indicated by a series of flashes. For example, code 23 is displayed as flash, flash, pause, flash, flash, flash. After a slightly longer pause, any other codes stored are displayed in numerical order.

5) The setting of a specific fault code is the result of a particular system failure, NOT a specific component. Therefore, the existance of a particular code denotes the probable area of the malfunction, not necessarily the failed component itself.

Fig. 4: Logic Module LED Location

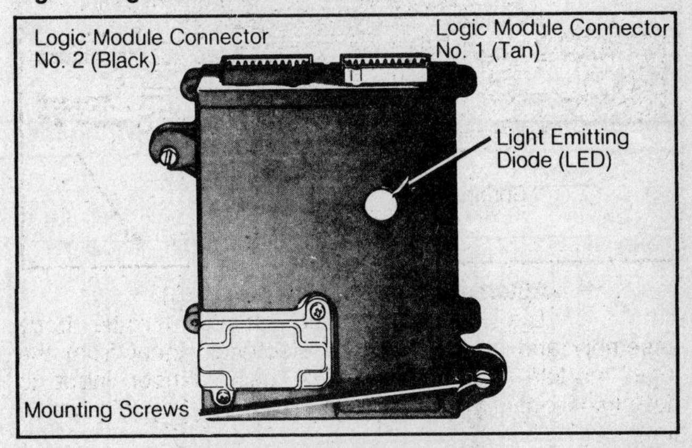

FAULT CODES

The Chrysler Throttle Body Fuel Injection system is equipped with a self-diagnostic capability which stores certain "fault codes" in the logic module when system malfunctions occur. These codes may be recalled to aid in system diagnosis. The following list presents these codes and the system malfunctions which they represent.

Code 11

Problem with distributor circuit. No distributor signal to logic module since restoration of battery voltage.

Code 13

Problem with MAP sensor pneumatic system. Appears if sensor vacuum level does not change between start and start/run transfer speed (500-600 RPM).

Code 14

Problem with MAP sensor electrical system. MAP sensor signal outside of .02-4.9 volt range..

Code 15

Problem with Speed Sensor circuit. Engine speed above 1470 RPM, sensor indicates less than 2 MPH. Code valid only if sensed while vehicle is moving.

Code 21

Problem with O_2 Sensor feedback circuit. Occurs if engine temperature is above 170°F (77°C), engine speed is above 1500 RPM, but O_2 sensor stays rich or lean for more than 60 seconds.

Code 22

Problem with Coolant Temperature Sensor circuit. Appears if the temperature sensor indicates an incorrect temperature or a temperature that changes too fast to be real.

Code 23

Problem with Charge Temperature Sensor circuit. Appears if the charge temperature sensor indicates an incorrect temperature or a temperature that changes too fast to be real.

Code 24

Problem with TPS circuit. Appears if the sensor signal is either below .16 volts or above 4.7 volts.

CHRYSLER CORP. 2.2L EFI ENGINE CONTROL SYSTEM (Cont.)

Code 25

Problem with AIS control circuit. Appears if proper voltage from AIS system is not present. An open harness or motor will not activate this code.

Code 31

Problem with Canister Purge Solenoid circuit. Appears when the proper voltage at the purge solenoid is not present (open or shorted system).

Code 32

Problem with Power Loss Lamp circuit. Appears when proper voltage to the circuit is not present (open or shorted system).

Code 33

Open or shorted circuit at air conditioning WOT cut-out relay circuit.

Code 34

Open or shorted circuit at EGR solenoid.

Code 41

Problem with charging system. Appears if battery voltage from the ASD relay is below 11.75 volts.

Code 42

Problem in the ASD relay circuit. Appears if, during cranking, battery voltage from ASD relay is not present for at least 1/3 of a second after first distributor

Fig. 5: Chrysler Corp. Engine Control System Wiring Diagram

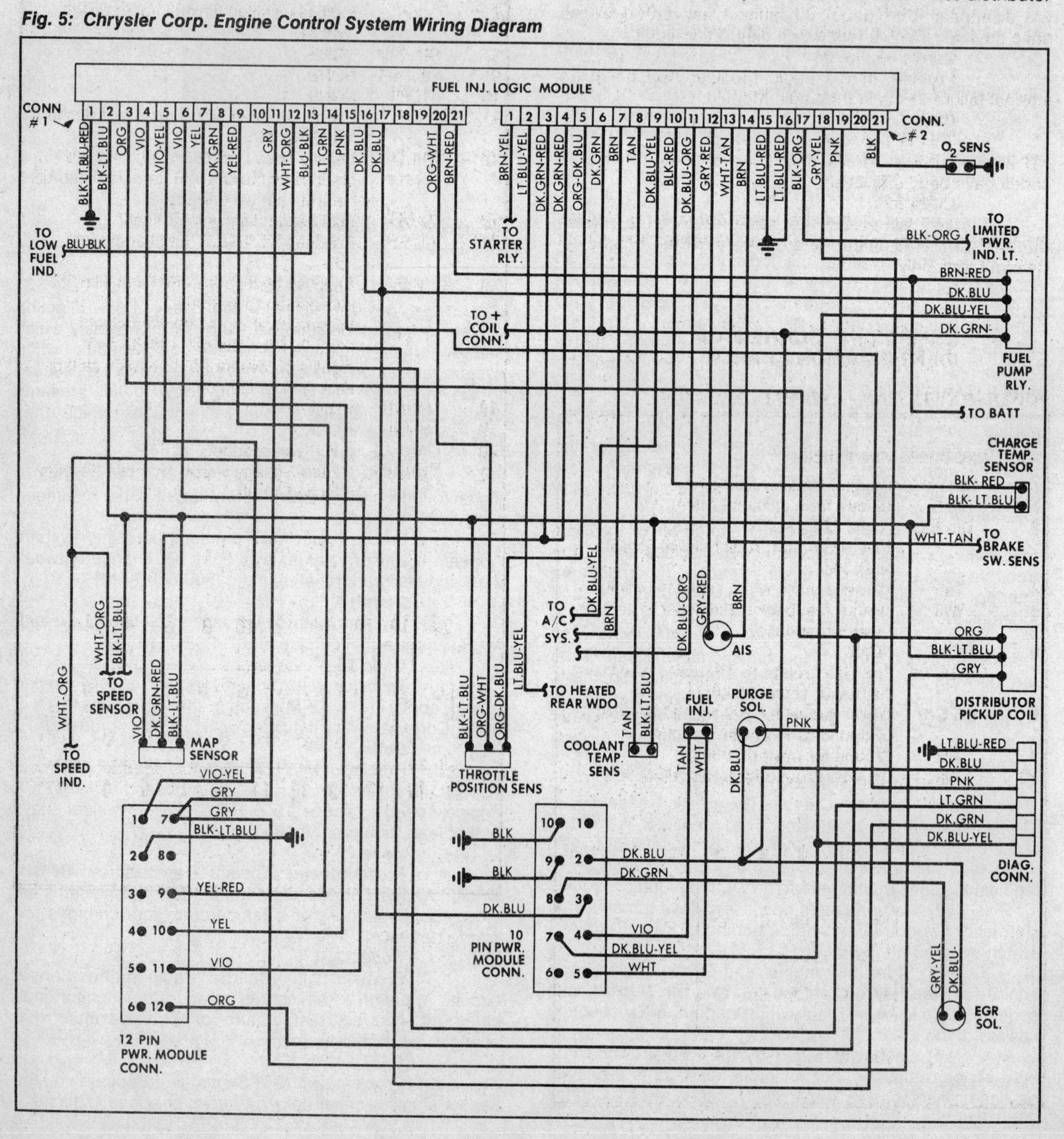

CHRYSLER CORP. 2.2L EFI ENGINE CONTROL SYSTEM (Cont.)

pulse, or if battery voltage is present for more than 3 seconds after engine stalls (last distributor pulse).

Code 43

Problem in the interface circuit. Appears if the anit-dwell or injector control signal is not present between the logic module and power module.

Code 44

Problem in the Logic Module. Appears if an internal failure exists in the logic module.

Code 51

Problem in Standby Memory. Appears if direct battery feed is interrupted to the logic module. This code will disappear after about 30 ignition key on/off cycles once the logic module receives a distributor signal.

Codes 52, 53, 54

Problem in the Logic Module. Appears if an internal failure exists in the Logic Module.

Code 55

This is the "end of message" code. This code will always appear as the final code after all other fault codes have been displayed.

Code 88

This will be the first code displayed. It implies the start of the message, and appears on the Diagnostic Readout tool, only.

COMPONENT CONNECTOR IDENTIFICATION CHARTS

POWER MODULE PINS — 10-PIN CONNECTOR

Pin No.	Wire Color	Wire Function
1	Blk/Yel	Triggers ignition coil (-).
2	Dk. Bl	J2 feed from ignition switch.
3	Dk. Bl	Fused J2 power to: Logic module to drive AIS motor; ASD relay to activate relay coil.
4	Tan	Provides pulse width signal to injector.
5	Wht	Injector feedback signal used to control injector response.
6	NONE	NONE
7	Dk. Bl/Yel	Provides ground to ASD relay when distributor signal present.
8	Dk. Grn	Power supply for spark and fuel drive components in power module.
9	Blk	Ground for power module.
10	Blk	Back-up ground for power module.

1 2 3 4 5

10 9 8 7 6

LOGIC MODULE PINS — CONNECTOR 1

Pin No.	Wire Color	Wire Function
1	Blk	Input ground to prevent "noise" on sensor signals.
2	Blk/Lt. Bl	Common ground for engine sensors.
3	Org	8 volt power supply from power module. Provides for 5 volt sensor supply.
4	Vio	5 volt power supply for MAP sensor.
5	Vio/Yel	Injector pulse width info. input.
6	Vio	NONE
7	Yel	Supplies ignition timing info. to power module.
8	Dk. Gry	NONE
9	Yel/Red	NONE
10	NONE	NONE
11	Gry	Distributor input signal. Provides timing and RPM info.
12	Wht/Org	Vehicle speed input. Provides vehicle stopped or moving info. to determine AIS control and fuel delivery.
13	Bl/Blk	Fuel gauge display information.
14	Lt. Grn	Provides for "HOLD" function on test box.
15	Pnk	Supplies fault codes and O_2 switching information to test box.
16 & 17	Dk. Bl	Fused power input (J2) from power module. Provides AIS voltage and signals processor not to accept sensor info. with ignition off.
18	NONE	NONE
19	NONE	NONE
20	Org/Wht	5 volt power supply for TPS.
21	Brn/Red	Battery voltage supply to retain memory with engine off.

20 18 16 14 12 10 8 6 4 2

21 19 17 15 13 11 9 7 5 3 1

CHRYSLER CORP. 2.2L EFI ENGINE CONTROL SYSTEM (Cont.)

LOGIC MODULE PINS — CONNECTOR 2

Pin No.	Wire Color	Wire Function
1	Brn/Yel	Neutral/Park switch input. Information modifies AIS control and timing at idle.
2	Lt Bl/Yel	Rear defrost input. AIS increases idle speed when extra engine load is sensed.
3	Dk Grn/Red	NONE
4	Dk Grn/Red	MAP sensor input. Provides engine load info., throttle limp-in as needed.
5	Org/Dk. Bl	TPS input. Informs logic module of wide open throttle. Provides signal to unload flooded engine and idle signal to adjust AIS position, timing, and fuel delivery rate. Informs logic module when MAP limp-in required.
6	Dk Grn	Battery voltage from ASD relay. Modifies pulse width in response to voltage variation.
7	Brn	A/C clutch input. Increases idle speed during A/C operation.
8	Tan	Coolant temp. sensor input. Modifies spark advance, injector pulse width, AIS control.
9	Dk. Bl/Yel	A/C switch input. Sets AIS at higher RPM in response to high engine loads.
10	Blk/Red	Charge temp. sensor input. Used for coolant temp. limp-in when needed.
11	Dk. Bl/Org	WOT relay output. Provides ground to shut off A/C clutch under wide open throttle conditions.
12	Gry/Red	AIS control output. Drive signal to AIS motor.
13	Wht/Tan	Brake switch input. Influences TPS position.
14	Brn	AIS control output. Drive signal to AIS motor.
15	Lt. Bl/Red	Power ground for logic module.
16	Lt. Bl/Red	Back-up power ground for logic module.
17	Blk/Org	Provides ground for POWER LOSS lamp on instrument panel when in limp-in mode.
18	Gry/Yel	Provides ground to activate EGR, or to turn EGR off when engine is cold.
19	Pnk	Provides ground to activate purge solenoid; removes canister purge when engine is cold.
20	NONE	NONE
21	Blk	O_2 sensor input. Provides logic module with O_2 sensor info. to modify fuel pulse width.

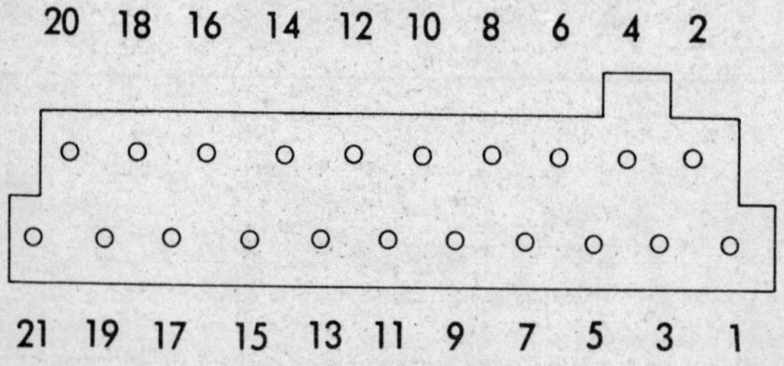

20 18 16 14 12 10 8 6 4 2

21 19 17 15 13 11 9 7 5 3 1

POWER MODULE PINS — 12-PIN CONNECTOR

Pin No.	Wire Color	Wire Function
1	Vio/Yel	Injector control input. Provides injector pulse width instructions from logic module.
2	Blk/Lt. Bl	Noise ground. Prevents "noise" on sensor signals.
3	NONE	NONE
4	NONE	NONE
5	NONE	NONE
6	NONE	NONE
7	Gray	Distributor signal input. Activates power module to supply ground for ASD relay.
8	NONE	NONE
9	Yel/Red	NONE
10	Yel	Anit-Dwell input. Receives spark advance info. from logic module.
11	Vio	NONE
12	Org	8 volt output. Supply voltage for Hall pick-up and logic module.

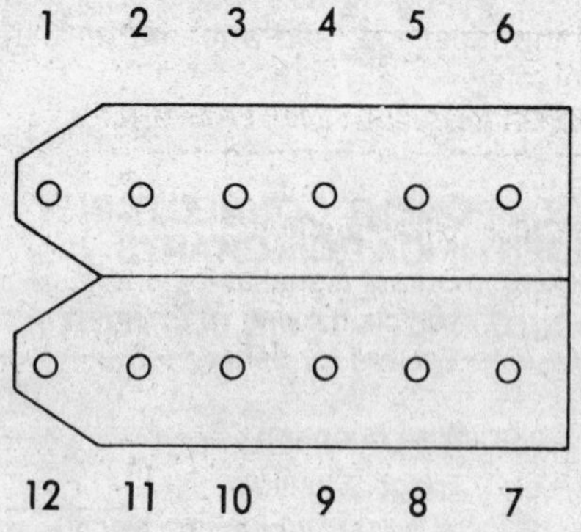

1 2 3 4 5 6

12 11 10 9 8 7

EGR/PURGE SOLENOID CONNECTOR TERMINALS

Pin No.	Wire Color	Wire Function
1	Gry/Yel	Ground through logic module to activate EGR solenoid or to remove EGR when engine is cold.
2	Pnk	Ground through logic module to activate purge solenoid, or to remove canister purge when engine is cold.
3	Dk. Bl	Voltage supply through ignition switch.

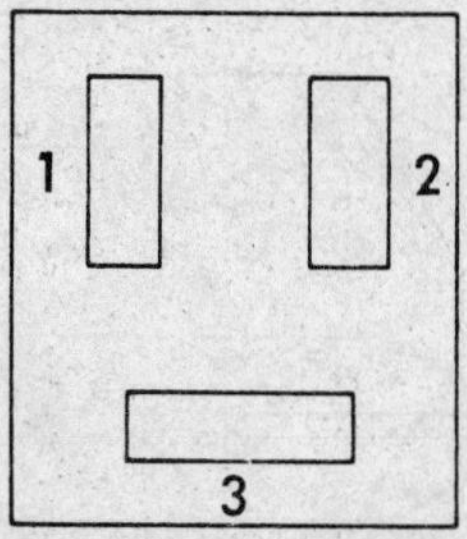

1 2

3

CHRYSLER CORP. 2.2L EFI ENGINE CONTROL SYSTEM (Cont.)

WIDE OPEN THROTTLE A/C RELAY CONNECTOR TERMINALS

Pin No.	Wire Color	Wire Function
1	Dk. Bl/Org	Ground input to turn off A/C clutch below 490 RPM or at wide open throttle (as indicated by TPS signal).
2	Dk. Bl/Yel	Output signal to set AIS at higher speed during A/C operation.
3	Brn	Connects A/C clutch circuit in series.
4	Dk. Bl	J2 voltage feed for relay coil.

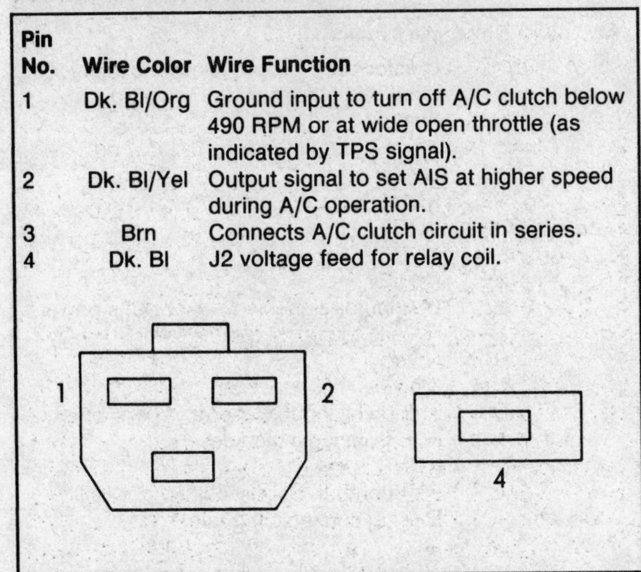

SPEED SENSOR CONNECTOR TERMINALS

Pin No.	Wire Color	Wire Function
1	Wht/Org	Output signal to logic module: indicates vehicle moving or stopped.
2	Blk/Lt. Bl	Ground for sensor through logic module.

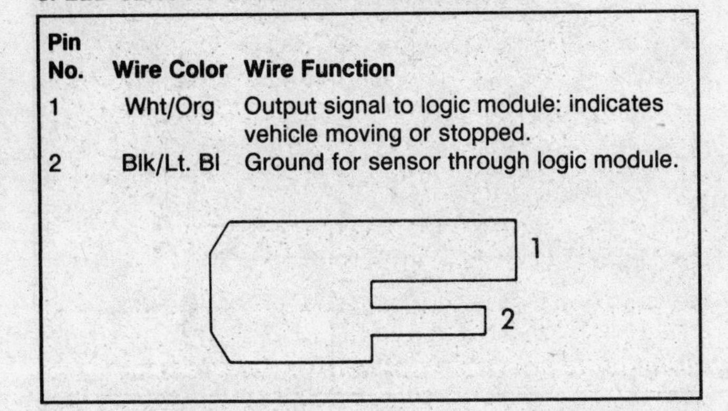

COOLANT TEMPERATURE SENSOR CONNECTOR TERMINALS

Pin No.	Wire Color	Wire Function
1	Not Used	NONE
2	Tan	Output signal to logic module connector 2, pin 8.
3	Black/Lt. Bl	Ground for sensor through logic module.

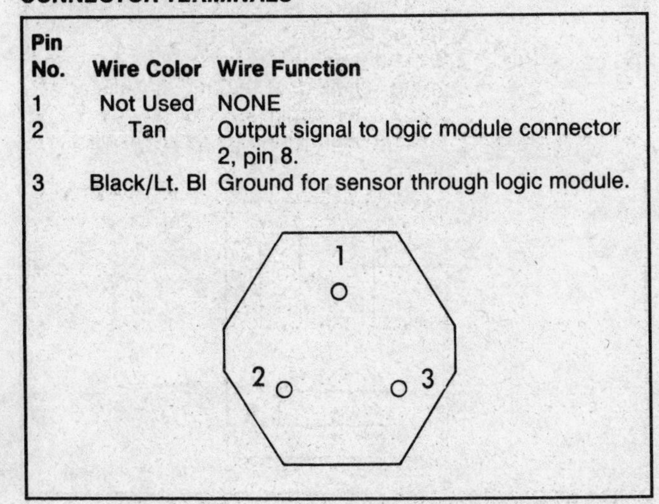

THROTTLE POSITION/AIS MOTOR CONNECTOR TERMINALS

Pin No.	Wire Color	Wire Function
1	Blk/Lt. Bl	Sensor ground through logic module.
2	Org/Wht	5 volt power supply from logic module.
3	Org/Dk. Bl	Sensor output signal to logic module connector 2, pin 5.
4	NONE	NONE
5	Brn	#2 drive signal to AIS motor.
6	Gry/Red	#1 drive signal to AIS motor.

3 2
4 1
5 6

MAP SENSOR CONNECTOR TERMINALS

Pin No.	Wire Color	Wire Function
1	Vio	5 volt power supply from logic module.
2	Dk. Grn/Red	Sensor output to logic module connector 2, pin 4.
3	Blk/Lt. Bl	Ground for sensor through logic module.

1 2 3

CHARGE TEMPERATURE SENSOR CONNECTOR TERMINALS

Pin No.	Wire Color	Wire Function
1	Blk/Red	Sensor output for coolant temp. sensor limp-in when needed.
2	Blk/Lt. Bl	Ground for sensor through logic module.

1
2

CHRYSLER CORP. 2.2L EFI ENGINE CONTROL SYSTEM (Cont.)

ASD RELAY CONNECTOR TERMINALS

Pin No.	Wire Color	Wire Function
1	Brn/Red	Voltage supply from battery.
2	Dk. Bl/Yel	Ground (through power module) when distributor signal present at power module.
3	Dk. Grn	Power supply to: (+) side of ignition coil, spark and fuel drive components in power module, fuel pump, and logic module to modify pulse width based on battery voltage.
4	Dk. Bl	Power module ground for relay coil with ignition "ON".

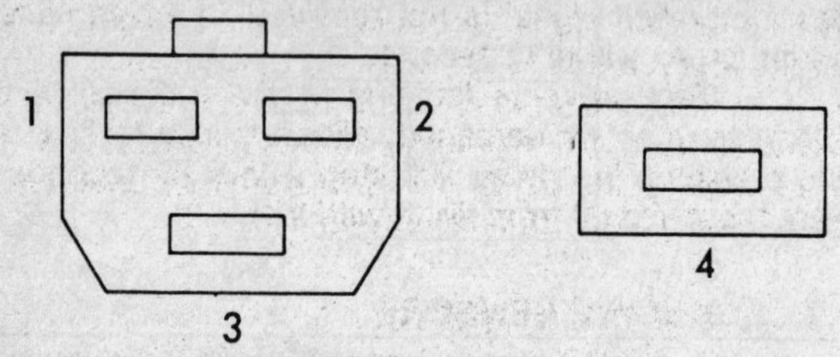

1 2 3 4

DISTRIBUTOR CONNECTOR TERMINALS

Pin No.	Wire Color	Wire Function
1	Org	8 volt power supply from logic module.
2	Gry	Output signal to logic module connector 2, pin 11; power module 12-pin connector, pin 7.
3	Blk/Lt. Bl	Distributor ground through logic module.

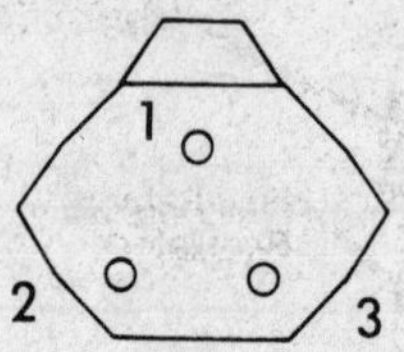

1 2 3

CHRYSLER CORP. COMBUSTION CONTROL COMPUTER

Imperial

NOTE: Information on this system is also covered in the FUEL SYSTEMS Section. Additional diagnostic information that relates strictly to the fuel portion of this system can be found in the CHRYSLER CORP. ELECTRONIC FUEL INJECTION article.

DESCRIPTION

The Combustion Control Computer (CCC) system is used on Imperial models with Electronic Fuel Injection. The computer controls the EFI system, spark timing and advance, idle speed, air injection switching and fuel evaporation purging.

The system is capable of self-calibration to compensate for changes in altitude or barometric pressure. It also has safety features that enable it to shut down the fuel supply pump if the engine stalls or will not start after prolonged cranking.

COMBUSTION CONTROL COMPUTER

The computer is located in a housing attached to the air cleaner. No servicing is possible and the housing should not be opened. The system inputs and outputs are routed through 2 connectors — one 10-pin and one 12-pin.

The CCC has 4 main circuits which control engine operation. These are the EFI circuit, which monitors air/fuel ratios; the Auto Calibration Circuit, which fine-tunes and corrects the EFI; the Electronic Spark Advance (ESA) circuit, which controls ignition power and advance; and the Automatic Idle Speed (AIS) circuit, which controls engine idle speed.

Two other modules are used that have controlling capability. One is the Power Module, located on the hydraulic support plate inside the air cleaner. The power module converts 12 volt battery power to 23 volts for use by the CCC and EFI circuits. It also amplifies signals from the CCC to the EFI control pump, and feeds the flowmeter signal to the CCC.

The other module is the Automatic Shut-Down (ASD) Module and is located on the right fenderwell or firewall. All electrical power to the system flows through the module when the ignition switch is in "Start" or "Run".

If the switch is in "Start" position, the ASD module allows the fuel pump to run. When the switch is in "Run" position, the ASD module allows the pump to run unless an ignition signal is not received, in which case it stops the pump within ½ second.

This prevents flooding or fire hazards. If the injectors were to be damaged, allowing fuel to flow out during cranking; the pump will stop within 20 seconds to prevent the manifold from filling with fuel.

ENGINE SENSORS

The CCC needs sensor inputs to determine engine operating characteristics. The following sensors are used with this system:

- Intake Air Flow Sensor
- Intake Air Temperature Sensor
- Fuel Flowmeter
- Fuel Temperature Sensor
- Fuel Pressure Switch
- Throttle Position Potentiometer

Fig. 1: Combustion Control Computer System Schematic

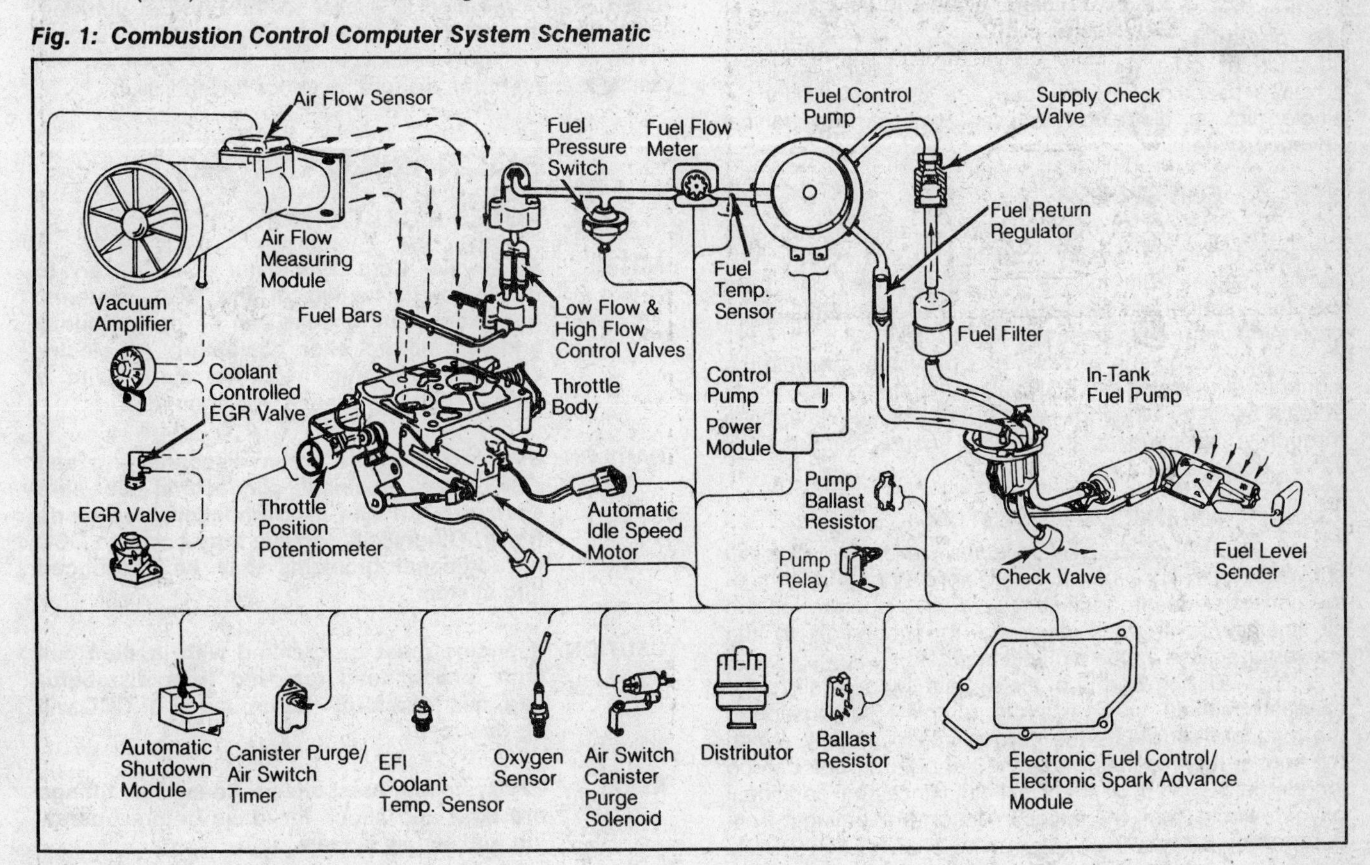

CHRYSLER COMBUSTION CONTROL COMPUTER (Cont.)

- Closed Throttle Switch (with Back-up Circuit)
- Coolant Temperature Sensor
- Oxygen Sensor
- Engine Speed (from a distributor signal)
- Air Conditioner "On" Switch
- Detonation Sensor

In addition to these sensors,the CCC also receives information from the ignition switch, has a timer to determine operating time, and determines engine load by comparing air flow with engine speed.

OPERATION

COMBUSTION CONTROL COMPUTER (CCC)

The CCC operates in open and closed loop. When the engine is cold or just being started, the system is in open loop operation. This means it operates based on information stored in the CCC programming. When the engine is warm and all conditions are favorable (sensors operating) then it operates in closed loop, where fuel enrichment is based on information from the oxygen sensor.

A unique feature of the Chrysler Combustion Control Computer system is its ability to calibrate itself. The Auto Calibration Circuit compares information with the oxygen sensor to see if it is the same as pre-programmed information would be under the same conditions.

If these 2 sources of information do not agree (due to temperature or altitude variations) the computer will adjust its memory to compensate. This calibration takes place at idle speed and around 55 miles per hour during steady cruising.

The Electronic Spark Advance cirucit is similar to other Chrysler Corp. vehicles. It provides no advance at idle or up to 1000 RPM, provides pre-programmed advance at other engine speeds, and adds additional advance based on engine load and throttle position. A single pick-up distributor is used, with no mechanical advance system.

EGR SYSTEM

The CCC system controls engine emission systems, but is not directly in control of EGR operation. A vacuum signal from the air flow sensor and one from manifold vacuum are compared by the vacuum amplifier to determine the proper amount of EGR.

A coolant sensor/valve prevents the vacuum signal from reaching the EGR valve until engine coolant is at least 54-64°F. When the valve opens, vacuum is applied through a 1-second delay valve to ensure smooth EGR valve operation.

AIR INJECTION SYSTEM

The CCC system uses a 3-way catalytic converter to reduce harmful emissions. The rear half of the converter needs additional oxygen to operate, so the air injection system is designed to supply air to the converter as well as the exhaust manifold.

During warm-up, the system supplies air to the exhaust manifold, which helps to complete combustion in the manifold and heats the oxygen sensor rapidly. When the sensor has reached operating temperature, air can no longer be supplied to the manifold, since the additional oxygen would "fool" the oxygen sensor; preventing it from determining the mixture.

An air switching timer (on firewall) is used by the CCC to provide air switching. As soon as the engine coolant sensor indicates to the computer that coolant is warm, it starts a 70 second timer. At the end of 70 seconds, a signal is sent to a vacuum solenoid, which allows vacuum to operate the air switching valve. Air is directed "downstream" to the converter. If the engine is warm when started, the 70 second timer begins immediately. *See Fig. 3.*

EVAPORATION CONTROL SYSTEM

The evaporation control system (ECS) is used to prevent fuel vapors from entering the atmosphere after the engine is stopped. Vapors that are emitted from the engine and fuel tank when it is stopped are channelled to the canister. When the engine starts, they cannot be immediately purged (drawn into the engine) or the air/fuel mixture will become too rich. However, when the oxygen sensor is operating, it can compensate for the vapors.

The ECS system operates in conjunction with the air switching system. When air injection is shifted downstream, the vacuum signal which keeps the canister purge valve closed is shut off. Engine vacuum draws vapors out of the canister and into the engine, where they are burned. When the engine is stopped, vapors again flow from the engine and fuel tank to the canister. *See Fig. 3.*

CRANKCASE VENTILATION

When the engine is operating, crankcase pressure is used to purge vapors through the PCV valve into the throttle body. Air to vent the crankcase is drawn through a hose from the air cleaner to the right valve cover. This operation is similar to the non-EFI vehicles. However, since all the air entering the engine is measured through the air flow sensor, leaks in the PCV system will cause leaning of the mixture and poor driveability.

DIAGNOSIS & TESTING

NOTES & CAUTIONS

NOTE: **A Chrysler Corp. EFI tester is necessary to do thorough testing of the CCC systems. However, some checks can be done visually and with normal shop equipment. All electrical measurements must be made with a digital, high-impedance volt-ohmmeter.**

CAUTION: **Use extreme care when disconnecting and connecting electrical connectors. Be sure system is off and all connections are made firmly. Otherwise, damage may occur to CCC or additional problems may be introduced into system.**

CAUTION: **If engine must be cranked with ignition coil high tension lead removed from distributor cap, this lead MUST be grounded or CCC will be destroyed.**

NOTE: **EFI system is pressurized. Be sure all fittings are tight and check for leaks before operating fuel supply system.**

CHRYSLER COMBUSTION CONTROL COMPUTER (Cont.)

NOTE: Whenever CCC is replaced, Auto-Calibration procedure must be performed to allow computer to adjust to vehicle conditions. See "Adjustment" in this article.

Before beginning diagnosis and testing, be sure to check systems that are not related to CCC and eliminate these from the list of possible problems. Such items are corroded battery wires, poor ground connections, and contaminated fuel filters or spark plugs. These will cause problems, but are not the fault of the CCC system.

NOTE: The following tests are performed without the use of an EFI tester. When further testing is required with an EFI tester, follow the equipment manufacturer's instructions and testing procedures.

SYSTEM VISUAL CHECK

Inside Air Cleaner

1) Check the following items: Proper wires connected to control pump, fuel pressure switch, and fuel flowmeter. *See Fig. 4 (wiring diagram) for identification.*

2) Power module ground wire connected to support plate screw. Fuel lines and pressure switch connected tight and not leaking.

3) No wires are cut or chafed by clips or hardware. Air cleaner cover tightly sealed.

NOTE: The CCC system measures intake air volume to calculate fuel flow and will not operate if the air cleaner cover is removed. Ensure that cover is sealed except when observing fuel flow during cranking.

Outside Air Cleaner

1) Check the following items: All electrical connections are tight and wires are in good condition. All electrical component mounting screws must be clean and tight to ensure a good ground connection.

2) Vacuum hoses connected between PCV valve and front throttle body port; charcoal canister and rear throttle body port. All other vacuum lines connected and in good condition.

3) Check fuses for EFI and in-tank pump. Check connection from in-tank pump to body harness near tank.

NO-START CHECKS

1) Remove air cleaner. Disconnect coil secondary wire and connect it to ground. Crank engine and check for fuel flow at injectors. If flow is okay, check ignition system.

CAUTION: Coil secondary wire must be grounded if not connected to cap while engine is being cranked. Otherwise, damage to computer may occur.

2) If no fuel is seen, perform "In-Tank Pump Test". If fuel flow is minimal, perform "Fuel Pressure Test". If fuel flow is excessive or evidence of flooding is seen, perform "Excessive Fuel Flow" test.

Ignition System Test

1) Remove 1 plug wire and crank engine, checking for a good spark to ground. If not okay, hold secondary coil wire $^3/_{16}$" from good ground and crank engine. If a good spark is seen, repair cap, rotor, or secondary wires. If no spark is seen, go to next step.

2) Remove 10-pin connector from CCC and connect ohmmeter across pins 5 and 9 in connector. If resistance is between 150-900 ohms, pick-up coil is okay. Check resistance between pin 9 and ground and pin 5 and ground. If resistance is very high, no short exists. If resistance is low, check for short between pick-up coil and computer.

3) If resistance of pick-up coil is zero, coil is shorted or grounded. Check at distributor connector for continuity between either connector wire and ground. If grounded, replace coil and attempt to restart. If coil is not grounded, go to step **5)**.

4) If resistance at pick-up coil is too high, check again across the 2 terminals in the distributor connector. If resistance is now between 150-900 ohms, repair circuit to computer. If not, the harness is okay and the pick-up coil must be replaced. Attempt to restart.

5) Voltage at coil positive terminal (during cranking) should be 9 volts or more. If not, check voltage at starter relay "BAL" terminal while cranking. If voltage is 9 volts or more, repair circuit to coil. If not, check battery and/or replace starter relay.

6) If voltage at coil terminal is 9 volts or more and engine will not start, disconnect 10-pin connector at computer and connect voltmeter between pin 1 in connector and ground. While cranking engine, voltage should be 9 volts or more. If not, repair wiring harness and attempt to restart. If so, go to next step.

7) Connect ohmmeter between pin 10 and ground. If continuity is not shown, repair ground connection to pin 10. If continuity is shown, disconnect ASD module and repeat step **1)**. If a good spark is shown, replace ASD module. If not replace CCC.

In-Tank Pump Test

1) Check continuity and resistance of in-tank pump ballast resistor. Resistor is at right top of cowl and should have 0.4 ohms resistance.

2) Continuity should be present between one side of ballast resistor and pin 3 of pump relay connector (right fender well). Continuity should exist between other side of resistor and pin 1 in connector. Pin 5 should be grounded.

3) Insert positive voltmeter probe into rear of relay connector at pin 3 while connector is hooked up. Connect other probe to ground and crank engine. Voltmeter should indicate 8-10 volts. Insert probe at pin 4 and crank engine. Voltmeter should indicate 9 volts. If not, check battery and voltage supply to pump relay.

4) If voltage is present, check continuity between pin 3 of relay connector and Dark Green wire at pump (fuel tank).

Excessive Fuel Flow

1) With air cleaner cover removed, turn key on. If fuel flows continuously from injectors, disconnect control pump connector.

2) If fuel continues to flow, replace fuel control plate (pump, injectors, flowmeter).

3) If fuel flow stops, problem is in computer. Substitute good computer and retest. If original proves defective, replace computer.

STARTS, THEN STALLS CHECKS

AIS Motor

1) Turn ignition on but do not start engine. Visually check position of throttle arm at AIS motor. Arm

CHRYSLER COMBUSTION CONTROL COMPUTER (Cont.)

should be pointing downward and toward rear of engine.

2) If throttle arm is in correct position, check ballast resistor. With ignition on, measure voltage between pin "A" and ground, then between pin "B" and ground. Voltage at "A" should be 6 volts, at "B", 10 volts. If not, check wiring harness.

3) Resistance (with connectors removed) between pins "C" and "D" should be 9-11 ohms, and between "D" and E" should be 4-6 ohms. If not correct, replace ballast resistor.

4) If arm at motor was in correct position, disconnect 10-pin connector at computer. Connect a voltmeter between pin 6 of connector and ground. At least 8 volts should be present. If not, check wiring harness. If harness is okay, replace AIS motor.

Fig. 2: Ignition/AIS Motor Ballast Resistor Connections

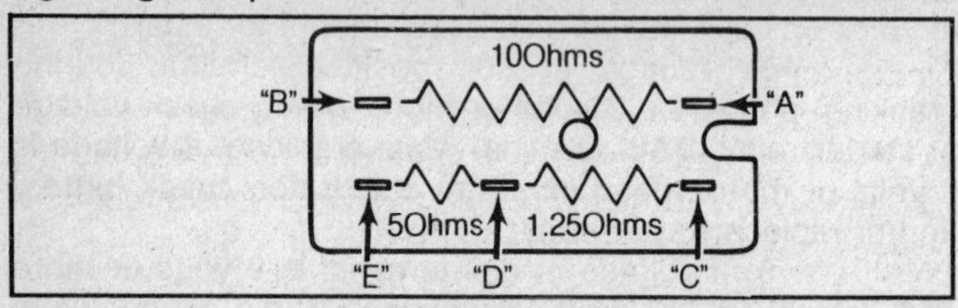

5) If 8 volts were measured at pin 6, computer must be replaced.

Fuel Supply

Perform test under "No-Start Checks" and inspect fuel flow, fuel pressure, and voltage to pump.

Computer Supply

1) Disconnect 12-pin EFI connector from module inside computer on air cleaner housing. Connect a voltmeter between pin 8 of connector and ground, then crank engine.

2) Voltmeter should indicate at least 9 volts. If not, reconnect connector and check wiring harness to starter relay. If voltage is correct, replace computer.

DRIVEABILITY CHECKS

Preliminary Check

1) Connect tachometer and adjustable timing light to engine. Start engine and allow to idle. Idle speed should be between 530-630 RPM. If not, adjust idle speed using EFI tester.

2) Ground closed throttle switch using jumper wire. Timing light should indicate 12° BTDC. If not, adjust basic timing. Raise engine RPM to 1500 RPM with switch still grounded. If timing changes, CCC must be replaced. If timing does not change, go to next step.

3) Remove jumper wire from closed throttle switch and decrease engine speed to 1000 RPM. Timing should be 27-35°. If not, replace CCC. If so, go to next step.

4) Increase engine speed to 2000 RPM. Timing should be 47-55°. If not, replace CCC. If so, engine has passed preliminary test. Other testing must be done with EFI tester.

Air Switching Operation

1) Engine must be warm. Stop engine and disconnect downstream air hose from air switching valve. Start engine, noting time with stop watch. For first 70 seconds, no air should come from downstream port of air switching valve. If okay, go to step **3)**. If air is emitted, check harness and connectors at CCC and air switching timer.

2) If connections are good, connect voltmeter between ground and air switching vacuum solenoid feed wire (leave feed wire connected). If voltage is less than 1 volt and air comes from valve, replace air switching valve. If voltage is about 12 volts and air comes from valve, replace air switching timer.

3) After 70 seconds following engine start, air should come from downstream port of air switching valve. If so, and driveability is still poor, replace CCC and retest. If no air comes from valve (and voltage at solenoid is less than 1 volt) check electrical connections.

Fig. 3: Air Switching/Canister Purging Control Circuits

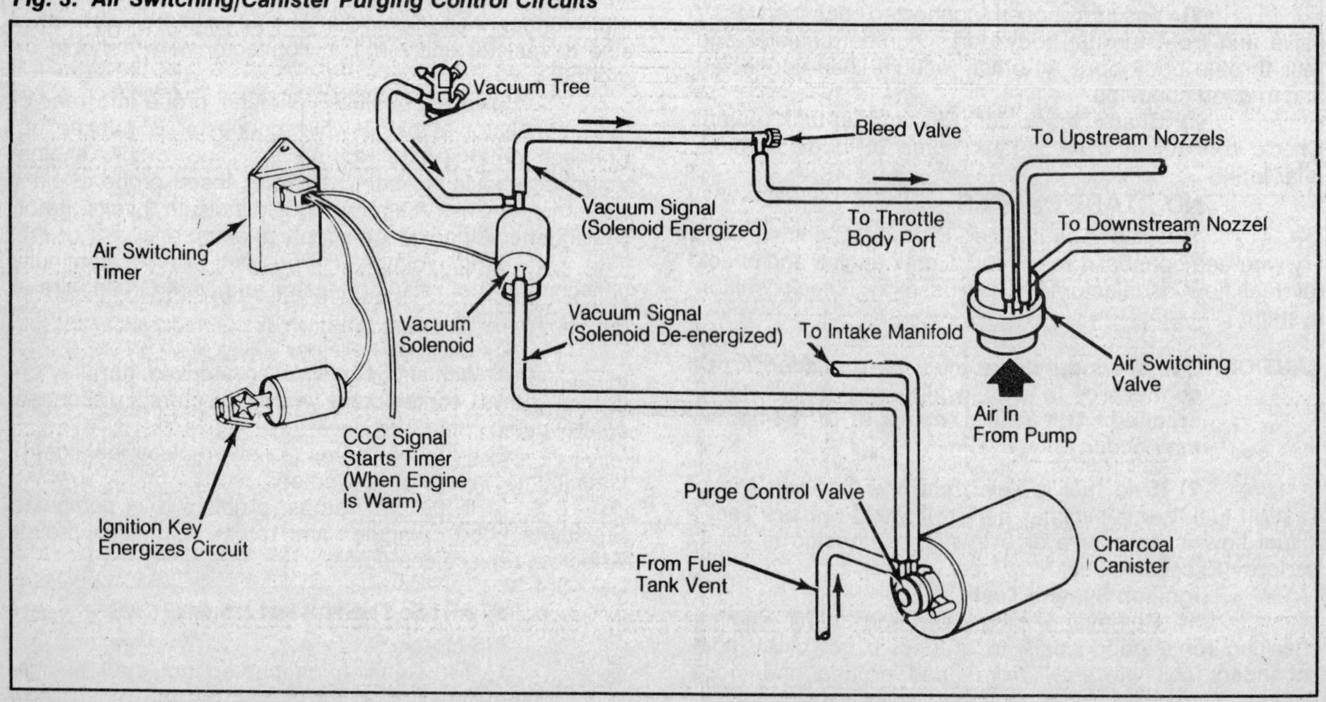

CHRYSLER COMBUSTION CONTROL COMPUTER (Cont.)

4) If connections are good, replace air switching timer. If voltage is above 12 volts and no air comes from downstream port, check vacuum hoses and source. If good, replace air switching valve and retest.

ADJUSTMENTS

THROTTLE POSITION POTENTIOMETER (TPP)

NOTE: **Throttle position potentiometer is mounted with break-off screws. Screws must be drilled and removed, then replaced before adjustment is possible.**

1) Connect EFI tester to vehicle. Place toggle switch to EFI position and rotary switch to throttle position, then turn ignition on. Move diagnostic aid switch to manual position, then move AIS control switch down and hold until AIS motor stops.

2) Depress AIS by-pass button and read TPP voltage. Adjust switch position to obtain 4.0-5.0 volts. Tighten break-off screws until heads snap off.

AUTOMATIC IDLE SPEED MOTOR

1) Turn ignition on. Motor should move arm rearward and open throttle blades. When vehicle is started, idle should be 580 RPM in "D" and should remain constant. If not, adjustment may be necessary.

2) Connect EFI tester with diagnostic aid. Connect tachometer pick-up to No. 1 spark plug lead, battery leads to battery, and place diagnostic aid switch to normal position.

3) Start engine and run until warm. Move diagnostic aid switch to manual position and depress control switch until engine speed no longer decreases. Place transmission selector in "D".

4) Idle speed should be 530-630 RPM. If not, adjust to 580 RPM by turning screw on end of AIS motor linkage. One turn of screw will change idle speed 50 RPM.

AUTO-CALIBRATION

NOTE: **Whenever computer is replaced, auto-calibration procedure must be performed to allow computer to adjust to vehicle conditions.**

1) Start and run engine until normal operating temperature is reached. If engine is already warm, idle for at least 90 seconds to allow timer to run out.

2) Increase speed to 2000-2500 RPM and hold constant for at least 90 seconds. Reduce engine speed to idle and allow to idle for at least 150 seconds.

3) Repeat step **2)** once more so computer can verify initial calibration. Procedure is now complete.

Fig. 4: Combustion Control Computer Wiring Diagram

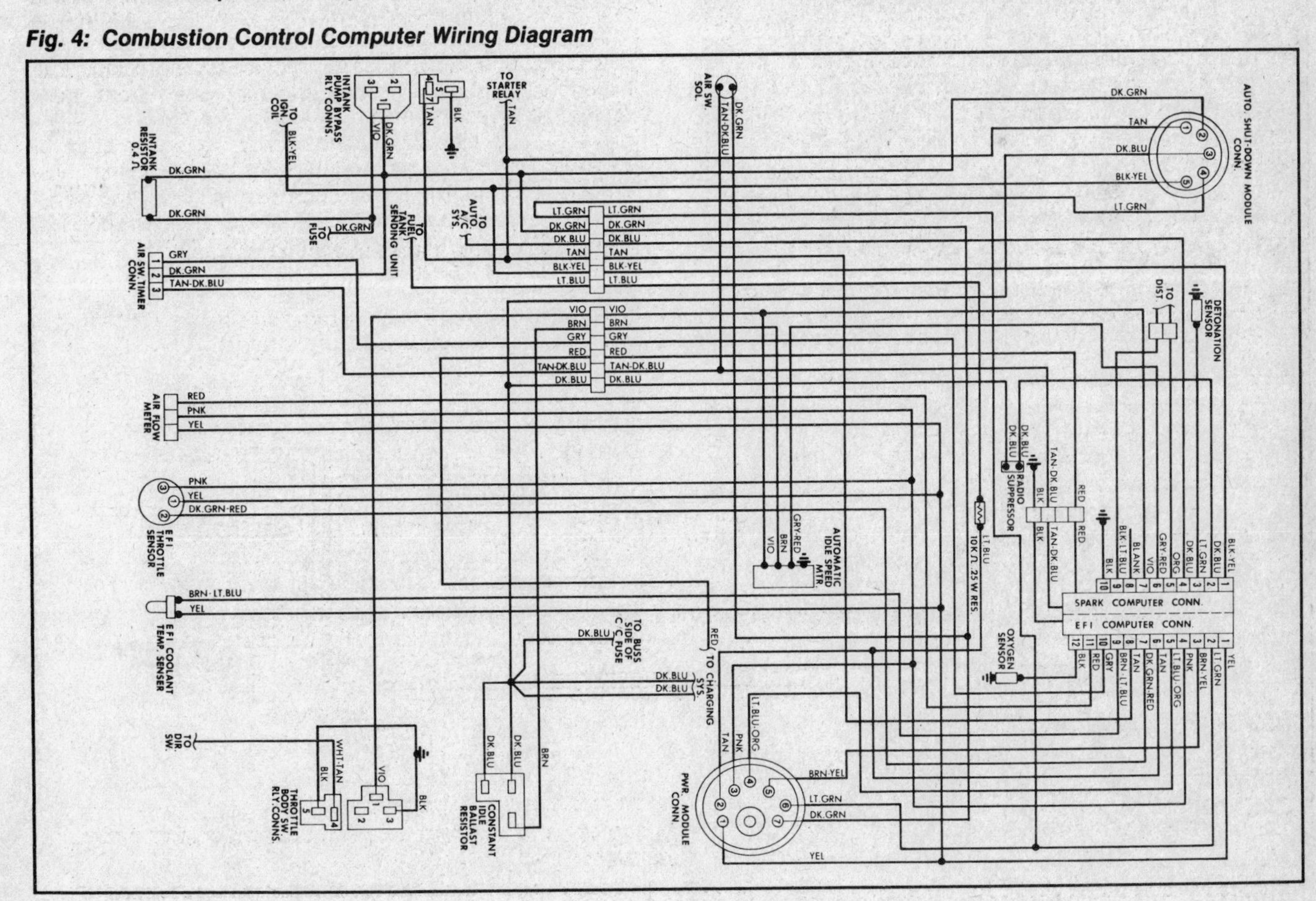

CHRYSLER COMBUSTION CONTROL COMPUTER (Cont.)

CALIBRATION VERIFICATION

NOTE: This procedure can be used to verify that the computer is operating properly. Engine must be at normal temperature.

1) Air cleaner cover must be tight and exhaust system must be checked to ensure no leaks or holes exist. Connect EFI tester to system and connect a CO meter to tailpipe.

2) Remove air pump hose from downstream air injection tube and plug tube. Connect diagnostic aid to AIS motor. Start engine, leave transmission selector in "P", and place speed control switch in manual position. Idle for at least 90 seconds.

3) Disconnect oxygen sensor wire and ground wiring harness side of connector. Increase engine speed to 2000-2500 RPM and hold it constant with diagnostic aid control.

4) CO reading must be between 0.5-3.5%. If higher than 3.5%, replace computer.

5) Remove test equipment and reconnect air injection tube.

CHRYSLER CORP.
HALL EFFECT ELECTRONIC SPARK CONTROL

Chrysler Corp. 1.6L, 1.7L & 2.2L

DESCRIPTION

NOTE: **The distributor used on the 2.2L EFI engine is the same as that used on the 1.6L, 1.7L and 2.2L engines. Information other than the system wiring diagram is not available from manufacturer for the 2.2L EFI distributor.**

Fig. 1: Wiring Diagram of Chrysler Corp. Hall Effect Electronic Spark Control System

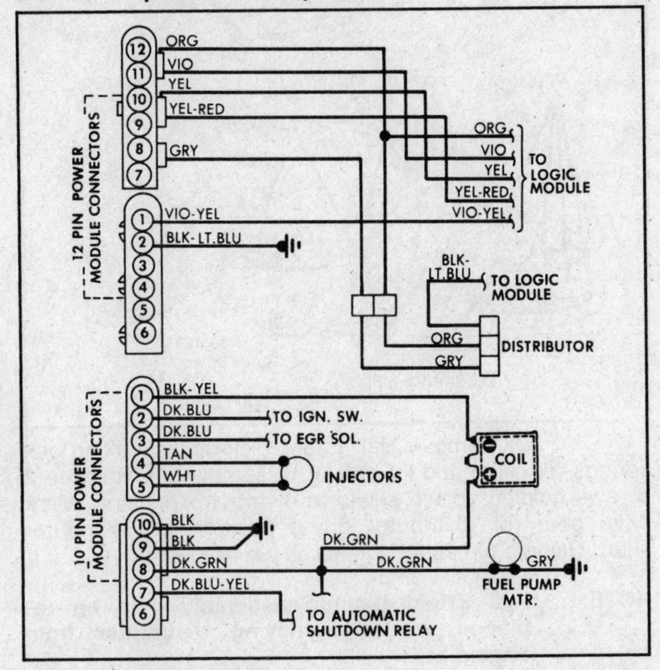

Used on 2.2L EFI engine.

The Electronic Spark Control system used on Chrysler Corp. front wheel drive vehicles with 1.6L, 1.7L and 2.2L engines features a Hall Effect distributor and a spark control computer.

Fig. 2: Wiring Diagram of Chrysler Corp. Hall Effect Electronic Spark Control System

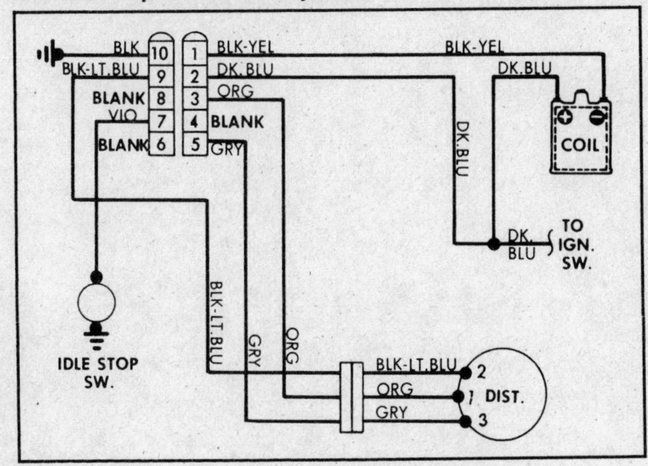

Used on 1.6L, 1.7L and non-EFI 2.2L engines.

The computer is really the heart of the system, providing capability of igniting a lean air/fuel mixture according to different modes of engine operation. It provides an infinite number of variable advance curves.

The computer contains an electronic printed circuit board, which simultaneously receives signals from various engine sensors, analyzes them to determine how the engine is operating and then advances or retards ignition timing.

The computer determines the exact instant when ignition is required, and then signals the ignition coil to produce the electrical impulses that fire the spark plugs. The computer is located on the fenderwell, near the battery.

The computer is connected to other fuel/ignition components by a 10-wire dual connector. Five engine sensors feed information to the computer. These include a vacuum transducer, mounted on the computer housing, the Hall Effect pick-up assembly in the distributor, an engine coolant temperature sensor, a carburetor switch, and an oxygen sensor.

The computer used with the spark control system eliminates need for either vacuum advance units or centrifugal advance weights. The Hall Effect distributor is connected to the rest of the system by a 3-terminal connector. *See Fig. 3.* It sends small alternating current signals to the computer as rotor shutter blades enter and leave the gap in the Hall Effect switching unit pick-up assembly.

Fig. 3: Components of Hall Effect Distributor for Electronic Spark Control System

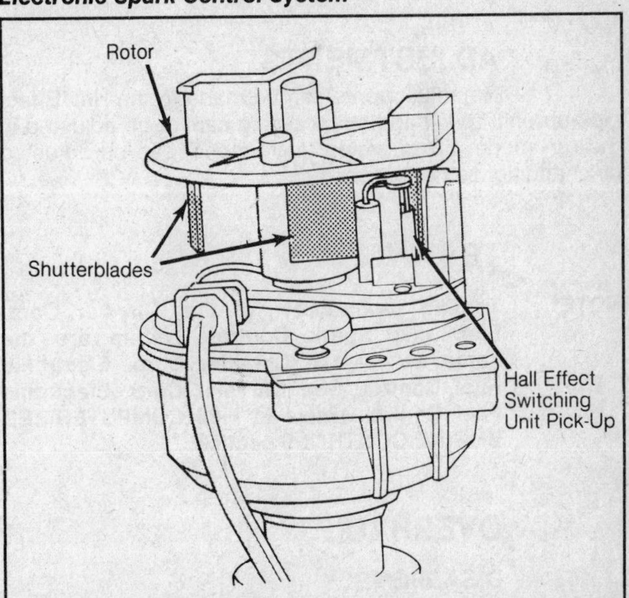

The carburetor switch reports when the engine is at idle. The coolant temperature switch or sensor keeps the computer informed on engine operating temperatures. The vacuum transducer informs the computer of engine manifold vacuum.

OPERATION

The computer has 2 functional modes, the start and run modes. The start mode functions only during

CHRYSLER CORP.
HALL EFFECT ELECTRONIC SPARK CONTROL (Cont.)

engine cranking and starting. A fixed amount of spark advance is provided, based on distributor position.

The run mode functions only when the engine starts and is operating normally. The Hall Effect pick-up assembly and the 4 other sensors provide information to the computer, which then varies spark advance to match engine operating conditions. Spark timing and dwell cannot be adjusted in the run mode.

Engine sensors work together. If engine temperature drops below a predetermined temperature, the coolant temperature switch signals the computer to prevent additional advance from the vacuum transducer signal. As temperatures rise, vacuum increases, and additional advance is called for. For maximum advance, the carburetor switch must remain open. During the time when advance will not occur quickly, vacuum advance is controlled by engine RPM and will build up at a slow rate. If the carburetor switch closes, this build-up of advance will be cancelled.

The Hall Effect pick-up signal is a reference signal, providing maximum amount of advance, based on sensor input. At the proper time, the computer shuts off current to the ignition coil primary circuit. As the magnetic field collapses, a high voltage surge occurs in the secondary, firing the spark plugs.

If the run mode of the computer fails, the system will go into the start mode. This enables the vehicle to be driven in for repair. However, performance and fuel economy will be poor. If the Hall Effect pick-up or the start mode of the computer fails, the engine will not start or run.

ADJUSTMENTS

No adjustments can be made to the Hall Effect pick-up unit. Dwell and spark timing cannot be adjusted in the run mode. Fixed timing (start mode) can be adjusted by changing distributor position.

TESTING

NOTE: **Testing procedures for the Chrysler Corp. Electronic Spark Control System are the same as for the Chrysler Corp. Electronic Fuel Control. See Chrysler Corp. Electronic Fuel Control article in 1983 COMPUTERIZED ENGINE CONTROLS section.**

OVERHAUL

DISASSEMBLY

1) Remove distributor from vehicle. Lightly clamp distributor in soft jawed vise. Remove distributor cap and rotor from shaft. Remove screw holding pick-up lead to distributor housing.

NOTE: **When removing spark plug wires from distributor cap, do not pull on wires. Positive-locking wires must be released from inside cap. See Fig. 4.**

Fig. 4: Use Pliers to Release Positive-Locking Spark Plug Wire Terminals

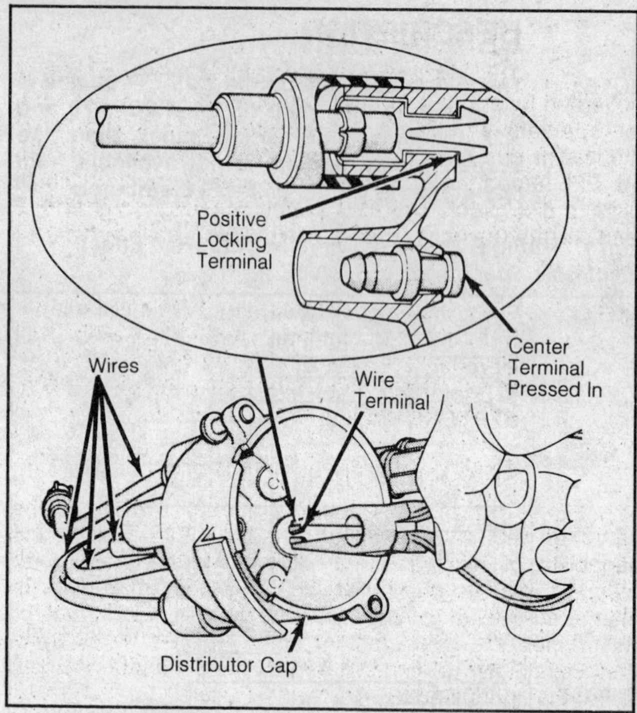

2) Remove Hall Effect pick-up assembly lock springs (or clips) and lift pick-up assembly out. Remove 2 screws holding splash shield to distributor housing. Mark drive gear (or distributor drive) position on distributor shaft. Using a pin punch, drive roll pin from shaft.

NOTE: **Hall Effect pick-up assembly may be replaced without removing distributor from engine.**

3) Remove drive gear (or distributor drive) and remove shaft from housing. If equipped, remove thrust washers, nylon spacers and block seals.

REASSEMBLY

To reassemble, reverse disassembly procedure. Correct rotor has "E.S.A." stamped in its top. Check rotor for proper grounding of shutterblades.

CHRYSLER CORP. ELECTRONIC SPARK CONTROL

Chrysler Corp. Models with 6-Cylinder & V8 Engines

DESCRIPTION

The Electronic Spark Control (ESC) system is governed by a Spark Control Computer, 7 engine sensors, a specially-calibrated carburetor and, on most models, a dual pick-up distributor. Models with the 5.2L V8 EFI (Electronic Fuel Injection) engine have a single pick-up distributor. The ESC system is designed to burn a lean air/fuel mixture, with a minimum of emissions. *See Fig. 1*.

NOTE: For a diagram of 10-wire and 12-wire connectors for the ignition and electronic fuel injection systems of 5.2L V8 EFI, see Chrysler Electronic Fuel Injection Articles in FUEL SYSTEMS Section.

SPARK CONTROL COMPUTER

The Spark Control Computer (SCC) is the heart of the entire system. It gives the system the capability of igniting a lean fuel mixture according to different modes of engine operation by delivering an infinite amount of variable advance curves. The computer determines the exact instant when ignition is required, then signals the ignition coil to produce the spark required to fire the spark plugs.

The computer consists of one electronic printed circuit board which receives signals from all the sensors and, within milliseconds, computes them so that proper advance or retard is immediately achieved.

Fig. 2: Electronic Spark Control Computer

Spark Control Computer is mounted on air cleaner.

SENSORS

The electronic spark control computer, mounted on the air cleaner, uses 7 engine sensors to determine when to fire the spark plugs. *See Fig. 2*. These include the distributor pick-up coil(s), coolant temperature sensor, carburetor switch, vacuum transducer, detonation sensor (5.2L V8 4-Bbl. only), oxygen sensor and charge temperature switch. Their functions are as follows:

Magnetic Pick-Up Assembly

The pick-up coil assembly is located in the distributor. The start pick-up coil supplies a signal to the computer, which will cause the spark plugs to fire at a fixed amount of advance during cranking only. Once the engine begins to run, the run pick-up coil takes over, supplying advance information to the computer. The computer then modifies advance information to reflect other engine operating conditions supplied by the ramaining sensors. The 5.2L V8 EFI engine has only one pick-up coil.

Fig. 1: Wiring Diagram for Chrysler Corp. Electronic Spark Control System

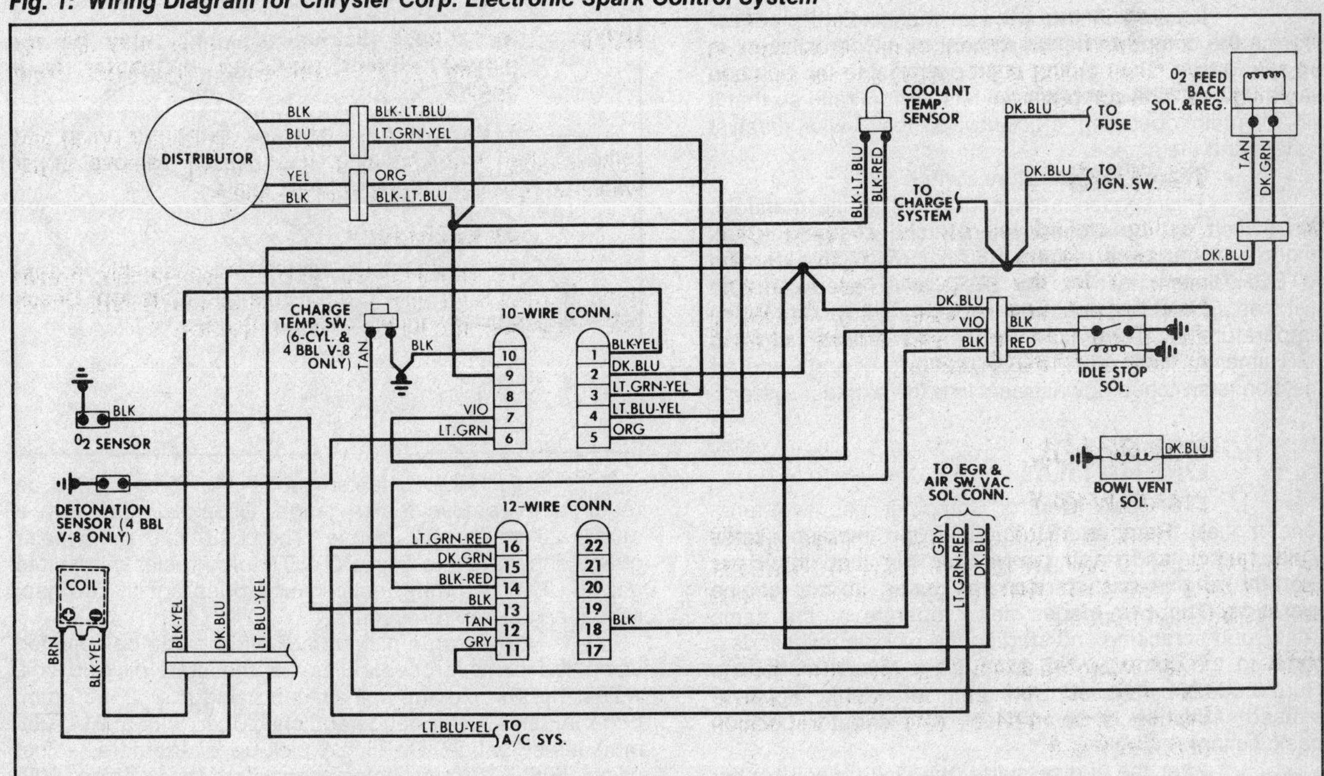

Models with 5.2L V8 EFI engines have only one pick-up coil.

CHRYSLER CORP. ELECTRONIC SPARK CONTROL (Cont.)

The start pick-up coil can be identified by its 2-prong male connector. The run pick-up coil can be identified by its connector having 1 male prong and 1 female prong.

Coolant Temperature Sensor

The coolant sensor is located in the cylinder head of 6-cylinder engines and in the intake manifold of most V8 engines. The 5.2L V8 2-Bbl. engine has the coolant temperature switch in the charge temperature switch location on the intake manifold. The coolant sensor informs the computer when the engine has reached a predetermined temperature, so that proper adjustment can be made to the air/fuel ratio. It also prevents changes until such a temperature is reached.

Vacuum Transducer

This sensor, located on the spark control computer, signals the computer to inform it of engine operating vacuum. Vacuum is one of the factors used to determine whether the computer will advance or retard ignition timing or change the air/fuel ratio.

Carburetor Switch

Located on the end of idle stop, the carburetor switch informs the computer when the engine is at idle. When carburetor switch contacts throttle lever ground, the computer will cancel spark advance and prevent air/fuel ratio from being adjusted.

Detonation Sensor

Used on only 5.2L V8 4-Bbl. engines, this sensor is mounted in the intake manifold and sends a low voltage signal to the computer whenever engine knock is detected. The computer then retards timing a maximum of 11°, the actual amount being in proportion to the strength and frequency of the detonation. When the condition no longer exists, timing is advanced to its original value.

Oxygen Sensor

Located in the exhaust manifold, this sensor informs the computer of the amount of oxygen present in exhaust gases. The amount is proportional to the rich and lean mixtures. The computer adjusts air/fuel ratio so that it will maintain operating efficiency of the 3-way catalyst system and the engine.

Charge Temperature Switch

This sensor is located in the intake manifold. The switch will be closed when intake charge (air/fuel mixture) temperature is below 60°F (16°C). This permits no EGR timer function, no EGR valve operation and switches air injection upstream into exhaust system. When temperature is above 60°F, the switch opens, allowing EGR timer to time out, the EGR valve to operate and air injection is switched downstream into the exhaust system.

OPERATION

The Spark Control Computer has two functional modes, "Start" and "Run". The "Start" mode operates while cranking and starting only. The "Run" mode operates after the engine has started and during normal engine operation. The two modes never operate at the same time. During cranking and starting the pick-up coil sends a signal to the computer which is in the "Start" mode, the "Run" mode is by-passed. During this time a fixed advance is used. Advance is determined by distributor position (basic timing).

After the engine starts, the pick-up coil continues to send a signal to the computer, but the computer is now in the "Run" mode and "Start" mode is by-passed. The amount of timing advance is now controlled by the computer, based upon information received from the engine sensors.

The amount of spark advance is determined by two factors, engine speed and engine vacuum. At what point it occurs depends upon computer programming. Advance from vacuum will be provided when the carburetor switch is open. The amount of advance is programmed into the computer and is proportional to the amount of vacuum and engine RPM. Advance from speed will be given by the computer when the carburetor switch is open and is programmed to engine RPM.

If for some reason, there is a failure of the "Run" mode of the computer, the "Start" mode will come back into service and allow the vehicle to be driven in for repair. Performance and economy will be greatly reduced because of the fixed timing.

ADJUSTMENTS

PICK-UP COIL AIR GAP

1) Align one reluctor tooth with start pick-up coil. Loosen pick-up coil hold down screw. Insert a .006" (.15 mm) non-magnetic feeler gauge between reluctor tooth and start pick-up coil. Adjust air gap so that contact is made between reluctor tooth, feeler gauge, and pick-up coil. Tighten hold down screw. *See Fig. 3.*

Fig. 3: Checking Distributor Pick-Up Coil Air Gap

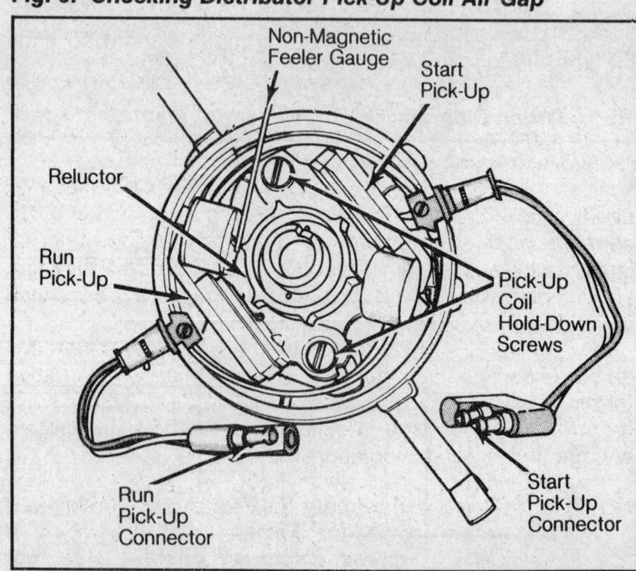

2) Remove feeler gauge. No force should be required to remove feeler gauge. Check air gap with a .008" (.20 mm) feeler gauge. The .008" (.20 mm) feeler guage should fit into gap. DO NOT force feeler gauge into gap. If .008" (.20 mm) feeler gauge does not fit into gap, repeat adjustment procedure.

3) The run pick-up coil air gap can be adjusted using the same procedure as for the start pick-up coil. Adjust the run pick-up coil air gap using a .012" (.30 mm) non-magnetic feeler gauge and check gap with a .014" (.35 mm) feeler gauge. On single pick-up distributors, adjust using .006" (.15 mm) feeler gauge and check using .008" (.20 mm) feeler gauge.

CHRYSLER CORP. ELECTRONIC SPARK CONTROL (Cont.)

TESTING

IGNITION SYSTEM STARTING

1) Turn ignition switch "ON". Remove ignition coil wire from distributor cap. Hold end of wire 1/4" from a good engine ground. Intermittently jump coil negative terminal to ground, while watching for spark at ignition coil wire. If there is a spark, it must be constant and bright blue.

2) If spark is good, continue to intermittently jumper coil negative terminal to ground, while slowly moving coil wire away from ground. Check for arcing at coil tower. If arcing occurs, replace ignition coil.

3) If spark is weak or not constant, or if there is no spark, proceed to "Failure to Start Test."

4) If spark is good and there is no arcing at ignition coil tower, ignition system is producing necessary high secondary voltage. Make sure this spark is getting to plugs by checking distributor rotor, cap, spark plugs, and plug wires.

5) If all this checks out okay, but engine still will not start, the ignition system is not the problem. It will be necessary to check fuel system and mechanical engine components.

FAILURE TO START

NOTE: **Perform Ignition System Starting Test first. Failure to do so may result in lost diagnostic time or incorrect test results.**

1) Measure and record battery voltage. Measure specific gravity, which must be at least 1.220 (temperature corrected) to deliver proper voltage.

2) Turn ignition switch "OFF". Disconnect 10-wire connector from spark control computer. Repeat step **1)** of Ignition System Starting Test. If spark results, replace spark control computer.

3) If no spark is obtained, check voltage at positive terminal of ignition coil. With ignition switch "ON", connect positive voltmeter lead to positive terminal of ignition coil and negative lead to a good ground. Reading should be within 1 volt of battery voltage. If not, check wiring between battery and coil positive terminal.

4) If voltage at positive terminal of ignition coil was correct, connect positive voltmeter lead to negative terminal of ignition coil and negative lead to a good ground. Again, voltage should be within 1 volt of battery voltage. If not, replace ignition coil.

NOTE: **Check coil primary and secondary resistance before replacing ignition coil. However, if battery voltage exists on positive side, but not on negative side of coil, ignition coil normally requires replacement.**

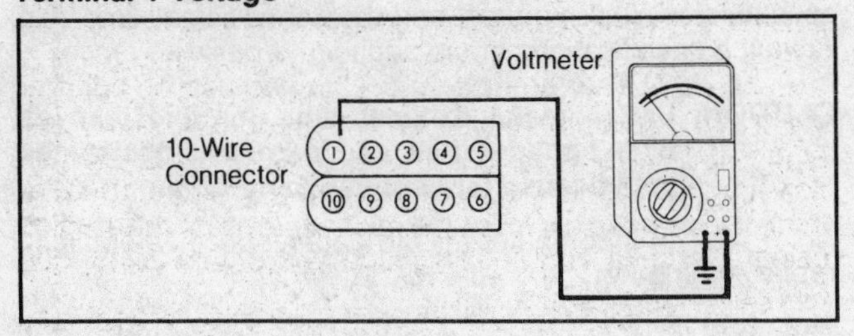

Fig. 4: Voltmeter Hookup for Checking Terminal 1 Voltage

5) If voltage was correct at negative coil terminal, but no spark resulted in step **1)** of Ignition System Starting Test, replace ignition coil.

6) If spark results, but engine will not start, turn ignition switch to the "RUN" position. Connect positive voltmeter lead to terminal 1 of 10-wire connector and negative lead to a good ground. *See Fig. 4*.

7) Reading should be within 1 volt of battery voltage. If not, check wire for open and repair it, repeating this step once more. Reconnect 10-wire connector to computer.

8) If battery voltage was recorded in step **6)**, place a thin insulator (piece of paper) between curb idle adjusting screw and carburetor switch or make sure screw does not touch switch. *See Fig. 5*.

Fig. 5: Checking Voltage at Carburetor Switch

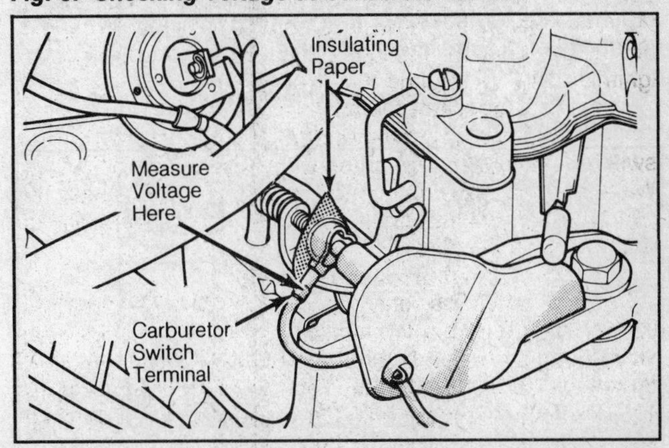

9) Connect negative lead of voltmeter to a good ground. Turn ignition switch to "RUN" position, and touch positive voltmeter lead to carburetor switch terminal. Reading should be approximately 5 volts. If so, proceed to step **15)**.

10) If voltage was not at least 5 volts, turn ignition switch "OFF". Disconnect 10-wire connector from computer. Turn ignition switch back to "RUN" position. Connect positive voltmeter lead to terminal 2 of 10-wire connector and negative lead to ground. *See Fig. 6*.

Fig. 6: Voltmeter Hookup for Checking Terminal 2 Voltage

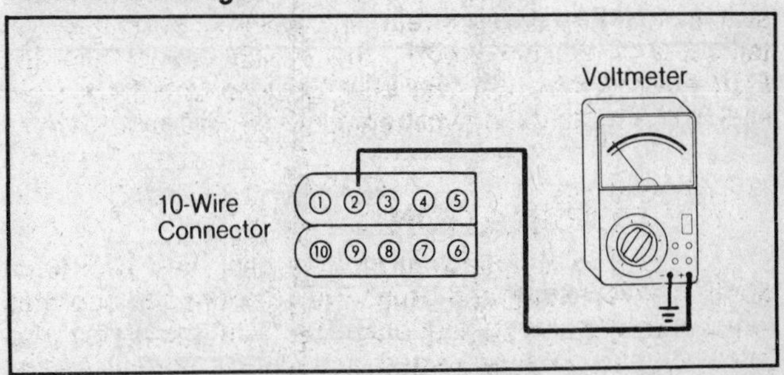

11) Voltage reading should again be within 1 volt of battery voltage. If not correct, check wiring between terminal 2 and ignition switch for opens, shorts or poor connections.

12) If voltage at terminal 2 was correct, turn ignition switch "OFF". Using an ohmmeter, check continuity between terminal 7 of 10-wire connector and carburetor switch terminal. *See Fig. 7*.

CHRYSLER CORP. ELECTRONIC SPARK CONTROL (Cont.)

Fig. 7: Ohmmeter Hookup for Checking Carburetor Switch Wiring Harness

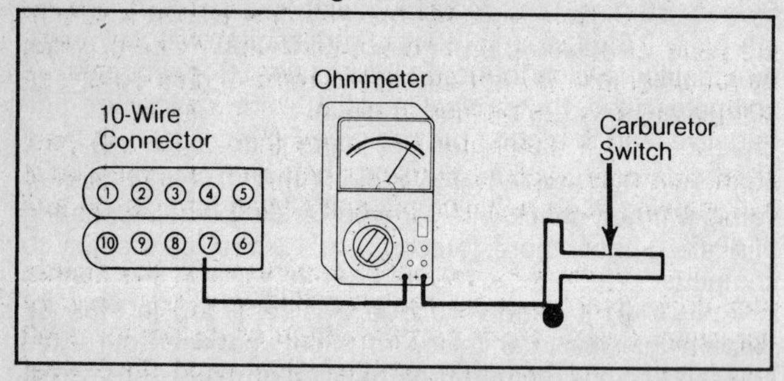

13) Continuity should exist. If not, check wire between connections for opens, shorts or poor connections. If continuity is present, use an ohmmeter with leads attached to terminal 10 and engine ground to check continuity of ground circuit. *See Fig. 8*.

Fig. 8: Ohmmeter Hookup for Checking Computer Ground Circuit

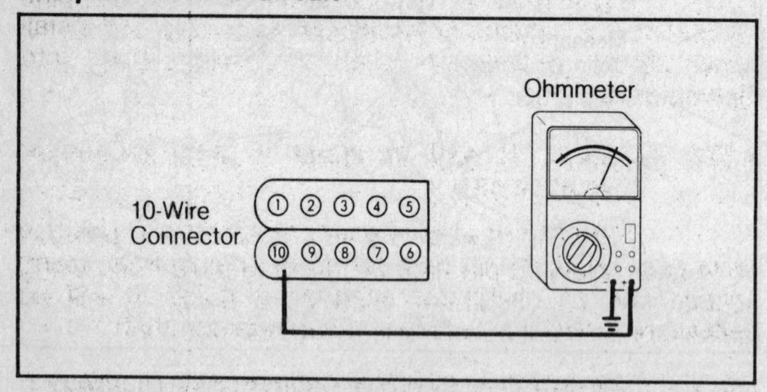

14) If there is continuity, replace spark control computer. If there is no continuity, check wire from terminal 10 to ground. If engine fails to start, proceed to step **15)**.

15) Turn ignition switch "OFF". Attach ohmmeter leads to terminals 5 and 9 of 10-wire harness connector to check run pick-up coil resistance and to terminals 3 and 9 to check start pick-up coil resistance. *See Fig. 9*. Resistance should be 150-900 ohms for both pick-up coils. If so, proceed to step **17)**.

Fig. 9: Ohmmeter Hookup for Checking Pick-Up Coil Resistance

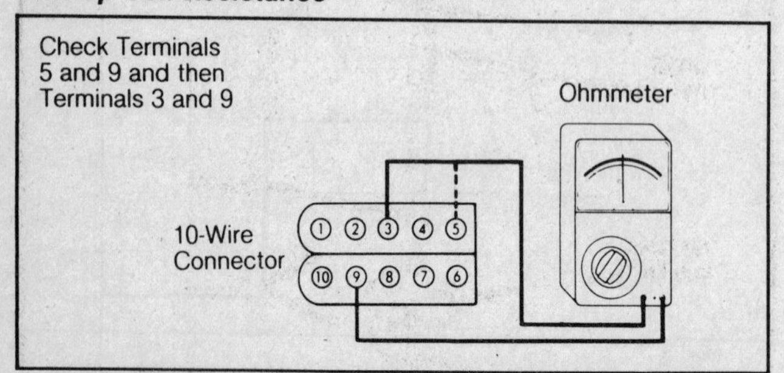

16) If resistance is not 150-900 ohms, disconnect distributor connectors and attach ohmmeter leads to run pick-up coil leads and then to start pick-up coil leads coming from distributor. If resistance is now okay, wiring harness is defective. If resistance is still not 150-900 ohms, replace pick-up coil(s), as necessary.

17) Connect one lead of an ohmmeter to engine ground and touch other lead to each terminal of leads coming from 2 distributor pick-up coils. There should be no continuity. If continuity is indicated, replace pick-up coil.

18) Remove distributor cap and rotor and check reluctor-to-pick-up coil(s) air gap as described previously. Install distributor cap and reinstall all wiring. If engine fails to start, replace spark control computer. If it still fails to start, install original computer and retest.

IGNITION COIL RESISTANCE

1) If ignition coil is suspected, connect ohmmeter leads to positive and negative ignition coil primary terminals. Ignition switch should be "OFF" and coil wires removed. Primary resistance should read 1.60-1.79 ohms for Prestolite coils; 1.34-1.55 ohms for Essex coils.

2) Then move ohmmeter leads to ignition coil negative terminal and ignition coil tower. Ohmmeter resistance reading should be 9,400-11,700 for Prestolite coils, 9,000-12,200 ohms for Essex coils.

3) Replace ignition coil if either specification is not obtained.

BASIC ADVANCE TIMING

1) Connect an adjustable timing light to engine so that total timing advance at crankshaft can be checked. Connect a jumper wire between carburetor switch and a good ground.

2) Be sure vacuum line is connected to vacuum transducer on computer. Observe timing mark immediately after engine starts to run, and adjust timing light so basic timing signal is seen at timing plate.

3) The meter on timing light should then show amount of advance, as indicated on vehicle emission control label.

SPARK ADVANCE OF COMPUTER

NOTE: **The Spark Control Computer has various spark advance schedules incorporated into its microprocessor for operation at differing engine temperatures. Therefore, be sure engine is at normal operating temperature before testing.**

1) Start engine and allow it to warm to normal operating temperature. Place transmission in neutral and set parking brake.

2) Place a thin insulator (piece of paper) between curb idle adjusting screw and carburetor switch, or make sure screw is not touching switch. *See Fig. 5*. Remove and plug vacuum line at vacuum transducer.

3) Connect an auxiliary vacuum supply to vacuum transducer and apply 10 in. Hg vacuum for 3.7L engines or 16 in. Hg vacuum for 5.2L engines. Increase engine speed to 2000 RPM, wait one minute for specified accumulator clock up time, and then check specifications. Advance specifications are in addition to basic advance.

CAUTION: **Use a metal exhaust tube for this test, as high temperatures and extended test times could cause rubber hose to catch fire.**

4) If computer fails to obtain specified settings, replace computer.

CHRYSLER CORP. ELECTRONIC SPARK CONTROL (Cont.)

CARBURETOR SWITCH

NOTE: Grounding the carburetor switch eliminates all spark advance.

1) Turn ignition key off and disconnect 10-wire harness connector from computer. With throttle completely closed, check continuity between terminal 7 of harness connector and a good ground. If no continuity is indicated, check wire and carburetor switch.

2) Recheck basic timing. With throttle opened, check continuity between terminal 7 of harness connector and a good ground. There should be no continuity. If continuity exists, replace carburetor switch.

COOLANT TEMPERATURE SENSOR

1) Connect ohmmeter leads to sensor terminals. With engine cold and ambient temperature below 90°F (32°C), resistance should be 500-1000 ohms. With engine hot (normal operating temperature), resistance should be more than 1300 ohms.

2) If not to specifications, replace coolant temperature sensor. The sensor will continually change its resistance with changes in engine operating temperature. This device is NOT a switch.

CHARGE TEMPERATURE & COOLANT SWITCH

1) Turn ignition switch "OFF" and disconnect wire from charge temperature switch. Connect one lead of ohmmeter to a good engine ground (or to switch's ground terminal). Connect other lead to center terminal of coolant switch. Check for continuity.

2) For a cold engine, continuity should be present with a resistance less than 100 ohms. If not, replace the switch. The charge temperature switch must be cooler than 60°F (15°C) to obtain this reading.

3) For an engine at normal operating temperature, the terminal should show no continuity. If it does, replace coolant switch or charge temperature switch.

DETONATION SENSOR TEST

NOTE: This test applies to 5.2L V8 4-Bbl. engine only.

1) Connect a variable timing light to engine. Start engine and run it on second highest step of fast idle cam (at least 1200 RPM). Connect an auxiliary vacuum supply of 16 in. Hg vacuum to vacuum transducer.

2) Using a small end wrench, lightly tap on manifold near sensor. Using the timing light, look for a decrease in spark advance. The amount of decrease in timing should be in proportion to the strength and frequency of the tapping.

3) Maximum decrease in timing would be 11°. Shut off engine and disconnect timing light. If ignition timing retards more than 11°, or timing does not retard at all, replace detonation sensor.

OVERHAUL

DISASSEMBLY

1) Remove distributor cap. Using 2 screwdrivers, pry off rotor from shaft. Remove reluctor by prying up from bottom of reluctor using 2 pry bars or screwdrivers with a maximum width of 7/16". Be careful not to distort or damage reluctor teeth.

2) Remove 2 screws and lock washers attaching plate to housing, and lift out plate and pick-up coil(s) as an assembly. Do not attempt to remove distributor cap clamps, as they are peened in place.

3) If distributor has more than .006" (.15 mm) shaft side play, replace housing shaft and reluctor sleeve by removing shaft retaining pin and sliding retainer off end of shaft.

4) On 3.7L 6-cylinder engines only, the distributor drive gear must be replaced if it is either worn or damaged. Scribe a line on the bottom of distributor shaft in a direct line with the original distributor drive gear retaining pin hole. Remove drive gear retaining pin and drive gear.

5) Use a file to clean burrs from around pin hole in shaft and remove lower thrust washer. Push shaft up and remove shaft through top of distributor housing.

REASSEMBLY

1) Inspect all bearing surfaces and pivot pins for roughness, binding, or looseness. Lubricate and install upper thrust washer on shaft and slide shaft into distributor housing.

NOTE: Steps 2) and 3) apply to 3.7L 6-Cylinder engines only.

2) Slide new drive gear onto shaft and position drive gear retaining pin hole 90° from original hole, using scribed line on distributor shaft as a guide. It will be necessary to drill a new hole in the distributor shaft.

Fig. 10: Exploded View of 3.7L 6-Cylinder ESC Distributor

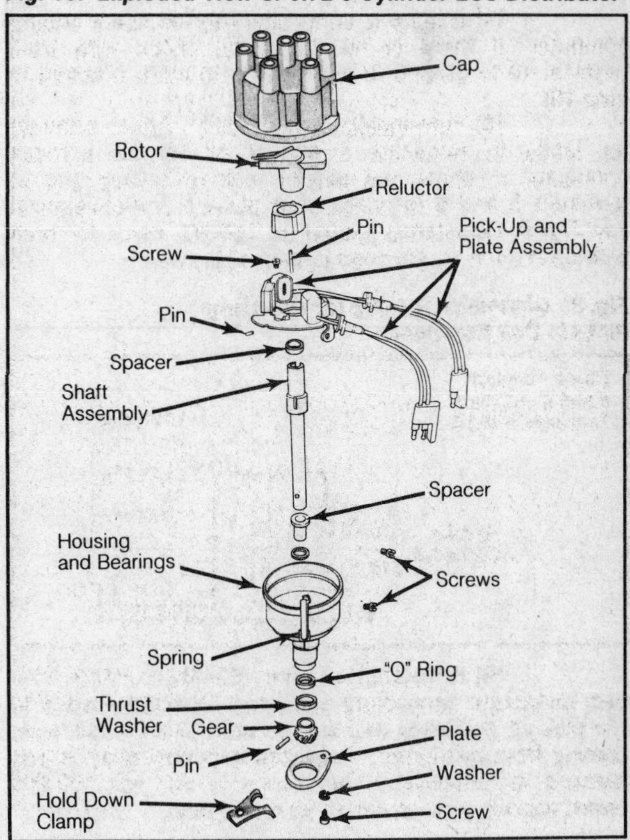

CHRYSLER CORP. ELECTRONIC SPARK CONTROL (Cont.)

3) Before drilling new hole, .124-.129" (3.15-3.28 mm) in diameter, be sure that clearance between drive gear and thrust washer is .007" (.18 mm). Drill new hole and install new drive gear and drive gear retaining pin.

4) Install distributor shaft retainer and pin (5.2L V8 engines only). Install lower plate, upper plate, and pick-up coil(s) as an assembly.

5) Position reluctor keeper pin into place on reluctor sleeve and firmly press reluctor into place. Make sure keeper pin is in place. Lubricate felt pad in top of reluctor sleeve and install rotor and cap.

Fig. 11: Exploded View of 5.2L V8 ESC Distributor

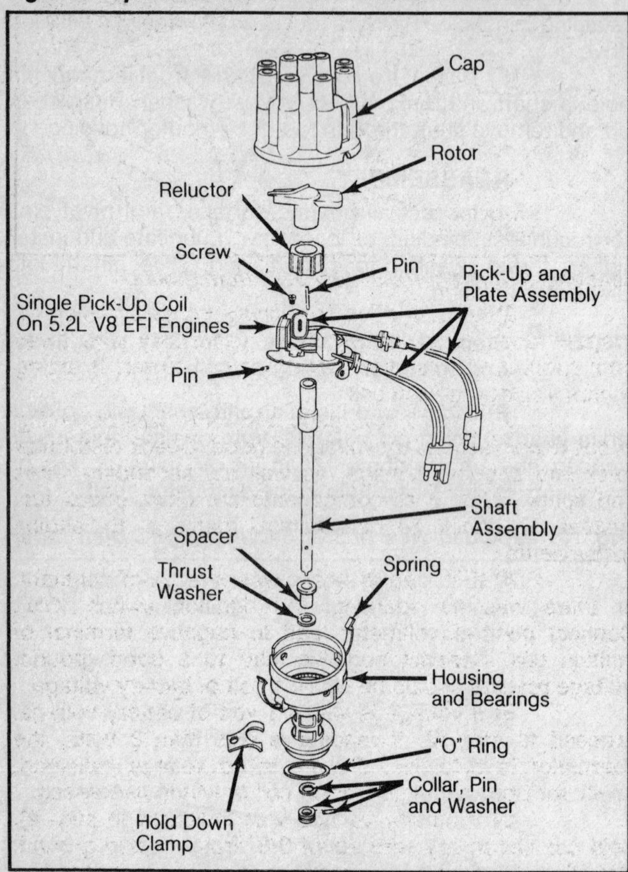

Models with EFI use a single pick-up coil.

CHRYSLER CORP. (MITSUBISHI) ELECTRONIC IGNITION

Chrysler Corp. Models with 2.6L Engines

DESCRIPTION

The Electronic Ignition System used with the 2.6L engine consists of a battery, ignition switch, ignition coil, IC ignitor (electronic control unit), spark plugs and wiring. *See Fig. 1*. The IC (integrated circuit) ignitor is built into the distributor.

The distributor consists of a power distributing section, a signal generator (reluctor and pick-up coil assembly), an IC ignitor, drive gear and both centrifugal and vacuum advance mechanisms.

Fig. 1: Location of 2.6L Ignition System Components

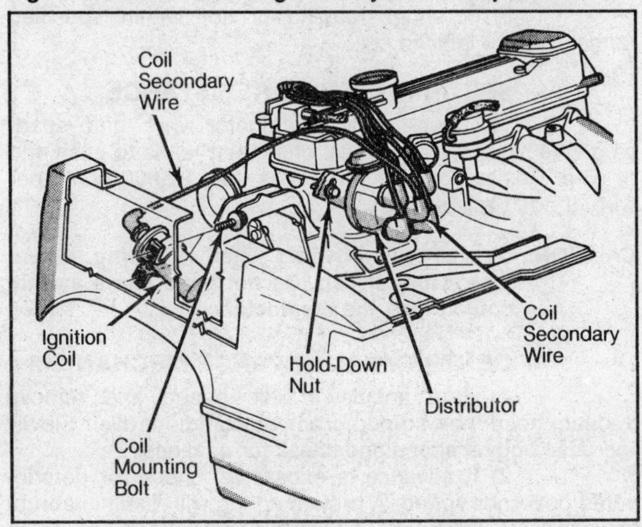

OPERATION

As the distributor shaft turns, a reluctor rotates inside a pick-up coil assembly. As the reluctor teeth pass the pick-up coil, a signal is generated similar to that produced by a small magneto generator.

The signal is produced in exact synchronization with distributor shaft rotation, four times per rotation and at equally spaced intervals.

The signal generated is sent to the IC ignitor, which then switches current on or off in the ignition coil primary circuit. As current is shut off, the magnetic field in the coil primary collapses. This results in a voltage surge in the secondary, firing the spark plugs.

The centrifugal advance mechanism is located below the rotor assembly. As engine speed increases, the weights move outward, causing the reluctor to rotate ahead of the distributor shaft, advancing timing.

The vacuum advance has a spring-loaded diaphragm connected to the breaker assembly. As engine vacuum increases, the diaphragm pivots the movable breaker assembly in a direction opposite to shaft rotation. This, too, advances ignition timing.

ADJUSTMENTS

The only adjustments that can be made to this system are basic ignition timing (changing distributor position) and spark plug gap.

TESTING

IGNITION SYSTEM

1) Remove secondary wire from distributor center tower. Hold end of wire approximately 3/8" from a good engine ground. Crank engine and check for a bright blue spark at gap. *See Fig. 2.*

Fig. 2: Testing Ignition System for Spark

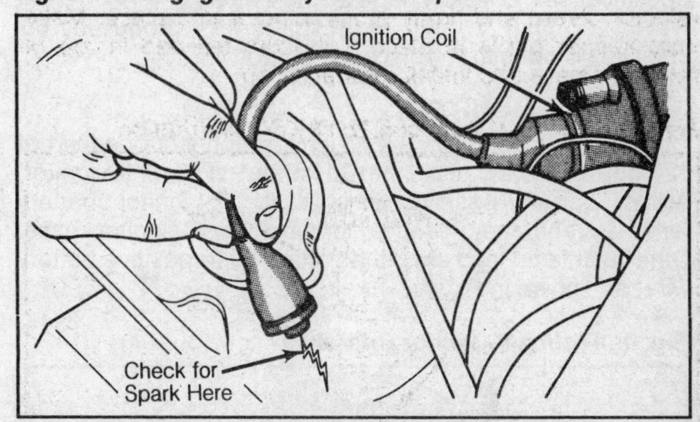

Hold end of wire approximately 3/8" from ground.

2) If spark does not occur, proceed to step **4)**. If spark does occur, slowly move secondary wire away from ground, checking for arcing at coil tower. If arcing occurs, replace ignition coil.

3) If spark was good and there was no arcing at coil tower, secondary voltage is good. Check distributor rotor and cap for damage, as well as, secondary wires and spark plugs. If all components are okay, check fuel system or check for mechanical damage to engine components.

4) If in step **2)** spark was weak, not constant, or there was no sparking, turn ignition switch "ON". Connect positive voltmeter lead to negative terminal of ignition coil. Connect negative lead to a good ground. Voltage reading should be within 1 volt of battery voltage.

5) If voltage is within 1 volt of battery voltage, proceed to step **6)**. If reading is less than 3 volts, the distributor is defective. If there is no voltage indicated, check for open circuit in ignition coil or wiring harnesses.

6) If battery voltage was indicated in step **4)**, hold coil secondary wire about 3/8" from a good ground. *See Fig. 3*. Using a special jumper wire assembly, momentarily touch ignition coil negative terminal to ground. A spark should result.

Fig. 3: Special Ignition System Jumper Wire Assembly

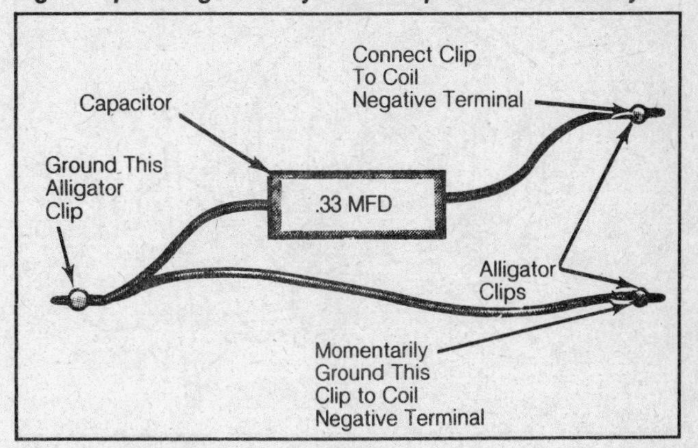

CHRYSLER CORP. (MITSUBISHI) ELECTRONIC IGNITION (Cont.)

7) If spark results, but engine does not start, proceed to step **9)**. If there was no spark, check for voltage at positive terminal of ignition coil with ignition switch on (voltmeter positive lead to positive terminal, negative lead to ground). Reading should be at least 12 volts.

8) If proper voltage is read, ignition coil is defective and must be replaced. If voltage was not to specifications, check wiring back to battery.

9) If in step **6)** a spark was produced, but vehicle will not start, replace distributor.

IC IGNITOR

1) To check the IC ignitor, connect one lead of 12-volt, 3-30 watt test lamp to output side of IC ignitor. Attach battery positive terminal to IC ignitor battery terminal, and the negative terminal to IC ignitor base. Other test lamp lead should be attached to positive battery wire, as shown in *Fig. 4*.

Fig. 4: Testing IC Ignitor Operation

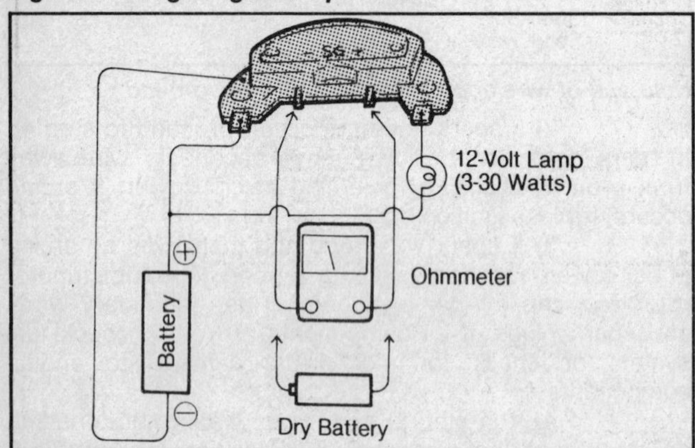

Polarity of ohmmeter or dry battery may be reversed.

2) Using a dry battery or ohmmeter, apply small voltage to signal input terminals of IC ignitor. Test lamp should light when signal voltage is applied and go out when it is removed. If not, replace IC ignitor.

3) If lamp does not operate as stated, IC ignitor is defective. However, if lamp does operate properly, IC ignitor still could be faulty. Part substitution is recommended as a final test in such cases.

Fig. 5: Measuring Pick-Up Coil Resistance

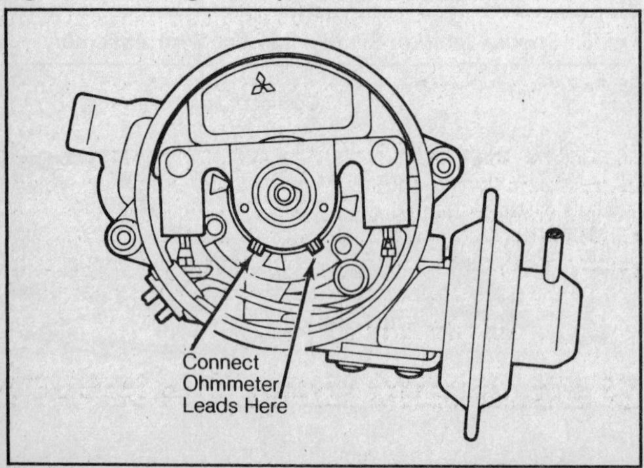

PICK-UP COIL RESISTANCE

Connect an ohmmeter to terminals shown in *Fig. 5*. With ignition switch "OFF", resistance should read 920-1120 ohms. If not, replace pick-up coil assembly.

IGNITION COIL RESISTANCE

1) Connect ohmmeter leads to positive and negative terminals of ignition coil. Ignition switch should be "OFF" and wire should be removed from positive terminal of ignition coil to isolate it from system. Primary resistance should be 0.70-0.85 ohm.

2) With ignition switch still "OFF", connect ohmmeter leads to coil negative terminal and coil tower terminal. Secondary resistance should read 9,000-11,000 ohms.

3) If either reading is not within specified range, replace ignition coil.

SECONDARY WIRE RESISTANCE

To check coil-to-distributor wire and spark plug wire resistance, connect ohmmeter leads to each end of wire. Resistance should be less than 22,000 ohms per wire. If not, replace wires.

CAUTION: Do not pull on wires when removing. Grasp wire's rubber cap. Do not bend wires as this could break the conductor.

CENTRIFUGAL ADVANCE MECHANISM

1) Run engine at idle speed and remove vacuum hose (non-striped) from vacuum controller. Slowly increase engine speed and check for advance.

2) If advance is excessive, check for deteriorated governor spring. A broken spring will result in abrupt advance. If advance is insufficient, check governor weights and cam for faulty operation.

VACUUM ADVANCE MECHANISM

1) Set engine speed at 2500 RPM. Check for advance by disconnecting and connecting distributor vacuum hose.

2) If available, connect a vacuum pump after removing distributor vacuum hose. Run engine at idle and slowly apply vacuum to check for advance.

3) If advance is excessive, check for deteriorated or sagging vacuum controller. If advance is insufficient or there is no advance, breaker plate is not operating properly or vacuum diaphragm is damaged.

OVERHAUL

DISASSEMBLY

1) Remove distributor cap and rotor. *See Fig. 6*. Remove centrifugal advance components as an assembly by removing screw in top of shaft. Due to extreme tightness of bolt, a socket or box wrench should be used for this purpose.

2) If governor assembly is further disassembled, be sure 2 different springs are properly identified for correct reassembly. Remove wire clamp screw and remove clamp. Remove 2 screws securing pick-up coil assembly and IC ignitor and remove them as an assembly.

3) Remove 2 screws securing vacuum diaphragm assembly. Disengage vacuum diaphragm from

CHRYSLER CORP. (MITSUBISHI) ELECTRONIC IGNITION (Cont.)

breaker assembly. Remove 2 screws retaining breaker assembly, and lift assembly from distributor housing.

4) Remove 2 screws from bearing retainer plate. Lift out plate. Mark location of drive gear on distributor shaft for later reassembly alignment. Drive out roll pin and remove drive gear. Lift distributor shaft and bearing assembly from housing. Remove housing seal.

REASSEMBLY

Reassemble in reverse order of disassembly. Check distributor cap for cracks, flashover, damage to carbon brush, and burned or worn terminals. Remove light scaling from terminals. Be sure that grease on back side of IC ignitor is not removed, as it is necessary for heat dissipation. Also, apply grease to all sliding surfaces.

Fig. 6: Exploded View of Distributor Used on 2.6L Engines

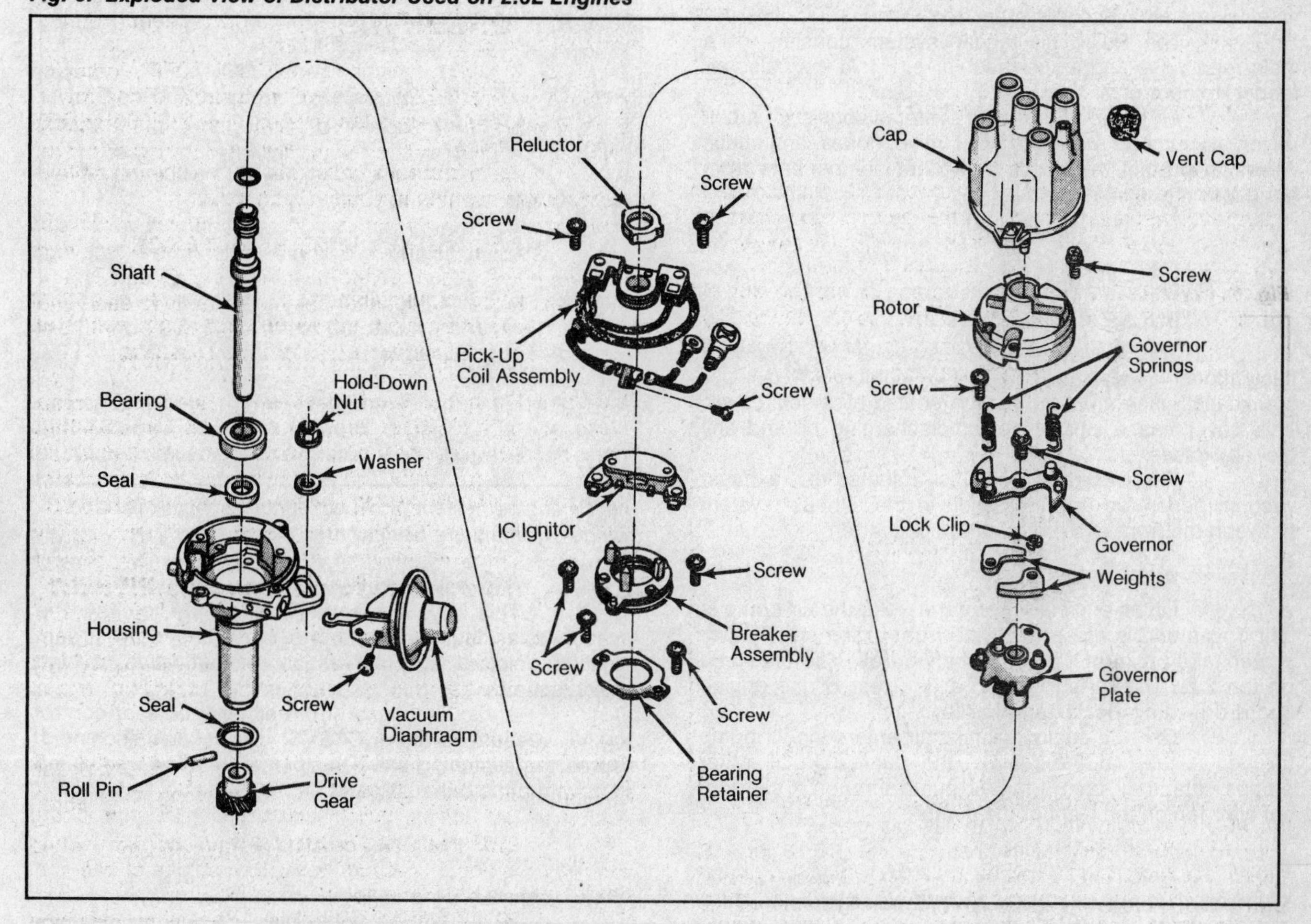

CHRYSLER CORP. AIR INJECTION SYSTEMS

DESCRIPTION

The air injection system adds a controlled amount of fresh air to the exhaust gases, at the exhaust manifold or downstream, to aid in complete oxidation of the exhaust gases. This results in reduced levels of carbon monoxide (CO) and hydrocarbon (HC) emissions.

The 2.6L engine uses a pulse air feeder (PAF) system to supply this additional air. All other engines use an air pump air injection system.

The Pulse air feeder system consists of a main-reed valve and a sub-reed valve, within the pulse air feeder, to control air flow.

Air pump air injection systems consist of a belt driven air pump, a switching/relief valve, hoses, and check valves to protect the hoses and other components from hot gases in the injection tubes.

OPERATION

PULSE AIR FEEDER

The main-reed valve responds to pressure fluctuations generated within the number 3 cylinder crankcase, since the crankcase is sealed by a seal cover. This cover has a small hole for discharging oil and any blow-by gases.

The sub-reed valve is actuated by exhaust vacuum generated from pulsation in the exhaust system between the front and rear catalytic converters.

AIR PUMP

On all engines except the 2.2L, the air pump is belt driven and is mounted at the front of the engine with power take-off from the crankshaft pulley. The air pump on the 2.2L engine is mounted at the rear of the engine and is driven by the camshaft pulley.

On 1.7L engines, intake air enters the air pump through a tube at the rear of the pump. On all other pumps, intake air enters the air pump through a centrifugal filter fan on the front of the pump.

CAUTION: The intake tube at the rear of the pump used on 1.7L engines is larger in diameter than the discharge tube. If hoses are not connected properly, pump damage may occur.

Fig. 2: Air Pump Air Injection System

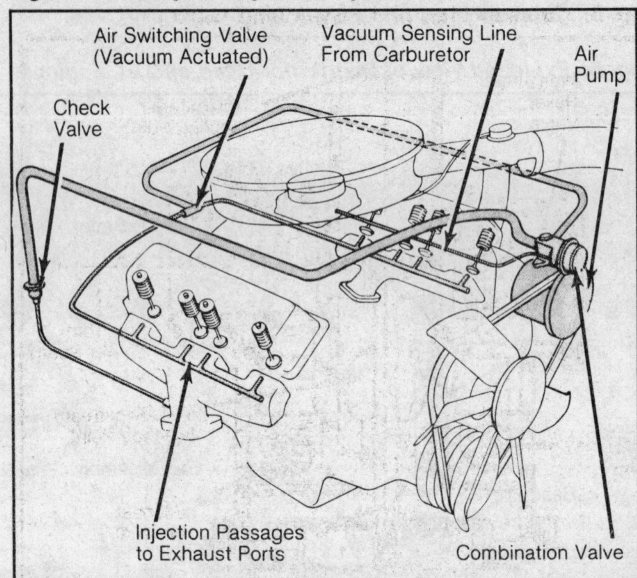

The V8 engine system is shown although 4-cylinder and 6-cylinder systems are basically the same.

AIR SWITCHING VALVE

This valve directs air injection flow to either the location near the exhaust ports or to the downstream injection point. It also serves as a relief valve at high engine speeds.

A vacuum signal, from either a coolant control engine vacuum switch (CCEVS) or vacuum solenoid, causes the switching valve to open. This allows air pump air flow into the exhaust ports.

Fig. 1: 2.6L Pulse Air Feeder Air Injection System

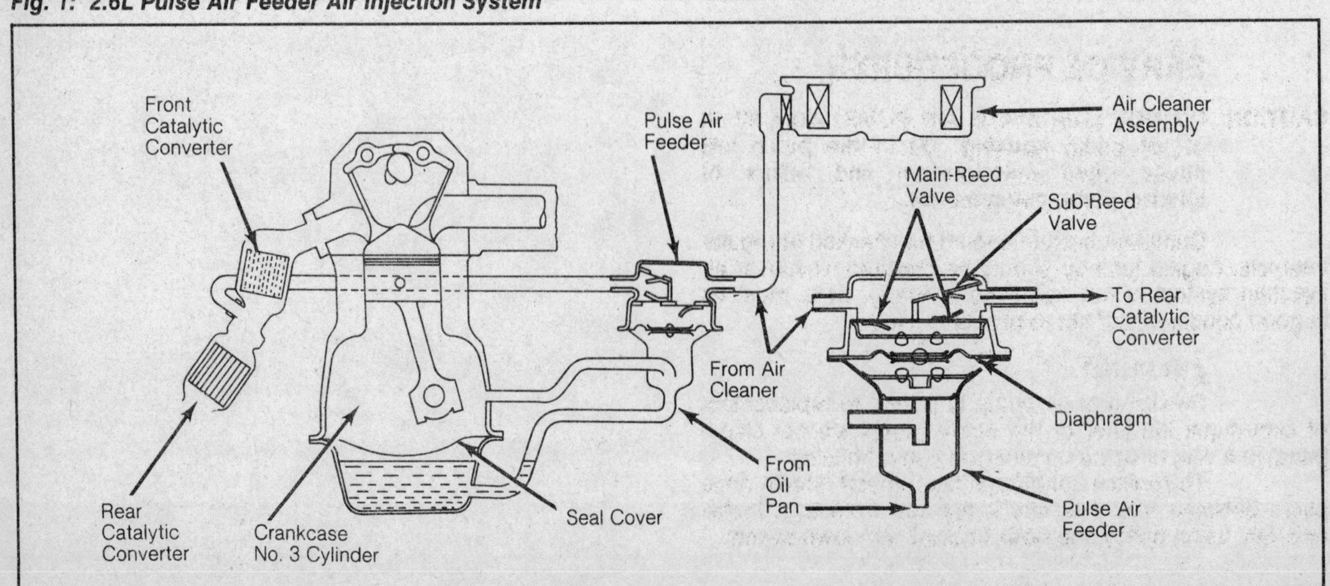

CHRYSLER CORP. AIR INJECTION SYSTEMS (Cont.)

When the CCEVS shuts off vacuum to the switching valve, a bleed orifice in the vacuum line of the combination valve allows vacuum to go to zero. This causes the valve to switch air pump air to the downstream injection point.

Fig. 3: Cutaway View of Air Switching Valve

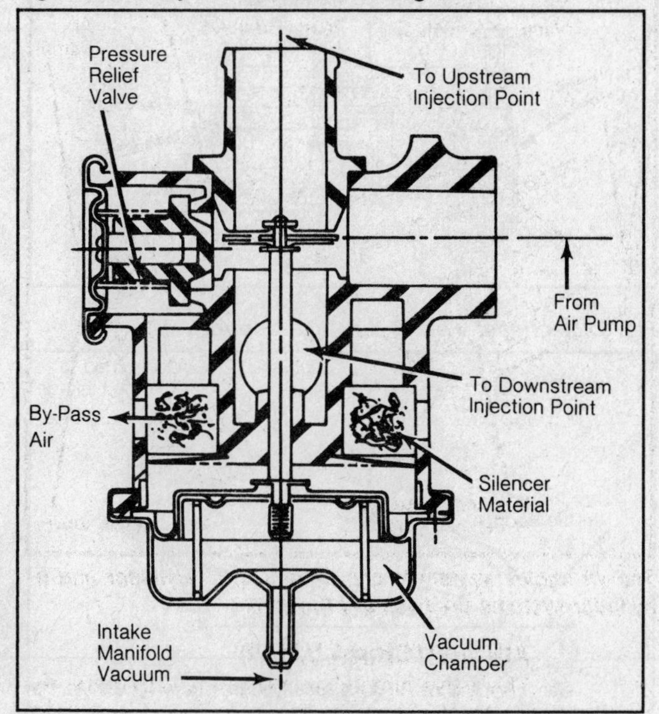

CHECK VALVE

This valve is located in the injection tube assemblies that lead to the exhaust manifolds or to the downstream injection point. The valve has a one-way diaphragm which prevents hot exhaust gases from backing up into the hoses and pump.

This valve will protect the system in the event of air pump belt failure, abnormally high exhaust system pressure or air hose rupture.

SERVICE PROCEDURES

CAUTION: DO NOT LUBRICATE AIR PUMP. Wipe all oil off of pump housing. Oil in the pump will cause rapid deterioration and failure of internal pump components.

Complete system should be checked at regular intervals. Engine tune-up should be checked whenever air injection system is not operating properly. Belts must be in good condition and set to proper tension.

AIR PUMP

Servicing of air pump is limited to replacement of centrifugal fan filter or the entire pump. Do not clamp pump in a vise or use a hammer on pump housing.

To replace centrifugal filter, insert needle nose pliers between filter fins and break fan from hub. Install new fan, using pulley and bolts to draw fan down evenly.

NOTE: Fan might have a slight squeal until sealing lip is worn in. Air injection system is not completely noiseless. Normal noise increases in pitch as engine speed increases.

CAUTION: If the engine compartment is to be cleaned with steam or high pressure liquids, fan filter should be masked off to prevent liquid from entering air pump.

TESTING

PULSE AIR FEEDER VALVE

1) With engine running, remove hose from air cleaner. Check for vacuum at hose opening by covering with hand.

2) If no vacuum is generated, check hoses for a leak and evidence of oil leaks.

AIR SWITCHING VALVE

1) With engine running, apply vacuum to valve. Air should be injected upstream only.

2) If air escapes from silencer ports or is applied upstream and downstream, valve is faulty and must be replaced.

CHECK VALVE

1) To check operation of this valve, remove air supply hose from check valve inlet tube.

2) With engine operating, listen for exhaust leakage at check valve. If exhaust gases escape from valve, valve must be replaced. Also check for leaks at all other connections.

CHRYSLER CORP. EXHAUST GAS RECIRCULATION

DESCRIPTION

The exhaust gas recirculation (EGR) system allows a predetermined amount of exhaust gas to recirculate to the intake manifold. This dilutes the incoming air/fuel mixture.

This diluting of the air/fuel mixture reduces peak flame temperatures during combustion. The reduced temperature reduces emissions of oxides of nitrogen (NOx).

OPERATION

Ported vacuum control provides signals for EGR operation on 1.6L, 1.7L and 2.2L 4-cylinder engines. The 2.6L 4-cylinder engine utilizes a carburetor vacuum controlled dual EGR control valve in addition to a mechanically-linked sub-EGR control valve. Venturi vacuum control is used for EGR operation on 6-cylinder and V8 engines.

PORTED VACUUM CONTROL SYSTEM

1.6L, 1.7L & 2.2L 4-Cylinder Engines

As the throttle blade opens, a slot type port in the carburetor throttle body is exposed to an increasing percentage of manifold vacuum. This port is connected through an external nipple directly to the EGR valve.

The flow rate is dependant on manifold vacuum, throttle position and exhaust gas back-pressure.

Fig. 1: Ported Vacuum Control EGR System Used on 1.6L, 1.7L & 2.2L 4-Cylinder Engines

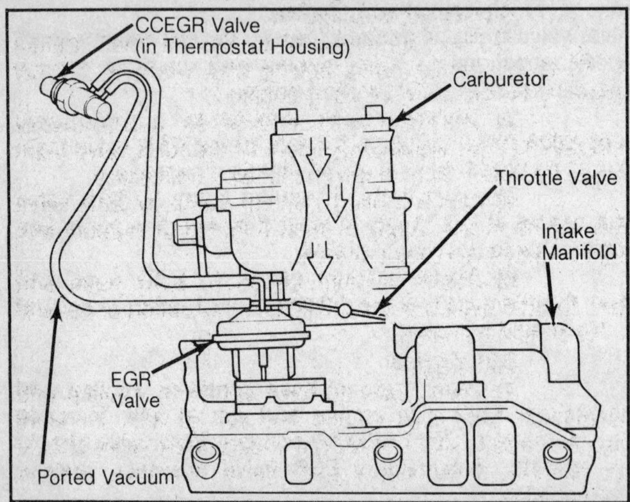

DUAL EGR SYSTEM CONTROL VALVE

2.6L 4-Cylinder Engine

The dual EGR system has primary and secondary valves which respond to different carburetor vacuums in response to throttle opening. EGR operation is suspended at idle and wide open throttle.

The primary valve controls EGR flow at relatively small throttle opening angles. The secondary control valve allows recirculation of exhaust gas into the intake mixture at larger throttle opening angles.

Vacuum applied to the dual EGR control valve is controlled by a thermo valve. The sub-EGR valve is directly opened and closed with motion of the throttle valve though mechanical linkage.

Fig. 2: Sectional View of Dual EGR Control Valve

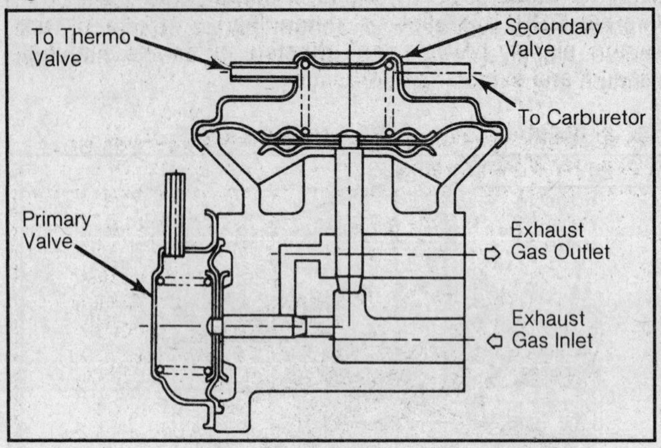

Fig. 3: Sectional View of Sub-EGR Control Valve

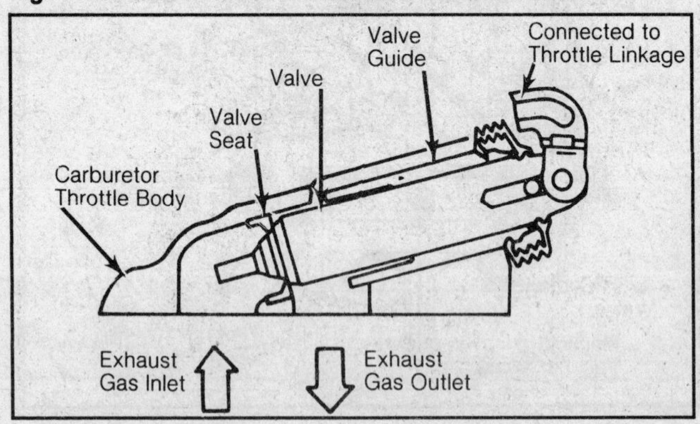

Two thermo valves sense coolant temperature at the intake manifold and prevent operation of the dual EGR valve below the preset temperature of the thermo valve.

Fig. 4: EGR System for 2.6L 4-Cylinder Engine

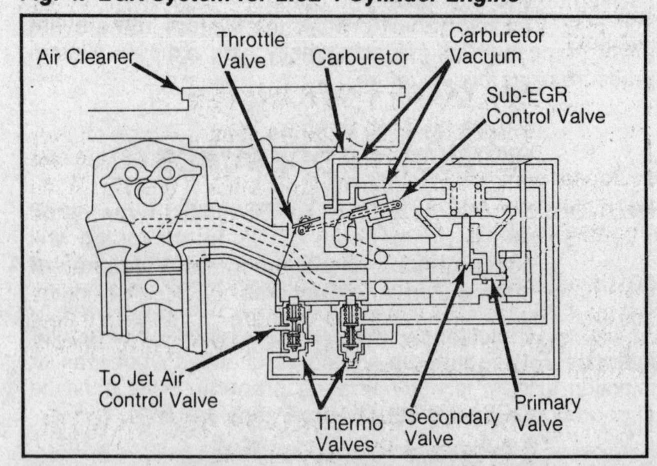

VENTURI VACUUM CONTROL SYSTEM

6-Cylinder & V8 Engines

Vacuum is tapped at the throat of the carburetor venturi or air flow sensor (EFI models) to provide control vacuum to the vacuum amplifier. This low amplitude vacuum signal is increased in the amplifier to a level which will operate the EGR valve.

CHRYSLER CORP. EXHAUST GAS RECIRCULATION (Cont.)

A dump diaphragm compares venturi and manifold vacuum to prevent EGR operation at wide open throttle. EGR operation is determined primarily by the venturi signal, but is also effected by intake manifold vacuum and exhaust gas pressure.

Fig. 5: Venturi Vacuum Control EGR System Used on 6-Cylinder & V8 Engines

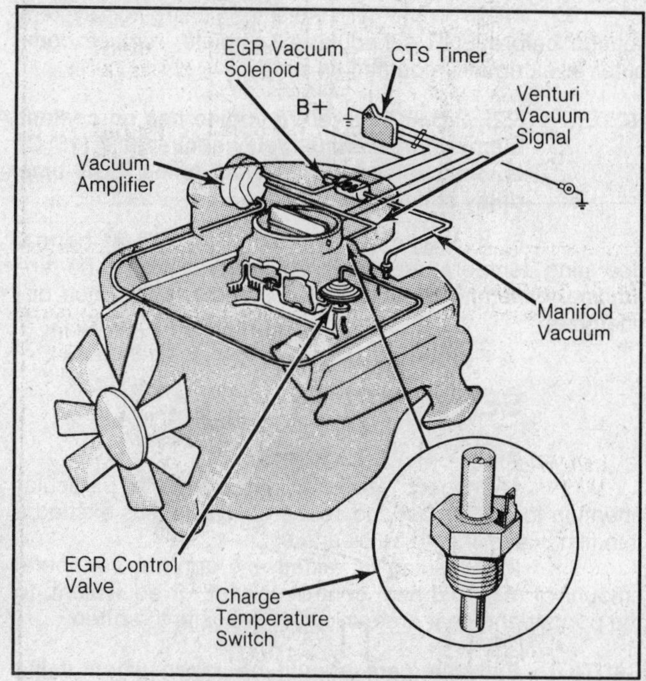

COOLANT CONTROL EGR VALVE (CCEGR)

The CCEGR valve is located in the thermostat housing on 4-cylinder engines. On 6-cylinder engines, the CCEGR valve is located in the cylinder head. On V8 engines, the CCEGR valve is located in the intake manifold.

EGR DELAY TIMER SYSTEM

6-Cylinder & V8 Engines Only

Vehicles having a 6-cylinder or V8 engine are equipped with EGR delay system which consists of an electrical timer which in turn is connected to an engine mounted solenoid.

The purpose of the delay device is to not allow EGR function for a preset amount of time following engine start-up. The CCEGR valve will override this system if cold engine start is made. Amount of time delay differs between model applications.

CHARGE TEMPERATURE SWITCH (CTS)

6-Cylinder & V8 Engines Only

The CTS is installed in the number 6 runner of the intake manifold on 6-cylinder engines and in the number 8 runner of the intake manifold on V8 engines.

When air/fuel mixture temperature is below 60°F (16°C), the switch closes. This prevents EGR timer and EGR valve operation. When air/fuel temperature is above 60°F (16°C), the switch opens. This again allows the EGR timer and EGR valve to operate

EGR CTS TIMER

6-Cylinder & V8 Engines Only

Used with CTS, the CTS timer is not interchangable with earlier models. Due to wiring harness and function changes, 3 timers are used. They are color coded Black, Orange or Red to correspond with various applications.

Fig. 6: Charge Temperature Switch (CTS) Used on 6-Cylinder and V8 Engines

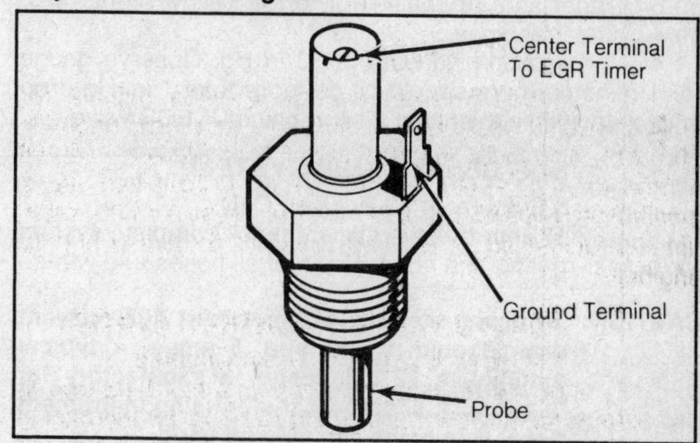

TESTING

SYSTEM FUNCTIONAL CHECK

All Except 2.6L Engine

1) Place transmission in Neutral (man. trans.) or "P" (auto. trans.). Start engine and warm to normal operating temperature by idling engine.

2) Abruptly open throttle to approximately 2000-3000 RPM. Visible movement of the EGR valve stem should be noted. Repeat several times if necessary.

3) Attach a hand vacuum pump to EGR valve with engine at idle. Apply at least 5 in. Hg of vacuum and engine should run rough or stall.

4) Attach vacuum gauge to EGR hose and open throttle quickly several times. A fluctuation of several in. Hg should be noted.

2.6L Engine

1) Check vacuum hose condition, routing and installation. Start cold engine and run at idle. Increase engine speed to 2500 RPM. Secondary EGR valve should not operate. If secondary EGR valve operates, replace thermo valve.

2) Warm engine to at least 150°F (66°C). Accelerate engine to 2500 RPM. Secondary EGR valve should operate. If it does not, inspect EGR valve or thermo valve and replace as necessary.

3) Disconnect Green striped hose from nipple on carburetor. Connect vacuum pump to hose. Pull sub-EGR valve by hand and apply 6 in. Hg vacuum.

4) If engine idling speed becomes unstable, the secondary valve is operating properly. If no change, the EGR valve or thermo valve is not operating properly.

5) Disconnect vacuum pump. Reconnect Green striped hose to carburetor. Disconnect Yellow striped hose. Connect vacuum pump to Yellow striped hose. Apply 6 in. Hg vacuum with hand pump.

CHRYSLER CORP. EXHAUST GAS RECIRCULATION (Cont.)

6) If engine idling speed becomes unstable, primary valve is operating properly. If no change, the EGR valve or thermo valve is not operating properly.

CCEGR VALVE

1) Remove CCEGR valve from vehicle. Place it in an ice bath to bring temperature of coolant sensing portion to below 40°F (4°C).

2) Attach a hand vacuum pump with gauge to the CCEGR nipple corresponding to the Blue stripe hose on 6-cylinder and V8 engines or to the Yellow stripe hose on 4-cylinder engines.

3) Apply vacuum of 10 in Hg. Observe gauge for 1 minute. There should be no more than 1 in. Hg drop in vacuum within this time. If so, replace CCEGR valve.

EGR DELAY TIMER SYSTEM

6-Cylinder & V8 Engines Only

1) Before testing timer, check complete system for proper routing and connections of all hoses and wires.

CAUTION: **To avoid overload of timer, test light current draw should not exceed .5 amps. A typical automotive 12 volt tester is satisfactory for this test. A shop built tester using instrument panel size bulbs can also be used.**

2) With ignition switch off, remove wiring connector from time delay solenoid valve. Connect a test light across wiring connector terminals just removed.

3) Start engine. Test light should come on and remain on for the amount of time as shown in color code application chart.

4) If light does not come on, remains on indefinitely, or does not react within the time limit shown, replace timer and repeat this test.

EGR TIMER SPECIFICATIONS

Delay Solenoid Color Code	Time Delay in Seconds
Black	35
Orange	60
Red	90

EGR TIME DELAY SOLENOID

6-Cylinder & V8 Engines Only

1) Make sure that all vacuum hoses are routed properly, correctly connected and not leaking. Disconnect electrical plug from solenoid valve.

2) Connect either solenoid terminal to a ground. Connect other terminal to positive battery terminal. This should activate the solenoid valve and shut off control vacuum to the EGR system.

3) You should hear a "click" from the solenoid as it is connected to the battery positive terminal.

4) To test valve operation, start engine and let it idle. Raise engine speed to about 2000 RPM. Watch EGR control valve stem. EGR control valve stem should move. If it does not, replace delay solenoid.

ELECTRONIC EGR SYSTEM

6-Cylinder & V8 Engines Only

1) With engine cold and not running, connect a voltmeter to Gray wire at EGR solenoid. Set parking brake and start engine.

2) Voltmeter should read less than 1 volt. This 1 volt reading should remain until engine has reached normal operating temperature and electronic EGR schedule has timed out.

3) Solenoid will de-energize when EGR schedule has timed out. At this point voltage should read charging system voltage. If not, replace solenoid and repeat this test.

4) If voltmeter indicates charging system voltage before EGR schedule is complete, replace computer or externally mounted timer.

NOTE: **5.2L 2-Bbl. Federal V8 engine has no coolant temperature thermal delay above 60°F (16°C) ambient temperature. It will follow EGR time delay schedule only.**

5) If engine is restarted while still at normal operating temperature, EGR solenoid will only be energized for length of time delay schedule. It will then de-energize.

SERVICING

EGR VALVE

1) Inspect valve for deposits with particular attention to the poppet and seat area. If deposits exceed a thin film, valve should be cleaned.

2) Cleaning is aided by applying a liberal amount of manifold heat control solvent, or equivalent, to the poppet and seat area, allowing deposits to soften

CAUTION: **Extreme care should be taken when using solvent cleaners to prevent spilling of solvent on valve diaphragm.**

3) Use an external vacuum source to open poppet and then scrape deposit from this area. If wear of stem or other moving components is noted, valve should be replaced.

NOTE: **Do not push valve stem manually, use an external vacuum source only.**

TROUBLE SHOOTING

NOTE: **All tests must be made with engine fully warm and running for at least 2 minutes.**

EGR VALVE STEM DOES NOT MOVE ON SYSTEM TEST

1) Check for cracked, leaking, disconnected or plugged vacuum. Replace any defective hoses.

2) Connect an external vacuum source to EGR valve diaphragm. Apply at least 10 in. Hg to valve. If no valve movement occurs, Diaphragm is ruptured or stem is frozen. Replace EGR valve.

3) If valve opens 1/8" (3 mm), pinch off supply hose to check for diaphragm leakage. Valve should remain open for at least 30 seconds. If leakage occurs, replace EGR valve.

CHRYSLER CORP. EXHAUST GAS RECIRCULATION (Cont.)

EGR VALVE STEM DOES NOT MOVE ON SYSTEM TEST, BUT OPERATES NORMALLY ON EXTERNAL VACUUM SOURCE

1) Disconnect CCEGR valve and by-pass valve with a short length of 3/16" tubing. If normal movement of EGR valve is restored, replace CCEGR valve.

2) On venturi vacuum type systems, disconnect Orange and Blue (or unstriped) hoses at time delay solenoid valve and by-pass valve with at short piece of tubing.

3) If normal EGR valve stem movement is restored, reconnect hoses to valve and disconnect electrical plug from solenoid. If EGR valve stem does not move, solenoid should be replaced.

4) If solenoid does move, timer should be further tested as previously described.

5) If plugged passages are suspected with the ported vacuum type system, carburetor should be removed and slots inspected and cleaned as necessary. Recheck for normal EGR operation.

6) If plugged passages are suspected with the venturi vacuum system, carburetor cleaner should be used to clean deposits from venturi passage. Use light air pressure to verify that passage is clean.

7) To check for defective vacuum amplifier (venturi vacuum systems), remove venturi vacuum signal hose from carburetor. With engine at idle, apply approximately 2 in. Hg vacuum to the signal hose.

8) Engine speed should drop at least 150 RPM and EGR valve stem should move 1/8" (3 mm) or more. If not, replace vacuum amplifier.

ENGINE WILL NOT IDLE, DIES ON RETURN TO IDLE OR ROUGH IDLE (EGR VALVE OPEN AT IDLE)

1) On venturi vacuum systems, disconnect and plug vacuum hose from EGR valve. If idle is unsatisfactory, replace EGR valve.

2) If idle is okay, reconnect hose to valve and disconnect hose from carburetor. If idle is okay, clean venturi tap. If idle not okay, replace vacuum amplifier.

3) On ported vacuum systems, disconnect an plug vacuum hose from EGR valve. If idle is not okay, replace EGR valve.

4) If idle is still rough, install vacuum gauge on ported signal tap. If more than 1" of vacuum is present, check idle setting. If vacuum is okay, check linkage and carburetor for binding.

ENGINE WILL NOT IDLE, DIES ON RETURN TO IDLE OR ROUGH IDLE (EGR VALVE CLOSED AT IDLE)

If removal of vacuum hose from EGR valve does not correct rough idle, remove EGR valve and inspect to ensure that poppet is seated. Clean deposits from valve or replace EGR valve if necessary.

1983 Exhaust Emission Systems

FORD MOTOR CO. SYSTEMS AND TUNE-UP PROCEDURES

DESCRIPTION

Control of exhaust emissions is accomplished by a combination of engine modifications and special control components. Component usage varies depending on engine and transmission combinations.

MANAGED THERMACTOR AIR (MTA) SYSTEM

The MTA system uses an air pump for the thermactor air source, special devices to control air by-pass and a one-way check valve to provide flow to air injection points (to catalytic converter or intake manifolds).

EXHAUST GAS RECIRCULATION (EGR)

Engine vacuum is used to operate the EGR valve which admits exhaust gases into the intake manifold to control oxides of nitrogen (NOx) emissions. On engines equipped with an Electronic Engine Control system, the control assembly signals the EGR solenoids for more precise control of EGR valve operation.

ELECTRONIC ENGINE CONTROL (EEC) SYSTEMS

The EEC-III system is used on all 5.0L V8 EFI engines. The EEC-IV system is used on 1.6L EFI, 2.3L HSC and 2.3L EFI/Turbo engines.

Various engine and vehicle sensors monitor engine and vehicle operating conditions. Information from these sensors is sent to the electronic control assembly (ECA) where they are analyzed. The ECA then computes correct operating modes and signals other modules to adjust ignition timing, air/fuel ratio, EGR flow rate, thermactor air flow, canister vapor flow and idle speed.

The major functions of these systems are to control air/fuel mixture, ignition timing and emission control. For additional information, see appropriate Electronic Engine Control System article.

MICROPROCESSOR CONTROL UNIT (MCU) SYSTEM

The MCU system is used on 2.3L 1-barrel engines and on 5.8L 2-barrel engines. The micro-computer is programmed to montior engine operations and driver demands under all operating conditions and to adjust engine operation accordingly.

Typical sensor inputs to the MCU are coolant temperature, air/fuel ratio signal, RPM signal and detonation sensor signals. For additional information, see appropriate Ford Motor Co. MCU Engine Control System article.

DURA-SPARK II IGNITION SYSTEM

This system is basically a solid state ignition system consisting of a breakerless distributor, electronic control module, ignition coil, battery, ignition switch, secondary wires and various wiring harnesses. For additional information, see Motorcraft Dura-Spark II Ignition article.

DURA-SPARK III IGNITION SYSTEM

This system is a solid state ignition system which provides power switching of the ignition coil. The EEC-III system controls the ignition input signal. The distributor assembly is unique to the Dura-Spark III system.

The Dura-Spark III distributor is equipped with only a distributor cap, rotor, and adapter. For additional information, see Motorcraft Dura-Spark III Ignition article.

THICK FILM INTEGRATED (TFI) IGNITION SYSTEMS

The TFI (Thick Film Integrated) ignition system is used on all vehicles equipped with 1.6L, 2.3L HSC or 2.3L EFI/Turbo engines. There are 2 different versions of the TFI ignition system. Carbureted 1.6L engines use TFI-I. Fuel injected (EFI) 1.6L engines, 2.3L High Swirl Combustion (HSC) engines and turbocharged 2.3L engines use TFI-IV.

The TFI ignition module is mounted on the distributor housing and is electrically connected to the distributor pick-up coil assembly (TFI-I) or Hall Effect switch assembly (TFI-IV) without the use of a wiring harness between the ignition module and the pick-up coil or Hall Effect switch assembly. For additional information, see Motorcraft TFI Ignition article.

ELECTRIC ASSIST CHOKE SYSTEM

A thermostatic spring heater to aid in fast choke release is installed on some models. This system does not heat when ambient temperatures are below a certain level or when the engine is not running. This system receives power from the alternator (battery on some models) and is grounded through the oil pressure sender switch.

CATALYTIC CONVERTER

The catalytic converter is designed to reduce exhaust emissions of carbon monoxide (CO), hydrocarbons (HC) and oxides of nitrogen (NOx). Various types of catalytic converters are used depending on engine and vehicle applications. For additional information, see Catalytic Converters article.

THERMOSTATIC AIR CLEANER (TAC)

The TAC is used on all models to control the temperature of incoming air. This allows for better control of the air/fuel mixture during all engine operating temperatures. For additional information, see Thermostatic Air Cleaners article.

POSITIVE CRANKCASE VENTILATION

The PCV system removes engine crankcase vapors which result from normal engine combustion. The vapors are drawn through a metered PCV valve and routed back to the intake manifold to be burned in the combustion chamber. For additional information, see Positive Crankcase Ventilation System article.

EVAPORATIVE EMISSION CONTROL

This system is used on all vehicles and is designed to keep fuel system vapors from escaping into the atmosphere. This closed system separates fuel vapors and routes them to the engine to be burned.

A carbon canister stores the vapors until the engine draws them in for burning. For additional information, see Ford Motor Co. Fuel Vapor Emission Control System article.

FORD MOTOR CO. SYSTEMS AND TUNE-UP PROCEDURES (Cont.)

TUNE-UP SERVICE PROCEDURES

In addition to servicing of the individual emission systems, it is important that all ignition timing and carburetor adjustments are properly set.

Due to late changes and corrections, always refer to the Engine Tune-Up Decal in the engine compartment before performing tune-up procedures. In the event that specifications in this manual and decal specifications differ, always use the decal specifications.

IGNITION TIMING

NOTE: **Timing instrument should be connected to number one spark plug wire using an adapter or snap-on connector. Do not puncture spark plug wire or boot to make connection. On 5.0L EFI engine, ignition timing is controlled by the EEC-III computer and is not adjustable.**

1.6L & 2.3L Engines

1) Place transmission in Neutral (man. trans.) or "P" (auto. trans.). Turn air conditioner and heater off. On all except 1.6L EFI engines, disconnect and plug vacuum lines at distributor. On all models, connect a timing light to engine.

2) On 1.6L EFI engines only, disconnect White single wire connector near distributor. On 2.3L engines only, disconnect barometric pressure switch and connect a jumper wire across connector pins that mate with Black and Yellow wires.

3) On all models, start engine and warm to normal operating temperature. With engine at timing RPM, adjust initial ignition timing. Remove jumper wire. Reconnect all connectors and vacuum hoses. Remove all test equipment.

3.3L, 3.8L, 5.0L 4-Bbl. & 5.8L Engines

1) Place transmission in Neutral (man. trans.) or "P" (auto. trans.). Disconnect and plug vacuum lines at distributor. Connect timing light and tachometer to engine.

2) If engine is equipped with a barometric pressure sensor, disconnect it from ignition module and place a jumper wire across Yellow and Black wire pins in ignition module connector.

3) Warm engine to normal operating temperature. With engine at timing RPM, check timing.

4) If timing is within 2° of specified timing, do not adjust. If not, loosen distributor hold-down bolt and turn distributor to adjust. Tighten bolt, then recheck timing.

5) Remove all test equipment and reconnect lines to distributor. Remove jumper wire from ignition module connector and reconnect to sensor.

Fig. 1: 1.6L Firing Order & Timing Marks

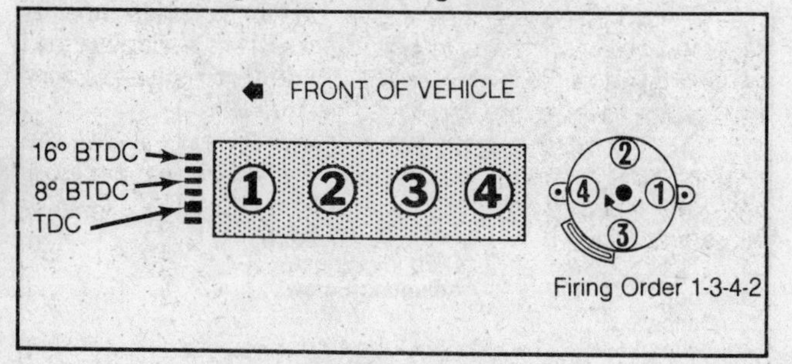

IGNITION TIMING SPECIFICATIONS

Application	Degrees BTDC @ RPM
1.6L 2-Bbl.	
Man. Trans.	8 @ 800
Auto. Trans.	10 @ 800
1.6L 2-Bbl. High Output	
Federal & Calif.	14 @ 800
High Alt.	
Man. Trans.	10 @ 800
Auto. Trans.	14 @ 800
1.6L EFI	
Man. Trans.	10 @ 800
Auto. Trans.	10 @ 750
2.3L 1-Bbl.	9 @ 700
2.3L HSC	[1]
2.3L EFI/Tubro	[1]
3.3L	
Federal & Calif.	10 @ 900
High Alt.	12 @ 900
3.8L	
Federal	
Capri & Mustang	[2] 10 @ 800
Cougar, LTD, Marquis & T-Bird with AOT Trans.	12 @ 800
Cougar & T-Bird with C5 Trans.	10 @ 800
Calif.	
Capri & Mustang	8 @ 800
All Others	10 @ 800
High Alt.	
Capri & Mustang	18 @ 800
Cougar, LTD, Marquis & T-Bird	12 @ 800
5.0L 4-Bbl.	10 @ 800
5.8L	12 @ 600

[1] — Information not available from manufacturer.
[2] — Mustang convertible is 12 @ 800.

Fig. 2: 2.3L Firing Order & Timing Marks

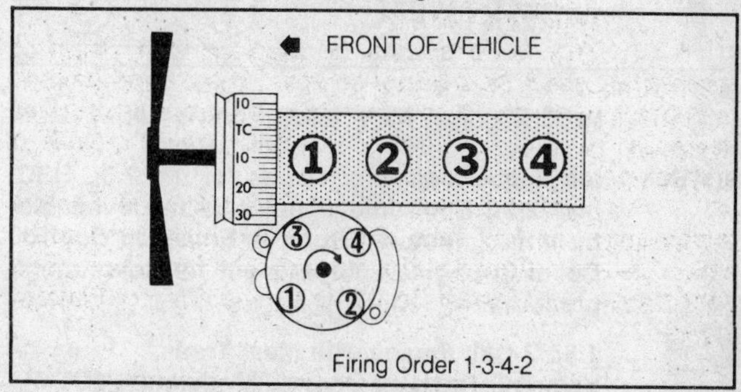

Fig. 3: 3.3L Firing Order & Timing Marks

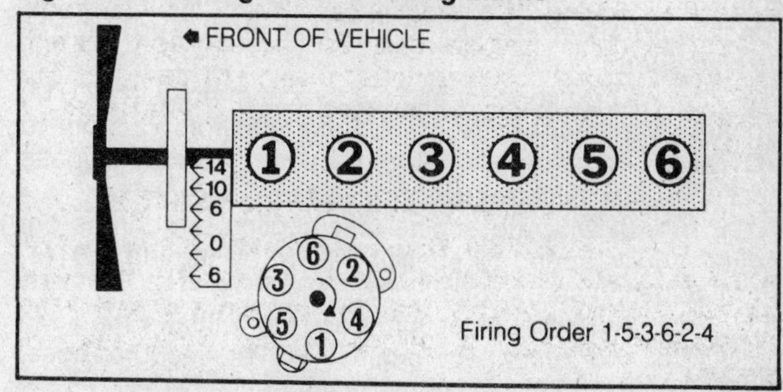

FORD MOTOR CO. SYSTEMS AND TUNE-UP PROCEDURES (Cont.)

Fig. 4: 3.8L Firing Order & Timing Marks

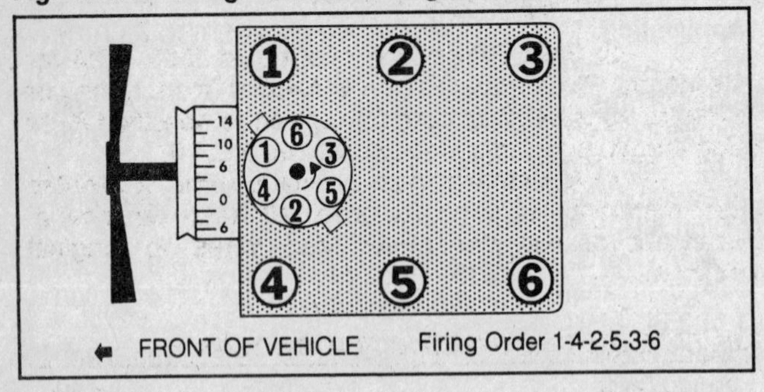

Fig. 5: 5.0L Firing Order & Timing Marks

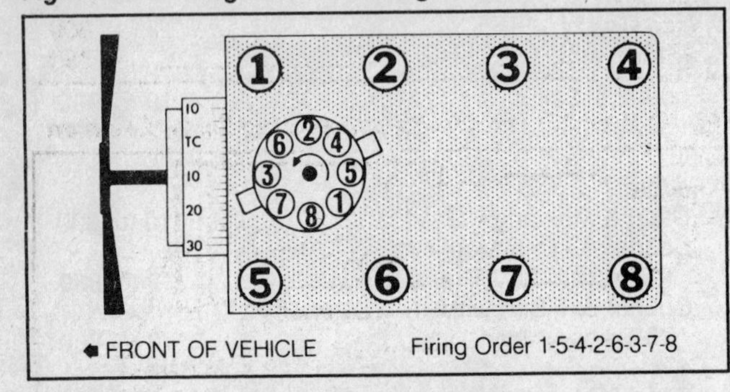

Fig. 6: 5.8L Firing Order & Timing Marks

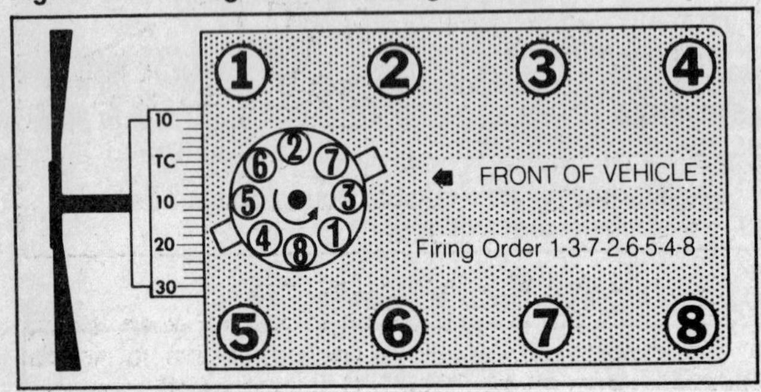

HOT (SLOW) IDLE RPM

NOTE: Idle adjustment procedures for the 2.3L HSC and 2.3L EFI/Turbo engines is not available from manufacturer. Refer to Emission Control Decal in engine compartment for adjustment procedures.

1.6L 2-Bbl. Engine with Man. Trans.
Vacuum Operated Throttle Modulator (VOTM)

1) Place transmission in Neutral. Start engine and warm to normal operating temperature. Place air conditioner/heater selector in HEAT position. Turn blower on high speed.

2) Disconnect and plug vacuum hose at VOTM. Connect a vacuum hose from intake manifold vacuum to VOTM. Disconnect and plug vacuum hose at bypass section of thermactor air control valve.

3) Operate engine until cooling fan comes on. Adjust VOTM speed to specified RPM by turning VOTM-RPM adjusting screw. *See Fig. 7.*

4) Remove vacuum hose from intake manifold to VOTM and reconnect original VOTM vacuum hose. Reconnect vacuum hose to thermactor system.

Fig. 7: 1.6L VOTM-RPM Adjusting Screw Location

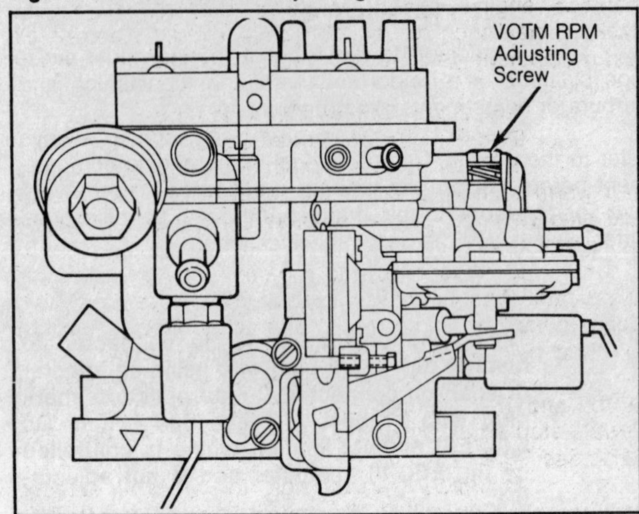

VOTM is used only on 1.6L 2-Bbl. engine with manual transmission.

1.6L VOTM CURB IDLE SPEED (RPM)
(Models with Man. Trans. Only)

Application	VOTM "Off"	VOTM "On"
1.6L 2-Bbl.	800	1200
1.6L 2-Bbl. H.O.	900	1500

1.6L 2-Bbl. Engine with Auto. Trans.
Models Without Idle Speed Control (ISC)

1) Place transmission in "P" or "N". Connect a tachometer to engine. Start engine and warm to normal operating temperature.

2) Disconnect and plug vacuum hose at bypass section of thermactor air control valve. Allow engine to run until cooling fan begins to operate.

3) Place transmission in "D" and adjust curb idle to specified RPM using curb idle speed adjusting screw. *See Fig. 8.*

Fig. 8: 1.6L Curb & Fast Idle Adjusting Screw Locations

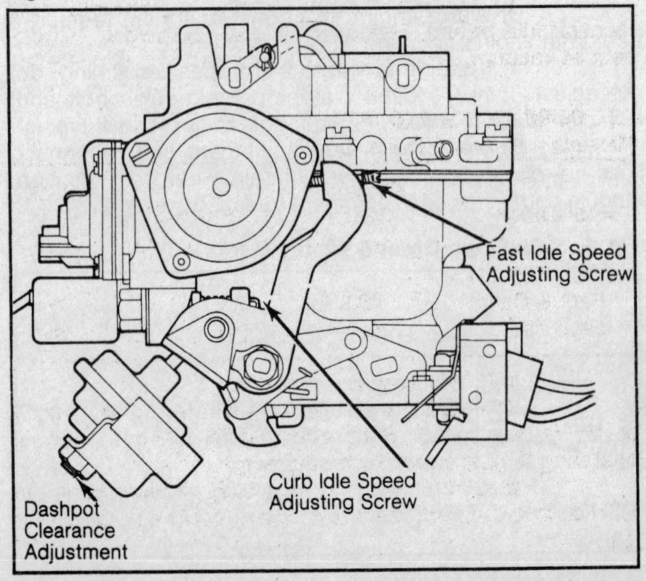

FORD MOTOR CO. SYSTEMS AND TUNE-UP PROCEDURES (Cont.)

4) Place transmission in "N" and momentarily increase engine speed. Recheck idle speed. Adjust dashpot clearance to .14-.18" (3.5-4.5 mm). Remove all test equipment and return vacuum hoses to original positions.

1.6L 2-Bbl. Engine with Auto. Trans. Models With Idle Speed Control (ISC)

1) Place transmission in "P" or "N". Start engine and warm to normal operating temperature. Disconnect and plug vacuum hose at by-pass section of thermactor air control valve.

2) Allow engine to run until cooling fan begins to operate. Disconnect and plug vacuum hose from ISC. Connect vacuum pump to ISC and apply enough vacuum to retract ISC plunger clear of ISC adjusting screw.

3) Place transmission in "D". With transmission in "D" and ISC plunger clear of adjusting screw, turn throttle stop adjusting screw to obtain specified ISC "Off" RPM. *See Fig. 8.*

4) Place transmission in "P" and remove vacuum pump from ISC. Reconnect vacuum line to ISC. With transmission in "D", turn ISC adjusting screw to obtain specified ISC "On" RPM. *See Fig. 9.*

Fig. 9: 1.6L ISC "On" Adjusting Screw Location

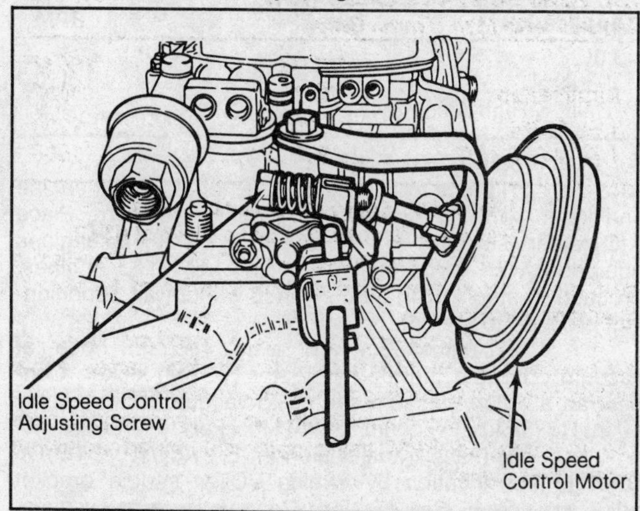

5) Increase engine speed momentarily and recheck idle speed. Removal all test equipment. Reconnect all vacuum lines to original locations.

1.6L CURB IDLE SPEED (RPM)
(Models with Auto. Trans. Only)

Application	Without ISC	With ISC "Off"	With ISC "On"
1.6L 2-Bbl.	750	720	750
1.6L 2-Bbl. H.O.			
Fed. & Calif.	750	720	750
High Alt.	850	820	850

1.6L EFI Engine

1) Place transmission in Neutral (man. trans.) or "P" (auto. trans.). Start engine and warm to normal operating temperature. Turn engine off.

2) Disconnect and plug both vacuum hoses at EGR solenoid. Disconnect idle speed control (ISC) power lead.

NOTE: Make sure that cooling fan is operating when idle adjustment is made.

3) Start engine and operate at 2000 RPM for 60 seconds. Place transmission in Neutral (man. trans.) or "D" (auto. trans.). Adjust curb idle speed to specified RPM using throttle plate adjusting screw. *See Fig. 10.*

4) Adjustment must be made within 2 minutes after restarting engine. Remove all test equipment. Reconnect all vacuum hoses and wires to original locations.

1.6L EFI CURB IDLE SPEED SPECIFICATIONS

Application	RPM
1.6L EFI	
Man. Trans.	800
Auto. Trans.	750

Fig. 10: 1.6L EFI Throttle Plate Adjusting Screw Location

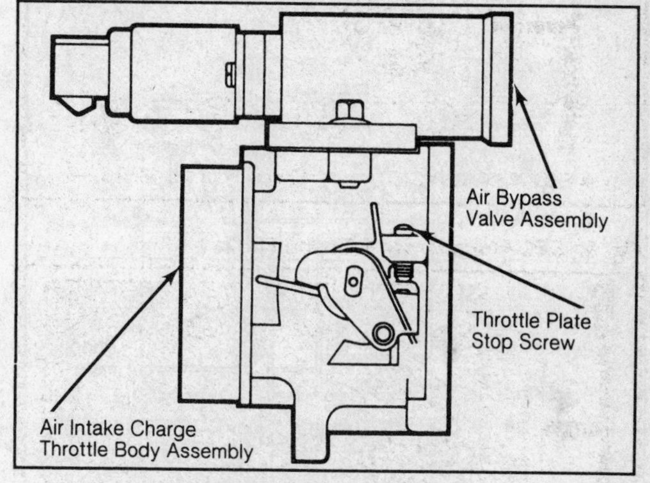

2.3L 1-Bbl. Engine (Exc. HSC)

1) Place transmission in Neutral (man. trans.) or "P" (auto. trans.). Start engine and warm to normal operating temperature. Place A/C selector in off position.

Fig. 11: 2.3L 1-Bbl. Curb Idle Speed Adjusting Screw Location

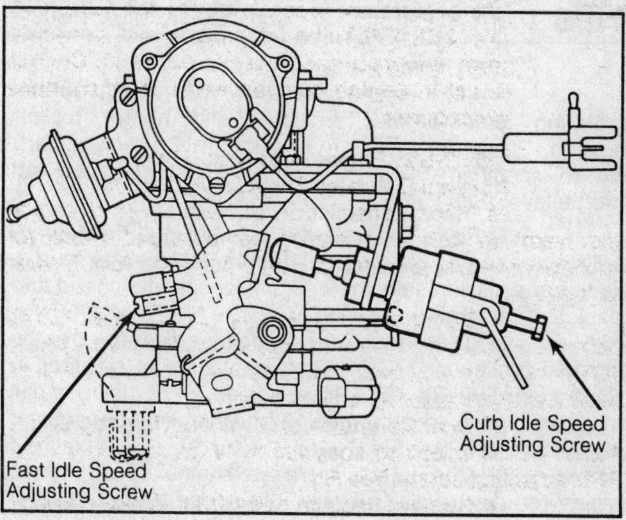

Feedback carburetor shown, other models similar.

FORD MOTOR CO. SYSTEMS AND TUNE-UP PROCEDURES (Cont.)

2) Place transmission in Neutral (man. trans.) or "D" (auto. trans.). Adjust curb idle speed to specified RPM by turning hex head adjusting screw on rear of throttle solenoid positioner (TSP) or vacuum operated throttle modulator (VOTM/TSP) housing. *See Fig. 11.*

3) Place transmission in Neutral and momentarily increase engine speed. Recheck curb idle speed. Remove test equipment from engine.

4) Turn ignition switch to "On" position. Open throttle so that TSP plunger extends. Secure choke plate in wide open position. Open throttle so that throttle vent lever does not contact bowl vent rod.

5) Close throttle to idle set position and measure travel of fuel bowl vent rod from idle to full throttle. *See Fig. 12, Dimension "A".*

6) Travel of bowl vent rod should be .10-.15" (2.5-3.8 mm). If adjustment is required, bend the throttle vent lever at point shown in *Fig. 12.*

Fig. 12: 2.3L 1-Bbl. Bowl Vent Rod Travel Adjustment

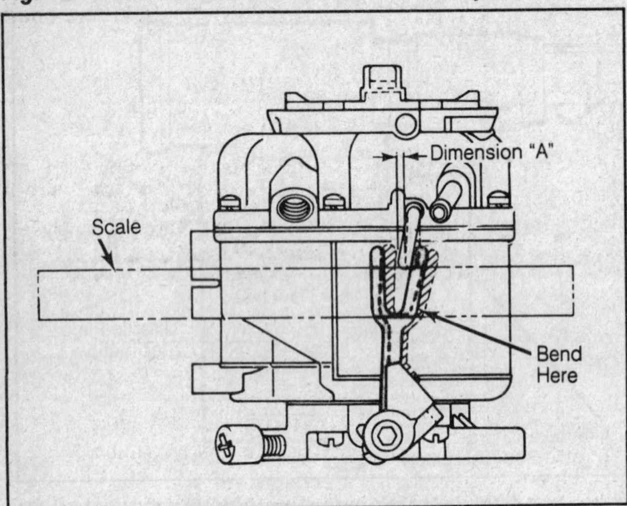

2.3L 1-Bbl. CURB IDLE SPEED SPECIFICATION

Application	RPM
2.3L 1-Bbl.	
Man. Trans.	850
Auto. Trans.	800

3.3L Engine

1) Start engine and allow it to reach normal operating temperature. Turn A/C and heater to off position. Place transmission selector in "D". Adjust curb idle to specified RPM by turning adjusting screw on throttle lever. *See Fig. 13.*

2) Place transmission selector in "P". Momentarily increase engine speed. When engine returns to idle, place transmission selector in "D". Recheck idle speed and readjust if necessary.

3) Disconnect wiring connector to throttle solenoid positioner (TSP). Place transmission selector in "P". Adjust TSP-Off RPM to specified RPM using small adjusting screw located behind throttle linkage against carburetor base. *See Fig. 13.*

4) Momentarily increase engine speed. When engine returns to idle, recheck idle speed and readjust if necessary.

Fig. 13: 3.3L Curb Idle, TSP-Off RPM & Fast Idle Speed Adjusting Screw Locations

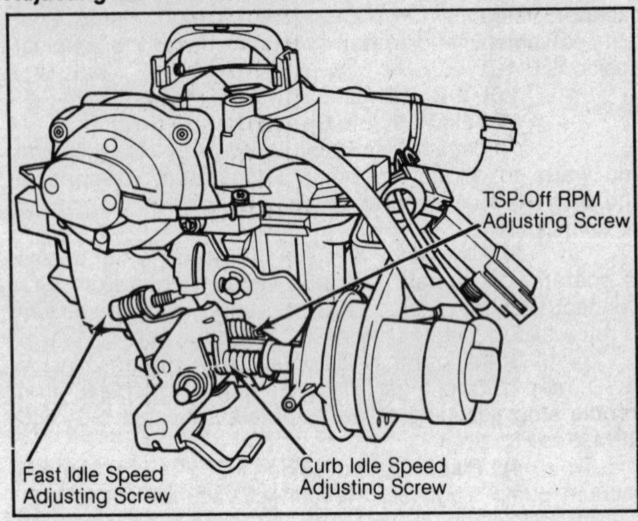

3.3L ENGINE IDLE SPEED SPECIFICATIONS

Application	Curb Idle RPM	TSP-Off RPM
3.3L		
Federal	550	450
Calif. & High Alt.	600	450

3.8L & 5.8L Engines

1) Place transmission in "P" or "N". Start engine and let it warm to normal operating temperature. Place A/C-heater selector in off position. On 3.8L engines equipped with air conditioning and all 5.8L engines, proceed to step **2)**. On 3.8L engines without air conditioning, proceed to step **4)**.

2) Disconnect and plug vacuum hose at vacuum operated throttle modulator (VOTM) kicker. Connect an auxiliary vacuum source to vacuum kicker. Apply 10 in. Hg (34 kpa) vacuum to VOTM kicker.

3) Place transmission in "D". Adjust VOTM-On RPM to specification by turning VOTM saddle bracket adjusting screw. *See Fig. 14.* Remove external vacuum source. Remove plug from vacuum hose and reconnect hose to VOTM kicker. Proceed to step **4)**.

Fig. 14: Idle Adjustment Screw Locations for 3.8L Engines with Air Conditioning

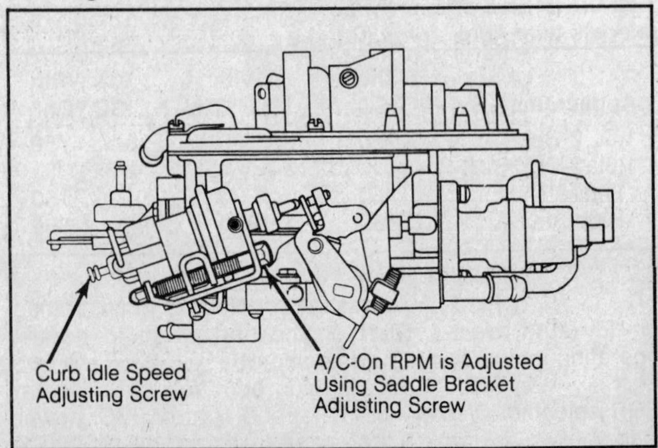

1983 Exhaust Emission Systems

FORD MOTOR CO. SYSTEMS AND TUNE-UP PROCEDURES (Cont.)

4) Place transmission in "D". Adjust curb idle to specified RPM using saddle bracket adjusting screw on models without A/C *(See Fig. 15)*, or hex head screw protruding from rear of throttle solenoid positioner (TSP) on models with A/C *(See Fig. 14)*.

Fig. 15: Idle Adjustment Screw Locations for 3.8L Engines without Air Conditioning

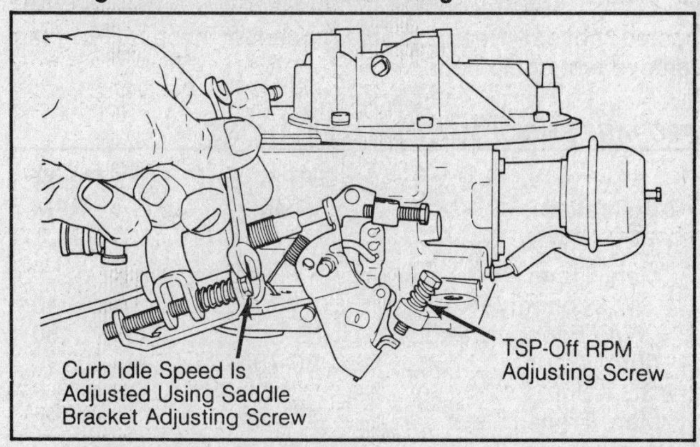

5) Place transmission in "P" or "N". Momentarily increase engine speed. Place transmission in "D" and recheck curb idle speed. Disconnect TSP feed wire. Adjust TPS-Off RPM to specification. Reconnect TSP feed wire.

3.8L & 5.8L IDLE SPEED SPECIFICATIONS

Application	VOTM-On RPM	Curb Idle RPM	TSP-Off RPM
3.8L			
Federal			
Cougar & T-Bird			
with C5 Trans.	700	550	450
All Others	650	550	450
Calif. & High Alt.			
Capri & Mustang	650	550	450
All Others	700	550	450
5.8L	700	600	.....

5.0L 4-Bbl. Engine

1) Place transmission in Neutral. Start engine and let it warm to normal operating temperature. Place A/C-heater selector in off position.

Fig. 16: 5.0L 4-Bbl. Curb Idle Adjusting Screw Location

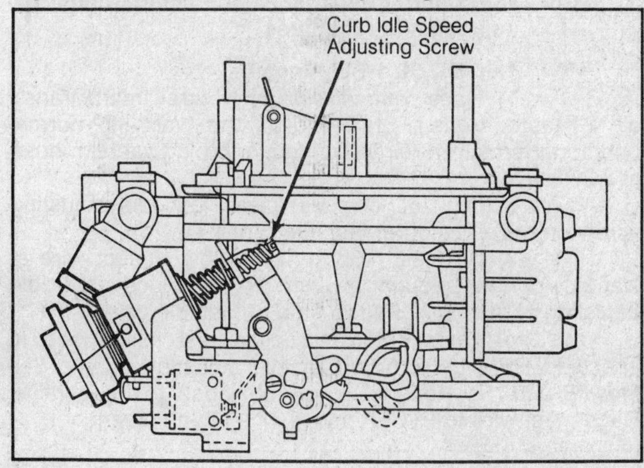

2) Disconnect and plug vacuum hose at thorttle kicker. Adjust curb idle to specified RPM using curb idle speed adjusting screw on throttle lever. *See Fig. 16*.

3) Increase engine speed momentarily. Let engine return to idle and recheck curb idle speed. Remove plug and reconnect vacuum hose to throttle kicker.

5.0L EFI Engine

1) Place transmission in "N" or "P" and set parking brake firmly. Start engine and let it warm to normal operating temperature. Place A/C-heater selector in off position.

2) Turn engine off. Restart engine and run at 2000 RPM for 60 seconds. Allow engine to return to idle and stabilize for 15 seconds. Place transmission in "R". Adjust curb idle speed to specified RPM using saddle bracket adjusting screw. *See Fig. 17*.

Fig. 17: 5.0L EFI Curb Idle Adjustment

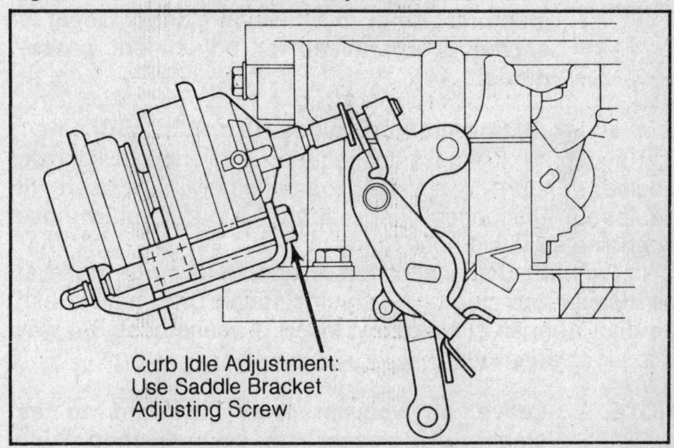

3) If RPM is low, turn engine off and turn adjusting screw 1 full turn clockwise, and repeat steps **1)** and **2)** until correct RPM is obtained.

5.0L CURB IDLE SPEED (RPM)

Application	Specification
5.0L 4-Bbl.	700
5.0L EFI	550

IDLE MIXTURE PLUG REMOVAL

1.6L Carbureted Engine

1) Remove carburetor from vehicle. Center punch a mark on mixture screw plug. Drill a 3/32" hole through both the steel and plastic plug.

2) Install a screw extractor into hole and remove steel and plastic plugs. Reinstall carburetor on vehicle. After mixture adjustment procedures have been completed, install a new plug.

2.3L 1-Bbl. Engine (Exc. HSC)

1) Remove carburetor from engine. Drain fuel from carburetor. Using a hacksaw, carefully cut a lengthwise slot through the metal cup around the mixture screw.

NOTE: **DO NOT contact throttle body with hack saw blade.**

2) Insert a screwdriver into slot just cut and twist screwdriver to spread cup. Spread cup just enough to remove mixture screw plug. Reinstall carburetor on vehicle.

FORD MOTOR CO. SYSTEMS AND TUNE-UP PROCEDURES (Cont.)

3.3L & 5.0L Carbureted Engines

Remove carburetor from vehicle. Drain fuel bowl. Drill a 3/32" hole in mixture screw plug. Use a screw extractor to remove plug. Reinstall carburetor and make adjustments. After adjustment, install new mixture plug.

3.8L Engine

Remove carburetor and mount upside-down on a carburetor stand. Place support under plug caps, then use punch and hammer to tap spring tang on plug out. Reinstall carburetor.

IDLE MIXTURE ADJUSTMENT

NOTE: **No idle mixture adjustments are required or possible on 1.6L EFI, 2.3L EFI/Turbo, 5.0L EFI and 5.8L engines.**

NOTE: **Idle mixture adjustment procedures for the 2.3L HSC engine is not available from manufacturer. Refer to Emission Control Decal in engine compartment for adjustment procedures.**

All Carbureted Engines (Exc. 2.3L HSC)

1) Connect tachometer and timing light to engine. Ensure hot idle compensator is closed (if equipped). Disconnect fuel evaporative purge return hose at engine and plug hose fitting.

2) Disconnect fuel evaporative purge hose at air cleaner and plug fitting on air cleaner. Disconnect fresh air duct from air cleaner, and insert propane hose 3/4 way into air cleaner duct.

NOTE: **Leave all vacuum lines attached to air cleaner. Air cleaner may be positioned aside for adjustments, but must be in place during speed checks.**

3) Revise air injection dump valves as follows: If valve has 2 vacuum fittings, disconnect and plug the hoses. If only 1 vacuum fitting, disconnect and plug hose, then run a vacuum hose from fitting to manifold vacuum.

4) On 2.3L 1-Bbl. engines with feedback carburetors, disconnect electrical lead wire from electric ported vacuum switch (PVS). On 1.6L engines with automatic transmissions, disconnect and plug vacuum hose at ISC. Connect a vacuum pump to ISC and apply enough vacuum to retract ISC plunger clear of throttle linkage.

5) On all models, check and adjust curb idle and engine timing. Remove PCV valve from valve cover and allow to draw fresh air. Run engine briefly at 2500 RPM.

NOTE: **Propane bottle must be in a vertical position.**

6) With engine idling and transmission in Neutral (man. trans.) or "D" (auto. trans.), slowly open propane valve and watch for RPM gain. When RPM begins to drop off, note maximum speed gain. If gain is within "RPM Gain" specifications, do not adjust.

7) If not within specifications, remove carburetor and mixture screw plug. Reinstall carburetor and run engine until warm, then accelerate briefly to 2500 RPM. Proceed with adjustment.

8) If measured speed gain was higher than specified, turn mixture screw counterclockwise (rich) slightly, then repeat propane procedure until gain matches "Reset RPM".

NOTE: **After turning mixture screw, allow 15 seconds for idle to stabilize before turning screw again.**

9) If measured speed gain was lower than specified, turn mixture screw clockwise (lean) slightly, then repeat propane procedure until gain matches "Reset RPM".

10) Reconnect PCV valve and other disconnected hoses. Readjust idle speed if necessary, then remove test equipment.

PROPANE ENRICHMENT SPECIFICATIONS

Application	RPM Gain	Reset RPM
1.6L		
Man. Trans.		
W/ Economy Pkg.	10-70	40
W/O Economy Pkg.	10-120	80
Auto. Trans.	20-70	40
2.3L 1-Bbl.		
Man. Trans.	60-100	80
Auto. Trans.		
Federal	150-200	175
Calif.	160-240	200
3.3L		
Federal	30-50	40
Calif. & High Alt.	10-30	20
3.8L		
Federal	30-90	60
Calif.		
Cougar, LTD, Marquis & Thunderbird with AOT Trans.	50-150	100
All Others	30-90	60
5.0L 4-Bbl.	[1]	[1]

[1] — Information not available from manufacturer.

COLD (FAST) IDLE RPM

NOTE: **No fast idle adjustment is required or possible on 1.6L EFI engines.**

NOTE: **Fast idle adjustment procedures for the 2.3L HSC and 2.3L EFI/Turbo engines is not available from manufacturer. Refer to Emission Control Decal in engine compartment for adjustment procedures.**

1.6L & 2.3L 1-Bbl. Engines

1) Place transmission in Neutral (man. trans.) or "P" (auto. trans.). Start engine and warm to normal operating temperature. Disconnect and plug vacuum hose at EGR valve.

2) On 1.6L engines, place fast idle adjusting screw on second step of fast idle cam.

3) On 2.3L 1-Bbl. engines, disconnect wire at electric ported vacuum switch (PVS). Place fast idle adjusting screw on kickdown step of fast idle cam.

4) On all models, adjust fast idle speed to specified RPM by turning fast idle adjusting screw. *See Figs. 8 and 11.* Reconnect vacuum hose to EGR valve. Reconnect wire to PVS. Remove all test equipment.

FORD MOTOR CO. SYSTEMS AND TUNE-UP PROCEDURES (Cont.)

3.3L & 5.8L Engines

1) Warm engine to normal operating temperature. Disconnect and plug vacuum lines at EGR valve and at canister purge valve.

2) Place fast idle screw on 2nd step of fast idle cam and adjust fast idle RPM. *See Figs. 13 and 18.* Reconnect vacuum lines and remove test equipment.

Fig. 18: 5.8L Fast Idle Adjusting Screw Location

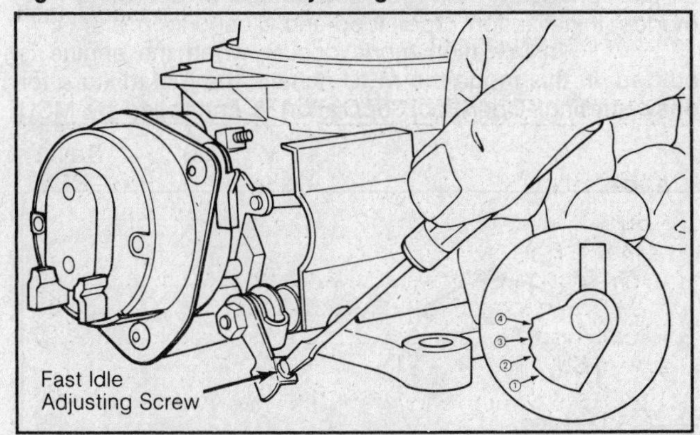

3.8L & 5.0L 4-Bbl. Engines

1) Place transmission in Neutral (man. trans.) or "P" (auto. trans.). Start engine and let it warm to normal operating temperature. Disconnect and plug vacuum hose at EGR valve.

2) Place fast idle screw on highest step of fast idle cam. Adjust fast idle screw to obtain specified RPM. *See Figs. 19 and 20*. Momentarily increase engine speed.

Fig. 19: 3.8L Fast Idle Adjusting Screw Location

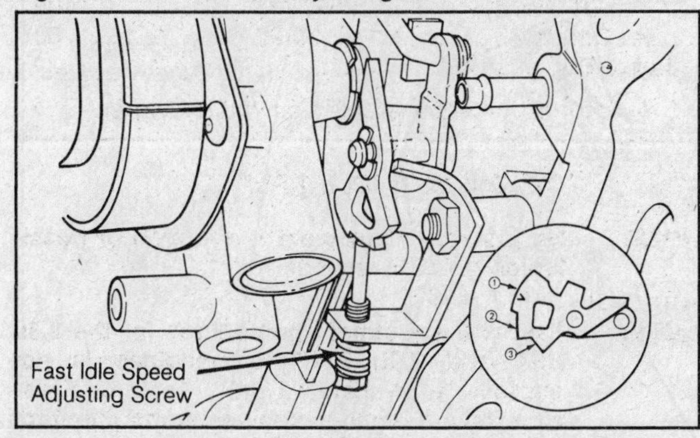

Fig. 20: 5.0L 4-Bbl. Fast Idle Adjusting Screw Location

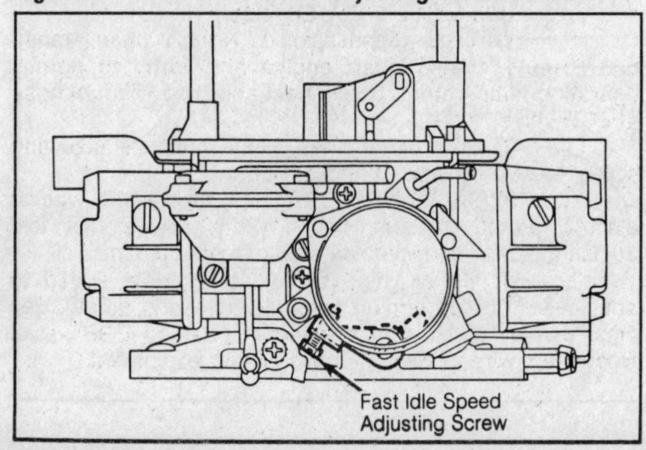

3) Again place fast idle adjustment screw on highest step of fast idle cam. Recheck fast idle speed. Remove plug from EGR valve vacuum hose and reconnect hose to EGR valve.

5.0L EFI Engine

1) Place transmission in "N" or "P". Start engine and warm to normal operating temperature. Disconnect and plug vacuum hose at EGR valve. Disconnect and plug vacuum hose at fast idle pulldown motor. Stop engine.

2) Set fast idle lever on highest step of fast idle cam. Start engine and check fast idle speed within 20-60 seconds after engine is started. Adjust if necessary. *See Fig. 21*.

NOTE: If speed is not checked between 20-60 seconds after engine starts, stop engine and repeat procedure.

3) Reconnect vacuum hose to EGR valve and fast idle pulldown motor. Remove all test equipment.

Fig. 21: 5.0L EFI Fast Idle Adjusting Screw Location

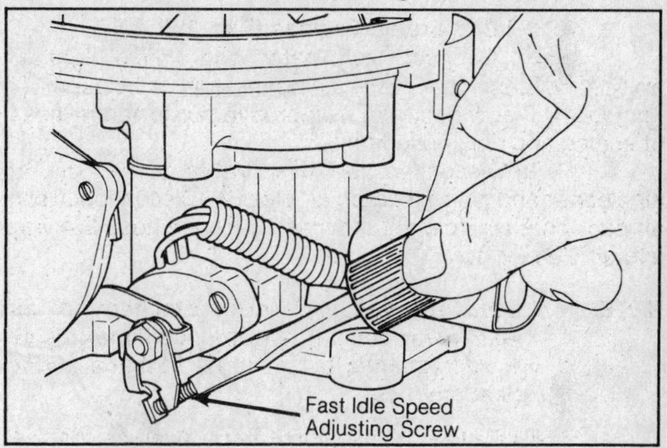

FAST IDLE SPEED SPECIFICATIONS

Application	RPM
1.6L 2-Bbl.	
Man. Trans.	
W/Economy Pkg.	2100
W/O Economy Pkg.	2200
Auto. Trans.	2400
1.6L 2-Bbl. H.O.	2400
2.3L 1-Bbl.	
Man. Trans.	1800
Auto. Trans.	
Federal	2600
Calif.	2000
3.3L	
Federal	
LTD & Marquis	2200
Fairmont & Zephyr	2000
Calif	
LTD & Marquis	2100
Fairmont & Zephyr	2000
3.8L	
Federal & Calif.	2200
High Alt.	2100
5.0L	
4-Bbl.	2400
EFI	2200
5.8L	1650

FORD MOTOR CO. 4-CYL. MCU ENGINE CONTROL SYSTEM

All Models W/2.3L (Exc. EFI Turbo)

DESCRIPTION

The MCU control system is named for and commanded by a Microprocessor Control Unit. This micro-computer is located in the engine compartment and is capable of controlling engine air/fuel ratios, air injection, and on some models, canister purge, spark retard and idle speed. The system consists of the MCU module, air/fuel control and air injection solenoids, engine sensors, feedback carburetor, and related circuitry.

OPERATION

MICROPROCESSOR CONTROL UNIT (MCU)

The MCU is a solid-state micro-computer located on the left fender panel. It is the "brain" of the system and receives inputs and sends signals through a 24-pin connector. The MCU is capable of operating in 3 modes: Initialization, Open loop and Closed loop.

Initialization mode occurs when the engine is started. In this mode the MCU richens the fuel mixture for easy starting. Open loop operation is controlled by MCU

Fig. 1: 4-Cylinder MCU System Layout

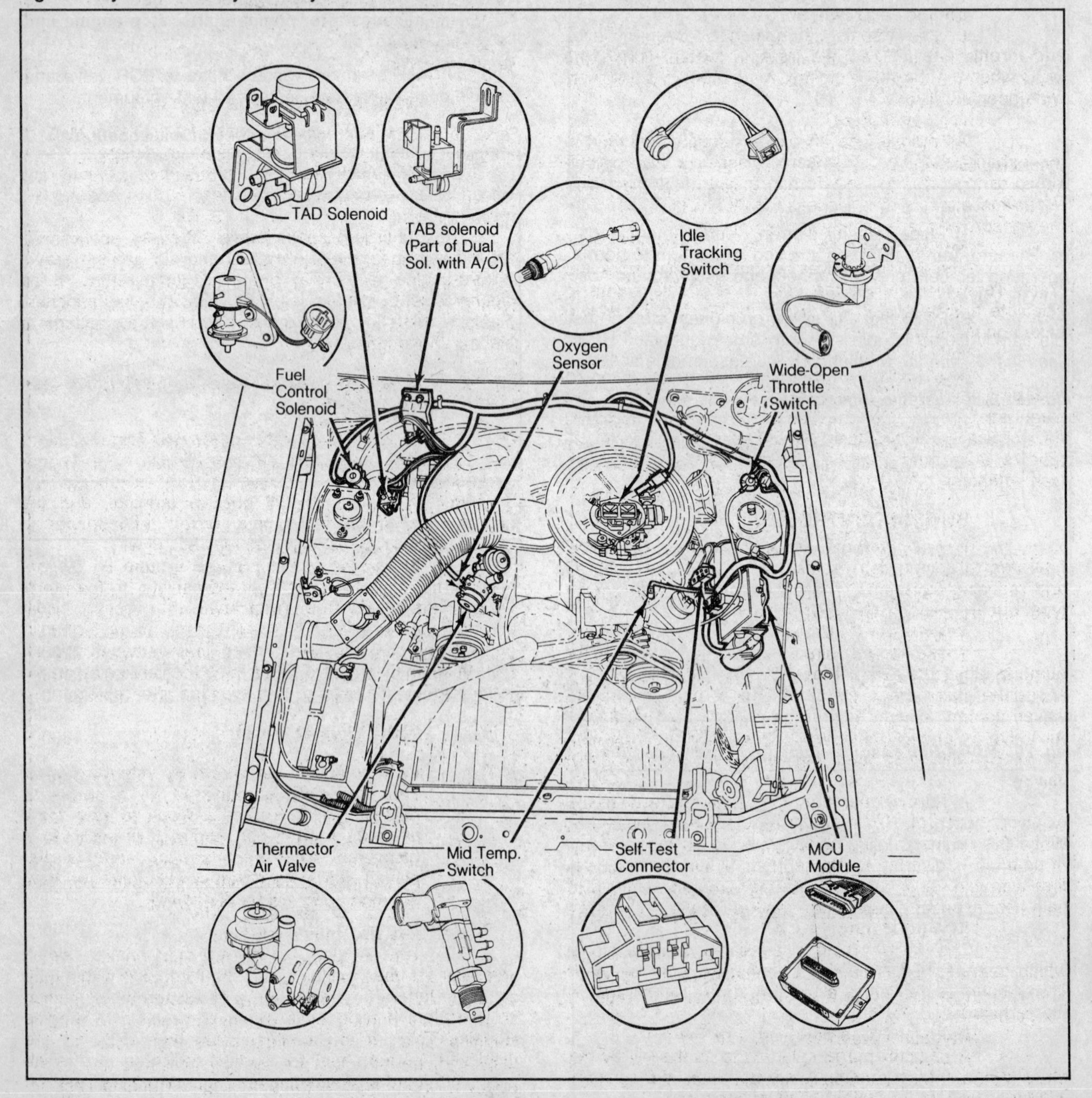

FORD MOTOR CO. 4-CYL. MCU ENGINE CONTROL (Cont.)

programming. Air/fuel ratio is fixed at a pre-determined level and allows good driveability at idle, moderate-to-heavy acceleration, and deceleration.

Closed loop operation occurs when the engine is warm and vehicle is operated at light load conditions. In closed loop, the MCU controls the air/fuel mixture in response to signals from an oxygen sensor in the exhaust manifold.

ENGINE SENSORS

Coolant Temperature

The coolant temperature switch is used to signal temperature changes to the MCU. The MCU uses this signal to improve cold engine operation. The coolant switch is mounted on the Ported Vacuum Switch (PVS).

Engine Load Sensor

Engine load is determined by vacuum level, and throttle position. An idle tracking switch signals the MCU when the throttle is closed. A vacuum switch signals wide open conditions.

Oxygen Sensor

All models use an oxygen sensor mounted in the exhaust manifold. This sensor sends a low voltage signal to the MCU to indicate rich or lean mixture. When mixture is lean, the signal is less than 0.2 volts. When rich, the sensor voltage is slightly above 0.6 volts.

Engine Speed

The MCU receives a direct signal from the "Tach Test" terminal on the coil. It uses this signal to calculate engine speed and alters the air/fuel correction based on this speed.

Self-Test Connector

The MCU can self-diagnose most common operating problems. In order to initiate and read the diagnostic program, connections are made to the Self-Test connector. It provides voltage pulses which can be read by a specialized tester (Rotunda 07-0004) or a dial-type voltmeter.

ENGINE CONTROLS

Engine controls are the devices the MCU operates to accomplish its task of improving driveability and reducing emissions. These devices vary with engine type, but are all controlled electrically.

Thermactor Controls

These controls direct the flow of air from an air pump to either the exhaust manifold, the catalytic converter, or the atmosphere. On all models, a pair of solenoid valves control vacuum flow which operates a Thermactor Air Valve assembly. These valves are called the Thermactor Air By-Pass (TAB) and Thermactor Air Diverter (TAD) valves.

In normal operation, the air is injected into the catalytic converter to improve reduction of emissions. When the engine is idling or decelerating for long periods of time, air is diverted to atmosphere. When the engine is first warming, air is injected into the exhaust manifold to help heat exhaust gases before they reach the converter.

Air/Fuel Controls

The MCU provides a pulsed voltage signal which operates a fuel control solenoid/vacuum regulator. The vacuum is applied to a mixture control diaphragm in the carburetor.

Canister Purge Solenoid

A canister purge solenoid is controlled by the MCU. When engine conditions are optimum, the solenoid is opened and the fuel vapor canister is purged.

DIAGNOSIS & TESTING

The MCU system is capable of diagnosing some problems which may occur. To determine which components should be checked, perform the "Functional Test" which follows. If problems do exist, a service code will be displayed (as pulses on a voltmeter). Locate the appropriate test chart and follow the repair procedure as instructed. Do not use the test charts unless referred to them by the "Functional Test", or you may replace some components unnecessarily. Testing procedures require the following equipment:

- Dial Voltmeter (0-20v scale)
- Digital Voltmeter (DVOM — Min. impedance 10 megohms)
- Vacuum Gauge (0-30 in. Hg)
- Vacuum pump
- Tachometer
- Jumper Wire

PREPARATION FOR TESTING

1) Check vacuum hoses for leaks, cracks, or improper routing. Repair or replace as necessary.

2) Check electrical connections. Repair any frayed or broken wires. Ensure that all connections are clean and tight.

3) Check coolant level. Turn all accessories off. Place transmission in neutral and set parking brake. Warm engine to normal operating temperature. If air cleaner must be moved, leave all vacuum hoses attached. If engine will start, start engine and check for voltage at electric choke terminal.

NOTE: If vehicle does not start, proceed to No Start Test (No. 1).

4) Turn ignition off. Locate Self-Test connector and insert a jumper wire between ground and Trigger sockets. Connect the positive lead of a needle-type voltmeter to vehicle battery positive terminal, and the negative lead to Self-Test output socket. Set voltmeter on 15-20 volt scale. Battery voltage may be shown.

5) Disable canister purge system by disconnecting the hose that runs from the canister to the purge valve (if equipped). Reconnect hose after testing. Make sure that the carburetor throttle linkage is off the high cam and that the choke is open. On engines equipped with an EGR vacuum load control valve, plug the vent holes on the valve with a piece of tape. Remove tape after testing.

FUNCTIONAL TEST

NOTE: Service codes are shown by voltage pulses. The first digit is indicated by a series of pulses, then the needle drops to zero for 2 seconds, then the second digit of the code is displayed. After each service code is displayed, a 5 second pause will occur and then the next code will be displayed.

Key On, Engine Off Test

Turn key on, but do not start engine. Watch voltmeter for code pulses which should appear within 5-30 seconds. Ignore any initial surge of voltage when ignition is turned on. If code 11 is displayed proceed to "Engine Running Test". If any code(s) other than code 11 are displayed, perform test for code(s) indicated and repair problem(s) before proceeding to "Engine Running Test".

FORD MOTOR CO. 4-CYL. MCU ENGINE CONTROL (Cont.)

NOTE: If voltmeter does not pulse, but shows steady high or low readings, see "Functional Test Not Operating".

Fig. 2: Connections for Functional Test

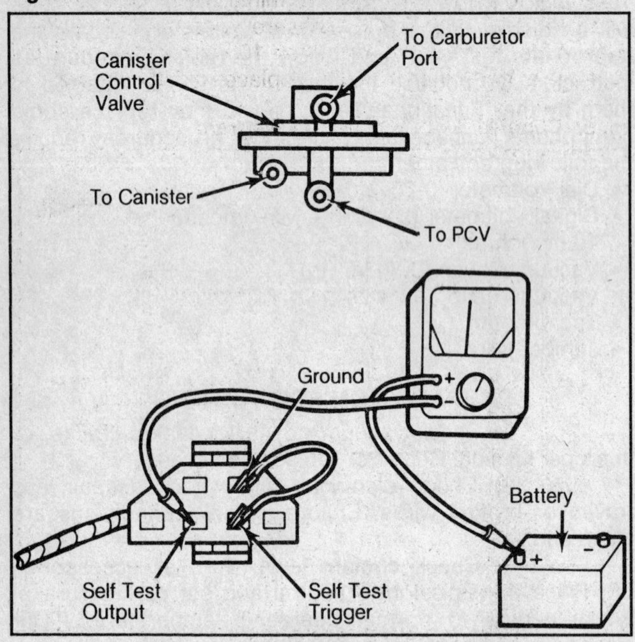

Engine Running Test

1) Start engine and raise speed to 3000 RPM within 20 seconds after start. Hold RPM until initial pulses appear (2-3). Continue holding speed until code pulses begin (10-40 seconds).

2) Return engine to idle when codes begin. If code 11 is displayed proceed to "Cold Drive Complaint Test". If any code(s) other than code 11 are displayed, perform test for code(s) indicated and repair problem(s) before proceeding to "Cold Drive Complaint Test".

NOTE: If no initial pulses or more than 3 initial pulses occur, perform "Tachometer Lead Test".

NOTE: If voltmeter does not pulse, but shows steady high or low readings, see "Functional Test Not Operating".

Cold Drive Complaint Test

If complaint occurred when engine was cold, recheck mid temperature switch for proper operation. Go to "Mid Temperature Switch Test".

SUB-ROUTINE TESTS

INSTRUCTIONS FOR USING THE SUB-ROUTINE TESTS

Sub-routines are the following checks which are performed to correct a service code. Be sure to perform check as instructed. After replacing components or repairing circuits, repeat "Functional Test" and check engine operation.

Observe the following instructions when performing sub-routines:

- Do not measure voltage or resistance at MCU module, or connect test lamps to it (unless specific instructions say to do so).
- Disconnect both ends of a circuit when looking for continuity or shorts. Be sure ignition is turned off.
- Disconnect solenoids and switches from harness before measuring resistance or continuity.
- When more than one service code is indicated, start service with the first code received.
- Use wiring diagrams to locate pin locations and connectors.

NOTE: Complete system wiring diagram is located before Sub-Routine Tests. Each individual test has a partial schematic to aid in servicing.

DIAGNOSTIC CODE 11 NO START TEST

This test detects faults in the MCU only.

1) Check Tach lead for a ground short. Leave harness connected to MCU; disconnect coil and ignition

Fig. 3: 4-Cylinder MCU System Wiring Diagram

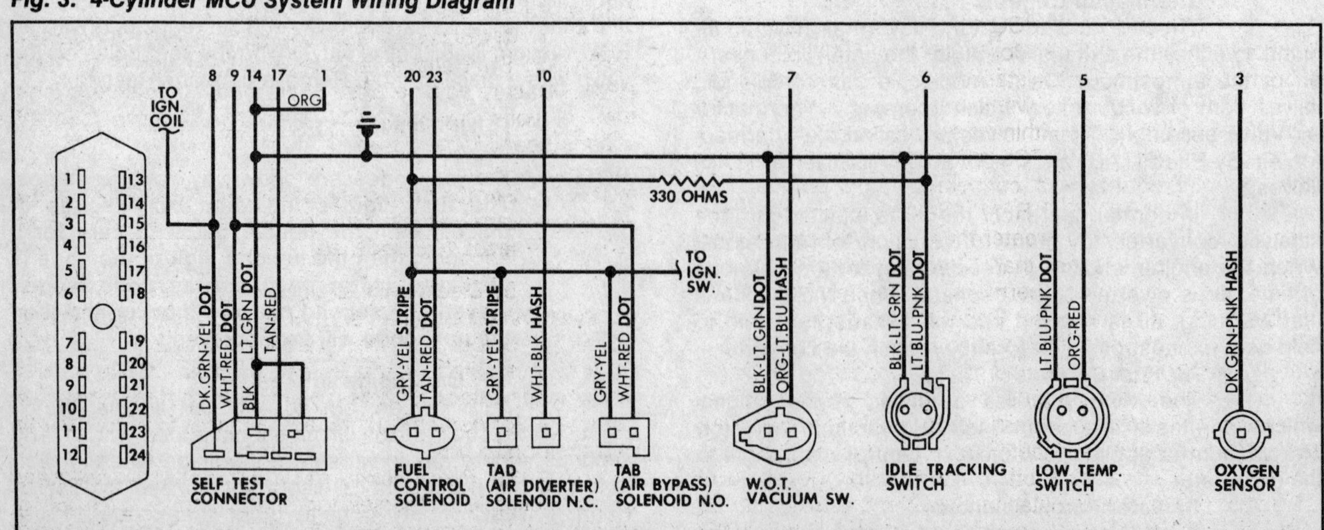

FORD MOTOR CO. 4-CYL. MCU ENGINE CONTROL (Cont.)

module connectors. Measure resistance between ground and self-test connector, then Tach connector. If resistance is less than 1000 ohms, go to step **2)**. If higher than 1000 ohms, MCU is not shorted.

2) Disconnect harness from MCU and measure resistance again. If resistance is less than 1000, repair circuit. If greater than 1000, replace MCU module.

Fig. 4: No Start Test Wiring Diagram

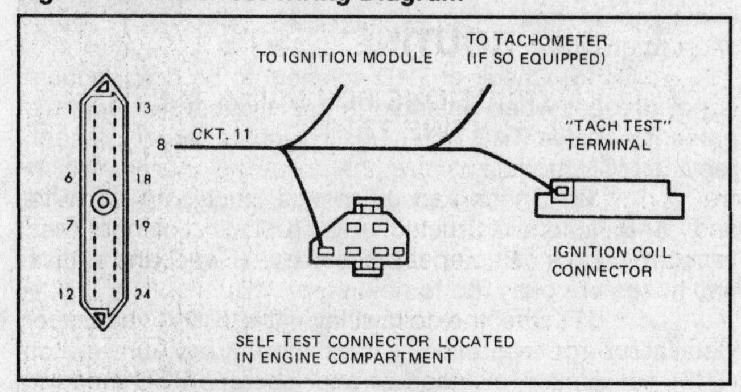

DIAGNOSTIC CODE 33 RUNNING TEST NOT INITIATED

It is necessary to increase speed to more than 2500 RPM within 20 seconds after start in order to initiate "Functional Test". Turn key off and repeat procedure.

DIAGNOSTIC CODE 41 FUEL ALWAYS LEAN

After starting engine, allow at least 2 minutes of idling before testing. Disconnect "Functional Test" trigger wire. Do not block throttle open as Idle Tracking Switch will be activated and invalidate test results.

1) Disconnect MCU connector and oxygen sensor. Turn all accessories off. Measure resistance between ground and MCU connector pins 3 and 23. If resistance is less than 1000 ohms in either case, repair short. If resistance is greater than 1000 ohms, go to next step.

2) Check continuity between MCU connector pin 3 and oxygen sensor connector (harness side). If resistance is greater than 5 ohms, repair wire. If less than 5 ohms, go to next step.

3) Reconnect MCU and oxygen sensor. Disconnect harness from Fuel Control Solenoid (FCS). Check resistance of FCS coil. Resistance should be between 28-66 ohms. If resistance is within range, proceed to next step. If resistance is not within range, replace FCS.

4) Reconnect FCS and connect voltmeter to back of solenoid harness connector. Start engine and maintain a speed of 2500 RPM. Observe voltmeter after 55 seconds. If voltage is greater tham 10 volts, proceed to next step. If voltage is less than 12 volts, replace MCU.

5) Disconnect thermactor air supply hose from the air pump, and plug hose. Raise engine speed to 2500 RPM and hold choke 3/4 closed to force the system rich. With voltmeter still connected to FCS, observe voltage after 55 seconds. If voltage is less than 10 volts, proceed to next step. If voltage is more than 10 volts, check for lean carburetor, and thermactor air.

6) Turn engine off. Disconnect oxygen sensor connector and check resistance between harness side of connector and ground. If resistance is less than 1000 ohms, replace MCU module. If greater than 1000 ohms, go to next step.

7) With oxygen sensor disconnected, start engine. With engine idling, connect a jumper wire to harness side of oxygen sensor connector. Be sure this connection cannot contact ground. Connect the other end of jumper to battery positive terminal, then raise engine speed to 2500-2800 RPM. Measure voltage at FCS after 55 seconds. If voltage is less than 10 volts, replace MCU. If voltage is more than 10 volts, replace oxygen sensor.

Fig. 5: Code 41 & 42 Test Wiring Diagram

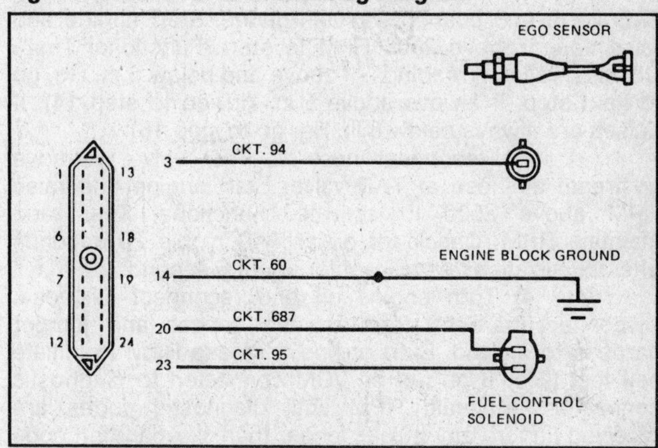

Also see system wiring diagram.

DIAGNOSTIC CODE 42 FUEL ALWAYS RICH

After starting engine, allow at least 2 minutes at idle before testing. Disconnect "Functional Test" trigger jumper. Do not block throttle open as Idle Tracking Switch will be activated and invalidate test.

1) Check choke valve for sticking or binding and repair as necessary.

2) Disconnect MCU connector and connector at Fuel Control Solenoid (FCS). Measure resistance between MCU pin 20 and FCS connector, then between MCU pin 23 and FCS connector. Resistance in both wires should be less than 5 ohms. If so, go to next step. If resistance is higher, repair wiring.

3) Check resistance of FCS. If within 28-66 ohms, go to next step. If resistance is not within 28-66 ohm range, replace FCS.

4) Connect a voltmeter to back of FCS harness connector. Start engine and raise engine speed to 2500 RPM. Measure voltage after 55 seconds. If voltage is less than 10 volts, replace MCU. If voltage is more than 10 volts, proceed to next step.

NOTE: **For the following step, a digital VOM must be used which has an input impedance of at least 10 megohms.**

5) Disconnect oxygen sensor from harness. Connect DVOM between sensor and ground, with switch in lowest voltage position. Start engine and run at 2000 RPM for 1 minute to warm up sensor. Turn engine off and immediately check DVOM reading. If greater than 0.4 volts, go to next step. If less than 0.4 volts, check carburetor (too rich).

6) Purge exhaust system by immediately disconnecting coil "horseshoe" connector and cranking engine for 10 seconds with throttle wide open. Observe DVOM. If greater than 0.4 volts, replace oxygen sensor. If less than 0.4 volts, check carburetor (too rich).

FORD MOTOR CO. 4-CYL. MCU ENGINE CONTROL (Cont.)

DIAGNOSTIC CODE 44 THERMACTOR SYSTEM

1) Remove vacuum hose from TAB valve and connect gauge to hose. Start engine and increase RPM to above 2500 to activate "Functional Test". Observe vacuum gauge. If vacuum pulses are above and below 5 in. Hg, proceed to next step. If pulses are always above 5 in. Hg, proceed to step **7)**. If pulses are below 5 in. Hg, proceed to next step.

2) Reconnect hose to TAB. Disconnect hose at TAD valve and connect vacuum gauge. Start engine and raise speed above 2500 RPM to start "Functional Test". Observe vacuum readings. If above and below 5 in. Hg, go to next step. If always above 5 in. Hg, go to step **14)**. If pulses are always below 5 in. Hg, go to step **16)**.

3) Reconnect hose to TAD valve. Remove upstream air hose at TAD valve. Start engine and raise RPM above 2500 to activate "Functional Test" and maintain RPM. Check for air at TAD nipple 20 seconds after initialization (air will last for about 6 seconds).

4) Turn engine off and reconnect air hose. Disconnect harness from oxygen sensor and jumper harness to ground. Start engine, increase RPM to initiate self test (2 or 3 pulses on VOM connected to diagnostic connector). Maintain RPM until diagnostic codes are received (ignore any pulses longer than 1 second). If code 41 is read on voltmeter, check choke system, then go to next step. If code 44 is received, replace MCU module.

CAUTION: For the next step, a digital VOM must be used which has an input impedance of at least 10 megohms.

5) Place DVOM selector in lowest voltage position and connect it between oxygen sensor and ground. Start engine and run at 2000 RPM for 1 minute to warm up sensor. Turn engine off and immediately check DVOM. If voltage is less than 0.4 volts, check carburetor (too rich). If voltage is greater than 0.4 volts, go to next step.

6) Immediately purge exhaust system. Disconnect coil "horseshoe" connector and crank engine for 10 seconds with throttle wide open. If voltage is greater than 0.4 volts, replace oxygen sensor. If voltage is less than 0.4 volts, check carburetor (too rich).

7) Disconnect MCU connector, then connectors at TAD and TAB solenoids. Check continuity between MCU connector pin 20 and TAD solenoid, then between pin 9 and TAB solenoid. If less than 5 ohms resistance, go to next step. If greater than 5 ohms resistance is measured, repair wiring.

8) Measure resistance of TAB solenoid. If between 50-110 ohms, go to next step. If not within 50-110 ohms, replace TAB solenoid.

9) Check at TAB solenoid output to be sure vacuum is not present when solenoid is energized (12 volts). If vacuum is present, replace TAB solenoid. If no vacuum, replace MCU module.

10) Check vacuum hose between TAD and TAB solenoid, then between source and TAB solenoid. Repair as necessary. If hoses are okay, go to next step.

11) Check vacuum switch (TVS) and retard delay valve (RDV) for proper installation and operation. Check vacuum schematic for usage and location. Service valves if necessary, otherwise go to next step.

12) Check at TAB solenoid output to be sure vacuum is present when the solenoid is energized (12 volts). If vacuum is not present, replace TAB solenoid. If vacuum is present, go to next step.

13) Disconnect TAB solenoid connectors and MCU connector. Measure resistance between pin 20 and TAB connector, then pin 9 and TAB connector. If resistance is less than 5 ohms, replace MCU module. If higher than 5 ohms, repair circuits.

14) Disconnect MCU connector. Measure resistance from pin 10 to ground. If greater than 1000 ohms, go to next step. If less than 1000 ohms, repair short to ground.

15) Check at TAD solenoid to be sure vacuum is not present when solenoid is deactivated. If vacuum is present, replace TAD solenoid. If vacuum is not present, replace MCU module.

16) Check vacuum hoses between TAD valve and TAD solenoid, then between TAD solenoid and vacuum source. Repair if necessary. If vacuum source and hoses are okay, go to next step.

17) Check retard delay valve (RDV) for proper installation and operation. Check thermal vacuum switch (TVS) for proper installation and operation (if used on vehicle). Replace if necessary. If okay, go to next step.

18) Measure resistance of TAD solenoid. If not between 50-110 ohms, replace solenoid. If resistance is okay, go to next step.

19) Check at TAD solenoid to be sure vacuum is present when solenoid is energized (12 volts). If vacuum is not present, replace solenoid. If vacuum is present, go to next step.

20) Disconnect wiring at TAD solenoid and MCU. Measure between MCU pin 20 and TAD solenoid, then between pin 10 and solenoid. If resistance is greater than 5 ohms, repair wiring. If less than 5 ohms, replace MCU module.

Fig. 6: Code 44 Test Wiring Diagram

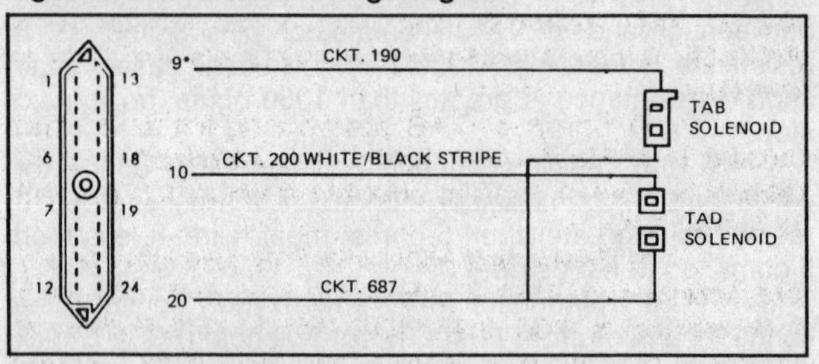

DIAGNOSTIC CODE 45 THERMACTOR AIR DIVERTER

1) Remove vacuum hose from TAD valve and connect vacuum gauge to hose. Start engine and raise speed to 2500 RPM to begin "Functional Test". Observe gauge during initial pulses. If pulses are above and below 5 in. Hg, MCU is okay, check Thermactor pump. If pulses are always above 5 in. Hg, check Thermactor pump. If pulses are always below 5 in., Hg, go to next step.

2) Check vacuum hoses between vacuum source, TAD solenoid, and TAD valve. If vacuum source or hoses are faulty, repair. If okay, go to next step.

3) Measure resistance of TAD solenoid. If within 50-110 ohms, go to next step. If not, replace TAD solenoid.

4) Check at TAD solenoid output for vacuum when solenoid is energized (12 volts). If no vacuum, replace solenoid. If vacuum is present, go to next step.

FORD MOTOR CO. 4-CYL. MCU ENGINE CONTROL (Cont.)

5) Disconnect MCU connector and TAD connector. Measure resistance between MCU pin 10 and TAD connector, then between pin 20 and TAD connector. If resistance is less than 5 ohms, replace MCU module. If resistance is greater than 5 ohms, repair circuit.

6) Check at TAD solenoid output to ensure vacuum is not present when solenoid is deactivated. If vacuum is present, replace solenoid. If no vacuum, go to next step.

7) Measure resistance between MCU pin 10 and ground. If resistance is less than 1000 ohms, repair short circuit to ground. If resistance is more than 1000 ohms, replace MCU module.

Fig. 7: Code 45 Test Wiring Diagram

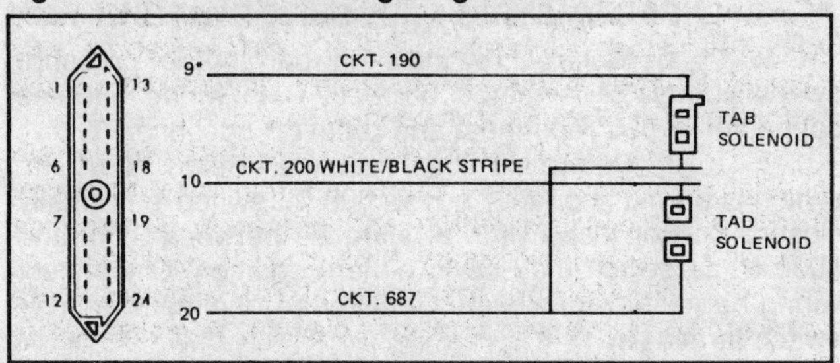

DIAGNOSTIC CODE 46
THERMACTOR AIR BY-PASS

1) Remove vacuum hose at TAB valve and connect gauge to hose. Start engine and raise speed above 2500 RPM to start "Functional Test". Observe gauge during initial pulses. If pulses are above and below 5 in. Hg, MCU is okay, check Thermactor pump. If pulses are always above 5 in. Hg, check Thermactor pump. If pulses are always below 5 in. Hg, go to next step.

2) Check vacuum hoses between vacuum source, TAD solenoid, and TAB valve for leaks or blockage. Repair if necessary. If hoses are okay, go to next step.

3) Check at TAB solenoid output to be sure vacuum is present when solenoid is deactivated. If no vacuum is present, replace solenoid. If vacuum is present, go to next step.

4) Disconnect MCU and TAB solenoid connectors. Measure resistance between ground and MCU pin 9. If resistance is less than 1000 ohms, repair short to ground. If resistance is greater than 1000 ohms, replace MCU module.

5) Check TAB solenoid output to make sure vacuum is not present when solenoid is deactivated. If vacuum is present, replace solenoid. If vacuum is not present, go to next step.

Fig. 8: Code 46 Test Wiring Diagram

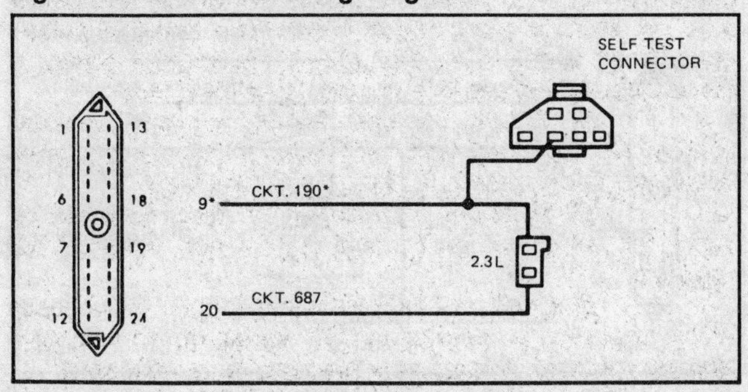

6) Disconnect MCU and TAB solenoid connectors. Measure resistance between ground and MCU pin 11. If resistance is less than 1000 ohms, repair short to ground. If greater than 1000 ohms, replace MCU module.

DIAGNOSTIC CODE 51
MID TEMPERATURE SWITCH

1) Ensure that coolant temperature was above 128°F (53°C) during "Functional Test" when code was observed.

2) Check contacts of mid temperature switch (should be closed above 128°F/53°C). If resistance measures less than 5 ohms, go to step **3)**. If above 5 ohms, replace mid temperature switch.

3) Measure resistance in wiring between MCU (pins 5 & 14) and mid temperature switch. If resistance is less than 5 ohms, replace MCU module. If greater than 5 ohms, repair wiring.

4) Disconnect harness from mid temperature switch and measure resistance between wire leading to MCU pin 14 and ground. If resistance is less than 1000 ohms, repair wire leading to MCU pin 14. If resistance is greater than 1000 ohms, replace MCU.

Fig. 9: Code 51 Test Wiring Diagram

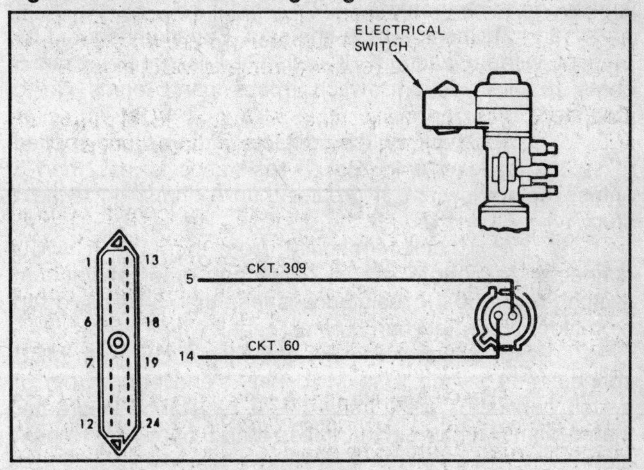

DIAGNOSTIC CODES 52 & 62
IDLE TRACKING SWITCH

1) Ensure throttle was off fast idle cam and contacting Idle Tracking Switch (ITS) during "Functional Test" when code was observed.

2) Check switch contacts. Switch should be open when throttle is closed, and continuity should be present when throttle is partially open. If switch is okay, go to next step. If not, go to step **5)**.

3) Check continuity between MCU connector pin 6 and switch, then pin 14 and switch. Be sure wire between pin 6 and switch is not shorted to ground. If wiring is okay, go to next step. If not, repair circuit.

4) Be sure ignition is off, then disconnect wiring connectors from MCU and ITS. Measure resistance between pins 6 and 20 in MCU connector. If not within 280-380 ohm range, replace resistor. If resistance is correct, replace MCU module.

5) Be sure ignition is off, then disconnect wiring connectors from MCU and ITS. Measure resistance between pins 6 and 20 in MCU connector. If not within 280-380 ohm range, replace resistor and ITS. If within range, replace only ITS. Repeat "Functional Test".

FORD MOTOR CO. 4-CYL. MCU ENGINE CONTROL (Cont.)

Fig. 10: Codes 52 & 62 Test Wiring Diagram

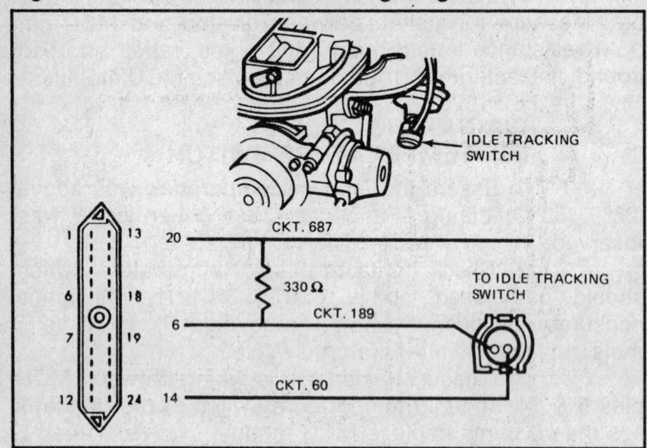

DIAGNOSTIC CODES 53 & 63 WOT VACUUM SWITCH

1) Verify correct amount of vacuum is present at switch (use vacuum gauge). At least 8 in. Hg should be present at wide open throttle switch. If vacuum level is too low, check vacuum lines and thermal switches. If vacuum is okay, go to next step.

2) Check switch contacts. Continuity should be present without vacuum. If resistance is greater than 5 ohms, replace vacuum switch. If less than 5 ohms, go to next step.

3) Check switch contacts with vacuum applied to switch (at least 3 in. Hg). If resistance is less than 5 ohms, replace switch. If greater than 5 ohms, go to next step.

4) Check continuity from pin 14 in MCU connector to bottom pin in 2-wire connector at vacuum switch (circuit 60). If resistance is less than 5 ohms, go to next step. If greater than 5 ohms, repair wiring.

5) Check continuity of switch circuit from MCU connector to switch. Use MCU pin 7, and bottom pin of switch connector pin (circuit 73). If resistance is greater than 5 ohms, repair circuit. If less than 5 ohms, go to next step.

6) Check same circuit for short to ground. Measure between MCU pin 7 and ground. If resistance is less than 1000 ohms, repair short in circuit. If greater than 1000 ohms, MCU module must be replaced.

Fig. 11: Codes 53 & 63 Test Wiring Diagram

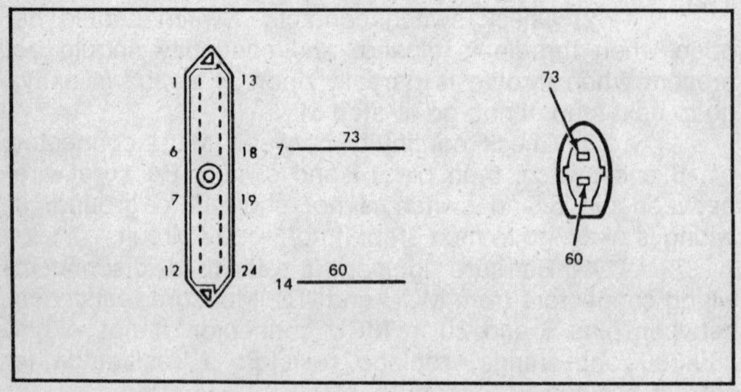

DIAGNOSTIC CODE 56 DUAL TEMPERATURE SWITCH

1) Ensure water temperature was above 55°F (13°C) during Self-Test when code was observed.

2) Check contacts of dual temperature switch (should be closed above 55°F/13°C). If resistance measures less than 5 ohms, go to step **3)**. If above 5 ohms, replace dual temperature switch.

3) Measure resistance in wiring between MCU (pins 19 & 14) and dual temperature switch. If resistance is less than 5 ohms, replace MCU module. If greater than 5 ohms, repair wiring.

4) Disconnect harness from mid temperature switch and measure resistance between wire leading to MCU pin 19 and ground. If resistance is less than 1000 ohms, repair wire leading to MCU pin 19. If resistance is greater than 1000 ohms, replace MCU.

DIAGNOSTIC CODE 65 BAROMETRIC PRESSURE SWITCH

1) Make sure that the barometric pressure switch connector is mated correctly with wiring harness connector. If not, reconnect and repeat "Functional Test".

2) Determine local altitude. Below 3500 ft., switch is normally open. Above 4000 ft., switch is normally closed. Do not test switch at altitudes between 3500 and 4000 ft. as switch may be in either condition. Disconnect wiring harness from switch. Connect an ohmmeter across switch terminals.

3) If resistance is greater than 10 ohms at altitudes above 4000 ft. or less than 1000 ohms below 3500 ft., replace switch and repeat functional test. If resistance is less than 10 ohms at altitudes above 4000 ft. or more than 1000 ohms below 3500 ft., proceed with test.

4) Disconnect harness plug from MCU. Check wires leading from MCU pins 14 and 18 to switch for continuity. If resistance of either wire is less than 10 ohms replace MCU. If resistance is over 10 ohms in either wire, repair open circuit. Repeat "Functional Test".

NO DIAGNOSTIC CODE FUNCTIONAL TEST NOT OPERATING

1) Ensure that test connections, jumper wires, and VOM were all correctly hooked up.

2) Disconnect MCU connector. With ignition on, battery voltage should be present at pin 20. If not, check fuse. With ignition off, pin 14 should have continuity to ground. If not, repair. If wiring is okay, go to next step.

3) Check for continuity between Self-Test connector and MCU. See wiring diagram at end of this test for wire connections. Check to ensure circuit from MCU to TAD solenoid is not shorted to ground.

4) Measure TAB solenoid resistance. If within 50-110 ohms, replace MCU module. If not within 50-110 ohms, replace solenoid. Repeat "Functional Test".

Fig. 12: Diagnostic Circuit Wiring Diagram

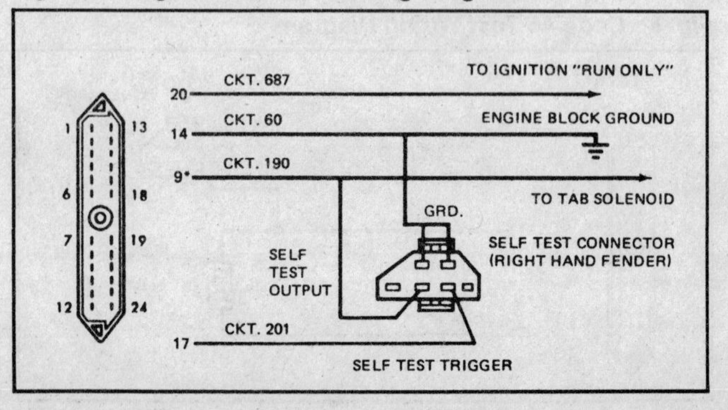

FORD MOTOR CO. 4-CYL. MCU ENGINE CONTROL (Cont.)

TACHOMETER LEAD TEST

Disconnect MCU connector and "horseshoe" connector at ignition coil. Check continuity between pin 8 in MCU connector and "Tach Test" terminal in coil connector. If circuit is open, repair. If continuity is found, replace MCU module.

Fig. 13: Tachometer Lead Test Wiring Diagram

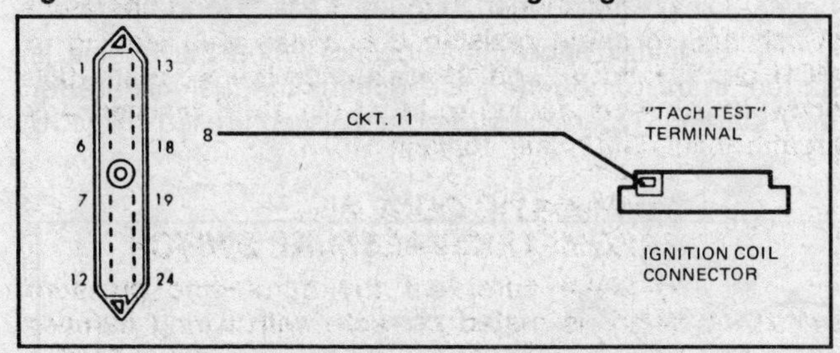

CANISTER PURGE SOLENOID

1) Check vacuum hoses for leaks or blockage and check vacuum source. Repair leaks or blockage, if present and proceed with testing.

2) Check to ensure canister purge solenoid passes vacuum when energized with 12 volts, and blocks vacuum when de-energized. Check housing and hose for leaks. If solenoid is okay, proceed to next step. If not, replace solenoid and retest.

3) Disconnect MCU and canister purge connector. Check continuity between MCU connector pin 12 and canister purge connector. Also check between pin 20 and canister purge connector. If resistance of each circuit is less than 5 ohms, go to next step. If not, repair circuits.

4) Connect ohmmeter between ground and MCU connector pin 12. If resistance is greater than 1000 ohms, replace MCU. If less, repair short circuit to ground.

Fig. 14: Canister Purge Test Wiring Diagram

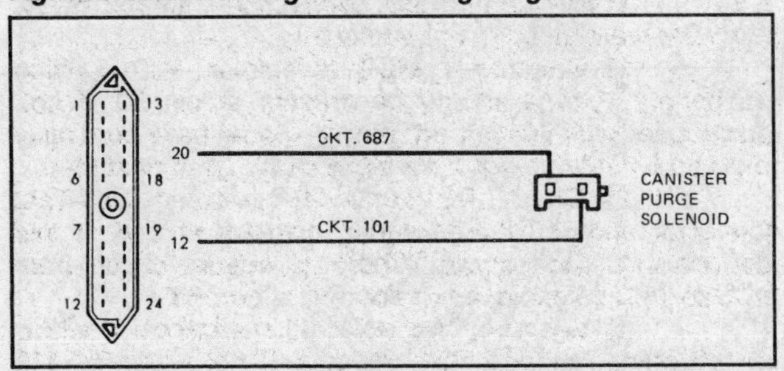

Fig. 15: 4-Cylinder MCU System Vacuum Diagram

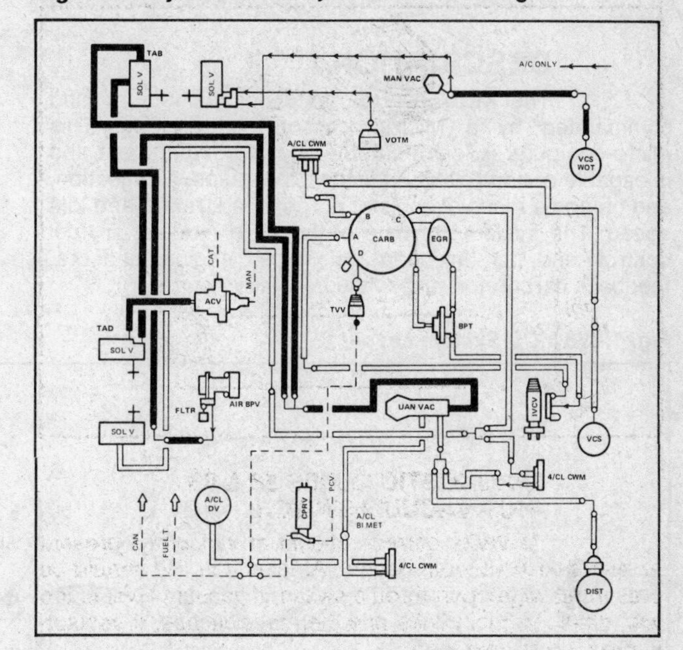

FORD MOTOR CO. V8 MCU ENGINE CONTROL SYSTEM

All Models W/2-Bbl.

DESCRIPTION

The MCU control system is named for and commanded by a Microprocessor Control Unit. This micro-computer is located in the engine compartment and is capable of controlling engine air/fuel ratios, air injection, and on some models, canister purge, spark retard and idle speed. The system consists of the MCU module, air/fuel control and air injection solenoids, engine sensors, feedback carburetor, and related circuitry.

OPERATION

MICROPROCESSOR CONTROL UNIT (MCU)

The MCU is a solid-state micro-computer located on the left fender panel. It is the "brain" of the system and receives inputs and sends signals through a 24-pin connector. The MCU is capable of operating in 3 modes: Initialization, Open loop and Closed loop.

Initialization mode occurs when the engine is started. In this mode the MCU richens the fuel mixture for easy starting. Open loop operation is controlled by MCU

Fig. 1: V8 MCU System Layout

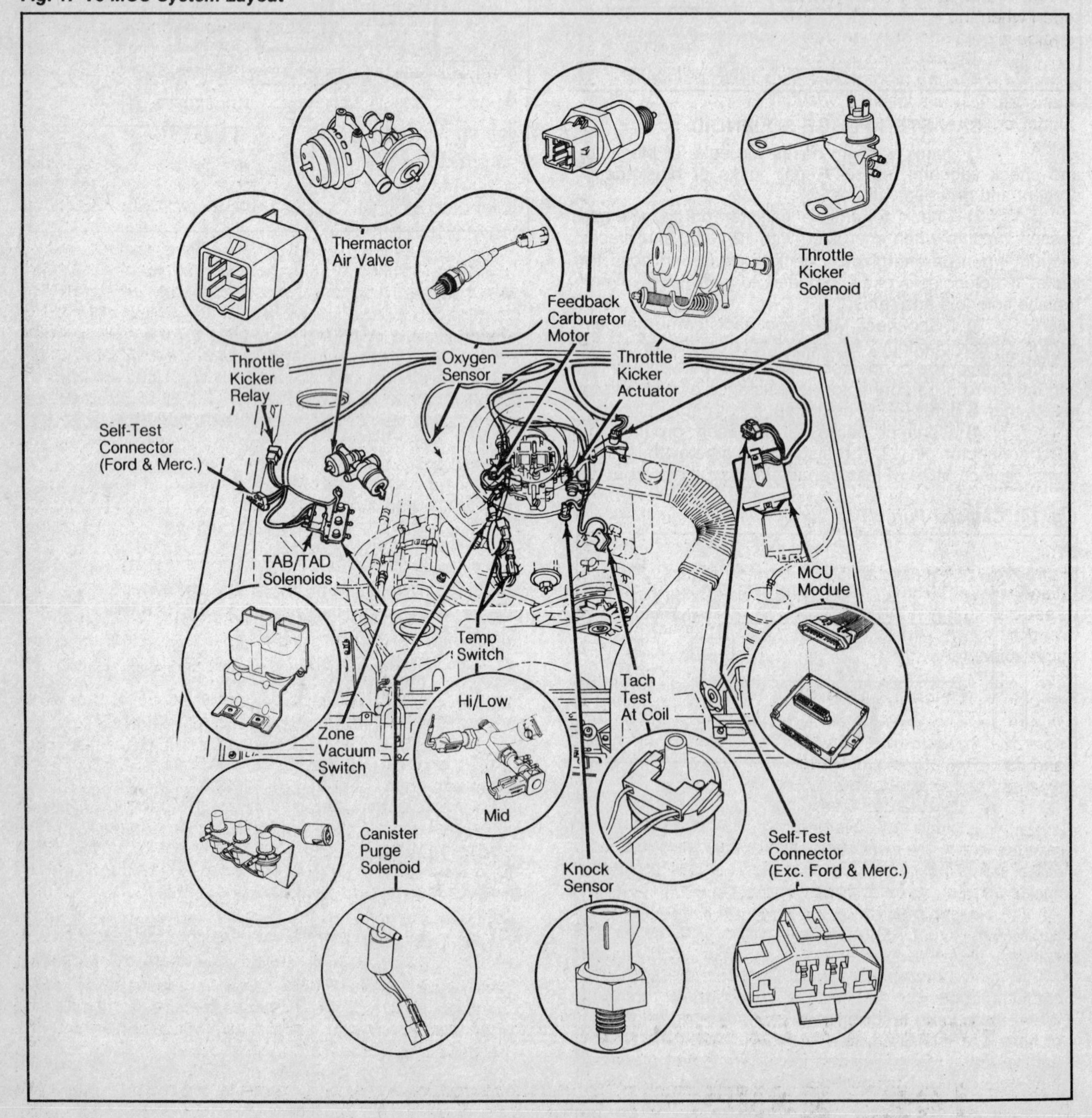

FORD MOTOR CO. V8 MCU ENGINE CONTROL SYSTEM (Cont.)

programming. Air/fuel ratio is fixed at a pre-determined level and allows good driveability at idle, moderate-to-heavy acceleration, and deceleration.

Closed loop operation occurs when the engine is warm and vehicle is operated at light load conditions. In closed loop, the MCU controls the air/fuel mixture in response to signals from an oxygen sensor in the exhaust manifold.

ENGINE SENSORS

Coolant Temperature

There are 2 switches are used to signal temperature changes to the MCU. The 2 switches are mounted with sensors in a coolant passage. One switch is open when the engine is warm; the other is open when the engine is cold and/or when it has overheated.

Engine Load Sensor

Engine load is determined by vacuum level. To measure vacuum level, 3 vacuum switches are used to signal cruise, deceleration, and wide-open-throttle conditions.

Oxygen Sensor

All models use an oxygen sensor mounted in the exhaust manifold. This sensor sends a low voltage signal to the MCU to indicate rich or lean mixture. When mixture is lean, the signal is less than 0.2 volts. When rich, the sensor voltage is slightly above 0.6 volts.

Engine Speed

The MCU receives a direct signal from the "Tach Test" terminal on the coil. It uses this signal to calculate engine speed and alters the air/fuel correction based on this speed.

Knock Sensor

The knock sensor is used on some engines to help reduce detonation. It allows a voltage signal to pass through when it senses detonation. The MCU uses this information to signal ignition module. The MCU otherwise does not control ignition timing.

Self-Test Connector

The MCU can self-diagnose most common operating problems. In order to initiate and read the diagnostic program, connections are made to the Self-Test connector. It provides voltage pulses which can be read by a specialized tester (Rotunda 07-0004) or a dial-type voltmeter.

ENGINE CONTROLS

Engine controls are the devices the MCU operates to accomplish its task of improving driveability and reducing emissions. These devices vary with engine type, but are all controlled electrically.

Thermactor Controls

These controls direct the flow of air from an air pump to either the exhaust manifold, the catalytic converter, or the atmosphere. On all models, a pair of solenoid valves control vacuum flow which operates a Thermactor Air Valve assembly. These valves are called the Thermactor Air By-Pass (TAB) and Thermactor Air Diverter (TAD) valves.

In normal operation, the air is injected into the catalytic converter to improve reduction of emissions. When the engine is idling or decelerating for long periods of time, air is diverted to atmosphere. When the engine is first warming, air is injected into the exhaust manifold to help heat exhaust gases before they reach the converter.

Air/Fuel Controls

The MCU provides current to a feedback motor in the carburetor, also known as a Feedback Carburetor Actuator (FBCA). This motor extends and retracts a shaft which alters a bleed-air orifice in the carburetor.

Canister Purge Solenoid

The canister purge solenoid is controlled by the MCU. When engine conditions are correct, the solenoid is opened and the fuel vapor canister is purged.

Throttle Kicker

The throttle kicker is used to improve idle. The MCU applies voltage to a solenoid, providing vacuum to operate the kicker.

Ignition Control

Some applications have a knock sensor to reduce detonation. The MCU sends a signal to a 3-connector ignition module, which then retards timing.

DIAGNOSIS & TESTING

The MCU system is capable of diagnosing some problems which may occur. To determine which components should be checked, perform the Functional Test which follows.

If problems do exist, a service code will be displayed (as pulses on a voltmeter). Locate the appropriate test chart and follow the repair procedure as instructed. Do not use the test charts unless referred to them by the Functional Test, or you may replace some components unnecessarily. Testing procedures require the following equipment:

- Dial Voltmeter (0-20v scale)
- Digital Voltmeter (DVOM — Min. impedance 10 megohms)
- Vacuum Gauge (0-30 in. Hg)
- Vacuum pump
- Tachometer
- Jumper Wire
- Timing Light
- Test lamp (12v)
- Torque Wrench with deep 1 1/8" socket
- Steel Rod (socket extension) & Tap Hammer
- Watch with second hand

PREPARATION FOR TESTING

1) Check vacuum hoses for leaks, cracks, or improper routing. Repair or replace as necessary.

2) Check electrical connections. Repair any frayed or broken wires. Ensure that all connections are clean and tight.

3) Turn all accessories off. Place transmission in neutral and set parking brake. Warm engine to normal operating temperature. If air cleaner must be moved, leave all vacuum hoses attached. Check to see that battery voltage is present at electric choke terminal.

NOTE: If vehicle will not start, see No Start Test.

4) Turn ignition off. Locate Self-Test connector and insert a jumper wire between ground and Trigger sockets. Connect the positive lead of a needle-type voltmeter to vehicle battery positive terminal, and the negative lead to Self-Test output socket.

5) Set voltmeter on 15-20 volt scale. Battery voltage may be shown. Remove PCV valve from valve

FORD MOTOR CO. V8 MCU ENGINE CONTROL SYSTEM (Cont.)

cover. Using a vacuum tee, connect a vacuum gauge into the vacuum hose leading from the carbon canister to the canister purge valve.

FUNCTIONAL TEST

NOTE: **Service codes are shown by voltage pulses. The first digit is indicated by a series of pulses, then the needle drops to zero for 2 seconds, then the second digit of the code is displayed. After all service codes are displayed, the throttle kicker will retract.**

Key On, Engine Off Test

Turn key on, but do not start engine. Watch voltmeter for code pulses which should appear within 5-30 seconds. Ignore any initial surge of voltage when ignition is turned on. Record code(s) and repair any problems indicated by codes.

NOTE: **If voltmeter and vacuum gauge do not pulse, or show steady high or low readings, see No Self-Test Output.**

Fig. 2: Connections for Functional Test

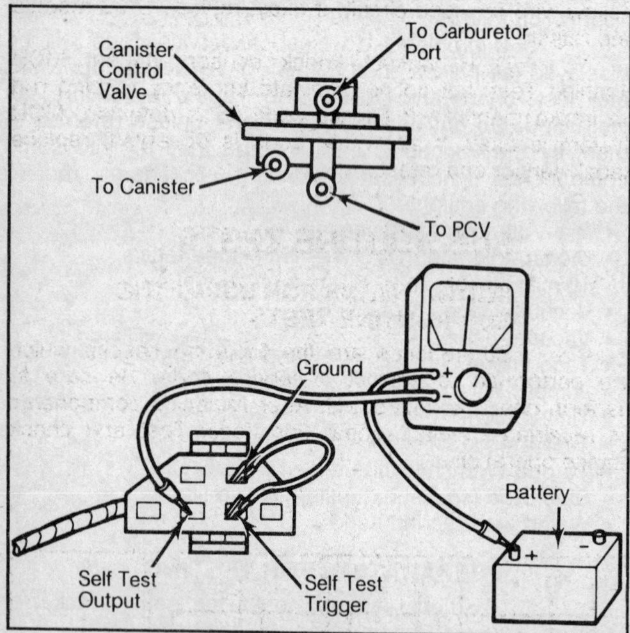

Engine Running Test

1) Verify that engine is at normal operating temperature. Run engine at 2000 RPM for 2 minutes, turn key off and immediately restart engine. Observe voltmeter and vacuum gauge for initialization pulses after restarting engine. The throttle kicker should also come on at this time and remain on throughout test.

2) Check to see if engine has knock sensor. If so, have steel bar (socket extension) and tap hammer ready. As soon as initialization pulses appear, hold steel bar against manifold near knock sensor and tap bar lightly with hammer for 15 seconds (on models with knock sensor only).

NOTE: **If more than 4 pulses appear, check for open circuit between coil and pin 8 of MCU module connector.**

3) Observe and record service codes. When codes are complete, throttle kicker will retract. Stop engine and reconnect PCV valve. Perform tests for codes in the order that codes were displayed.

NOTE: **A service code 11 may be considered a failure and code 62 may be considered a pass (MCU okay) on vehicles equipped with an altitude switch operating above 4000 ft. or vehicles without an altitude switch that have MCU pin 6 grounded to the engine.**

NOTE: **When code 11 is displayed for vehicles with a drive complaint of detonation (at WOT only) and/or poor performance, and vehicle is equipped with a universal igntion module, perform Spark Knock Test. On all other vehicles, testing is complete and MCU is functioning.**

NON-CODE TESTS

No Start Test

This test identifies faults in the MCU only, not other causes of No-Start condition.

1) Turn ignition off. Disconnect coil "horseshoe" shaped connector from coil, and vehicle harness from ignition module (4-wire connector). Check resistance between coil connector "Tach Test" terminal and ground. If resistance is less than 1000 ohms, go to next step. If greater than 1000 ohms, MCU is okay.

2) Disconnect vehicle harness connector at MCU. Measure resistance between pin 8 and ground. If greater than 1000 ohms, replace MCU module. If less than 1000 ohms, repair circuit from MCU module to coil connector to ignition module connector.

Fig. 3: No Start Test Connections

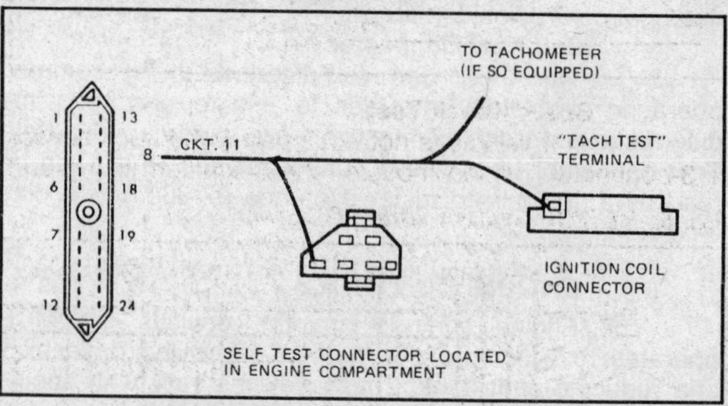

No Self-Test Output

Disconnect jumper wire from Self-Test Trigger in Self-Test connector.

1) Disconnect harness connector at MCU. Connect a voltmeter between pins 14 and 20 in MCU connector. With ignition on, 10.5 volts or more should be present. If so, go to step **3)**. If not, go to next step.

2) Connect voltmeter between pin 20 and ground. If voltage is now more than 10.5 volts, repair circuit from pin 14 to ground. If not, repair circuit from pin 20 to battery.

3) With ignition off, check continuity of circuit from Self-Test Connector (Blk/Lt Grn) to ground. If resistance is less than 1,000 ohms, go to next step. If not, repair circuits.

FORD MOTOR CO. V8 MCU ENGINE CONTROL SYSTEM (Cont.)

4) Check for continuity between MCU connector pin 19 and Self-Test Trigger socket (Tan/Red). If resistance is less than 5 ohms, go to next step. If not, repair circuit.

5) Check continuity between MCU connector pin 8 and "Tach Test" lead at coil "horseshoe" connector (remove connector from coil). If resistance is 5 ohms or less, go to next step. If not, repair circuit.

6) Disconnect canister purge connector. Check continuity between MCU connector pin 9 and Gry/Yel Hash wire at canister purge connector. Also check between pin 20 and Gry/Yel Stripe wire. If resistance of each circuit is less than 5 ohms, go to next step. If not, repair circuits.

7) Connect ohmmeter across canister purge solenoid. Resistance should be 50-100 ohms. If not, replace solenoid. If so, go to next step.

8) Connect ohmmeter between engine ground and Gry/Yel Hash wire at canister purge solenoid. If resistance is greater than 1000 ohms, go to next step. If less, repair short circuit to ground.

9) Check to ensure canister purge solenoid passes vacuum when energized with 12 volts, and blocks vacuum when de-energized. Check housing for leaks. If solenoid is okay, replace MCU module. If not, replace solenoid and retest.

Fig. 4: No Self-Test Output Test Connections

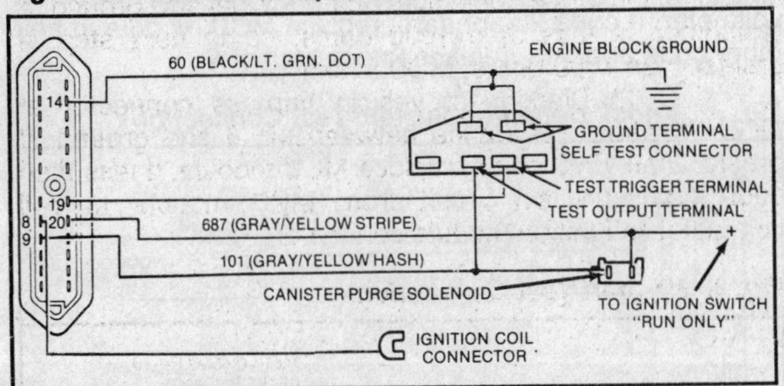

Spark Knock Test

1) If vehicle is not equipped with knock sensor or 3-connector ignition module, check ignition timing and reset as necessary. Testing is now complete. MCU system is functional and problem must be in some other area.

2) If vehicle is equipped with knock sensor or 3-connector module, disconnect knock sensor and set timing. Disconnect 2-wire connector (Yel and Blk/Wht wires) and jumper wires together at module.

3) Check ignition timing. If timing retards 16-20°, reconnect module and go to next step. If timing does not retard, replace module and repeat Spark Knock Test.

4) With vehicle at normal operating temperature, set fast idle screw on cam step that will maintain engine speed above 1200 RPM. Read and record ignition timing.

5) Locate zone vacuum switch, then remove and plug hose from it. Recheck timing, if timing retards more than 5 degrees and system has a knock sensor, go to step **7)**. If no knock sensor, testing is complete, MCU system okay. If timing does not retard 5 degrees, go to next step.

6) While engine is still at 1200 RPM, disconnect 2-wire connector at ignition module. If timing retards, check Yellow wire for short to ground. If okay, replace MCU module and retest. If timing does not retard, check Yellow wire for open circuit. If okay, replace MCU module and retest.

7) Reconnect knock sensor. Repeat MCU Running Test, but do not simulate knock by tapping rod on intake manifold. If service code 25 is obtained, MCU system is okay. If any other code is observed, replace knock sensor and retest.

SUB-ROUTINE TESTS

INSTRUCTIONS FOR USING THE SUB-ROUTINE TESTS

Sub-routines are the following checks which are performed to correct a service code. Be sure to perform check as instructed. After replacing components or repairing circuits, repeat Functional Test and check engine operation.

Fig. 5: V8 MCU System Wiring Diagram

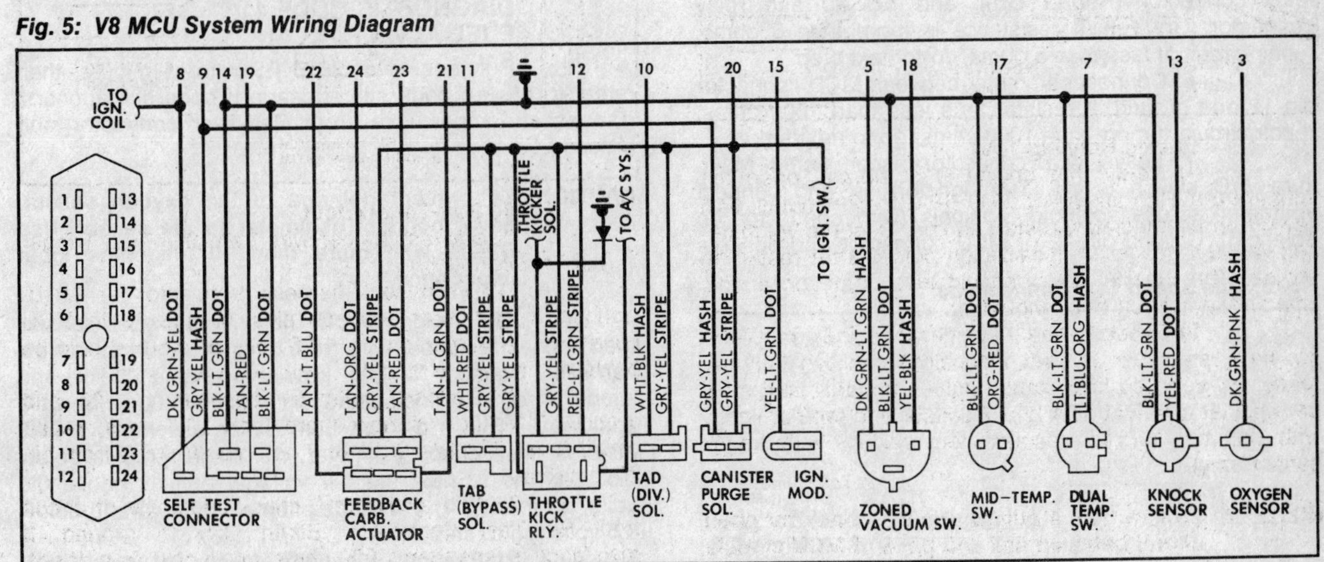

FORD MOTOR CO. V8 MCU ENGINE CONTROL SYSTEM (Cont.)

Observe the following instructions when performing sub-routines:

- Do not measure voltage or resistance at MCU module, or connect test lamps to it (unless specific instructions say to do so).
- Disconnect both ends of a circuit when looking for continuity or shorts. Be sure ignition is turned off.
- Disconnect solenoids and switches from harness before measuring resistance or continuity.
- When more than one service code is indicated, start service with the first code received.
- Use wiring diagrams to locate pin locations and connectors.

NOTE: **Partial wiring diagrams are provided for most Sub-Routine Tests to aid in servicing. For complete system wiring diagram and connector terminal locations, see Fig. 5.**

DIAGNOSTIC CODE 12
IDLE SPEED INCORRECT

Adjust carburetor idle speed and retest. Check all connections to carburetor and throttle actuator or kicker. If not equipped with vacuum throttle kicker, start test at step **3)**.

1) If equipped with vacuum actuated throttle kicker, check for manifold vacuum at kicker at idle. If vacuum is present, stop engine and go to next step. If no vacuum is present, repair vacuum lines and retest.

2) Apply 10 in. Hg vacuum to throttle actuator. Arm should extend and hold position while vacuum is applied. If not, repair or replace actuator, then retest. If actuator does operate, go to next step.

3) Disconnect wiring from throttle kicker solenoid and measure resistance of solenoid. If resistance is between 45-90 ohms, go to next step. If not, replace solenoid and retest.

4) Check circuit resistance between throttle kicker relay connector and solenoid, then between solenoid and ground. If resistance is less than 5 ohms, go to next step. If greater than 5 ohms, repair circuit.

5) Disconnect MCU connector. Check circuits for continuity between MCU pin 12 and throttle kicker relay connector (Red/Lt Grn), and pin 20 and relay connector (Gry/Yel). If resistance is more than 5 ohms, repair circuit. If less than 5 ohms, go to next step.

6) Connect ohmmeter between MCU connector pin 12 and ground. If resistance is less than 1000 ohms, repair circuit. If more than 1000 ohms, go to next step.

7) Leave MCU connector disconnected. Make sure A/C switch is off. Turn ignition on and connect voltmeter across solenoid terminals (with connector on solenoid). Ground pin 12 of MCU connector and observe voltmeter. If greater than 10 volts, replace MCU module. If less than 10 volts, replace relay.

Fig. 6: Idle Speed Test Connections

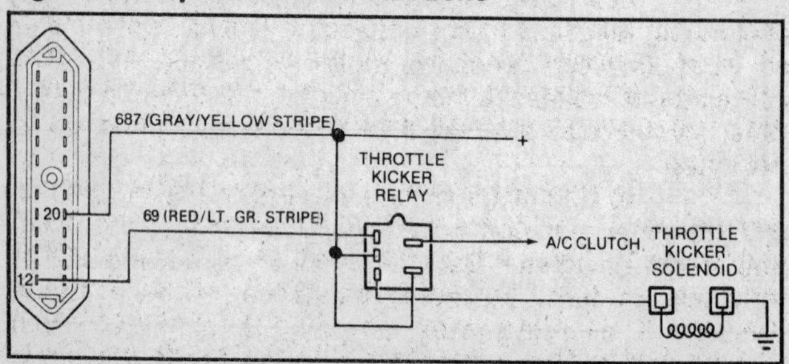

DIAGNOSTIC CODE 25
KNOCK DETECTION SYSTEM

Ensure that intake manifold was tapped with steel object within 2" from knock sensor. If not, retest, then remove jumper wire from Self-Test Trigger.

1) With ignition off, disconnect harness from knock sensor. Using 1 1/8" deep socket, loosen sensor and torque to 12-18 ft. lbs. (16-24 N.m). Do not overtighten. Go to next step.

2) Disconnect MCU connector. Connect ohmmeter between engine ground and pin 13 in MCU connector. If resistance is less than 1000 ohms, repair circuit. If more than 1000 ohms, go to next step.

3) Check continuity between pin 13 and knock sensor connector (Yel/Red). If less than 5 ohms, go to next step. If not, repair circuit.

4) Check continuity between pin 14 and knock sensor connector (Blk/Lt Grn). If less than 5 ohms, go to next step. If not, repair circuit.

5) Reconnect Self-Test Trigger jumper on Self-Test connector. Connect a 12v test lamp to battery positive terminal, then disconnect knock sensor. Perform steps **1)** and **2)** of Engine Running Test, then instead of tapping manifold with rod, tap test lamp to Yel/Red contact in knock sensor connector for 5 seconds. Observe voltmeter. If code 25 appears, replace MCU module. If any other code appears, replace knock sensor.

Fig. 7: Knock Detection System Test Connections

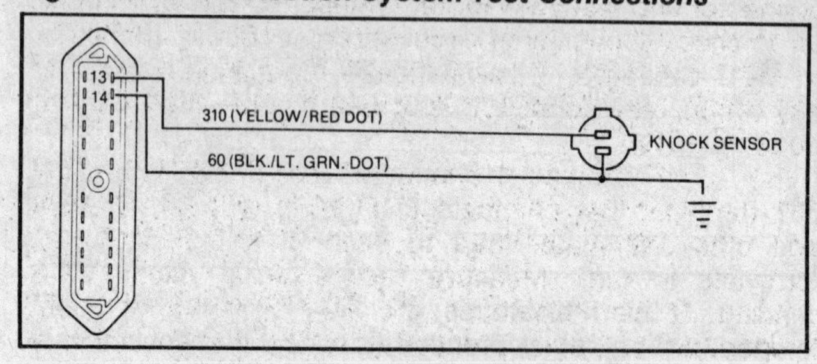

DIAGNOSTIC CODE 41
FUEL ALWAYS LEAN

Run engine at 2000 RPM for 1 minute, then retest to ensure code still appears. If code still appears, disconnect jumper wire from Self-Test connector and proceed.

CAUTION: **To prevent damage to the oxygen sensor, never connect ohmmeter to the sensor. Use DVOM with more than 10 megohms input impedance.**

1) Turn ignition off. Disconnect oxygen sensor, then connect a jumper wire from oxygen sensor to vehicle harness. Connect DVOM between engine block and jumper wire. Start engine and run at 2000-2300 RPM while applying 9-18 in. Hg to vacuum switch assembly. Wait 2 minutes, then check voltmeter. If voltage remains below 0.5 volts, go to next step. If voltage remains above 0.5 volts, go to step **4)**. If voltage alternates above and below 0.5 volts, go to step **13)**.

2) Reconnect oxygen sensor to vehicle harness, then disconnect Thermactor air hose at pump.

FORD MOTOR CO. V8 MCU ENGINE CONTROL SYSTEM (Cont.)

Disconnect MCU connector and connect DVOM between MCU connector pin 3 and engine ground. Place carburetor on high idle cam, then depress CVR rod on top of carburetor to force system rich. If voltage is less than 0.5 volts, go to next step. If greater than 0.5 volts, proceed to step **5)**.

3) Turn ignition off. Disconnect oxygen sensor from vehicle harness (with MCU still disconnected). Connect ohmmeter between MCU connector pin 14 and ground. If resistance is 5 ohms or less, proceed with test. If resistance is more than 5 ohms, repair circuit.

4) With ignition off, disconnect MCU harness connector and oxygen sensor. Connect ohmmeter to oxygen sensor connector (vehicle harness side) and MCU connector pin 3. If resistance is less than 5 ohms, proceed with test. If greater than 5 ohms, repair circuit. Check for a grounded oxygen sensor circuit by connecting an ohmmeter from MCU connector pin 3 to ground. If resistance is less than 1000 ohms, repair circuit. If resistance is 1000 ohms or more, replace oxygen sensor.

5) Reconnect all wiring, then start engine and run on low step of fast idle cam. Disconnect harness from feedback motor (FBCA) on carburetor. Let engine run 2 minutes, then apply at least 15 in. Hg vacuum to zone switch assembly. Connect a known good feedback motor (with shaft fully depressed) to vehicle harness. While observing motor shaft, disconnect PCV hose from carburetor. If shaft does not extend, go to next step. If shaft extends within 10-15 seconds, reconnect PCV and Thermactor hoses and go to step **9)**.

6) Turn ignition off. Disconnect MCU harness connector and feedback motor connector. Use an ohmmeter to check continuity of circuits from feedback connector to MCU connector. If resistance is more than 5 ohms in any circuit, repair circuit. If less than 5 ohms in all circuits, go to next step.

7) Connect 1 ohmmeter lead to FBCA terminal 687 (terminal that connects to Gry/Yel wire of harness) and other ohmmeter lead to each of 4 outside FBCA terminals in turn. Measure resistance of each FBCA winding. If all resistances are 50-175 ohms at room temperature or above, proceed with test. If any winding is more or less than 50-175 ohms, replace FBCA motor.

8) Connect 1 ohmmeter lead to engine ground. Check all circuits in feedback harness connector (except Gry/Yel) for continuity with ground. If resistance is more than 1000 ohms in all circuits, go to next step. If not, repair circuit.

9) With ignition off, connect ohmmeter lead to feedback motor case (FBCA) and other lead to terminal 687 of motor. If resistance is less than 190,000 ohms, replace motor. If greater than 190,000 ohms, go to next step.

10) Remove feedback motor from carburetor. Check for sticking shaft or dirt. Connect harness to motor and turn ignition on. Shaft should extend, then retract when ignition is turned off. If motion is uneven or shaft rotates, replace motor. Reinstall motor in carburetor.

11) Turn ignition off and disconnect vehicle harness from TAD solenoid. Connect an ohmmeter across TAD solenoid leads. If resistance is 50-100 ohms, go to next step. If not, replace TAD solenoid.

12) Disconnect MCU connector and TAD connector. Measure resistance between ground and pin 10 in MCU connector. If less than 1000 ohms, repair circuit. If more than 1000 ohms, reconnect MCU and go to next step.

13) Check connections and operation of TAD solenoid and valve. If wiring and hoses are properly connected, check for carburetor leaks, hose routing errors, and operation of bowl vent solenoid.

Fig. 8: Fuel Always Lean Test Connections

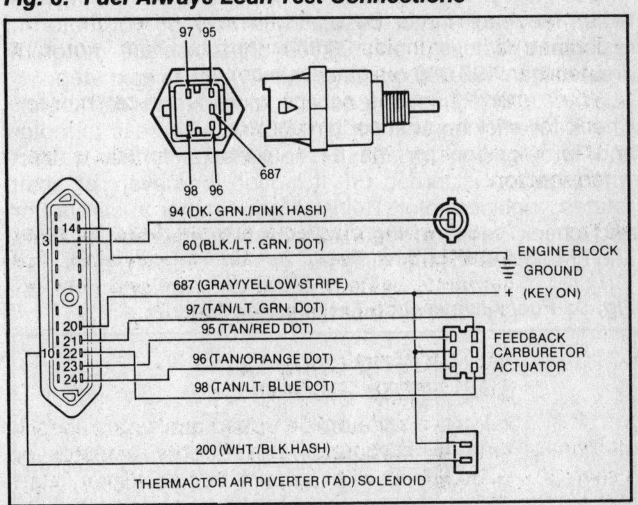

DIAGNOSTIC CODE 42
FUEL ALWAYS RICH

Vehicle must be at normal operating temperature. Disconnect jumper wire between ground and Self-Test trigger. Ensure power is present at choke cap, cold enrichment circuit works, and choke is off.

1) Disconnect Thermactor air hose at pump, and vehicle harness at oxygen sensor. Connect a voltmeter between oxygen sensor and ground, then disconnect PCV hose from carburetor. Run engine at 1800 RPM for 60 seconds, then observe voltmeter. If voltage is greater than 0.5 volts, replace oxygen sensor. If voltage varies at less than 0.5 volts, reconnect PCV and oxygen sensor. Go to next step.

2) Disconnect vehicle harness from feedback motor on carburetor. Connect a known good motor (with shaft fully depressed) to harness, but leave original motor in carburetor. Turn ignition on. If shaft extends, then retracts slightly, go to next step. If motor does not extend, go to step **4)**.

3) Apply 10-12 in. Hg vacuum to vacuum switches. Start engine and place on high step of fast idle cam. Let engine run for 2 minutes, then force system rich by depressing CVR rod on top of carburetor. Observe test feedback motor. If shaft does not retract, disconnect motor and go to next step. If shaft retracts until flush, turn ignition off, reconnect Thermactor hose to pump, and go to step **7)**.

4) Disconnect MCU connector from MCU, and disconnect feedback motor connector. Check continuity of all wires between feedback motor connector and MCU connector. If resistance in any circuit is more than 5 ohms, repair circuit. If all are less than 5 ohms resistance, go to next step.

5) Connect 1 ohmmeter lead to FBCA terminal 687 (terminal that connects to Gry/Yel wire of harness) and other ohmmeter lead to each of 4 outside FBCA terminals in turn. Measure resistance of each FBCA winding. If all resistances are 50-175 ohms at room temperature or above, proceed with test. If any winding is more or less than 50-175 ohms, replace FBCA motor.

FORD MOTOR CO. V8 MCU ENGINE CONTROL SYSTEM (Cont.)

6) Connect one lead of ohmmeter to engine ground, and test pins from feedback motor connector (except Gry/Yel). If resistance of each circuit is more than 1000 ohms, replace MCU. If resistance of any circuit is less than 1000 ohms, repair circuit.

7) With ignition off, connect ohmmeter between feedback motor case and terminal 687 of motor. If resistance is less than 190,000 ohms replace motor. If greater than 190,000 ohms (or infinity), go to next step.

8) Remove feedback motor from carburetor. Check for sticking shaft or dirt. Connect harness to motor and turn ignition on. Shaft should extend, then retract when ignition is turned off. If motion is uneven, or shaft rotates, replace motor. Reinstall good motor in carburetor and check vacuum lines, evaporative emission system, and crankcase for fuel dilution.

Fig. 9: Fuel Always Rich Test Connections

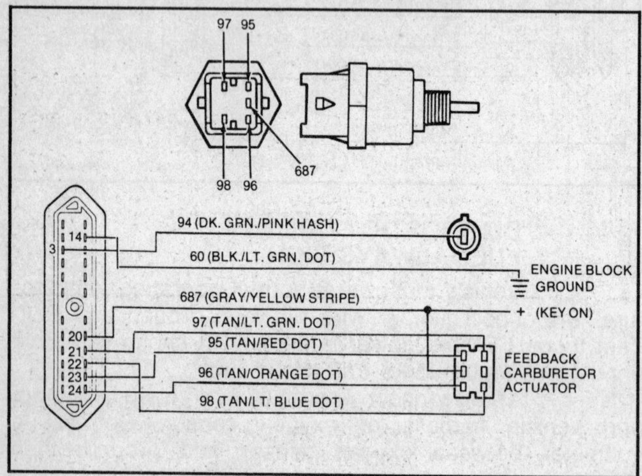

DIAGNOSTIC CODE 44 THERMACTOR SYSTEM

1) Check for manifold vacuum at input to TAB-TAD solenoids. If vacuum is present, go to next step. If not, check hose condition and routing.

2) Remove vacuum hose from TAB valve and connect vacuum gauge to hose. Start engine and run at 2000 RPM for 2 minutes. Stop engine, then immediately restart and allow to idle. Begin Functional Test and watch vacuum gauge. If pulses are above and below 5 in. Hg, go to next step. If gauge is always above 5 in. Hg, go to step **4)**. If always below 5 in. Hg, go to step **6)**.

3) Reconnect hose to TAB valve. Remove hose from TAB valve and connect vacuum gauge to hose. Start engine, run for 2 minutes above 2000 RPM, then stop engine. Restart immediately and observe vacuum gauge as Self-Test starts. If vacuum pulses above and below 5 in. Hg, check Thermactor pump operation. If vacuum is always above 5 in. Hg, go to step **10)**. If below 5 in. Hg, go to step **12)**.

4) Disconnect MCU connector and TAB connector. Measure resistance between MCU connector pin 11 and ground. If less than 1000 ohms, repair short to ground. If greater than 1000 ohms, go to next step.

5) Check at TAB solenoid output to make sure vacuum is not present when solenoid is deactivated (engine idling, harness disconnected). If vacuum is present, replace TAB solenoid. If no vacuum, replace MCU module.

6) Check vacuum hose between TAB valve and TAB solenoid for damage. If damaged, repair or replace. If hose is okay, go to next step.

7) Measure TAB solenoid resistance. If not within 50-110 ohms, replace solenoid. If resistance is correct, go to step **8)**.

8) Check at TAB solenoid output to be sure vacuum is present when solenoid is activated (engine idling, 12 volts applied). If no vacuum, replace TAB solenoid. If vacuum is present, go to next step.

9) Disconnect MCU connector and TAB solenoid connector. Continuity should exist between MCU pin 11 and Wht/Red wire at connector, and between pin 20 and Gry/Yel wire at connector. If resistance is more than 5 ohms, repair circuit. If less than 5 ohms, replace MCU module.

10) Disconnect MCU connector and TAD solenoid connector. Measure resistance between MCU pin 10 and ground. If resistance is less than 1000 ohms, repair short. If more than 1000 ohms, go to next step.

11) Check at TAD solenoid output to ensure vacuum is not present with engine idling and TAD solenoid connector disconnected. If vacuum is present, replace TAD solenoid. If no vacuum, replace MCU module.

12) Check vacuum hose between TAD valve and TAD solenoid for blocks or leaks. If problems are found, repair. If hose is okay, go to next step.

13) Remove TAD solenoid connector and measure resistance across TAD solenoid. If not between 50-110 ohms, replace solenoid. If resistance is between 50-110 ohms, go to next step.

14) Check at TAD solenoid output to ensure vacuum is present with engine idling and solenoid energized with 12 volts. If vacuum is present, go to next step. If not, replace solenoid.

15) Measure resistance of Wht/Blk wire between MCU pin 10 and TAD connector, then resistance of Gry/Yel wire between pin 20 and TAD connector. If resistance in either circuit is more than 5 ohms, repair circuit. If less than 5 ohms, replace MCU module.

Fig. 10: Thermactor System Test Connections

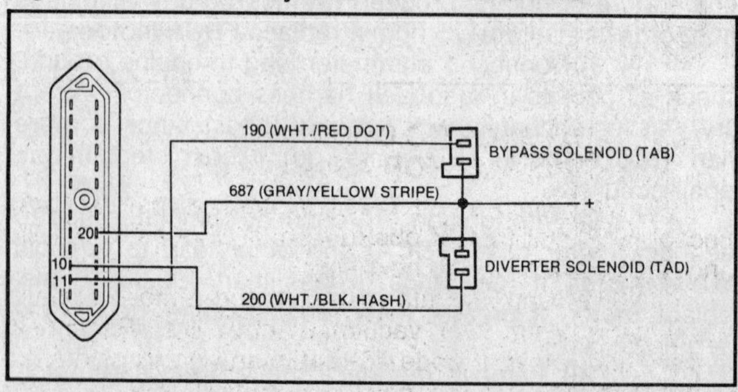

DIAGNOSTIC CODE 45 THERMACTOR AIR DIVERTER

1) Ensure that TAD vacuum line restrictor was uncapped and is free of obstruction. If plugged, clean out and retest. If okay, go to next step.

2) Cap vacuum restrictor and remove vacuum delay valve from TAD vacuum control line. Reconnect system and retest. If code 45 reappears, go to next step. If not, replace vacuum delay valve with new part and retest.

FORD MOTOR CO. V8 MCU ENGINE CONTROL SYSTEM (Cont.)

3) Remove vacuum hose from TAD valve and connect a vacuum gauge to hose. Start engine and run above 2000 RPM for 2 minutes, then stop engine. Restart engine and initiate Funtional Test, then watch vacuum gauge. If vacuum pulses above and below 5 in. Hg, check Thermactor pump. If vacuum is always above 5 in. Hg, go to step **8)**. If vacuum is always below 5 in. Hg, go to next step.

4) Check vacuum hoses between TAD valve and solenoid, then between solenoid and source. Repair if necessary. If hoses are okay, go to next step.

5) Remove TAD connector and measure TAD solenoid resistance. If between 50-110 ohms, go to next step. If not, replace solenoid.

6) Check at TAD solenoid output to ensure vacuum is present when solenoid is energized by 12 volts. If no vacuum, replace solenoid. If vacuum is present, go to next step.

7) Disconnect both TAD and MCU connectors. Measure resistance between MCU pin 20 and TAD Gry/Yel wire, and between pin 10 and Wht/Blk wire. If resistance is less than 5 ohms, replace MCU module. If greater than 5 ohms, repair circuits.

8) Check that vacuum is not present at TAD solenoid output when solenoid is deactivated (engine idling, solenoid disconnected). If vacuum is present, replace solenoid. If not present, go to next step.

9) Disconnect MCU and TAD connectors. Connect ohmmeter between MCU connector pin 10 and ground. If resistance is less than 1000 ohms, repair short to ground. If more than 1000 ohms, replace MCU module.

Fig. 11: Thermactor Diverter Test Connections

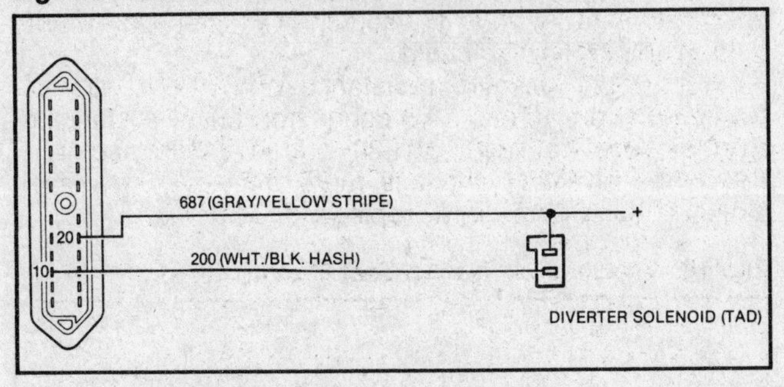

DIAGNOSTIC CODE 46
THERMACTOR AIR BYPASS

1) Ensure that TAB vacuum line restrictor was uncapped and is free of obstruction. If plugged, clean out and retest. If okay, go to next step.

2) Cap vacuum restrictor and remove vacuum delay valve from TAB vacuum control line. Reconnect system and retest. If code 46 reappears, go to next step. If not, replace vacuum delay valve with new part and retest.

3) Remove vacuum hose from TAB valve and connect vacuum gauge to hose. Start engine and run above 2000 RPM for 2 minutes, then stop engine. Restart engine and initiate Functional Test. Watch vacuum gauge. If vacuum pulses above and below 5 in. Hg, check Thermactor pump. If vacuum is always above 5 in. Hg, go to step **7)**. If always below 5 in. Hg, go to next step.

4) Check vacuum hoses between TAB valve, solenoid, and vacuum source. If hoses are leaking or blocked, repair. If hoses are okay, go to next step.

5) Check at TAB solenoid output to ensure vacuum is present with engine idling and 12 volts applied to solenoid. If no vacuum, replace solenoid. If vacuum is present, go to next step.

6) Disconnect TAB connector and MCU connector. Measure resistance between TAB connector wire (Wht/Red) and MCU connector pin 11. If less than 10 ohms, replace MCU. If more than 10 ohms, repair circuit.

7) Check TAB solenoid output to ensure vacuum is not present when solenoid is deactivated. If vacuum is present, replace solenoid. If vacuum is not present, go to next step.

8) Measure resistance between MCU connector pin 11 and ground. If resistance is less than 1000 ohms, repair short. If greater than 1000 ohms, replace MCU module.

Fig. 12: Thermactor Bypass Test Connections

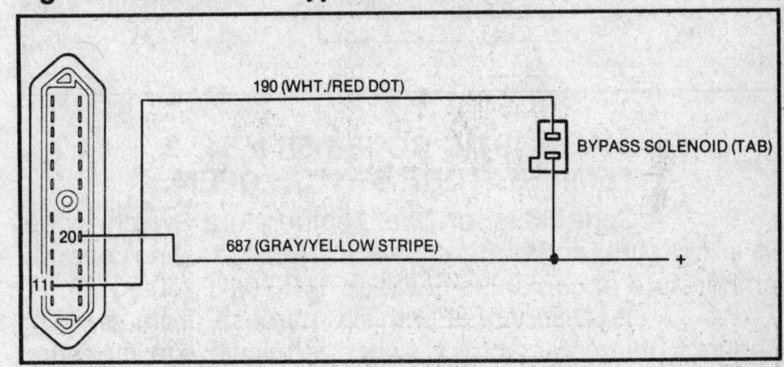

DIAGNOSTIC CODES 51 & 55
VACUUM SWITCH OPEN

Code 51 is for Hi/Low Vacuum Switch, code 55 is for Mid Vacuum Switch. Use steps **1)** and **2)** for code 51, and steps **3)** through **5)** for code 55. Be sure vacuum is present at switch during idle conditions while testing.

1) Turn ignition off. Disconnect switch from harness. Measure resistance across Hi/Low Vacuum Switch by inserting ohmmeter probes into switch connector. If resistance is less than 5 ohms, go to next step. If greater than 5 ohms, replace switch.

NOTE: Not all calibrations use a Hi Vacuum Switch.

2) Disconnect MCU harness connector. Measure continuity from MCU connector pin 5 to switch connector (Dk Grn/Lt Grn), then measure from pin 14 to switch connector (Blk/Lt Grn). If resistance is 5 ohms or less, replace MCU module. If greater than 5 ohms, repair circuits.

3) Start engine and run at idle. Disconnect Mid Vacuum Switch hose. Check for manifold vacuum at hose. If vacuum exists, go to next step. If not, check hose for plugs, leaks, or wrong connections.

4) Turn ignition off. Disconnect harness from switch connector. Apply a minimum of 15 in. Hg vacuum to switch. Check resistance of switch. If resistance is less than 5 ohms, reconnect hose and go to next step. If resistance is greater than 5 ohms, replace switch assembly.

5) Disconnect MCU harness connector. Measure continuity from MCU connector pin 18 to switch connector (Yel/Blk), then measure from pin 14 to switch connector (Blk/Lt Grn). If resistance is less than 5 ohms, replace MCU module. If greater than 5 ohms, repair circuit.

FORD MOTOR CO. V8 MCU ENGINE CONTROL SYSTEM (Cont.)

Fig. 13: Vacuum Switch Test Connections

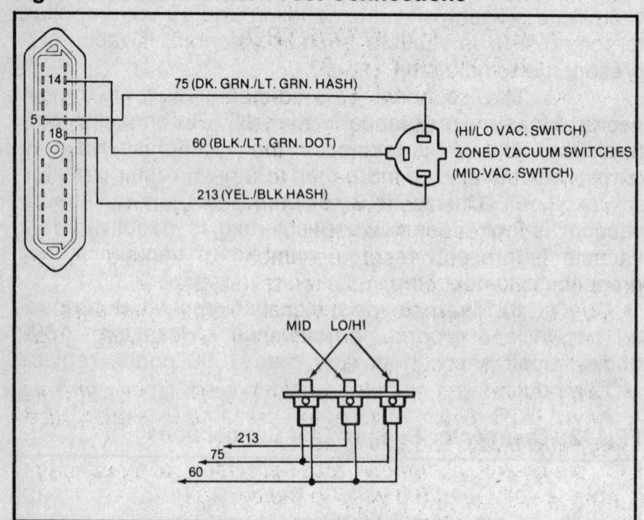

DIAGNOSTIC CODES 53 & 54 TEMPERATURE SWITCH OPEN

Code 53 is for Dual Temperature Switch, code 54 is for Mid-Temperature Switch. Before testing, ensure temperature of coolant is between 140-200°F (60-93°C).

1) Disconnect vehicle harness from switch. Connect ohmmeter across switch terminals and measure resistance. If resistance is greater than 5 ohms, replace switch. If less than 5 ohms, go to next step.

2) Connect one lead of ohmmeter to MCU pin 7, then 17, and the other lead to ground. If resistance is 1000 ohms or less in either location, repair circuit. If resistance is 1000 ohms or more, proceed with test.

3) Disconnect MCU harness connector. Check continuity of circuits from MCU connector to switch connector. (Pins 7 & 14 for Dual-Temp. Switch; pins 14 & 17 for Mid-Temp Switch). If resistance is greater than 5 ohms, repair circuit. If less than 5 ohms, replace MCU module.

Fig. 14: Temperature Switch Test Connections

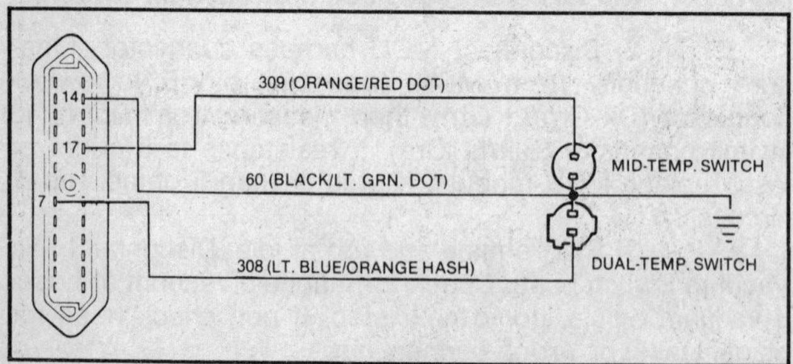

DIAGNOSTIC CODE 62 BAROMETRIC PRESSURE SWITCH

1) Make sure that the barometric pressure switch connector is mated correctly with wiring harness connector. If not, reconnect and repeat Functional Test.

2) Determine local altitude. Below 3500 ft., switch is normally open. Above 4000 ft., switch is normally closed. Do not test switch at altitudes between 3500 and 4000 ft. as switch may be in either condition. Disconnect wiring harness from switch. Connect an ohmmeter across switch terminals.

3) If resistance is greater than 10 ohms at altitudes above 4000 ft. or less than 1000 ohms below 3500 ft., replace switch and repeat functional test. If resistance is less than 10 ohms at altitudes above 4000 ft. or more than 1000 ohms below 3500 ft., proceed with test.

4) Disconnect harness plug from MCU. Check wires leading from MCU pins 14 and 6 to switch for continuity. If resistance of either wire is less than 10 ohms replace MCU. If resistance is over 10 ohms in either wire, repair open circuit. Repeat Functional Test.

DIAGNOSTIC CODE 65 VACUUM SWITCH CLOSED

Ensure that vacuum hoses are connected to switch and engine coolant is between 140-200°F (60-93°C).

1) Turn engine and ignition off and disconnect vacuum switch from vehicle harness. Connect ohmmeter across switch connector (Blk/Lt Grn and Yel/Blk) to measure switch resistance. If resistance is greater than 1000 ohms, reconnect switch. If less than 1000 ohms replace switch assembly.

2) Disconnect vehicle harness from MCU. Connect ohmmeter between MCU connector pin 18 and engine ground. If resistance is greater than 1000 ohms, replace MCU. If less than 1000 ohms, repair circuits.

1983 Exhaust Emission Systems

FORD MOTOR CO. ELECTRONIC ENGINE CONTROL III

Ford, Lincoln & Mercury Models W/EFI

NOTE: Information on this system is also covered in the FUEL SYSTEMS Section. Additional diagnostic information that relates strictly to the fuel portion of this system can be found in the FORD MOTOR CO. ELECTRONIC FUEL INJECTION article.

DESCRIPTION

The EEC system consists of an Electronic Control Assembly (ECA), several sensors located on the engine or in the various engine systems, special actuators governed by the ECA, and various connecting electrical and vacuum lines. This system adjusts the engine to the best settings for various conditions of load, speed, temperature and altitude by controlling the following functions:

- Ignition Timing
- Carburetor Air/Fuel Ratio
- Engine Speed At Idle
- Exhaust Gas Recirculation (EGR) Flow Rate
- Secondary (Thermactor) Air Flow Rate
- Fuel Evaporation Canister Purging

OPERATION

ELECTRONIC CONTROL ASSEMBLY (ECA)

The ECA is a solid-state, micro-computer consisting of a processor assembly and a calibration assembly. This unit is located in the passenger compartment under the instrument panel, to the left of the steering column. The ECA is the "brain" of the EEC system.

Processor Assembly

The processor assembly is housed in an aluminum case and contains circuits designed to:

- Continuously sample input signals from the sensors.
- Calculate the proper spark advance, air/fuel ratio, EGR flow and thermactor air flow.
- Send out control signals to adjust spark timing, air/fuel ratio, EGR flow, thermactor air mode, evaporation canister purge and idle speed.

The processor assembly also provides a continuous reference voltage of 9.0 volts to the sensors.

Calibration Assembly

The calibration assembly is contained in a black plastic housing which is attached to the top of the processor assembly. It contains the "memory" and programming used by the processor assembly. The calibration assembly is capable of:

Fig. 1: EEC-III Component Locations

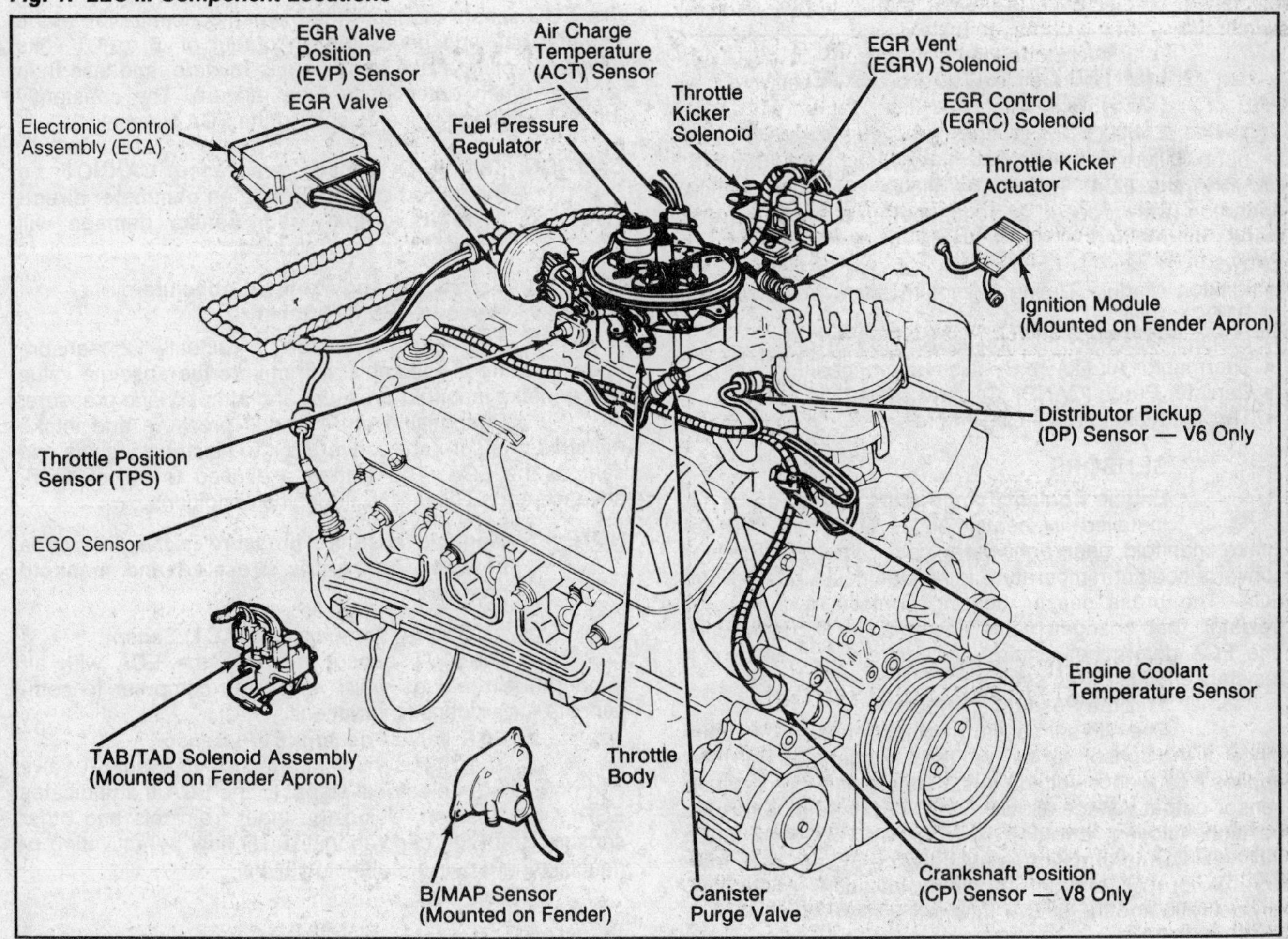

FORD MOTOR CO. ELECTRONIC ENGINE CONTROL III (Cont.)

- Providing operating information for that particular vehicle, for use by the processor assembly.
- Recalling information from its memory when required.

Power Relay

Activated by the ignition switch to supply battery voltage to the EEC. The power relay is mounted under the hood on the left fender apron. Also protects ECA from possible damage due to reversed voltage polarity.

Fig. 2: EEC Electronic Control Assembly (ECA)

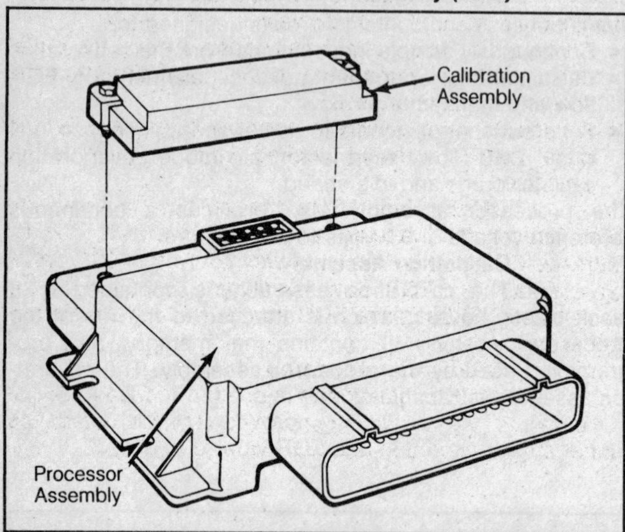

LIMITED OPERATION STRATEGY (LOS) MODE

The LOS mode functions during engine start, or upon failure of the ECA detected by a "safeguard" circuit in the ECA. This mode allows continued vehicle operation (with reduced performance) until repairs can be made. In this mode the actuator functions are set as follows:

- Ignition Module Timing; Minimum spark advance (10° BTDC).
- Exhaust Gas Recirculation (EGR): No EGR.
- Thermactor Air (TAB): By-pass (dump) position.
- Canister Purge (CANP): Canister sealed, no purge.
- Throttle Kicker (TK): Low RPM idle.

SENSORS

Engine Coolant Temperature (ECT) Sensor

Installed in heater outlet fitting at front of intake manifold near right valve cover, the ECT sensor converts coolant temperature to an electrical signal for the ECA. The brass sensor housing contains a thermistor (resistor that changes value according to temperature). The ECA determines engine coolant temperature by the resistance value of the sensor.

Throttle Position (TP) Sensor

The TP sensor is a potentiometer. The resistance of the sensor varies with throttle opening. The ECA applies a reference voltage to the sensor and the resultant sensor output voltage allows the ECA to determine throttle position (closed throttle, part throttle or wide open throttle). This information is used by the ECA in determining the proper amount of spark advance, EGR flow, air/fuel ratio and the proper thermactor air mode.

NOTE: **The throttle position (TP) sensor mounting holes are slotted to permit rotational adjustment. If sensor is replaced, it must be correctly positioned or misleading throttle information will be sent to the ECA.**

Crankshaft Position (CP) Sensor (V8 Models Only)

To provide the EEC system with an accurate timing reference (when pistons reach 10° BTDC), the crankshaft vibration damper is fitted with a 4-lobe "pulse ring".

As the crankshaft rotates, the pulse ring interrupts a magnetic field at the tip of the CP sensor (mounted on right front of engine). When the field is interrupted, an output signal is generated and sent to the ECA.

The ECA uses these signals to determine the exact position of the crankshaft. From the pulse frequency, the ECA can determine engine RPM. By knowing these two factors, the ECA can determine amount of ignition timing advance required for best engine operation.

NOTE: **Once the CP sensor is installed, no field adjustment is necessary.**

Exhaust Gas Oxygen (EGO) Sensor

Installed in the exhaust manifold, the EGO sensor provides the ECA with the oxygen concentration of the exhaust gas.

The EGO sensor monitors the oxygen concentration of the exhaust gas and generates an output of .6 to 1.1 volts when detecting a rich exhaust gas mixture, and less than .2 volts when detecting a lean mixture. The constantly changing voltage signal is sent to the ECA for analysis.

CAUTION: **The EGO sensor resistance CANNOT be measured by connecting an ohmmeter directly to its output lead. Sensor damage will result if this is attempted.**

Barometric and Manifold Absolute Pressure (BMAP) Sensor

The BMAP sensor is actually 2 sensors combined into 1 assembly. It monitors the absolute value of the intake manifold pressure and atmospheric pressure.

Changes in atmospheric pressure and intake manifold pressure are converted into electrical signals and sent to the ECA. The signals are used to adjust spark advance and EGR rate to fit engine conditions.

NOTE: **Manifold absolute pressure is the difference between barometric pressure and manifold pressure.**

Air Charge Temperature (ACT) Sensor

The ACT sensor provides the ECA with air temperature readings which allow the computer to compensate for air density variations.

EGR Valve Position (EVP) Sensor

The EVP sensor is attached to the EGR valve and provides an electrical signal to the ECA that indicates EGR valve position. Using the input from this and other sensors, the ECA can regulate EGR flow by activating or deactivating a pair of solenoid valves.

FORD MOTOR CO. ELECTRONIC ENGINE CONTROL III (Cont.)

THROTTLE KICKER SYSTEM

The throttle kicker system consists of a Throttle Kicker Solenoid (TKS) and a Throttle Kicker Actuator (TKA). The system is designed to increase engine RPM when the A/C is on, at high altitude, and when coolant temperature is above or below a specific range.

With A/C "ON", the ECA energizes the TKS, allowing intake manifold vacuum to reach the TKA. The TKA is positioned on the carburetor against the throttle lever. With vacuum applied, the TKA will increase engine RPM for increased cooling and smoother idle. The TKA is also energized during engine warm-up or if an engine overheat condition exists.

EXHAUST GAS RECIRCULATION (EGR) SYSTEM

The EGR system used with EEC-III has 3 major components: an EGR valve and sensor assembly, an EGR cooler, and a 2-solenoid EGR control assembly.

Utilizing engine manifold vacuum to operate the EGR valve, the ECA controls EGR gas flow. When EGR valve is open, exhaust gas from exhaust manifold is directed into the intake manifold and becomes part of the combustion cycle, helping to reduce NOx emission levels.

EGR Valve and Sensor Assembly

The EGR valve is mounted to the intake manifold under the carburetor. The valve controls EGR flow through a pintle valve and seat. An EGR valve position sensor (EVP) is attached to the valve and provides an electrical signal to the ECA indicating EGR valve position.

The EGR valve, unlike standard EGR valves, has no opening to observe pintle valve movement. The EGR valve and position sensor are serviced as individual units.

Dual EGR Control Solenoids

EGR valve flow rate is controlled by two solenoid valves mounted on the left valve cover. Proper control of vacuum needed to operate the EGR valve requires two types of solenoid valves:

- A vent valve, which is normally open; that is, the outlet port is normally connected to the inlet port when the solenoid is not energized.
- A vacuum valve, which is normally open; that is, the outlet port is normally blocked when solenoid is not energized.

Utilizing input from the various sensors, the ECA directs the vacuum and vent solenoids to: (1) Increase EGR flow by applying vacuum to the EGR valve, (2) Maintain the EGR flow by trapping vacuum in the system, and (3) Decrease EGR flow by venting the system to the atmosphere.

EGR Cooler Assembly

An EGR gas cooler is used to reduce EGR gas temperature, thus providing improved flow characteristics, better engine operation and EGR valve durability.

Fig. 3: Electronic Engine Control Sensors

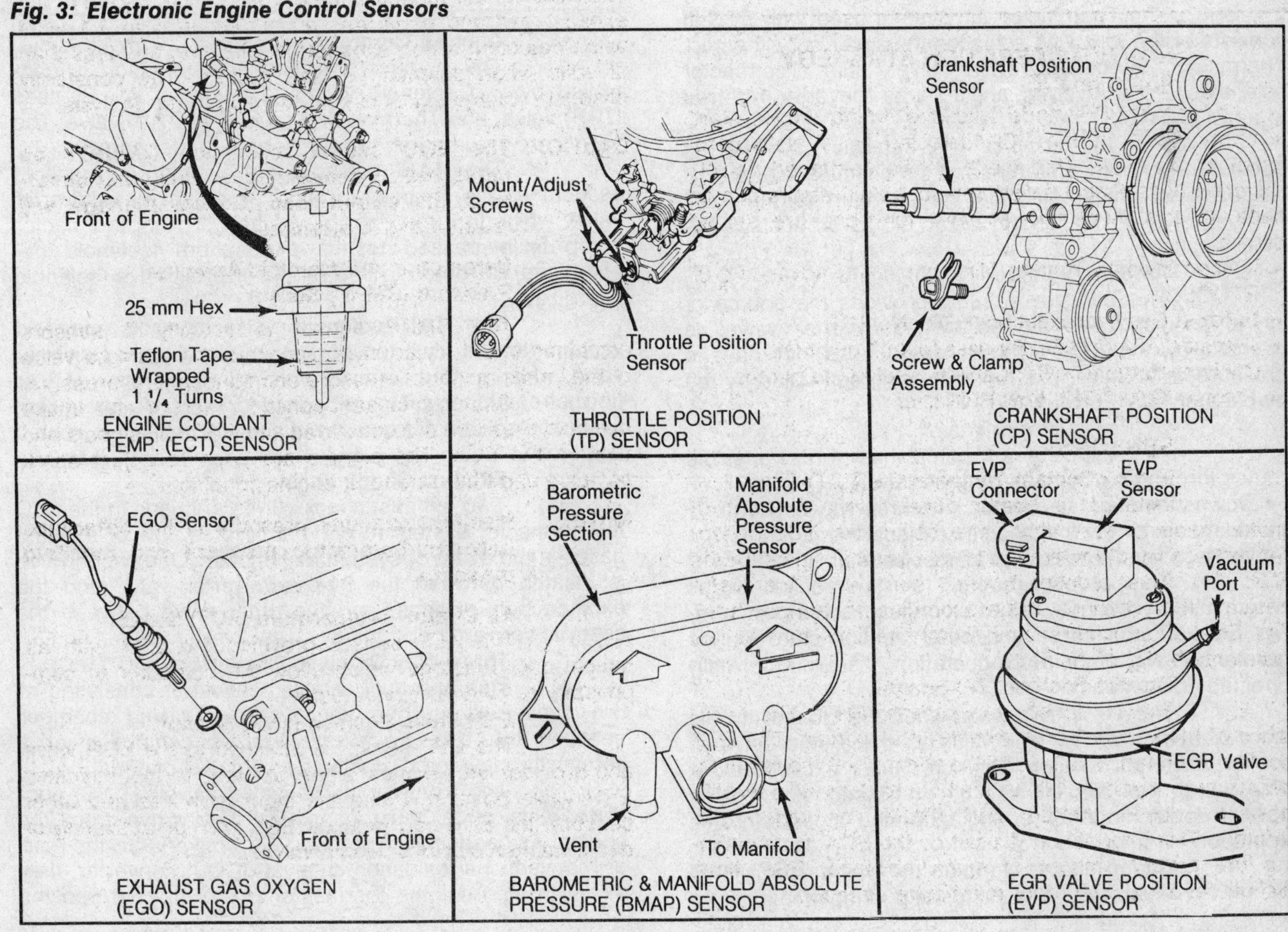

FORD MOTOR CO. ELECTRONIC ENGINE CONTROL III (Cont.)

Fig. 4: Dual EGR Control Solenoids

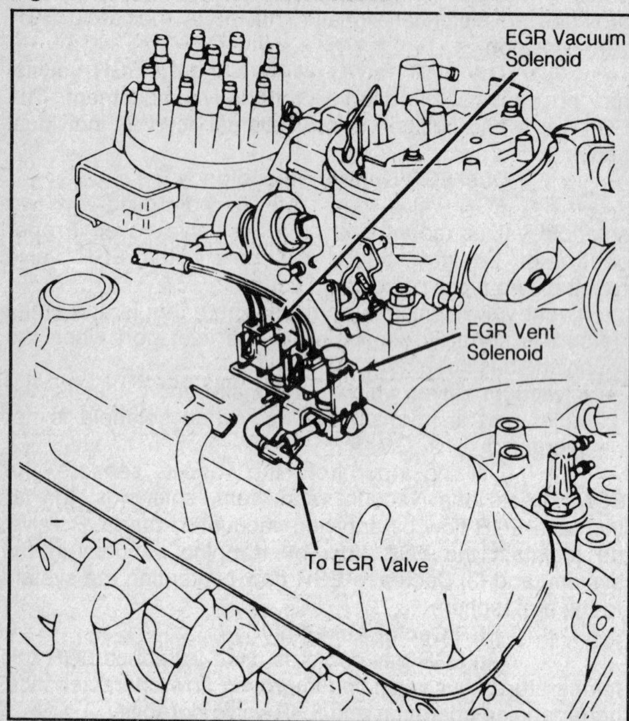

THERMACTOR AIR SYSTEM

The Thermactor Air System used with EEC-III consists of the following components: an air supply pump, Thermactor By-pass/Diverter valve, dual Thermactor solenoids, 2 check valves, and a 3-way converter (referred to as COC/TWC).

The efficiency of the catalytic converter is dependent upon temperature and the chemical makeup of the exhaust gases. Air must be provided to the COC catalyst for the oxidation of HC and CO by-products of the TWC catalyst.

Air Supply Pump

This belt driven pump provides the source of air to be controlled by the by-pass/diverter valve as directed by the ECA. The air pump does not have a pressure relief valve, this function being controlled by the by-pass/diverter valve.

By-Pass/Diverter Valve

Air from the air pump has three possible routes through the by-pass/diverter valve:

- Downstream air (air injected into three-way catalyst).
- Upstream air (air injected into exhaust manifold).
- By-pass (air by-passed to atmosphere).

The proper routing for thermactor air is determined by the ECA based on engine coolant temperature versus time curve and other sensor data. During normal coolant temperature operation, the air is normally directed downstream.

The air is by-passed when the closed throttle time exceeds a preset time value, or if the time between the Exhaust Gas Oxygen lean/rich sensor exceeds a set time value. The air will also be by-passed during wide open throttle mode or during extended closed throttle operation.

During engine warm-up the thermactor air will be routed upstream. This is to help remove excessive amounts of HC and CO produced during the warm-up period.

Fig. 5: Thermactor Air System By-Pass/Diverter Valve

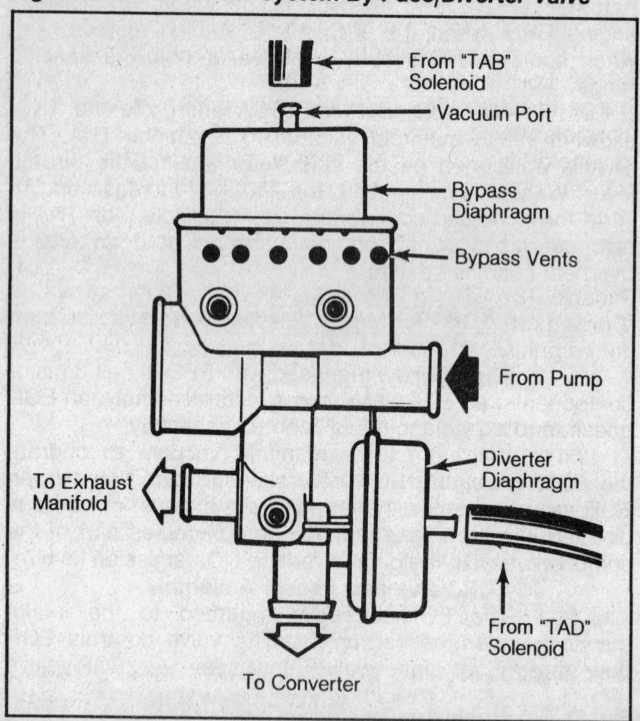

Dual Air Control Solenoids

The by-pass/diverter valve operation is controlled by two solenoid valves: Thermactor Air By-pass (TAB) valve, and Thermactor Air Diverter (TAD) valve. The valves are mounted on top of the right fender apron.

The TAB solenoid valve controls manifold vacuum to the by-pass portion of the by-pass/diverter valve, which in turn controls whether air from thermactor pump is by-passed to the atmosphere (solenoid de-energized) or routed to control the diverter valve (solenoid energized).

The TAD solenoid valve controls manifold vacuum to the diverter portion of the by-pass/diverter valve, which in turn controls which direction (upstream or downstream) thermactor air is routed. When de-energized, air is routed downstream. When energized, air is routed upstream.

Exhaust Check Valve

Two exhaust check valves are used in the EEC III Thermactor system to prevent reverse flow of exhaust gases in the event of system malfunction. One check valve is located between the by-pass/diverter valve and the exhaust port drillings, and the other valve between the catalytic converter and the by-pass/diverter valve.

Three-Way Catalytic Converter (COC/TWC)

This is a dual catalytic converter consisting of two converters in one shell, with a mixing chamber between the two. Each converter is composed of a ceramic "honey-comb" coated with catalyst material.

The front, or "three-way catalyst" (TWC) converter acts on exhaust gases as they arrive from the engine. As gases flow from the TWC converter to the rear, or "conventional oxidation catalyst" (COC) converter, they mix with air from the thermactor pump injected into the

FORD MOTOR CO. ELECTRONIC ENGINE CONTROL III (Cont.)

mixing chamber. This air is required for proper oxidation of HC and CO in the COC converter.

CANISTER PURGE SYSTEM

Canister Purge (CANP) Solenoid

This solenoid is a combination solenoid and valve. Located in the line between the intake manifold purge fitting and the carbon canister, the CANP solenoid controls the flow of vapors from the canister to the intake manifold during various engine operating modes. The valve is opened and closed by a signal from the ECA.

DURA-SPARK III IGNITION SYSTEM

The EEC-III system uses a Dura-Spark III module (Brown grommet where wires emerge) and a Dura-Spark II ignition coil. A resistance wire is also used in the primary circuit.

Distributor

The EEC distributor eliminates conventional mechanical and vacuum advance mechanisms. All timing is controlled by the ECA, which is capable of firing the spark plug at any point within a 50° range depending on calibration. This increased spark capability requires greater separation of adjacent distributor cap electrodes to prevent cross-fire.

Fig. 6: EEC III Ignition Distributor Assembly

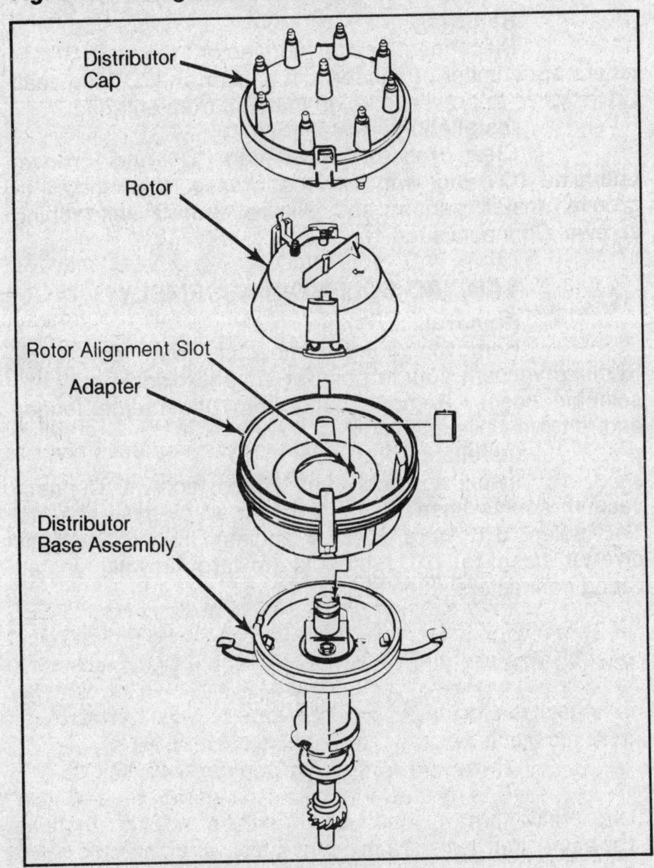

DIAGNOSIS & TESTING

NOTE: **Due to the complexity of the EEC III system, full testing cannot be done unless an EEC III tester (T79L-50-EEC-II or T80L-50-EEC-II, and T78L-50-DVOM or T79L-50-DVOM) is used. Instructions for testing come with the tester, which is available from Owatonna Tool Co. However, some checks can be made using regular shop equipment. These checks are outlined in the following procedures.**

TESTING NOTES & CAUTIONS

NOTE: **No repairs or adjustments can be made to the ECA components. If diagnosis shows Processor or Calibration units are not functioning properly, they must be replaced.**

CAUTION: **Shorting the wiring harness across a solenoid valve can burn out circuitry in the ECA that controls the solenoid valve actuator.**

CAUTION: **The EEC system contains transistors which CANNOT tolerate excessive voltage surges or transient voltage. Never try to jump-start the vehicle with 24 volts.**

CAUTION: **The Exhaust Gas Oxygen (EGO) sensor resistance CANNOT be measured by connecting an ohmmeter directly to its output lead. Sensor damage will result if this is attempted.**

BASIC EEC TROUBLE SHOOTING

1) Perform basic fuel system and ignition system checks, to ensure there is gas and spark.

2) Remove air cleaner assembly and inspect all vacuum and pressure hoses for proper connection to fittings, or any broken, cracked or pinched conditions.

3) Inspect EEC sub-system harness for proper connections to EGR solenoid valves. Red wire to both, Yellow wire to vacuum solenoid and Green wire to vent solenoid.

4) Check for any loose or detached connectors or broken or detached wires. Ensure all terminals are completely seated.

5) Repair items as required and replace air cleaner.

6) Check battery charge, cable connections and main electrical wiring.

7) Test resistance of all sensors and solenoids, using values given in COMPONENT RESISTANCE VALUES Chart. Be sure to disconnect component from circuit before checking resistance.

REMOVAL & INSTALLATION

BMAP SENSOR

Removal

Disconnect wiring harness from BMAP sensor. Disconnect vacuum hose, remove retaining nuts, and remove sensor.

Installation

Position sensor and tighten retaining nuts. Connect vacuum hose to "Manifold" port. Do not connect any hose to "Vent" port. Connect wiring harness.

FORD MOTOR CO. ELECTRONIC ENGINE CONTROL III (Cont.)

EEC III COMPONENT RESISTANCE VALUES

Component	Wire Colors	Resistance (Ohms)
Crank Position (CP) Sensor	Gry—Dk Blu	100-640
Distributor Position (DP) Sensor	Gry—Dk Blu	300-800
Coolant (ECT) Sensor	Lt Grn/Yel—Blk/Wht	1100-8000
Air Charge Temp (ACT)	Lt Grn/Ppl—Blk/Wht	1700-60,000
Throttle Position (TP) Sensor		
Closed Throttle	Org/Wht—Blk/Wht	3000-5000
Closed Throttle	Dk Grn/Lt Grn—Blk/Wht	550-1100
Wide Open Throttle	Dk Grn/Lt Grn—Blk/Wht	2100 or more
EGR Control Solenoid	Red-Yel	30 or more
EGR Vent Solenoid	Red—Dk Grn	30 or more
TK Solenoid	Red—Red/Lt Grn	45 or more
TAB Solenoid	Red—Wht/Red	45-90
TAD Solenoid	Red—Lt Grn/Blk	45-90
Fuel Pump Relay	Red—Tan/Lt Grn	40 or more
By-Pass Ballast Resistor	.....	3 or less

CANISTER PURGE SOLENOID VALVE

Removal

Remove air cleaner. Disconnect 2-wire connector and 2 vacuum hoses from solenoid. Remove valve.

Installation

Connect hose from manifold to nipple at end of valve. Connect hose from "T" to nipple toward middle of valve. Position valve so end with wires faces upward, then connect wiring and install air cleaner.

CRANKSHAFT POSITION (CP) SENSOR

Removal

Disconnect both sensor connectors. Remove sensor retaining clamp and pull sensor carefully out of holder.

Installation

Clean holder, then insert sensor fully (clamping surface about .025" from holder surface). Install retaining clamp and tighten to 70-100 INCH Lbs. (8-11 N.m). Route wires up water pump and under spark plug wires along manifold to right of carburetor.

ELECTRONIC CONTROL ASSEMBLY

Removal

1) Remove 10 mm retaining bolt and remove harness connector. Remove 2 bracket nuts, then remove gasket around connector.

2) From inside passenger compartment, remove 2 screws holding ECA to bracket. Slide out ECA and remove 2 screws to lift off calibration assembly.

Installation

1) Attach calibration assembly with 2 screws. Slide ECA into bracket, engaging clip in ECA flange. Position connector surface through firewall, then install 2 mounting screws.

2) Install gasket carefully and replace bracket mounting nuts. Install connector and tighten retaining bolt to 40 INCH Lbs. (4.5 N.m).

OXYGEN SENSOR

Removal

Allow exhaust manifold to cool. Disconnect wiring and remove sensor with crow's foot socket or special tool (T79P-9472-A).

Installation

Clean mounting surface and install sensor with fingers. Use tool to tighten sensor until compression washer crushes, about 27-33 ft. lbs. (37-45 N.m), then connect wiring.

EGR VALVE POSITION SENSOR

Removal

Disconnect wiring connector. Remove 3 fasteners at perimiter of sensor. Lift sensor and "O" ring seal. Cover valve to prevent foreign material from entering.

Installation

Clean top of valve and "O" ring groove. Lubricate "O" ring with silicone grease, then install in groove. Install sensor and secure with 3 self-tapping screws. Connect wiring.

TAB/TAD SOLENOID ASSEMBLY

Removal

Remove wiring connector from solenoids. Remove vacuum source hose at "T" and disconnect both solenoid hoses. Remove bolts from underneath fender and remove valve assembly.

Installation

Install assembly and tighten screws. Connect vacuum source hose to "T". Connect air by-pass hose to TAB solenoid (toward front of engine), then connect air diverter hose to TAD solenoid (toward firewall). Install wiring connectors.

FORD MOTOR CO. ELECTRONIC ENGINE CONTROL III (Cont.)

Fig. 7: Ford Motor Co. Electronic Engine Control (EEC III) Wiring Diagram

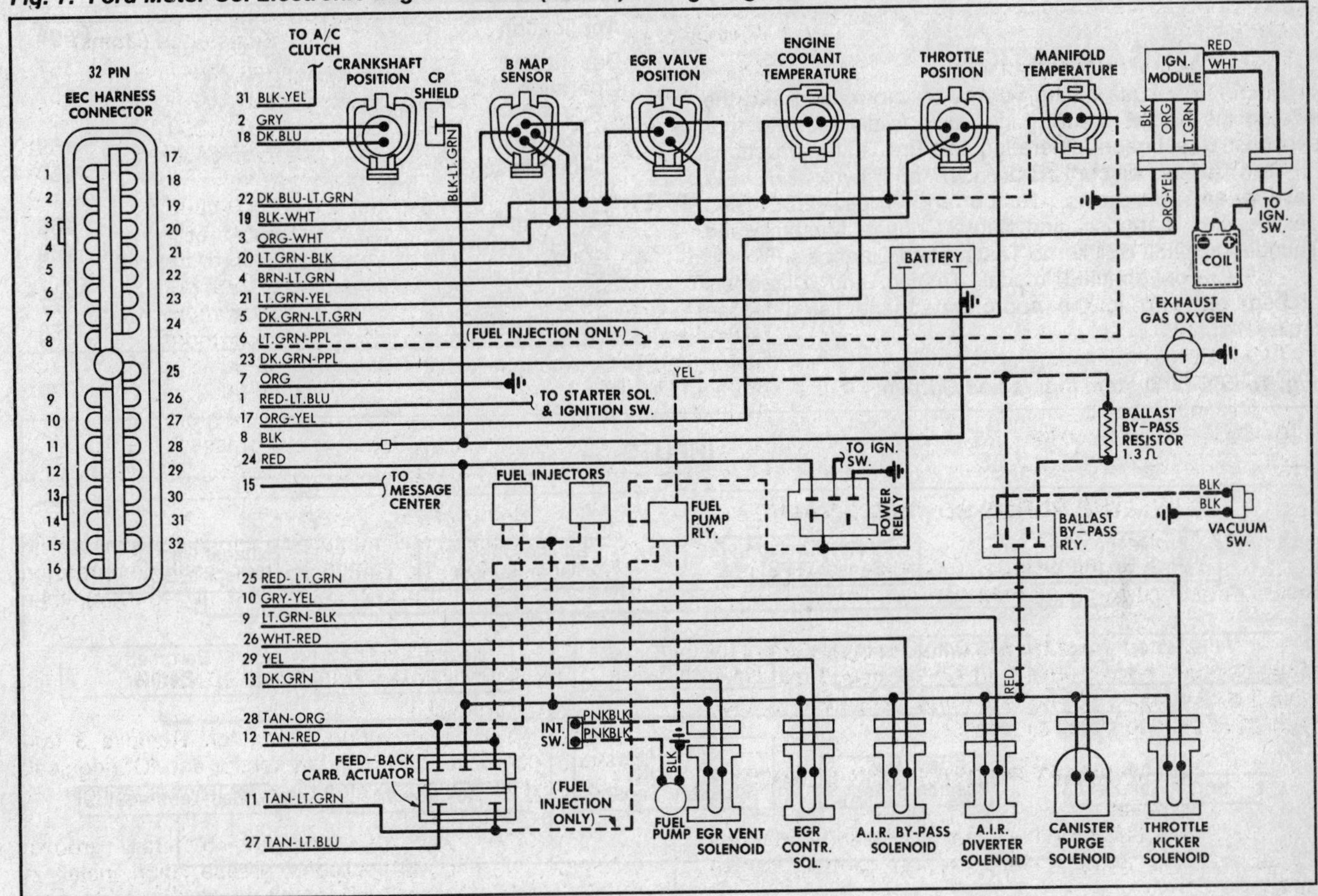

Fig. 8: Typical EEC III Vacuum Schematic

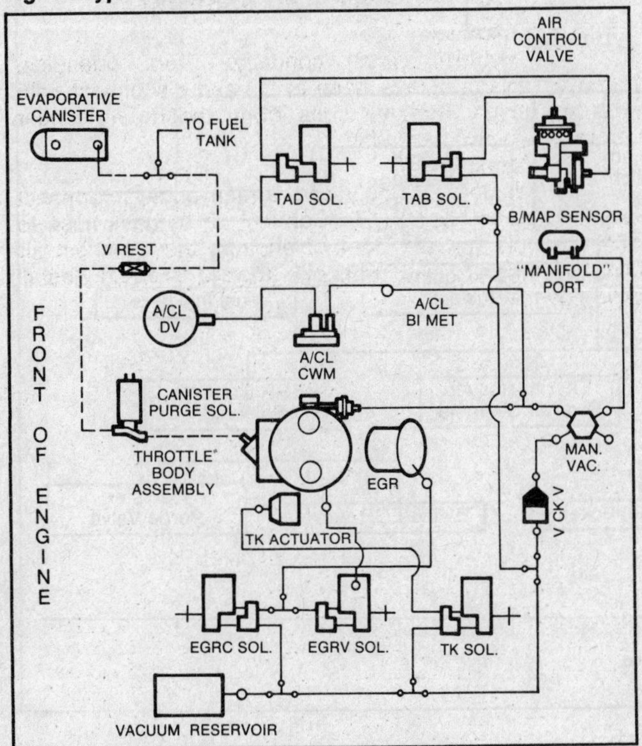

FORD MOTOR CO. ELECTRONIC ENGINE CONTROL IV

1.6L EFI, 2.3L HSC, 2.3L EFI Turbo

ORGANIZATION

Because of the volume of information and the size of the article, the EEC-IV article is divided into four sections: Description, Operation and Pre-Test Instructions for all models; Escort, EXP, LN7 and Lynx 1.6L EFI Testing and Diagnosis; Tempo and Topaz 2.3L HSC Testing and Diagnosis and Capri, Cougar, Mustang and Thunderbird 2.3L EFI Turbo Testing and Diagnosis.

For specific model Testing and Diagnosis procedures, turn to the appropriate page listed in the table.

EEC-IV DIRECTORY

Fig. 1: EEC-IV System Inputs and Outputs

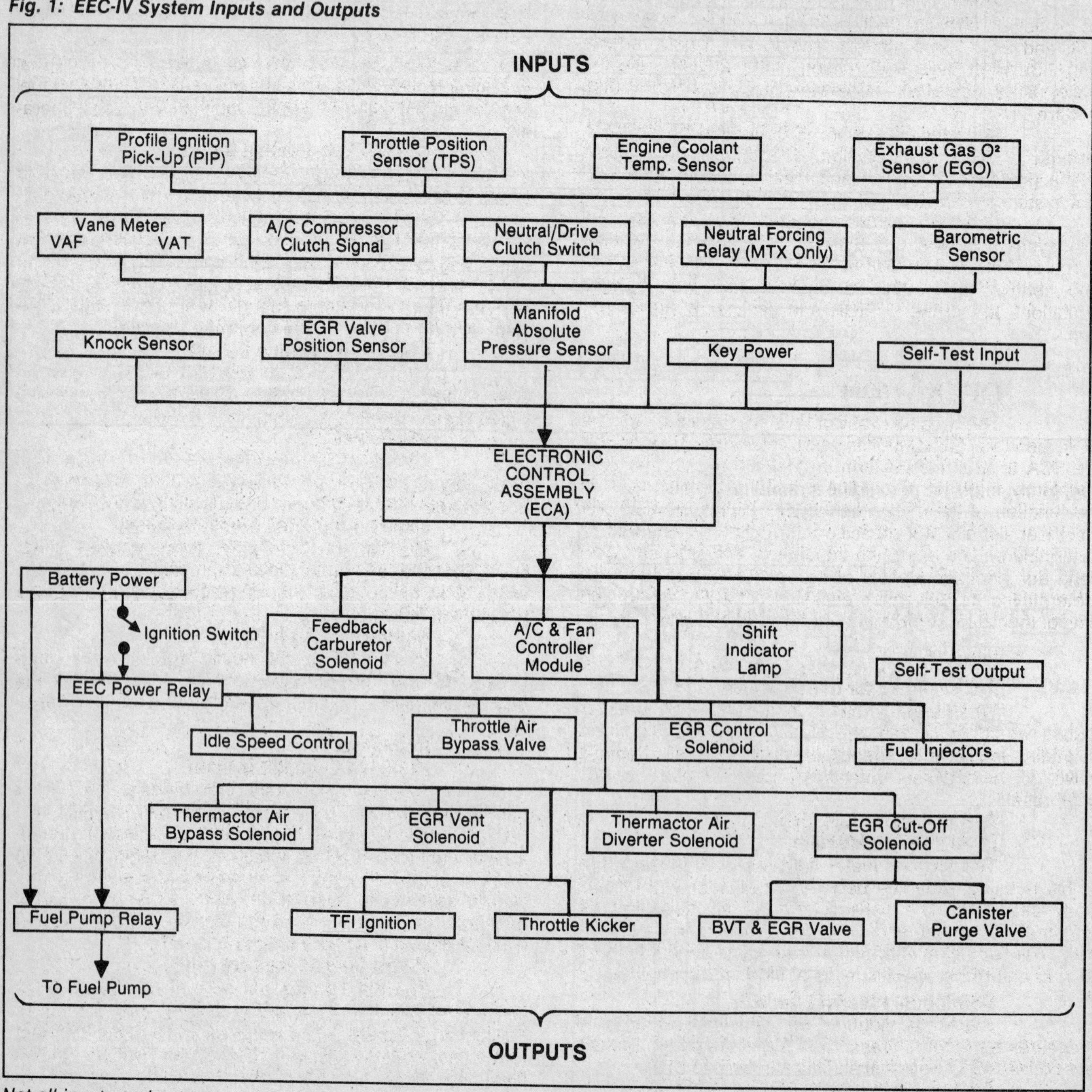

Not all inputs and outputs are used on all engines.

FORD MOTOR CO. ELECTRONIC ENGINE CONTROL IV (Cont.)

DESCRIPTION

The center of the EEC-IV system is the Electronic Control Assembly (ECA). The ECA receives information from several sensors and other electronic devices. Based on information received and the operation program in the ECA's memory, the ECA generates output signals to control engine operation. The calibration module for EEC-IV systems is mounted inside the ECA. The ECA is located in the passenger compartment, under the center console.

The EEC-IV system controls 3 major areas of engine operation: Air/fuel mixture, ignition, and emission control. Additionally the system controls A/C compressor clutch operation and provides self-diagnostic capabilities.

The air/fuel mixture control is accomplished by an air flow controlled, multi-point, fuel injection system on 1.6L and 2.3L Turbo models. Tempo and Topaz models with 2.3L High Swirl Combustion (HSC) engines use the Holley 6149 Feedback carburetor to control the air/fuel mixture.

The ignition system is controlled by the ECA through a Thick Film Ignition (TFI-IV) module. Ignition timing (advance or retard) and dwell are controlled with this system to improve ignition system performance.

Emission control components controlled by this system include the EGR system and the canister purge system. These systems are shut off until the engine and controls are ready to operate with the changed conditions presented by EGR and canister purge operation.

OPERATION

The engine control system consists of the ECA, sensors and switches, and actuators. In order for the ECA to properly perform its function, it must be kept constantly informed of engine operating conditions. It is the function of the engine sensors to supply the ECA, via electrical signals, with specific information as required to determine engine operating conditions. The ECA can then send out electrical signals of its own to control fuel flow (determining air/fuel ratio), emission controls and ignition timing. Individual component operation is as follows:

INPUTS

A/C Compressor Clutch Signal

When battery voltage is applied to compressor clutch, a signal is sent to ECA. ECA uses signal to maintain engine idle speed, using throttle air by-pass valve, to compensate for added load created by A/C compressor.

Air Flow Meter Assembly (Fuel Injected Models)

The air flow meter consists of 2 sensors in a single housing, mounted between air cleaner and throttle body assembly. The sensors are an air flow and air temperature sensor and both are exposed to intake air flow. The combined information from these sensors allows ECA to determine specific mass of air entering engine.

Barometric Pressure Sensor

Sensor is mounted on right inner fender and measures barometric pressure of atmospheric air. Signals are converted to electrical signals and sent to ECA.

Engine Coolant Temperature (ECT) Sensor

This sensor, threaded into heater supply tube, monitors and signals the ECA of engine coolant temperature. The ECA interprets this as either cold or normal operating temperature. This influences ECA control of fuel mixture enrichment, idle speed, ignition, and EGR operation.

Fig. 2: Air Flow Meter Installation

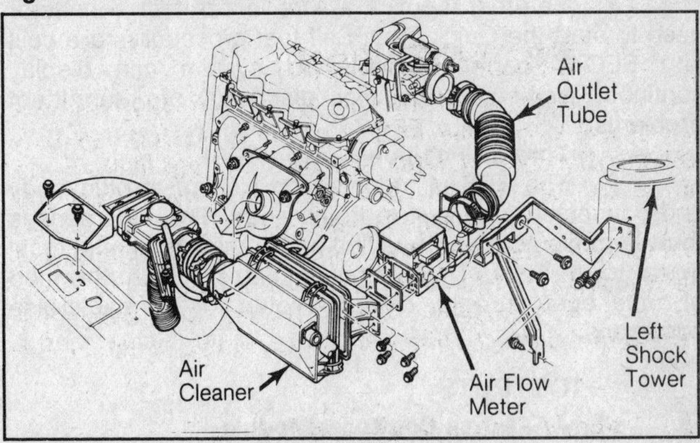

1.6L EFI and 2.3L Turbo EFI only.

Exhaust Gas Oxygen Sensor

This sensor is threaded into exhaust manifold where it constantly monitors oxygen content of exhaust gases. A voltage signal is produced which varies according to difference in oxygen content between exhaust gases and surrounding atmosphere. This signal is sent to the ECA which translates exhaust gas oxygen content to air/fuel ratio. It then alters fuel delivery rate to aquire the ideal ratio for current engine operating conditions.

EGR Valve Position Sensor

Sensor located on top part of EGR valve on 2.3L Tempo and Topaz models. Sensor provides system with a signal indicating position of EGR valve.

Key Power

This is simply the test input for Quick Test using Key On-Engine Off Self-Test routine. These tests are to detect hard faults only, not intermittent problems.

Manifold Absolute Pressure Sensor

Mounted on right inner fender, sensor measures absolute pressure of mixture in intake manifold and sends a signal to ECA that is proportional to absolute pressure in manifold.

Neutral Forcing Relay

In start mode, the neutral forcing relay simulates a no-load condition to the ECA. This enables the ECA to maintain a fast idle speed to aid in engine warm-up.

Neutral Switch (& Clutch Engaged Switch)

Automatic transaxle 1.6L models use only a neutral start switch. Manual transaxle 1.6L models use both a clutch engaged switch and a transaxle neutral switch. Function of either circuit is the same, indicating whether engine is loaded or unloaded and ensuring that vehicle cannot be started in gear. ECA uses signal generated by these switches to maintain same idle speed whether engine is under a load or not.

Profile Ignition Pick-Up (PIP)

The PIP informs the ECA of crankshaft position and speed. PIP assembly is integral with distributor. PIP has an armature with 4 windows and 4 metal tabs that rotate past a stator assembly (Hall-Effect Switch). Ignition distributor does not have any mechanical or vacuum advance. Distributor is adjustable for resetting base timing if necessary.

FORD MOTOR CO. ELECTRONIC ENGINE CONTROL IV (Cont.)

Self-Test Input

Self-test input is a wire in self-test connector used to start the Quick Test. Self test procedures are built into EEC-IV control module so system can display continous self-test codes for diagnosis of intermittent problems.

Throttle Position Sensor (TPS)

The TPS is mounted on side of throttle body and connected directly to throttle shaft. The TPS senses throttle movement and position and transmits an electrical signal to the ECA. These signals keep the ECA informed of wide open throttle, closed throttle, or normal cruise conditions.

OUTPUTS

A/C & Fan Controller Module

A/C and Cooling Fan Controller Module is operated by ECA, coolant temperature switch and stoplamp switch. Controller module provides an output signal which controls operation of A/C compressor clutch and engine cooling fan.

EGR Control Solenoid

Solenoid switches manifold vacuum to operate EGR valve on command from ECA. Vacuum opens EGR valve when solenoid is energized.

EGR Shut-Off Solenoid

EGR shut-off solenoid is an electrically operated vacuum valve located between manifold vacuum source and EGR valve. Located between solenoid and EGR valve is a controlled vacuum bleed. This vacuum bleed is a Backpressure Variable Transducer. These 2 devices operate EGR for optimum performance. Vacuum switched by solenoid is also supplied to canister purge valve.

EGR Vent Solenoid

Solenoid vents EGR control solenoid vacuum line. When vent solenoid is energized, control solenoid can open EGR valve.

Feedback Carburetor Solenoid

Feedback control is accomplished by this solenoid which regulates idle, off idle and main system air/fuel ratios according to ECA signals.

Fuel Injectors

On 1.6L and 2.3L Turbo models, each cylinder has a solenoid-operated injector which sprays fuel toward back of each inlet valve. Each injector is energized through ignition circuit and grounded through ECA to complete circuit. ECA controls length of time each injector is open.

The "open" time of injector governs amount of fuel delivered. Injectors deliver 1/2 the amount of fuel required for an operating cycle each time they open (twice per cycle).

Fuel Pump Relay

Fuel pump relay is activated by ECA with ignition switch in "ON" or "CRANK" positions. When ignition switch is turned to "ON" position, relay is activated to supply initial line pressure to system.

Idle Speed Control Solenoid

This is an air valve solenoid used to by-pass throttle plate to provide idle speed control according to signals from ECA.

Self-Test Output

Part of the self-test connector, service codes are transmitted on the output in the form of timed pulses to be read as diagnostic codes.

Shift Indicator Lamp

Used on Tempo and Topaz to indicate to driver when to shift gears for optimum fuel economy. ECA signals lamp when to light according to information received on engine speed and manifold vacuum levels.

Thermactor Air By-pass Solenoid

Solenoid provides a vacuum signal to by-pass valve, which then by-passes thermactor pump air to atmosphere.

Thermactor Air Diverter Solenoid

Solenoid provides a vacuum signal to diverter valve to divert thermactor pump air to either exhaust manifold or catalytic converter.

TFI Ignition Module

The TFI module triggers ignition coil and determines dwell. Module is mounted on side of distributor. ECA uses signal from Profile Ignition Pick-up to determine crankshaft position. Ignition timing is determined within ECA. ECA then signals TFI module when to fire coil.

Throttle Air By-pass Valve

Throttle Air By-pass Valve is a solenoid operated valve controlled by ECA. Solenoid operates a variable area metering valve. Responding to commands from ECA, valve controls both cold and warm idle air flow. Valve operates by by-passing air around throttle plate. Idle speed is adjusted to meet varying conditions by altering amount of air flowing into engine.

Throttle Kicker Solenoid

Two port valve with an atmospheric vent. A vacuum diaphragm is used to maintain nominal idle speed on command from ECA.

TESTING & DIAGNOSIS

TEST EQUIPMENT

The following equipment is recommended to perform the Quick Tests and Pinpoint Tests on EEC-IV systems. Some equipment is REQUIRED to perform tests. DO NOT attempt to test this system without proper equipment. Damage to vehicle components will result if improper equipment is used.

- Self-Test Automatic Read-Out (STAR) Tester. This tool is recommended, but not required. It is specially built for the EEC-IV system and is used to display the two digit service codes that are programmed into the control module.
- Analog Volt-Ohmmeter with 0-20V DC range. This can be used as an alternate to the STAR tester.
- Jumper wire about 15" long.
- Vacuum Gauge with 0-30 in. Hg range, and resolution in the 1 in. Hg. range.
- Tachometer with 0-6000 RPM range, accuracy plus/minus 40 RPM and resolution within 20 RPM.
- Vacuum Pump with 0-25 in. Hg range.
- Digital Volt-Ohmmeter (DVOM) with 10 meg-ohm minimum input impedance.
- Timing light.
- Spark tester. A modified spark plug with side electrode removed and alligator clip attached may be used.
- Breakout Box. For 2.3L HSC and 2.3L EFI Turbo models. This is a jumper wire assembly which connects between the vehicle harness and the processor assembly. The Breakout Box is REQUIRED to perform certain tests on the processor. Ford Motor Co. DOES

FORD MOTOR CO. ELECTRONIC ENGINE CONTROL IV (Cont.)

NOT recommend using a DVOM to probe the processor pin connector as permanent damage to the pins will result.

- Fuel injection pressure gauge for EFI and EFI Turbo models.
- Non-powered test light for EFI and EFI Turbo models.

PREPARATION

Correct test results for this system are dependent on the correct operation of several related non-EEC components and systems. All non-EEC problems should be corrected before attempting to diagnose the EEC system.

Before hooking up any equipment to diagnose the EEC system, make the following checks:

- Verify the condition of the air cleaner and air ducting.
- Check all vacuum hoses for leaks, restrictions and proper routing.
- Check the EEC system wiring harness electrical connections for loose or detached connectors, wires or terminals.
- Check the ECA, sensors and actuators for physical damage.
- Perform all necessary safety precautions to prevent personal injury or vehicle damage.
- Set parking brake and place shift lever in "P" for automatic transmission, Neutral for manual transmission. Do not move shift lever during testing unless specifically directed to do so.
- Turn off all lights and accesories, and make sure that vehicle doors are closed when making readings.
- Check coolant level and correct as necessary.
- Start engine and idle until upper radiator hose is hot and pressurized and throttle is off fast idle. Check for leaks around exhaust manifold, EGO sensor and vacuum connections
- Turn ignition key off.

NOTE: **If vehicle is towed in or is suspected of having intermittent problems, do not turn the ignition key off. Diagnostic codes may be stored in the continuous testing memory.**

QUICK TESTS
1.6L EFI

Test Connections

Connect a timing light to engine. Connect a jumper wire from the self-test input to ground. Connect a DC voltmeter (0-20V range) to battery positive terminal and self-test output terminal. Temporarily disconnect jumper wire (1 end only) from self-test input terminal. *See Fig. 3.*

Fig. 3: 1.6L EFI Meter Hook-Up for Reading Codes

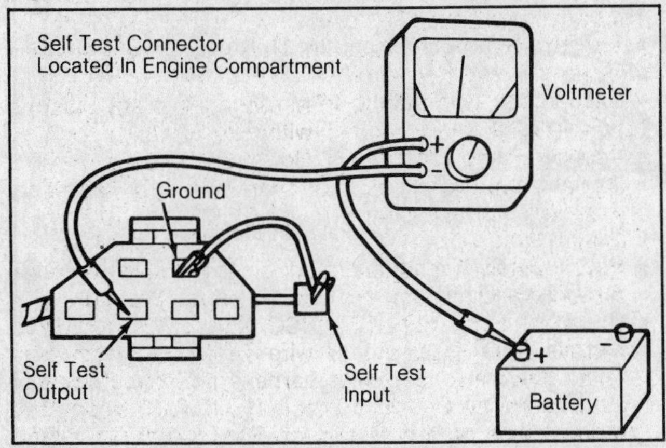

NOTE: **Service codes are shown by voltage pulses. The first digit is indicated by a series of pulses, then the needle drops to zero for 2 seconds, then the second digit of the code is displayed. After each service code is displayed, a 5 second pause will occur and then the next code will be displayed.**

Quick Tests

Key On-Engine Off Self-Test

Turn ignition switch on. Reconnect grounded jumper wire to self-test input terminal. Observe and record service codes until code 10 is displayed. When more than 1 code is displayed, always repair problems in the order that codes were displayed. Do not move shift lever or clutch during test. Repair codes as follows:

- If code 11 is displayed, Key On/Engine Off Test has been passed. Proceed to Timing Check.
- If code 15 is displayed, replace ECA and retest vehicle.
- If code 21 is displayed, go to Test F.
- If code 23 is displayed, go to Test E.
- If code 24 is displayed, go to Test D.
- If code 26 is displayed, go to Test D.
- If code 67 is displayed, go to Test V.
- If no codes, or any codes other than those listed are displayed, go to Test P.

Timing Check

Disconnect grounded jumper wire from self-test input. Start engine and reconnect grounded jumper wire to self-test input. Check timing. If timing is 27-33° BTDC, proceed to Engine Running Self-Test. If timing is not 27-33° BTDC, proceed to Test Q.

NOTE: **If engine stalls while testing, go to Test T.**

Engine Running Self-Test

1) Disconnect grounded jumper wire from self-test input. Start engine and run at 2000 RPM for 2 minutes.

NOTE: **If engine will not start, perform Test A, No Start Test.**

2) Restart engine and run at idle. Reconnect grounded jumper wire to self-test input. Code 20 will be displayed and followed within 60 seconds by the service codes. Observe and record service codes until code 10 is displayed. If engine stalls while testing, perform Test T. If more than 1 code is displayed, correct problems in order that codes were received. Repair codes as follows:

- If code 11 is displayed, Engine Running Self-Test has been passed. If problems still exist, go to Test T. If problem is intermittent, proceed to Continuous Testing.
- If code 12 is displayed, go to Test K.
- If code 13 is displayed, go to Test K.
- If code 21 is displayed, go to Test F.
- If code 23 is displayed, go to Test E.
- If code 24 is displayed, go to Test D.
- If code 26 is displayed, go to Test D.
- If code 41 is displayed, go to Test H.
- If code 42 is displayed, go to Test H.
- If no codes, or any codes other than those listed are displayed, go to test P.

FORD MOTOR CO. ELECTRONIC ENGINE CONTROL IV (Cont.)

Continuous Test

NOTE: **Service codes are lost when ignition key is turned off.**

1) Turn ignition key off. Disconnect grounded jumper wire from self-test input. Perform this test once with key on/engine off and then repeat test with engine running. If engine stalls, do not turn key off or codes will be lost. Wiggle, move and twist the wiring harness. Tap and/or shake sensors. Operate sensors through full range of normal operation (start with cold engine and test until operating temperature is reached, operate throttle from closed to W.O.T., etc.).

2) Observe voltmeter while performing test. If a needle deflection occurs, an intermittent open or short has occured in one of the sensor circuits. After performing test, the intermittent problems will be stored in the memory as service codes. Do not turn key off. Reconnect grounded jumper wire to self-test input. Observe and record service codes.

NOTE: **Continuous test can only be run once without turning ignition key off. Do not miss reading any of the service codes.**

3) Vehicle may be operated with voltmeter connected to verify that intermittent problem is stored by computer when symptom occurs. If voltmeter deflects, do not turn ignition key off. Reconnect grounded jumper wire to self-test input and display codes.

4) Check circuit(s) indicated by codes for shorted or open circuits. Disassemble the associated harness connector and check for proper terminal connection. If no problem is found, repeat Continuous Test while shaking and moving the harness. If problem still cannot be isolated, substitute the affected sensor and retest. If fault is still present, substitute ECA and retest using original sensor.

5) If code 41 or 42 is displayed as an intermittent problem, all non-electrical sources of fuel mixture problems should be eliminated before testing for an intermittent electrical problem.

CIRCUIT TESTS

Test Instructions

1) Do not run any of the following circuit tests unless directed to do so during the Quick Test. Each circuit test assumes that a fault has already been detected in the circuit. Performing a circuit test without being directed to do so by the Quick Test may result in incorrect results or replacement of good components.

2) Correct test results for the Quick Test are dependent on the proper operation of related non-EEC systems and components. It may be necessary to correct any problems in these areas before the vehicle will pass any tests.

3) Do not replace any parts unless specifically directed to do so by the tests.

4) When more than 1 code is displayed, always diagnose and correct problems in the order that codes were displayed.

5) Do not measure voltage or resistance at the ECA or connect any test lights to it unless otherwise specified.

6) Isolate both ends of a circuit and turn key off whenever checks are being made for continuity or short circuits unless directed to do otherwise.

7) Disconnect solenoids and switches from the harness before measuring resistance, continuity or applying battery voltage.

8) When performing circuit tests, follow steps in proper order until fault is found.

9) After completing repairs, make sure that all components are securely reconnected and repeat the Quick Test to verify that problem has been corrected.

10) An open circuit is any resistance reading of greater than 5 ohms (unless otherwise specified).

11) A short circuit to ground is any resistance reading less than 10,000 ohms to ground (unless otherwise specified).

Fig. 4: Front View of 1.6L EFI Engine Showing Sensor Locations

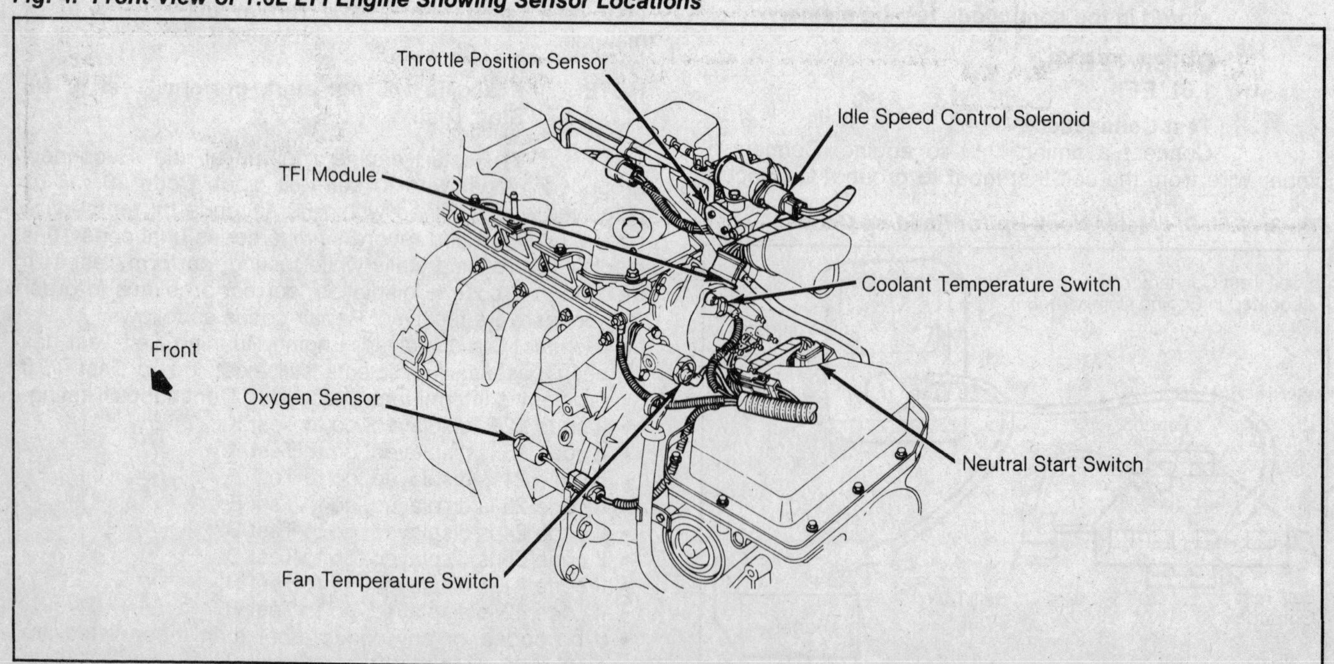

FORD MOTOR CO. ELECTRONIC ENGINE CONTROL IV (Cont.)

Fig. 5: 1.6L EFI EEC-IV Wiring Diagram

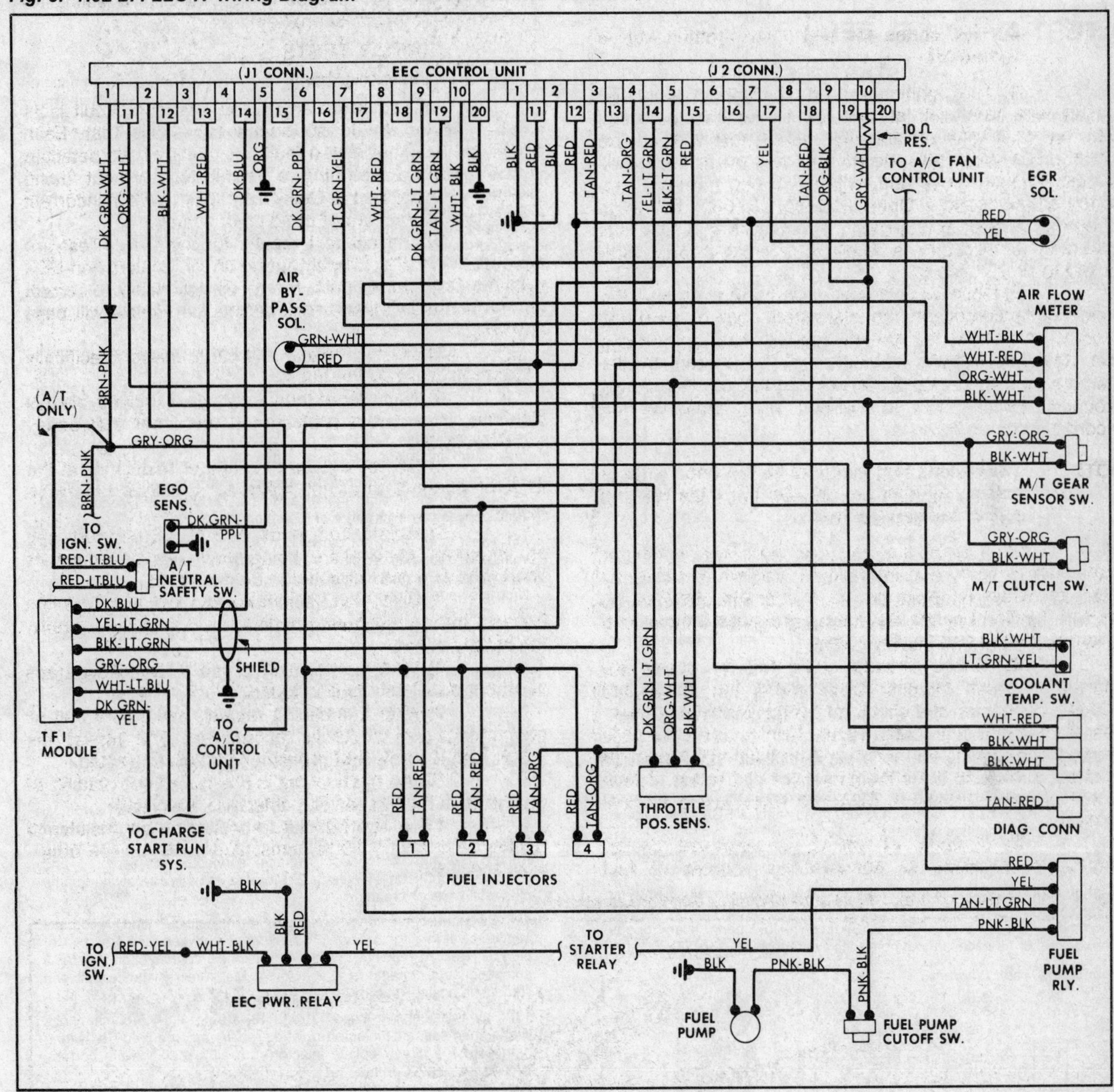

FORD MOTOR CO. ELECTRONIC ENGINE CONTROL IV (Cont.)

TEST A — 1.6L EFI

NO START TEST

1) Connect a fuel pressure gauge to the schrader valve on the fuel rail. Cycle the ignition switch off and on several times to pressurize the fuel system. Correct any fuel leaks before proceeding with test.

2) Try to start engine. If engine does not crank, check for excess fuel in cylinders (hydraulic lock) and check the starting/charging system. If engine cranks, but does not start or continue to run, proceed with test.

3) Check for spark at spark plugs. If present, proceed to step **9)**. If not, proceed to step **4)**.

4) Check for spark at ignition coil. If present, check cap, rotor and spark plug wires. If not present, proceed to step **5)**.

Ignition Module Circuit Diagram

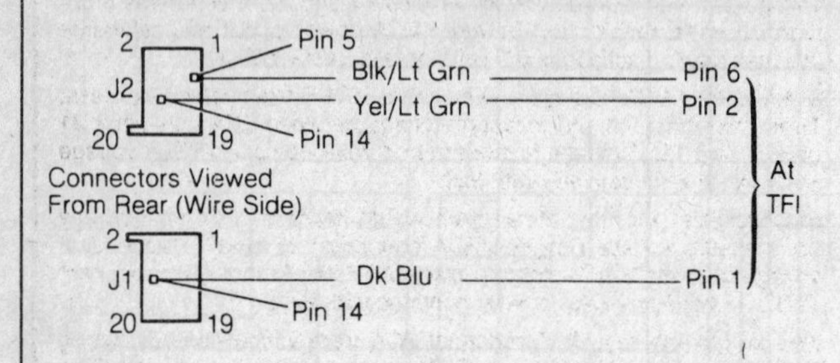

5) Connect DVOM to ECA connector J2 pin 14 and chassis ground. Crank engine and record voltage. If voltage is 3-6 volts, EEC portion of ignition system is operating. Problem is in TFI system. If voltage is not 3-6 volts, continue with test.

6) Turn ignition key off and disconnect ECA connector J2. Check connector J2 pin 14 for shorts to ground. If resistance is less than 2000 ohms, repair short in wiring harness. If resistance is more than 2000 ohms, continue with test.

7) Disconnect ECA connectors J1 and J2. Connect a digital voltmeter to ECA connector J1 pin 14 and J2 pin 5. Crank engine and measure voltage. If voltage is 3-6 volts, check ECA connectors for damaged or corroded terminals. If connectors are good replace ECA. If voltage is not 3-6 volts, continue with test.

8) Disconnect ECA connector J1 and the TFI harness connector. Check circuit from ECA connector J1 pin 14 to TFI pin 1 (Dk Blu) for shorts or opens. If any shorts or opens exist, repair wiring as necessary. If no shorts or opens exist, check circuit from ECA connector J2 pin 5 to TFI pin 6 (Blk/Lt Grn) for opens. If any opens exist, repair as necessary. If no opens exist, problem is in TFI.

Injector Circuit Diagram

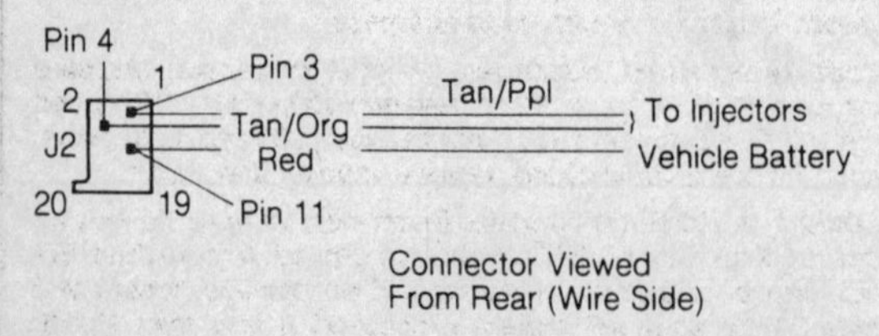

9) Disconnect wiring connections from all 4 injectors. Connect a pressure gauge to schrader valve on fuel rail. Note initial pressure reading. Observe pressure gauge while pressurizing fuel system by cycling the ignition key off and on several times. Turn key off and reconnect injectors. If pressure increased from initial reading, proceed to step **11)**. If pressure did not increase, proceed to step **10)**.

10) Locate fuel pump inertia switch in left rear of vehicle. Push button on inertia switch to reset it. Observe pressure gauge while attempting to pressurize fuel system. If fuel pressure increases, repeat Quick Test. If fuel pressure does not increase, fuel pump is not operating.

11) With injector wiring harnesses disconnected, pressurize fuel system by turning ignition off and to "RUN" position several times. Fuel pressure should be 35-45 psi (2.5-3.0 kg/cm²). If pressure is not correct, check to ensure ignition coil is connected. Ensure that injectors, fuel pressure regulator or fuel delivery lines and connections are not leaking. If no pressure reading can be obtained, check fuel pump circuit.

12) When fuel pressure is obtained, turn key off. Reconnect all injectors. Pressure must not drop more than 4 psi (.3 kg/cm²) within 2 minutes after ignition is turned off.

13) Pressurize the fuel system and verify fuel quality (no water or air in fuel). Disable the electric fuel pump by disconnecting the fuel pump relay. Crank engine for 5 seconds. Take a fuel pressure reading at the end of the cranking period. If fuel pressure is 10-20 psi (.7-1.4 kg/cm²), No Start problem is not related to the EEC system. If pressure was more or less than specified; or if pressure was correct and engine runs rough and misses, continue with testing.

14) Connect a non-powered 12 volt test lamp between pins 11 and 3 of ECA plug J2. Crank engine and note results. Then connect test lamp between pins 11 and 4 of ECA plug J2.

15) If test lamp does not glow on 1 or both tests, verify that battery voltage is recorded at pin 11 of plug J2. If voltage is not present, repair wire or replace battery. If voltage is present, replace ECA. If test lamp glows brightly on 1 or both tests, check circuits 95 (Tan/Purple dot) and 96 (Tan/Orange dot) to injectors. If no problem is found replace ECA. If test lamp glows dimly on both tests, circuits are okay. Continue test.

16) Remove test lamp and fuel pump relay. Using a DVOM, measure the voltage between the same pins tested in step **14)** while cranking engine. If the difference between the voltage readings is more than 1 volt, disconnect ECA plugs and inspect for corroded or damaged pins. Reconnect plugs and retest. If voltage readings still vary more than 1 volt, replace ECA. If voltage difference is less than 1 volt, circuits are okay. Continue test.

17) Reconnect fuel pump relay. Turn ignition off. Disconnect electrical connectors at injectors 2, 3, and 4. Set DVOM on 20 ohm range and measure resistance between pins 3 and 11 of ECA plug J2 (injector 1). Record reading. Disconnect electrical connector at injector 1 and reconnect connector at injector 2. Measure resistance between same pins again. Record reading.

18) Disconnect electrical connector at injector 2 and reconnect connector at injector 3. Measure resistance between pins 4 and 11 of plug J2. Record reading. Disconnect electrical connector at injector 3 and reconnect connector at injector 4. Measure resistance between same pins again. Record reading.

19) If all 4 readings in steps **17)** and **18)** are not 2.0-3.5 ohms, check wiring harness on injector(s) and repair as required. If wiring harness(es) is okay, replace injector(s). If all 4 readings are correct, circuits are okay. Continue test.

20) Disconnect all injector electrical connectors and connect pressure gauge to pressure relief valve. Pressurize fuel system. Connect electrical connector at injector 1. Crank engine for 5 seconds and record pressure reading immediately after end of 5 second crank cycle. Repeat procedure on remaining injectors, testing only 1 injector at a time.

21) If all 4 readings in step **20)** are not within 4 psi (.3 kg/cm²) of each other, replace injector(s) that is incorrect. If all readings are acceptable, check for fuel contamination or other engine malfunctions and test again. If problem remains, disconnect ECA plugs and check for corroded or damaged pins. Retest. If problem still exists, replace ECA.

FORD MOTOR CO. ELECTRONIC ENGINE CONTROL IV (Cont.)

TEST B — 1.6L EFI

BATTERY VOLTAGE TEST

1) Turn ignition on and measure voltage across battery terminals. If voltage is 10.5 volts or more, proceed with test. If voltage is less than 10.5 volts, battery service is required.

2) With ignition on and processor connected, measure voltage between battery negative terminal and Blk/Wht wire in self-test connector. If voltage is less than 0.5 volts, proceed to step **3)**. If voltage is more than 0.5 volts, proceed to step **4)**.

3) Measure voltage from battery positive terminal to ECA connector J2 pin 11 and then pin 12. If both readings are less than 0.5 volts, perform Reference Voltage Test. If either or both readings are more than 0.5 volts, proceed to step **7)**.

4) Measure voltage from battery negative terminal to ECA connector J2 pin 1 and then pin 2. If both readings are less than 0.5 volts, proceed to step **5)**. If either or both readings are more than 0.5 volts, ECA ground circuit has open circuit or high resistance. Repair as necessary.

5) Turn ignition off and leave processor connected. Measure resistance between ECA connector J1 pin 12 to J2 pin 1, then from J1 pin 12 to J2 pin 2. If both readings are less than 1 ohm, proceed to step **6)**. If either or both readings are more than 1 ohm, disconnect and inspect ECA connectors for damaged or corroded terminals. Reconnect and retest. If problem still exists, replace ECA.

6) Measure resistance between ECA connector J1 pin 12 and Blk/Wht wire in self-test connector. If reading is less than 5 ohms, system is good. Repeat Quick Test. If reading is 5 ohms or more, repair wiring harness.

7) With ignition on and ECA connected, connect negative lead of a digital voltmeter to the battery negative terminal and make the voltage checks outlined in the following steps. If an open fusible link is found, check for shorts to ground before replacing the fusible link.

8) Connect voltmeter positive lead to Yellow wire at EEC power relay. If voltage is more than 10.5 volts, proceed to step **9)**. If voltage is 10.5 volts or more, check Yellow wire from battery positive terminal to EEC power relay for opens or shorts to ground. Check Red wires from EEC power relay to ECA connector J2 pins 11 and 12 for shorts to ground. Repair as necessary.

9) Connect voltmeter positive lead to Red/Yellow wire at power relay. If voltage is more than 10.5 volts, proceed to step **10)**. If voltage is 10.5 volts or less, check for open fuse or open in ignition switch start and run circuits.

10) Connect voltmeter positive lead to Black wire at power relay. If voltage is 0.5 volts or less, proceed to step **11)**. If voltage is more than 0.5 volts, repair open in wires leading from battery negative terminal to ECA connector J2 pins 1 and 2.

11) Connect voltmeter positive lead to Red wire at power relay. If voltage is less than 10.5 volts, replace relay. If voltage is 10.5 volts or more, repair open circuit in Red wires leading from power relay to ECA connector J2 pins 11 and 12.

Battery & Reference Voltage Circuit Diagram

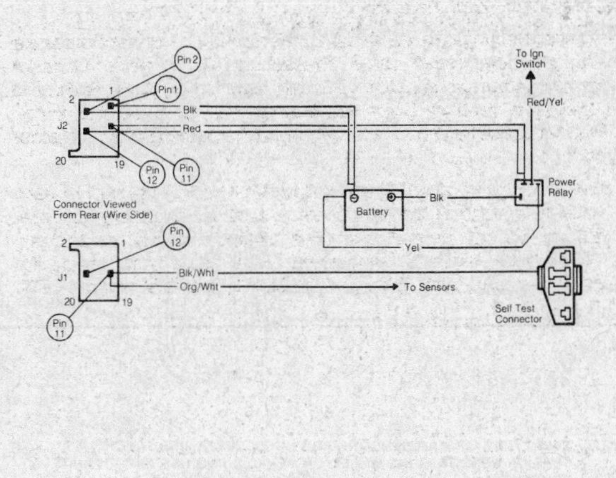

TEST C — 1.6L EFI

REFERENCE VOLTAGE TEST

1) Connect a voltmeter between pin 11 of ECA plug J2 and the Black/White wire in the self-test connector. Turn ignition switch on and note voltage. If below 10.5 volts, perform Battery Voltage Test.

2) If voltage measured is 10.5 volts or above, move voltmeter leads to pins 11 and 12 of ECA plug J1. Voltmeter should now read 4.0-6.0 volts. If voltage reading is too high, proceed to step **3)**. If voltage reading is too low, proceed to step **5)**. If voltage is correct, repeat Quick Test.

3) With voltmeter leads connected to pins 11 and 12 of ECA plug J1, turn ignition key off and measure voltage. If voltage is more than 0.5 volts, repair short between battery power and reference voltage circuits. If voltage is 0.5 volts or less, continue with test.

4) Disconnect ECA from wiring harness. Turn ignition key on. Measure voltage between ECA connector J1 pins 11 and 12. If voltage is more than 0.5 volts, repair short between ECA power circuit and reference voltage circuit. If voltage is 0.5 volts or less, replace ECA.

5) Reconnect ECA harness and disconnect TPS from vehicle harness. Turn ignition key on and measure voltage between ECA connector J1 pins 11 and 12. If voltage is more than 4 volts, replace TPS. If voltage is 4 volts or less, continue with test.

6) Disconnect Air Flow Meter from wiring harness. With ignition key on, measure voltage between ECA connector J1 pins 11 and 12. If voltage is more than 4 volts, replace Air Flow Meter and reconnect TPS. If voltage is 4 volts or less, continue with test.

7) Turn ignition key off. Disconnect ECA from wiring harness. Using DVOM, check continuity from ECA connector J2 pins 1 and 2 to battery negative post and from pins 11 and 12 to Red terminal on power relay. If any circuit measures more than 1 ohm, repair open circuit or bad connection in harness. If all circuits are less than 1 ohm, proceed with test.

8) Disconnect TPS and Air Flow Meter from wiring harness. With ECA harness disconnected, check for short circuits between ECA connector J1 pin 11 and remaining pins on connectors J1 and J2. If all readings are 10,000 ohms or more, replace ECA. If any reading is below 10,000 ohms, repair short circuit. Reconnect all sensors.

TEST D — 1.6L EFI

VANE AIR FLOW METER TEST

1) Connect DVOM to J1 pin 10 and pin 12. Repeat Quick Test that led to this test. With key on, voltage should be .2-.5 volts. With engine running, 1.35-2.70 volts. If not, go to next step. If so, disconnect connector and check for damage. Repeat test. If problem still exists, replace processor.

2) With processor and TP sensor disconnected, check circuits 200, 351 and 359 for opens. If no opens or shorts to ground, replace vane air flow meter. If opens or shorts, repair harness.

3) If a code 24 appeared, disconnect J1 from processor. Measure resistance from J1 pin 8 to pin 12. If between 100 ohms (270°F) and 4000 ohms (40°F), go to next step. If not between 100 and 4000 ohms, check circuit for opens. If no opens, replace vane air flow meter.

4) Place DVOM on 200,000 ohm scale. Disconnect vane air flow meter and processor. Check circuit 357 for short to ground. If more than 10,-000 ohms, inspect connector for damage. If no damage, repeat test and if code 24 still appears, replace processor. If less than 10,000 ohms, correct short to ground in circuit 357.

Vane Air Flow Meter Circuits

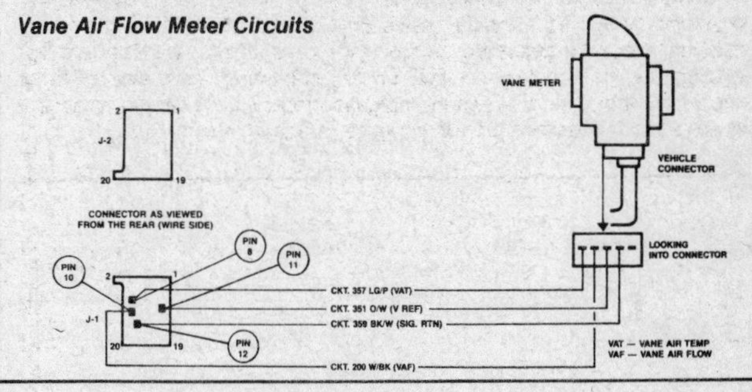

FORD MOTOR CO. ELECTRONIC ENGINE CONTROL IV (Cont.)

TEST E — 1.6L EFI

THROTTLE POSITION SENSOR TEST DIAGNOSTIC CODE 23

1) Disconnect ISC solenoid and verify curb idle per emission decal. Adjust as necessary (except for No Start problems). With ECA connected, connect voltmeter to rear of ECA connector J1 pins 9 and 12.

2) Repeat Quick Test while observing meter. If voltage is 0.5-1.3 volts during test, disconnect ECA connectors and inspect for corrosion and damage. Reconnect ECA and retest. If problem is still present, replace ECA. If voltage is not 0.5-1.3 volts proceed with test.

3) With key on and ECA connected, measure voltage at ECA connector J1 pins 11 and 12. Voltage should be 4-6 volts. If not, proceed to reference voltage test.

4) Disconnect Air Flow Meter harness connector. Disconnect ECA plug J1. Connect an ohmmeter between ground and pins 9, 11, and 12 of plug. No continuity should exist between ground and any pin. Connect ohmmeter to all combinations of the 3 pins. No open circuits should exist.

5) If circuit does not perform as specified, disconnect harness from sensor and repeat test at sensor. If continuity to ground or an open circuit between pins still exists, replace sensor. If sensor performs as specified, check and repair wiring harness as needed.

Throttle Position Sensor Circuit Diagram

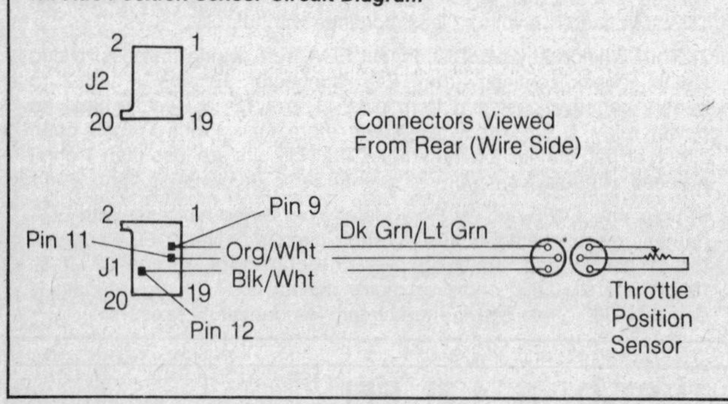

TEST F — 1.6L EFI

COOLANT TEMPERATURE SENSOR TEST DIAGNOSTIC CODE 21

1) Turn ignition key on. With ECA connected, measure voltage at ECA connector J1 pins 11 and 12. Voltage should be 4-6 volts. If not, proceed to Reference Voltage Test. Disconnect plug J1 from ECA. Connect an ohmmeter to pins 7 and 12 of connector. Resistance should be as follows: At 40°F, 155,000 ohms. At 60°F, 95,000 ohms. At 200°F, 2350 ohms. At 240°F, 1300 ohms. If not, check wiring harness for open circuits or replace sensor.

2) Connect an ohmmeter between pin 7 and ground. If resistance is greater than 10,000 ohms, disconnect ECA connectors and inspect for damage or corrosion. Reconnect ECA and retest. If code 21 is still present, replace ECA. If resistance is less than 10,000 ohms, check wiring harness for a short to ground.

Temperature Sensor Circuit Diagram

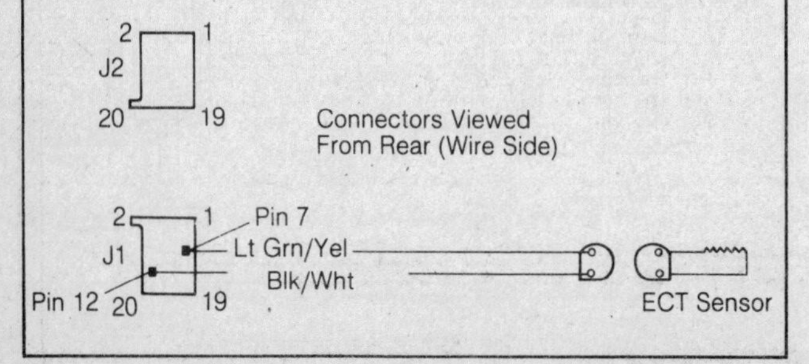

TEST G — 1.6L EFI

MANIFOLD ABSOLUTE PRESSURE SENSOR

1) Turn all accessories off. Check vacuum line to Manifold Absolute Pressure (MAP) sensor for opens, leaks, etc. Repair any problems as required.

2) Check for Engine Running Self-Test codes 31 or 41. If code 31 is present, go to Test H. If code 41 is present, to go Test J. If no codes, go to next step.

3) Disconnect vacuum line and attach vacuum pump to MAP sensor nipple. Apply 20 in. Hg vacuum. If sensor holds vacuum, go to next step. If not, replace sensor and repeat Quick Test.

4) Turn key on. Disconnect MAP sensor. Place DVOM on 20 volt scale. Connect positive lead to harness circuit 351 and negative lead to circuit 359. If voltage is between 4 and 6 volts, go to next step. If less than 4 volts, go to step **10)**. If more than 6 volts, go to Test C.

5) Connect DVOM positive lead to circuit 358 and negative lead to circuit 359. If reading is less than 4 volts, go to next step. If more than 4 volts, go to step **8)**.

6) Turn key off. Inspect 60 pin processor connector for damage, corrosion, etc. Connect breakout box. Place DVOM on 2000 ohm scale. Measure continuity from MAP circuit 359 to box pin 46, circuit 351 to pin 26 and circuit 358 to pin 45. If all readings are 5 ohms or less, go to next step. If any reading is more than 5 ohms, repair open circuit in harness and repeat Quick Test.

7) Turn key off. Place DVOM on 200,000 ohm scale. Disconnect processor. Connect breakout box. Measure resistance of circuits 351 and 358 to box pins 40 and 60. If all read 10,000 ohms or more, go to next step. If any are less than 10,000 ohms, repair short circuit and repeat Quick Test.

8) Turn key off and wait 10 seconds. Connect breakout box to harness, leaving processor disconnected. Disconnect MAP sensor. Measure resistance from pin 45 to pins 2 through 60. If all show 10,000 ohms or more, go to next step. If any show less than 10,000 ohms, repair harness short circuit and retest.

9) Plug in substitute MAP sensor and hook up vacuum line. Run in self-test mode where sensor failed. If code 22 appears, replace processor and repeat Quick Test with original sensor. If no code 22, install substitute sensor and repeat Quick Test.

10) Disconnect sensor from harness. Inspect terminals for damage, corrosion, etc. Disconnect processor from harness. Inspect connectors for damage, corrosion, etc. Clean and repair any problems and go to next step.

11) Reconnect processor. Place DVOM on 20 volt scale. Turn key on. Measure voltage across harness circuits 351 and 359. If less than 4 volts, go to next step. If more than 4 volts, VREF is okay and test is complete.

12) Disconnect processor and connect breakout box, leaving processor disconnected. Place DVOM on 200 ohm scale. Measure resistance between circuit 359 and box pin 46 and circuit 351 and box pin 26. If either is less than 5 ohms, replace processor and repeat Quick Test. If either is more than 5 ohms, repair problem in harness and repeat Quick Test.

Manifold Absolute Pressure Sensor Test Circuits

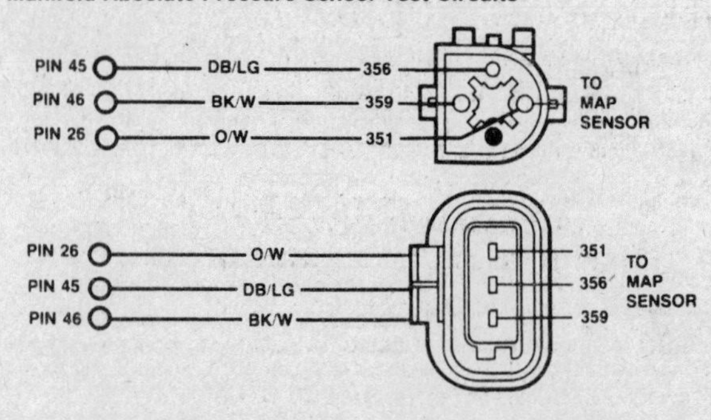

NOTE: TWO TYPES OF MAP SENSORS ARE USED. DETERMINE WHICH TYPE OF SENSOR IS INSTALLED ON VEHICLE AND USE APPROPRIATE SCHEMATIC.

FORD MOTOR CO. ELECTRONIC ENGINE CONTROL IV (Cont.)

TEST H — 1.6L EFI

FUEL CONTROL CIRCUIT TEST DIAGNOSTIC CODES 41 & 42

Code 41

1) Turn ignition key off. With oxygen sensor disconnected, connect a digital voltmeter between the sensor and ground. Remove air cleaner to gain access to air meter inlet. Using a pencil or similar device, prop the air meter vane part-way open. Run engine at 2000 RPM for 2 minutes while observing voltmeter. If meter reads less than 0.5 volts at end of 2 minutes, replace oxygen sensor. If meter reads more than 0.5 volts at end of 2 minutes, proceed to step **2)**.

2) Check continuity from ECA connector J1 pin 5 to oxygen sensor ground (Org wire). Check continuity from ECA connector J1 pin 6 to sensor connector (Dk Grn/Ppl wire). If both circuits are less than 5 ohms, disconnect ECA connectors and inspect for damaged or corroded terminals. If connectors are good, replace ECA. If either or both circuits are above 5 ohms, repair the wiring harness.

Fuel Control Circuit Diagram

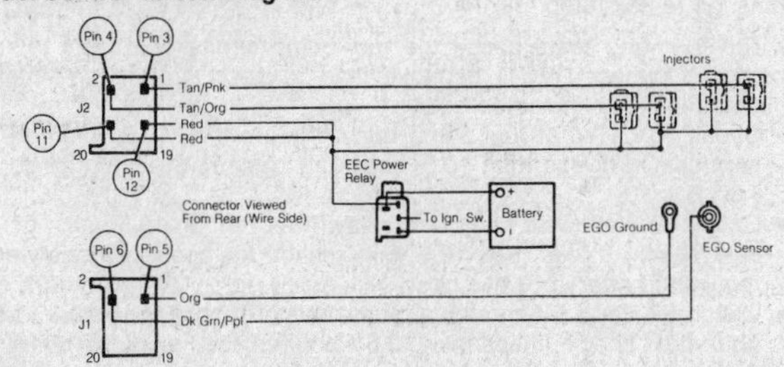

Code 42

1) Disconnect wiring harness at oxygen sensor. Using a jumper wire, ground the oxygen sensor wire (Dk Grn/Ppl) to the engine block. Repeat Engine Running Self-Test portion of Quick Test. If code 41 results, proceed to step **3)**. If not, proceed to step **2)**.

2) Check continuity from ECA connector J1 pin 5 to oxygen sensor ground (Org wire). Check continuity from ECA connector J1 pin 6 to sensor connector (Dk Grn/Ppl wire). If both circuits are less than 5 ohms, disconnect ECA connectors and inspect for damaged or corroded terminals. If connectors are good, replace ECA. If either or both circuits are above 5 ohms, repair the wiring harness.

3) With oxygen sensor disconnected, connect a digital voltmeter between the sensor and ground. Run engine at 2000 RPM for 2 minutes while observing voltmeter. Disconnect manifold vacuum hose located just downstream of the throttle plate. If voltmeter reads less than 0.4 volts, sensor is good, proceed to step **4)**. If voltmeter reads more than 0.4 volts, replace sensor and retest.

4) Connect fuel pressure gauge to fuel rail. Start and run engine. Fuel pressure should be 25-45 psi (1.76-3.16 kg/cm²). If engine will not start, cycle ignition key on and off several times to pressurize the fuel system. Fuel pressure should remain at 35-45 psi (2.46-3.16 kg/cm²) for at least 60 seconds after key is turned off. If fuel pressure is not to specifications, problem is in fuel injection system.

5) Turn ignition off. Disconnect electrical connectors at injectors 2, 3, and 4. Set DVOM on 20 ohm range and measure resistance between pins 3 and 11 of ECA plug J2 (injector 1). Record reading. Disconnect electrical connector at injector 1 and reconnect connector at injector 2. Measure resistance between same pins again. Record reading. Disconnect electrical connector at injector 2 and reconnect connector at injector 3. Measure resistance between pins 4 and 11 of plug J2. Record reading.

6) Disconnect electrical connector at injector 3 and reconnect connector at injector 4. Measure resistance between same pins again. Record reading. If all 4 readings are not 2.0-3.5 ohms, check wiring harness on injector(s) and repair as required. If wiring harness(es) is okay, replace injector(s). If all 4 readings are correct, circuits are okay. Continue test.

7) Connect a non-powered 12 volt test lamp between pins 11 and 3 of ECA plug J2. Crank engine and note results. Then connect test lamp between pins 11 and 4 of ECA plug J2. If test lamp does not glow on 1 or both tests, verify that battery voltage is recorded at pin 11 of plug J2.

8) If voltage is not present, repair wire or replace battery. If voltage is present, replace ECA. If test lamp glows brightly on 1 or both tests, check circuits 95 (Tan/Purple dot) and 96 (Tan/Orange dot) to injectors. If no problem is found replace ECA. If test lamp glows dimly on both tests, circuits are okay. Continue test.

9) Connect a tachometer to engine. Raise engine speed to 2000 RPM and maintain. (May be necessary to disconnect ISC and use throttle body stop screw to maintain speed.) Disconnect and reconnect injectors one at a time. Note RPM drop for each injector. Reconnect ISC and reset curb idle. If all injectors produce an RPM drop of about 150 RPM, injectors are operating properly. If not, replace suspect injector.

TEST K — 1.6L EFI

IDLE SPEED CONTROL TEST DIAGNOSTIC CODES 12 & 13

1) Check and adjust curb idle if needed. Disconnect the ECA from the vehicle wiring harness. Connect an ohmmeter across terminals 9 and 10 of ECA plug J2. Resistance should be 6-14 ohms.

2) If resistance is incorrect, check resistance at solenoid terminals. If resistance is correct (6-14 ohms), locate and repair short in wiring harness leading to solenoid. If resistance between terminals 9 and 10 is still incorrect, replace ISC solenoid. Reconnect ECA and ISC solenoid.

3) Turn ignition switch on and check voltage at Red wire in ISC solenoid connector. If voltage is not 10.5 volts or greater, find and repair open circuit in Red wire leading to solenoid. Check for 10.5 or more volts at Purple wires in ISC connector. If not present, check for short circuits in Purple wires leading to ISC.

4) Connect voltmeter (0-20V) to rear of ISC harness connector with ISC connected. Repeat Quick Test while observing voltmeter. If meter reading varies during Quick Test, replace ISC solenoid.

5) Connect voltmeter to rear of ECA connector J2 pins 11 and 9. Repeat Quick Test. If meter reading varies during Quick Test, isolate and repair open circuits in Purple wires leading to ISC. If meter reading does not vary during Quick Test, check ECA connectors for bent or damaged pins. If connectors are good, replace ECA.

ISC Circuit Diagram

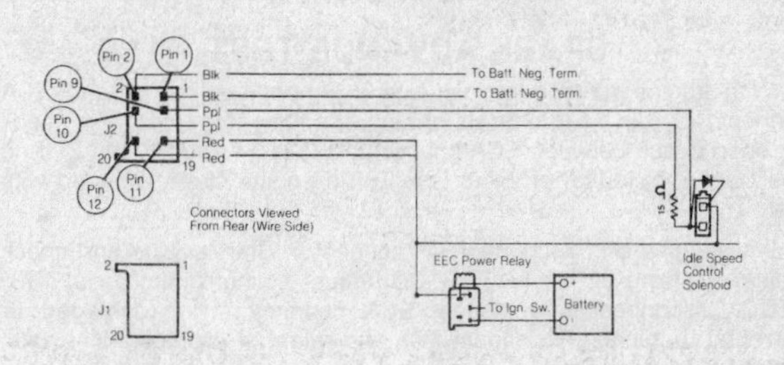

FORD MOTOR CO. ELECTRONIC ENGINE CONTROL IV (Cont.)

TEST P — 1.6L EFI

VEHICLE STALLS IN SELF-TEST

1) With ECA connected, turn ignition on. Measure voltage from ECA connector J1 pin 11 to J1 pin 12. If voltage is 4-6 volts, proceed with test. If voltage is not 4-6 volts, perform Reference Voltage Test.

2) Turn ignition on and measure voltage from Blk/Wh wire in self-test connector to battery negative post. If voltage is greater than 0.5 volts, perform Battery Voltage Test. If voltage is less than 0.5 volts, proceed with test.

3) With ignition on and processor connected, measure voltage between battery positive post and ECA connector J2 pin 11, then between battery positive post and J2 pin 12. If either or both readings are greater than 0.5 volts, perform battery voltage test. If both readings are less than 0.5 volts, proceed with test.

4) Turn ignition off and disconnect ECA connector J1. Check continuity from ECA connector J1 pin 13 to Wh/Red wire at self-test plug. If resistance is 5 ohms or more, repair open circuit. If resistance is less than 5 ohms, proceed with test.

5) Turn ignition off and disconnect ECA connector J2. Check continuity from ECA connector J2 pin 18 to Tan/Red wire at self-test plug. If resistance is 5 ohms or more, repair open circuit. If resistance is less than 5 ohms, proceed with test.

6) With ignition off and ECA disconnected, measure resistance between EGO ground point and ECA connector J1 pin 5. If resistance is more than 5 ohms, repair ground wire circuit. If resistance is 5 ohms or less, inspect ECA connectors for damaged or corroded terminals. Reconnect ECA and retest. If problem is still present, replace ECA.

Diagnostic Circuit Diagram

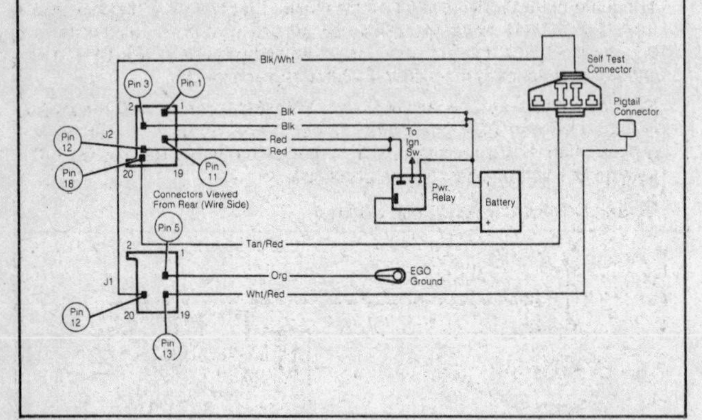

TEST Q — 1.6L EFI

SPARK ADVANCE TEST

1) With engine running at idle, use a jumper wire to ground ECA connector J2 pin 14 to chassis ground. If engine does not stall, check for open circuit between ECA connector J2 pin 14 and TFI pin 2. If no open circuit is found, problem is in TFI. If engine stalls, proceed with test.

2) With engine off, disconnect TFI connector. Start engine and check timing. If timing is not 7-13° BTDC, adjust timing. If timing is 7-13° BTDC, disconnect and inspect ECA connectors for damaged or corroded terminals. Reconnect ECA and retest. If problem still exists, replace ECA.

TEST S — 1.6L EFI

FUEL PUMP CIRCUIT TEST

1) Turn key on and off several times and check that fuel pump operates. If pump runs, check fuel system. If pump does not run, go to next step.

2) Turn key to run position. Connect DVOM negative lead to ground and measure voltage at J2 pins 11 and 12. If 10.5 volts or more, go to next step. If less than 10.5 volts, go to Test B.

3) Connect negative DVOM lead to battery negative post and probe J2 pins 1 and 2 with other lead. If less than 1 volt on both circuits, go to next step. If less than 1 volt on either circuit, correct faulty ground on circuit 57.

4) Disconnect fuel pump relay. Place DVOM on 200 ohm scale. Measure resistance across two small pins of relay. If less than 50 ohms or more than 100 ohms, replace relay. If between 50 and 100 ohms, go to next step.

5) The following tests check the fuel pump ciruits. Turn key to run position. Connect DVOM negative lead to good ground and make voltage checks as indicated below.

- Circuit 361, Red at fuel pump relay. If more than 10.5 volts, go to next check. If less than 10.5, check for open in 361. If okay go to Test B.
- Circuit 37, Yellow at fuel pump relay. If more than 10.5 volts, go to next check. If less than 10.5 volts, check for open in 37 between relay and battery positive post.
- Circuit 97 Tan/Lt. Grn at fuel pump relay. If more than 10.5 volts, go to next check. If less than 10.5 volts, replace fuel pump relay.
- Circuit 97 Tan/Lt/ Grn. at fuel pump relay during crank mode. If 1 volt or less, go to next check. If 1 volt or more, check 97 to processor for opens, If okay, replace processor.
- Circuit 787, Pink/Blk at fuel pump relay during crank mode. If more than 10.5 volts, go to next check. If less than 10.5 volts, replace fuel pump relay.
- Circuit 787, Pink/Blk at inertia switch terminals during crank mode. If more than 10.5 volts, go to next check. If less than 10.5 volts at one terminal, replace inertia switch. If less than 10.5 volts at both terminals, check for open in 787 between relay and inertia switch.
- Circuit 787, Pink/Blk at fuel pump during crank mode. If more than 10.5 volts, go to next check. If less than 10.5 volts, check for opn in 787 between fuel pump and inertia switch.
- Circuit 57. Blk at fuel pump during crank mode. If more than 1 volt, correct faulty ground circuit from fuel pump to chassis ground. If less than 1 volt, service fuel pump.

Fuel Pump Circuits

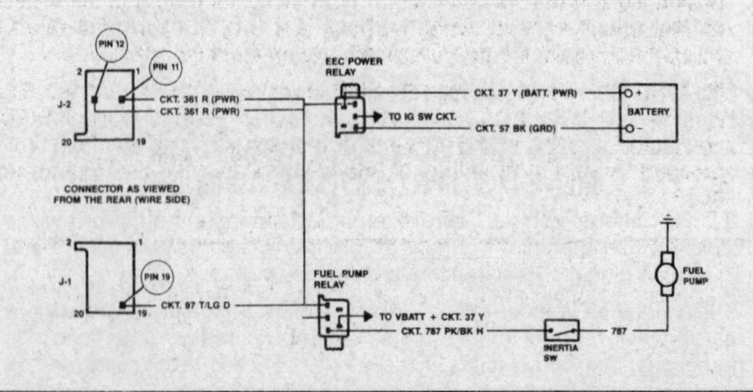

ELECTRONIC CONTROL UNIT TEST

The only means of testing the ECA itself is to substitute a good ECA for the suspect ECA. Substitution of a new ECA should only be carried out after all other components and systems have been tested and repaired. Installing a new ECA while a problem still exists elsewhere in the system can result in destroying the new ECA.

TEST T — 1.6L EFI

SYMPTOM DIAGNOSIS TEST

- If engine stalls on deceleration, or at idle, proceed to step **1)**.
- If engine has high idle speeds on every restart, proceed to step **2)**.
- If incorrect or incomplete service codes are displayed, perform Diagnostic Circuit Test.
- If drive complaints are intermittent, perform Continuous Testing portion of Quick Test.
- If engine stalls, runs rough or misses, check electrical connections, ignition system. If no problems are found, proceed to step **4)**. After completing test, perform No Start Test.

1) Disconnect and plug vacuum hose from EGR valve. Start and run engine until it reaches normal operating temperature. Perform Quick Test. If vehicle does not stall, EGR service is required. If vehicle stalls, perform Idle Speed Control Test.

2) Turn ignition key off. Connect voltmeter negative lead to self-test output wire and positive lead to battery positive terminal. Do not connect grounded jumper to self-test input wire. Turn ignition key on and observe voltmeter. If no pulsing codes are displayed, perform Idle Speed Control Test. If pulsing codes are displayed, proceed to step **3)**.

3) Disconnect ECA connector J1. Measure resistance from ECA connector J1 pin 13 to chassis ground. If resistance is less than 10,-000 ohms, repair short to ground in White/Red wire leading from pin 13 to self-test input connector. If resistance is 10,000 ohms or more, disconnect and inspect ECA connectors for damaged or corroded terminals. If connectors are good and fault is still present, replace ECA.

4) Disconnect and plug all vacuum lines connected to EGR on-off solenoid. Connect a hand-held vacuum pump to lower port on solenoid. Start and run engine until it reaches normal operating temperature. Let engine idle for 3 minutes, then apply 10 in. Hg vacuum to solenoid using vacuum pump.

5) Vacuum should hold. While observing vacuum gauge, rapidly accelerate engine. Vacuum should bleed off. If vacuum holds at idle and bleeds off during acceleration, EEC system is ok. Check EGR valve and Backpressure Variable Transducer Valve. If vacuum does not hold, proceed to step **6)**. If vacuum does not bleed off, proceed to step **7)**.

6) Disconnect harness from EGR solenoid. apply 10 in. Hg vacuum to solenoid. If solenoid does not hold vacuum, replace solenoid. If solenoid holds vacuum, check circuit from ECA connector J2 pin 17 for shorts to ground. If ok, disconnect and inspect ECA connectors for damaged or corroded terminals. If connectors are good, reconnect ECA and retest. If problem is still present, replace ECA.

7) Turn ignition key off and disconnect wiring harness from EGR solenoid. Measure resistance of EGR solenoid coil. If resistance is not within 45-90 ohms, replace solenoid. If resistance is within 45-90 ohms, proceed to step **8)**.

8) With ignition key on, solenoid and ECA connected, measure voltage at Yellow wire at EGR connector. If voltage is less than 10.5 volts, repair poor connection or open circuit in Red wire connected to solenoid. If voltage is more than 10.5 volts, check Yellow wire connected to solenoid for opens. If ok, disconnect and inspect ECA connectors for damaged or corroded terminals. If ok, reconnect ECA and retest. If problem is still present, replace ECA.

TEST V — 1.6L EFI

NEUTRAL SWITCH-A/C INPUT TEST
DIAGNOSTIC CODE 67

NOTE: On manual transaxle models, begin with step 1). On automatic transaxle models, begin at step 3).

1) Turn A/C off (if equipped). Shift transaxle into Neutral and release clutch. With ignition turned off, disconnect ECA connector J1 and measure resistance between pins 1 and 12. If resistance is less than 5 ohms, proceed to step **5)**. If not, proceed to step **2)**.

2) Locate the gear switch (on transaxle) and the clutch switch (under dash). Disconnect wiring harness from both switches. Measure resistance accross each switch. If both switches read 5 ohms or less, correct open circuit in wiring harness (Dk Grn/Wht wire and Blk/Wht wire). If not, replace defective switch, reconnect and retest.

3) Turn A/C off (if equipped). Shift transaxle into "N" or "P". Turn ignition on. With ECA connected, measure voltage between ECA connector J1 pin 1 and ground. If voltage is less than 0.5 volts, proceed to step **5)**. If voltage is more than 0.5 volts, proceed to step **4)**.

4) Locate neutral/drive switch on transaxle. Disconnect wiring harness from switch and measure resistance across switch. If resistance is less than 5 ohms, correct open circuit in wiring harness (Dk Grn/ Wht wire). If resistance is more than 5 ohms, replace switch.

5) Turn ignition key on and A/C off. With ECA connected, measure voltage between ECA connector J1 pin 2 and ground. If reading is greater than 1 volt, correct short to power circuit in Blk/Yel wire. If voltage is 1 volt or less, replace processor.

Neutral Drive-A/C Input Circuit Diagram

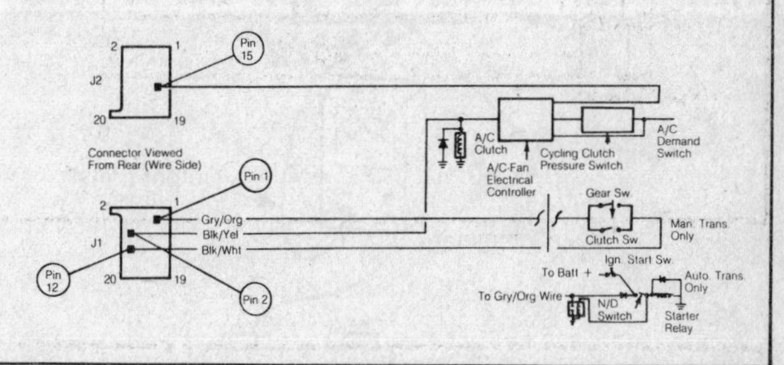

QUICK TESTS
2.3L HSC

Reading Self-Test Codes

Service codes are transmitted on the Self-Test Output and are shown as voltage pulses on a Digital Volt-Ohmmeter (DVOM). Key On-Engine Off Self-Tests will show three codes for each step. The first code is On Demand, the second code is a Separator code and the third code is the Continuous code. The On Demand code first digit is indicated by a pulse, then the needle drops to zero for 2 seconds, then the second digit of the code is displayed. After 9 seconds, the Separator code will be displayed for 1/2 second. After 6 seconds, the first digit of the Continuous code will be displayed, the needle will drop to zero for 2 seconds, then the second digit of the Continuous code will display.

Engine Running Self-Tests will display codes in the same manner, except there will be an Engine ID code, a Dynamic Response Code and an On Demand code. On Demand codes are same as Continuous codes in Key On-Engine Off Self-Test. The Engine ID code has no application in the field, and is for factory use only. The codes will be displayed in the same manner as Key On-Engine Off Self-Test codes.

Equipment Hook-Up

With ignition key off, connect a jumper wire from the self-test input to pin 2 on the self-test connector. *See Fig. 5.* Set needle-type volt-ohmmeter (DVOM) on DC 0-15 volt scale. Connect DVOM from battery positive side to pin 4 on self-test connector.

Fig. 6: Meter Hook-Up for Reading Codes-All 2.3L

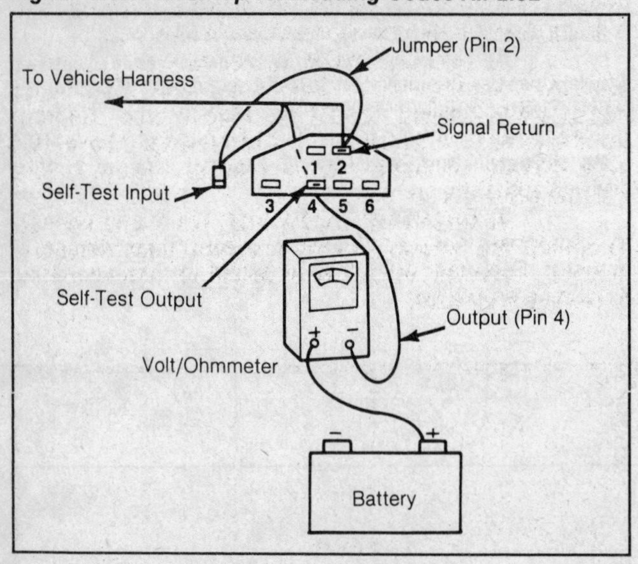

Key On/Engine Off Self-Test

Turn ignition switch on. Reconnect grounded jumper wire to self-test input terminal. Observe and record On Demand and Continuous codes. When more than 1 code is displayed, always repair problems in the order that codes were displayed. Do not depress throttle during test. Repair codes as follows:

NOTE: **If vehicle is being serviced because shift indicator lamp is always on or off, proceed to Test Z, Shift Indicator Light.**

KEY ON-ENGINE OFF SELF-TEST RESULTS

On Demand Codes	Continuous Codes	Proceed to Test
11	11	Timing Check
Any	11	See Code No.
Any	Any	See Code No.
11	Any	Timing Check
None	None	Test P
15	.....	Replace processor, retest.
21	.....	Test F
22	.....	Test G
23	.....	Test E
51	.....	Test F
53	.....	Test E
61	.....	Test F
63	.....	Test E
None	None	Test P

Timing Check

Engine Running Self-Test must be activated while checking or adjusting timing. Connect timing light. Start engine and check timing for no longer than 25 seconds. Refer to vehicle emission decal for base timing specification. Timing is calculated as follows: Base timing plus 20°, plus or minus 3°, equals initial timing. Results are as follows:

- If timing is base, plus 20°, plus or minus 3°: Go to Engine Running Self-Test.
- If timing is not base, plus 20°, plus or minus 3°: Go to test Q, Spark Timing Check and check spark output circuit to TFI module.
- Vehicle does not start: go to test A: No Start Problem.
- Vehicle stalls during 25 second timing check: Go to test P: No Codes or Invalid Codes.

Engine Running Self-Test

This test checks sensors under actual operating conditions. Fault must be present at time of test to be detected. This test will display an Engine ID Code, a Dynamic Response Code and an On Demand Service Code. After a Dynamic Response Code is received, quickly press and release accelerator once only. If test is not performed properly, a series 70 code (77, 76, 73, 72) will appear and the test will have to be repeated.

NOTE: **On vehicles with a vacuum delay valve, there is a tee and a restrictor in thermactor vacuum line. Uncap restrictor during test.**

Start and run engine at more than 2000 RPM for 2 minutes. Ignore any output codes at this time. Turn engine off and wait 10 seconds. Verify self-test is activated. Start engine. Test will proceed with Engine ID Code, Dynamic Response code and Engine Running On Demand service codes. If a 10 or 1 pulse occurs during Dynamic Response code, open throttle wide open momentarily. Record codes and proceed as follows:

Continuous Test

1) Unless instructed to do so, do not disconnect any sensor with key on or service codes will be stored. Should Keep Alive Power pin 1 to processor be interrupted, all stored Continuous codes will be lost. If pin 1 fails, invalid codes may be received during test.

FORD MOTOR CO. ELECTRONIC ENGINE CONTROL IV (Cont.)

2) Correct method for clearing memory is to exit Key On-Engine Off Self-Test during code output sequence. Exit self-test by removing self-test jumper. Before using stored information, first verify that previous tests indicated code 11.

3) If during tests an On Demand code is detected, this must be repaired first, since some hard failures also request a code in the continuous memory. Once On Demand testing is complete, clear memory of Continuous codes and operate vehicle to verify repair.

4) Before repairing any Continuous Test service codes, verify that a code 11 was received from both previous tests. Repair only those codes that are not repeated from previous tests.

5) With vehicle prepared as in Key On-Engine Off Self-Test, record all Continuous codes. Perform Key On-Engine Off Self-Test. When first service code is output, exit self-test by removing jumper from self-test input to signal return pin 2. This will erase any Continuous codes.

6) With self-test deactivated, key on and engine off, self-test output is checked. Wiggle system harness, connectors or sensors while observing DVOM. A fault will be indicated by meter deflection of 10.5 volts or more, and a service code will be stored.

7) After checking all system components, perform Key On-Engine Off Self-Test to retrieve any codes stored during wiggle test. Remain in continuous monitor mode and service Continuous codes as follows:

NOTE: Record service codes before removing or replacing processor. Codes will be erased whenever processor is disconnected.

CONTINUOUS TEST CODES

Code	Proceed to Test
Code 11	[1]
21	Test U
22	Test U

[1] — If no intermittent problems, test is complete. If intermittent problems exist, go to test X, Invalid Codes-Continuous Test and generate a fault in keep alive memory.

CONTINUOUS TEST CODES (Cont.)

Code	Proceed to Test
31	Test U
51	Test U
53	Test U
61	Test U
63	Test U
No codes	Test P
Invalid codes	Test X

CIRCUIT TESTS

Test Instructions

1) Do not run any test unless instructed to do so by the Quick Test. Make sure all non-EEC related faults are corrected. Do not replace any part unless directed to do so. Always start with lowest code first.

2) Do not make measurements at control module or connect test lamps to it, unless specified. Measurements are made by probing REAR of connectors. Isolate both ends of circuit and turn key off whenever checking for shorts or continuity, unless specified.

3) Disconnect solenoids and switches from harness before measuring continuity, resistance or energizing with a 12 volt source. Follow each step in order until fault is found. After any repairs, check all component connections and repeat Quick Test.

Output State Test

1) Output State Test is used to diagnose actuators. Perform test in Key On-Engine Off mode after codes have been sent. Do not disable self-test but quickly depress throttle and release, to activate auxiliary EEC outputs. Another throttle depression will turn them off.

2) Connect DVOM to self-test output pin 4. Start Key On-Engine Off Self-Test. When Continuous codes are completed, DVOM will read 0 volts. Depress throttle to turn on actuators. DVOM readings above 10.5 volts indicate actuators are on, readings below 2 volts indicate actuators are off.

3) Disconnect DVOM from pin 4 and connect to appropriate actuator. Measure output state voltage of actuator. Each test will tell what action to take according to reading on DVOM.

Fig. 7: 2.3L HSC EEC-IV System Wiring Diagram

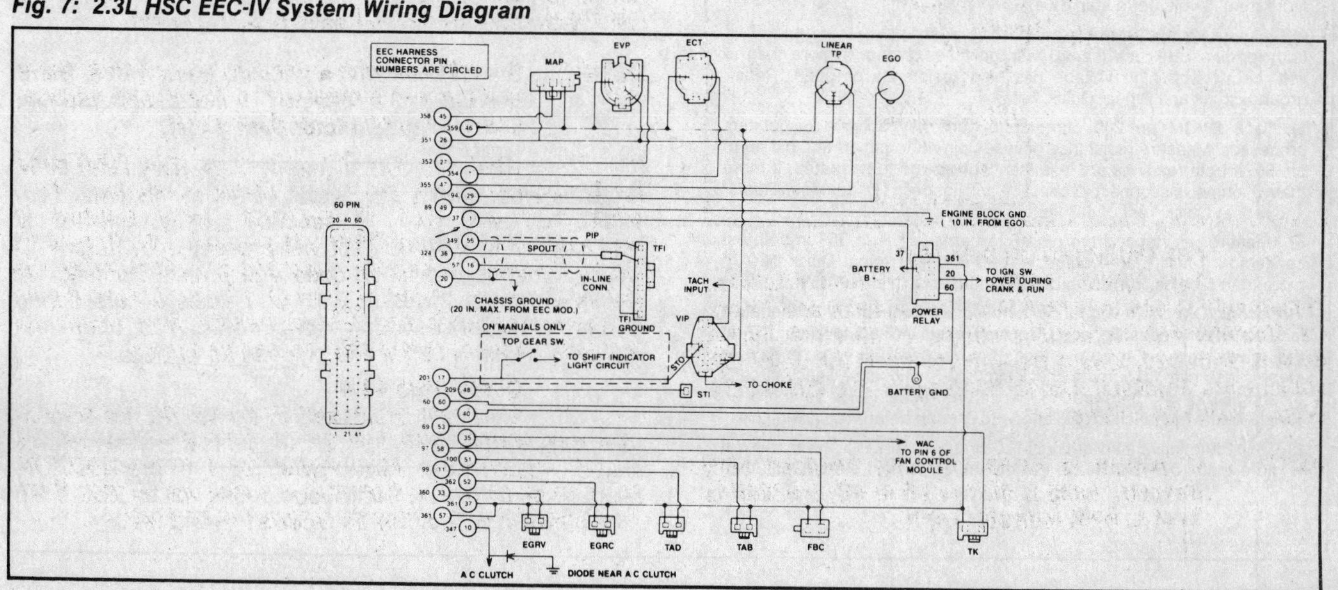

FORD MOTOR CO. ELECTRONIC ENGINE CONTROL IV (Cont.)

TEST A — 2.3L HSC

NO START PROBLEM

1) Attempt to start engine. If engine cranks but does not start, go to next step. If engine does not crank, check charging circuit.

2) Disconnect coil harness clip. Disconnect any spark plug wire. Connect spark tester between plug wire and ground. Crank engine. If no spark, go to next step. If spark occurs, diagnose ignition system. Reconnect plug wire.

3) Remove coil wire from distributor and install spark tester. Check for spark while cranking. If no spark, go to next step. If spark occurs, diagnose ignition system. Reconnect coil wire.

4) With key off, disconnect processor connector. Check for damaged pins, frayed wires, corrosion, etc., and repair. Connect breakout box and reconnect processor. Place DVOM on 20 volt scale. Turn key on. Measure voltage from breakout box pin 37 to pin 40 and pin 57 to pin 60. If both readings are 10.5 volts or more, go to next step. If either reading less than 10.5 volts, go to test B.

5) Place DVOM on 2000 ohm scale. Measure resistance from box pin 16 to pin 40 and pin 16 to pin 60. If less than 5 ohms, go to next step. If more than 5 ohms, repair open circuit and repeat Quick Test.

6) Place DVOM on 20 volt scale. Connect one lead of DVOM to pin 56 and other lead to pin 16. Turn key on. Observe voltage while cranking. If under 3 volts or more than 6 volts, go to next step. If between 3 and 6 volts, go to step **9)**.

7) Turn key off. Place DVOM on 2000 ohm scale. Disconnect processor. Connect DVOM from pin 56 of box to circuit 349 on TFI connector. Measure resistance. If 5 ohms or less, go to next step. If more than 5 ohms, repair open in circuit 349 and repeat Quick Test.

8) Turn key off. Disconnect TFI connector. Place DVOM on 200,000 ohm scale. Measure resistance between box pin 56 to pins 26, 40, 46 and 57. If any resistance is 10,000 ohms or less, repair circuit 349 and repeat Quick Test. If all are more than 10,000 ohms, go to next step.

9) Turn key off. Disconnect TFI. Disconnect processor. Measure resistance between box pin 36 and pins 26, 40, 46 and 57. If any resistance is less than 10,000 ohms, repair circuit 324 and repeat Quick Test. If all are more than 10,000 ohms, go to next step.

10) Connect TFI. Disconnect processor from harness. Turn key to start. If vehicle starts, replace processor. If vehicle does not start, diagnose ignition system.

No Start Test Circuits

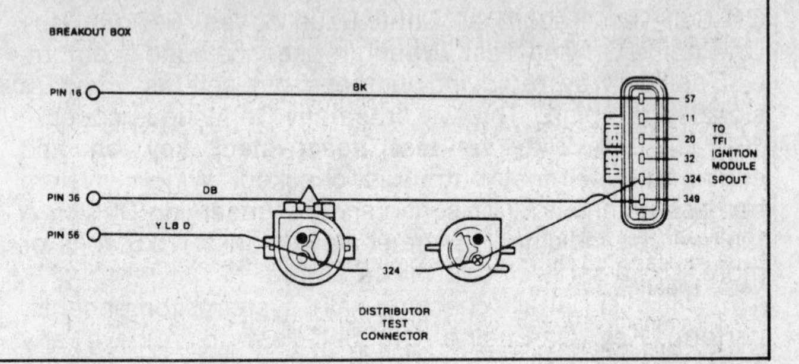

TEST B — 2.3L HSC

VEHICLE BATTERY

1) Place DVOM on 20 volt scale, turn key on. Measure voltage across battery terminals. If 10.5 volts or less, service battery, If more than 10.5 volts, go to next step.

2) Measure voltage from battery negative post to circuit 359 in self-test connector. If reading is less than .5 volt, go to next step. If more than .5 volt, go to step **4)**. Turn key off.

3) Disconnect processor and install breakout box. Connect processor. Turn key on and measure voltage from battery positive post to box pin 37 and pin 57. If both readings are less than .5 volt, go to test C. If more than .5 volt, go to step **7)**.

4) Measure voltage from battery positive post to pin 40 and pin 60. If both readings are less than .5 volt, go to next step. If more than .5 volt, circuit with high voltage has high resistance or open. Repair ground circuit and repeat Quick Test.

5) Place DVOM on 200 ohm range, turn key off and disconnect processor. Measure resistance between pin 46 to pin 40 and pin 46 to pin 60. If both readings are less than 5 ohms, go to next step. If more than 5 ohms, disconnect processor and inspect for damage. Repair and repeat Quick Test. If still faulty, replace processor.

6) Measure resistance from pin 46 to harness circuit 359 in self-test connector. If less than 5 ohms, system is okay, repeat Quick Test. If more than 5 ohms, correct excessive resistance in circuit 359.

7) Place DVOM on 20 volt range, turn key on. Connect DVOM negative lead to battery negative post. Connect positive lead to circuit 37 at EEC power relay. Measure voltage. If more than 10.5 volts, to to next step. If less than 10.5 volts, check circuit 37 for opens. Check circuits 37 and 361 for shorts to ground. Repair and repeat Quick Test. If open fusible link is found, check for shorts to ground before replacing link.

8) Connect positive lead of DVOM to circuit 20 at EEC power relay. If is more than 10.5 volts, leave key on and go to next step. If less than 10.5 volts, check for opens in ignition switch circuits 16, 37 and 20. Repair and repeat Quick Test.

9) Connect DVOM positive lead to circuit 60 at EEC power relay. If .5 volt or less, leave key on and go to next step. If more than .5 volt, repair open or short in circuit 60 and repeat Quick Test.

10) Connect DVOM positive lead to circuit 361 at EEC power relay. If less than 10.5 volts, repair open in circuit 361 to pins 37 and 57 and repeat Quick Test. If more than 10.5 volts, replace power relay and repeat Quick Test.

Vehicle Battery Test Circuits

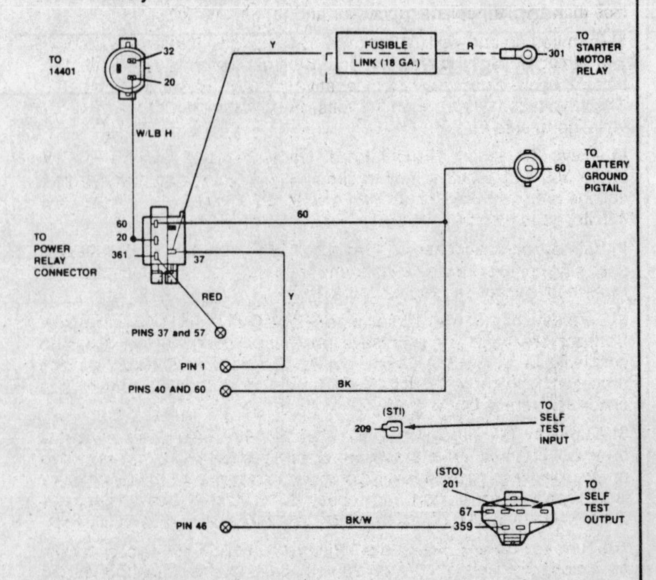

FORD MOTOR CO. ELECTRONIC ENGINE CONTROL IV (Cont.)

TEST C — 2.3L HSC

REFERENCE VOLTAGE

1) With key off, disconnect processor and connect breakout box. Reconnect processor. Turn key on. Measure voltage from box pin 37 to circuit 359 in self-test connector. If more than 10.5 volts, go to next step. If less than 10.5 volts, go to Test B, step **1)**.

2) Place DVOM on 20 volt scale. Disconnect processor from breakout box. Turn key on. Measure voltage from pin 26 to pin 46. If 6 volts or more, go to next step. If less than 6 volts, go to step **5)**.

3) Turn key off. Measure same circuit as in step **2)**. If .5 volt or less, go to next step. If more than .5 volt, service short between VREF and battery power circuits and repeat Quick Test.

4) Disconnect processor from harness, and turn key on. Place DVOM on 20 volt scale. Measure between pin 26 and pin 46. If .5 volt or less, replace processor and repeat Quick Test. If more than .5 volt, service short between VREF and battery power in EEC harness. Repeat Quick Test.

5) Disconnect throttle position sensor from harness. Turn key on. Measure voltage between pin 26 and 46. If 4 volts or less, go to next step. If more than 4 volts, replace Throttle Position sensor and repeat Quick Test.

6) Disconnect Manifold Absolute Pressure (MAP) sensor from harness. Turn key on and measure voltage between pin 26 and 46. If 4 volts or less, go to next step. If more than 4 volts, replace MAP sensor and repeat Quick Test.

7) Disconnect EGR Valve Position (EVP) sensor from harness. Turn key on and measure voltage between pin 26 and 46. If 4 volts or less, go to next step. If more than 4 volts, replace EGR-EVP sensor and repeat Quick Test.

8) Turn key off. Disconnect EEC connector from module. Place DVOM on 200 ohm scale. Check continuity from pins 40 and 60 to battery negative terminal and pins 37 and 57 to circuit 361 on power relay. If all readings are less than 5 ohms, go to next step. If any is more than 5 ohms, service open or faulty circuit and repeat Quick Test.

9) Turn key off. Place DVOM on 200,000 ohm scale. Disconnect harness connector from module and check for shorts between VREF pin 26 and pins 20, 40 and 60. If 10,000 ohms or more, replace processor and repeat Quick Test. If less than 10,000 ohms, service short and repeat Quick Test.

Reference Voltage Test Circuits

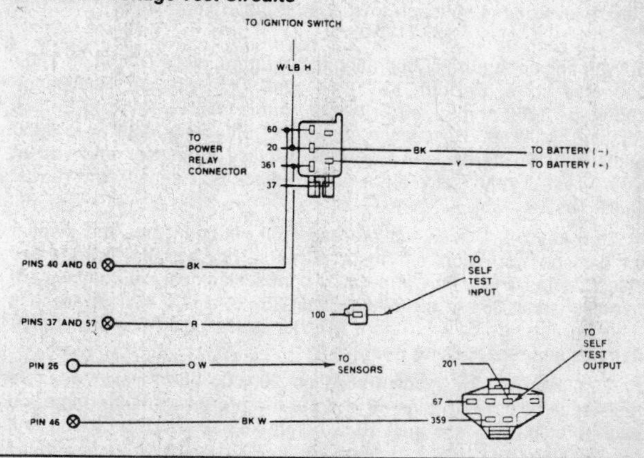

TEST D — 2.3L HSC

THROTTLE POSITION SENSOR

1) With key off, check that sensor is seated properly. If so, go to next step, If not, install sensor correctly and repeat Quick Test.

2) Disconnect sensor, and connect DVOM positive lead to sensor harness circuit 351. Connect negative lead to harness circuit 359. Turn key on and measure voltage. If between 4 and 6 volts, go to next step. If more than 6 volts, go to test C. If less than 4 volts, go to step **14)**.

3) Repeat Key On-Engine Running Self-Test with TP sensor disconnected. If service code 63 appears, replace sensor and repeat Quick Test. If code 23 appears, go to next step.

4) Place DVOM on 20 volt scale, connect positive meter lead to circuit 55 and negative lead to ground. Turn key on and observe voltage reading. If more than 2 volts, repair harness and repeat Quick Test. If less than 2 volts, replace processor and repeat Quick Test.

5) Turn key off and wait 10 seconds. Disconnect TP sensor and check for damaged pins, corrosion, etc. Connect meter positive lead to battery positive terminal and negative lead to harness circuit 359. Check voltage. If more than 10 volts, go to next step. If less than 10 volts, go to step **8)**.

6) Leave TP sensor disconnected. Connect meter positive lead to circuit 355 and negative lead to circuit 359. Turn key on and measure voltage on circuit 355. If less than 4 volts, go to next step. If more than 4 volts, go to step **9)**.

7) With sensor disconnected, perform Key On-Engine Off Self-Test. If code 63 appears, replace sensor and repeat Quick Test. If no code 63, replace processor and repeat Quick Test.

8) Turn key off and wait 10 seconds. Place DVOM on 2000 ohm scale. Connect breakout box and leave processor disconnected. Measure continuity of circuit 359 to box pin 46. If less than 5 ohms, replace processor and repeat Quick Test. If more than 5 ohms, repair open circuit and repeat Quick Test.

9) Turn key off and place DVOM on 200,000 ohm scale. Connect breakout box and leave processor disconnected. Measure resistance on box pin 47 to pins 26 and 57. If either resistance is 10,000 ohms or less, repair harness short and repeat Quick Test. If both resistances are more than 10,000 ohms, replace processor and repeat Quick Test.

10) Turn key off and disconnect TP sensor. Inspect for damaged pins, corrosion, etc. Place DVOM on 20 volt scale. Connect positive lead to circuit 351 and negative lead to circuit 359. Turn key on. If reading is between 4 and 6 volts, go to step **11)**. If reading is less than 4 volts, go to step **13)**. If more than 6 volts, go to test C.

11) Turn key off and connect a jumper wire between circuit 351 and 355. Perform Key On-Engine Off Self-Test. Check for code 53. If no code 53, turn key off and go to next step. If code 53 appears, replace TP sensor and repeat Quick Test.

12) Turn key off and disconnect processor 60 pin connector and inspect for damage, corrosion, etc. Repair as required. Place DVOM on 200,000 ohm scale. Connect one lead to circuit 355 at sensor connector and other lead to ground. If reading is less than 10,000 ohms, repair circuit short and repeat Quick Test. If more than 10,000 ohms, go to next step.

13) Turn key off and wait 10 seconds. Connect breakout box and leave processor disconnected. Place DVOM on 2000 ohm scale. Check continuity of circuit 355 to box pin 47. Check continuity of circuit 351 to box pin 26. If either reading is more than 5 ohms, repair faulty circuit and repeat Quick Test. If both are 5 ohms or less, replace processor and repeat Quick Test.

14) Disconnect TP sensor and processor from harness and inspect terminals. If okay, go to next step. If not okay, clean and repair as required and repeat Quick Test.

15) Reconnect processor. Place DVOM on 20 volt scale. Turn key on. Measure voltage across circuit 351 and 359 at sensor harness connector. If less than 4 volts, go to next step. If more than 4 volts, VREF is okay and test is complete.

16) Disconnect processor and connect breakout box. Leave processor disconnected. Measure resistance from TP sensor connector circuit 359 to box pin 46, and between circuit 351 to box pin 26. If either reading is less than 5 ohms, replace processor and repeat Quick Test. If either reading is 5 ohms or more, repair harness for opens, bad connections, etc., and repeat Quick Test.

Throttle Position Sensor Test Circuits

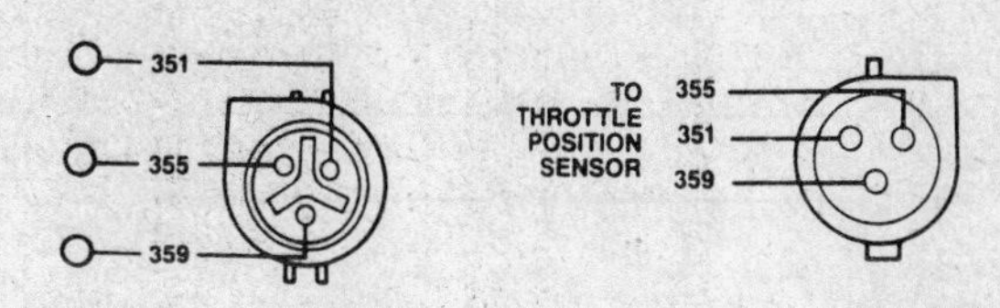

FORD MOTOR CO. ELECTRONIC ENGINE CONTROL IV (Cont.)

TEST F — 2.3L HSC

ENGINE COOLANT TEMPERATURE SENSOR

1) Start engine and operate at 2000 RPM for 5 minutes. Check that upper radiator hose is hot and pressurized. Repeat Engine Running Self-Test. If code 21 is present go to next step. If no code 21, continue tests as necessary.

2) Place DVOM on 20 volt scale. Turn key on and disconnect ECT sensor connector and connect DVOM to circuits 359 and 354 at harness connector. If reading is between 4 and 6 volts, go to next step. If less than 4 volts, go to step **4)**. If more than 6 volts, go to test C.

3) With engine at normal operating temperature, place DVOM on 200,-000 ohm scale. Perform Key On-Engine Off Self-Test. Resistance should be 1300 ohms (240°F) to 7450 ohms (140°F). Perform Engine Running Self-Test. Resistance should be 1550 ohms (230°F) to 4250 ohms (170°F). If readings are okay, replace processor and repeat Quick Test. If readings are not okay, replace ECT sensor and repeat Quick Test.

4) Turn key off. Disconnect processor 60 pin connector and inspect for damage, corrosion, etc. Install breakout box and leave processor disconnected. Place DVOM on 2000 ohm scale. Measure continuity of harness circuit 354 to pin 7 and circuit 359 to pin 46. If both are less than 5 ohms, go to next step. If either is less than 5 ohms, repair harness and repeat Quick Test.

5) Turn key off and place DVOM on 200,000 ohm scale. Measure resistance of pin 7 to pins 40 and 60. If more than 10,000 ohms, go back to step **3)**. If less than 10,000 ohms, repair short to ground and repeat Quick Test.

6) Turn key off. Disconnect ECT connector and inspect for damage, corrosion, etc. Create opposite failure by inserting jumper wire across ECT harness connector. Perform Key On-Engine Off Self-Test. If code 61 appears, replace sensor and repeat Quick Test. If no code 61, go to next step.

7) Remove jumper wire and connect breakout box, leaving processor disconnected. Place DVOM on 2000 ohm scale. Measure continuity of harness circuit 354 to box pin 7 and circuit 359 to box pin 46. If either resistance is more than 5 ohms, repair open in harness and repeat Quick Test. If both are less than 5 ohms, replace processor and repeat Quick Test.

8) Disconnect sensor connector. Perform Key On-Engine Off Self-Test. If code 51 appears, replace ECT sensor and repeat Quick Test. If no code 51, go to next step.

9) Connect breakout box, leaving processor disconnected. Place DVOM on 200,000 ohm scale. Disconnect ECT. Measure resistance of box pin 7 to pins 40 and 60. If either is less than 10,000 ohms, repair short to ground and repeat Quick Test. If both are more than 10,000 ohms, replace processor and repeat Quick Test.

Coolant Temperature Sensor Test Circuits

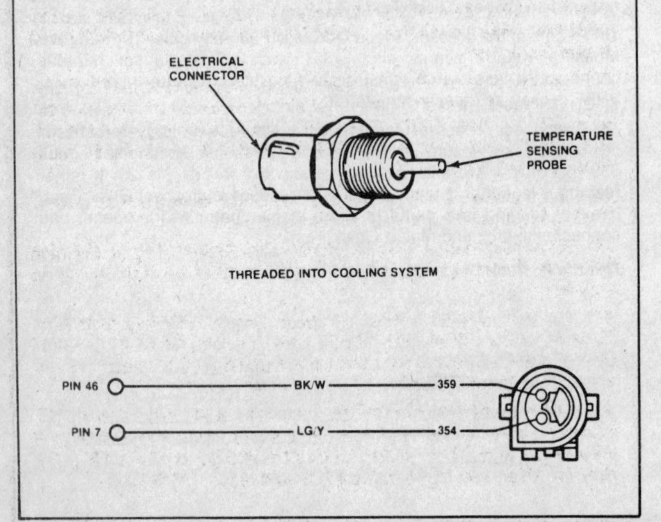

TEST H — 2.3L HSC

EGR VALVE POSITION

1) Disconnect EGR vacuum line at valve and plug. Perform Engine Running Self-Test. If code 31 appears, go to next step. If no code 31, go to step **10)**.

2) Turn key off. Place DVOM on 200,000 ohm scale. Measure resistance from circuit 351 (pin 1) to 352 (pin 3), and 359 (pin 2) to 352 (pin 3) on sensor. If both are between 100 and 5500 ohms, go to next step. If either is less than 100 or more than 5500 ohms, replace EVP sensor and repeat Quick Test.

3) With key off, disconnect vacuum line from EGR valve, and connect vacuum pump to EGR valve. Measure resistance of EVP sensor circuits 351 (pin 1) to 352 (pin 3) while gradually increasing vacuum to 10 in. Hg. If resistance gradually decreases from 5500 to no less than 100 ohms, go to next step. If resistance reads less than 100, or more than 5500 ohms, replace EVP and repeat Quick Test. If unable to hold vacuum or resistance does not decrease, replace EGR valve and repeat Quick Test.

4) Place DVOM on 20 volt scale. Turn key on. Connect DVOM positive lead to harness circuit 351 and negative lead to circuit 359. If voltage reads between 4 and 6 volts, go to next step. If reading is less than 4 volts, go to step **9)**. If more than 6 volts, go to Test C.

5) Connect DVOM positive lead to harness circuit 351 and negative lead to circuit 352. If reading is between 4 and 6 volts, go to step **10)**. If less than 4 volts, go to next step.

6) Turn key off. Inspect processor 60 pin connector for damage, corrosion, etc. Place DVOM on 200,000 ohm scale. Measure resistance of circuit 352 to 359, and 352 to ground. If either is less than 10,000 ohms, repair short and repeat Quick Test. If both are 10,-000 ohms or more, go to next step.

7) Turn key off. Connect breakout box, leaving processor disconnected. Place DVOM on 2000 ohm scale. Measure continuity between box pin 46 to circuit 359, pin 26 to circuit 351 and pin 27 to circuit 352. If all are less than 5 ohms, go to next step. If any are more than 5 ohms, repair faulty circuits and repeat Quick Test.

8) Turn key off and disconnect EVP sensor. Measure resistance between box pin 27 and pins 26 and 37. If either is less than 10,000 ohms, repair short and repeat Quick Test. If both are 10,000 ohms or more, replace processor and repeat Quick Test.

9) Turn key off. Place DVOM on 2000 ohm scale. Disconnect solenoid and connect DVOM across terminals on both EGRV and EGRC soleniods. Measure resistance. If resistance between 30-70 ohms, reconnect solenoids and go to step **10)**. If less than 30 or more than 70 ohms, replace solenoid assembly and repeat Quick Test.

10) Turn key off. Place DVOM on 20 volt scale. Connect negative lead to Self-Test Output and positive lead to positive battery post. Perform Key On-Engine Off Self-Test until completion of continuous test. DVOM should read 0 volts. Depress and release accelerator. If 10.5 volts or more, go to next step. If reading did not reach 10.5 volts, go to Test P.

11) Connect negative lead to output circuit 360 and positive lead to EGRV solenoid circuit 361. Record voltage while depressing and releasing throttle. Connect negative lead to output circuit 362 and positive lead to EGRC solenoid circuit 361. Depress and release throttle and record voltage. If both inputs cycle on and off, remain in output state check and go to next step. If inputs do not cycle, go to step **16)**.

12) Install vacuum pump to EGRC solenoid bottom port and install vacuum gauge to output port. Disconnect vacuum vent line. Cycle inputs on and off by hitting throttle and observe vacuum gauge while maintaining vacuum at source. If vacuum cycles on and off, go to next step. If not, replace solenoid and repeat Quick Test.

13) Turn key off and check all vacuum lines for kinks, breaks, etc. If okay, go to next step. If not okay, repair as required and repeat Quick Test.

14) Inspect EVP sensor connector for damage, corrosion, etc. Place DVOM on 200,000 ohm scale. Connect vacuum pump to EGR valve. Connect one DVOM lead to EVP sensor circuit 351 (pin 1) and other lead to circuit 352 (pin 3). Observe resistance while gradually increasing vacuum to 10 in. Hg. If reading decreases to between 5500 and 100 ohms, replace processor and repeat Quick Test. If reading does not decrease or resistance is more than 5500 or less than 100 ohms, go to next step.

FORD MOTOR CO. ELECTRONIC ENGINE CONTROL IV (Cont.)

TEST H — 2.3L HSC (Cont.)

15) Remove EVP sensor from EGR valve. Place DVOM on 200,000 ohm scale. Measure resistance from pin 1 to pin 3, while using finger to gradually move EVP shaft. Watch for sudden jumps in readings. If reading decreases, replace EGR valve and repeat Quick Test. If no decrease or jumps in readings, replace EVP sensor and repeat Quick Test.

16) Turn key on. Place DVOM on 20 volt scale. Measure voltage across both EGR solenoids (circuit 361 to battery ground). If both readings more than 10.5 volts, go to next step. If either reading is less than 10.5 volts, repair open in harness and repeat Quick Test.

17) Turn key off. Inspect 60 pin processor connector for damage, corrosion, etc. Connect breakout box to harness, leaving processor disconnected. Place DVOM on 2000 ohm scale. Measure continuity of box pin 33 to harness circuit 361 and pin 52 to circuit 362. If both less than 5 ohms, go to next step. If either more than 5 ohms, repair open circuit and repeat Quick Test.

18) Turn key off. Disconnect EGR solenoid connectors. Measure resistance between box pins 33 to pins 40, 46 and 57, and from pin 52 to pins 40, 46 and 57. If all readings are 10,000 ohms or more, go to next step. If any are less than 10,000 ohms, repair short in circuit and repeat Quick Test.

19) Place DVOM on 2000 ohm scale. Measure resistance of both EGR solenoids. If both readings are between 30-70 ohms, replace processor and repeat Quick Test. If any are more than 70 or less than 30 ohms, replace EGR solenoid and repeat Quick Test.

EGR Valve Test Circuits

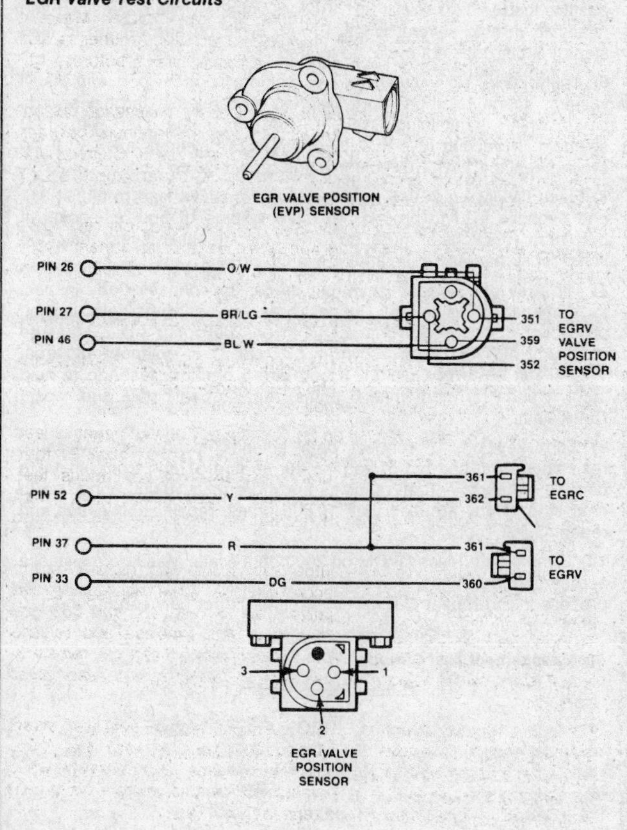

TEST J — 2.3L HSC

FUEL CONTROL

1) If service code 41 was present, check that vehicle was prepared properly for test. Vehicle should have been run for 2 minutes prior to test. If so, go to next step. If not, prepare vehicle properly and repeat test.

2) Check that Exhaust Gas Oxygen sensor is grounded and connected properly, and that there are no manifold leaks. Repair faults as required.

3) Disconnect oxygen sensor and processor. Place DVOM on 200,000 ohm scale. Connect DVOM positive lead to sensor circuit 94 and negative lead to ground. Measure resistance. If less than 1000 ohms, repair short and go to next step. If more than 1000 ohms, reconnect sensor and go to next step.

4) Disconnect thermactor air supply hose to air pump and cap hose. Perform Engine Running Self-Test. If code 41 appears, leave thermactor disconnected and go to next step. If no code 41, repair any other service codes which may have appeared.

5) Disconnect Feedback Carburetor Solenoid (FCS) connector. Perform Engine Running Self-Test. If code 41 is present, leave FCS disconnected and go to next step. If no code 41, go to step **7)**.

6) Run vehicle for 2 minutes at part throttle. Perform Engine Running Self-Test with choke plate 3/4 closed. If code 41 appears, go to step **11)**. If no code 41, EEC system okay. Problem is in carburetor.

7) Connect FCS. Turn key off. Connect breakout box, leaving processor disconnected. Place DVOM on 200,000 ohm scale. Measure resistance of box pin 58 to pins 20, 40 and 46. If 10,000 ohms or more, go to next step. If less than 10,000 ohms, repair short in circuit 97 and repeat Quick Test.

8) Check all FCS vacuum hoses to carburetor for leaks, restrictions, etc. Repair as required.

9) Run vehicle at part throttle for 2 minutes. Perform Engine Running Self-Test with choke plate 3/4 closed. If code 41 appears, replace FCS and repeat Quick Test. If no code 41, go to next step.

10) Place DVOM on 2000 ohm scale. Disconnect FCS. Connect DVOM between circuit 97 in FBC harness and engine ground, and between circuit 360 in FCS harness and engine ground. If either is less than 1000 ohms, replace FCS and repeat Quick Test. If either is more than 1000 ohms, replace processor and repeat Quick Test.

11) Turn key off. Connect processor. Disconnect oxygen sensor. Place DVOM on 200,000 ohm scale. Measure resistance between circuit 94 and battery ground. If more than 10,000 ohms, go to next step. If less than 10,000 ohms, replace processor and repeat Quick Test.

12) Start vehicle and run for 2 minutes. Place DVOM on 20 volt scale. Disconnect oxygen sensor. With engine running, hold choke plate 3/4 closed and measure voltage between sensor and ground. If .45 volt or more, go to next step. If less than .45 volt, replace sensor.

13) With key on, connect DVOM positive lead to circuit 94 and negative lead to battery ground. Measure voltage. If less than 2 volts, go to next step. If more than 2 volts, repair harness short to VREF and repeat Quick Test.

14) Turn key off and connect breakout box. Place DVOM on 1000 ohm scale. Measure resistance from box pin 29 to circuit 94 and from pin 49 to pins 40 or 60. If both measure 5 ohms or less, replace processor and repeat Quick Test. If either is more than 5 ohms, repair faulty circuit and repeat Quick Test.

15) Check choke plate for sticking or binding. If okay go to next step. If not, correct as required and repeat Quick Test.

16) Disconnect oxygen sensor connector. Repeat Engine Running Self-Test. If code 41 appears, go to next step. If no code 41, go to step **26)**.

17) Connect oxygen sensor. Repeat Engine Running Self-Test. Remove vacuum hose from PCV. Check for code 42 or 47. If either code present, replace sensor and repeat Quick Test. If neither code is present, go to next step.

18) Turn key off. Place DVOM on 2000 ohm scale. Disconnect FCS. Connect DVOM across terminals on solenoid. Measure resistance. If between 30 and 60 ohms, reconnect FCS and go to next step. If not between 30 and 60 ohms, replace FCS and repeat Quick Test.

FORD MOTOR CO. ELECTRONIC ENGINE CONTROL IV (Cont.)

TEST J — 2.3L HSC (Cont.)

19) Enter Output State Check. Place DVOM on 20 volt scale. Connect DVOM positive lead to battery positive post and negative lead to Self-Test Output connector. Jumper Self-Test Input connector. Perform Key On-Engine Off Self-Test until completion of continuous codes. DVOM will indicate 0 volts. Depress and release throttle. If DVOM indicated high voltage (10.5 V) remain in test mode and go to next step. If no high reading, depress throttle to wide open and release. If voltage does not go high, go to Test P.

20) Connect DVOM positive lead to circuit 361 on FCS and negative lead to circuit 97. While observing DVOM, depress and release throttle several times. FCS should cycle on and off. If not, go to next step. If so, go to step **23)**.

21) Connect one DVOM lead to circuit 361 and other lead to battery ground. Turn key on. If voltage is 10 volts or more, go to next step. If less than 10 volts, repair open and repeat Quick Test.

22) Disconnect processor 60 pin connector and inspect for damage, corrosion, etc. Connect breakout box, leaving processor disconnected. Place DVOM on 200,000 ohm scale. Measure continuity from circuit 97 to box pin 58. If more than 5 ohms, repair open in circuit 97 and repeat Quick Test. If less than 5 ohms, replace processor and repeat Quick Test.

23) Disconnect FCS connector and check for damage, corrosion, etc. Measure resistance of solenoid. If between 30 and 65 ohms, go to next step. If not between 30 and 65 ohms, replace FCS and repeat Quick Test.

24) Check all carburetor hosee from FCS to carburetor for leaks, restrictions, etc. Repair as required.

25) Connect oxygen sensor and FCS. Run engine for 2 minutes. Perform Engine Running Self-Test. With engine running, disconnect vacuum hose from PCV. If code 42/47 appears, replace FCS and repeat Quick Test. If no code 42/47, problem is in carburetor.

26) Connect oxygen sensor. Disconnect processor 60 pin connector and check for damage, corrosion, etc. Connect breakout box, leaving processor disconnected. Place DVOM on 20 volt scale. Turn key on. Connect DVOM between box pin 29 and battery. If more than .4 volt, repair short in circuit 94 and repeat Quick Test. If less than .4 volt, replace processor and repeat Quick Test.

27) Disconnect breakout box. Run engine at 2000 RPM for 2 minutes. Perform Engine Running Self-Test. If code 43 appears, go to step **28)**. If no code 43, service any other codes as required.

28) Check exhaust system for leaks and repair as required.

29) Start vehicle and let idle. If idle quality deteriorates and remains constantly poor before, during and after test, idle needs to be adjusted. If idle quality is okay, replace oxygen sensor and repeat Quick Test.

Fuel Control Test Circuits

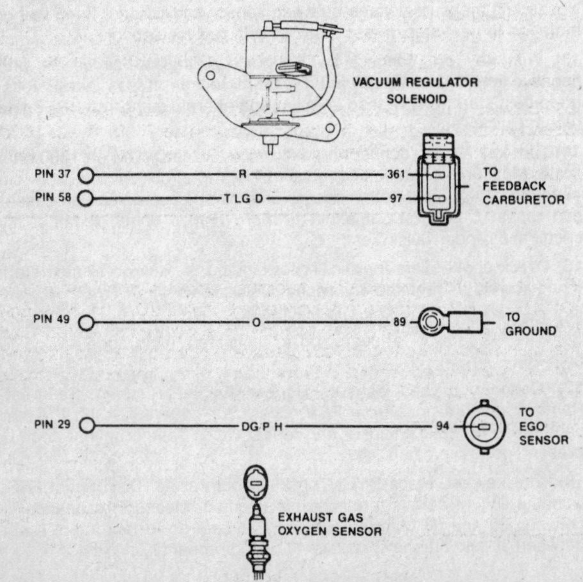

TEST L — 2.3L HSC

AIR MANAGEMENT SYSTEM

1) Check that restrictor teed into Thermactor Air Diverter (TAD) vacuum line is uncapped and free from contamination. Service as required.

2) Start engine and bring to normal operating temperature. Turn key off. Ground Self-Test Input. Perform Engine Running Self-Test and record codes. If code 11 appears, repeat Quick Test. If code 44 or 46 appears, go to step **3)**. If any other codes appear repair as required and repeat Quick Test.

3) Turn key off and wait 10 seconds. Place DVOM on 2000 ohm scale. Disconnect Thermactor Air Bypass and Diverter (TAB/TAD) solenoid. Connect DVOM across solenoid terminals. Measure resistance. If between 50 and 110 ohms, reconnect solenoid and go to next step. If not between 50 and 110 ohms, replace solenoid and repeat Quick Test.

4) Turn key off and wait 10 seconds. Place DVOM on 20 volt scale. Connect DVOM positive lead to battery positive post and negative lead to Self-Test Output connector. Jumper Self-Test Input. Perform Key On-Engine Off Self-Test until continuous codes completed. DVOM should indicate 0 volts. Depress and release throttle. If DVOM changed to higher voltage, go to next step. If no change, depress throttle to wide open and release. If Self-Test Output voltage does not go high, go to Test P.

5) Install DVOM negative lead to output circuit 100 and positive lead to TAB solenoid circuit 361. Install negative lead to output circuit 99 and positive lead to TAD circuit 361. Record voltage while depressing and releasing throttle several times. If both cycle on and off, go to next step. If either does not cycle, go to step **7)**.

6) Apply 20 in. Hg vacuum to TAB solenoid bottom port and install vacuum gauge to upper port. Depress and release throttle several times while manitaining vacuum. Perform same test with TAD solenoid. If vacuum cycles on and off, EEC system is okay. If no cycling, replace TAB/TAD solenoid and repeat Quick Test.

7) Place DVOM on 20 volt scale. Connect positive lead to circuit 361 and negative lead to ground. Measure voltage of both solenoids. If both read 10.5 volts or more, go to next step. If either is less than 10.5 volts, repair harness open and repeat Quick Test.

8) Turn key off. Disconnect 60 pin processor connector and inspect for damage, corrosion, etc. Connect breakout box to harness, leaving processor disconnected. Place DVOM on 2000 ohm scale. Measure continuity of TAB circuit 100 from box pin 51 to solenoid and from TAD circuit 99 to box pin 11. If both are 5 ohms or less, go to next step. If either is more than 5 ohms, repair open circuit and repeat Quick Test.

9) Turn key off. Disconnect both solenoid connectors. Measure resistance from box pin 51 to pins 40, 46 and 57 and from pin 11 to pins 40, 46 and 57. If all readings are more than 10,000 ohms, go to next step. If any are less than 10,000 ohms, repair short circuit and repeat Quick Test.

10) Turn key off. Place DVOM on 2000 ohm scale. Measure resistance across both solenoids. If both are between 50 and 110 ohms, replace processor and repeat Quick Test. If either is not between 50 and 110 ohms, replace solenoid and repeat Quick Test.

Air Management Test Circuits

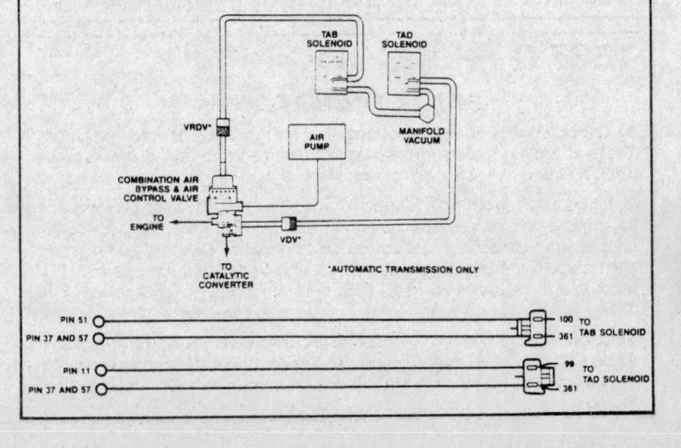

FORD MOTOR CO. ELECTRONIC ENGINE CONTROL IV (Cont.)

TEST M — 2.3L HSC

RPM FAILED SELF-TEST

1) Check that Manifold Absolute Pressure (MAP) sensors are properly seated. Correct as required.

2) Tee a vacuum gauge in vacuum line to MAP sensor. Repeat Engine Running Self-Test. Record codes. If vacuum decreased more than 7 in. Hg and code 72 appears, replace MAP sensor and repeat Quick Test. If vacuum decreased more than 7 in. Hg and no code 72, disconnect vacuum equipment and repeat self-test. Verify wide open throttle test was performed. If vacuum decreased less than 7 in. Hg. check vacuum line for kinks, breaks and for proper line routing. Repeat Quick Test.

3) Check that Throttle Position sensor is properly mounted and repair as required.

4) Disconnect Throttle Position sensor. Place DVOM on 200,000 ohm scale. Connect DVOM leads across sensor connector between circuit 355 and 359. Move throttle to wide open and record resistance. If 1000 ohms or more, repeat Engine Running Self-Test and verify that WOT test was performed. If less than 1000 ohms, replace TP sensor and repeat Quick Test.

TEST P — 2.3L HSC

NO CODES/INVALID CODES

1) Ensure that auto. trans. vehicles are fully seated in "P". Disconnect processor and MAP sensor. Connect breakout box. Reconnect processor. Place DVOM on 20 volt scale. With key on, measure voltage between MAP circuit 351 and battery ground. If 4-6 volts, go to next step. If less than 4 volts, go to step **6)**. If more than 6 volts, go to Test C.

2) With MAP sensor disconnected, repeat Engine Running Self-Test and check for codes. If no codes, go to next step. If any codes appear, replace MAP sensor and repeat Quick Test.

3) Turn key off. Place DVOM on 200,000 ohm scale. Connect breakout box. Reconnect processor. Connect one DVOM lead to box pin 49 and other lead to engine ground. If reading is less than 5 ohms, go to next step. If 5 ohms or more, repair open in circuit 89 to engine block and repeat Quick Test.

4) Disconnect processor and inspect connectors. Repair and retest if required. Measure continuity from box pin 46 to circuit 359 of self-test connector, box pin 48 to circuit 209 of self-test input and box pin 17 to circuit 201 of self-test output. If all readings are 5 ohms or less, go to next step. If any are more than 5 ohms, repair open circuit and repeat Quick Test.

5) Turn key off. Disconnect processor. Measure resistance from box pin 17 to pin 40. If more than 10,000 ohms, go to step **9)**. If less than 10,000 ohms, repair short in circuit 201 and repeat Quick Test.

6) Disconnect MAP sensor. Perform Key On-Engine Off Self-Test. Check for codes. If codes appear, go to next step. If no codes, go to step **8)**.

7) Disconnect processor and inspect connectors. Repair and retest as required. Connect breakout box, leaving processor disconnected. Measure continuity from box pin 26 to MAP sensor harness circuit 351. If more than 5 ohms, repair open circuit and repeat Quick Test. If less than 5 ohms, replace processor and repeat Quick Test.

8) Disconnect processor. Connect breakout box, leaving processor disconnected. Turn key on. Connect positive DVOM lead to pin 37 and negative lead to pin 40. If reading is 10.5 volts or less, go to Test B. If 10.5 volts or more, go to Test C.

9) Turn key off. Place DVOM on 20 volt scale. Connect DVOM negative lead to battery negative post and positive lead to circuit 37 at EEC power relay. If 10.5 volts or less, repair circuit 37 open and repeat Quick Test. If more than 10.5 volts, go to next step.

10) Turn key off. Connect DVOM negative lead to engine ground. Check circuit 20 at EEC power relay. If 10.5 volts or less, go to next step. If more than 10.5 volts, replace power relay and repeat Quick Test.

11) Perform same test as in step **10)**, except turn key on. If more than 10.5 volts, go to step **13)**. If less than 10.5 volts, check for open in ignition switch circuits 20, 16 and 37.

12) Turn key on. Connect DVOM negative lead to circuit 60 at EEC power relay. If .50 volt of less, go to step **14)**. If more than .50 volt, repair open to circuit 60.

13) Turn key off. Disconnect EEC power relay. Connect DVOM positive lead to harness connector circuit 361 and other lead to ground. If 10.5 volts or less, EEC system is okay. If 10.5 volts or more, repair short between circuits 361 and 37.

14) Activate Key On-Engine Off Self-Test. When first service code appears, deactivate self-test. This will erase continuous codes. Perform Key On-Engine Off Self-Test and record codes. Valid codes are 11, 22, 31, 51, 53, 61 and 63. If valid codes appear, go to Quick Test results for appropriate service code action. If no valid codes appear, go to next step.

15) Disconnect processor harness connector and inspect for damage, corrosion, etc., and repair as required. Connect breakout box, leaving processor disconnected. With DVOM on 20 volt scale, turn key on. Measure voltage from box pin 1 to pins 40 and 60. If 10 volts or more, replace processor and repeat Quick Test. If less than 10 volts, repair open in circuit 37 and repeat Quick Test.

16) Turn key off and wait 10 seconds. Connect tachometer. Perform Engine Running Self-Test and try to maintain engine RPM at 2000. If engine stalls, fuel system is suspect. If engine does not stall, record service codes and go to next step.

17) Check for vacuum leaks and repair as required. Check for codes 31, 33 and 41. Ignore all other codes. If no codes appear, go back to step **1)**. If code 31 or 33 appears, to Test H. If code 41 appears, go to step **19)**.

18) Turn key off. Disconnect FCS connector and deactivate self-test. Start engine and maintain 2000 RPM for 2 minutes. Perform Engine Running Self-Test. Check for code 41. If code 41 appears, check for vacuum leaks. If no code 41, go to test J.

19) Turn key off. Perform Key On-Engine Off Self-Test. Leave key on to enter Output State Check. Codes 23, 53 or 63 should appear. If so, go to Quick Test results for appropriate service code action. If no codes, leave key on and go to next step.

20) Depress throttle to wide open position and release several times. Observe self-test output. It should cycle on and off. If so, check throttle and linkage for binding and repair as required. If no cycling, replace TP sensor and repeat Quick Test.

TEST Q — 2.3L HSC

SPARK TIMING CHECK

1) Check engine timing according to Timing Check at front of Quick Tests. If timing is okay (base plus 20°), perform Engine Running Self-Test. If timing not okay, go to next step.

2) Disconnect spout test connector at distributor. Connect jumper wire to ground for circuit 324 going to distributor. Start engine. Install jumper from distributor test connector to ground. If vehicle stalls, go to next step. If vehicle does not stall, check circuit 324 for open to TFI module and repair. If no fault, EEC system is okay, and problem is in TFI.

3) Disconnect jumper wire. Leave spout connector disconnected. Start engine and check base timing. If timing is plus or minus 3° to specifications, go to next step. If not plus or minus 3°, reset engine timing.

4) Turn key off and wait 10 seconds. Connect breakout box to harness, leaving processor disconnected. With DVOM on 2000 ohm scale, measure continuity from box pin 36 to circuit 324 at distributor test connector. If 5 ohms or less, replace processor, reconnect spout connector and check timing. If more than 5 ohms, repair open circuit, reconnect spout connector and recheck timing.

Spark Timing Test Circuits

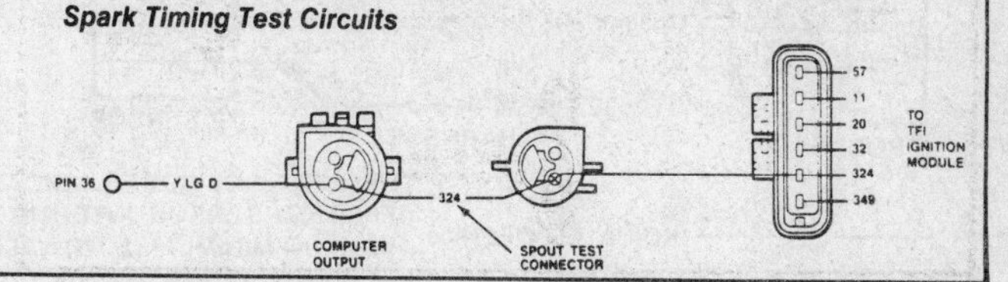

FORD MOTOR CO. ELECTRONIC ENGINE CONTROL IV (Cont.)

TEST R — 2.3L HSC

THROTTLE KICKER

1) Check that all accessories are off. If so, go to next step. If not, turn accessories off and repeat Quick Test.

2) Apply 20 in. Hg vacuum to Throttle Kicker (TK). If vacuum holds, go to next step. If vacuum does not hold, replace TK and repeat Quick Test.

3) With vacuum applied to TK, perform Engine Running Self-Test. If code 35 appears, EEC system is okay, and idle needs adjustment. If any other code appears, go to next step.

4) Turn key off. Disconnect TK solenoid. Place DVOM on 2000 ohm scale. Connect DVOM across solenoid terminals. If resistance is between 50 and 110 ohms, reconnect TK and go to next step. If not 50-110 ohms, replace TK solenoid and repeat Quick Test.

5) Turn key off. Connect DVOM negative lead to self-test output and positive lead to battery positive lead. Jumper self-test input. Perform Key On-Engine Off Self-Test until Continuous codes completed. Depress and release throttle. If meter changed to high voltage reading, go to next step. If not, depress throttle to WOT and release. If self-test output voltage does not go high. go to Test P, step **19)**.

6) Connect DVOM across TK solenoid terminals. Depress and release accelerator. If reading changes from high to low, go to next step. If not, repair open in circuit and repeat Quick Test.

7) Depress and release accelerator. Reading should change from low to high. If so, EEC circuit to TK solenoid is okay, go to next step. If not, repair short in circuit 361 and repeat Quick Test.

8) Check vacuum hoses from TK solenoid to vacuum source and TK. Repair any problems as required and repeat Quick Test.

9) With engine running, check TK solenoid output. With 12 volts applied, vacuum should be present. If so, go to next step. If not, replace TK solenoid and repeat Quick Test.

10) Turn key off. Disconnect TK solenoid connector. Disconnect processor and connect breakout box, leaving processor disconnected. Place DVOM on 200 ohm scale. Measure continuity from box pin 53 and TK solenoid connector circuit 69, and from box pin 37 and TK connector circuit 361. If both are 5 ohms or less, replace processor and repeat Quick Test. If either is more than 5 ohms, repair circuit and repeat Quick Test.

TEST U — 2.3L HSC

WIGGLE TEST

1) Service Code 21. Turn key off and wait 10 seconds. Disconnect all self-test equipment. Drive vehicle and attempt to simulate complaint. After completing drive test, perform Key On-Engine Off Self-Test. If code 21 appears, check thermostat operation. If okay, replace Engine Coolant Temperature sensor and repeat Quick Test. If no code 21, testing complete.

2) Service Code 22. Connect vacuum pump to MAP sensor. Slowly apply 25 in. Hg. vacuum to sensor. Slowly bleed off vacuum. Lightly tap on sensor, and wiggle connector. If a service code is indicated (high DVOM deflection), disconnect and inspect connectors. If good, replace MAP sensor and repeat Quick Test. If no code, go to step **8)**, and see Circuit U2.

3) Service Code 31. Connect vacuum pump to EGR valve. Slowly apply 10 in. Hg to valve, then bleed off vacuum. Lightly tap on EVP sensor, and wiggle connector. If a service code is indicated (high DVOM deflection), disconnect and inspect connectors. If good, replace EVP sensor and repeat Quick Test. If no codes, go to step **8)**, and see Circuit U3.

4) Service Code 51. Lightly tap on ECT sensor, and wiggle connector. If a service code is indicated (high DVOM deflection), disconnect and inspect connectors. If good, replace ECT sensor and repeat Quick Test. If no codes, go to step **8)**, and see Circuit U4.

5) Service Code 61. Perform same test as step **5)**. Results are the same, except see Circuit U5.

6) Service Code 63. Move throttle slowly to WOT position. Release throttle slowly to closed position. Lightly tap on TP sensor and wiggle connectors. If service code is indicated (high DVOM deflection), disconnect and inspect connectors. If good, replace TP sensor and repeat Quick Test. If no codes, go to step **8)**, and see Circuit U6.

7) Service Code 53. Perform same test as in step **6)**. Results are the same, except see Circuit U7.

8) Observe voltmeter. Using circuit number from step that brought you to this step, grasp harness as close to sensor connector as possible. Wiggle, shake or bend a small section of EEC system harness while working toward bulkhead. Do same to harness from bulkhead-to-processor. If a service code is indicated, isolate fault and make necessary repairs. Repeat Quick Test. If no codes, go to next step.

9) Turn key off and wait 10 seconds. Disconnect processor 60 pin connector. Inspect connector for damage, corrosion, etc. Repair as required and repeat Quick Test. If unable to duplicate fault, but problem still exists, drive vehicle and check for continuous codes. Repair as required and repeat Quick Test.

Wiggle Test Service Code Circuits

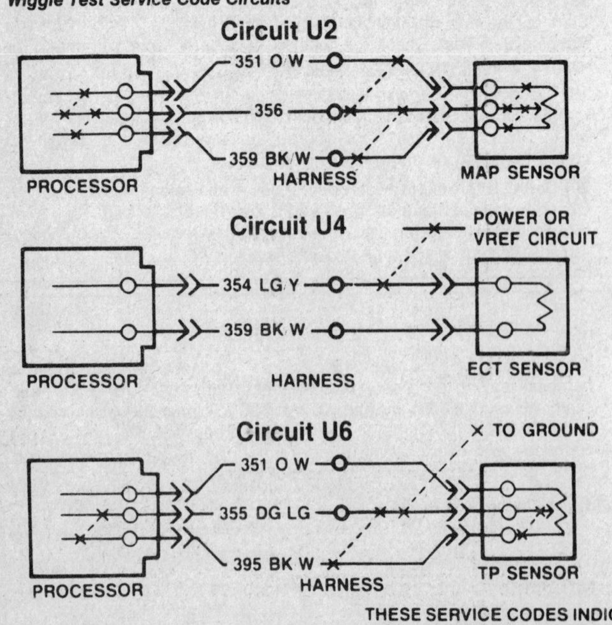

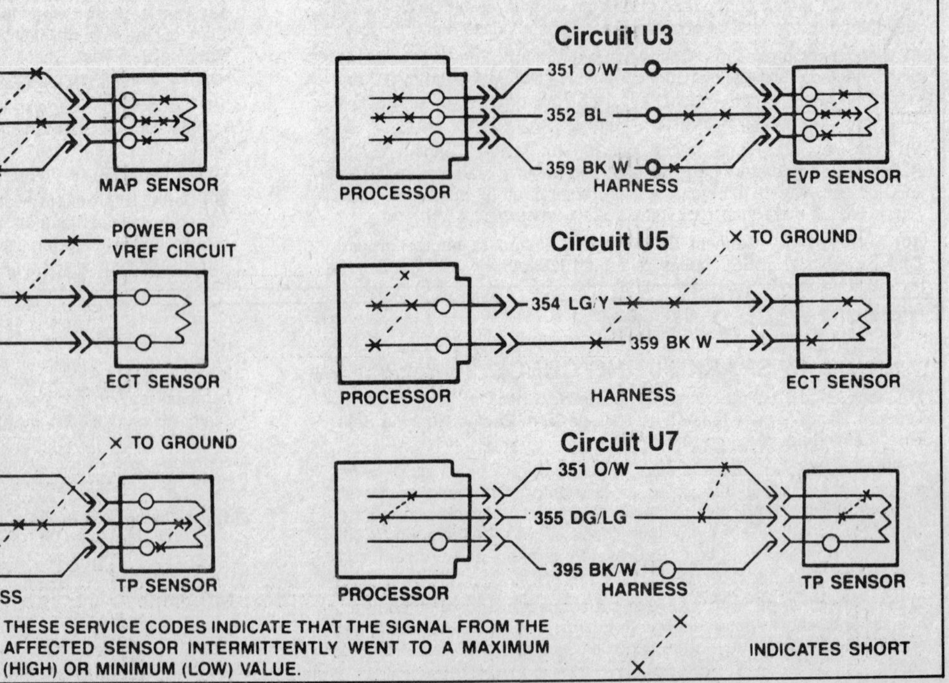

FORD MOTOR CO. ELECTRONIC ENGINE CONTROL IV (Cont.)

TEST X — 2.3L HSC

INVALID CODES CONTINUOUS TEST

1) Check if any EEC components are routed too close to high electrical energy components. If so, reroute them.

2) Turn key on. Activate self-test until first code is output, then deactivate self-test. This will erase continuous codes. Turn key off. Perform Key On-Engine Off Self-Test and record any codes. Valid codes are 11, 22, 31, 51, 53, 61 and 63. If all codes are valid, go back to Continuous test. If no valid codes, go to next step.

3) Turn key off. Deactivate self-test. Disconnect engine coolant temperature sensor. Turn key on and wait 15 seconds. Turn key off. Connect ECT sensor. Activate self-test. Turn key on and record codes. If code 51 is present, Keep Alive Memory is functional. Repeat Quick Test. If no code 51, go to next step.

4) Check power circuit to Keep Alive Memory for voltage. Turn key off. Disconnect processor and inspect 60 pin connectors. Connect breakout box to harness, leaving processor disconnected. Place DVOM on 20 volt scale. Connect DVOM positive lead to box pin 1 and negative lead to box pin 60. Turn key on. If is less than 10 volts, repair open to power circuit and repeat Quick Test. If more than 10 volts, replace processor and repeat Quick Test.

Invalid Codes Test Circuit

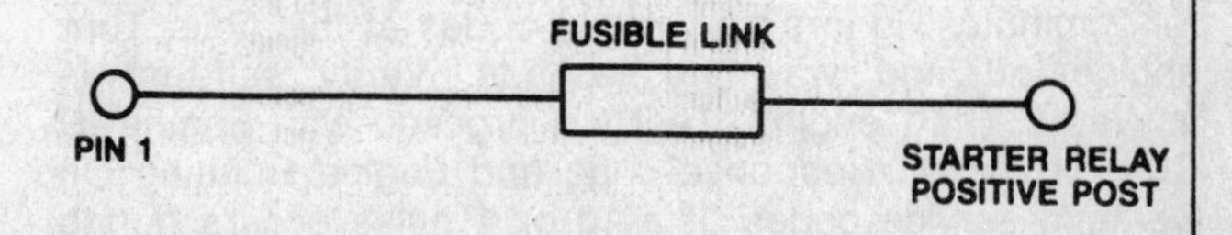

TEST Z — 2.3L HSC

SHIFT INDICATOR LIGHT

NOTE: Before proceeding with this test, service code 11 must be present in both Quick Tests.

1) Check light operation by driving vehicle. If light is always off, go to next step. If light is on intermittently or always on, go to step **4)**.

2) Turn key off and wait 10 seconds. Disconnect harness from top gear switch. Place DVOM on 200 ohm scale. Measure continuity of top gear harness connector circuit 201 to self-test circuit connector. If less than 5 ohms, go to next step. If more than 5 ohms, repair open in circuit 201, and retest light function.

3) Turn key off. Disconnect harness from top gear switch. Place transmission in 1st gear. Measure continuity of top gear switch. If less than 5 ohms, check fuse and bulb. If okay, repair open in circuit 46 or 640. Retest light function. If 5 ohms or more, replace top gear switch and retest light function.

4) Turn key off and wait 10 seconds. With top gear harness disconnected, place transmission in top gear. Measure continuity of top gear switch. If less than 5 ohms, replace top gear switch and retest light function. If more than 5 ohms, repair short in circuit 46 and retest light function.

QUICK TESTS 2.3L EFI TURBO

Reading Self-Test Codes

Service codes are transmitted on the Self-Test Output and are shown as voltage pulses on a Digital Volt-Ohmmeter (DVOM). Key On-Engine Off Self-Tests will show three codes for each step. The first code is On Demand, the second code is a Separator code and the third code is the Continuous code. The On Demand code first digit is indicated by a pulse, then the needle drops to zero for 2 seconds, then the second digit of the code is displayed. After 9 seconds, the Separator code will be displayed for 1/2 second. After 6 seconds, the first digit of the Continuous code will be displayed, the needle will drop to zero for 2 seconds, then the second digit of the Continuous code will display.

Engine Running Self-Tests will display codes in the same manner, except there will be an Engine ID code, a Dynamic Response Code and an On Demand code. The Engine ID code has no application in the field, and is for factory use only. The codes will be displayed in the same manner as Key On-Engine Off codes.

Equipment Hook-Up

With ignition key off, connect a jumper wire from the self-test input to pin 2 on the self-test connector. *See Fig. 6.* Set needle-type volt-ohmmeter on DC 0-15 volt scale. Connect VOM from battery positive side to pin 4 on self-test connector.

Key On-Engine Off Self-Test

Turn ignition switch on. Reconnect grounded jumper wire to self-test input terminal. Observe and record On Demand and Continuous codes. When more than 1 code is displayed, always repair problems in the order that codes were displayed. Do not depress throttle during test. Repair codes as follows:

KEY ON-ENGINE OFF SELF-TEST RESULTS

On Demand Codes	Continuous Codes	Proceed to Test
11	11	Timing Check
Any	11	See Code No.
Any	Any	See Code No.
11	Any	Timing Check
None	None	Test P
15		Replace processor, retest.
21		Test F
22		Test R
23		Test E
24		Test D
26		Test G
51		Test F
53		Test E
54		Test D
56		Test G
61		Test F
63		Test E
64		Test D
66		Test G
67		Test W
None	None	Test P

Timing Check

If vehicle is in a no-start condition, go directly to Test A. Turn key off. Verify that self-test trigger has been activated. Restart engine and check timing while in self-test. If timing is 27-33° BTDC, go to Engine Running Self-Test. If timing is not 27-33° BTDC, go to Test Q.

NOTE: If engine stalls while testing, go to Test X.

FORD MOTOR CO. ELECTRONIC ENGINE CONTROL IV (Cont.)

Engine Running Self-Test

This test checks sensors under actual operating conditions. Fault must be present at time of test to be detected. This test will display an Engine ID Code, a Dynamic Response Code and an On Demand Service Code. After a Dynamic Response Code is received, quickly press and release accelerator once only. If test is not performed properly, a series 70 code (77, 76, 73, 72) will appear and the test will have to be repeated.

Start and run engine at more than 2000 RPM for 2 minutes. Ignore any output codes at this time. Turn engine off and wait 10 seconds. Verify self-test is activated. Start engine. Test will proceed with Engine ID Code, Dynamic Response code and Engine Running On Demand service codes. If a 10 or 1 pulse occurs during Dynamic Response code, open throttle wide open momentarily. Record codes and proceed as follows:

ENGINE RUNNING SELF-TEST RESULTS

On Demand Codes	Proceed to Test
11	Continuous Code [1]
Any	See Code No.
None	Repeat self-test. [2]
12	Test N
13	Test N
21	Test F
22	Test R
23	Test E
24	Test D
26	Test G
31	Test H
34	Test V
41	Test H
42	Test H
73	Test E
76	Test G
77	Test T
None	Test P

[1] — If drive problem still exists, go to Test X.
[2] — Verify service codes, then go to Test P.

Continuous Test

1) Unless instructed otherwise, do not disconnect any sensor with key on, or a service code may be stored. Should Keep Alive Power pin 1 (circuit 37) to processor be interrupted momentarily, all stored Continuous Codes may be lost. Should power pin 1 fail, invalid codes may be received during Continuous Test.

2) Correct method for clearing processor memory of stored codes is to exit Key On-Engine Off Self-Test during code output sequence at point where service codes begin. Exit self-test by removing self-test jumper.

3) Before using stored codes, verify that self-tests indicated a pass (code 11). If an On Demand code is detected during test, this must be repaired first, since some hard failures also request a code in the continuous memory.

4) Once On Demand testing is completed, clear memory of Continuous Codes and operate vehicle to verify repair. If a drive complaint still exists, repeat Quick Test and follow Continuous Test directions.

5) Perform Key On-Engine Off Self-Test. When first service code is output, exit self-test by removing jumper from self-test input to signal return pin 2. This will erase any Continuous codes.

6) Place key in run position but do not start engine. This places system in Continuous Monitor Mode. Self-test output will be activated whenever a monitored sensor is interrupted. Perform Continuous Monitor Test.

Continuous Monitor Test

Continuous Monitor Test codes are separated from Key On-Engine Off codes by a single separator pulse. After service codes have been received, observe DVOM while moving, wiggling, tapping heating or cooling the system harness, connectors and sensors. If an intermittent condition is created, the monitor will indicate this by producing a service code. Perform Key On-Engine Off Self-Test to retrieve codes. If any codes are indicated, go to proper test as shown in Continuous Test Results. If no codes appear, fault is not in a monitored EEC sensor circuit. EEC functional test is complete. Refer to Test X for additional symptom diagnostic information.

CONTINUOUS TEST RESULTS

Code	Proceed to Test
14	Test Y
21	Test F
22	Test R
41	Test H
42	Test H
51	Test F
53	Test E
54	Test D
56	Test G
61	Test F
63	Test E
64	Test D
66	Test G

CIRCUIT TESTS

Test Instructions

1) Do not run any test unless instructed to do so by Quick Test. Make sure all non-EEC related faults are corrected. Do not replace any part unless directed to do so. Always start with lowest codes first.

2) Do not make measurements at control module or connect test lamps to it, unless specified. All measurements are made by probing REAR of connector. Isolate both ends of a circuit and turn key off when checking for shorts or continuity, unless specified.

3) Disconnect solenoids and switches from harness before measuring continuity, resistance or energizing with a 12 volt source. Follow each step in order until fault is found. After repairs, check component connections and repeat Quick Test.

Output State Test

1) This test is used to diagnose actuators. Test is performed in Key On-Engine Off mode after Continuous codes have been sent. Do not disable self-test but quickly press throttle and release. All EEC outputs will be activated. Depress throttle again to turn them off.

2) Connect DVOM to self-test output pin 4. Start Key On-Engine Off On Demand Test. When codes are completed, DVOM will read 0 volts. Depress throttle. DVOM readings above 10.5 volts indicate actuators are on, readings below 2 volts indicate actuators are off.

3) Disconnect DVOM from pin 4 and connect to appropriate actuator. Measure output state voltage of actuator. Each test will tell what action to take according to reading on DVOM.

FORD MOTOR CO. ELECTRONIC ENGINE CONTROL IV (Cont.)

TEST A — 2.3L EFI TURBO

NO START PROBLEM

NOTE: Do not smoke or have an open flame when performing fuel checks. If a fuel leak is detected, stop test immediately and correct leaks.

1) Check fuel delivery system for leaks. Correct leaks before proceeding. If no leaks, go to next step.

2) Attempt to start the vehicle. If engine does not crank, diagnose engine starting system. If engine cranks, but does not start, or runs rough, go to next step.

3) Using a spark tester (modified spark plug), check for spark at a plug wire while cranking. A good sharp, hot white spark should appear. If so, go to step **9)**. If not, go to next step. Reconnect plug wire.

4) Remove coil wire from distributor and install spark tester. Check for hot, white spark while cranking. If a spark appears, diagnose TFI system. If no spark, go to next step.

5) Turn key off, disconnect processor and connect breakout box. Leave processor disconnected. Place DVOM on 20 volt range, and connect between box pins 56 and 16. Crank engine. If reading is between 3-6 volts, go to next step. If not between 3-6 volts, go to step **7)**.

Ignition Module Signal Check

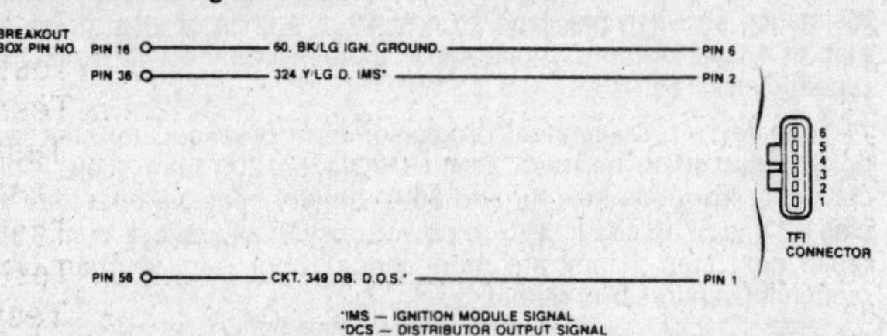

6) With breakout box connected, and processor disconnected, turn key off. Place DVOM on 2000 ohm scale. Disconnect TFI module connector at distributor. Check continuity between box pin 16 and TFI terminal connector 6, and between box pin 56 and TFI terminal 1. If both are less than 5 ohms, TFI system is faulty. If either is 5 ohms or more, repair circuits as required and repeat Quick Test.

7) With DVOM on 20 volt range, disconnect breakout box from processor. Connect DVOM to pins 36 and 16. Crank engine. If between 3-6 volts, TFI system is faulty. If not between 3-6 volts, go to next step.

8) With key off, install breakout box, leaving processor disconnected. Place DVOM on 2000 ohm scale. Connect TFI module connector to distributor. Connect DVOM between box pins 36 and 16. If more than 2000 ohms, TFI system is faulty. If less than 2000 ohms, disconnect TFI module. If short present, repair harness. If no short, TFI system is faulty.

9) Disconnect all electrical connections at fuel injectors. Connect pressure gauge to Schrader valve on injector bar. Note initial pressure reading. Turn key to run for 1 second, then turn key off. Repeat 5 times. Turn key off. If pressure increased in run position, go to step **11)**. If no increase, go to next step. Reconnect injectors.

Schrader Valve Locations

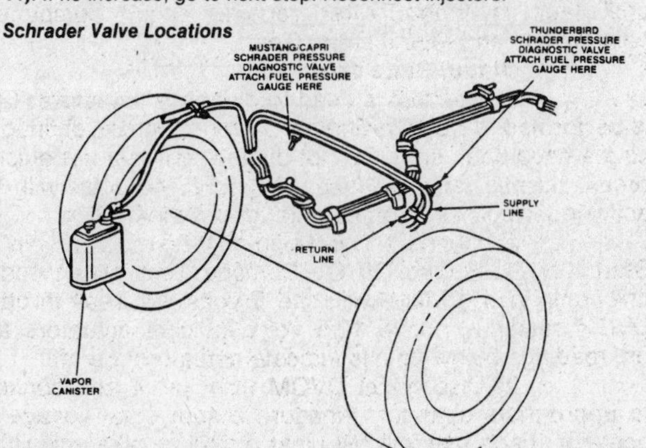

10) Locate inertia switch in trunk. Push switch button to reset switch. If switch will not reset, replace it. Repeat step **9)**, and note pressure readings. If reading increased, repeat Quick Test. If no increase, go to Test S.

11) Pressurize system as in step **9)**. Turn key off. Wait for pressure to become steady. If pressure is between 35-45 psi, go to next step. If not between 35-45 psi, check that coil is connected. Otherwise check for leaking injectors or fuel regulator.

12) Wait 2 minutes after pressure gauge reading in step **11)**, then note drop in pressure. If 4 psi or less drop in 2 minutes, go to next step. If more than 4 psi drop, turn key off. Check for hydraulic lock-up, fuel fouled spark plugs, leaking injectors or fuel regulator.

13) Pressurize system as in step **9)**. Disconnect fuel pump relay to disable fuel pump. Crank engine for 5 seconds. Take pressure reading. If pressure is about 10-20 psi at end of cycle, EEC system is okay. No start problem is in another vehicle system. If original complaint was vehicle runs rough, go to step **14)**. If pressure is not about 10-20 psi, go to step **14)**. Reconnect fuel pump relay.

NOTE: The colder the engine the more the pressure drop. Coolant temperature of 200°F equals about a 10 psi drop in 5 seconds. 60°F equals a 20 psi drop in 5 seconds.

14) Connect breakout box. Connect non-powered 12 volt test lamp from box pin 37 to pin 58, then from pin 37 to pin 59. Crank engine. If dim glow at light on both tests, go to next step. If no light at one of tests, check for battery power at pin 37, and/or service circuit 361. If okay, replace processor and repeat Quick Test. If bright light on any test, check circuit 95 and 96 for shorts to ground. If okay, replace processor and repeat Quick Test.

Injector Signal Check

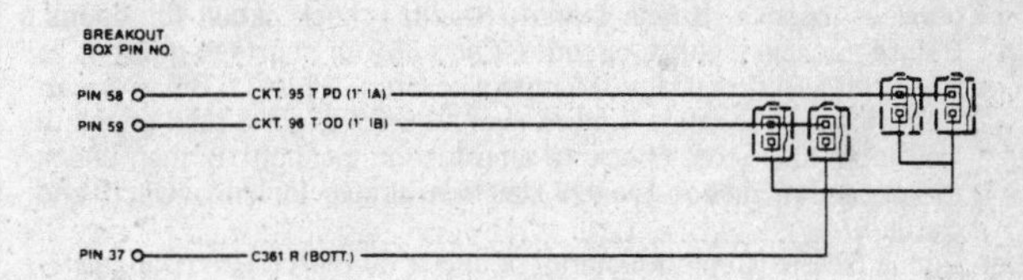

15) Remove fuel pump relay. Using DVOM, measure average voltage between pins 37 and 58 during cranking. Also measure between pins 37 and 59. If more than 1 volt difference between circuits, disconnect processor and inspect for damage. Reconnect processor and repeat Quick Test. If problem still present, replace processor. If less than 1 volt difference between circuits, go to next step.

16) Turn key off, and place DVOM on 20 ohm range. Disconnect injectors 2, 3 and 4 electrically. Through the vehicle harness, measure the resistance of injectors as follows.

- Injector 1 between pins 58 and 37.
- Disconnect injector 1. Reconnect injector 2. Read resistance between pins 58 and 37.
- Disconnect injector 2, reconnect injector 3. Read resistance between pins 59 and 37.
- Disconnect injector 3, reconnect injector 4. Read resistance beteen pins 59 and 37.

All four readings should be between 2-3.5 ohms. If so, go to next step. If not, check harness on suspect injector. If okay, replace injector. Reconnect all injectors and repeat Quick Test.

17) Electrically disconnect all injectors at intake manifold. Pressurize system as in step **9)**. Connect injector for cylinder 1 only. Crank engine for 5 seconds. Record reading at end of 5 seconds. Repeat procedure for each injector in turn. If all readings are not within 4 psi of each other, replace injector(s) not within reading and repeat Quick Test. If all readings within 4 psi, disconnect processor. Inspect connector for damage and repeat Quick Test. If problem still present, replace processor and repeat Quick Test.

FORD MOTOR CO. ELECTRONIC ENGINE CONTROL IV (Cont.)

TEST B — 2.3L EFI TURBO

VEHICLE BATTERY

1) Turn key to run. Measure voltage across battery terminals. If more than 10.5 volts, go to next step. If less than 10.5 volts, service discharged battery.

2) Turn key to run. Place DVOM on 20 volt scale. Measure voltage between battery negative post to signal return circuit 359 in self-test connector. If less than .5 volts, go to next step. If more than .5 volts, go to step **4)**.

3) Turn key to run. Measure voltage from battery positive post to pin 37 and pin 57. If both are less than .5 volts, go to Test C. If either is more than .5 volts, go to step **7)**.

4) Connect breakout box. With processor connected, place DVOM on 20 volt scale. Turn key to run. Measure voltage from battery positive post to box pin 40 and pin 60. If both less than .5 volts, go to next step. If either less than .5 volts, circuit has high resistance or open. Correct faulty ground circuit 57 and repeat Quick Test.

5) With breakout box and processor connected, place DVOM on 200 ohm scale. Turn key off. Measure resistance between pins 40 and 46, and between pins 46 and 60. If both less than 1 ohm, go to next step. If either more than 1 ohm, disconnect processor. Inspect for damage and repeat Quick Test. If fault still present, replace processor and repeat Quick Test.

6) Turn key off. Measure resistance between pin 37 and circuit 359 signal return in self-test connector. If less than 5 ohms, system okay, repeat Quick Test. If more than 5 ohms, excessive resistance in circuit 359 is indicated. Correct fault and repeat Quick Test.

7) If an open fusible link is found, check for shorts to ground before replacing link. Place DVOM on 20 volt scale. With processor connected, turn key to run. Connect DVOM negative lead to battery negative post and make the following voltage checks. Key must remain in run for these checks.

- Circuit 37 Yellow at EEC power relay. If more than 10.5 volts, continue checks. If less than 10.5 volts, check circuit for opens. Before servicing, check circuits 37 and 361 for shorts to ground.
- Circuit 175 Bk/Yel (Capri, Mustang) or circuit 20 W/Lt. Blu (Cougar, T-Bird) at power relay. If more than 10.5 volts, go to next check. If less than 10.5 volts, check 10 amp fuse in location 18, then check for opens in ignition switch start/run circuit, ignition switch and circuit 37.
- Circuit 57 Blk (Capri, Mustang) or circuit 60 Blk/Lt. Grn (Cougar, T-Bird) at power relay. If .5 volt or less, go to next check. If more than .5 volt, correct open in ground circuit.
- Circuit 361 Red at EEC power relay. If 10.5 volts or more, correct open in 361 from relay to pins 37 and 57. If 361 okay, replace processor. If less than 10.5 volts, replace power relay.

Battery Test Circuits

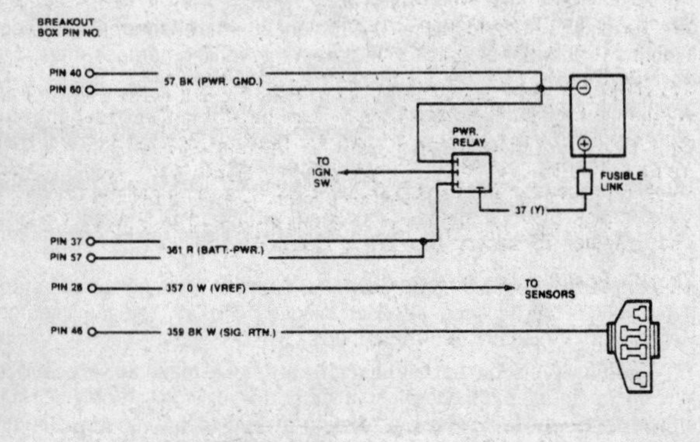

TEST C — 2.3L EFI TURBO

REFERENCE VOLTAGE

1) Place DVOM on 20 volt scale. Connect breakout box between processor and vehicle harness. Place key in Run position. Measure voltage between pins 37 and 40. If more than 10.5 volts, go to next step. If less than 10.5 volts, go to Test B.

2) With key in Run, measure voltage between box pins 26 and 46. If 4-6 volts, repeat Quick Test. If less than 4 volts, go to step **5)**. If more than 6 volts, go to next step.

3) With connections as in step **2)**, turn key off. If less than .5 volt, go to next step. If more than .5 volt, service short between VREF and battery power circuits and repeat Quick Test.

4) Disconnect processor from breakout box. Turn key to Run. Measure voltage between box pins 26 and 46. If .5 volt or less, replace processor and repeat Quick Test. If more than .5 volt, service short between VREF and battery power in EEC harness and repeat Quick Test.

5) With processor reconnected to breakout box, disconnect Throttle Position (TP) sensor from harness. Turn key to Run. Measure resistance between box pins 26 and 46. If 4 volts or less, go to step **6)**. If more than 4 volts, replace TP sensor and repeat Quick Test.

6) Disconnect Vane Air Flow (VAF) sensor from harness. Measure resistance between box pins 26 and 46. If 4 volts or less, go to next step. If 4 volts or more, replace VAF meter. Reconnect TP sensor and repeat Quick Test.

7) Turn key off. Disconnect processor from breakout box, but leave box connected to harness. Place DVOM on 200 ohm scale. Check continuity from box pins 40 and 60 to battery negative post and from pins 37 and 57 to circuit 361 on power relay. If all are less than 1 ohm, go to next step. If any are more than 1 ohm, service open circuit, reconnect sensors and repeat Quick Test.

8) With breakout box connected to vehicle harness, disconnect harness connector from module and check for shorts between VREF pin 26 and remaining pins on breakout box. TP, VAF/VAT sensors should remain disconnected. If all are 10.000 ohms or more, replace processor and repeat Quick Test. If any are less than 10,000 ohms, service short, reconnect sensors and repeat Quick Test.

Reference Voltage Test Circuits

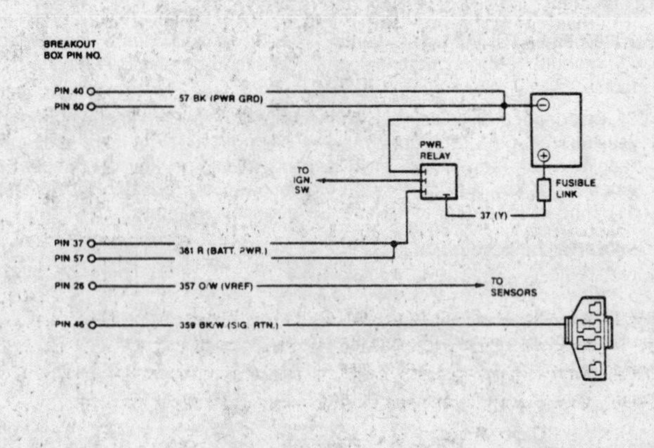

FORD MOTOR CO. ELECTRONIC ENGINE CONTROL IV (Cont.)

TEST D — 2.3L EFI TURBO

VANE AIR TEMPERATURE METER

NOTE: Outside temperature must be at least 50°F to perform this test.

1) Disconnect Vane Air Flow and Vane Air Temperature (VAF/VAT) sensor. Place DVOM on 20 volt scale. Turn key on. Measure voltage at VAT harness connector from signal circuit 357 to signal return circuit 359. If between 4-6 volts, go to next step. If less than 4 volts, go to step **3)**. If more than 6 volts, go to Test C.

2) Turn key on. Place DVOM on 200,000 ohm scale. Measure resistance at VAT sensor. In either Key On-Engine Off, or Engine Running Self-Test, reading should be 3700 ohms at 50°F, or 125 ohms at 240°F. If not within specifications, replace VAF/VAT meter assembly and repeat Quick Test. If within specifications, replace processor and repeat Quick Test.

3) Turn key off. Connect breakout box to harness, leaving processor disconnected. Check continuity of VAT circuit 357 from harness connector to box pin 25, and from circuit 359 to box pin 46. If both less than 5 ohms, go to next step. If either more than 5 ohms, repair circuit and retest. Repeat Quick Test.

4) Turn key off. Place DVOM on 200,000 ohm scale. Measure resistance of box pin 25 to box pins 40, 46 and 60. If any reading is less than 10,000 ohms, repair circuits and repeat Quick Test. If all are more than 10,000 ohms, go back to step **2)**.

5) Code 54. Turn key off. Generate opposite code by inserting jumper between harness connector VAT circuit 357 and signal return circuit 359. Perform Key On-Engine Off Self-Test. If code 64 appears, replace VAT sensor and repeat Quick Test. If no code 64, remove jumper and go to next step.

6) Turn key off. Connect breakout box to harness, leaving processor disconnected. Place DVOM on 200 ohm scale. Check continuity of VAT circuit 357 from connector to box pin 25, and from circuit 359 to pin 46. If both are less than 5 ohms, replace processor and repeat Quick Test. If either is more than 5 ohms, repair circuit and repeat Quick Test.

7) Code 64. Turn key off. Generate opposite code by disconnecting harness connector from VAF/VAT. Perform Key On-Engine Off Self-Test. If code 54 appears, replace VAT/VAF sensor and repeat Quick Test. If no code 54, go to next step.

8) Turn key off. Disconnect processor from vehicle harness. Install breakout box, leaving processor disconnected. Disconnect VAF/VAT sensors. Place DVOM on 200,000 ohm scale. Measure resistance between box pin 25 and pins 40, 46 and 60. If one or more is less than 10,000 ohms, repair circuit and repeat Quick Test. If all are more than 10,000 ohms, replace processor and repeat Quick Test.

Vane Air Temperature Test Circuits

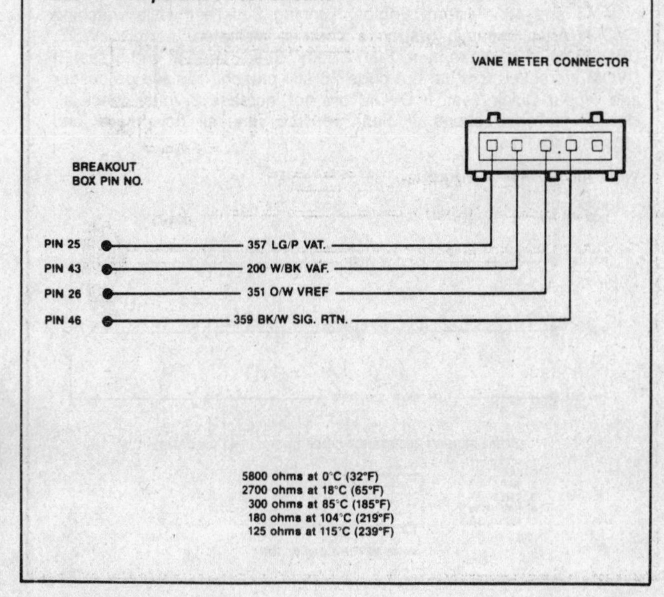

TEST E — 2.3L EFI TURBO

THROTTLE POSITION SENSOR

1) Code 23. Code 23 indicates throttle position (TP) sensor input to processor is out of closed throttle limits (.25-1.4 volts). No opens or shorts exist or a code 53 or 63 would have been generated. Check that throttle linkage is at mechanical closed throttle. Check for binding linkage, vacuum line or electrical harness interference. If throttle plate is closed go to next step. If not closed, repair as required and repeat Quick Test.

2) Refer to emission decal and verify that throttle plate opening is at proper RPM set point. If so, replace TP sensor as it cannot be adjusted. If RPM adjustment required, adjust and repeat Quick Test.

3) Turn key off. Disconnect TP sensor and inspect for damage, corrosion, etc. Repair as required. Place DVOM on 20 volt scale. Measure voltage from TP connector circuit 359 to battery positive post. If 10 volts or more, go to next step. If less than 10 volts, go to step **6)**.

4) Disconnect TP sensor. Turn key on. Measure voltage between TP connector circuit 355 and circuit 359. If less than 4 volts, go to next step. If more than 4 volts, go to step **7)**.

5) With TP sensor disconnected, perform Key On-Engine Off Self-Test. If code 63 appears, replace TP sensor and repeat Quick Test. If no code 63, replace processor and repeat Quick Test.

6) Turn key off. Connect breakout box to vehicle harness. Leave TP sensor processor disconnected. Place DVOM on 200 ohm scale. Check continuity between circuit 359 of TP harness connector and box pin 46. If 5 ohms or less, replace processor and repeat Quick Test. If more than 5 ohms, repair open in circuit and repeat Quick Test.

7) Disconnect processor from vehicle harness, leaving TP sensor disconnected. Turn key on. Measure voltage between TP sensor harness circuits 355 and 359. If 4 volts or more, correct short in circuit and repeat Quick Test. If less than 4 volts, replace processor and repeat Quick Test.

8) With TP sensor disconnected, turn key on. Measure voltage between circuits 351 and 359. If 4-6 volts, go to next step. If less than 4 volts, go to step **12)**. If more than 6 volts, reconnect TP sensor and go to Test C.

9) Turn key off. Disconnect TP sensor. Jumper circuit 355 to circuit 351 at harness connector. Perform Key On-Engine Off Self-Test. If code 53 appears, replace TP sensor and repeat Quick Test, If no code 53 or any other codes, remove jumper and go to next step.

10) Turn key off. Place DVOM on 200,000 ohm scale. Measure resistance between TP sensor harness circuits 355 and 359. If 10,000 ohms or more, go to next step. If less than 10,000 ohms, repair short in circuit and repeat Quick Test.

11) Turn key off. Connect breakout box, leaving processor disconnected. Measure resistance between TP harness connector circuit 355 and box pin 47. If less than 5 ohms, replace processor and repeat Quick Test. If more than 5 ohms, repair open in circuit 355 and repeat Quick Test.

12) With same connections as in step **11)**, measure resistance between circuit 351 and box pin 26. If less than 5 ohms, replace processor and repeat Quick Test. If more than 5 ohms, repair open in circuit 351 and repeat Quick Test.

13) Code 73. Code 73 indicates TP sensor did not exceed 25% of its rotation in Engine Response Check. Turn key off. Install breakout box. Connect DVOM to box pins 46 and 47. Perform Engine Running Self-Test. If reading exceeds 3.5 volts during brief wide open throttle, replace processor and repeat Quick Test. If reading did not reach 3.5 volts, check that TP sensor is properly attached to throttle body. If okay, replace TP sensor and repeat Quick Test.

Throttle Position Sensor Circuits

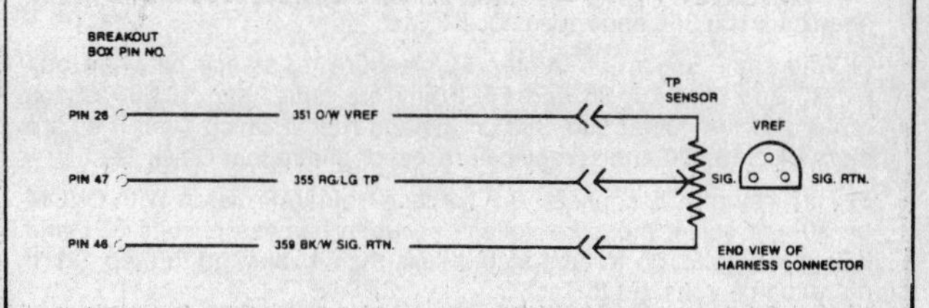

FORD MOTOR CO. ELECTRONIC ENGINE CONTROL IV (Cont.)

TEST F — 2.3L EFI TURBO

ENGINE COOLANT TEMPERATURE SENSOR

NOTE: To pass this test, coolant temperature must be 50-240°F for Key On-Engine Off Self-Test and 180-240°F for Engine Running Self-Test.

1) Code 21. Start engine and bring to normal operating temperature. Check that upper radiator hose is hot and pressurized. Perform Quick Tests before continuing. If code 21 still appears, go to next step. If no code 21, service other codes if required. If vehicle stalls, service cause of stalling.

2) Disconnect Engine Coolant Temperature (ECT) sensor and inspect connectors. Place DVOM on 20 volt scale. Turn key on. Measure voltage between harness connector circuit 354 and 359. If between 4 and 6 volts, go to next step. If less than 4 volts, go to step **4)**. If more than 6 volts, go to Test C.

3) With vehicle warm, turn key off. Place DVOM on 200,000 ohm scale. Measure resistance of ECT sensor. In Key On-Engine Off Self-Test, reading should be 1300-58,000 ohms. In Engine Running Self-Test, reading should be 1300-3500 ohms. If both are within limits, replace processor and repeat Quick Test. If not within limits, replace ECT sensor and repeat Quick Test.

4) Turn key on. Disconnect processor 60 pin connector and inspect connectors. Connect breakout box to harness, leaving processor disconnected. With DVOM on 200 ohm scale, measure continuity of circuit 354 to box pin 7 and circuit 359 to box pin 46. If both less than 5 ohms, go to next step. If either more than 5 ohms, repair harness and repeat Quick Test.

5) With same connections as in step **4)**, place DVOM on 200,000 ohm scale and measure resistance of box pin 7 to pins 40 and 60. If more than 10,000 ohms, go back to step **3)**. If any is less than 10,000 ohms, repair short to ground and repeat Quick Test.

6) Turn key off. Disconnect ECT connector. Inspect connector and sensor. Connect jumper across terminals 354 and 359. Perform Key On-Engine Off Self-Test. If code 61 appears, replace ECT and repeat Quick Test. If no code 61, go to next step.

7) Turn key off. Remove jumper. Install breakout box to harness, leaving processor disconnected. Place DVOM on 200 ohm scale and measure continuity of ECT circuit 354 to box pin 7 and circuit 359 to pin 46. If either is more than 5 ohms, repair open in harness and repeat Quick Test. If both are less than 5 ohms, replace processor and repeat Quick Test.

8) Disconnect ECT connector. Induce an open failure. Perform Key On-Engine Off Self-Test. If code 51 appears, replace ECT and repeat Quick Test. If no code 51, go to next step.

9) Turn key off and wait 10 seconds. Install breakout box to harness, leaving processor disconnected. Disconnect ECT. Place DVOM on 200,000 ohm scale and measure resistance between box pin 7 to pins 40 and 60. If any are less than 10,000 ohms, repair short in harness and repeat Quick Test. If both are more than 10,000 ohms, replace processor and repeat Quick Test.

Coolant Temperature Sensor Circuits

PIN 7 — 354 LG/Y ECT

BREAKOUT BOX PIN NO.

RESISTANCE VALUES
10°C (50°F) = 57,800 OHMS
18°C (65°F) = 40,000 OHMS
82°C (180°F) = 3,500 OHMS
104°C (220°F) = 1,800 OHMS
115°C (239°F) = 1,300 OHMS

PIN 46 — 359 BK SIG. RTN.

TEST G — 2.3L EFI TURBO

VANE AIR FLOW

1) Code 26. Code 26 indicates vane air flow input to processor is out of closed limits (Engine Off) or idle limits (Engine Off .15-.50 volts; Engine at Idle 1.5-2.7 volts). There are no shorts or opens in circuit or code 56 or 66 would have been generated. Check for air or vacuum leaks. Remove air filter and check for contamination. If code 26 appears in Key On-Engine Off Self-Test, replace vane air flow meter and repeat Quick Test. If no code 26, go to next step.

2) Turn key off. Install breakout box. Reconnect processor and VAF meter. Place DVOM on 20 volt scale and connect DVOM leads between box pins 43 and 46. Turn key on. Place an unsharpened wooden pencil through vane meter opening. Pencil must pass completely through opening. If 2.8-3.7 volts, vane meter is capable of outputting signals. Code 26 has been caused by incorrect engine speed, or vacuum leak. Repair and repeat Quick Test. If voltage not 2.8-3.7, replace VAF meter and repeat Quick Test.

3) Turn key off. Disconnect Vane Air Flow (VAF) sensor. Measure voltage between VAF harness connector circuit 359 and battery positive post. If reading is 10 volts or more, go to next step. If less than 10 volts, go to step **6)**.

4) With VAF sensor disconnected, turn key on. Measure voltage between circuits 200 and 359. If less than 4 volts, go to next step. If more than 4 volts, go to step **7)**.

5) With VAF meter disconnected, perform Key On-Engine Off Self-Test. If code 66 appears, replace VAF/VAT meter and repeat Quick Test. If no code 66, replace processor and repeat Quick Test. Disregard all other codes.

6) Turn key off. Connect breakout box to vehicle harness. Do not connect VAF meter or processor. Check continuity between VAF harness connector circuit 359 and box pin 46. If 5 ohms or less, replace processor and repeat Quick Test. If more than 5 ohms, repair open in circuit 359 and repeat Quick Test.

7) With same set up as in step **6)**, measure resistance between box pin 43 and pins 26, 35 and 57. If any are more than 10,000 ohms, repair short in circuit 200, 359 or 361 and repeat Quick Test. If all are more than 10,000 ohms, replace processor and repeat Quick Test.

8) Turn key off. Disconnect VAF harness from VAF meter. With DVOM on 20 volt scale, measure voltage between harness circuits 351 and 359. If 4-6 volts, go to next step. If less than 4 volts, go to step **12)**. If more than 6 volts, go to Test C.

9) Turn key off. With VAF meter disconnected, jumper circuit 200 to circuit 351 at harness connector. Perform Key On-Engine Off Self-Test. If code 56 appears, replace VAF meter and repeat Quick Test. If no code 56, go to next step.

10) Turn key off. Place DVOM on 200,000 ohm scale. Measure resistance between harness connector circuits 200 and 359. If 10,000 ohms or more, go to next step. If less than 10,000 ohms, repair short in circuit 200 and repeat Quick Test.

11) Turn key off. Connect breakout box, leaving processor disconnected. Measure resistance between circuit 200 and box pin 43. If less than 5 ohms, replace processor and repeat Quick Test, If more than 5 ohms, repair open in circuit 200 and repeat Quick Test.

12) With same connections as in step **11)**, measure resistance between connector circuit 351 and box pin 26. If less than 5 ohms, replace processor and repeat Quick Test. If more than 5 ohms, repair open in circuit 351 and repeat Quick Test.

13) Code 76. Place DVOM on 20 volt scale and connect between box pins 43 and 46. Perform Engine Running Self-Test while watching DVOM. After dynamic response code is indicated, perform WOT. DVOM should increase more than 2 volts. Check code at end of test. If DVOM increased 2 volts, but code 76 still present, replace processor and repeat Quick Test. If DVOM did not increase 2 volts, check air cleaner for obstructions. If clear, replace vane air flow meter and repeat Quick Test.

Vane Air Flow Test Circuits

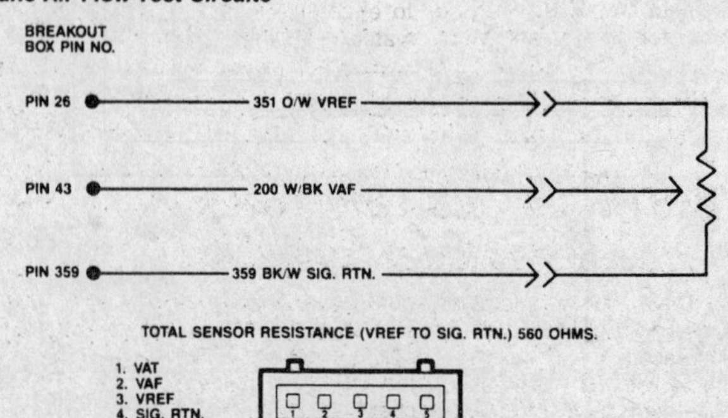

FORD MOTOR CO. ELECTRONIC ENGINE CONTROL IV (Cont.)

TEST H — 2.3L EFI TURBO

FUEL CONTROL

NOTE: Fuel contaminated engine oil may affect 4-1 and 4-2 service codes. If this is suspected, remove PCV from valve cover and repeat Quick Test. If problem corrected, change engine oil and filter.

1) Install fuel pressure gauge. Start and run engine. Fuel pressure must be 25-45 psi. If within specifications, go to next step. If not within specifications, check fuel pump and fuel pressure regulator. If engine will not run, cycle key on and off several times. After final key off, fuel pressure should remain at 35-45 psi for 60 seconds.

2) The following tests check the fuel injection harness resistance. Connect breakout box to injector harness. Turn key off and place DVOM on 200 ohm scale. Electrically disconnect injectors for cylinders 2, 3 and 4. Through the vehicle harness, measure the resistance of the following circuits:

- Injector 1, between box pins 37 and 58.
- Disconnect injector 1. Reconnect injector 2. Measure between box pins 37 and 58.
- Disconnect injector 2. Reconnect injector 3. Measure between box pins 37 and 59.
- Disconnect injector 3. Reconnect injector 4. Measure between box pins 37 and 59.

All four readings should be 2-3.5 ohms. If so, go to next step. If any are not 2-3.5 ohms, service harness/connector on suspect injector for opens or shorts. If okay, replace injector and repeat Quick Test. Reconnect all injectors.

3) With breakout box connected, connect a non-powered 12 volt test lamp between box pins 37 and 58. Crank engine. Repeat test between box pins 37 and 59. If lamp is dim in both tests, go to next step. If lamp does not light on one or more tests, check that battery power exists at pins 37 and 57. If so, replace processor and repeat Quick Test. If lamp is bright on one or more tests, check circuits 95 and 96 for shorts to ground. If okay, replace processor and repeat Quick Test.

4) Connect tachometer to engine. Run engine at 2000 RPM. If may be necessary to disconnect Idle Speed Control (ISC) motor and use throttle body stop screw to set engine RPM. Disconnect and reconnect injectors one at a time. Note RPM drop for each injector. Each should produce at least a 150 RPM drop. If so, fuel delivery system is okay. Problem may be air/vacuum leak, fuel contamination, or EGR. If no 150 RPM drop, replace faulty injector and repeat Quick Test. Reconnect ISC, and reset curb idle if required.

5) Code 42. Non-EEC problems can cause a code 42. Check for fuel contaminated engine oil, ignition misfire or canister purge malfunctions. Disconnect vehicle harness at Exhaust Gas Oxygen sensor. Using jumper wire, ground vehicle harness circuit 94. Repeat Engine Running Self-Test. If code 41 appears, go to step **7)**. If no code 41, go to next step.

6) Check continuity of oxygen sensor ground circuit 890 between breakout box pin 49 and sensor ground at engine block. Also check sensor circuit 94 between box pin 29 and sensor harness connector. If both are less than 5 ohms, disconnect processor connector and inspect for damage. If okay, replace processor and repeat Quick Test. If not less than 5 ohms, correct circuit with improper resiatance.

7) Place DVOM on 20 volt scale. Disconnect oxygen sensor harness. Connect DVOM from sensor to engine ground. Run engine at 2000 RPM for 2 minutes. While watching DVOM, disconnect manifold vacuum hose to create vacuum leak. If reading is less than .4 volts, sensor is okay, go to step **11)**. If more than .4 volts, replace oxygen sensor and repeat Quick Test.

8) Code 41. Vacuum/air leaks in non-EEC areas can cause a code 41. Check for leaks and correct as required. Turn key off. Place DVOM on 20 volt scale. Disconnect oxygen sensor from harness. Connect DVOM to sensor and engine ground. Remove air cleaner. Using standard wooden pencil, prop air meter inlet door part way open. Start engine and run at 2000 RPM for 2 minutes. If reading is more than .5 volt at end of 2 minutes, go to next step. If less than .5 volt, replace oxygen sensor and repeat Quick Test.

9) Check continuity of oxygen sensor circuit 89, between breakout box pin 49 and engine block ground. Also check circuit 94 between box pin 29 to harness connector Dk. Grn/Pink at sensor. If both are less than 5 ohms, go to next step. If either is more than 5 ohms, repair circuit and repeat Quick Test.

10) Turn key off. Place DVOM on 200,000 scale. Disconnect oxygen sensor at harness. Measure resistance between box pins 29 and 40. If less than 150,000 ohms, correct cause of resistance and repeat Quick Test. If more than 150,000 ohms, oxygen sensor input circuit okay. Disconnect processor connector and inspect for damage. If okay, replace processor and repeat Quick Test.

11) Continuous testing codes 41/42. If code 41 appears it indicates that the fuel system was lean for more than 15 seconds, when it should have been under control of oxygen sensor. If code 42 appears, it indicates that the fuel system was rich for more than 15 seconds, when it should have been under control of oxygen sensor. Before attempting to correct a code 41/42, diagnose all other complaints such as rough idle, missing, etc., first. Areas to check to isolate fuel control problems are as follows:

- Unmetered Air. Vacuum/air leaks in canister purge system, PCV, engine sealing or air leaks between VAF meter and throttle body.
- Oxygen Sensor Fuel Fouled. If fuel fouled spark plugs are observed, make thorough check of ignition system. If oxygen sensor is fuel fouled, run vehicle at high sustained speeds, followed by a few hard accelerations. This will burn off contamination.
- Fuel Pressure. Perform Step H1.
- Ignition System. If always in deafult spark (10 degress), perform Timing Check.
- Improper Fueling. Lead fouled oxygen sensor.
- Throttle Position Sensor. If not moving, connect DVOM to pin 47, circuit 355 and to pin 46, circuit 359. Turn key to run. Observe meter while moving throttle. Reading must increase with throttle opening. If not, replace TP sensor as required. If, at this point drive problem is still present, perform steps H2 through H4 only.

Fuel Injector Resistance Check Circuits

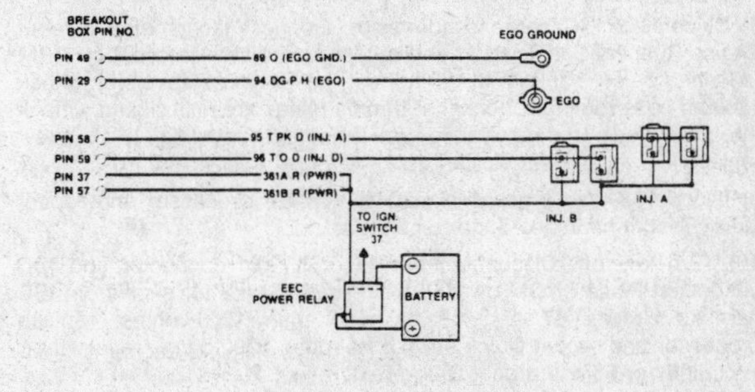

TEST K — 2.3L EFI TURBO

DETONATION/SPARK KNOCK

1) Drive vehicle and verify detonation. Disconnect vehicle harness from knock sensor at engine. Drive vehicle. If knock level has increased, knock sensor circuit is working. If knock level remains same with sensor disconnected, go to next step. If knock increases with sensor disconnected, check base timing, fuel octane, EGR, coolant temperature and boost pressure.

2) Turn key off. Disconnect knock sensor. Connect breakout box. Place DVOM on 200 ohm scale. Measure resistance between sensor connector circuit 310 and box pin 23. Also between circuit 359 and box pin 46. If both less than 5 ohms, repeat knock sensor and repeat step **1)**. If knock level remains same, replace processor. If one or more readings more than 5 ohms, repair circuit and repeat step **1)**.

FORD MOTOR CO. ELECTRONIC ENGINE CONTROL IV (Cont.)

TEST N — 2.3L EFI TURBO

IDLE SPEED CONTROL

NOTE: If engine is running rough or has rough idle, correct before using test. Causes may be ignition system, fuel system or EGR system.

1) Code 12. If engine exhibits other problems in addition to Idle Speed Control (ISC) problem, go to Test X. If not, go to next step.

2) Turn key off. Disconnect ISC harness. Place DVOM on 200,000 ohm scale. Measure ISC solenoid resistance. If 7-13 ohms, go to next step. If not 7-13 ohms, replace ISC solenoid and repeat Quick Test.

3) With same connections as in step **2)**, check for short from either ISC pin to ISC housing. If more than 10,000 ohms, go to next step. If less than 10,000 ohms, replace ISC solenoid and repeat Quick Test.

4) Connect ISC harness. Turn key on. Place DVOM on 20 volt scale. Measure vehicle power at ISC connector circuit 361. If more than 10.5 volts, go to next step. If less than 10.5 volts, repair open in 361 from ISC to EEC power relay. Repeat Quick Test.

Idle Speed Control Circuits

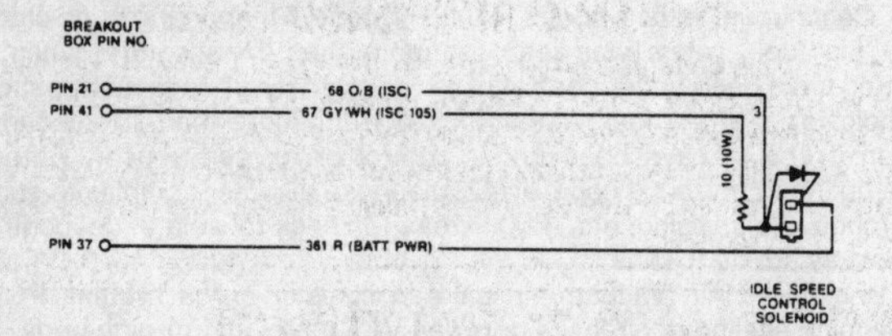

5) Turn key off. Disconnect ISC harness at ISC. Connect breakout box. Place DVOM on 200 ohm scale. Check continuity from circuit 68 to box pin 21. If less than 5 ohms, go to next step. If more than 5 ohms, repair circuit 68 and repeat Quick Test.

6) With vehicle prepared for Quick Test, place DVOM on 20 volt scale. Connect DVOM to rear of ISC harness connector with harness connected. Positive probe goes to Red wire, negative probe to Gray/White wire. Start engine and observe DVOM. If meter varies during Quick Test, replace ISC actuator and repeat Quick Test. If meter does not vary, go to next step.

7) With vehicle prepared for Quick Test, connect DVOM to breakout box pins 21 and 40. Start engine and observe DVOM during Self-Test. If meter varies, repair open in circuits 67 or 68 and repeat Quick Test. If meter does not vary, disconnect processor and inspect pins. If okay, replace processor and repeat Quick Test.

8) Disconnect ISC harness connector. Connect tachometer. Repeat Engine Running Self-Test. At end of test record service codes. If RPM remained below 1500 RPM during test, go to next step. If not, check vacuum hose routing. Check that throttle plates are fully closed. Check throttle linkage and speed control linkage for binding. If all okay, replace ISC and repeat Quick Test.

9) If code 13 was present in step **8)**, replace processor and repeat Quick Test. If no code 13, go to next step.

10) Turn key off. Disconnect processor 60 pin connector and ISC connector. Place DVOM on 2000 ohm scale. Check for short from ISC harness circuits 67 and 68. If more than 1000 ohms, replace processor and repeat Quick Test. If less than 1000 ohms, repair short in ciruit 67 or 68 and repeat Quick Test.

ISC Circuits 67 and 68 Test

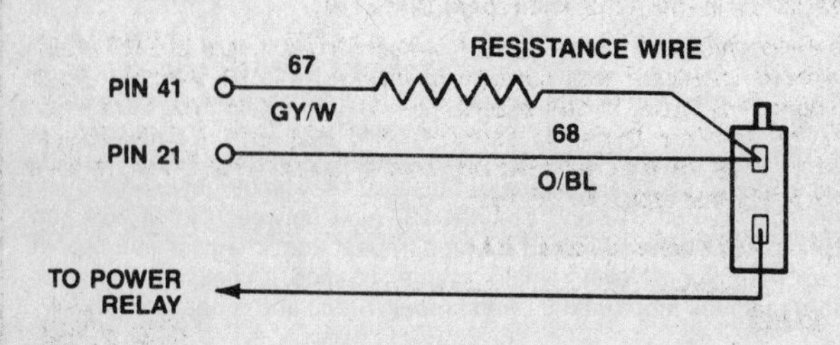

TEST P — 2.3L EFI TURBO

NO CODES IMPROPER CODES

1) Turn key on. Place DVOM on 20 volt scale. Disconnect Throttle Position (TP) sensor and measure voltage between harness connector circuits 351 and 359. If 6 volts or more, to to Test C, step **2)**. If less than 4 volts, to to Test C, step **1)**. If between 4-6 volts, reconnect TP and go to next step.

2) With key on, measure voltage between battery negative post and circuit 359 in self-test connector. If less than .5 volt, go to next step. If more than .5 volt, go to Test B, step **4)**.

3) Connect breakout box. Place DVOM on 200 ohm scale. Check self-test input circuit 100 from self-test pigtail connector to box pin 48. If less than 5 ohms, go to next step. If more than 5 ohms, repair open in circuit 100 and repeat Quick Test.

4) Check Self-Test output circuit 201 between self-test connector and box pin 17. If less than 5 ohms, go to next step. If more than 5 ohms, repair open in circuit 201 and repeat Quick Test.

5) Turn key off. Connect DVOM between oxygen sensor ground point on engine and box pin 49. If more than 5 ohms, repair oxygen sensor ground wire or open circuit bad connection and repeat Quick Test. If less than 5 ohms, disconnect processor and inspect connector. If okay, reconnect and repeat Quick Test. If problem still present, replace processor and repeat Quick Test.

Test Circuits for Test P

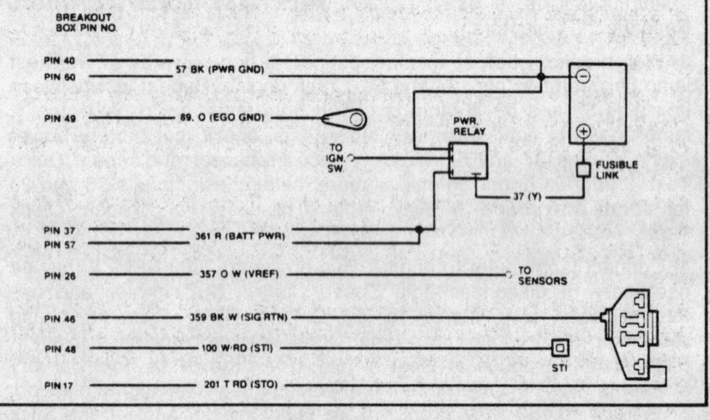

TEST Q — 2.3L EFI TURBO

SPARK ADVANCE OUT OF LIMITS

1) If spark advance was not 27-33° in self-test, place system in self-test. Once self-test is completed, system returns to normal and spark timing will no longer be locked at 30. Connect breakout box. With engine idling, connect jumper between box pin 36 and chassis. If engine stalls, ignition module circuit is okay, go to next step. If engine does not stall, check for open in circuit 324. If okay, problem is in TFI system.

2) With engine off, disconnect ignition module signal at in-line connector. Start engine and check timing. If timing is not 7-13°, reset timing. If timing okay, disconnect processor connector and inspect for damage. Reconnect and repeat Quick Test. If problem still present, replace processor and repeat Quick Test.

Spark Advance Test Circuit

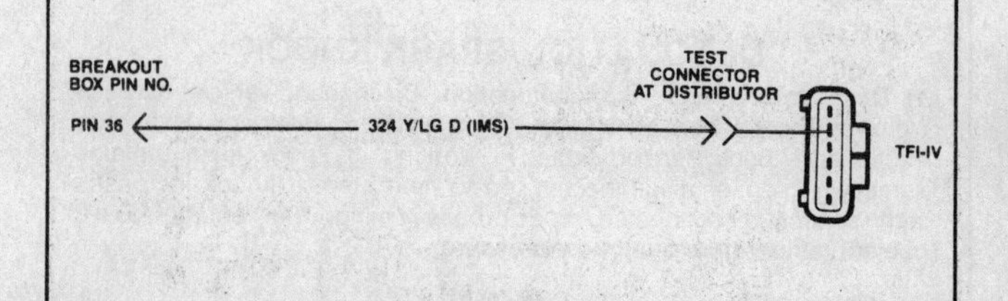

FORD MOTOR CO. ELECTRONIC ENGINE CONTROL IV (Cont.)

TEST R — 2.3L EFI TURBO

BAROMETRIC PRESSURE SENSOR

1) Code 22. Disconnect Barometric Pressure (BP) sensor. Turn key on. Place DVOM on 20 volt scale. Measure voltage between BP harness connector circuit 351 and battery negative post. If 4-6 volts, go to next step. If not 4-6 volts, go to Test C.

2) With BP sensor disconnected, turn key on. Measure voltage between circuit 359 and battery positive post. If 10 volts or more, go to next step. If less than 10 volts, repair open in circuit 359 and repeat Quick Test.

3) Turn key off. Place DVOM on 200,000 ohm scale. Measure resistance between BP circuits 358 and 359 and between circuits 358 and 351. If any reading is less than 10,000 ohms, go to next step. If both are more than 10,000 ohms, substitute a good BP sensor and repeat Quick Test. If code 22 appears, replace processor, using original BP sensor, and repeat Quick Test.

4) Turn key off. Disconnect processor and BP sensor. Connect breakout box, leaving processor disconnected. Place DVOM on 200,-000 ohm scale. Measure resistance between BP circuits 358 and 359, and 358 to 351. If one or more are less than 10,000 ohms, repair short and repeat Quick Test. If both are more than 10,000 ohms, substitute BP sensor and repeat Quick Test. If code 22 appears, replace processor, using original BP sensor and repeat Quick Test.

Barometric Pressure Sensor Test Circuits

TEST S — 2.3L EFI TURBO

FUEL PUMP CIRCUIT

1) Check if fuel pump runs. Cycle key from off to run several times. Pump should operate in Run mode. If so, check fuel system for problems. If not, go to next step.

2) Connect breakout box. Turn key on. Connect negative DVOM lead to good chassis ground. Measure battery voltage at box pins 37 and 57. If 10.5 volts or more, go to next step. If less than 10.5 volts, go to Test B.

3) Turn key on. Connect DVOM negative lead to battery negative post. Probe box pins 40 and 60 with positive lead. If less than 1 volt, ground okay, go to next step. If 1 volt or more on either circuit, repair faulty ground circuit 57.

4) Locate and disconnect fuel pump relay. Place DVOM on 200 ohm scale. Measure resistance of relay coil across two small pins in relay. If 50-100 ohms, go to next step. If not 50-100 ohms, replace fuel pump relay.

5) The following tests check the fuel pump ciruits. Turn key to On position. Connect DVOM negative lead to good ground and make voltage checks as indicated below. If an open fusible link is found, check for short to ground before replacing link.

- Circuit 361, Red at fuel pump relay. If more than 10.5 volts, go to next check. If less than 10.5, check for open in 361. If okay go to Test B.
- Circuit 37, Yellow at fuel pump relay. If more than 10.5 volts, go to next check. If less than 10.5 volts, check for open in 37 between relay and battery positive post.
- Circuit 97 Tan/Lt. Grn at fuel pump relay. If more than 10.5 volts , go to next check. If less than 10.5 volts, replace fuel pump relay.
- Circuit 97 Tan/Lt/ Grn. at fuel pump relay during crank mode. If 1 volt or less, go to next check. If 1 volt or more, check 97 to processor for opens, If okay, replace processor.
- Circuit 787, Pink/Blk at fuel pump relay during crank mode. If more than 10.5 volts, go to next check. If less than 10.5 volts, replace fuel pump relay.
- Circuit 787, Pink/Blk at inertia switch terminals during crank mode. If more than 10.5 volts, go to next check. If less than 10.5 volts at one terminal, replace inertia switch. If less than 10.5 volts at both terminals, check for open in 787 between relay and inertia switch.
- Circuit 787, Pink/Blk at both fuel pumps during crank mode. If more than 10.5 volts, go to next check. If less than 10.5 volts, check for open in 787 between fuel pump and inertia switch.
- Circuit 57. Blk at both fuel pumps during crank mode. If more than 1 volt at either pump, correct faulty ground circuit from fuel pump to chassis ground. If less than 1 volt at both pumps, service fuel pump.

Fuel Pump Test Circuits

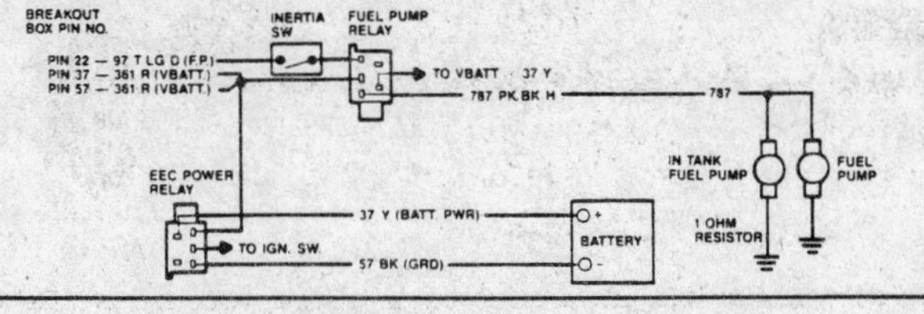

TEST T — 2.3L EFI TURBO

DYNAMIC RESPONSE TEST

Code 77. This code appeared because the system failed to recognize a brief Wide Open Throttle. Repeat Engine Running Self-Test. After Dynamic Response Code is received, perform a Wide Open Throttle. If code 77 is still present, replace processor and repeat Quick Test. If no code 77, Dynamic Response Test is passed. Repair any service codes received as required.

TEST V — 2.3L EFI TURBO

EGR ON-OFF CONTROL

1) Code 34. This code may result from a high volume monoxi-vent system which reduces backpressure. If this is suspected perform the test in a well-ventilated area, with monoxi-vent system disconnected. Install vacuum gauge at EGR valve. Start and idle engine. If gauge reading is less than 1 in. Hg, go to step **3)**. If more than 1 in. Hg, go to next step.

2) Electrically disconnect EGR solenoid. Restart and idle engine. If gauge reading is 1 in. Hg or less, repair short in circuit 362. If okay, replace processor and repeat Quick Test. If reading is more than 1 in. Hg, replace EGR solenoid and repeat Quick Test.

3) Check electrical connection at EGR solenoid. With vacuum gauge connected to EGR valve, perform Engine Running Self-Test. Note if vacuum changes and valve stem moves. If stem moves and vacuum increases to more than 8 in. Hg, EEC system is okay. Problem is in EGR system. If vacuum changes but stem does not move, EEC okay, EGR needs servicing. If vacuum is less than 8 in. Hg, go to next step.

4) With engine at idle, check for manifold vacuum at lower port of EGR solenoid. If vacuum present, reconnect line and go to next step. If no vacuum, repair cause of low vacuum.

5) Turn key off. Disconnect vehicle harness from EGR solenoid. With DVOM on 200 ohm scale, measure resistance of solenoid. If 65-110 ohms, go to next step. If not 65-110 ohms, replace EGR solenoid and repeat Quick Test.

6) Turn key on. Check voltage at EGR harness connector circuit 361. If 10.5 volts or more, go to next step. If less than 10.5 volts, repair cause of low battery voltage at circuit 361.

7) Turn key off. Connect breakout box. Check continuity of circuit 362 between box pin 35 and harness connector at EGR solenoid. If less than 5 ohms, go to next step. If more than 5 ohms, repair cause of resistance in circuit 362 and repeat Quick Test.

8) Place DVOM on 20 volt scale. Connect DVOM to rear of EGR on-off solenoid connector with harness connected to EGR solenoid. Enter Output Test Cycle. DVOM should indicate more than 10.5 volts when DVOM Self-Test Output is activated. and less than 1 when deacti-vated. If so, replace solenoid and repeat Quick Test. If not, replace processor and repeat Quick Test.

EGR On-Off Control Circuit Tests

FORD MOTOR CO. ELECTRONIC ENGINE CONTROL IV (Cont.)

TEST W — 2.3L EFI TURBO

A/C INPUT

1) Code 67. This code indicates that processor is receiving a 12 volt signal and that A/C clutch is energized in Quick Test. Turn Heater-A/C control off. If code 67 is received with controls off, proceed with test. Turn key off. Connect breakout box. Turn key on. Measure voltage between box pins 10 and 40. If 2 volts or less with A/C off, replace processor and repeat Quick Test. If more than 2 volts with A/C off, repair short to power in A/C clutch circuit and repeat Quick Test.

2) Prepare vehicle for Key On-Engine Off Self-Test. Perform test. If code 67 received, system is okay. If no code 67, go to next step.

3) Turn key off. Connect breakout box. Turn key and A/C system On. Measure voltage between box pins 10 and 40. If 2 volts or less with A/C On, repair open in vehicle harness A/C circuit. If more than 2 volts with A/C On, replace processor and repeat Quick Test.

A/C Input Test Circuits

BREAK OUT BOX PIN NO

PIN 40 — 347 BK/Y H — TO A/C CLUTCH

TEST X — 2.3L EFI TURBO

DIAGNOSTICS BY SYMPTOM

1) If engine stalls, stalls in Self-Test, runs rough or misses, check the following: Poor power/ground connections, ignition system problem, engine internal problem or fuel delivery problem (Test H).

2) If engine has detonation or spark knock, go to Test K.

3) If detonation occurs for 3-5 minutes with high idle speeds on restart, go to step **5)**.

4) If a lack of fast idle assist with A/C On occurs, go to Test W.

5) Check that system is not in self-test all the time. Turn key off. Connect Analog VOM to self-test connector. DO NOT insert jumper for self-test. Turn key on and observe meter. If any pulsing codes are displayed, go to next step. If no pulsing codes, go to Test N.

6) Connect breakout box, leaving processor disconnected. Place DVOM on 200,000 ohm scale. Measure resistance between box pin 17 and chassis ground. If more than 10,000 ohms, disconnect processor and check for damage. If fault still present, replace processor and repeat Quick Test. If less than 10,000 ohms, repair harness short to ground in circuit 100 and repeat Quick Test. Reconnect system after test

High Idle Speed Test Circuits

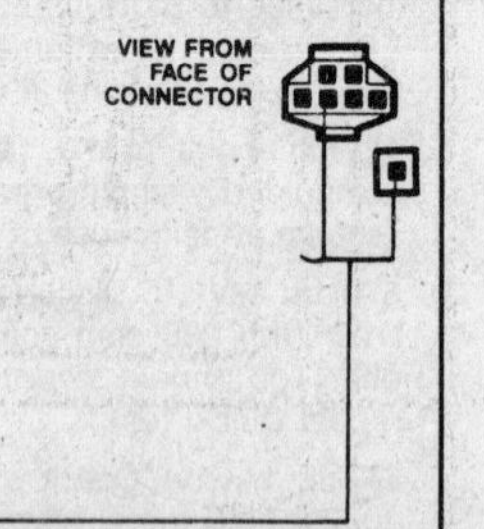

BREAKOUT BOX PIN NO.

PIN 17 ← 100 W RD (STI)

TEST Y — 2.3L EFI TURBO

ERRATIC IGNITION

Code 14. This code indicates 2 successive mistimed distributor output pulses were input to processor, resulting in possible engine miss or stall. Check vehicle for loose wires and connections, arcing secondary ignition components (coil, cap, wires, etc.) or an on-board 2-way radio. Make sure radio antenna and power leads are routed properly. If any of the above are present, repair as necessary and repeat Quick Test. If none are present, code 14 may be caused by external electromagnetic interference. Repeat Quick Test.

FORD MOTOR CO. ELECTRONIC ENGINE CONTROL IV (Cont.)

Fig. 8: 2.3L EFI Turbo EEC-IV System Wiring Diagram

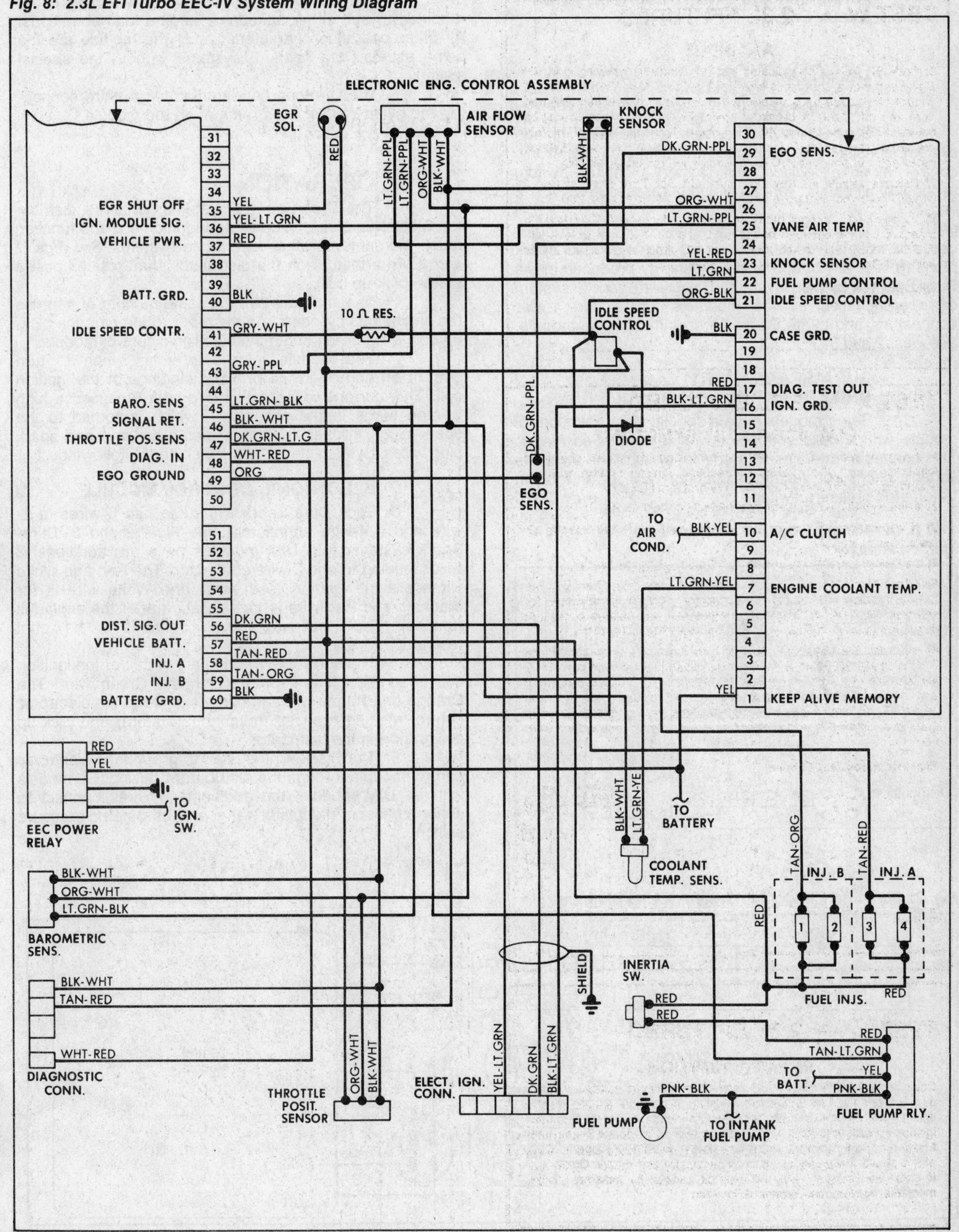

MOTORCRAFT DURA-SPARK II IGNITION

Ford Motor Co. Except 1.6L, 2.3L Turbo & 5.0L EFI

DESCRIPTION

DURA-SPARK II

Dura-Spark II is basically a solid-state ignition system, consisting of a breakerless distributor, electronic control module, ignition coil, battery, ignition switch, secondary wires and various wiring harnesses. *See Figs. 2 and 4.*

Most models use a large rotor, a distributor cap and adapter, secondary wires, and wide gap spark plugs to take advantage of higher energy produced in the Dura-Spark II ignition system. The Dura-Spark II system can be identified by the module's 2-wire and 4-wire connectors, and by its Blue wire grommet on the module. *See Figs. 2 and 3.*

DURA-SPARK II WITH UNIVERSAL IGNITION MODULE (UIM)

Some models have a special electronic control module with a third connector with 3 wires. *See Fig. 1.* This connector attaches to a special switch. The switch is either a distributor vacuum modulator valve or an ignition barometric pressure switch.

Fig. 1: Dura-Spark II System with Universal Ignition Module

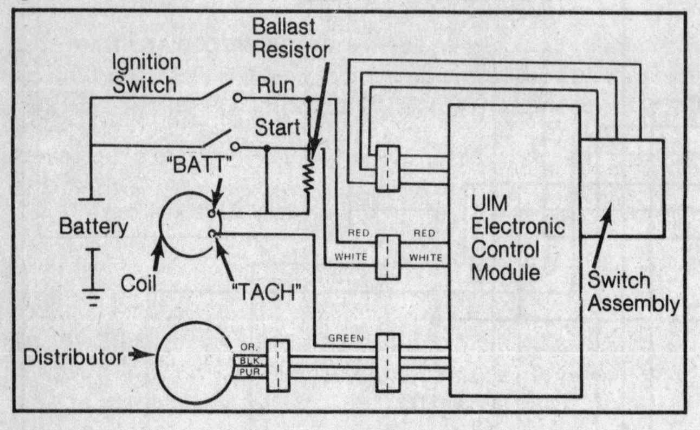

This switch allows base engine timing to be modified to suit either altitude or engine load conditions. All other operating characteristics of the module are the same as for Dura-Spark II systems without the special switch.

The UIM can be identified by its third connector and by its Yellow wire grommet on the module.

OPERATION

The Dura-Spark II systems contain a distributor, electronic control module and ignition coil and function much the same as other solid state systems. *See Figs. 1 and 2.* An armature on the distributor shaft rotates past a stator (pick-up coil).

The armature has the same number of teeth as the engine has cylinders. As the teeth rotate past the pick-up coil, a signal is sent to the electronic control module.

The module then determines when to turn current off and on in the primary windings of the ignition coil. This current collapse in the primary, causes a high voltage surge in the secondary, which is routed to the spark plugs through the rotor, distributor cap and spark plug wires. System components include the following:

ELECTRONIC CONTROL MODULE

Each Dura-Spark II module has 6 wires (a 2-wire and a 4-wire connector). *See Figs. 2 and 3.* Dura-Spark systems with UIM modules have an additional 3 wires leading to one 3-wire connector. The Red and White wires are the ignition feed wires (the White wire is for cranking and Red wire is for operation after the engine is running). The Red wire circuit contains a 1.1 ohm resistance wire.

The current to the primary circuit of the ignition coil is turned off and on through the Green wire. The Orange and Purple wires transmit signals to the electronic control module from the reluctor (armature) and pick-up coil (stator) in the distributor.

The Black wire is used to ground the electronic control module through the distributor housing. On models with an UIM module, the additional 3 wires connect to either a vacuum modulator valve or a barometric pressure switch.

Fig. 2: Dura-Spark II Ignition System Wiring Diagram

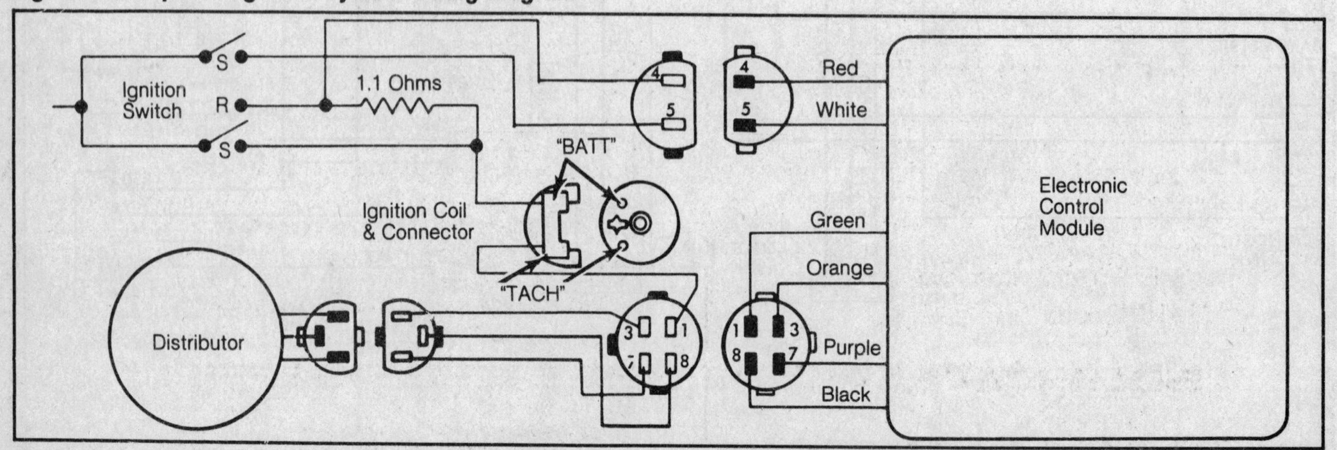

1983 Exhaust Emission Systems

MOTORCRAFT DURA-SPARK II IGNITION (Cont.)

DISTRIBUTOR

A reluctor, containing the same number of teeth as the engine has cylinders, turns with the distributor shaft. The pick-up coil contains a permanent magnet, causing a magnetic field around the pick-up coil.

As the teeth of the reluctor pass the pick-up coil the magnetic field builds and collapses, causing a signal to be sent to the electronic control module. In turn, the control module turns the ignition coil primary off and on, causing a high voltage surge in the secondary.

Fig. 3: Control Module and Distributor Connectors for Dura-Spark II Ignition Systems

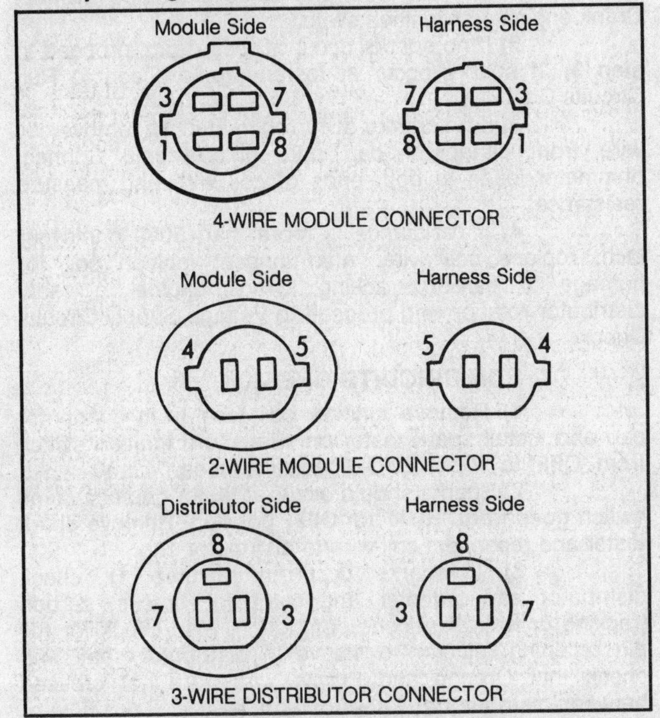

Dura-Spark II systems have an adapter between the distributor housing and cap. *See Fig. 4.* Distributor caps are larger than for conventional distributors and have male terminals. Distributors have both centrifugal and vacuum advance mechanisms.

On single diaphragm vacuum units, increased vacuum causes the movable pick-up coil to pivot on the lower plate assembly, advancing spark timing. On dual diaphragm units, the outer (primary) diaphragm operates from carburetor vacuum to provide timing advance during normal idle off driving conditions. It is connected to the pick-up coil assembly.

The inner (secondary) diaphragm operates from intake manifold vacuum and acts to retard ignition timing. The inner diaphragm is connected to the outer diaphragm by means of sliding linkage. Stronger intake manifold vacuum can override carburetor vacuum during closed throttle operation, retarding spark timing.

IGNITION COIL

Coils are oil filled and are energized whenever the ignition switch is in the "ON" or "START" position. They contain a positive "BATT" terminal and a negative "TACH" (sometimes called "DEC") terminal and a single secondary terminal. A special connector attaches the Green wire from the control module to the negative terminal ("TACH") and the wire from the ignition switch to the positive terminal ("BATT").

NOTE: **"DEC" refers to Distributor Electronic Control. This terminal is also referred to as the "Tach Test" terminal.**

RESISTANCE WIRE

The special ignition resistance wire in the Red wire circuit must be of specified length and diameter to reduce operating voltage. Under no circumstances should it be replaced by any other wire other than correct service resistance wire. When new wire is installed, old wire should be completely removed from system. Resistance value of wire is 1.1 ohms.

SYSTEM PROTECTION

Dura-Spark systems are protected against electrical currents produced or used by any other vehicle component during normal operation. However, damage to

Fig. 4: Schematic of Dura-Spark II Ignition System

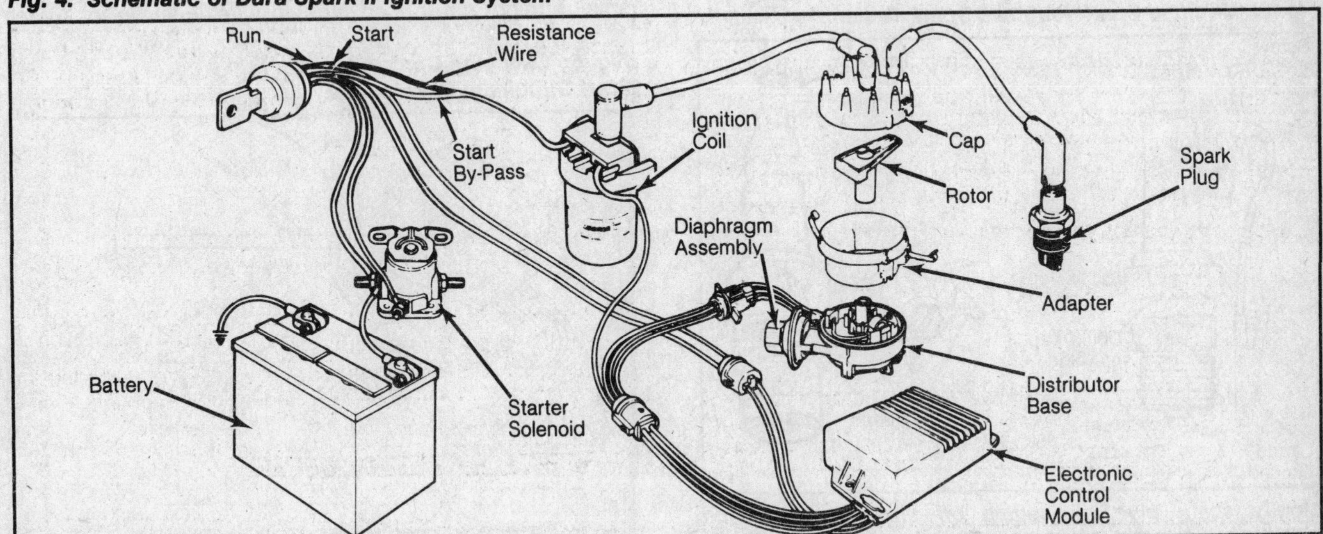

MOTORCRAFT DURA-SPARK II IGNITION (Cont.)

the ignition system can occur if proper testing procedures are not followed.

DURA-SPARK II SYSTEM PRECAUTIONS

Since the electronic control module and ignition coil are "ON" whenever the ignition switch is in the "ON" or "START" position, the system will generate a spark whenever the ignition switch is turned "OFF". This feature may be used as a diagnostic tool to check for continuity of circuit, coil and ignition switch.

As spark may occur if distributor cap is removed with switch "ON", keep switch "OFF" during underhood operations, unless you plan to start the engine or perform a test requiring the switch to be "ON". This will prevent accidental engine rotation during service or test procedures.

Silicone dielectric grease must be applied to all insulating areas at distributor, coil and spark plug boots.

A 3/4" clearance must be maintained at distributor cap mounting edge, spark plug wire terminals, and coil tower to prevent high voltage arc to ground.

To help prevent radio frequency interference, coat the entire brass rotor tip with silicone dielectric grease to a thickness of 1/32". Do not remove this grease, even if discolored, as the grease will maintain its insulating properties. The 3.3L engine uses a multipoint rotor which eliminates the need for dielectric grease on the rotor.

When removing distributor cap and adapter, do not remove the cap and adapter as an assembly. Always remove the distributor cap, the rotor, and then the adapter.

ADJUSTMENTS

No adjustments are to be made to the ignition system except initial engine timing and spark plug gap.

TESTING

NOTE: All wire colors shown refer to colors of electronic control module wires. When making tests, wires must be traced back to control module for proper color identification.

Fig. 5: Modified Spark Plug and Spark Tester

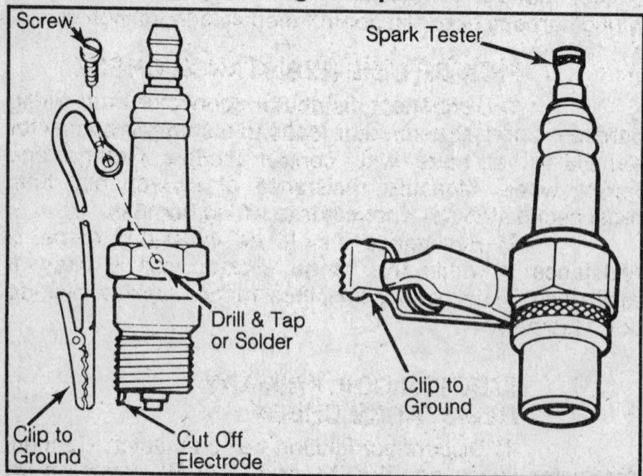

Modify spark plug by cutting off side electrode and installing spring clip for grounding plug housing.

Also, when a test is completed and a problem is found, make the necessary repair and repeat the failed test to be sure that problem has been corrected.

TEST SPARK PLUG

Use either a spark tester tool or modify a spark plug (cut off side electrode and install spring clip for grounding plug housing) for use in testing ignition system. *See Fig. 5.*

START CIRCUIT CHECK

1) Connect spark tester or modified spark plug between ignition coil wire and a good engine ground. Crank engine with ignition switch.

2) If no sparks occur at tester gap, proceed to step **3)**. If sparks occur at tester gap, proceed to Run Circuits Check.

3) If no sparks occurred in step **1)**, remove coil wire from distributor cap and ignition coil. Connect ohmmeter leads to both ends of coil wire and measure resistance.

4) If resistance is more than 5000 ohms per inch, replace coil wire. Also inspect ignition coil for damage or carbon tracking. Crank engine to verify distributor rotation and proceed to Voltage Supply Circuits Check.

RUN CIRCUITS CHECK

1) Remove ignition coil wire from distributor cap and install spark tester on wire. Turn ignition switch from "OFF" to "RUN" to "OFF" several times.

2) Sparks should occur at tester gap each time switch goes from "RUN" to "OFF" position. Remove spark tester and reconnect coil wire to distributor cap.

3) If sparks occurred in step **1)**, check distributor cap, adapter and rotor for cracks, carbon tracking or lack of silicone compound. Also check for roll pin retaining reluctor to sleeve in distributor shaft and check that Orange and Purple wires are not crossed between distributor and control module.

4) If no sparks occurred in step **1)**, proceed to Control Module Voltage Check.

CONTROL MODULE VOLTAGE CHECK

1) With ignition switch "OFF", carefully insert small straight pin in Red module wire. *See Fig. 6.* Attach

Fig. 6: Checking Control Module Run & Start Circuits with Voltmeter

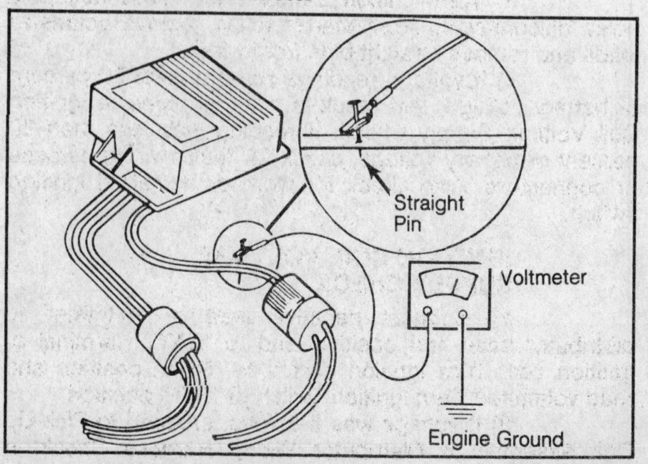

MOTORCRAFT DURA-SPARK II IGNITION (Cont.)

negative voltmeter lead to distributor base and positive lead to straight pin. Measure battery voltage.

CAUTION: Do not allow straight pin to contact an electrical ground.

2) Measure voltage at straight pin in Red wire but with ignition switch in "RUN" position. After reading voltmeter, turn ignition switch "OFF" and remove straight pin.

3) Voltmeter should read at least 90 percent of battery voltage. If so, proceed to Resistance Wire Check. If reading was less than 90 percent of battery voltage, check wiring harness between control module and ignition switch. Also check for a worn or damaged ignition switch.

RESISTANCE WIRE CHECK

1) Disconnect 2-wire control module connector and remove coil connector from coil. Connect ohmmeter leads to "BATT" terminal of coil connector and to harness connector terminal mating with Red control module wire. Read ohmmeter, then reconnect all connectors.

2) If resistance is .8-1.6 ohms, problem is either intermittent or not in ignition system. If resistance was less than .8 or more than 1.6 ohms, replace resistance wire.

VOLTAGE SUPPLY CIRCUITS CHECK

1) If starter relay has an "I" terminal, disconnect cable between relay and starter motor at starter relay. If starter relay does not have an "I" terminal, disconnect wire to "S" terminal of starter relay. Insert small straight pins in Red and White control module wires.

CAUTION: Do not allow straight pins to contact an electrical ground.

2) Measure battery voltage, connect negative voltmeter lead to distributor base, and note voltmeter reading in each of the following situations:

- Positive voltmeter lead connected to pin in Red wire with ignition switch in "RUN" position.
- Positive voltmeter lead connected to pin in White wire with ignition switch in "START" position.
- Positive voltmeter lead connected to "BATT" terminal of ignition coil with ignition switch in "START" position.

3) Turn ignition switch "OFF", reconnect any wires disconnected from starter relay, remove voltmeter leads and remove straight pins from wires.

4) If voltage readings were at least 90 percent of battery voltage, test result is okay, proceed to Ignition Coil Voltage Supply Check. If reading was less than 90 percent of battery voltage, check for faulty wiring harness or connectors. Also check for worn or damaged ignition switch.

IGNITION COIL VOLTAGE SUPPLY CHECK

1) Connect negative lead of voltmeter to distributor base and positive lead to "BATT" terminal of ignition coil. Turn ignition switch to "RUN" position and read voltmeter. Turn ignition switch to "OFF" position.

2) If voltage was 6-8 volts, proceed to Pick-Up Coil Assembly & Distributor Wiring Harness Check. If voltage was less than 6 volts or more than 8 volts, proceed to Ignition Coil Primary Resistance Check.

PICK-UP COIL ASSEMBLY & DISTRIBUTOR WIRING HARNESS CHECK

1) Disconnect control module 4-wire connector and inspect for dirt, corrosion or damage. Connect ohmmeter leads to connector terminals that mate with Orange and Purple control module wires.

2) Resistance should be 400-1300 ohms. If so, proceed to Control Module to Distributor Wiring Harness Check. If resistance is not to specifications, proceed to Pick-Up Coil Resistance Check.

CONTROL MODULE TO DISTRIBUTOR WIRING HARNESS CHECK

1) Disconnect 4-wire control module connector. Connect one lead of ohmmeter to distributor base. Alternately, connect the other ohmmeter lead to wiring harness connector terminals that mate with Orange and Purple wires of control module connector.

2) If resistance is greater than 70,000 ohms, test result is okay, proceed to Ignition Coil Secondary Resistance Check. If resistance was less than 70,000 ohms, check wiring harness between control module connector and distributor, including distributor grommet.

IGNITION COIL SECONDARY RESISTANCE CHECK

1) Disconnect ignition coil wire and ignition coil connector from coil. Connect ohmmeter leads to ignition coil "BATT" terminal and to high voltage terminal. Measure resistance and reconnect wire and connector.

2) If resistance is 7,700-10,500 ohms, coil is okay, proceed to Module-to-Coil Wire Check. If resistance is less than 7,700 or greater than 10,500 ohms, replace ignition coil.

MODULE-TO-COIL WIRE CHECK

1) Disconnect control module 4-wire connector and ignition coil connector. Connect one ohmmeter lead to distributor base and the other to "TACH" terminal of ignition coil connector. Measure resistance and reconnect all connectors.

2) If resistance is greater than 1 ohm, replace control module. If resistance is 1 ohm or less, inspect wiring harness between control module and ignition coil.

PICK-UP COIL RESISTANCE CHECK

1) Disconnect distributor connector from wiring harness. Connect ohmmeter leads to distributor connector terminals that mate with control module Orange and Purple wires. Measure resistance of pick-up coil then reconnect distributor connector to wiring harness.

2) Resistance should be 400-1,000 ohms. If resistance is within this range, pick-up coil is okay. If resistance is not within specified range, replace pick-up coil assembly.

IGNITION COIL PRIMARY RESISTANCE CHECK

1) Disconnect ignition coil connector. Connect ohmmeter leads to "BATT" and "TACH" terminals of ignition coil. Measure resistance and reconnect ignition coil connector.

MOTORCRAFT DURA-SPARK II IGNITION (Cont.)

2) If resistance is .8-1.6 ohms, coil is okay, proceed to Primary Circuit Continuity Check. If resistance is less than .8 or greater than 1.6 ohms, replace ignition coil.

PRIMARY CIRCUIT CONTINUITY CHECK

1) Insert a small straight pin in control module Green wire. Connect negative voltmeter lead to distributor base and positive lead to pin in Green wire. With ignition switch in "RUN" position, measure voltage. Turn ignition switch "OFF" and remove straight pin from Green wire.

2) If voltage reading was greater than 1.5 volts, proceed to Ground Circuit Continuity Check. If voltage reading was 1.5 volts or less, check wire between control module and ignition coil.

GROUND CIRCUIT CONTINUITY CHECK

1) Insert a small straight pin in control module Black wire. Connect negative voltmeter lead to distributor base and positive lead to straight pin in Black wire. Measure resistance and remove straight pin from wire.

2) If voltage reading was greater than .5 volt, proceed to Distributor Ground Circuit Continuity Check. If voltage was .5 volt or less, replace control module.

DISTRIBUTOR GROUND CIRCUIT CONTINUITY CHECK

1) Disconnect distributor connector from wiring harness. Connect ohmmeter leads to distributor base and to Black wire terminal in distributor connector. Measure resistance, then reconnect distributor connector to wiring harness.

2) If resistance was less than 1 ohm, circuit is okay. If resistance was greater than 1 ohm, check ground screw in distributor housing.

SPARK PLUG WIRE RESISTANCE CHECK

1) Remove distributor cap and disconnect spark plug end of suspected wire or wires. Connect ohmmeter leads to spark plug terminal and terminal inside distributor cap (each end of wire).

CAUTION: Never puncture a spark plug wire when measuring resistance.

2) If resistance is less than 5,000 ohms per inch, visually inspect wires for damage and remove spark plug for inspection and/or replacement. If resistance is greater than 5,000 ohms per inch, disconnect suspected wire from distributor cap and connect leads to each end of wire.

3) If resistance is now less than 5,000 ohms per inch, inspect distributor cap and spark plug wire terminals for damage. Repair as necessary. If resistance is still greater than 5,000 ohms per inch, replace wire(s).

OVERHAUL

DISASSEMBLY

1) Remove distributor cap, adapter and rotor. Disconnect distributor wiring harness plug. Using a small gear puller or two screwdrivers, carefully pry armature from sleeve and plate assembly. Remove roll pin.

Fig. 7: Components of Dura-Spark II Distributor

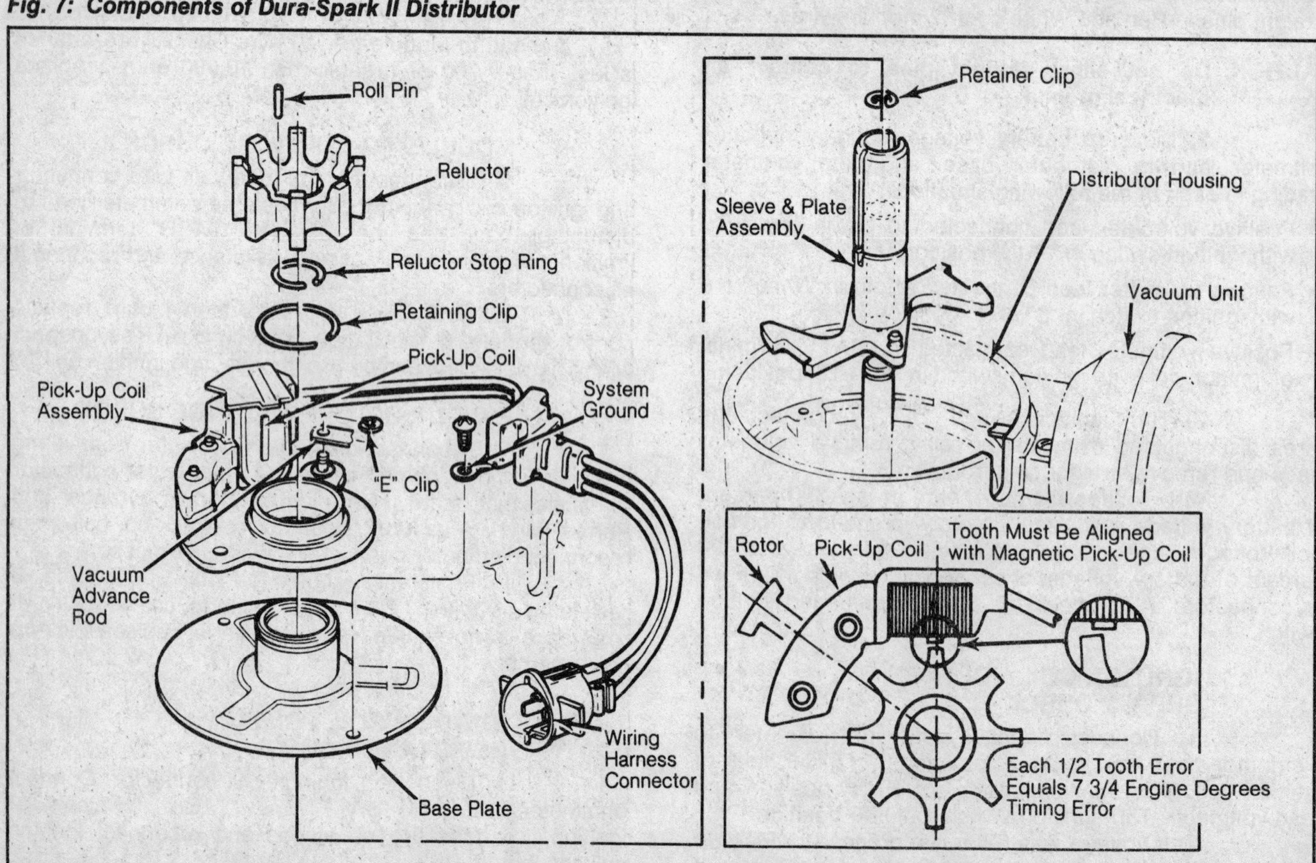

MOTORCRAFT DURA-SPARK II IGNITION (Cont.)

CAUTION: Do not pinch stator wires when removing armature.

2) On V8 engines, remove large wire retaining clip from base plate annular groove. Remove ground screw base and pull up to remove rubber grommet from base.

3) On all models, remove "E" clip securing diaphragm rod advance link to stator assembly. Lift diaphragm rod off post on stator assembly, and move it out against housing.

4) Remove 2 diaphragm attaching screws and remove diaphragm from housing. Remove screw retaining ground strap to housing. On V8 engines, remove stator assembly.

5) On 4-cylinder and 6-cylinder models, remove "E" clip, flat washer and wave washer securing stator assembly to lower plate. Remove stator assembly ground screw and lift assembly from distributor. Remove base plate from housing.

REASSEMBLY

Reverse disassembly procedure, but use new roll pin when installing armature.

1983 Exhaust Emission Systems

MOTORCRAFT DURA-SPARK III IGNITION (EEC)

Ford Motor Co. 5.0L V8 With EFI

DESCRIPTION

The ignition portion of the EEC III system is referred to as Dura-Spark III, a solid state system which provides power switching of the ignition coil. Dura-Spark III input signals are controlled by the EEC system.

Fig. 1: Exploded View of Dura-Spark III Distributor

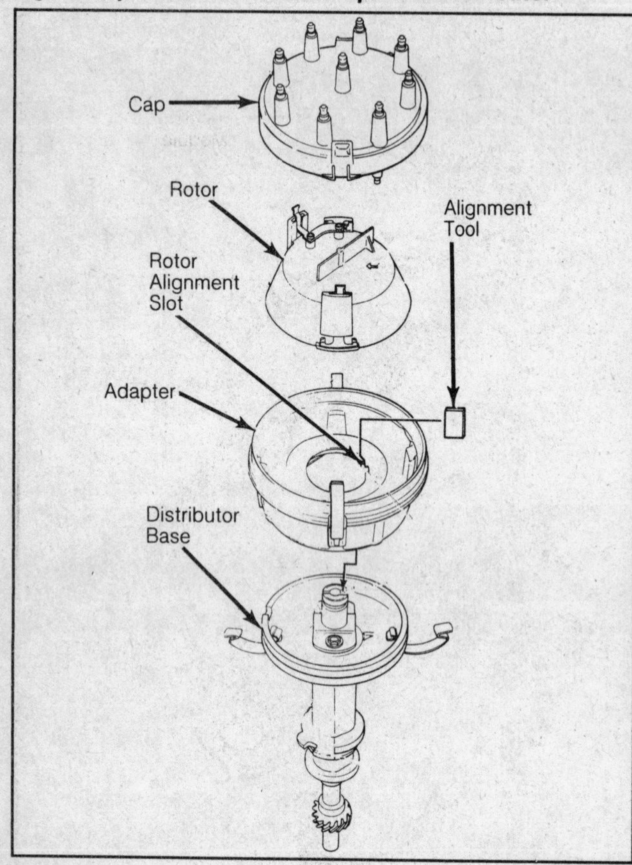

The EEC distributor, unlike Dura-Spark II, has no centrifugal or vacuum advance. Also, it has no armature (reluctor) or stator (pick-up coil). *See Fig. 1.* Secondary wires and spark plugs are the same, however, as used in Dura-Spark II systems.

Although control modules appear similar, they must not be interchanged. Dura-Spark III control modules have no Purple wire and can also be identified by a Brown grommet (Dura-Spark II modules have a Blue grommet).

Ignition timing is determined by the crankshaft position (CP) sensor and 6 or 7 other engine sensors. These sensors feed information to the EEC III system Electronic Control Assembly (ECA) through a special 32-pin connector. For further information on these sensors and the electronic control assembly, see *Ford Motor Co. Electronic Engine Control III article in COMPUTERIZED ENGINE CONTROLS Section.*

Unlike conventional distributors that are restricted to approximately 20° advance, the EEC system permits up to 50° distributor advance. Both distributor cap and rotor have upper and lower electrode levels. As the rotor turns, one of the high voltage electrode pick-up arms is aligned with one arm of the distributor cap center electrode plate. This allows high voltage to pass from the center plate arms through the rotor, distributor cap, and spark plug wires to the appropriate spark plug.

OPERATION

With the ignition switch turned on, the primary circuit is on and the ignition coil is energized. *See Fig. 2.* The EEC system (not the distributor as in Dura-Spark II systems) provides a signal telling the ignition module to turn off the coil primary circuit.

The length of time the primary circuit is turned on or off is controlled by the EEC Electronic Control Assembly (ECA). *See Fig. 3.* When the current is on, it flows from the battery through the ignition switch, primary windings of ignition coil, and ignition module circuits to ground.

When current is turned off, the magnetic field which is built up in the ignition coil collapses, inducing

Fig. 2: Wiring Schematic of Dura-Spark III Ignition System

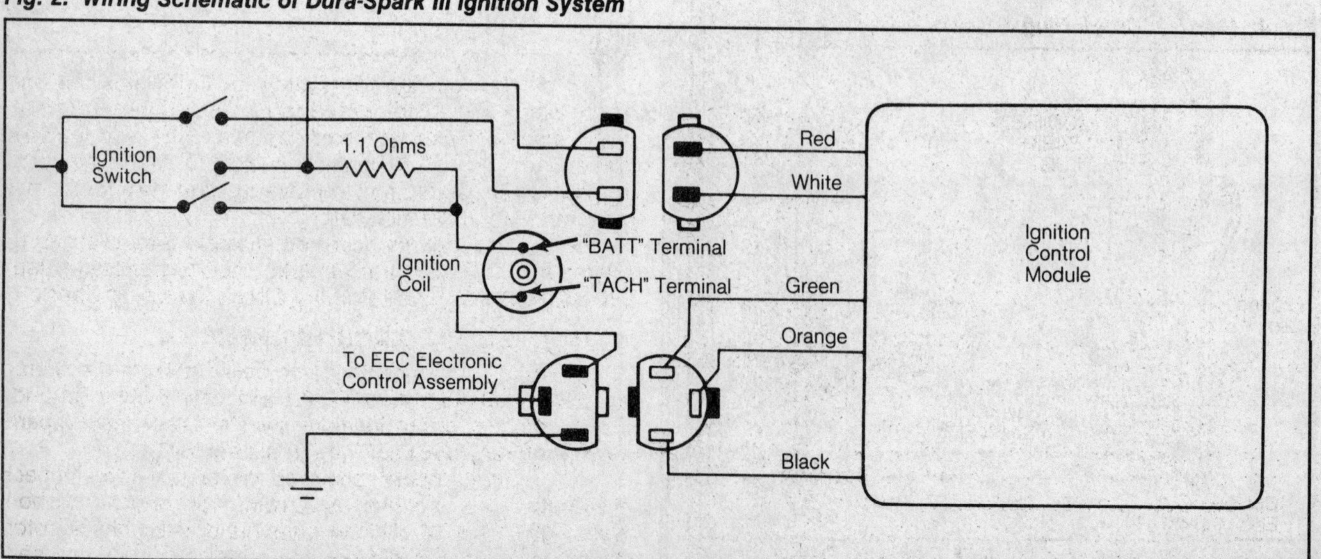

MOTORCRAFT DURA-SPARK III IGNITION (EEC) (Cont.)

high voltage to the secondary windings of the coil. This high voltage, produced each time the magnetic field builds and collapses, is transmitted by the coil to the distributor cap, rotor and to individual spark plugs.

Fig. 3: EEC III Electronic Control Assembly

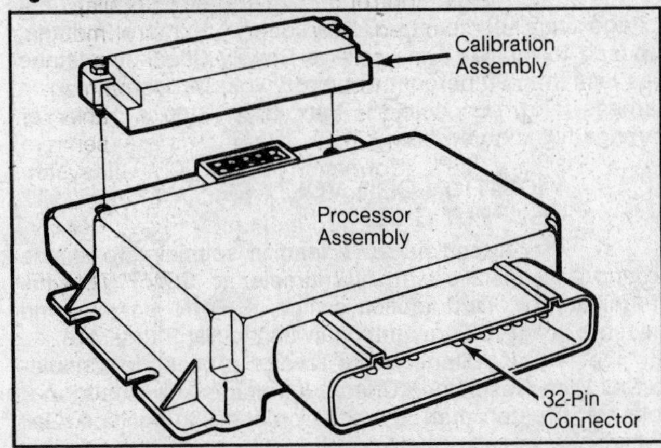

Located on left front inner fender well.

TESTING

NOTE: **Before testing, inspect the engine compartment to ensure all vacuum hoses and spark plug wires are properly routed and connected. Check all wiring harnesses and connectors for damage. Be sure battery is fully charged. All wire colors referred to are colors of ignition module wires. When test requires inspection of wiring harness, both visual and continuity checks should be performed. Wiggle the wires while measuring.**

SPARK TESTER

Use either a spark tester tool or modify a spark plug (cut off side terminal and install spring clip for grounding plug housing) for use in testing ignition system. *See Fig. 4*.

Fig. 4: Modified Spark Plug & Spark Tester

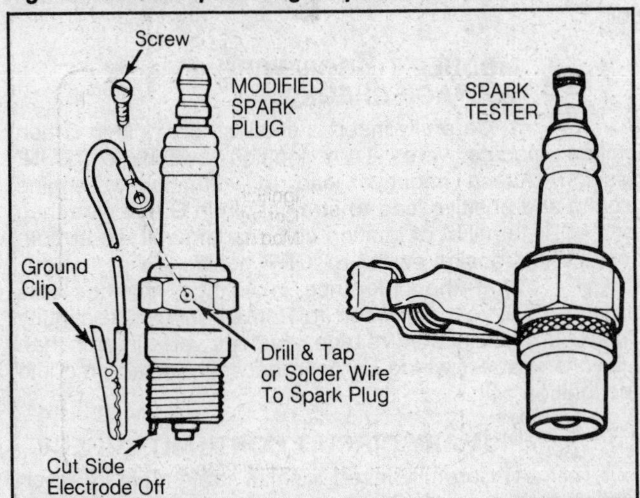

Spark plug modified by cutting off side terminal and installing spring clip.

RUN CIRCUITS CHECK

1) Disconnect ignition module 3-wire connector and install ignition diagnostic test adapter (T79P-12127-A or equivalent) as shown in *Fig. 5*. Disconnect ignition coil wire from distributor and connect spark tester to wire and engine ground.

Fig. 5: Ignition Diagnostic Test Adapter and Spark Tester Hook-Up for Run Circuits Checks

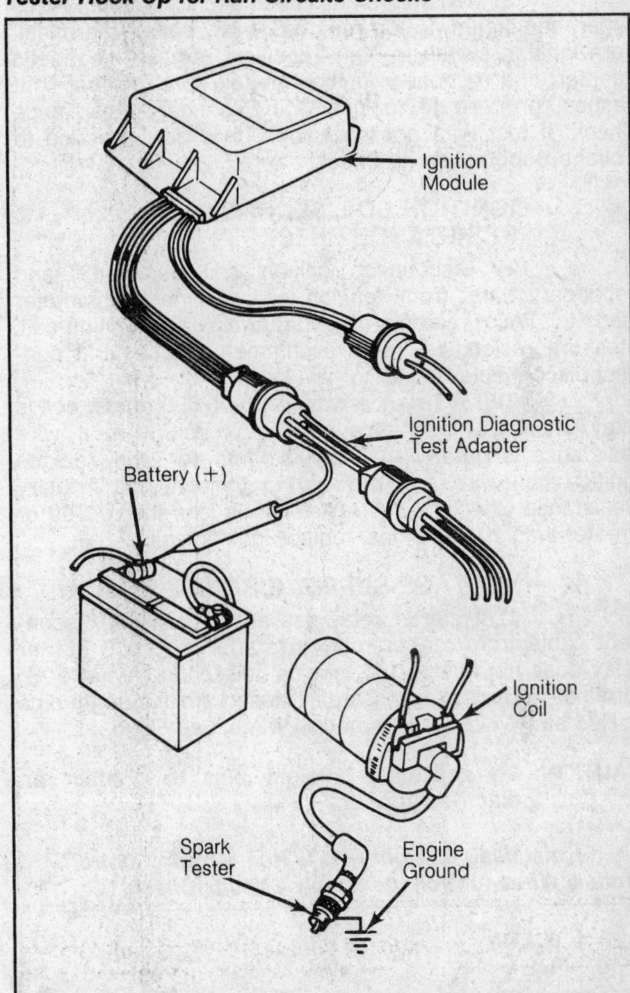

2) Turn ignition switch to "RUN" position and touch diagnostic adapter lead to positive battery terminal. Sparks should occur at tester gap each time lead touches battery terminal. Turn ignition switch to "OFF" position, remove spark tester and remove ignition diagnostic test adapter. Reconnect all wires.

3) If sparks occurred at tester gap, proceed to Start Circuits Check. If no sparks occurred at tester gap, proceed to Ignition Coil Primary Circuit Switching Check.

START CIRCUITS CHECK

1) Disconnect ignition coil wire from distributor cap and attach spark tester to wire and engine ground. Crank engine using ignition switch. Disconnect spark tester and reconnect coil wire to distributor.

2) If spark occurred at tester gap, inspect distributor cap, adapter and rotor for cracks, carbon tracking or lack of silicone compound. Also check rotor alignment. If sparks did not occur at tester gap, proceed to Voltage Supply Circuits Check.

MOTORCRAFT DURA-SPARK III IGNITION (EEC) (Cont.)

IGNITION COIL PRIMARY CIRCUIT SWITCHING CHECK

1) Disconnect ignition module 3-wire connector and install diagnostic adapter (T79P-12127-A or equivalent). Connect a test light between "TACH" terminal of ignition coil and on engine ground. With engine switch in "RUN" position, touch diagnostic adapter test lead to positive battery terminal.

2) Test light should flash each time test lead is either connected to or removed from battery terminal. Turn ignition switch to "OFF" position, remove diagnostic adapter, and reconnect ignition module wires. If test light flashes, proceed to Ignition Coil Secondary Resistance Check. If test light does not flash or is dim, proceed to Voltage Supply Circuits Check.

IGNITION COIL SECONDARY RESISTANCE CHECK

1) Disconnect ignition coil connector and secondary wire from ignition coil. Connect ohmmeter leads to "TACH" and high voltage terminals of ignition coil. Measure resistance, remove ohmmeter leads, and connect disconnected wires.

2) If resistance was 7,700-10,500 ohms, coil is okay, measure resistance of ignition coil wire. If wire resistance is greater than 5,000 ohms per inch, replace ignition coil wire and proceed to Ignition Coil Primary Resistance Check. If coil resistance is less than 7,700 or greater than 10,500 ohms, replace ignition coil.

VOLTAGE SUPPLY CIRCUITS CHECK

1) If starter relay has an "I" terminal, disconnect cable from starter relay to starter motor. If starter relay does not have an "I" terminal, disconnect wire to "S" terminal of starter relay. Carefully insert small straight pins in Red and White ignition module wires. *See Fig. 6.*

CAUTION: Do not allow straight pins to contact an electrical ground.

Fig. 6: Installing Straight Pins in Red & White Control Module Wires for Voltage Supply Circuits Check

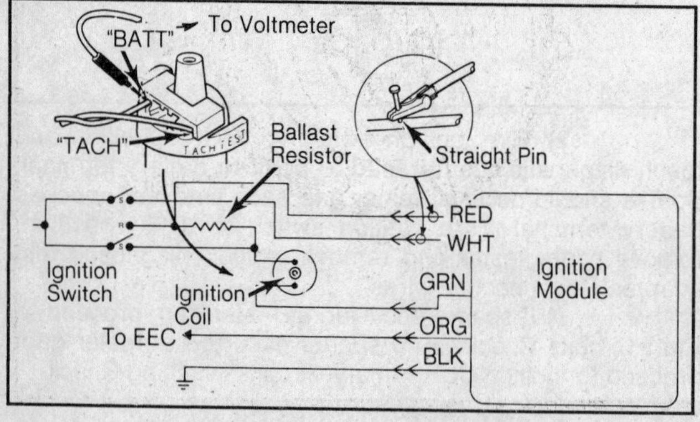

2) Measure battery voltage at battery. Measure voltage in each of the following situations at points indicated:

- With ignition switch in "RUN" position, connect negative lead of voltmeter to an engine ground and positive lead of voltmeter to straight pin in Red wire.
- With ignition switch in "START" position, connect negative lead of voltmeter to an engine ground and positive lead of voltmeter to straight pin in White wire.
- With ignition switch in "START" position, connect negative lead of voltmeter to an engine ground and positive lead of voltmeter to ignition coil "BATT" terminal.

3) Turn ignition switch "OFF", remove ohmmeter and straight pins, and reconnect starter relay cables. If voltage was at least 90 percent of battery voltage, proceed to Ignition Coil Voltage Supply Check. If voltage was less than 90 percent of battery voltage, inspect wiring harness and connectors. Also check for a worn or damaged ignition switch.

IGNITION COIL VOLTAGE SUPPLY CHECK

1) Attach negative lead of voltmeter to engine ground and positive lead of voltmeter to "BATT" terminal of ignition coil. Turn ignition switch to "RUN" position and measure voltage. Turn ignition switch to "OFF" position.

2) If voltage was 6-8 volts, proceed to Module-to-Coil Wire Resistance Check. If voltage was less than 6 volts or greater than 8 volts, proceed to Ignition Coil Primary Resistance Check.

MODULE-TO-COIL WIRE RESISTANCE CHECK

1) Disconnect ignition coil connector from ignition coil and disconnect ignition module 3-wire connector. Connect ohmmeter leads to engine ground and "TACH" terminal of ignition coil connector. Measure resistance. Remove ohmmeter leads and reconnect ignition module and coil connectors.

2) If resistance was greater than 1 ohm, replace ignition module. If resistance was 1 ohm or less, inspect wiring harness between ignition module and ignition coil.

IGNITION COIL PRIMARY RESISTANCE CHECK

1) Disconnect ignition coil connector. Connect ohmmeter leads to "BATT" and "TACH" terminals of ignition coil. Measure resistance, remove ohmmeter leads, and reconnect ignition coil connector.

2) If resistance was 0.8-1.6 ohms, proceed to Module-to-Coil Wire Voltage Check. If resistance was less than 0.8 ohms or greater than 1.6 ohms replace ignition coil.

MODULE-TO-COIL WIRE VOLTAGE CHECK

1) Carefully insert a small straight pin in Green ignition module wire. Turn ignition switch to "RUN" position. Attach negative lead of voltmeter to engine ground and positive lead to straight pin in Green wire then to "TACH" terminal of ignition coil, reading voltage at both points. Turn ignition switch to "OFF" position.

2) If the difference in voltage readings was less than 0.5 volts, proceed to Primary Circuit Continuity Check. If difference in voltage readings was greater than 0.5 volts, inspect wiring harness between ignition module and ignition coil.

PRIMARY CIRCUIT CONTINUITY CHECK

1) Carefully insert a small straight pin in Green ignition module wire. Connect negative voltmeter lead to engine ground and positive voltmeter lead to pin in Green wire. Turn ignition switch to "RUN" position and measure

MOTORCRAFT DURA-SPARK III IGNITION (EEC) (Cont.)

voltage. Turn ignition switch to "OFF" position, remove voltmeter, and remove straight pin.

2) If voltage was greater than 1.5 volts, proceed to Ground Circuit Continuity Check. If voltage was 1.5 volts or less, proceed to Ballast Resistor Check.

BALLAST RESISTOR CHECK

1) Disconnect ignition module 2-wire connector. Disconnect ignition coil connector from ignition coil. Connect ohmmeter leads to "BATT" terminal of ignition coil connector and to wiring harness terminal that mates with Red module wire. Measure resistance. Reconnect ignition coil and ignition module connectors.

2) If resistance was 0.8-1.6 ohms, replace ignition module. If resistance was less than 0.8 ohms or greater than 1.6 ohms, replace ballast resistor.

GROUND CIRCUIT CONTINUITY CHECK

1) Carefully insert a small straight pin in ignition module Black wire. Attach negative voltmeter lead to ground. Attach positive voltmeter lead to straight pin in black wire. Turn ignition switch to "RUN" position and measure voltage. Turn ignition switch to "OFF" position and remove straight pin.

2) If voltage was greater than 0.5 volts, proceed to Wiring Harness Ground Circuit Check. If voltage was less than 0.5 volts, replace ignition module.

WIRING HARNESS GROUND CIRCUIT CHECK

1) Disconnect ignition module 3-wire connector. Connect ohmmeter leads to engine ground and terminal in wiring harness connector that mates with Black wire of ignition module. Measure resistance. Reconnect ignition module 3-wire connector.

2) If resistance was less than 1 ohm, inspect Black wire, ignition module connector, and wiring harness connector. If resistance was greater than 1 ohm, inspect wiring harness and connectors between ignition module and ground connection.

SPARK PLUG WIRE CHECK

1) Disconnect spark plug end of suspected wire or wires. Remove distributor cap. Measure resistance of spark plug wires by touching ohmmeter probes to each end of wire. Measure from inside distributor cap. If resistance is less than 5,000 ohms per inch, wire is okay.

2) If resistance is more than 5,000 ohms per inch, remove wire from cap and measure resistance of wire only. If it is less than 5,000 ohms, wire is okay. Check distributor cap and spark plug terminal for corrosion. Also check spark plug. If more than 5,000 ohms, replace spark plug wire.

OVERHAUL

NOTE: Since EEC distributors have no vacuum or centrifugal advance mechanisms, overhaul is limited to removal, inspection and alignment of rotor or removal and inspection of cap.

ROTOR

Removal

Remove distributor cap. Remove rotor by pulling up on rotor pull tab. Rotor is held in place by a spring clip.

NOTE: Rotor removal is only necessary when replacing rotor or adapter or when checking rotor condition. No adjustment to distributor is needed when rotor is replaced.

Installation

1) Coat rotor lower electrode blade only (not upper blades) using silicone grease. Coat all 4 distributor cap center blade arms to a 1/32" thickness.

2) To check rotor alignment, set No. 1 piston on compression stroke. Rotate crankshaft until rotor alignment tool (T79P-12200-A) can be inserted into alignment slots in rotor and center of shaft. *See Fig. 7.*

Fig. 7: Rotor and Adapter for Dura-Spark III Distributor Showing Adapter-to-Distributor Shaft Alignment

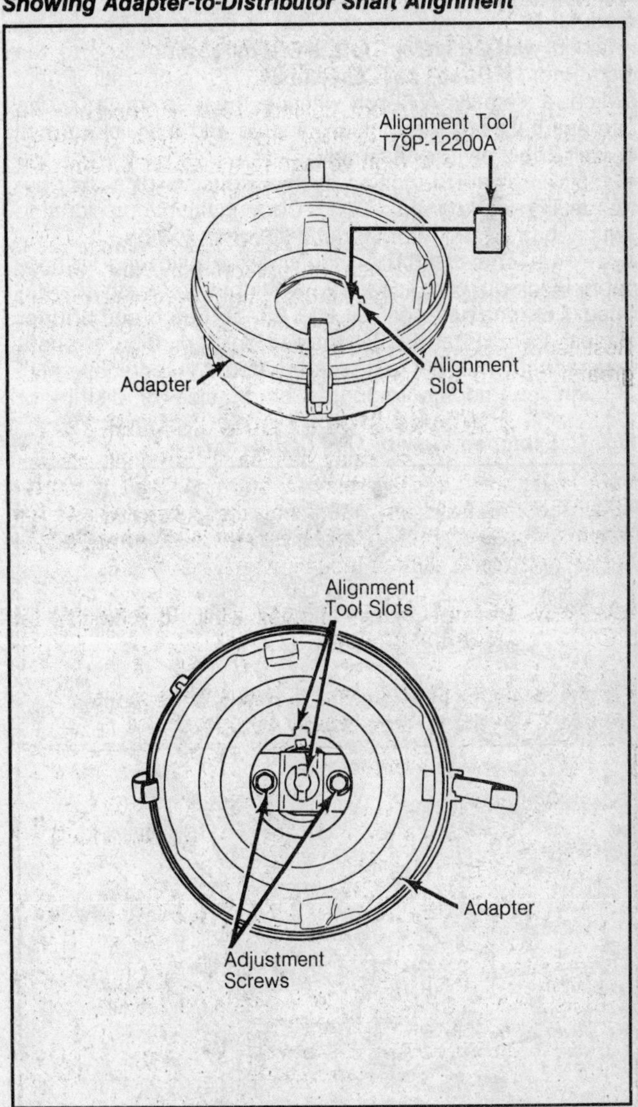

3) Read timing mark on damper that is aligned with pointer. If timing mark is within 4° of TDC, do not reset rotor alignment.

4) If alignment is not within 4° of TDC when installing rotor, remove alignment tool, position crankshaft at TDC and loosen 2 sleeve assembly adjustment screws.

5) Rotate sleeve until alignment tool fits into alignment slots. Tighten adjustment screws and remove alignment tool. Align rotor with large key way slot in distributor sleeve. Press rotor down into place.

MOTORCRAFT TFI IGNITION

Ford Motor Co. 1.6L, 2.3L HSC & 2.3L EFI/Turbo

DESCRIPTION

The TFI (Thick Film Integrated) ignition system is used on all vehicles equipped with 1.6L, 2.3L HSC or 2.3L EFI/Turbo engines. There are 2 different versions of the TFI ignition system. Carbureted 1.6L engines use TFI-I. Fuel injected (EFI) 1.6L engines, 2.3L High Swirl Combustion (HSC) engines and turbocharged 2.3L engines use TFI-IV.

In the TFI-I and the TFI-IV ignition systems, the small Blue plastic TFI ignition module replaces the bulky and much larger Dura-Spark module. The TFI ignition module is mounted on the distributor housing and is retained with 2 screws. It is electrically connected to the distributor pick-up coil assembly (TFI-I) or Hall Effect switch assembly (TFI-IV) without the use of a wiring harness between the ignition module and the pick-up coil or Hall Effect switch assembly.

The TFI ignition system consists of a distributor, a TFI ignition module, E-Core ignition coil, ignition switch, battery, and primary and secondary wiring.

The distributor contains the following components: Pick-up coil assembly with internal teeth (carbureted 1.6L engines only), a Hall Effect switch and shutter blades (1.6L EFI and 2.3L engines only), distributor shaft, reluctor with external teeth (carbureted 1.6L engines only), TFI ignition module (mounted on outside of distributor housing), octane rod (1.6L EFI and 2.3L engines only), centrifugal advance mechanism, vacuum advance mechanism (carbureted 1.6L engines only), rotor and distributor cap (with male terminals).

Vehicles equipped with the TFI-I or TFI-IV ignition system also use an E-Core ignition coil. The E-Core ignition coil is unlike any other Ford coil. It is encased in laminated plastic rather than being encased in an oil filled case, as most other coils are. This ignition coil has a very low primary resistance and is used without a ballast resistor in the electrical system. There are the usual primary connections on this coil.

Fig. 1: Exploded View of TFI-I Distributor

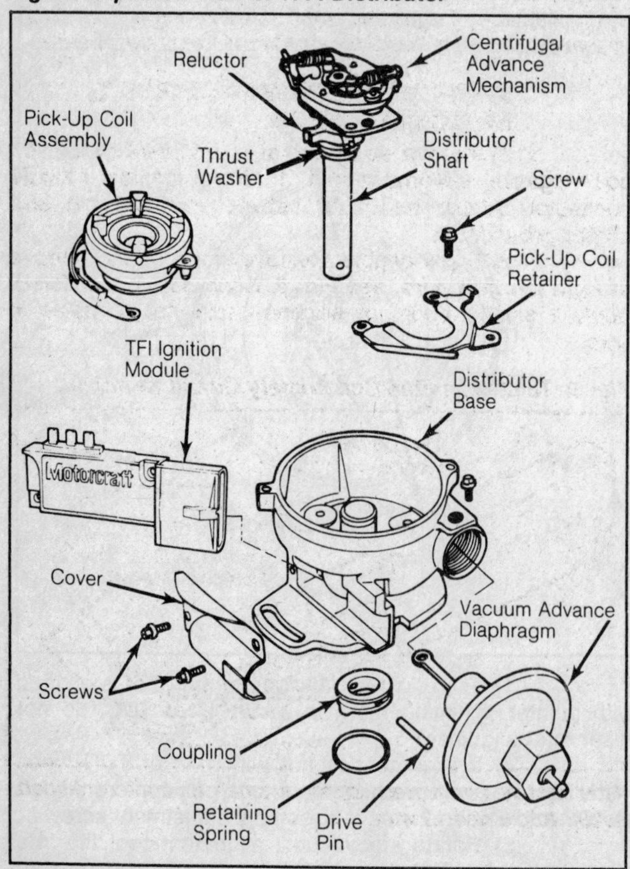

Used on carbureted 1.6L engines only.

Fig. 2: Exploded View of TFI-IV Distributor

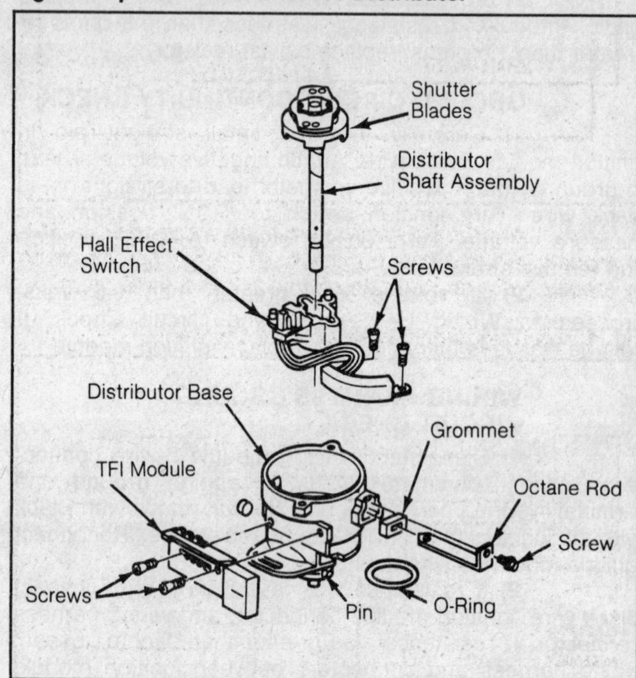

Used on 1.6L EFI and 2.3L engines only.

OPERATION

Each time the teeth on the reluctor pass the teeth on the pick-up coil, or the shutter blades pass through the Hall Effect switch, the magnetic field around the pick-up coil or Hall Effect switch builds and collapses. As this occurs, a pulse is generated in the pick-up coil or Hall Effect switch and sent to the TFI ignition module.

On 1.6L carbureted engines, the ignition module then turns the ignition coil primary circuit off and on causing a high voltage surge in the secondary which fires the spark plugs.

On 2.3L engines, the Hall Effect switch sends the pulse signal to the electronic control assembly (ECA) for modifications of the timing signal. Then, a modified spark timing signal is returned to the ignition module. This signals the ignition module when to turn the ignition coil primary circuit on and off. This causes a high voltage surge in the secondary which fires the spark plugs.

MOTORCRAFT TFI IGNITION (Cont.)

Fig. 3: TFI-I Ignition System Wiring Diagram

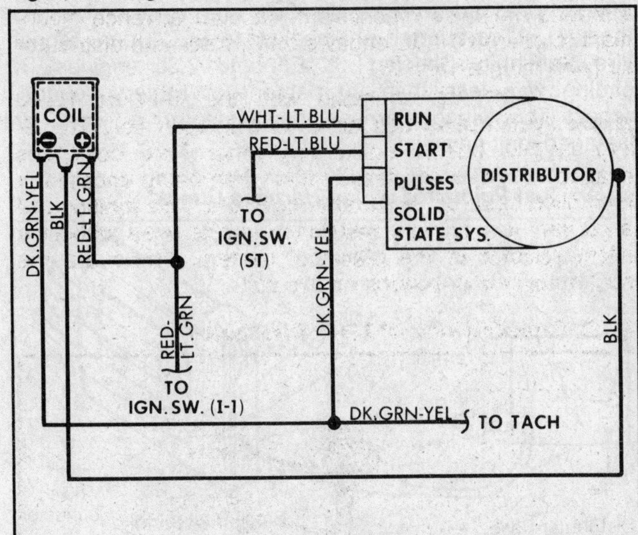

After initial ignition timing has been set on TFI-IV models, adjustments for octane concerns can be made by installing the appropriate octane link in the distributor.

Fig. 4: TFI-IV Ignition System Wiring Diagram

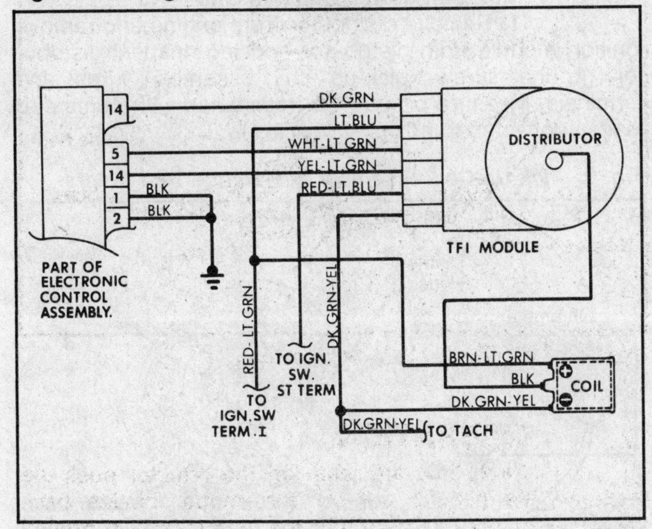

TESTING

NOTE: When a test requires the inspection of a wiring harness, both a visual inspection and a continuity test should be performed. When making measurements of a wire or connector, it is a good idea to wiggle the wires while measuring.

TEST SPARK PLUG

Use either a spark tester tool or modify a spark plug (cut off side terminal and install spring clip for grounding plug housing) for use in testing ignition system. *See Fig. 5.*

Fig. 5: Modified Spark Plug and Spark Tester

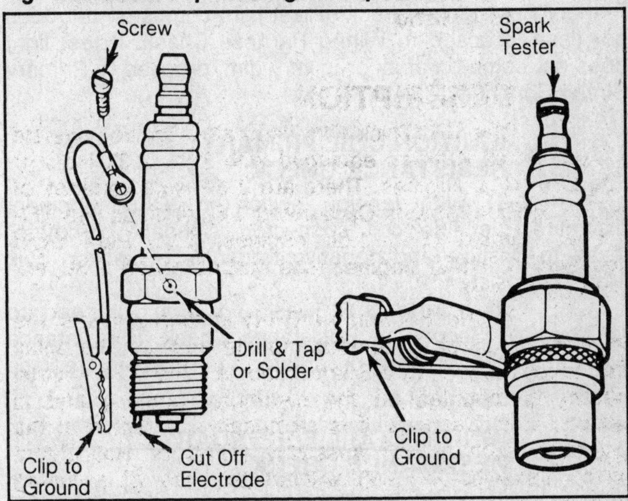

Modify spark plug by cutting off side electrode and installing spring clip.

IGNITION COIL SECONDARY VOLTAGE CHECK

1) Disconnect ignition coil secondary wire from distributor cap and attach spark tester to wire. Crank engine. Disconnect spark tester and reconnect secondary wire to distributor cap.

2) If sparks occurred at tester gap, inspect distributor cap and rotor for damage or carbon tracking. If no sparks occurred, measure resistance of ignition coil wire. Replace if greater than 5,000 ohms per inch. Proceed to Ignition Coil Primary Circuit Switching Check.

IGNITION COIL PRIMARY CIRCUIT SWITCHING CHECK

1) Insert a small straight pin in wire to ignition coil negative terminal about 1" from ignition module connector. Attach test light between straight pin and engine ground.

2) Crank engine. Remove test light and remove straight pin from wire. *See Fig. 6.* After test is completed, apply a small amount of silicone sealer to pin holes in wire.

Fig. 6: Testing Ignition Coil Primary Circuit Switching

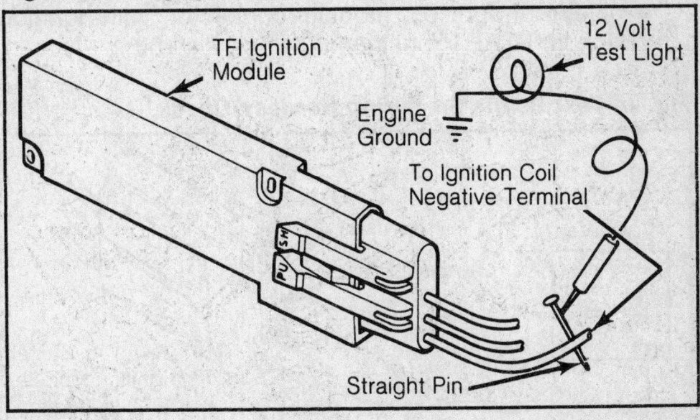

After test is completed, apply a small amount of silicone sealer to pin hole in wire.

MOTORCRAFT TFI IGNITION (Cont.)

3) If test light flashes, proceed to Ignition Coil Primary Resistance Check. If test light comes on but does not flash, proceed to Wiring Harness Check. If test light does not come on at all or is very dim, proceed to Primary Circuit Continuity Check.

IGNITION COIL PRIMARY RESISTANCE CHECK

1) With ignition switch in "OFF" position, disconnect ignition coil connector. Connect ohmmeter leads to positive and negative terminals of ignition coil. Measure resistance.

2) If resistance was .3-1 ohm, proceed to Ignition Coil Secondary Resistance Check. If resistance was less than .3 ohm or greater than 1 ohm, replace ignition coil.

IGNITION COIL SECONDARY RESISTANCE CHECK

1) With ignition switch in "OFF" position, disconnect ignition coil connector and secondary wire from ignition coil. Connect ohmmeter leads to ignition coil's negative and secondary terminals. Measure resistance.

2) If resistance was 8,000-11,500 ohms, proceed to Wiring Harness Check. If resistance was less than 8,000 ohms or greater than 11,500 ohms, replace ignition coil.

WIRING HARNESS CHECK

1) Disconnect ignition module connector from ignition module. Disconnect wire at "S" terminal of starter relay. Attach negative lead of voltmeter to distributor base and measure battery voltage at battery. With negative lead of voltmeter still connected to distributor base, check voltage in each of the following situations:

- Positive voltmeter lead connected to terminal No. 1 (1.6L carbureted engines) or terminal 2 (1.6L EFI and 2.3L engines) of ignition module connector with ignition switch in "RUN" position. *See Fig. 7 and 8*.
- Positive voltmeter lead connected to terminal No. 2 (1.6L carbureted engines) or terminal 3 (1.6L EFI and 2.3L engines) of ignition module connector with ignition switch in "RUN" position. *See Fig. 7 and 8*.
- Positive voltmeter lead connected to terminal 3 (1.6L carbureted engines) or terminal 4 (1.6L EFI and 2.3L engines) of ignition module connector with ignition switch in "START" position. *See Fig. 7 and 8*.

Fig. 7: Test Points for Wiring Harness Check

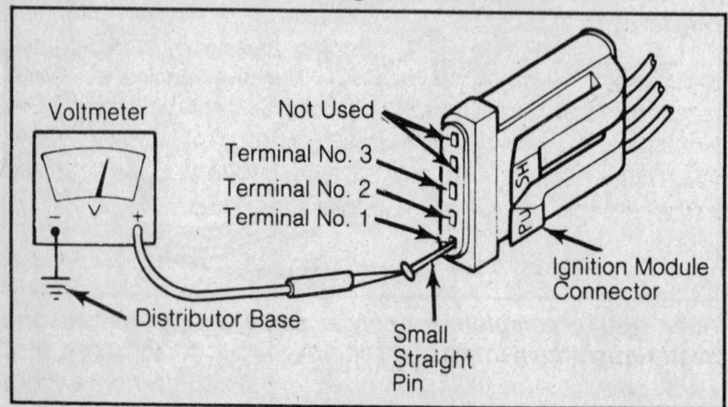

1.6L carbureted models.

2) If reading was at least 90 percent of battery voltage, proceed to Pick-Up Coil and Ignition Module Check (1.6L carbureted engines) or to EEC Spark Signal Wire Continuity Check (1.6L EFI and 2.3L engines). If reading was less than 90 percent of battery voltage, inspect for wiring harness problems or a worn or damaged ignition switch.

Fig. 8: Test Points for Wiring Harness Check

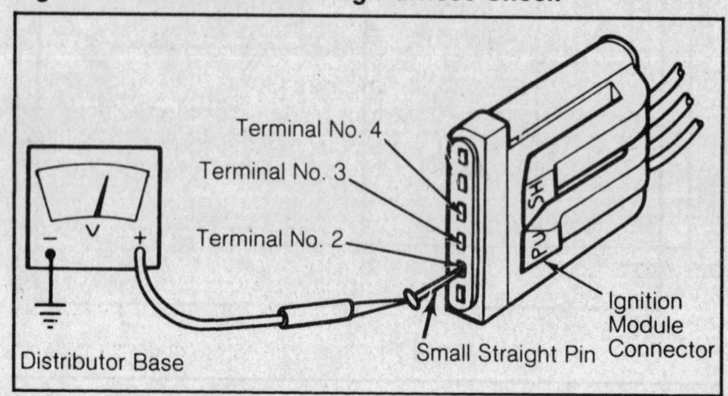

1.6L EFI and 2.3L engines.

PICK-UP COIL & IGNITION MODULE CHECK

1.6L Carbureted Engines Only

1) Remove distributor from engine and remove ignition module from distributor housing. Inspect distributor ground screw, pick-up coil assembly wires and terminals. Measure pick-up coil resistance with ohmmeter leads connected to points shown in *Fig. 9*.

Fig. 9: Pick-Up Coil Assembly Resistance Test Points

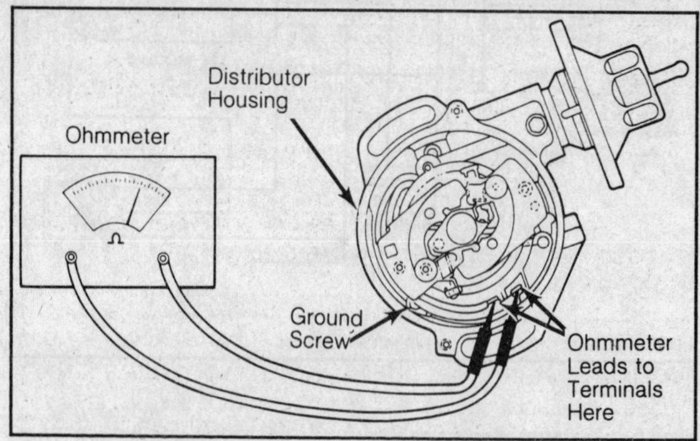

Pick-up coil resistance should be 650-1300 ohms.

2) If resistance was 650-1300 ohms, pick-up coil assembly is okay, replace ignition module. If resistance was less than 650 or greater than 1300 ohms, ignition module is okay, replace pick-up coil assembly. Reinstall ignition module on distributor housing and install distributor on engine.

EEC SPARK SIGNAL WIRE CONTINUITY CHECK

1.6L EFI & 2.3L Engines Only

1) Disconnect connector from electronic control assembly (ECA). Disconnect ignition coil wire from distributor cap and connect spark tester to wire. Crank engine and check for spark.

MOTORCRAFT TFI IGNITION (Cont.)

2) If sparks did not occur, proceed to Distributor and Module Check. If sparks did occur, disconnect ignition module connector and check for continuity in Dark Green wire between ignition module connector and terminal J1-14 of ECA.

3) If no continuity exists, repair wire or connectors as necessary. If continuity exists, proceed to testing procedures in *Ford Motor Co. EEC-IV System article in this section.*

DISTRIBUTOR & MODULE CHECK

1.6L EFI & 2.3L Engines Only

1) Remove distributor from engine with secondary coil wire still connected to distributor. Remove module from distributor. Install a new module on the distributor.

2) Connect a jumper lead from the distributor base to a good engine ground. Connect vehicle harness to module. Connect a spark tester to end of coil wire. Rotate distributor by hand and check for spark.

3) If sparks did occur, reinstall distributor with a new module. If sparks did not occur, install a new distributor but use original module.

IGNITION COIL PRIMARY VOLTAGE CHECK

1) Attach negative lead of voltmeter to distributor base and measure battery voltage. Turn ignition switch to "RUN" position. Connect positive lead of voltmeter to coil connector negative terminal (connector still connected to coil). Measure voltage. Turn ignition switch to "OFF" position.

2) If reading was at least 90 percent of battery voltage, inspect wiring harness between ignition module and ignition coil negative terminal. If reading was less than 90 percent of battery voltage, inspect wiring harness between ignition module and ignition coil negative terminal and proceed to Ignition Coil Voltage Supply Check.

IGNITION COIL VOLTAGE SUPPLY CHECK

1) Attach negative lead of voltmeter to distributor base. Measure battery voltage. Turn ignition switch to "RUN" position.

2) Connect positive voltmeter lead to positive terminal of ignition coil connector (connector still connected to ignition coil). Read voltmeter and turn ignition switch "OFF".

3) If reading was at least 90 percent of battery voltage, inspect ignition coil and ignition coil connector for dirt, corrosion or damage. Replace ignition coil if necessary.

4) If reading was less than 90 percent of battery voltage, repair wiring between ignition coil and ignition switch. Also check for a worn or damaged ignition switch.

OVERHAUL

NOTE: **On models equipped with TFI-IV ignition systems, only the distributor cap, rotor, TFI module, distributor shaft O-ring and octane rod can be replaced. If any other component is found to be defective, the entire distributor assembly must be replaced.**

TFI IGNITION MODULE

Removal

1) Disconnect wiring harness connector from ignition module. Remove distributor cap, with secondary wiring connected, and position out of way. Remove distributor hold down bolt and remove distributor from engine.

2) With distributor on work bench, remove the 2 ignition module retaining screws. Pull the right side of the ignition module down to the distributor mounting flange. Push ignition module back up and ignition module terminals will disengage from connector in distributor. Pull ignition module down and away from distributor to remove.

Installation

Reverse removal procedures and note the following: Coat the metal base plate of ignition module with about 1/32" of silicone grease before installing. Be sure that ignition module terminals are fully engaged in distributor connector. Tighten the 2 ignition module retaining screws to 9-16 INCH Lbs. (1.1-1.8 N.m).

OCTANE ROD (TFI-IV ONLY)

Removal & Installation

1) Remove distributor cap and rotor for visual access. Remove screw that retains octane rod to distributor housing.

2) Slide the octane rod and grommet out to a point at which the rod end can be disengaged from the pick-up coil retaining post.

3) Install grommet on new octane rod. Reinstall rod in distributor, making sure that rod is engaged with pick-up coil retaining post. Reinstall retaining screw, rotor and distributor cap.

DISTRIBUTOR (TFI-I ONLY)

Disassembly

1) Remove distributor cap and rotor. Using a small screwdriver or ice pick remove drive coupling spring. Using compressed air, blow any dirt or oil from drive end of distributor.

2) Put a small paint dot on drive coupling and distributor shaft for reassembly reference. Line up drive pin with slot in base of distributor housing. Support distributor in a vise and remove pin from distributor shaft using a 1/8" drift punch and hammer.

3) Remove distributor from vise. Remove drive coupling from distributor shaft. Before removing shaft from disributor housing, remove any burrs from end of shaft, especially around drive pin hole. After any burrs have been removed, carefully remove shaft from distributor base.

4) Remove 2 screws retaining pick-up coil connector to housing. If TFI module has not been removed, remove pick-up coil connector from top of TFI module. Remove TFI module. Remove pick-up coil retainer from pick-up coil assembly. Remove pick-up coil assembly from distributor housing.

Reassembly

Reassemble distributor in reverse order of disassembly while noting the following: Be sure to align paint dots, that were made during disassembly, on housing and shaft. Apply a light coat of oil to distributor shaft before installing in housing. Be sure that connectors are securely connected to TFI module.

FORD MOTOR CO. THERMACTOR SYSTEMS

DESCRIPTION

The Thermactor Exhaust Emission Control system reduces carbon monoxide (CO) and hydrocarbon (HC) content of exhaust gasses. It injects fresh air into the exhaust gas stream as it leaves the combustion chamber, allowing continued combustion of unburned gasses. A typical system consists of the following components: Air supply pump, air by-pass valve, check valve(s), air control valve, air manifold and air hoses.

Individual systems vary in number and type of components depending upon engine size and application, these are as follows: The Managed Thermactor Air (MTA) system uses the same basic components as the standard system, but "manages" thermactor air according to operating conditions. Some models are equipped with Thermactor II system which uses a pulse air valve instead of an air pump. Another system, the Extended Idle Air Bypass System is used to dump secondary thermactor air to the atmosphere. The Thermactor Air Timer system controls emissions that occur on hot starts. It uses a timer to direct carburetor spark port vacuum to the vacuum control valve.

OPERATION

Inlet air to air pump is drawn through a centrifugal air filter fan. The pump then supplies air under pressure to the exhaust port near the exhaust valve, by either an external air manifold, or through an internal drilled passage in cylinder head or exhaust manifold. The oxygen in the fresh air, plus the heating of the exhaust gasses, cause further burning which converts the gasses into carbon dioxide and water.

In the Managed Thermactor Air system, air is bypassed to the atmosphere by a Thermactor Air Bypass valve and is directed upstream near the exhaust manifold or downstream to the underbody catalytic converter by the Thermactor Air Control valve. Some models may use a combined Air By-Pass/Air Control valve.

In the Thermactor II system, the natural pulses present in the exhaust system are used to pull air into the exhaust manifold through a pulse air valve. The pulse air valve is connected to exhaust manifold through a tube and to the air cleaner with a hose.

In the Extended Idle Air bypass system, a normally closed Idle Tracking Switch opens when the throttle returns to idle, signaling the MCU to de-energize the normally open solenoid valve. Vacuum is then supplied to the normally open bypass valve which dumps thermactor secondary air to the atmosphere.

The Thermactor Air Timer System uses a timer to hold the solenoid valve open for 100-180 seconds thus directing carburetor spark port vacuum to both upper and lower ports of the vacuum control valve when the engine is started. If the engine is cold, only the upper port is open and thermactor air goes to the cylinder heads. If the engine is hot, only the lower port is open and vacuum is admitted to control valve only for duration of timed cycle. When cycle ceases, valve closes and vacuum is vented to atmosphere, while thermactor is directed to catalyst.

AIR PUMP

Air pump is a belt-driven, positive displacement, vane type pump. It is available in 11 cu. in. and 19 cu. in. sizes. The 11 cu. in. pump takes air through a filter attached to air inlet nipple. The 19 cu. in. pump takes air through an impeller type centrifugal air filter fan, thus eliminating the need for a separate air filter.

Dust and dirt particles cannot enter the pump because these heavier-than-air particles are thrown from the air intake by centrifugal force. The air pump does not have a pressure relief valve, this function being controlled by the air by-pass valve.

AIR BYPASS VALVES

Two types of valves are used by Ford Motor Co., normally open and normally closed valves. In addition, these valves may be mounted in-line with the air pump or mounted directly on the pump.

Normally Open Valves

These valves are available with and without vacuum vents. Valves without vents provide a timed dump of air for 1.1-2.8 seconds when a sudden high vacuum of about 20 in. Hg is applied to the signal port. This prevents backfire during deceleration.

Normally open valves with a vacuum vent provide a timed dump during deceleration and also dump when a vacuum pressure difference is maintained between the signal port and the vent port. The signal port must have 3 in. Hg more vacumm than the vent port to hold the dump. This is used to prevent the catalyst from overheating.

Fig. 1: Normally Open Air Bypass Valve

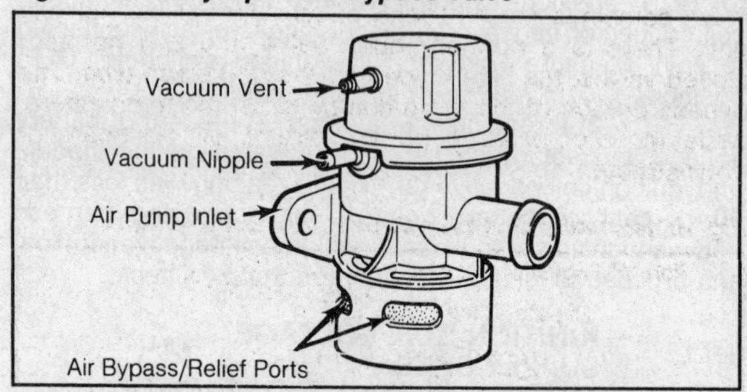

Valve with vacuum vent shown.

Normally Closed Valves

Normally closed valves supply air to the exhaust system with medium and high applied vacuum signals during cold start, short idles and some accelerations. With no or low vacuum applied to the pump, air is dumped through the silencer ports of the valve.

Fig. 2: Normally Closed Air Bypass Valve

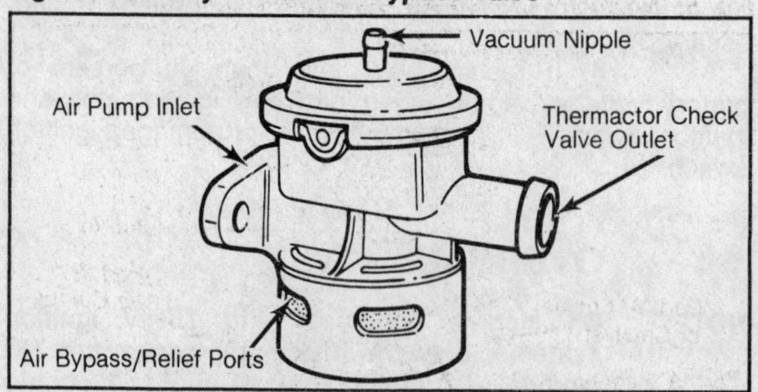

AIR CONTROL VALVE

Three basic types of air control valves are used: Standard air control valve, air control/shut-off valve

1983 Exhaust Emission Systems

FORD MOTOR CO. THERMACTOR SYSTEMS (Cont.)

and air control/shut-off valve with orifice. These valves direct air pump output to exhaust manifold or downstream to catalyst, depending upon engine control system. Air control and air control/shut-off valves are of similar construction except that bottom air outlet is capped on shut-off valves.

Fig. 3: Air Control/Shut-Off Valve With Orifice

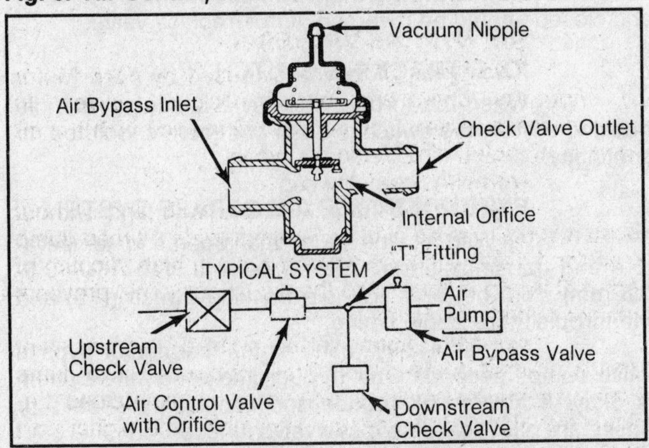

AIR BYPASS/AIR CONTROL VALVE

The combination air bypass/air control valve is used with some managed air thermactor systems. The valve combines the functions of the two valves into one unit. There is a normally open valve and two normally closed valves; the bleed type and the non-bleed type. The bypass portion of the valve dumps air to the atmosphere, while the control valve portion directs air upstream or downstream.

Fig. 4: Normally Open Air Bypass/Air Control Valve

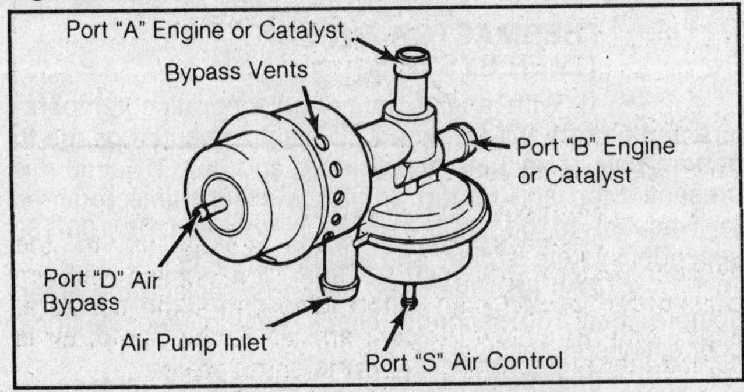

Fig. 5: Normally Closed Air Bypass/Air Control Valve

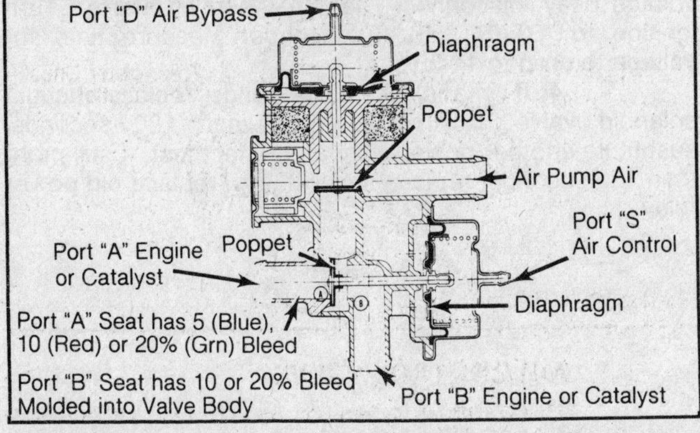

Valve with bleed shown; valve without bleed similar

CHECK VALVES

Check valves are used on all thermactor systems in various locations. These valves block air flow in one direction, and allow air flow in the other direction.

IDLE TRACKING SWITCH

Used on the Extended Idle Air Bypass system, this switch is a mechanically operated electric switch held open by the throttle linkage when the throttle is closed. It is located on the carburetor.

VACUUM CONTROL VALVE

Used in the Thermactor Air Timer system, this valve is a three port valve that switches the vacuum source from the top or bottom port to the center port. This vacuum is then routed to the thermactor control valve.

PULSE AIR VALVE

The pulse air valve replaces the thermactor pump on some vehicles. It permits air to be drawn into the exhaust system on vacuum exhaust pulses and blocks the backflow of high pressure exhaust pulses. The fresh air completes the oxidation of exhaust gas components.

TESTING

AIR PUMP

Check belt tension and adjust to specifications. Disconnect air supply hose from control valve. Observe air flow from pump outlet with engine running. Flow should increase as engine speed is increased.

AIR BYPASS VALVE

Normally Open Valve Without Vacuum Vent

1) With engine at normal operating temperature, parking brake applied and transmission in "P" or "N," disconnect air supply line at valve outlet. Disconnect vacuum line at vacuum nipple.

2) With engine at 1500 RPM, air should be heard and felt at valve outlet. Connect a direct vacuum line from any manifold vaccum source to vacuum nipple on valve. Air at outlet should be momentarily decreased or shut off.

3) At same time, air pump supply air should be heard at silencer ports. If valve fails any test and air pump checks okay, replace valve. Reconnect vacuum lines.

Normally Open Valve With Vacuum Vent

1) With engine at normal operating temperature, parking brake applied and transmission in "P" or "N," disconnect air supply line at valve outlet. Disconnect all vacuum lines from vacuum nipple and vent.

2) With engine at 1500 RPM, air pump supply should be heard and felt at outlet. Connect a vaccum line from vacuum nipple to one of the vacuum fittings on intake manifold. With vacuum vent open to atmosphere and engine at 1500 RPM, no air should be felt at outlet and all air should be bypassed through silencer ports.

3) Using the same direct line to an intake manifold vaccum source, cap vacuum vent. Accelerate engine to 2000 RPM and suddenly release throttle. A momentary interruption of air pump supply air should be felt at outlet.

FORD MOTOR CO. THERMACTOR SYSTEMS (Cont.)

4) If valve fails any test, and air pump is operating okay, replace valve. Reconnect all vacuum lines.

Normally Closed Valve

1) With engine at normal operating temperature, parking brake applied and transmission in "P" or "N," disconnect air supply line at valve outlet. Remove vacuum line and ensure that a vacuum signal is present at nipple.

2) Remove any delay valves or restrictors in line. Vacuum must be present at nipple before proceeding. With engine at 1500 RPM, and vacuum line connected to nipple, air pump supply air should be heard and felt at outlet.

3) With engine at 1500 RPM, disconnect vacuum line. Air at outlet should be significantly decreased or shut-off. Air pump supply air should be heard or felt at silencer ports.

4) If valve fails any test, and air pump is operating okay, replace valve. Reconnect all vacuum lines.

AIR BYPASS/AIR CONTROL VALVE

Normally Open Valve

1) With engine at normal operating temperature, parking brake applied and transmission in "P" or "N," disconnect hoses from outlets "A" and "B." *See Fig. 4.* Disconnect and plug vacuum line to ports "D" and "S."

2) With engine at 1500 RPM, air should flow out of port "B." Apply 8-10 in. Hg vacuum to port "S." With engine at 1500 RPM, air should flow from port "A."

3) Reconnect line to port "D" and ensure vacuum is present. With engine at 1500 RPM, air should flow from bypass vents. If valve fails any of these tests, replace valve. Reconnect hoses.

Normally Closed Valve

1) With engine at normal operating temperature, parking brake applied and transmission in "P" or "N," disconnect hoses from ports "A" and "B." *See Fig. 5* Disconnect and plug line to port "D." With engine at 1500 RPM, air should flow from bypass vents.

2) Reconnect line to port "D" and disconnect and plug line to port "S." Ensure vacuum is present in line to port "D." With engine at 1500 RPM, air should flow from port "B," and no air should flow from port "A."

3) Apply 8-10 in. Hg vacuum to port "S." With engine at 1500 RPM, air should flow from port "A." If the valve has a vacuum bleed, some lesser amount of air will flow from port "A" or "B" and main discharge will change when vacuum is applied to port "S."

4) If valve fails any test, replace valve. Reconnect hoses.

AIR CONTROL VALVE

1) Verify that air is being supplied to valve inlet by disconnecting inlet supply hose. Disconnect hose at valve outlet and hose from vacuum nipple. Some air flow should be heard and felt at valve outlet with engine at 1500 RPM.

2) Using a direct vacuum line from manifold vacuum source, connect line to vacuum nipple. An increase in air flow should be detected when vacuum is applied. If valve fails any test, replace valve. Reconnect all lines.

VACUUM CHECK VALVE

Apply 16 in. Hg vaccum to check side of valve and trap vacuum. If vacuum remains above 15 in. Hg for 10 seconds, valve operation is normal. If not, replace valve.

VACUUM CONTROL VALVE

With engine cold, top port should be closed to bottom port on two port valves. On three port valves, middle passage should be closed to bottom port, and should be open to top port. With engine warm, ports open and closed should be reversed. If not, replace valve.

IDLE TRACKING SWITCH

When the throttle stop lever is against the idle tracking switch, the switch is open and there should be no continuity.

EXTENDED IDLE AIR BYPASS SYSTEM

1) With engine at normal operating temperature and transmission in Neutral, insert a .140-.150" (3.5-3.8 mm) shim between the idle tracking switch (ITS) and the throttle stop. Begin timing.

2) If after 2-1/2 minutes the thermactor bypass valve dumps secondary air through the vents, the system is okay. If not, check routing and condition of hoses. If hoses are okay, check bypass valve function.

3) If valve is okay, check battery voltage to ITS and continuity through normally closed ITS while manually cycling switch. If okay, check that solenoid is functional and actually opens to close off vacuum. If solenoid is okay, turn engine off and ignition "ON" and check for battery voltage to MCU and to relay and for a signal to the solenoid.

PULSE AIR VALVE

With engine at normal operating temperature and curb idle, a suction should be felt at the valve inlet. If not replace the valve.

THERMACTOR AIR TIMER SYSTEM

1) With engine at normal operating temperature and battery fully charged, connect a vacuum gauge to bottom port of vacuum check valve and note if vacuum is present. Stop and restart engine. Measure time required for vacuum to be vented through solenoid. If 100-180 seconds, system is okay and test is complete.

2) If less than 100 seconds, replace the timer. If more than 180 seconds, check vacuum and electrical connections as follows:

3) Connect voltmeter between hot terminal of solenoid harness and ground. If no voltage, check B+ source to timer (not power relay). Repair as required. If voltage okay, disconnect I terminal lead on starter. Turn ignition to "START" for 3 seconds. Measure time for voltage to drop to 11.5 volts.

4) If time is 100-180 seconds, replace vacuum solenoid valve. If time is more than 180 seconds, susbtitute another power relay and repeat test. If still more than 180 seconds, replace timer. If less, replace old power relay.

1983 Exhaust Emission Systems

FORD MOTOR CO. EXHAUST GAS RECIRCULATION

DESCRIPTION

The Exhaust Gas Recirculation (EGR) system is designed to reintroduce small amounts of exhaust gas into the combustion cycle, thus reducing the amounts of NOx emissions. The amount of exhaust gas recycled and the timing of the cycle are controlled by such factors as engine vacuum, exhaust system backpressure, temperature, throttle angle and engine speed.

Typical systems consist of an EGR valve, a spacer plate on which the valve is mounted, a vacuum amplifier, a check valve, and a ported vacuum switch (PVS) or a temerature vacuum switch (TVS).

An EGR Vacuum Regulator Control system is used on some models. This system combines a ported EGR valve with with a backpressure variable transducer (BVT) to control NOx emissions.

Models with Electronic Engine Control (EEC) systems use an electronic EGR sytem with an electronic sonic EGR valve and a EGR valve position sensor. In addition, these vehicles use an exhaust cooler which uses coolant to reduce the temperature of exhaust flowing through the EGR valve and into the engine.

Some selected 2.0L and 2.3L engines use a EGR valve and transducer assembly which consists of an external entry ported EGR valve and a pressure tap to provide a backpressure signal to the remote transducer. This system operates the same as the Integral Backpressure Transducer valve system. Function checks are the same as that system.

OPERATION

EGR VALVES

Integral Backpressure Transducer Valve

This valve combines an exhaust gas backpressure transducer within the diaphragm housing of the EGR valve. The transducer modulates EGR flow by venting vacuum in relation to exhaust backpressure. Backpressure is sensed between the inlet and the poppet/tapered stem of the valve. Flow rate is dependent on source vacuum, exhaust pressure, control setting and orifice size.

Fig. 1: Integral Backpressure Transducer EGR Valve

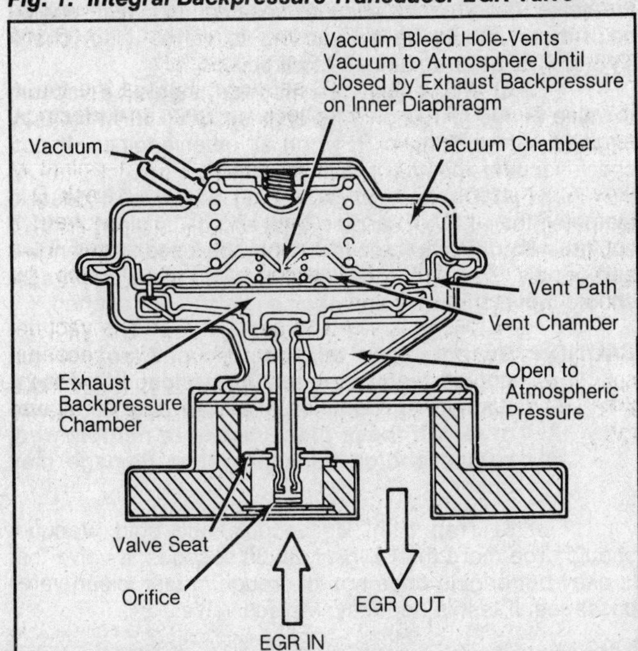

Poppet type valves are rapid opening. The flow rate through the valve is limited by the size of the valve orifice or the opening in the carburetor spacer plate.

Internal tapered stem type valves use a pintle which moves the tapered portion of the valve up or down against the valve seat. Gas flow rate is determined by the amount of movement of the taper off the seat.

Ported EGR Valve

This valve is operated by a vacuum signal from the carburetor EGR port which actuates the valve diaphragm. As vacuum increases enough to overcome the power spring, the valve is opened, allowing EGR flow. Amount of flow is dependent on the pintle or poppet position which is a direct result of the vacuum signal.

Fig. 2: Ported EGR Valve

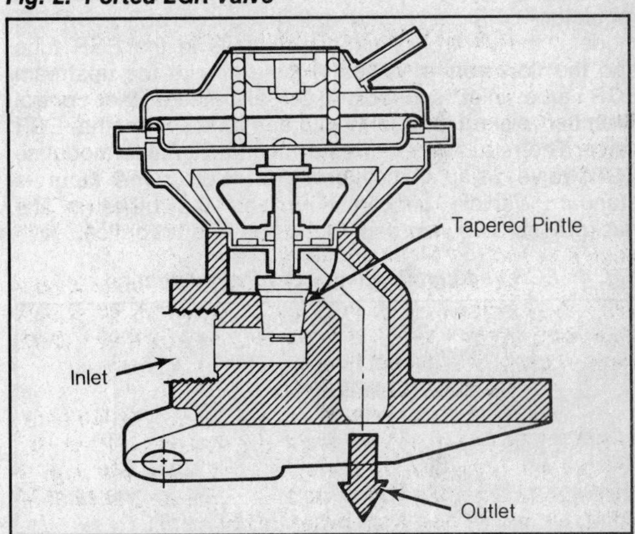

Valve with side entry, tapered pintle shown.

Electronic Sonic EGR Valve

This valve operates like a ported valve, except a tapered pintle is used for more exact flow control. A sensor mounted on top of this valve sends out electrical signals that tells the electronic control assembly (ECA) how far the EGR valve is open. The ECA then signals the

Fig. 3: Electronic Sonic EGR Valve System

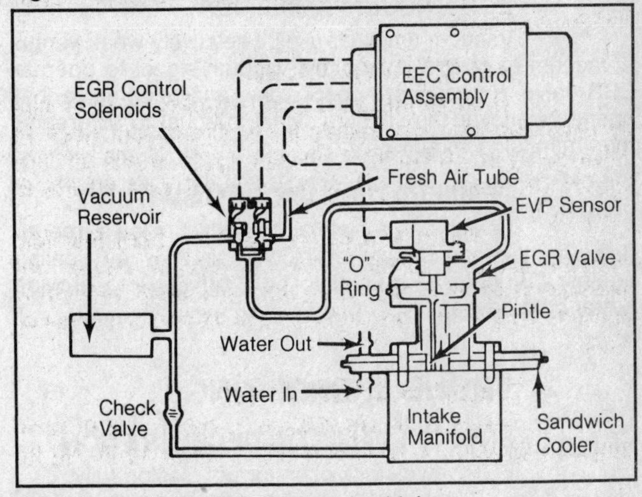

System used with EEC equipped vehicles.

FORD MOTOR CO. EXHAUST GAS RECIRCULATION (Cont.)

EGR control solenoids to maintain or alter EGR flow as required. Source vacuum is from manifold, and is bled off or applied to the diaphragm by the ECA. A cooler is sometimes used to reduce gas temperature, reduce detonation and allow better gas flow. This valve operates only a part throttle mode. It is closed in all other modes.

EGR LOAD CONTROL (WOT) VALVE

This valve dumps EGR vacuum at or near wide open throttle. Senses venturi vacuum at a predetermined level and causes valve to close or open when engine load is reduced from wide open throttle.

EGR VACUUM REGULATOR CONTROL SYSTEM

This system is used on most 1.6L engine applications. System consists of 3 components, a vacuum regulator, EGR valve and a flow control orifice. In EFI models, the control chamber pickup is in the EGR tube and the flow control orifice is integral with the upstream EGR tube inlet connector. On all others the control chamber pickup and orifice are integral with the EGR valve. The regulator receives a vacuum signal to modulate EGR valve using 2 backpressure inlets. One input is standard vehicle backpressure and the other is the backpressure downstream of the flow control orifice.

Fig. 4: EGR Vacuum Regulator Control System

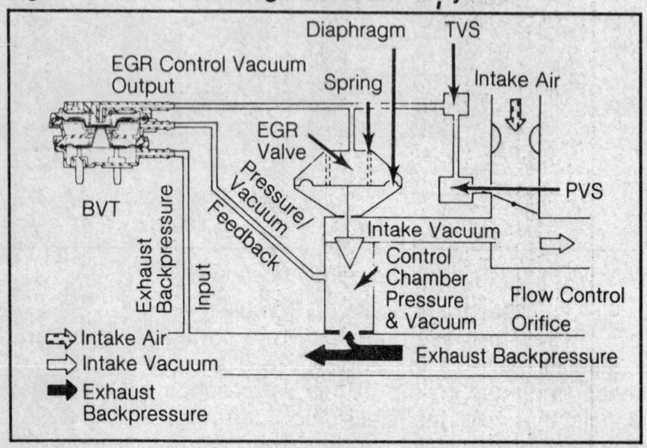

System used on most 1.6L engines.

EGR VACUUM AMPLIFIER

Vacuum amplifier uses a relatively weak venturi vacuum to control a manifold vacuum signal to operate EGR valve. It contains a check valve and relief valve that opens whenever the vacuum signal is equal to or greater than manifold vacuum.

TEMPERATURE VACUUM SWITCH

Switch has a bimetal disc which allows free air flow in the vacuum line or blocks air flow by sealing against "O" ring. It is used to hold off EGR to provide better cold driveability.

TROUBLE SHOOTING

ENGINE STALLS ON DECELERATION

EGR valve stuck open, or not closing fully.

ROUGH IDLE, STALLING, SURGE ROUGH RUNNING, HESITATION & POOR PART THROTTLE PERFORMANCE

EGR receiving vacuum from misrouted hoses. EGR valve not closing fully or stuck open, blown gasket or attachment loose, air bleeds plugged (backpressure valves). TVS or PVS opening too early when engine cold. EFI computer malfunction. Vacuum regulator leaking (EVR system).

PART THROTTLE ENGINE DETONATION

EGR valve stuck closed. Leaky valve diaphragm, vacuum restricted to EGR valve, EGR disconnected. TVS and/or PVS not opening, load control valve venting, EGR passages blocked. Insufficient backpressure. EVP sensor "O" ring leaking or sensor loose (EEC).

VERY LOW POWER AT FULL THROTTLE

Load control (WOT) valve not venting.

ENGINE HARD TO START, NO START, OR STARTS & STALLS

Vacuum at EGR. Hoses misrouted. EGR valve stuck open.

POOR FUEL ECONOMY

If EGR related, usually accompanied by detonation or other symptom of restricted or no EGR flow.

TESTING

EGR VALVES

Integral Backpressure Transducer Valves

1) Disconnect vacuum line to valve and plug. Connect vacuum pump to valve. Start engine and idle. Apply 6 in. Hg vacuum to valve. Vacuum should bleed off and valve should not operate.

2) If vacuum holds and valve opens, replace valve. With engine at idle, there should be no vacuum to the valve. If so, check vacuum hose routing. With engine cold, there should be no vacuum to valve. If so, check TVS or PVS and replace as required.

3) With engine warm, there should be vacuum to valve at 4000 RPM on 1.6L engines, 3000 RPM for 2.3L engines, and kickdown RPM on all other engines. If not, check vacuum lines from EGR to source.

4) Clamp a suitable plug about 1/16" less in diameter than I.D. of tailpipe into end of tailpipe. A drive socket with drive hole covered may be used. Idle engine and apply vacuum gradually. Valve stem/diaphragm should move smoothly and engine idle should roughen.

CAUTION: Do not block tailpipe fully and do not run engine faster than idle for prolonged periods. Be sure to remove plug from tailpipe at end of test. If these precautions are not followed, engine and/or exhaust system damage may occur.

5) Trap 6 in. Hg vacuum and hold. Vacuum should drop more than 1 in. Hg in 30 seconds. If valve test is okay but engine does not idle rough in test, clean valve passages. If test is not okay, replace valve.

FORD MOTOR CO. EXHAUST GAS RECIRCULATION (Cont.)

Ported EGR Valve

1) With engine cold there should be no vacuum to valve. If vacuum exists, check TVS or PVS function. At warm curb idle there should be no vacuum to valve.

2) With engine warm, there should be vacuum to valve at 4000 RPM on 1.6L engines, 3000 RPM for 2.3L engines, and kickdown RPM on all other engines. If not, check vacuum lines, TVS and PVS and replace as required.

3) With engine at idle, apply 8 in. Hg vacuum to valve. Valve stem should move, opening valve and idle should roughen. If stem moves but idle does not roughen, clean valve passages.

4) With engine idling, apply 4 in. Hg vacuum to valve and trap. Vacuum should not drop more than 1 in. Hg in 30 seconds. If so, replace valve.

Electronic Sonic EGR Valve

1) Connect vacuum gauge to valve. Apply 6 in. Hg vacuum to valve and trap. Vacuum should not drop more than 1 in. Hg in 30 seconds. If so, replace valve, "O" ring or EVP sensor.

2) As Sonic valve is part of EEC system, check all circuitry as described in EEC article. Machanical function can be checked as follows: Check vacuum lines for correct routing.

3) Disconnect vacuum hose at valve and connect vacuum gauge to hose. Accelerate engine to 2000-2500 RPM and release throttle. Repeat 8-10 times and check for consistent response.

4) With engine cold, if vacuum rises above zero, solenoid are leaking and should be replaced. With engine warm, vacuum should rise above 15 in. Hg and return to zero when throttle is released.

5) If vacuum does not go to 15 in. Hg, check vacuum source and service. If vacuum does not return to zero or is inconsistent, solenoids are worn and should be replaced. If solenoids are not damaged, and symptoms still exist, see Trouble Shooting.

VACUUM AMPLIFIER

1) Check for adequate manifold vacuum. With engine warm and at curb idle. Connect vacuum gauge to port on amplifier which leads to EGR/PVS valve. Vacuum should not read more than 2 in. Hg at idle.

2) Disconnect venturi hose at carburetor. Increase engine speed to 4000 RPM on 1.6L engines, 3000 RPM on 2.3L engines, and 2000 RPM on all other engines. Vacuum should not change. Maintain high engine speed and reconnect venturi hose.

3) Gauge should register at least 4 in. Hg vacuum. Return engine to idle. Gauge should return to initial reading. If not, replace amplifier.

1983 Exhaust Emission Systems

FORD MOTOR CO. EMISSION RELATED COMPONENTS

Ford Motor Co. vehicles utilize several types of devices to control emissions. Although originally intended for a specific purpose, many of the devices are now used in various parts of the system. These figures show the physical appearance of typical components and their identification symbols found on Emission Control Diagrams. Operation and method of actuation is provided for most devices. Refer to specific system within this section for testing procedures.

COMPONENT AND SYMBOL	OPERATION
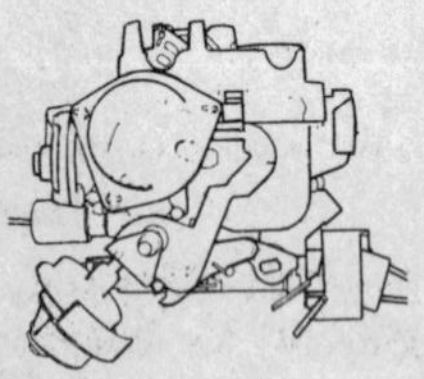 **A/C-WOT MICRO SWITCH**	Switch is mounted on carburetor to sense wide open throttle (WOT) position. On some applications, an adjusting screw is mounted on a lever that rotates with the throttle lever. As lever is rotated to WOT position, it contacts arm of micro switch that opens or closes an electrical circuit. On other applications, the adjusting screw can be set to any predetermined throttle angle before the WOT position. The switch is used on most carbureted models and cuts out the A/C compressor during WOT acceleration.
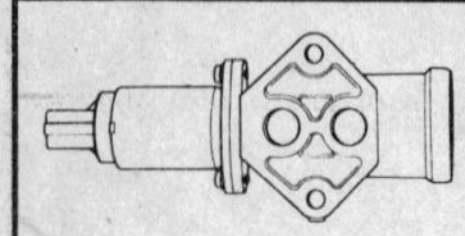 **AIR BY-PASS SOLENOID**	Solenoid is used to control engine idle speed and is operated by the EEC module.
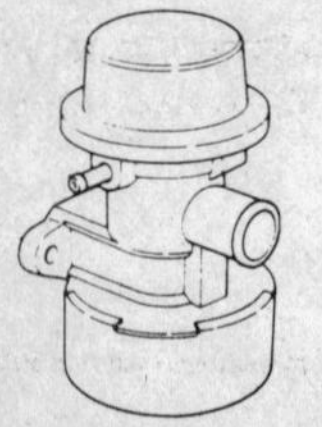 **AIR BY-PASS VALVE** 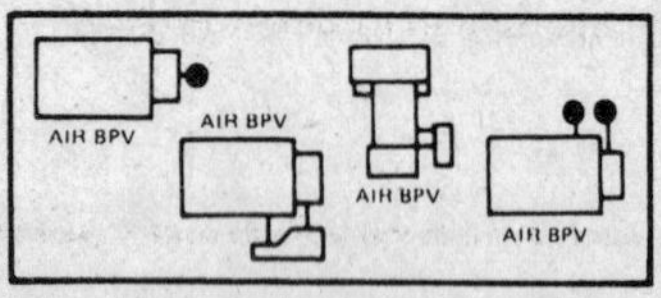 (symbols: AIR BPV, AIR BPV, AIR BPV, AIR BPV)	Vacuum operated valves may be normally open or closed. Valves direct air flow from thermactor air pump to exhaust system or atmosphere as required. May be mounted on air pump or in-line (remote).
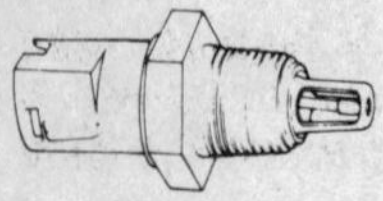 **AIR CHARGE TEMPERATURE (ACT) SENSOR**	Threaded into left rear of intake manifold on Electronic Fuel Injection models. Senses air/fuel mixture temperature and provides instant information to EFI system.
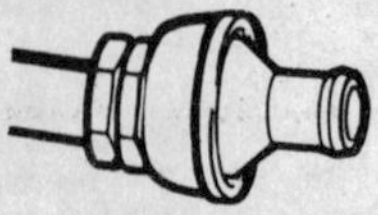 **AIR CHECK VALVE & PULSE AIR VALVE**	One way valve allows thermactor air to enter exhaust system. Pulse air valve IS NOT interchangeable with air check valve.
 **AIR CLEANER COLD WEATHER MODULATOR** 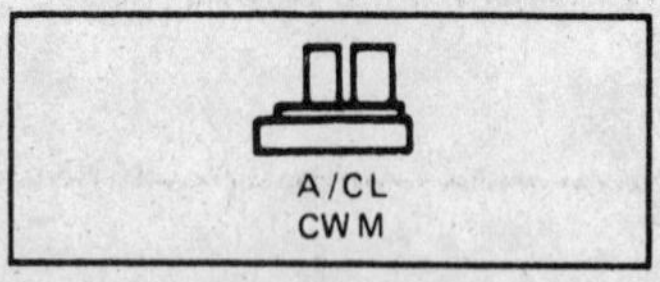 (symbol: A/CL CWM)	Bimetal sensor located in air cleaner to control flow of vacuum to air cleaner duct door motor. When air temperature rises sufficiently, cuts off vacuum to duct door motor, allowing outside air to air cleaner. Traps vacuum to prevent duct from going to hot position during cold weather acceleration.
 **AIR CLEANER TEMPERATURE CONTROL SENSOR** 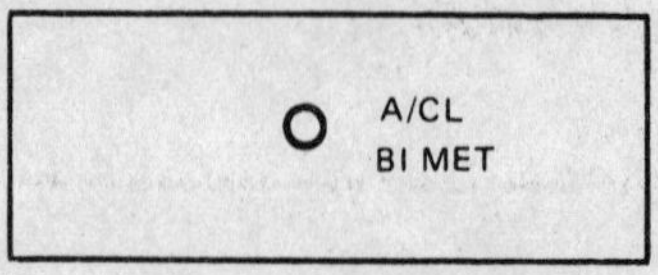 (symbol: A/CL BI MET)	Bimetal sensor installed in air cleaner tray. Also controls position of air duct door by bimetal switch action but does not trap vacuum during acceleration.
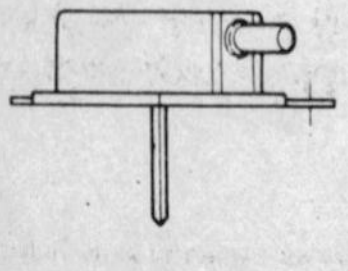 **AIR CLEANER VACUUM MOTOR** 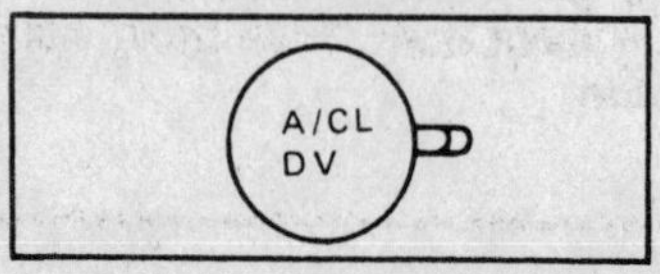 (symbol: A/CL DV)	Regulates position of door within air cleaner duct to allow warm or cold air as signaled by Air Cleaner Temperature Sensor and Cold Weather Modulator.

FORD MOTOR CO. EMISSION COMPONENTS (Cont.)

COMPONENT AND SYMBOL	OPERATION
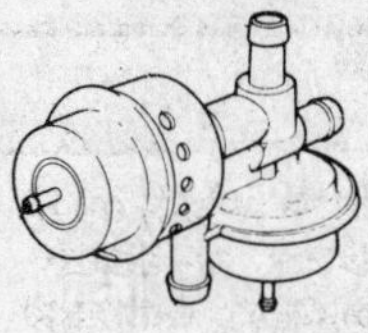 AIR SUPPLY CONTROL VALVES 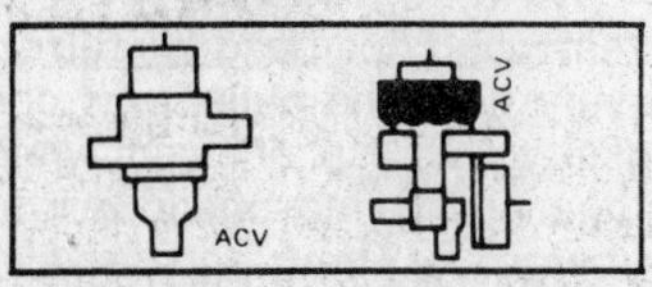 (ACV)	Operated by vacuum to direct air pump output to exhaust manifold or downstream to catalyst system depending on system requirements.
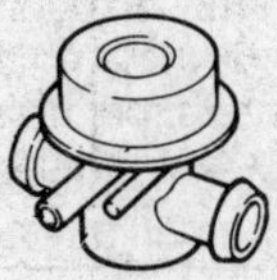 ANTI-BACKFIRE (GULP) VALVE 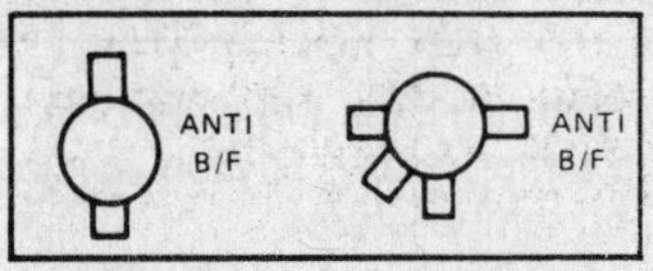 (ANTI B/F)	Vacuum operated valve downstream from air by-pass valve used to divert partial thermactor air to intake manifold when triggered by intake manifold vacuum during sudden deceleration.
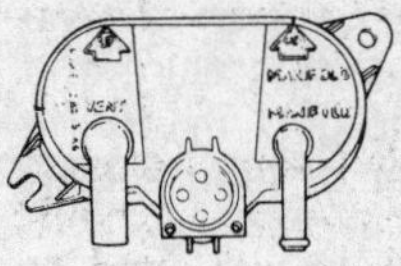 BAROMETRIC/MANIFOLD ABSOLUTE PRESSURE (B/MAP) SENSOR 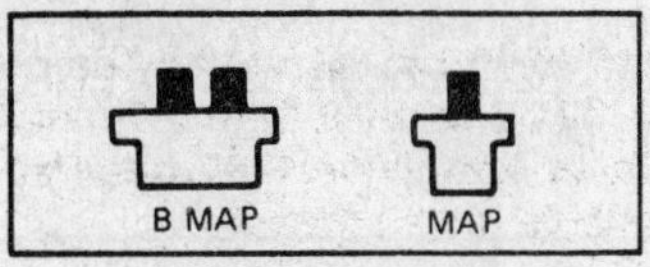 (B MAP, MAP)	Mounted on right inner fender, senses barometric pressure of atmosphere and manifold absolute pressure of air/fuel mixture in intake manifold.
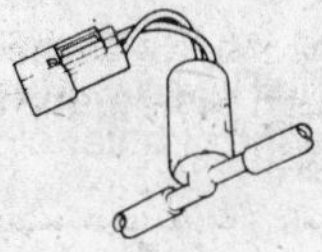 CANISTER PURGE SOLENOID & FUEL BOWL VENT VALVE 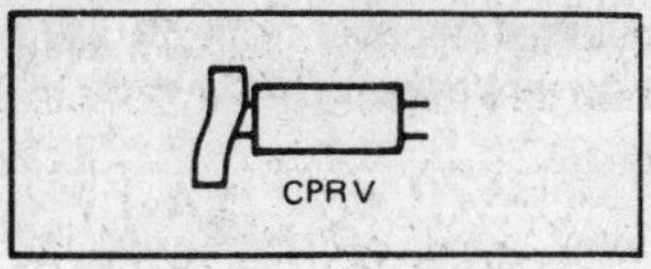 (CPRV)	Normally closed solenoid valve controls vapors from canister to intake manifold. Opened or closed by signal from electronic control assembly during various engine operating modes.
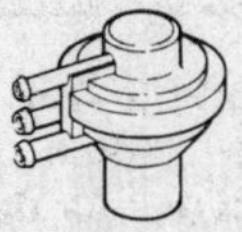 CANISTER PURGE VALVE  (PURGE CV)	Vacuum operated purge valve controls flow of vapors from carbon canister to engine.
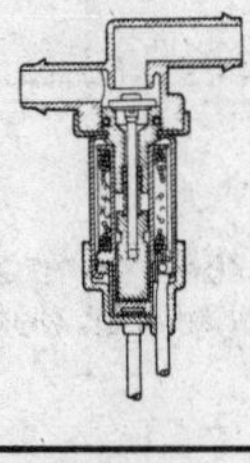 CARBURETOR FUEL BOWL SOLENOID VENT VALVE 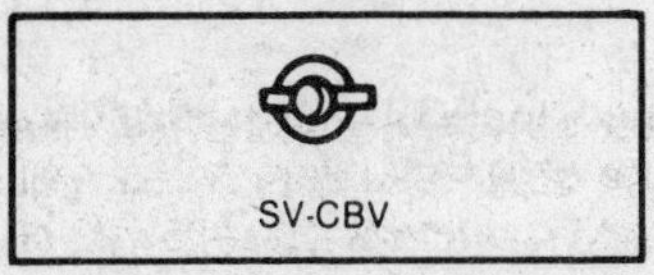 (SV-CBV)	A normally open valve located in fuel bowl vent line. The valve closes off the fuel bowl vent line when engine is running and returns to normally open position when ignition is turned off.
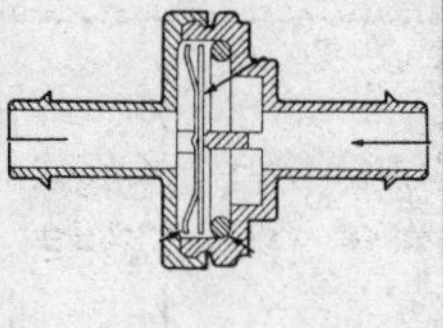 CARBURETOR FUEL BOWL THERMAL VENT VALVE 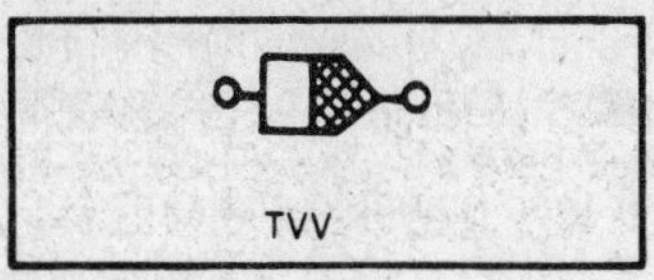 (TVV)	Inserted in carburetor-to-canister vent line. Valve is closed when engine compartment is cold. This prevents fuel tank vapors, generated when fuel tank heats up before engine compartment does, from being vented through carburetor fuel bowl.

FORD MOTOR CO. EMISSION COMPONENTS (Cont.)

COMPONENT AND SYMBOL		OPERATION
	DISTRIBUTOR MODULATOR SOLENOID VALVE 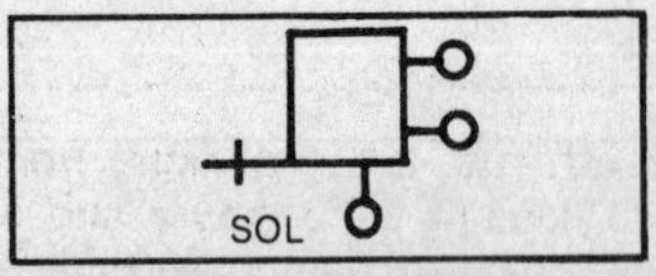 SOL	Two and three port valves are used. Two port valves are used in the Extended Idle Air Dump System, and some valves have an atmospheric vent. Those without a vent are at rest when open and energized when closed. Valves with a vent have the outlet port opened to the inlet port and closed to atmospheric vent when de-energized. Outlet port is opened to atmospheric vent and closed to inlet port when energized. Three port valves consist of 3 vacuum ports and operates the same as a two port valve with an atmospheric vent, except the 3rd port takes the place of the atmospheric vent.
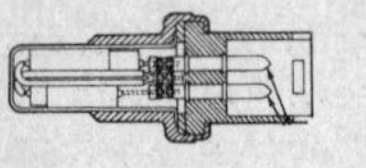	DUAL COOLANT TEMPERATURE SWITCH	This switch provides the electronic control system data on coolant temperature. Switch is closed at normal engine operating temperatures.
	EXHAUST GAS RECIRCULATION (EGR) VALVE 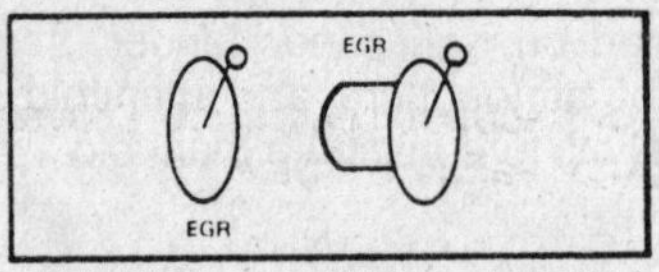 EGR EGR	Operated by engine vacuum directly or as signaled by EGR vacuum solenoids. Admits exhaust gas to the combustion cycle, lowering combustion temperature and reducing generation of Oxides of Nitrogen (NOx). In addition, EEC models use an EGR cooler to reduce EGR gas temperatures.
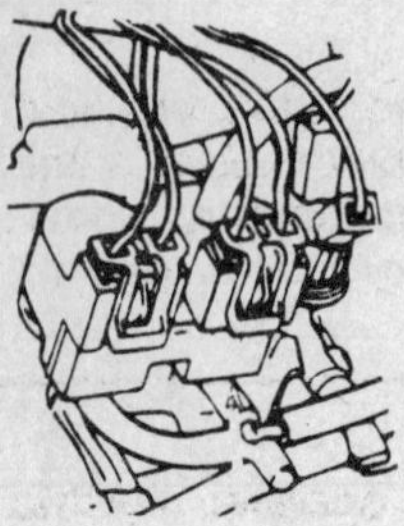	EGR & THERMACTOR SOLENOID VALVES 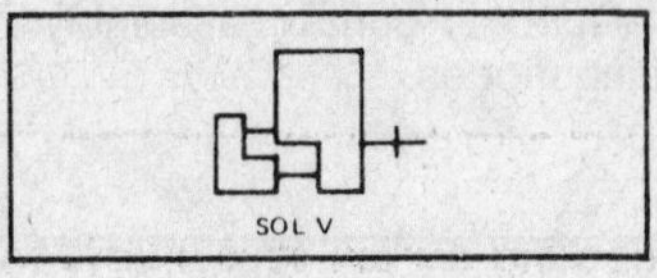 SOL V	Operated as signaled from EEC to control EGR valve. May be similar in appearance to thermactor air control solenoid valves.
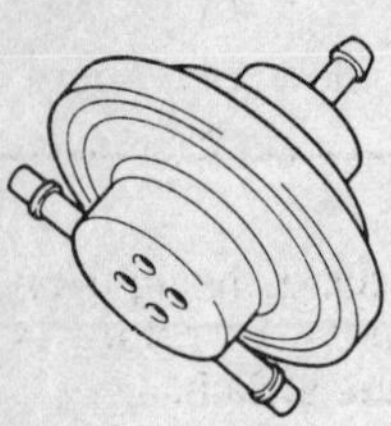	EGR VACUUM LOAD CONTROL (WOT) VALVE 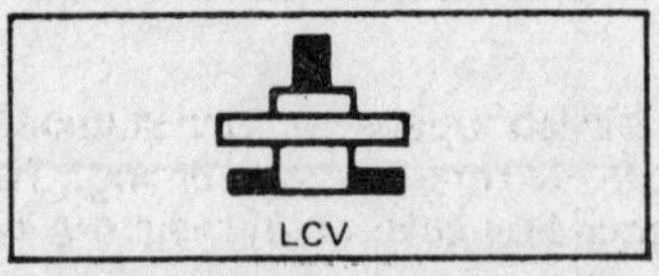 LCV	Operated by vacuum signal from carburetor venturi port. At or near wide open throttle (WOT), the valve interrupts vacuum to EGR valve.
	EGR VALVE POSITION (EVP) SENSOR	Attached to EGR valve assembly, indicates position of EGR valve to EEC.
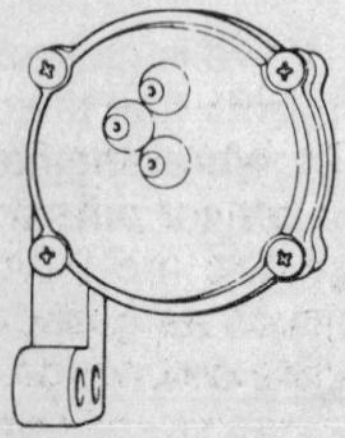	EGR VENTURI VACUUM AMPLIFIER (VVA) 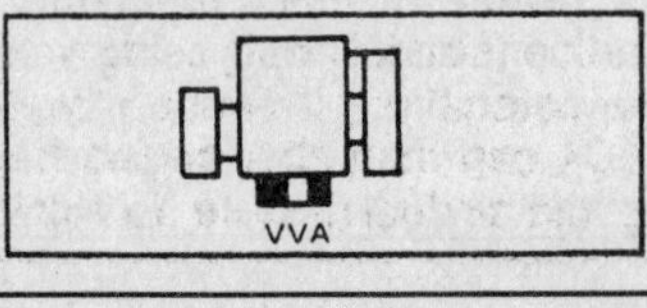 VVA	Uses relatively weak vacuum signal from venturi to control EGR valve. Contains a check valve and a relief valve that opens whenever venturi vacuum signal is equal to or greater than manifold vacuum.

FORD MOTOR CO. EMISSION COMPONENTS (Cont.)

COMPONENT AND SYMBOL	OPERATION
 EXHAUST HEAT CONTROL VALVE 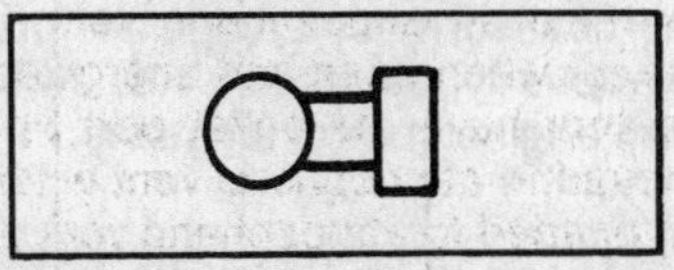	Used to divert hot gasses from exhaust manifold to intake manifold riser pad to heat incoming air/fuel charge. Two types are used, a bimetal spring type and a vacuum actuated type.
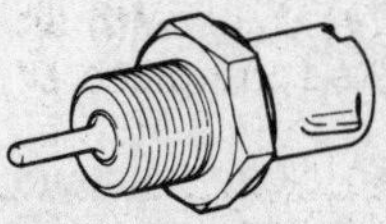 ENGINE COOLANT TEMPERATURE SENSOR (ECT)	Threaded into tube at right front of intake manifold. Detects coolant temperature and supplies information to Electronic Control Assembly (ECA).
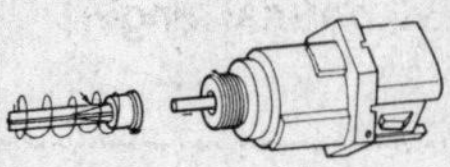 FEEDBACK CARBURETOR ACTUATOR MOTOR	Used on 7200 model carburetors, actuator is threaded into carburetor body. Its actuator shaft moves a fuel metering pintle valve to produce a leaner/richer air/fuel mixture. Actuator shaft moves in response to signals from oxygen sensor and EEC or MCU system.
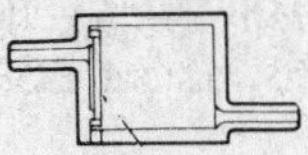 FUEL/VACUUM SEPARATOR  SA-FA	Used in vacuum system to prevent migration of fuel to distributor vacuum motor.
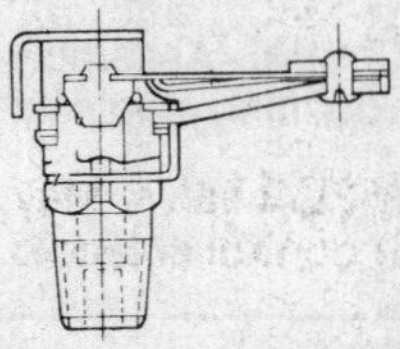 HOT IDLE COMPENSATOR 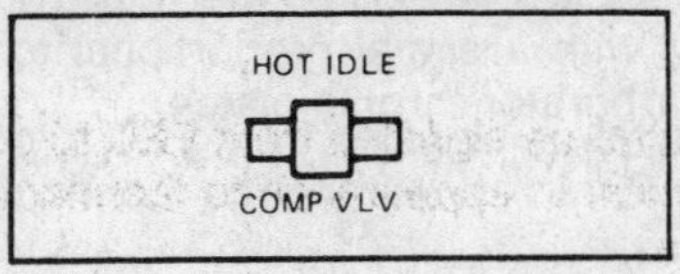 HOT IDLE COMP VLV	Bimetal spring causes air to be bled into intake manifold during extreme hot engine and idle operation. Engine idle speed also increases and results in engine cooling.
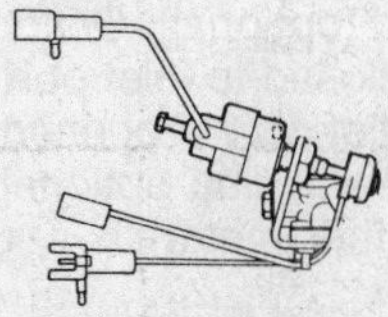 IDLE TRACKING SWITCH	Idle tracking switch is a mechanically operated electric switch held open by throttle linkage when throttle linkage is closed.
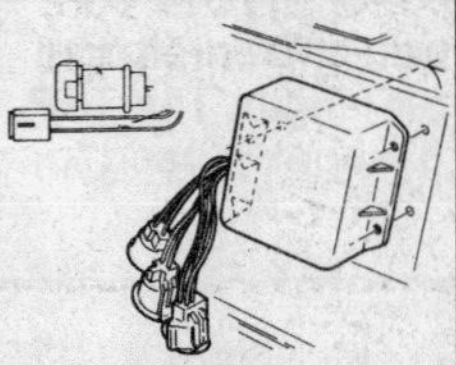 IGNITION BAROMETRIC PRESSURE SWITCH	This switch opens at low altitudes signaling the ignition module to retard spark timing. The amount of retard is controlled by calibration resistors inside the switch.
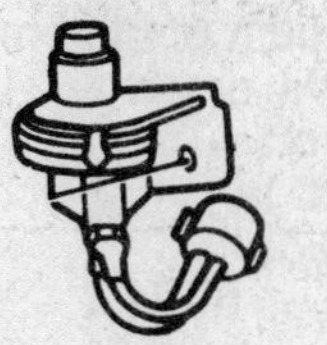 IGNITION TIMING VACUUM SWITCH 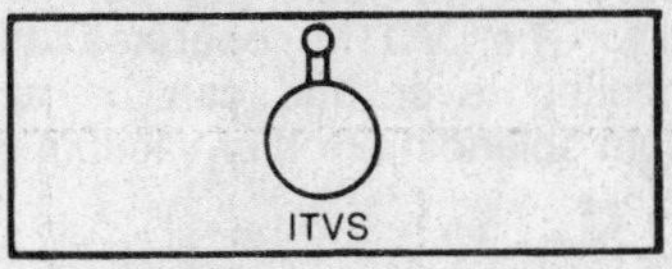 ITVS	This switch is open below a specified vacuum setting, signaling the ignition module to retard spark timing. Above the specified vacuum setting, the switch is closed and ignition module is in a non-retard spark timing mode. Amount of retard is controlled by calibration resistors inside switch assembly.
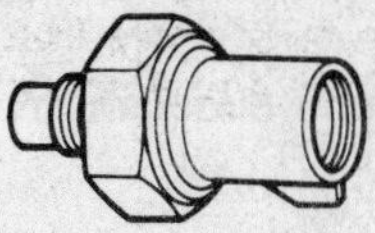 KNOCK SENSOR	Knock sensor is used to inform the ECA when engine detonation (spark knock) occurs. When the sensor detects engine detonation, it sends a voltage signal to the ECA. The ECA can then alter engine functions, such as ignition timing and air/fuel mixture, to eliminate engine detonation.

1983 Exhaust Emission Systems

FORD MOTOR CO. EMISSION COMPONENTS (Cont.)

COMPONENT AND SYMBOL		OPERATION
	MICROPROCESSOR CONTROL UNIT (MCU)	Microprocessor-based module is programmed to interface with various types of sensors, switches and actuators to perform engine control functions.
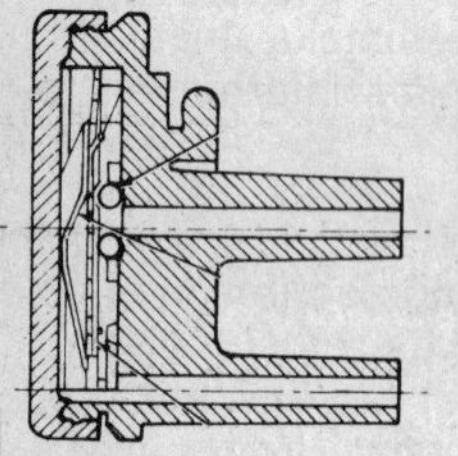	TEMPERATURE VACUUM SWITCH (TVS) 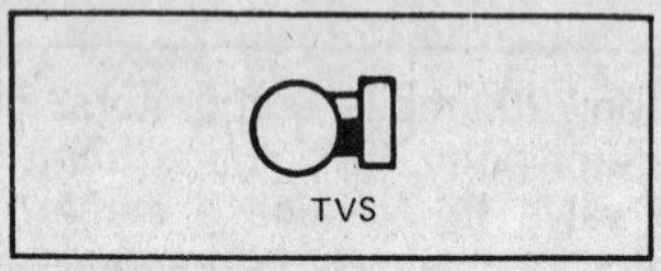 TVS	Incorporates a bimetal disc to open or close vacuum ports. May be used with distributor, purge or EGR systems.
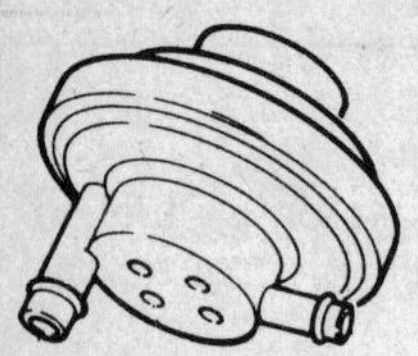	THERMACTOR IDLE VACUUM VALVE (TIV) 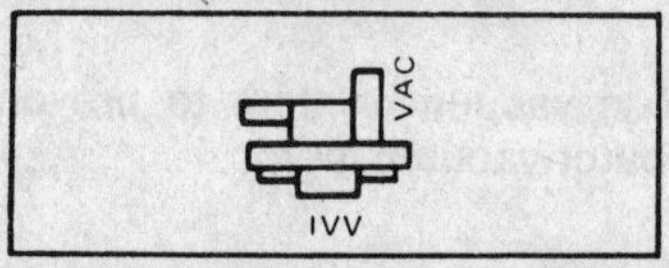 VAC IVV	Prevents excessive underbody temperature of exhaust system by diverting secondary air pump output during extended engine idling.
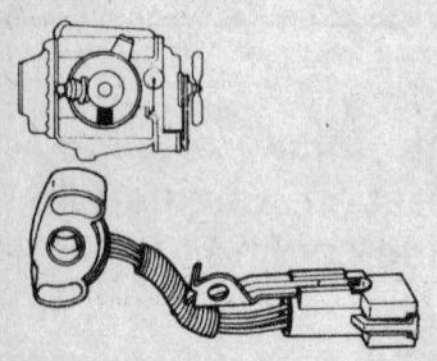	THROTTLE POSITION SENSOR	This sensor supplies the Electronic Control Assembly (ECA) with a signal proportional to the opening angle of the carburetor throttle plates.
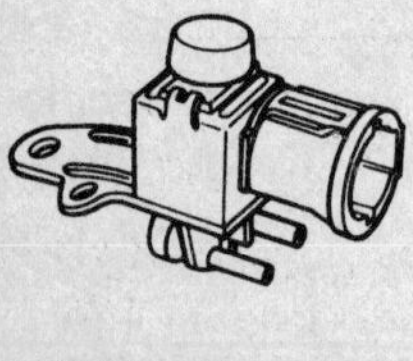	THROTTLE KICKER SOLENOID VALVE 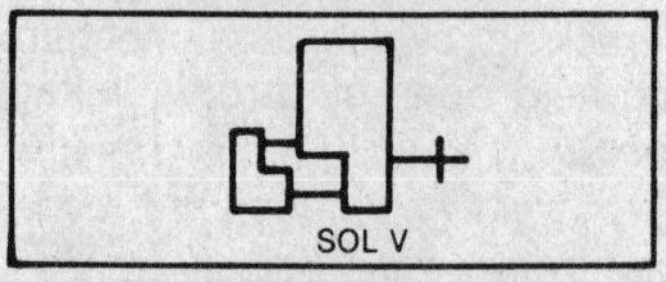 SOL V	Valve is normally closed and consists of 2 vacuum ports with an atmospheric vent to control bleed (optional). Outlet port is opened to atmospheric vent and closed to inlet port when de-energized. When energized, outlet port is opened to inlet port and closed to atmospheric vent. The optional control bleed is used to keep dirt and other materials out of the solenoid valve.
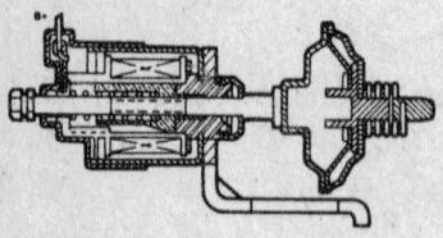	THROTTLE SOLENOID POSITIONER WITH DASHPOT	Two TSP with dashpots are used, one with a fixed plunger length and one with an adjustable plunger length. The TSP acts as a variable throttle stop and the dashpot is used for a gradual controlled throttle closing.
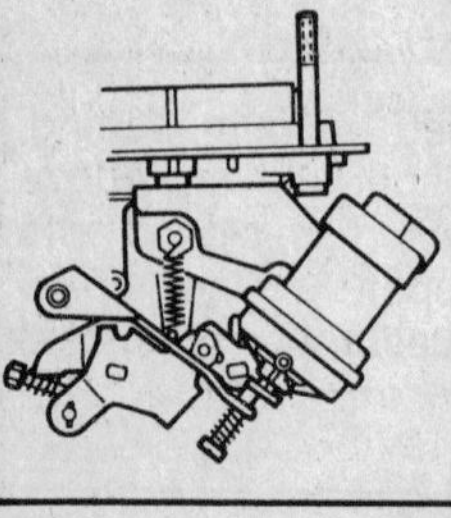	THROTTLE SOLENOID POSITIONER WITH VACUUM OPERATED THROTTLE MODULATOR (TSP-VOTM)  TSP-VOTM	The solenoid portion of this device is used as an anti-dieseling TSP and an A/C TSP. The vacuum portion may be used for maintaining a cold idle RPM or as an A/C VOTM. The VOTM operates the throttle through a connecting lever and can be actuated by an electric vacuum solenoid or other vacuum control device.
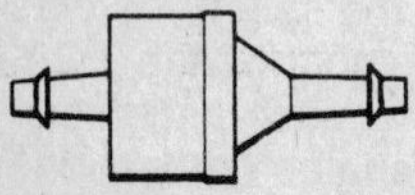	VACUUM CHECK VALVE 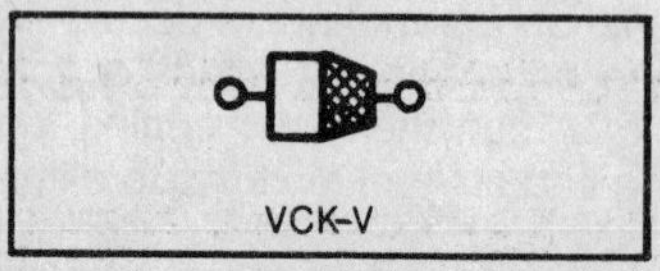 VCK-V	Vacuum check valves block air flow in one direction and allow free air flow in the other direction.

1983 Exhaust Emission Systems

FORD MOTOR CO. EMISSION COMPONENTS (Cont.)

COMPONENT AND SYMBOL	OPERATION
VACUUM CONTROL VALVES (VCV) 2-PORT VCV, 3-PORT VCV, 4-PORT VCV	Temperature operated vacuum switches with 2 or more ports. Utilize wax pellet or bimetal to either open or close vacuum ports. Normally mounted in some part of cooling system so that base is immersed in coolant. May be normally open or normally closed. One version includes an electrical vacuum switch at top end.
VACUUM DELAY VALVES VDV, DV-TW	Inserted in vacuum lines to provide for gradual application or release of vacuum to engine or emission control devices. May be one or two way valves, depending on function and part of system affected.
VACUUM OPERATED THROTTLE MODULATOR VOTM	When vacuum is applied, plunger extends to vary throttle stop position.
VACUUM REGULATOR VRV	May be 2, 3 or 4 port, used to control vacuum advance to distributor.
VACUUM REGULATOR & SOLENOID ASSEMBLY VENT, VR/S	Controls vacuum to the 6500 feedback carburetor on 2.3L engines. This assembly converts manifold vacuum to a variable vacuum output signal. The vacuum output signal is controlled by an electrical signal from the MCU module. It is used to vary the air/fuel ratio in the carburetor.
VACUUM RESTRICTOR V REST, T REST	Orifice-type flow restrictor used in vacuum lines of various systems to control flow rate and/or timing to components.
VACUUM VENT VALVES VACVV-T, VACVV-D	Controls induction of fresh air into system to prevent accumulation of fuel vapors which could cause decay of vacuum diaphragms. May be vent valve only or combined vent and delay valve. Valves should always be mounted so ports point downward.

1983 Exhaust Emission Systems

1982 FORD MOTOR CO. VACUUM DIAGRAMS

NOTE: **As Ford Motor Co. does not release its vacuum diagrams until the end of the model year, these 1982 vacuum diagrams were not included in the 1982 Emission Control Domestic Supplement. The following 1982 vacuum diagrams apply to Ford, Lincoln and Mercury models.**

1982 FORD MOTOR CO. VACUUM DIAGRAM INDEX

Engine & Model	Application	Transmission	A/C	Non A/C	Calibration	Fig. No.
1.6L (98") 4-Cylinder						
EXP, LN7	Exc. Hi. Alt.	Manual	X		1-3S-R0	1
EXP, LN7	Exc. Hi. Alt.	Manual		X	1-3S-R0	2
EXP, LN7	Exc. Hi. Alt.	Manual	X		1-3Y-R10	3
EXP, LN7	Exc. Hi. Alt.	Manual		X	1-3Y-R10	4
EXP, LN7	Exc. Hi. Alt.	Manual	X		1-3S-R11	5
EXP, LN7	Exc. Hi. Alt.	Manual		X	1-3S-R11	6
EXP, LN7	Federal	Auto.		X	1-4E-R0	7
EXP, LN7	Calif.	Auto.		X	1-4S-R0	7
EXP, LN7	Calif.	Auto.		X	1-4S-R10	7
EXP, LN7	Federal	Auto.	X		1-4E-R0	8
EXP, LN7	Calif.	Auto.	X		1-4S-R0	8
EXP, LN7	Calif.	Auto.	X		1-4S-R10	8
Escort, EXP, LN7, Lynx	Exc. Hi. Alt.	Manual			2-3B-R10	9
Escort, EXP, LN7, Lynx	Exc. Hi. Alt.	Manual	X		2-3C-R0	10
Escort, EXP, LN7, Lynx	Exc. Hi. Alt.	Manual			2-3C-R11	10
Escort, EXP, LN7, Lynx	Exc. Hi. Alt.	Manual	X		2-3E-R0	10
Escort, EXP, LN7, Lynx	Exc. Hi. Alt.	Manual		X	2-3C-R0	11
Escort, EXP, LN7, Lynx	Exc. Hi. Alt.	Manual		X	2-3E-R0	11
Escort, Lynx	Federal	Manual			2-3D-R0	12
Escort, Lynx	Federal	Manual			2-3D-R1	12
Escort, Lynx	Federal	Manual			2-3D-R16	12
Escort, EXP, LN7, Lynx	Hi. Alt.	Manual	X		2-3X-R0	13
Escort, EXP, LN7, Lynx	Hi. Alt.	Manual		X	2-3X-R0	14
Escort, EXP, LN7, Lynx	Federal	Auto.			2-4B-R10	15
Escort, EXP, LN7, Lynx	Calif.	Auto.			2-4T-R10	15
Escort, EXP, LN7, Lynx	Calif.	Auto.			2-4C-R0	16
Escort, EXP, LN7, Lynx	Calif.	Auto.			2-4C-R14	16
Escort, EXP, LN7, Lynx	Calif.	Auto.	X	X	2-4Q-R0	16
Escort, EXP, LN7, Lynx	Calif.	Auto.			2-4Q-R10	16
Escort, EXP, LN7, Lynx	Calif.	Auto.			2-4Q-R11	16
Escort, EXP, LN7, Lynx	Calif.	Auto.			2-4Q-R13	16
Escort, EXP, LN7, Lynx	Hi. Alt.	Auto.			2-4X-R0	17
Escort, EXP, LN7, Lynx	Hi. Alt.	Auto.			2-4X-R11	17
Escort, EXP, LN7, Lynx	Hi. Alt.	Auto.			2-4Y-R10	18
2.3L (140") 4-Cylinder						
Capri, Mustang Turbo	All	All			1-5F-R10	19
Capri, Cougar, Fairmont, Granada, Mustang, Zephyr	Federal	4-Spd. Man.			2-5B-R0	20
Capri, Cougar, Fairmont, Granada, Mustang, Zephyr	Federal	5-Spd. Man.			2-5B-R0	21
Capri, Fairmont, Mustang, Zephyr	Federal	Manual	X	X	2-5C-R0	22
Capri, Fairmont, Mustang, Zephyr	Federal	Manual	X	X	2-5C-R10	22
Capri, Fairmont, Mustang, Zephyr	Federal	Manual		X	2-5C-R11	23
Capri, Cougar, Fairmont, Granada, Mustang, Zephyr	Calif.	Manual	X	X	2-5N-R0	24
Capri, Cougar, Fairmont, Granada, Mustang, Zephyr	Calif.	Manual	X	X	2-5P-R0	24
Capri, Cougar, Fairmont, Granada, Mustang, Zephyr	Federal	Auto.	X	X	2-6A-R0	25
Capri, Cougar, Fairmont, Granada, Mustang, Zephyr	Federal	Auto.	X	X	2-6A-R10	25
Capri, Cougar, Fairmont, Granada, Mustang, Zephyr	Calif.	Auto.	X	X	2-6N-R0	26
Capri, Cougar, Fairmont, Granada, Mustang, Zephyr	Hi. Alt.	Auto.	X	X	2-6W-R0	27
Capri, Cougar, Fairmont, Granada, Mustang, Zephyr	Hi. Alt.	Man.			2-5W-R0	28

1982 FORD MOTOR CO. VACUUM DIAGRAMS (Cont.)

1982 FORD MOTOR CO. VACUUM DIAGRAM INDEX (Cont.)

Engine & Model	Application	Transmission	A/C	Non A/C	Calibration	Fig. No.
2.3L (140") 4-Cylinder (Cont.)						
Capri, Mustang	Federal	Manual			2-5A-R0	29
Cougar, Fairmont, Granada, Zephyr	Federal	Manual			2-5B-R1	30
3.3L (200") 6-Cylinder						
Thunderbird, XR7	All	Auto.	X	X	1-12B-R0	31
Capri, Cougar, Fairmont, Granada, Mustang, Zephyr	Calif.	Auto.	X	X	2-12B-R10	32
Cougar, Fairmont, Granada, Zephyr	Federal	Auto.	X	X	2-12T-R0	32
Capri, Cougar, Fairmont, Granada, Mustang, Zephyr	Federal	Auto.	X	X	2-12T-R2	32
Cougar, Granada	Federal	Auto.	X	X	2-12T-R4	33
Capri, Cougar, Fairmont, Granada, Mustang, Zephyr	Federal	Auto.	X	X	2-12T-R15	33
Capri, Fairmont, Mustang, Zephyr	Hi. Alt.	Auto.	X	X	2-12W-R0	34
3.8L (230") 6-Cylinder						
Cougar, Granada	Federal	Auto.			2-14A-R0	35
Cougar, Granada	Federal	Auto.			2-14A-R13	35
Cougar, Granada	Federal	Auto.			2-14B-R1	36
Cougar, Granada	Federal	Auto.	X	X	2-14B-R10	37
Thunderbird, XR7	Federal	Auto.			2-14C-R0	38
Thunderbird, XR7	Federal	Auto.			2-14C-R13	38
Lincoln Continental	Federal	Auto.			2-14D-R0	38
Thunderbird, XR7	Federal	Auto.		X	2-14C-R11	39
Thunderbird, XR7	Federal	Auto.	X	X	2-14E-R0	40
Thunderbird, XR7	Federal	Auto.	X	X	2-14E-R10	41
Cougar, Granada	Calif.	Auto.			2-14N-R0	42
Cougar, Granada	Calif.	Auto.			2-14N-R1	42
Cougar, Granada	Calif.	Auto.			2-14N-R10	42
Thunderbird, XR7	Calif.	Auto.			2-14Q-R1	42
Thunderbird, XR7	Calif.	Auto.			2-14Q-R11	42
Lincoln Continental	All	Auto.			2-14R-R1	43
Lincoln Continental	All	Auto.			2-14R-R11	43
Cougar, Granada	Hi. Alt.	Auto.			2-14W-R0	44
Cougar, Granada	Hi. Alt.	Auto.	X	X	2-14W-R10	45
Thunderbird, XR7	Hi. Alt.	Auto.	X	X	2-14X-R10	45
Thunderbird, XR7	Hi. Alt.	Auto.			2-14X-R0	46
Thunderbird, XR7	Hi. Alt.	Auto.			2-14X-R1	46
4.2L (255") V8						
Ford, Mercury	Exc. Hi. Alt.	Auto.			1-18U-R0	47
Ford, Mercury	Exc. Hi. Alt.	Auto.			2-18U-R10	47
Fairmont, Zephyr	Exc. Hi. Alt.	Auto.			2-18B-R0	48
Capri, Mustang	Exc. Hi. Alt.	Auto.			2-18B-R0	49
Capri, Mustang	Exc. Hi. Alt.	Auto.			2-18B-R13	50
Thunderbird, XR7	Federal	Auto.			2-18C-R4	51
Thunderbird, XR7	Federal	Auto.		X	2-18C-R5	51
Thunderbird, XR7	Federal	Auto.			2-18C-R11	52
Thunderbird, XR7	Exc. Hi. Alt.	Auto.			2-18Q-R0	53
Ford, Mercury	All	Auto.			2-18U-R11	54
Capri, Mustang	Hi. Alt.	Auto.			2-18W-R0	55
Fairmont, Zephyr	Hi. Alt.	Auto.			2-18W-R0	56
Thunderbird, XR7	Hi. Alt.	Auto.			2-18X-R0	57
5.0L (302") V8 Carbureted						
All 5.0L Models	Exc. Hi. Alt.	Auto.			1-20B-R1	58
Ford, Mercury	Exc. Hi. Alt.	Auto.			1-20N-R10	59
Ford, Mercury	Federal	Auto.			2-20B-R0	60
All 5.0L Models	Exc. Hi. Alt.	Auto.			2-20D-R1	61
Lincoln Continental	Exc. Hi. Alt.	Auto.			2-20R-R2	62
Lincoln Continental	Exc. Hi. Alt.	Auto.			2-20R-R16	63
Lincoln Continental	Hi. Alt.	Auto.			2-20Y-R0	64

1982 FORD MOTOR CO. VACUUM DIAGRAMS (Cont.)

1982 FORD MOTOR CO. VACUUM DIAGRAM INDEX (Cont.)

Engine & Model	Application	Transmission	A/C	Non A/C	Calibration	Fig. No.
5.0L (302") V8 Carbureted (Cont.)						
Ford, Mercury	Hi. Alt.	Auto.			2-20Z-R0	65
Capri, Mustang	Federal	Manual			2-21E-R10	66
Capri, Mustang	Federal	Manual			2-21E-R11	66
Capri, Mustang	Calif.	Manual			2-21S-R0	67
Capri, Mustang	Hi. Alt.	Manual			2-21Y-R10	68
5.0L (302") V8 Central Fuel Injection (CFI)						
Lincoln Mark VI, Town Car	Hi. Alt.	Auto.			1-22B-R0	69
Lincoln Mark VI, Town Car	Calif.	Auto.			1-22P-R0	69
Lincoln Mark VI, Town Car	Federal	Auto.			2-22A-R0	70
Lincoln Mark VI, Town Car	Exc. Calif.	Auto.			2-22Y-R11	71
5.8L W (351") V8						
Ford, Mercury	Calif.	Auto.			2-24P-R6	72
Ford, Mercury	Exc. Calif.	Auto.			2-24P-R10	73

CALIBRATION NUMBER IDENTIFICATION

To identify the calibration number, find the engine code label, generally located at the front of the engine. Although there are several label styles, the engine calibration number is shown on each label. Calibration codes will begin with the digit indicating current model year. For example, calibrations currently listed for 1982 Ford Vacuum Diagrams all begin with "2".

Each vehicle is also equipped with a decal containing emission control data applying to that vehicle and its engine. These decals are usually located on the underside of the hood, the radiator support, zip tube, fan shroud or other visible engine compartment location.

Exhaust Emission Control Label

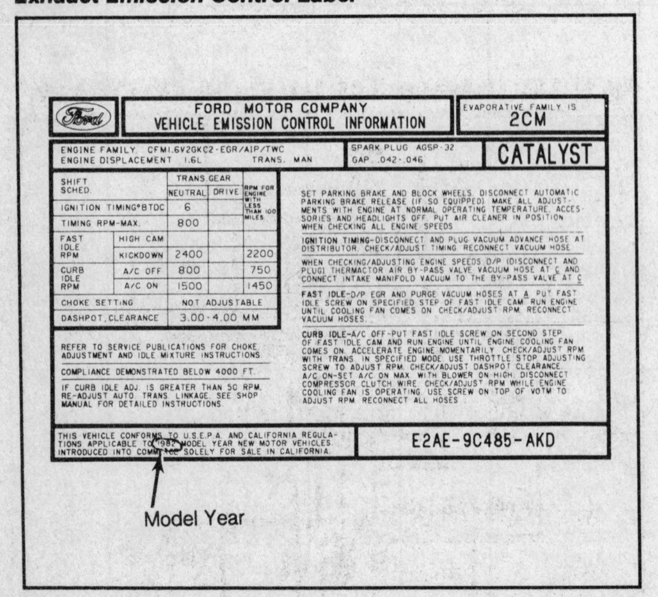

Engine Code Labels

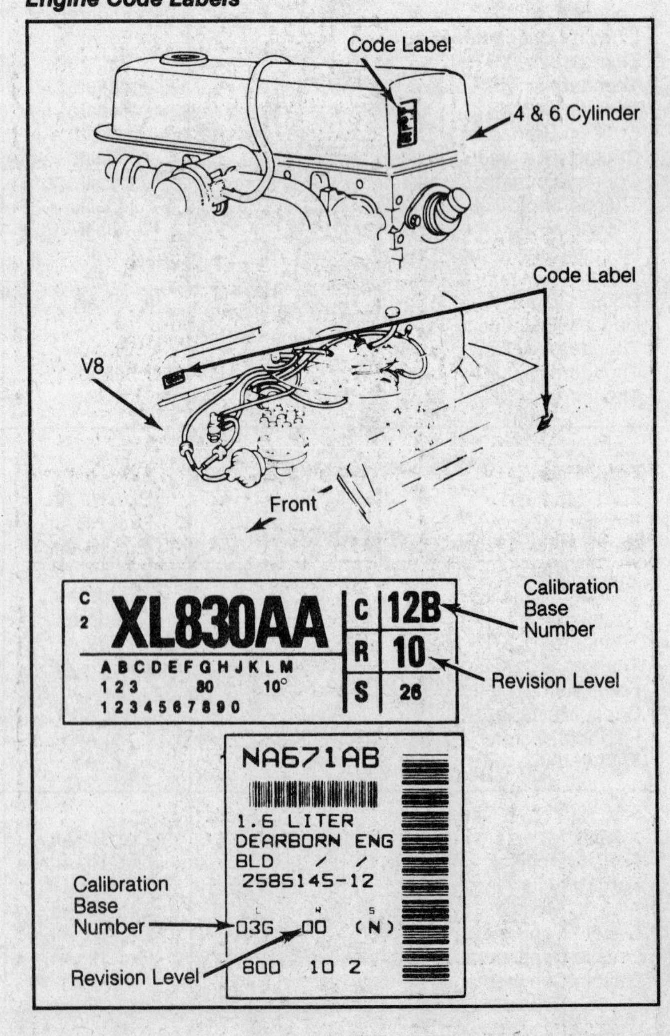

1983 Exhaust Emission Systems

1982 FORD MOTOR CO. VACUUM DIAGRAMS

Fig. 1: **1.6L; Calibration 1-3S-R0; Exc. Hi. Alt.; EXP & LN7**

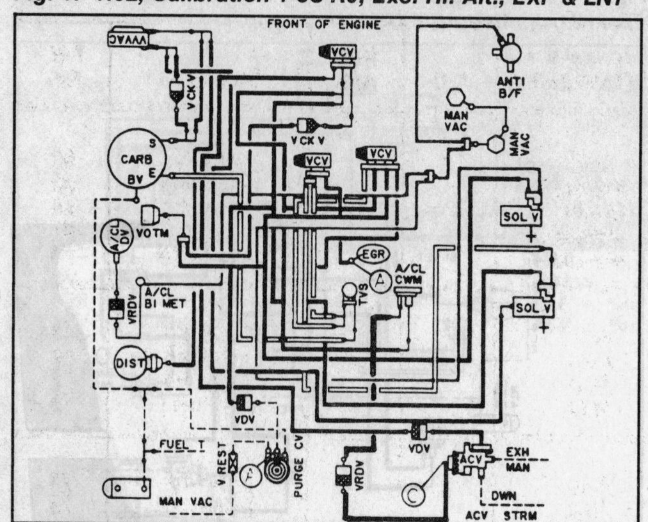

Fig. 2: **1.6L; Calibration 1-3S-R0; Exc. Hi. Alt.; EXP & LN7**

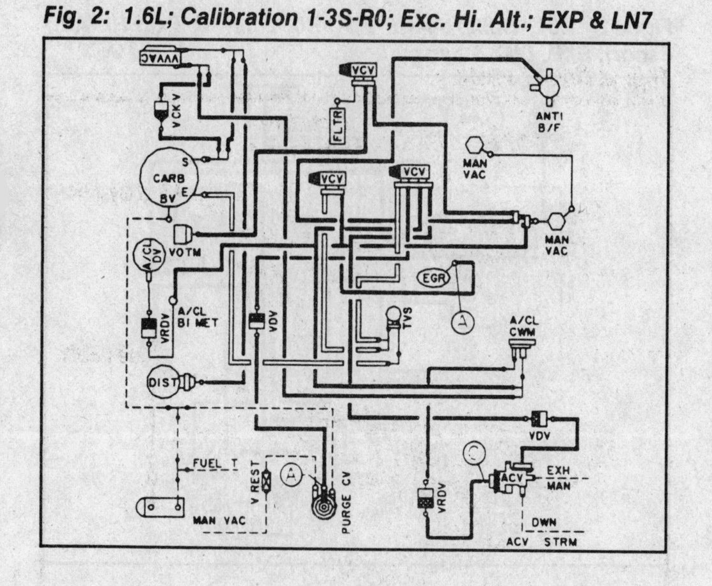

Fig. 3: **1.6L; Calibration 1-3Y-R10; Exc. Hi. Alt.; EXP & LN7**

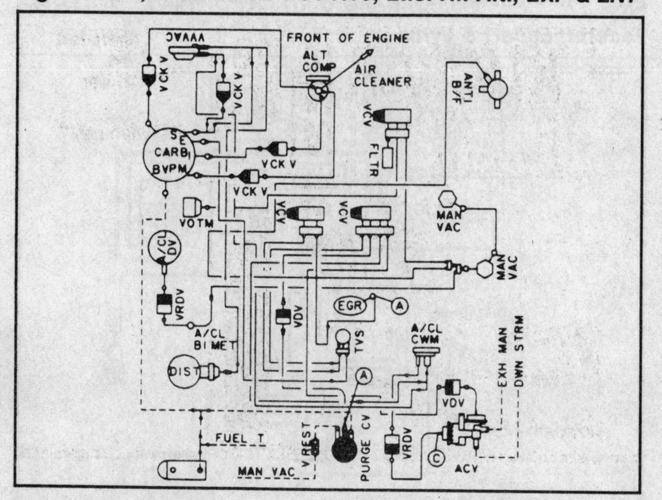

Fig. 4: **1.6L; Calibration 1-3Y-R10; Exc. Hi. Alt.; EXP & LN7**

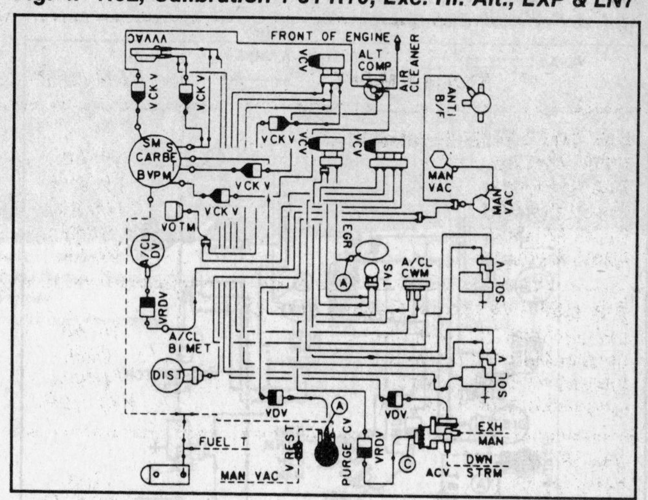

Fig. 5: **1.6L; Calibration 1-3S-R11; Exc. Hi. Alt.; EXP & LN7**

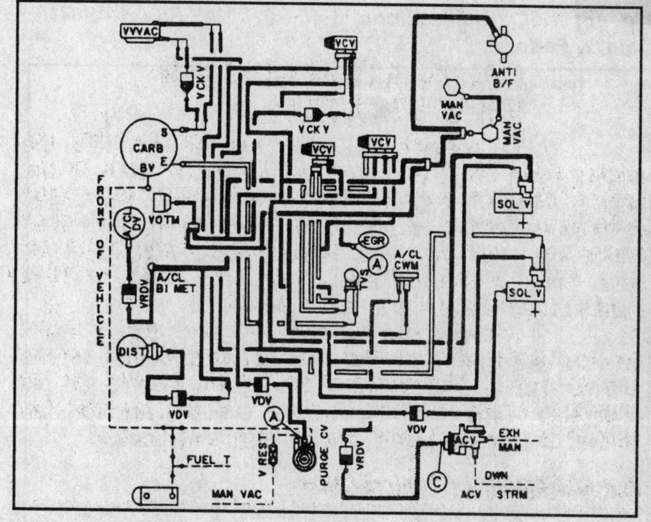

Fig. 6: **1.6L; Calibration 1-3S-R11; Exc. Hi. Alt.; EXP & LN7**

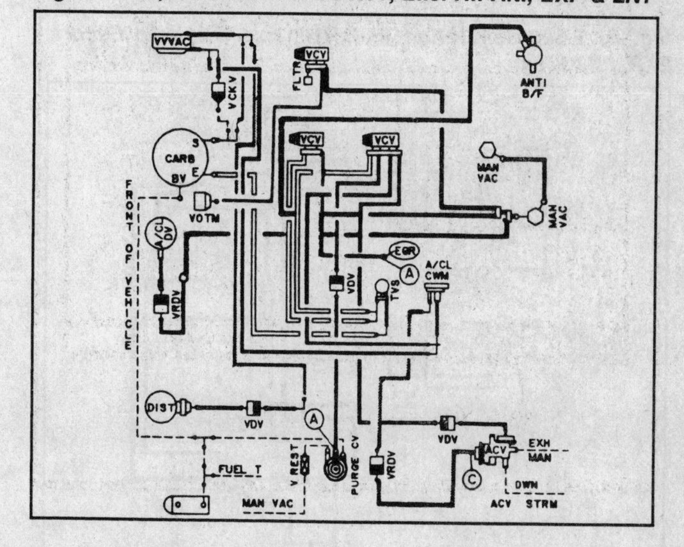

1982 FORD MOTOR CO. VACUUM DIAGRAMS (Cont.)

Fig. 7: 1.6L; Calibrations 1-4E-R0, 1-4S-R0, 1-4S-R10; Calif. & Federal; EXP & LN7

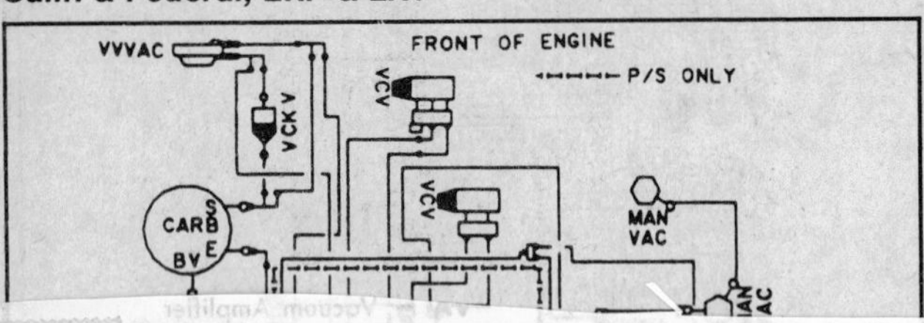

Fig. 10: 1.6L; Calibrations 2-3C-R0, 2-3C-R11, 2-3E-R0; Exc. Hi. Alt.; Escort, EXP, LN7 & Lynx

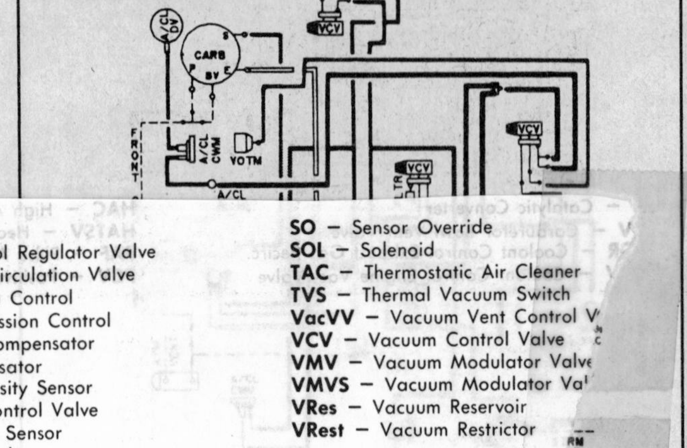

A/CL – Air Cleaner
ACkV – Air Check Valve
ACV – Air Control Valve
AIR – Air Injection Reactor
AIVV – Air Idle Vacuum Valve
ANTI-BFV – Anti-Backfire Valve
BiMet – Air Temperature Control Sensor
B/P – Back Pressure Transducer
BPV – By-pass Valve
CAT – Catalytic Converter
CV – Control Valve
DIST – Distributor
ECRV – Emission Control Regulator Valve
EGR – Exhaust Gas Recirculation Valve
FDC – Fuel Deceleration Control
FVEC – Fuel Vapor Emission Control
HAC – High Altitude Compensator
HIC – Hot Idle Compensator
KS – Spark Knock Intensity Sensor
LCV – Vacuum Load Control Valve
OXS – Exhaust Oxygen Sensor
PCV – Purge Control Valve
SO – Sensor Override
SOL – Solenoid
TAC – Thermostatic Air Cleaner
TVS – Thermal Vacuum Switch
VacVV – Vacuum Vent Control V
VCV – Vacuum Control Valve
VMV – Vacuum Modulator Valve
VMVS – Vacuum Modulator Val
VRes – Vacuum Reservoir
VRest – Vacuum Restrictor

Fig. 8: 1.6L; Calibrations 1-4E-R0, 1-4S-R0, 1-4S-R10; Calif. & Federal; EXP & LN7

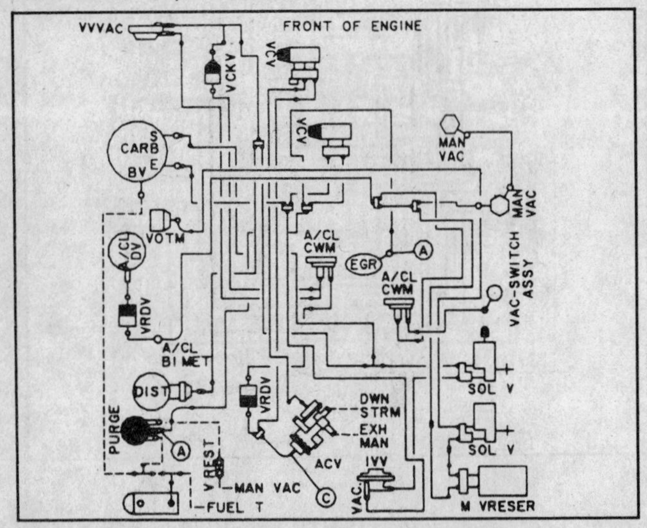

Fig. 11: 1.6L; Calibrations 2-3C-R0, 2-3E-R0; Exc. Hi. Alt.; Escort, EXP, LN7 & Lynx

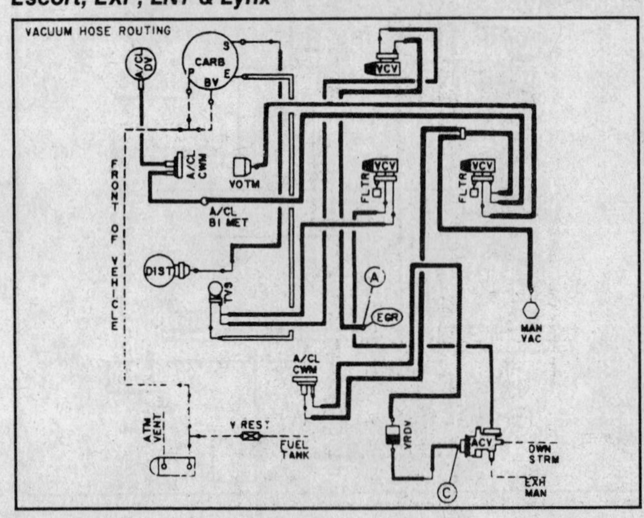

Fig. 9: 1.6L; Calibration 2-3B-R10; Exc. Hi. Alt.; Escort, EXP, LN7 & Lynx

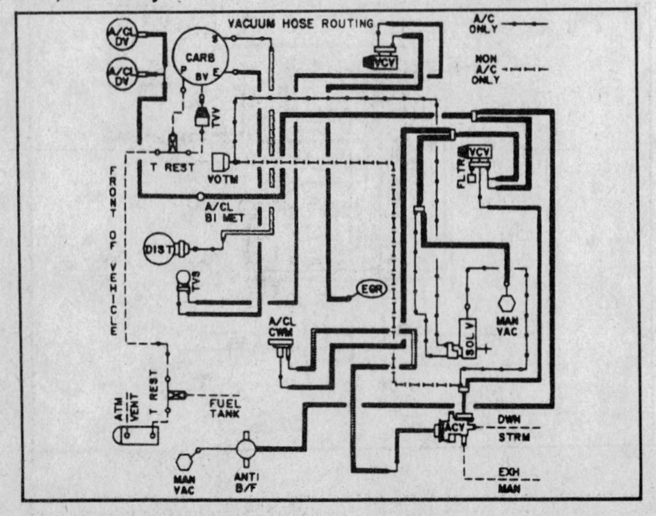

Fig. 12: 1.6L; Calibrations 2-3D-R0, 2-3D-R1, 2-3D-R16; Federal; Escort & Lynx

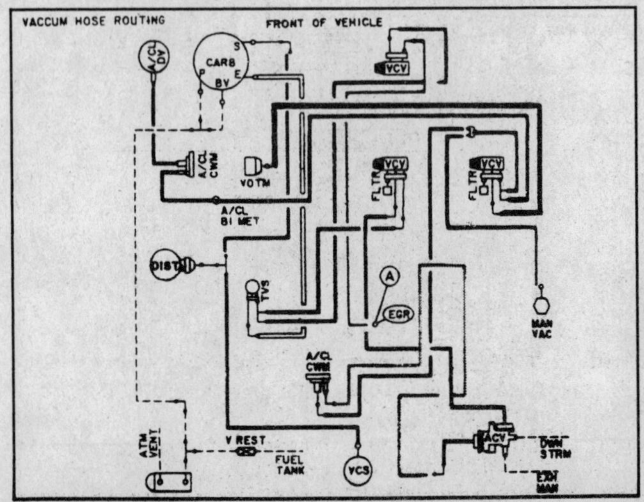

1982 FORD MOTOR CO. VACUUM DIAGRAMS (Cont.)

Fig. 13: 1.6L; Calibration 2-3X-R0; Hi. Alt.; Escort, EXP, LN7 & Lynx

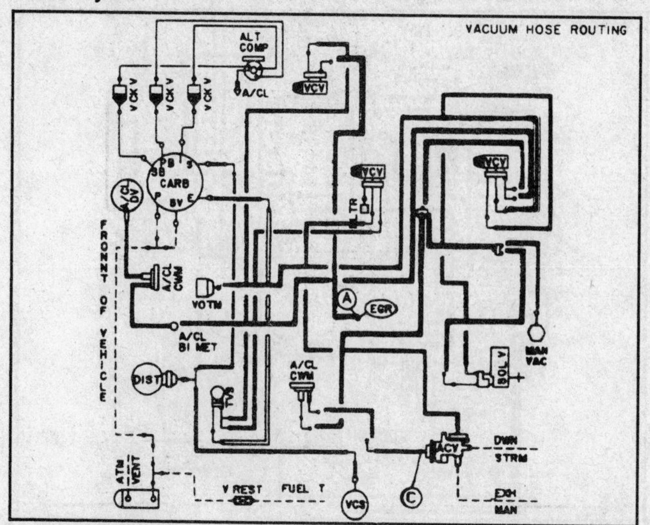

Fig. 14: 1.6L; Calibration 2-3X-R0; Hi. Alt.; Escort, EXP, LN7 & Lynx

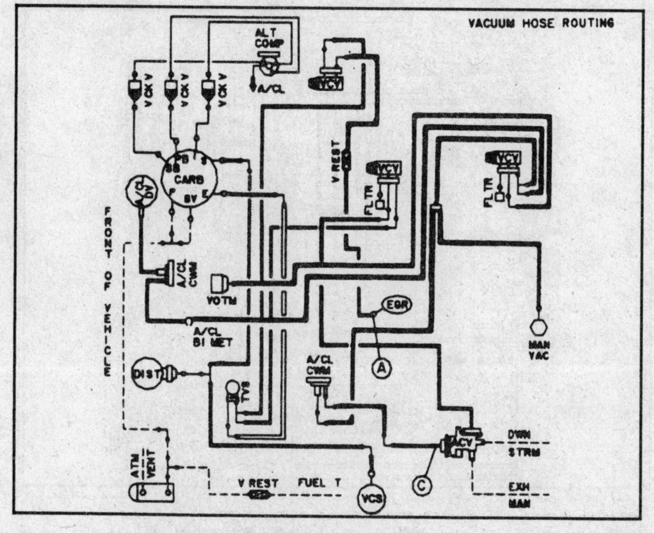

Fig. 15: 1.6L; Calibrations 2-4B-R10, 2-4T-R10; Calif. & Federal; Escort, EXP, LN7 & Lynx

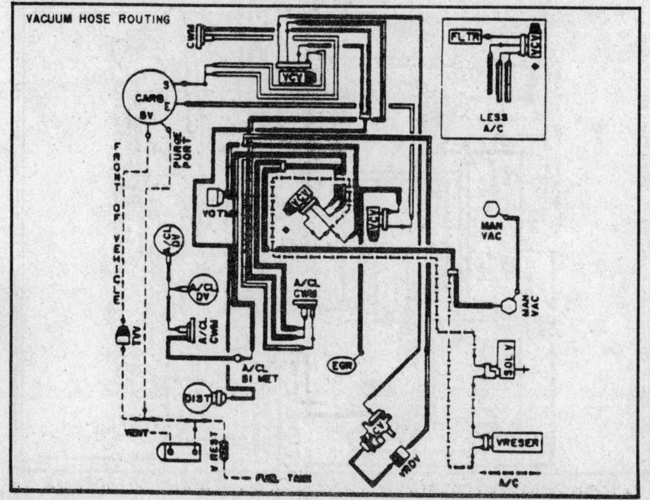

Fig. 16: 1.6L; Calibrations 2-4C-R0, 2-4C-R14, 2-4Q-R0, 2-4Q-R10, 2-4Q-R11, 2-4Q-R13; Calif.; Escort, EXP, LN7 & Lynx

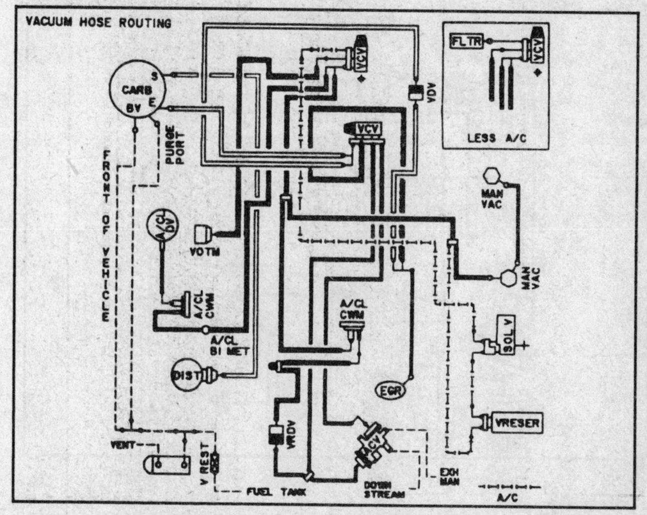

Fig. 17: 1.6L; Calibrations 2-4X-R0, 2-4X-R11; Hi. Alt.; Escort, EXP, LN7 & Lynx

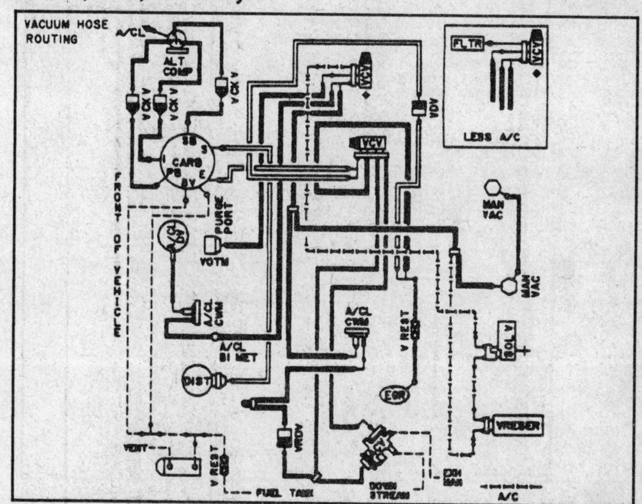

Fig. 18: 1.6L; Calibration 2-4Y-R10; Hi. Alt.; Escort, EXP, LN7 & Lynx

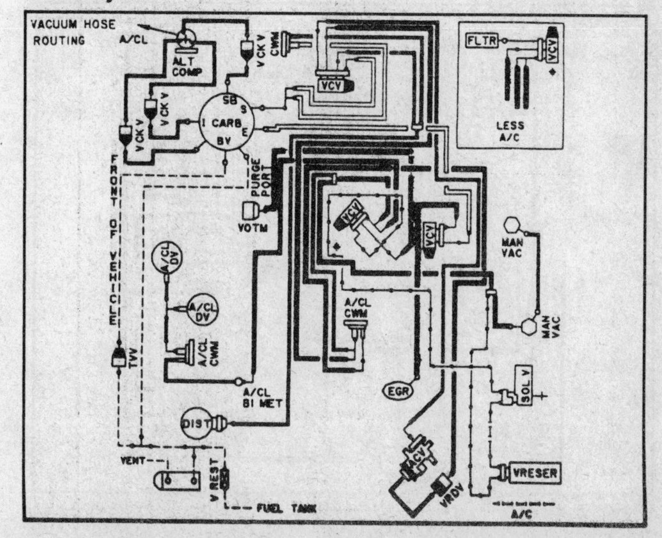

1982 FORD MOTOR CO. VACUUM DIAGRAMS (Cont.)

Fig. 19: 2.3L; Calibration 1-5F-R10; Nationwide; Capri & Mustang Turbo

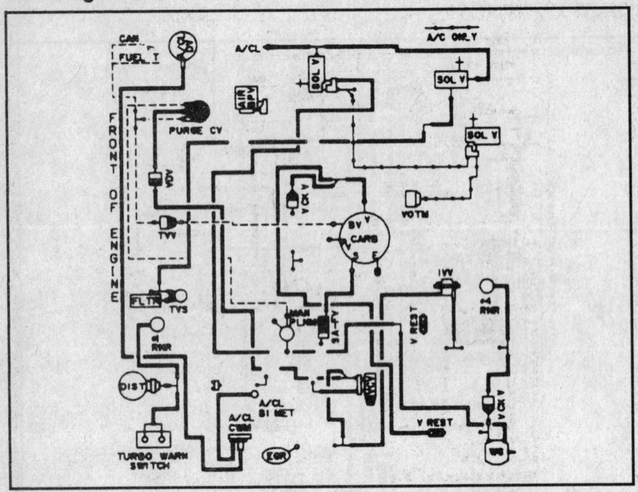

Fig. 20: 2.3L; Calibration 2-5B-R0; Federal; Capri, Cougar, Fairmont, Granada, Mustang & Zephyr

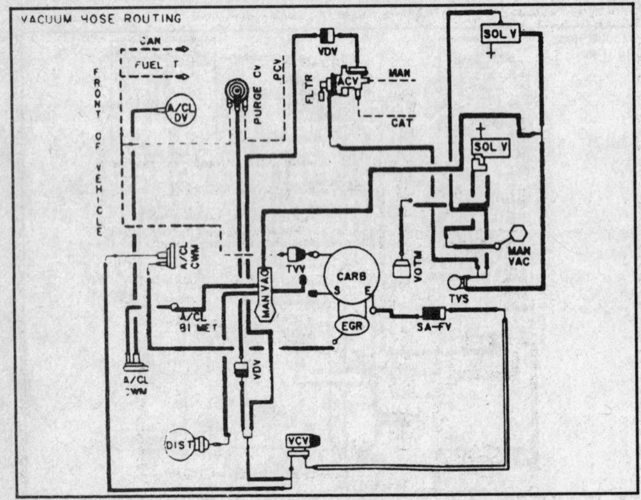

Fig. 21: 2.3L; Calibration 2-5B-R0; Federal; Capri, Cougar, Fairmont, Granada, Mustang & Zephyr

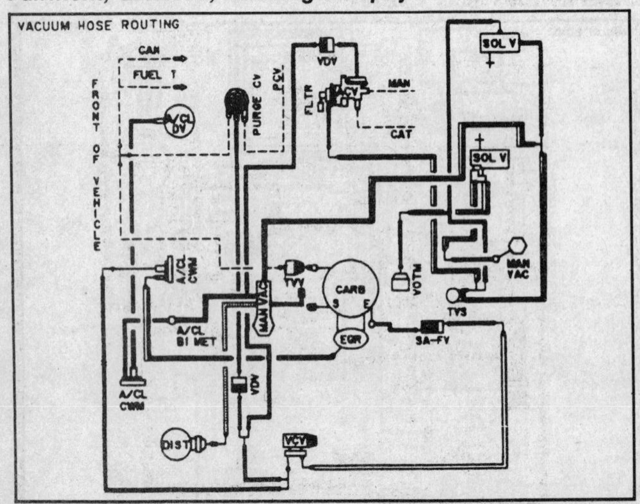

Fig. 22: 2.3L; Calibrations 2-5C-R0, 2-5C-R10; Federal; Capri, Fairmont, Mustang & Zephyr

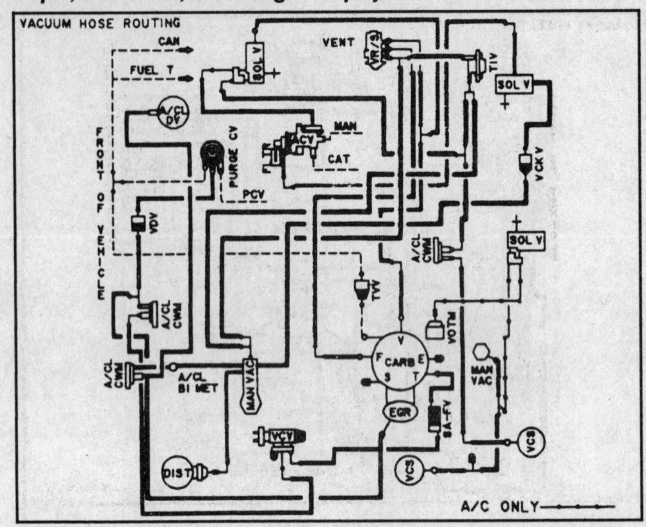

Fig. 23: 2.3L; Calibration 2-5C-R11; Federal; Capri, Fairmont, Mustang& Zephyr

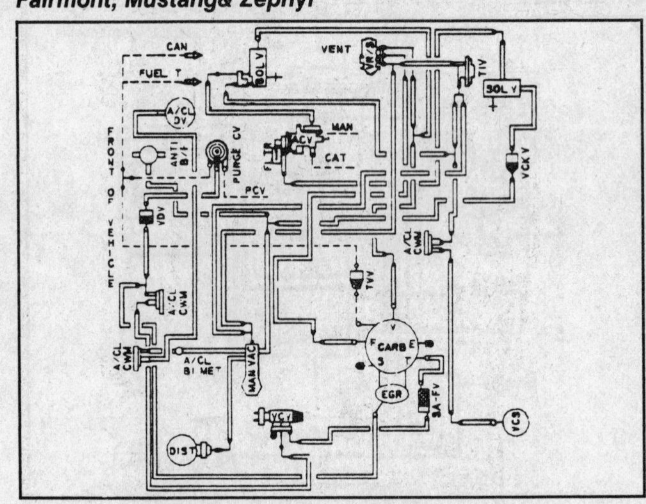

Fig. 24: 2.3L Calibrations 2-5N-R0, 2-5P-R0; Calif.; Capri, Cougar, Fairmont, Granada, Mustang & Zephyr

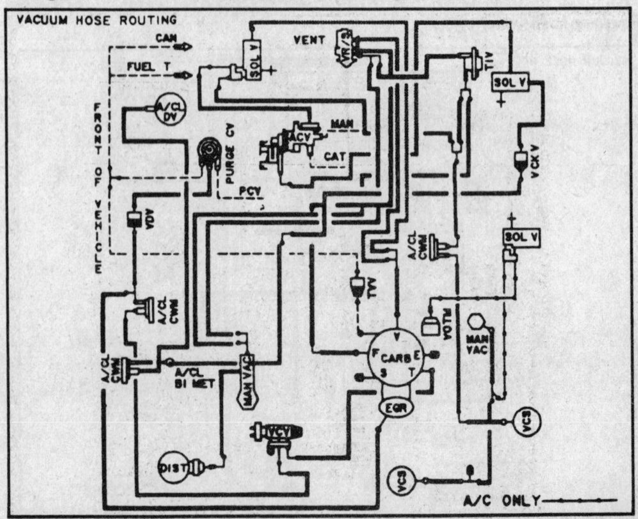

1982 FORD MOTOR CO. VACUUM DIAGRAMS (Cont.)

Fig. 25: 2.3L; Calibrations 2-6A-R0, 2-6A-R10; Federal; Capri, Cougar, Fairmont, Granada, Mustang & Zephyr

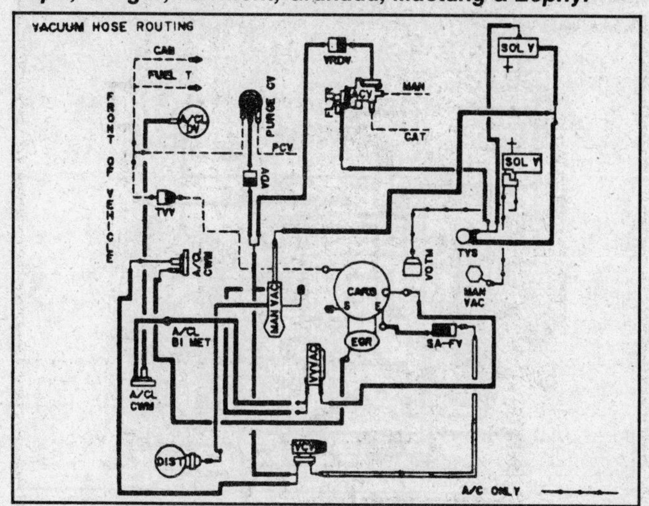

Fig. 26: 2.3L; Calibration 2-6N-R0; Calif.; Capri, Cougar, Fairmont, Granada, Mustang & Zephyr

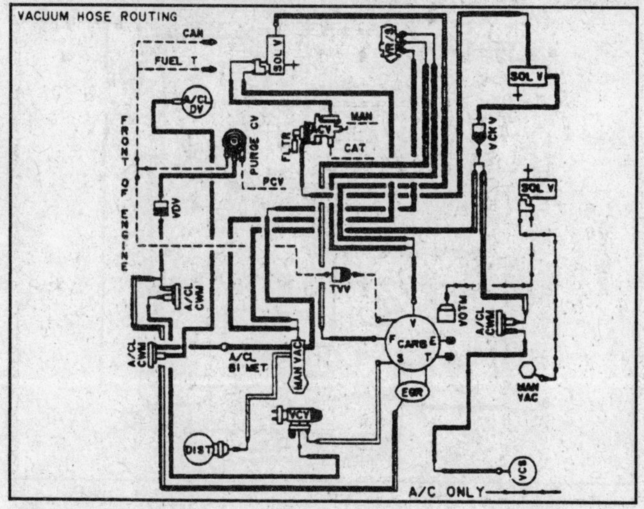

Fig. 27: 2.3L; Calibration 2-6W-R0; Hi. Alt.; Capri, Cougar, Fairmont, Granada, Mustang & Zephyr

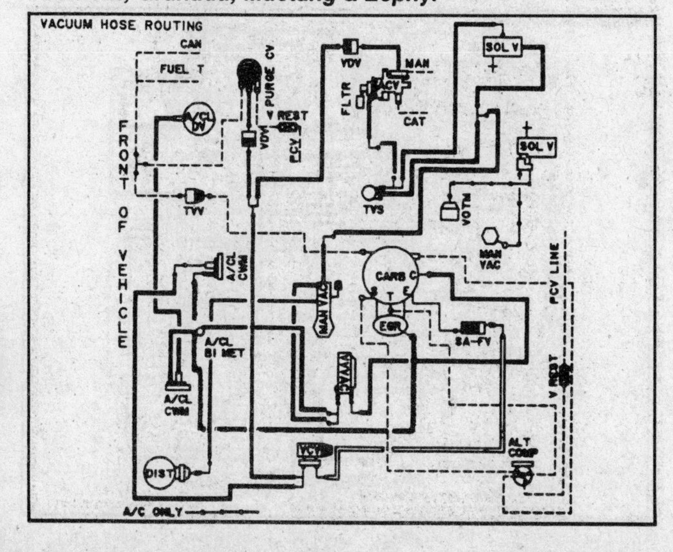

Fig. 28: 2.3L; Calibration 2-5W-R0; Hi. Alt.; Capri, Cougar, Fairmont, Granada, Mustang & Zephyr

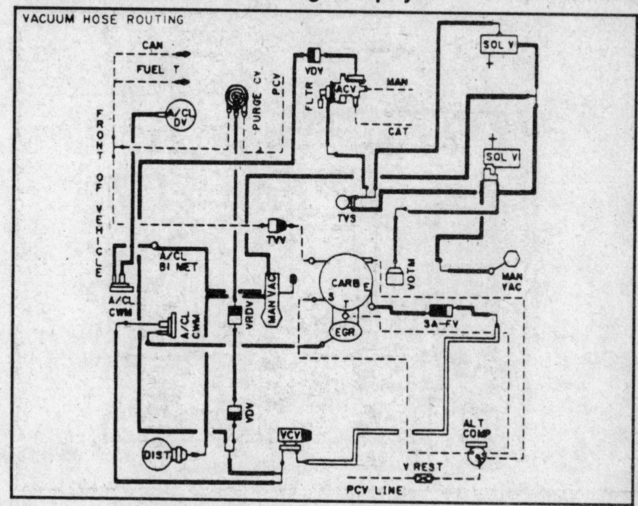

Fig. 29: 2.3L; Calibration 2-5A-R0; Federal; Capri & Mustang

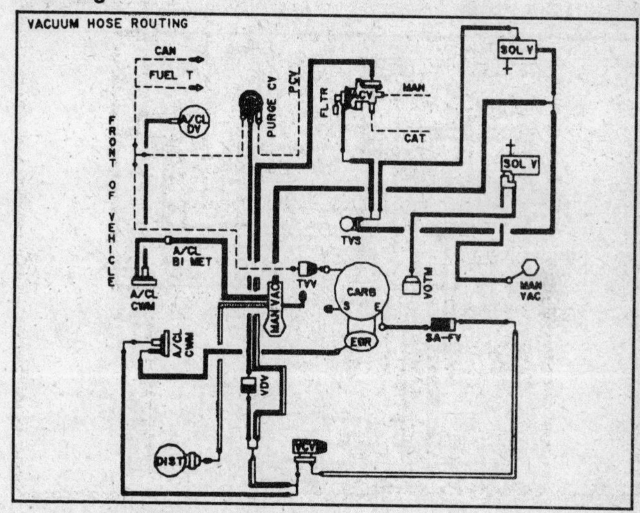

Fig. 30: 2.3L; Calibration 2-5B-R1; Federal; Cougar, Fairmont, Granada & Zephyr

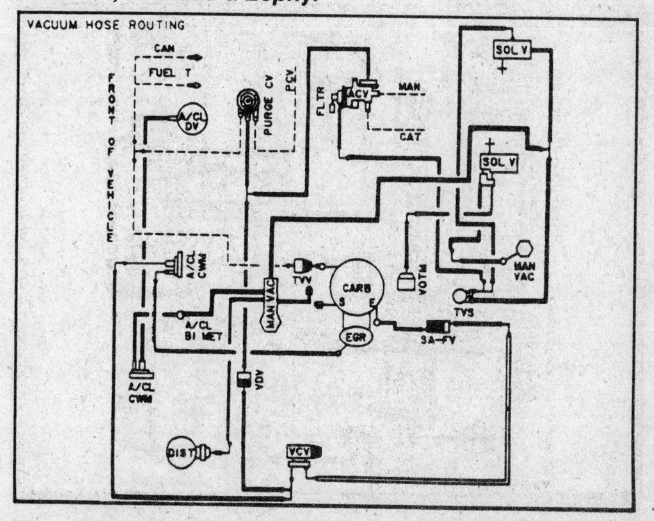

1982 FORD MOTOR CO. VACUUM DIAGRAMS (Cont.)

Fig. 31: 3.3L; Calibration 1-12B-R0; Nationwide; Thunderbird & XR7

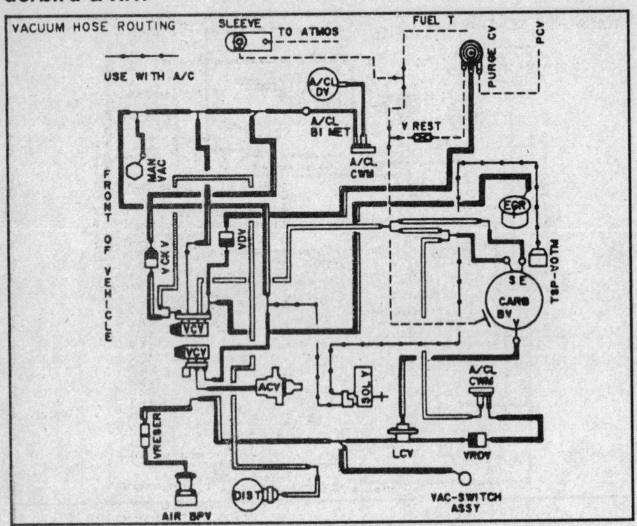

Fig. 32: 3.3L; Calibrations 2-12B-R10, 2-12T-R0, 2-12T-R2; Calif. & Federal; Capri, Cougar, Fairmont, Granada, Mustang & Zephyr

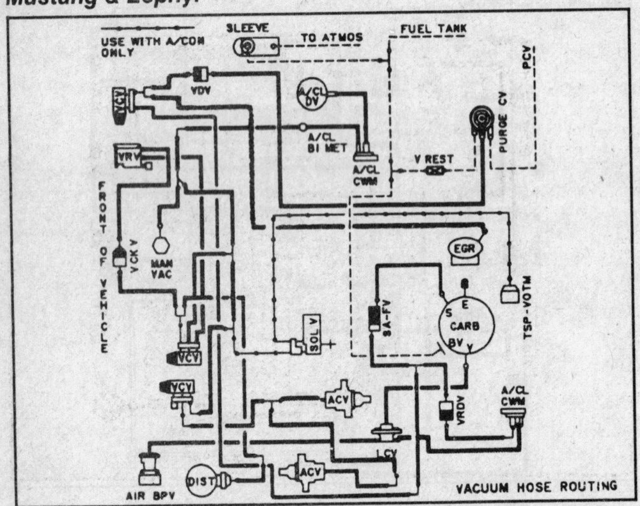

Fig. 33: 3.3L; Calibrations 2-12T-R4, 2-12T-R15; Federal; Capri, Cougar, Fairmont, Granada, Mustang & Zephyr

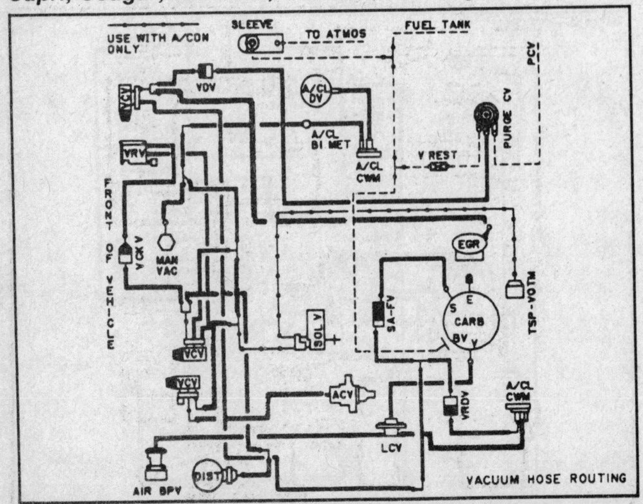

Fig. 34: 3.3L; Calibration 2-12W-R0; Hi. Alt.; Capri, Fairmont, Mustang & Zephyr

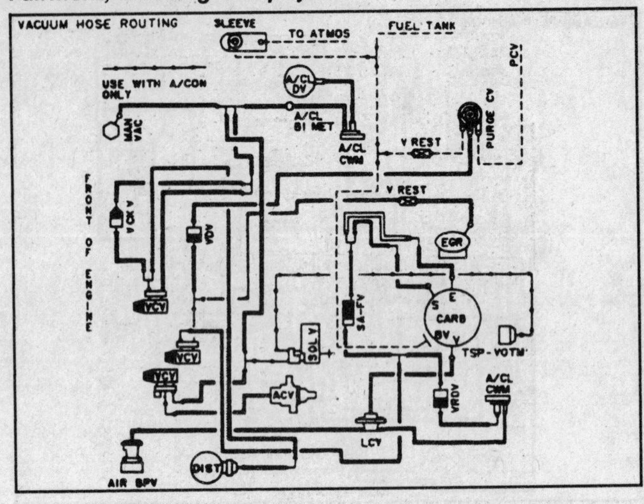

Fig. 35: 3.8L; Calibrations 2-14A-R0, 2-14A-R13; Federal; Cougar & Granada

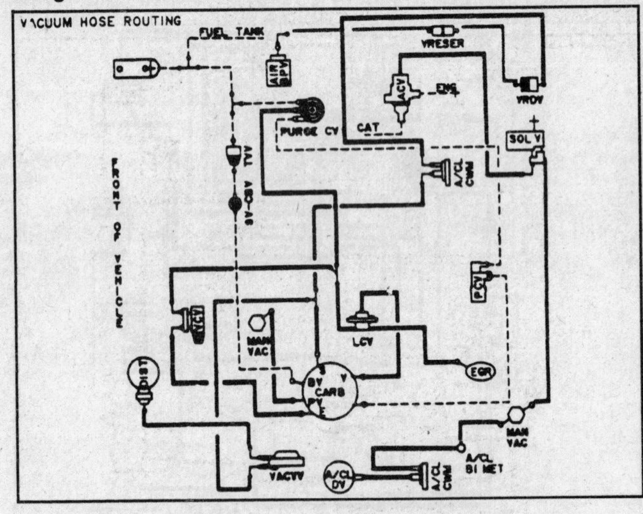

Fig. 36: 3.8L; Calibration 2-14B-R1; Federal; Cougar & Granada

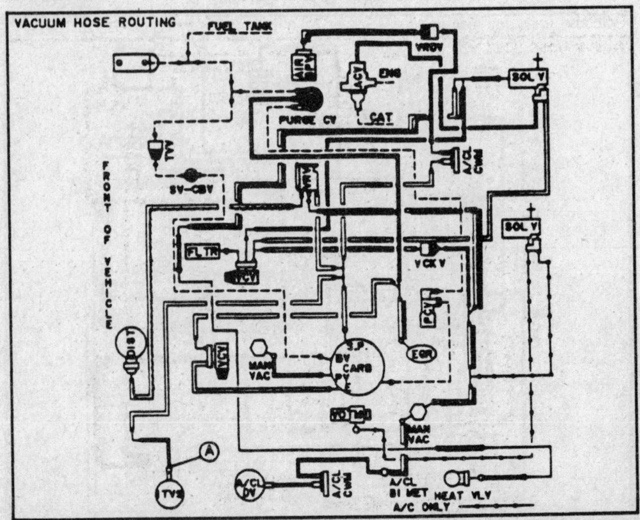

1982 FORD MOTOR CO. VACUUM DIAGRAMS (Cont.)

Fig. 37: 3.8L; Calibration 2-14B-R10; Federal; Cougar & Granada

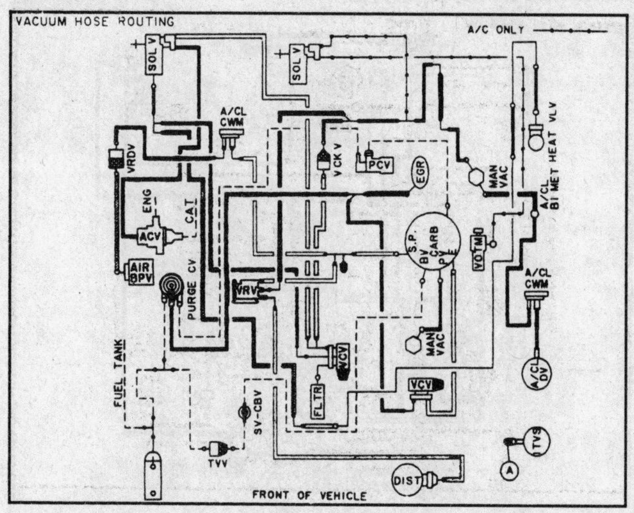

Fig. 38: 3.8L; Calibrations 2-14C-R0, 2-14C-R13, 2-14D-R0; Federal; Continental, Thunderbird & XR7

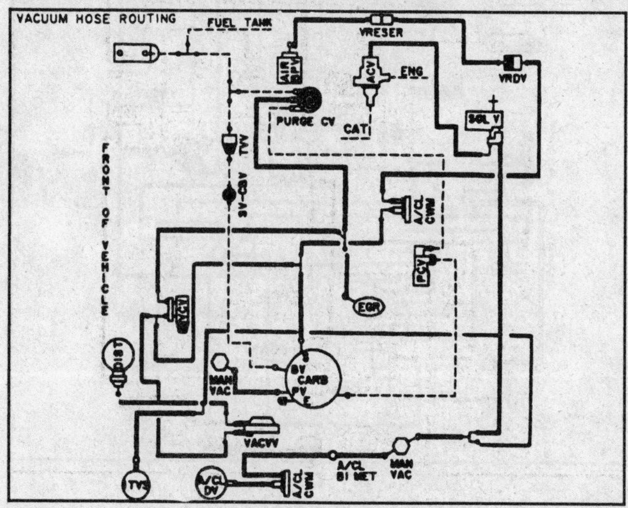

Fig. 39: 3.8L; Calibration 2-14C-R11; Federal; Thunderbird & XR7

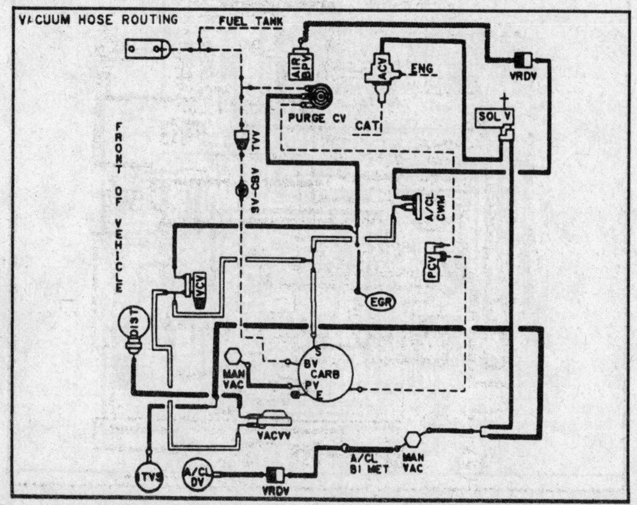

Fig. 40: 3.8L; Calibration 2-14E-R0; Federal; Thunderbird & XR7

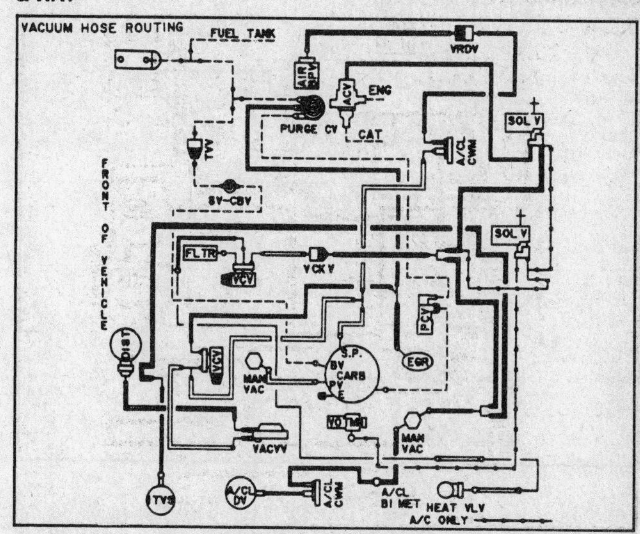

Fig. 41: 3.8L; Calibration 2-14E-R10; Federal; Thunderbird & XR7

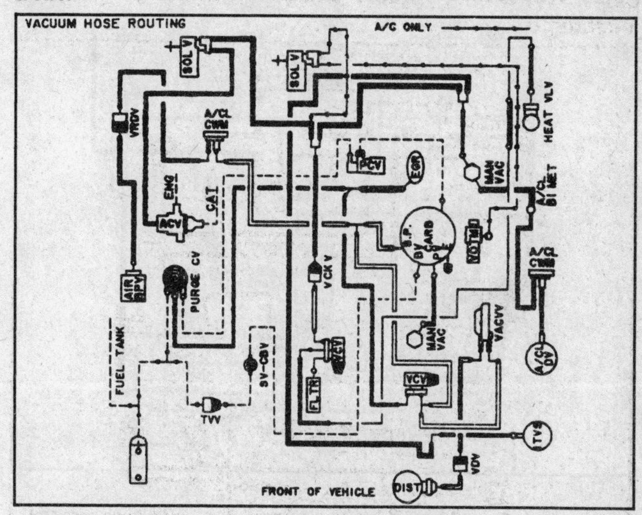

Fig. 42: 3.8L; Calibrations 2-14N-R0, 2-14N-R1, 2-14N-R10, 2-14Q-R1, 2-14Q-R11; Calif.; Cougar, Granada, Thunderbird & XR7

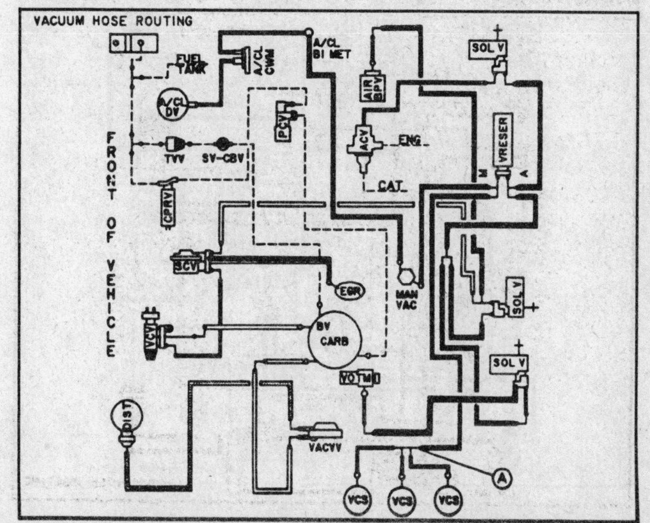

1982 FORD MOTOR CO. VACUUM DIAGRAMS (Cont.)

Fig. 43: 3.8L; Calibrations 2-14R-R1, 2-14R-R11; Nationwide; Lincoln Continental

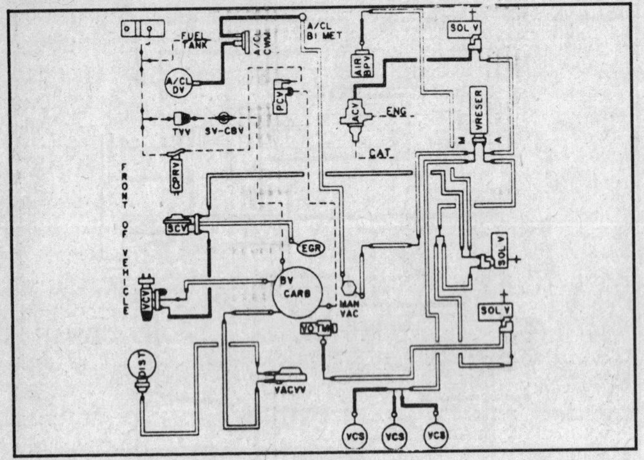

Fig. 44: 3.8L; Calibration 2-14W-R0; Hi. Alt.; Cougar & Granada

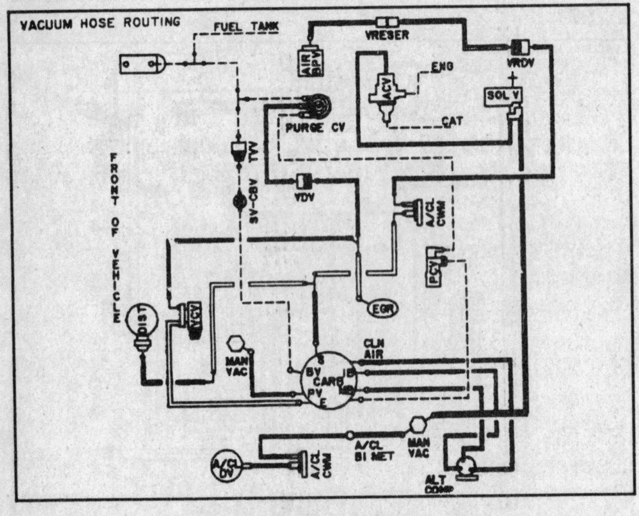

Fig. 45: 3.8L; Calibrations 2-14W-R10, 2-14X-R10; Hi. Alt.; Cougar, Granada, Thunderbird & XR7

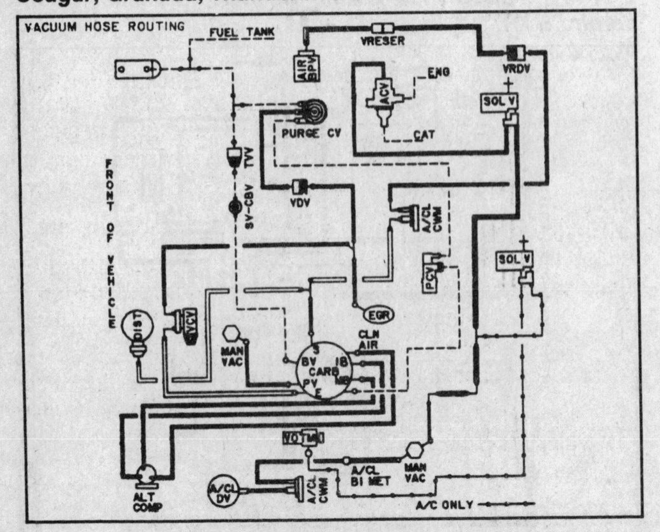

Fig. 46: 3.8L; Calibrations 2-14X-R0, 2-14X-R1; Hi. Alt.; Thunderbird & XR7

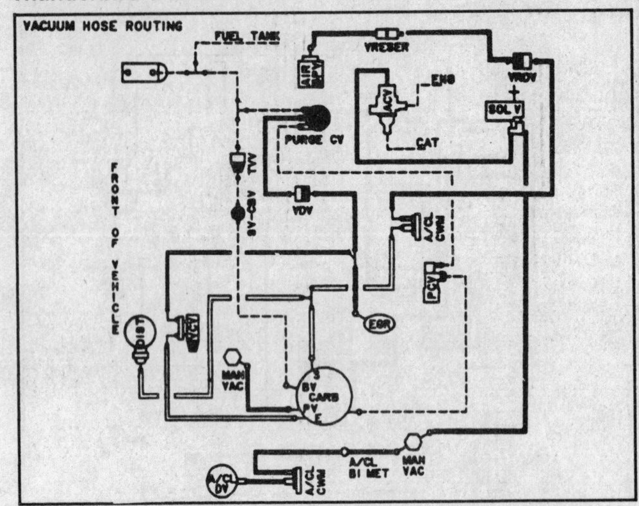

Fig. 47: 4.2L; Calibrations 1-18U-R0, 2-18U-R10; Exc. Hi. Alt.; Ford & Mercury

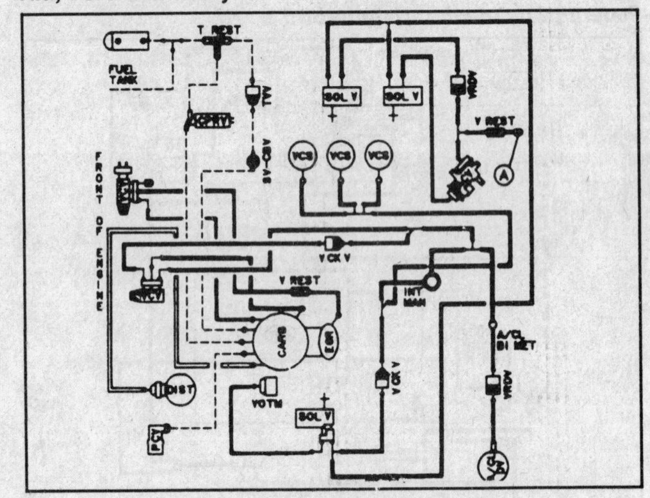

Fig. 48: 4.2L; Calibration 2-18B-R0; Exc. Hi. Alt.; Fairmont & Zephyr

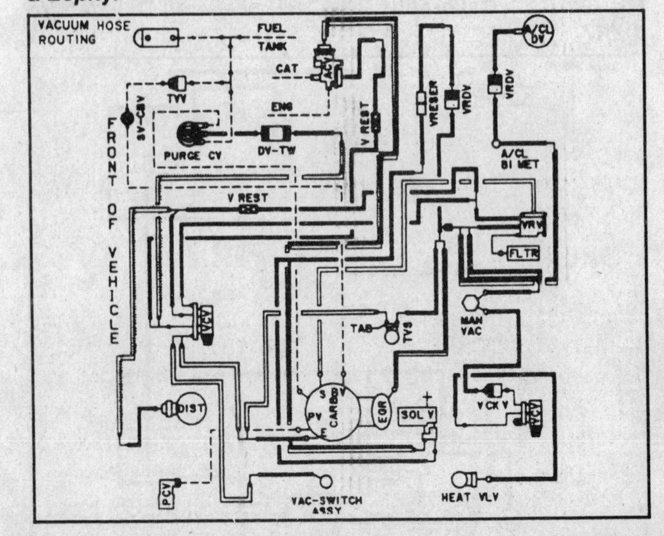

1982 FORD MOTOR CO. VACUUM DIAGRAMS (Cont.)

Fig. 49: 4.2L; Calibration 2-18B-R0; Exc. Hi. Alt.; Capri & Mustang

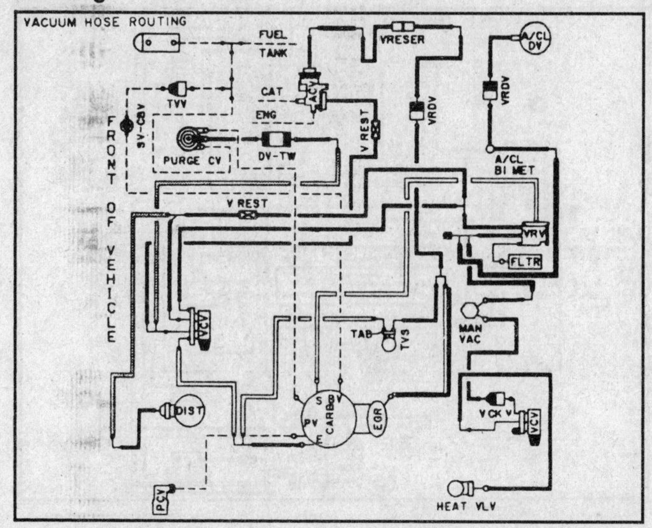

Fig. 50: 4.2L; Calibration 2-18B-R13; Exc. Hi. Alt.; Capri & Mustang

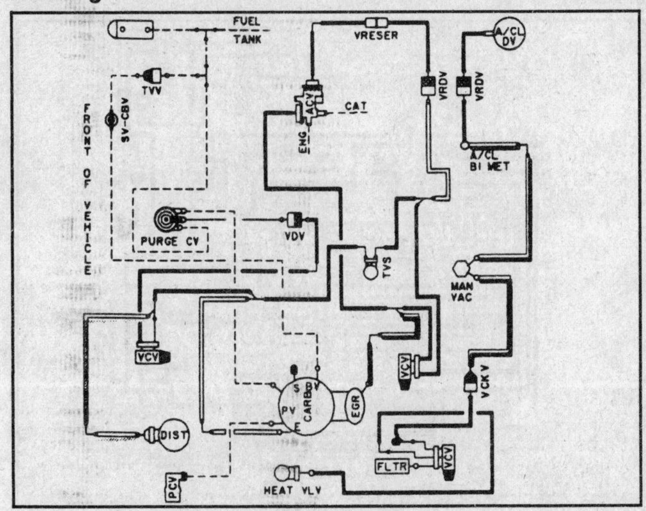

Fig. 51: 4.2L; Calibrations 2-18C-R4, 2-18C-R5; Federal; Thunderbird & XR7

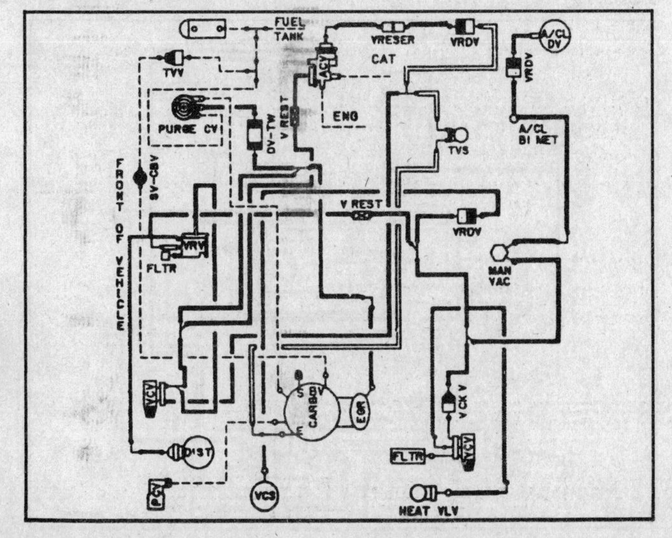

Fig. 52: 4.2L; Calibration 2-18C-R11; Federal; Thunderbird & XR7

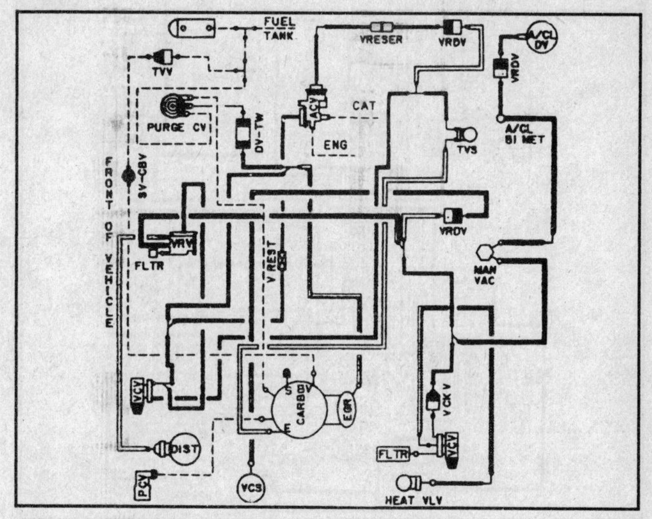

Fig. 53: 4.2L; Calibration 2-18Q-R0; Exc. Hi. Alt.; Thunderbird & XR7

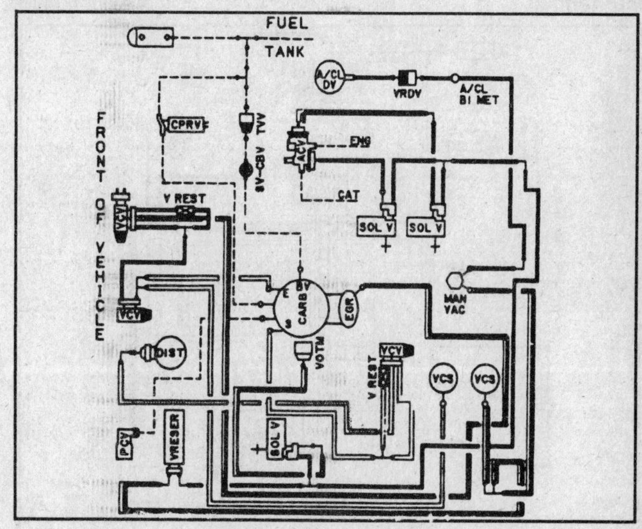

Fig. 54: 4.2L; Calibration 2-18U-R11; Nationwide; Ford & Mercury

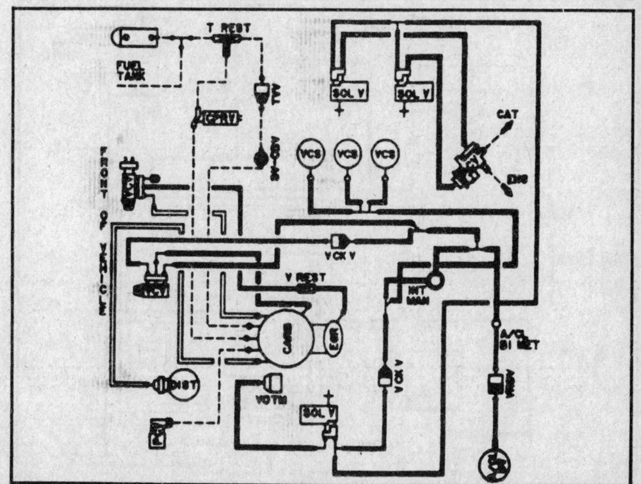

1982 FORD MOTOR CO. VACUUM DIAGRAMS (Cont.)

Fig. 55: 4.2L; Calibration 2-18W-R0; Hi. Alt.; Fairmont & Zephyr

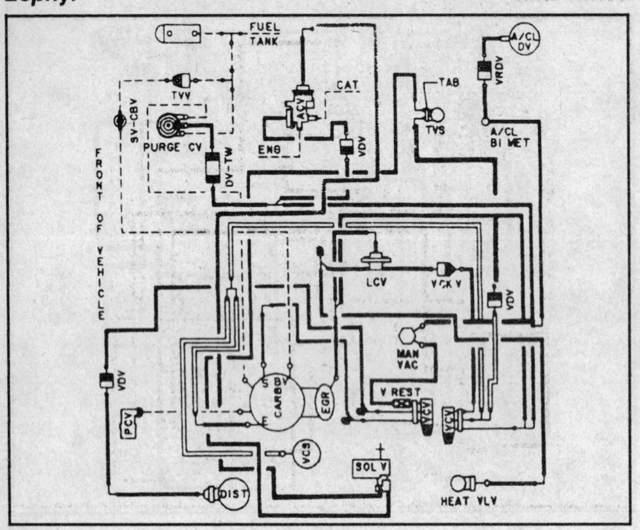

Fig. 56: 4.2L; Calibration 2-18W-R0; Hi. Alt.; Capri & Mustang

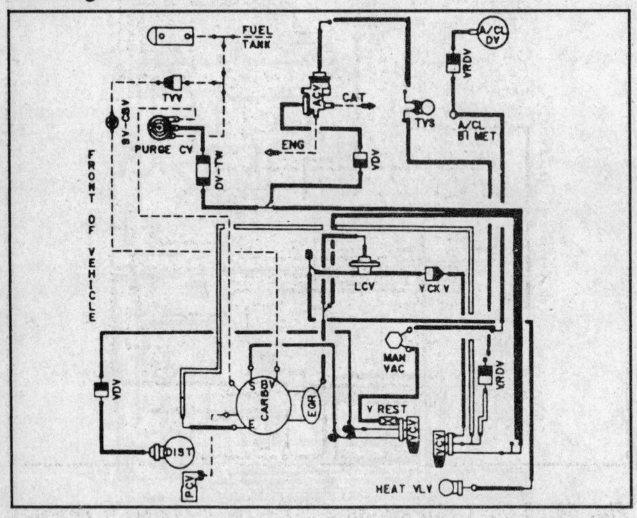

Fig. 57: 4.2L; Calibration 2-18X-R0; Hi. Alt.; Thunderbird & XR7

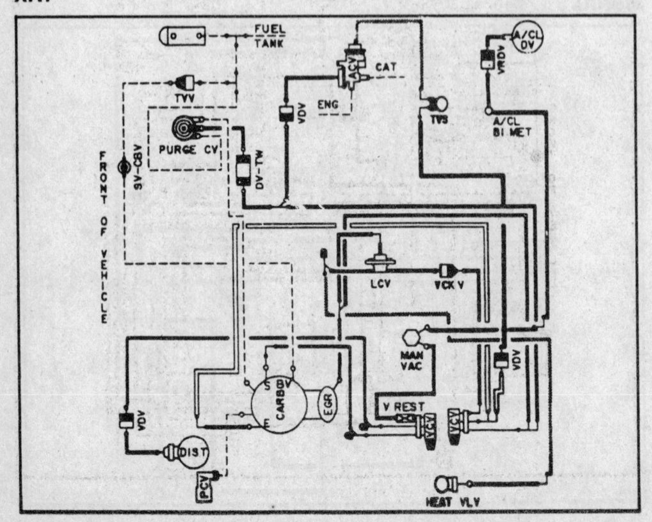

Fig. 58: 5.0L; Calibration 1-20B-R1; Exc. Hi. Alt.; All 5.0L carbureted models

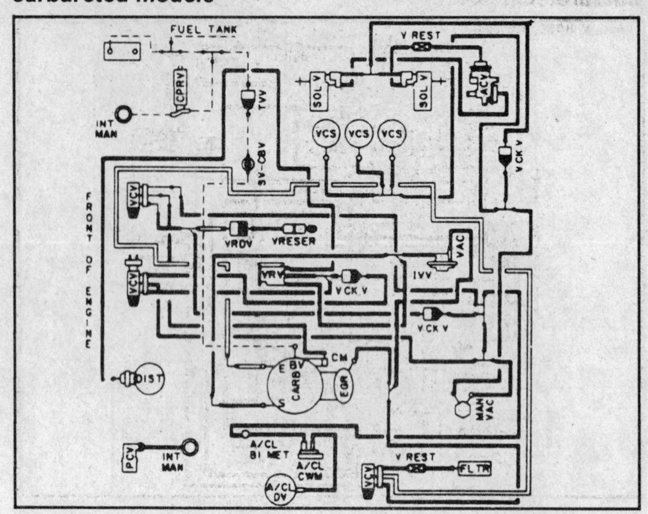

Fig. 59: 5.0L; Calibration 1-20N-R10; Exc. Hi. Alt.; Ford & Mercury

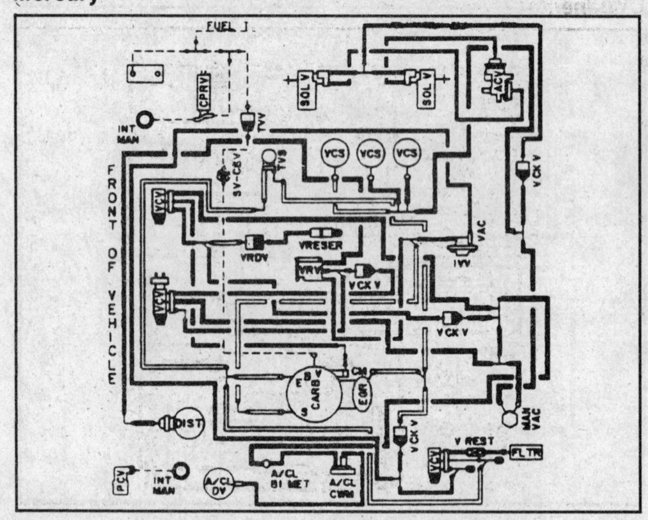

Fig. 60: 5.0L; Calibration 2-20B-R0; Federal; Ford & Mercury

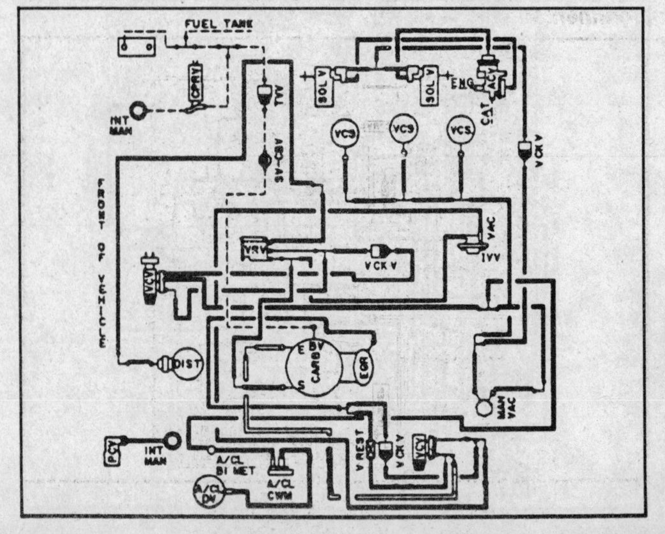

1982 FORD MOTOR CO. VACUUM DIAGRAMS (Cont.)

Fig. 61: 5.0L; Calibration 2-20D-R1; Exc. Hi. Alt.; All 5.0L Carbureted Models

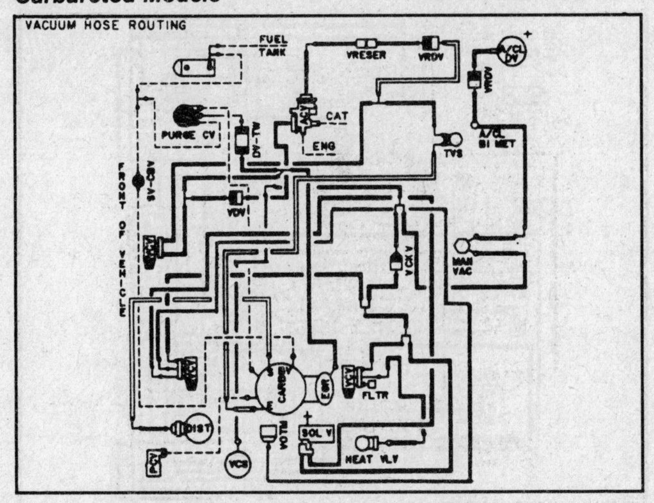

Fig. 62: 5.0L; Calibration 2-20R-R2; Exc. Hi. Alt.; Lincoln Continental

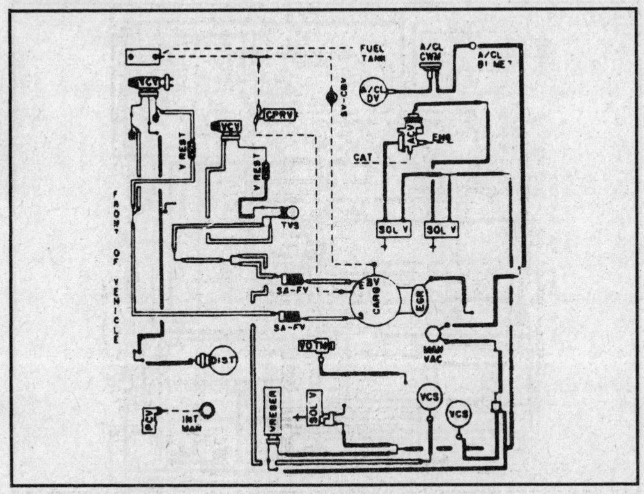

Fig. 63: 5.0L; Calibration 2-20R-R16; Exc. Hi. Alt.; Lincoln Continental

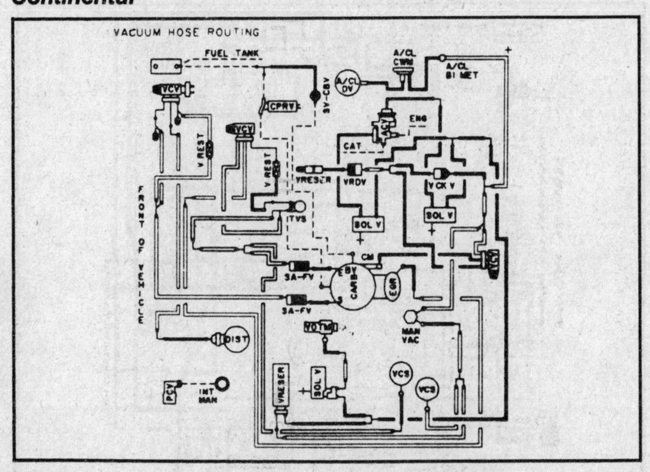

Fig. 64: 5.0L; Calibration 2-20Y-R0; Hi. Alt.; Lincoln Continental

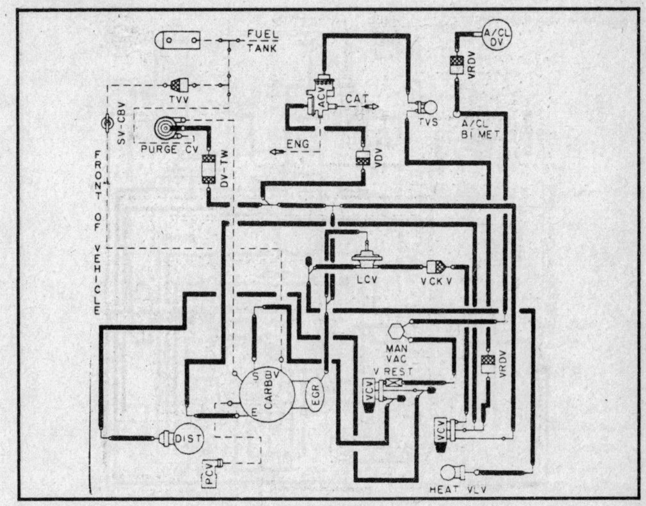

Fig. 65: 5.0L; Calibration 2-20Z-R0; Hi. Alt.; Ford & Mercury

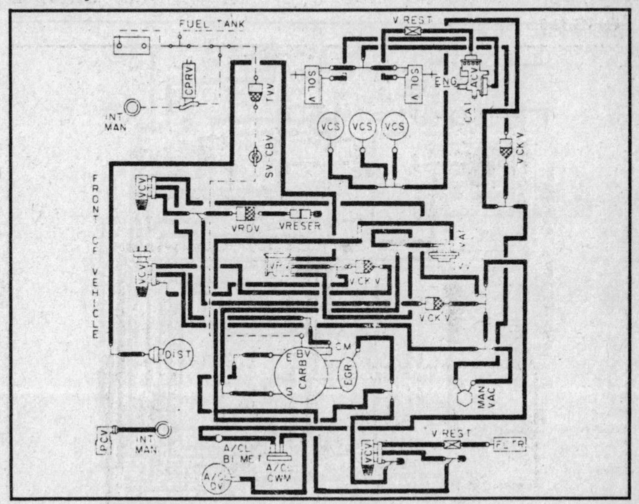

Fig. 66: 5.0L; Calibrations 2-21E-R10, 2-21E-R11; Federal; Capri & Mustang

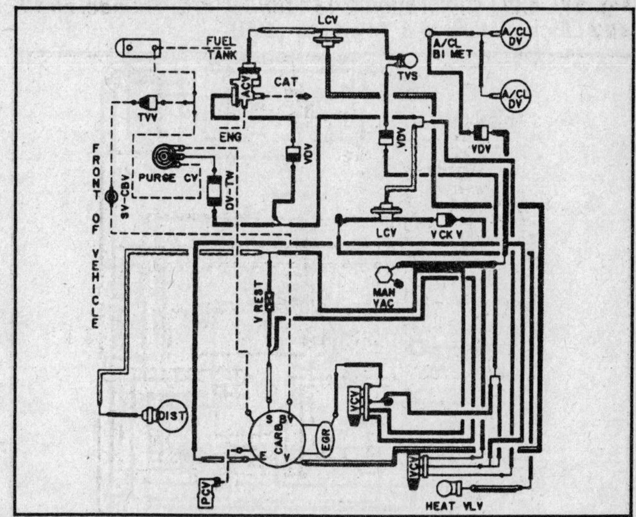

1983 Exhaust Emission Systems

1982 FORD MOTOR CO. VACUUM DIAGRAMS (Cont.)

Fig. 67: 5.0L; Calibration 2-21S-R0; Calif.; Capri & Mustang

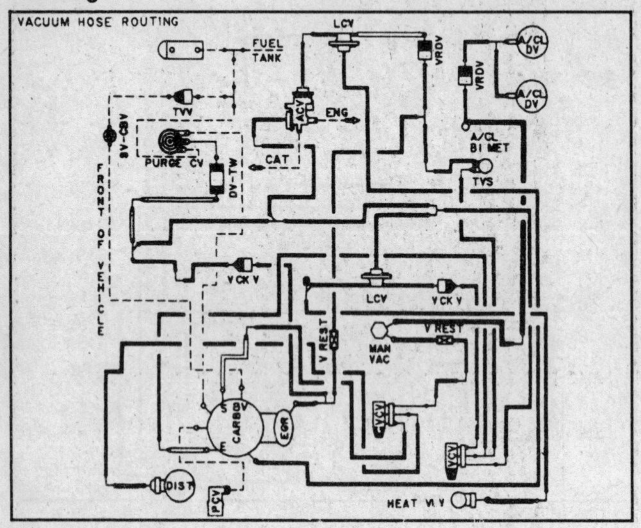

Fig. 68: 5.0L; Calibration 2-21Y-R10; Hi. Alt.; Capri & Mustang

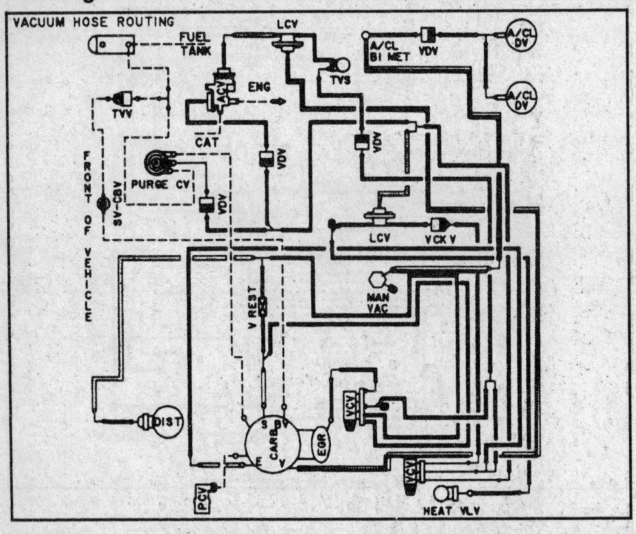

Fig. 69: 5.0L; Calibrations 1-22B-R0, 1-22P-R0; Calif. & Hi. Alt.; Lincoln Mark VI & Town Car (CFI)

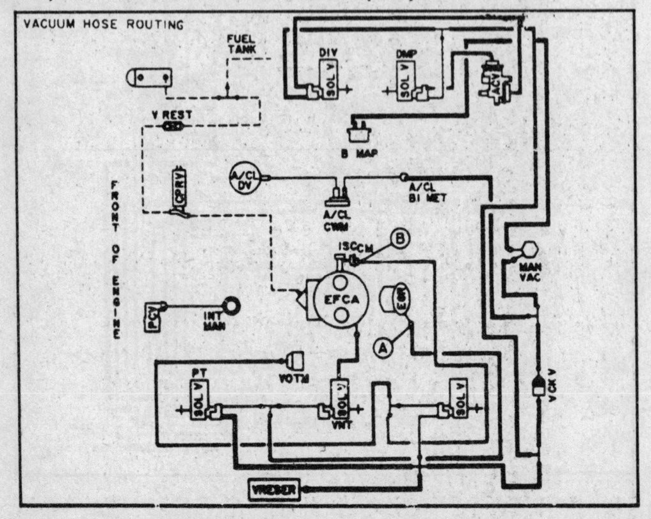

Fig. 70: 5.0L; Calibration 2-22A-R0; Federal; Lincoln Mark VI & Town Car (CFI)

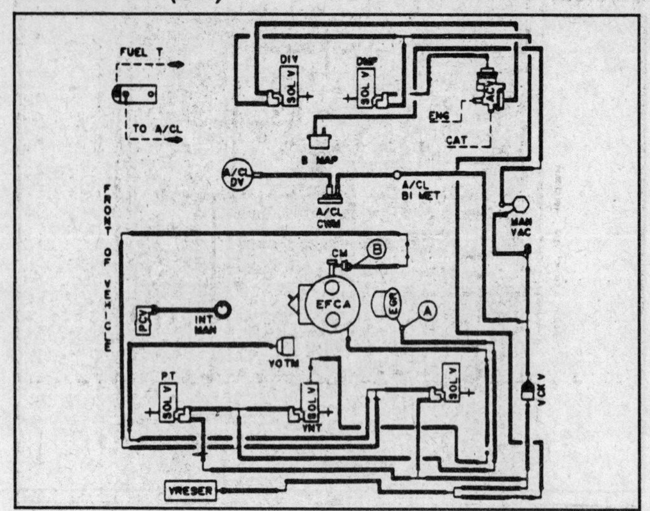

Fig. 71: 5.0L; Calibration 2-22Y-R11; Exc. Calif.; Lincoln Mark VI & Town Car (CFI)

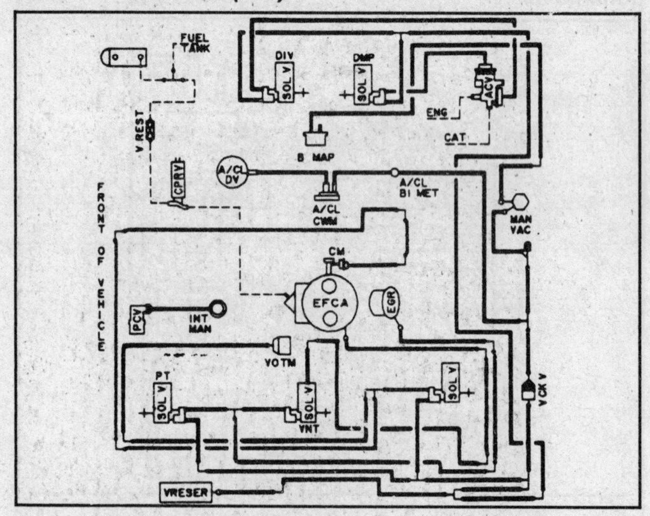

Fig. 72: 5.8L (W); Calibration 2-24P-R6; Calif.; Ford & Mercury

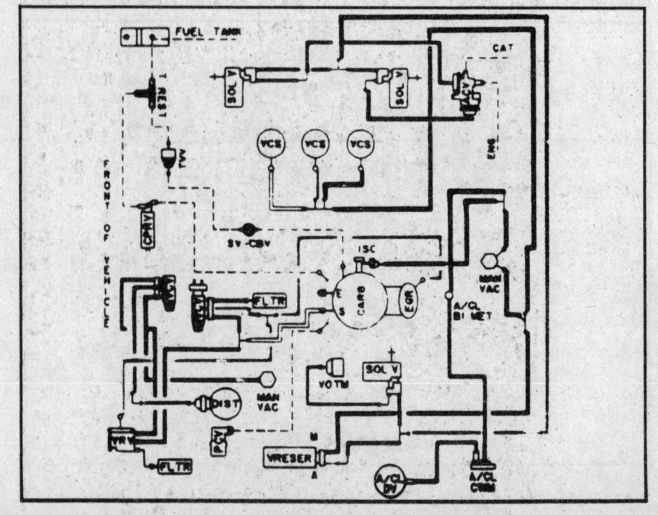

1982 FORD MOTOR CO. VACUUM DIAGRAMS (Cont.)

Fig. 73: *5.8L (W); Calibration 2-24P-R10; Exc. Calif.; Ford & Mercury*

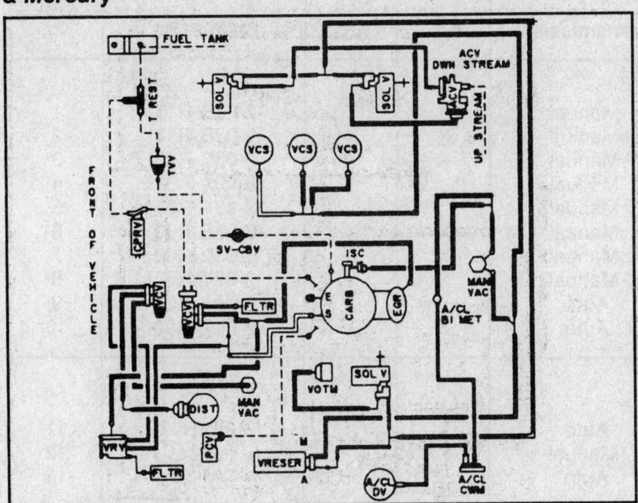

1983 FORD MOTOR CO. VACUUM DIAGRAMS

1983 FORD MOTOR CO. VACUUM DIAGRAM INDEX

Engine & Model	Application	Transmission	A/C	Non A/C	Calibration	Fig. No.
1.6L (98") 4-Cylinder						
Escort, EXP, LN7, Lynx	Federal	Manual	X	X	2-03B-R17	1
Escort, EXP, LN7, Lynx	Calif.	Manual	X	X	2-03B-R18	2
Escort, EXP, LN7, Lynx	Calif.	Manual	X	X	2-03B-R20	3
Escort, EXP, LN7, Lynx (EFI)	Exc. Calif.	Manual			3-03A-R01	4
Escort, EXP, LN7, Lynx (EFI)	Calif.	Manual			3-03A-R05	5
Escort, EXP, LN7, Lynx	Exc. Hi. Alt.	Manual	X	X	3-03B-R00	6
Escort, EXP, LN7, Lynx	Calif.	Manual	X	X	3-03C-R09	7
Escort, EXP, LN7, Lynx	Hi. Alt.	Manual	X	X	3-03Y-R00	8
Escort, EXP, LN7, Lynx (EFI)	Federal	Auto.			3-04A-R01	9
Escort, Lynx	Federal	Auto.	X	X	3-04Q-R00	10
2.3L (140") 4-Cylinder						
Capri, Fairmont, LTD Marquis, Mustang, Zephyr	Exc. Calif.	Auto.	X	X	3-6B-R02	11
1984 Tempo, Topaz	All	Manual			Typical	12
1984 Tempo, Topaz	All	Auto.			Typical	13
3.3L (200") 6-Cylinder						
Capri, Fairmont, LTD Marquis, Mustang, Zephyr	Federal	Auto.	X	X	3-12A-R10	14
3.8L (230") 6-Cylinder						
LTD, Marquis	Federal	Auto.		X	3-14B-R11	15
5.0L (302") V8						
Capri, Mustang (1-Pc. ACV)	Exc. Calif.	Manual			3-21A-R11	16
Capri, Mustang (2-Pc. ACV)	Exc. Calif.	Manual			3-21A-R11	17
Lincoln Continental (CFI)	Exc. Hi. Alt.	Auto.			3-22D-R00	18
Cougar, Thunderbird (CFI)	Exc. Hi. Alt.	Auto.			3-22D-R00	19
Cougar, Thunderbird (CFI)	Hi. Alt.	Auto.			3-22W-R00	20
5.8L (351") V8						
LTD & Marquis	All	Auto.			2-24P-R10	21

CALIBRATION NUMBER IDENTIFICATION

To identify calibration number, find engine code label, located at front of engine. Engine calibration number is shown on label. Calibration codes will begin with number indicating current model year. For example, calibrations listed for 1983 Ford Vacuum Diagrams begin with "3". Each vehicle is also equipped with a emission control data decal applying to that vehicle and its engine. These decals are usually located on the underside of the hood, or other visible engine compartment location.

Exhaust Emission Control Label

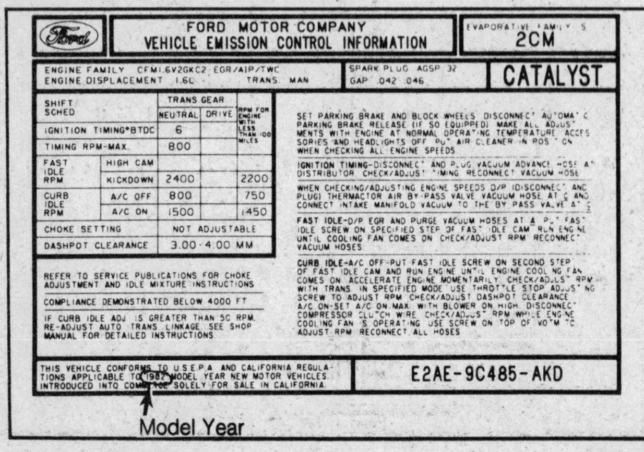

Engine Code Labels

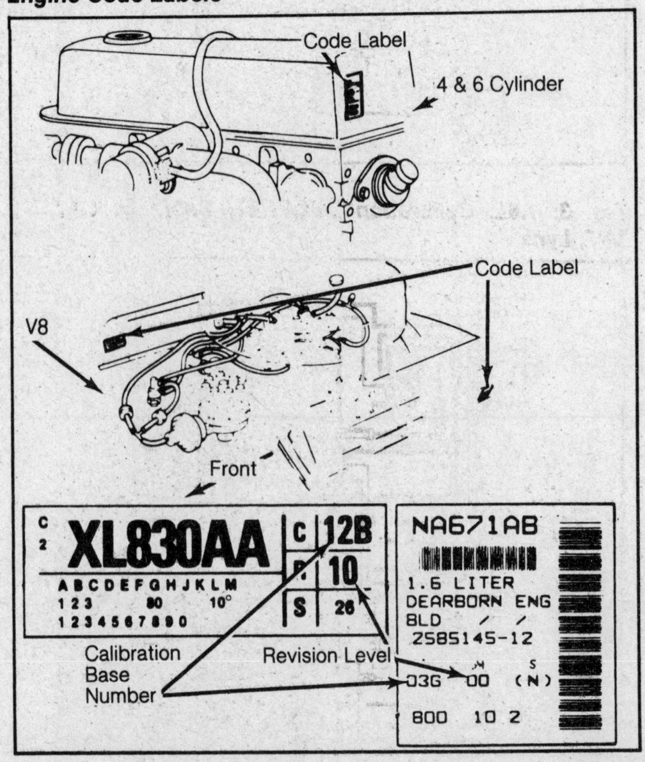

1983 FORD MOTOR CO. VACUUM DIAGRAMS (Cont.)

Fig.1: 1.6L; Calibration 2-03B-R17; Federal; Escort, EXP, LN7, Lynx

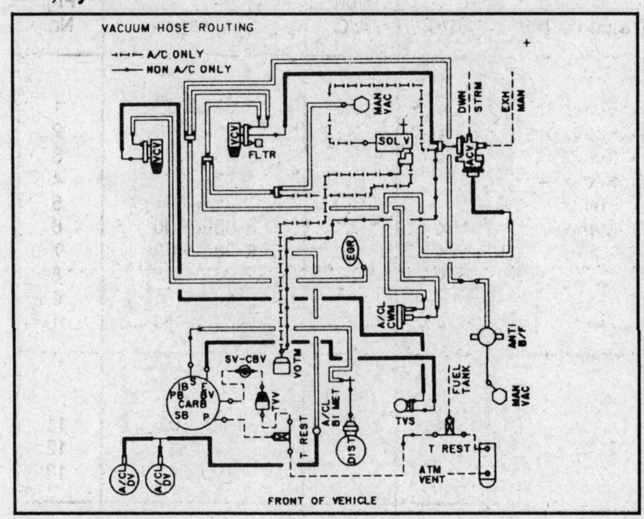

Fig. 2: 1.6L; Calibration 2-03B-R18; Calif.; Escort, EXP, LN7, Lynx

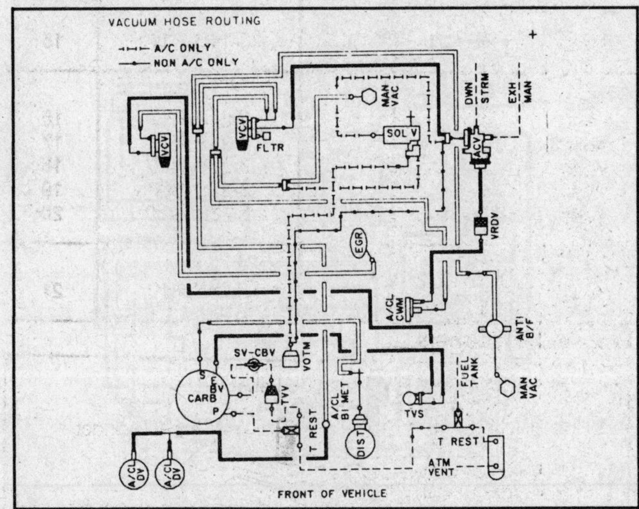

Fig. 3: 1.6L; Calibration 2-03B-R20; Calif.; Escort, EXP, LN7, Lynx

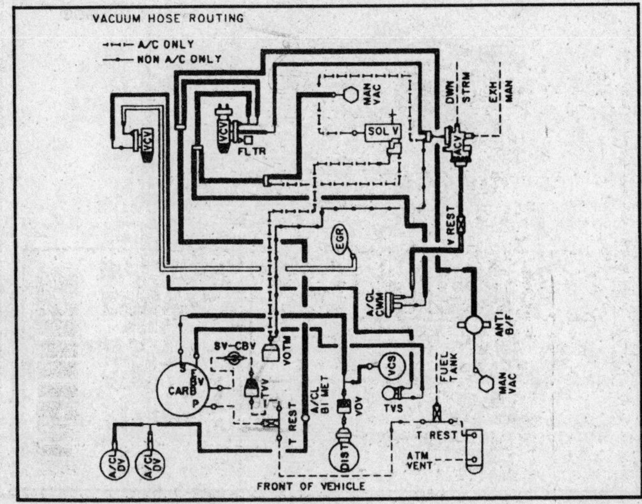

Fig. 4: 1.6L; Calibration 3-03A-R01; Exc. Calif.; Escort, EXP, LN7, Lynx

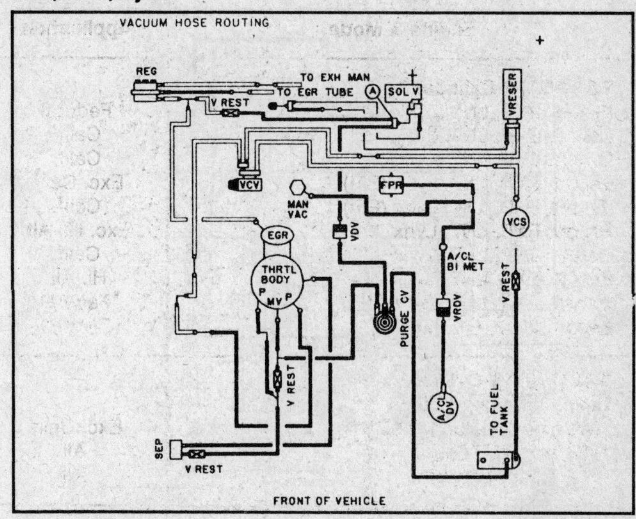

Fig. 5: 1.6L; Calibration 3-03A-R05; Calif.; Escort, EXP, LN7, Lynx (EFI)

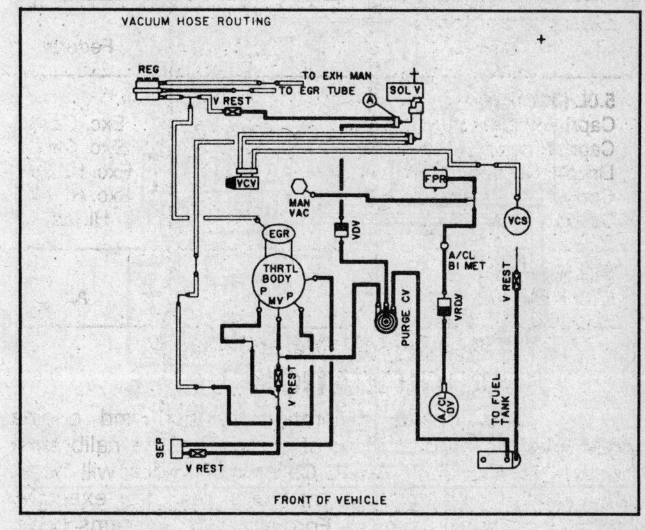

Fig. 6: 1.6L; Calibration 3-03B-R00; Exc. Hi. Alt.; Escort, EXP, LN7, Lynx

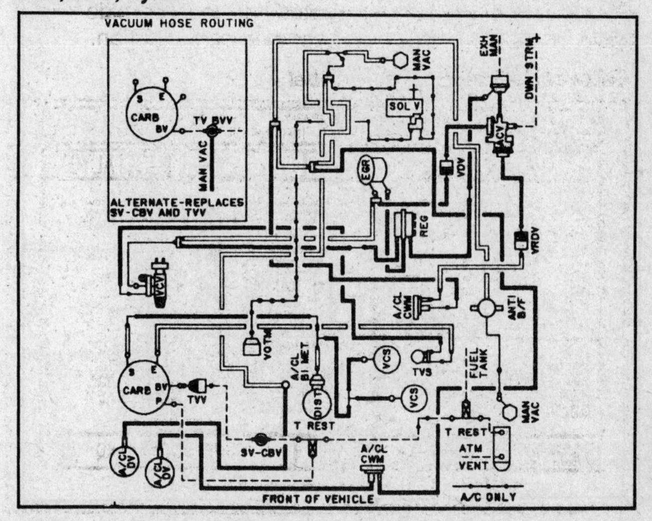

1983 FORD MOTOR CO. VACUUM DIAGRAMS (Cont.)

Fig. 7: 1.6L; Calibration 3-03C-R09; Calif.; Escort, EXP, LN7, Lynx

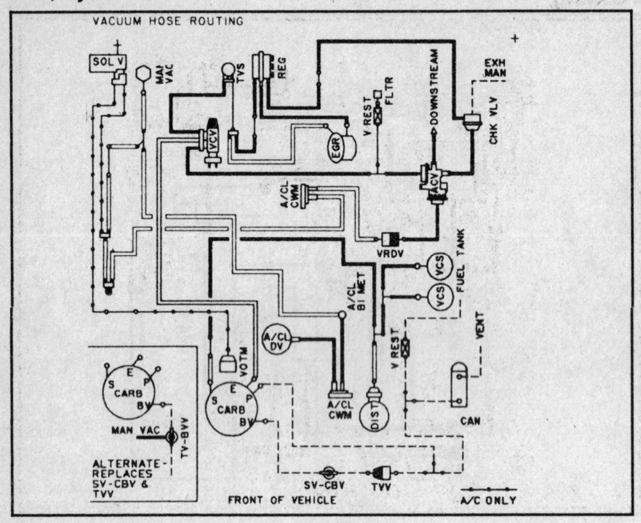

Fig. 8: 1.6L; Calibration 3-03Y-R00; Hi. Alt.; Escort, EXP, LN7, Lynx

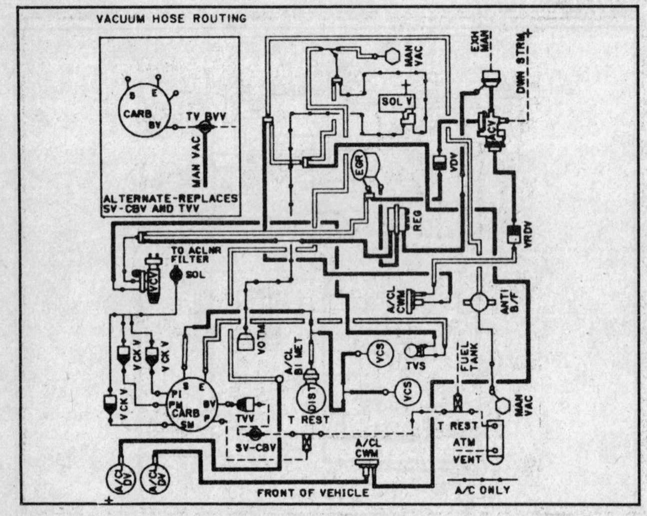

Fig. 9: 1.6L; Calibration 3-04A-R01; Federal; Escort, EXP, LN7, Lynx (EFI)

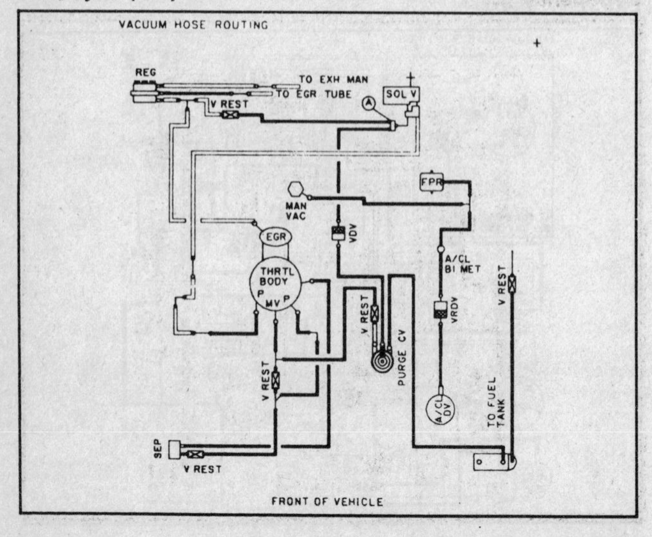

Fig. 10: 1.6L; Calibration 3-04Q-R00; Federal; Escort, Lynx

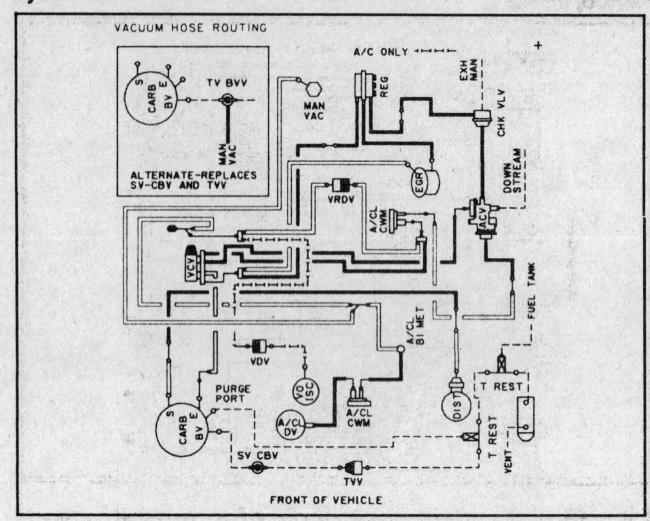

Fig. 11: 2.3L; Calibration 3-6B-R02; Exc. Calif.; Capri, Fairmont, LTD, Marquis, Mustang, Zephyr

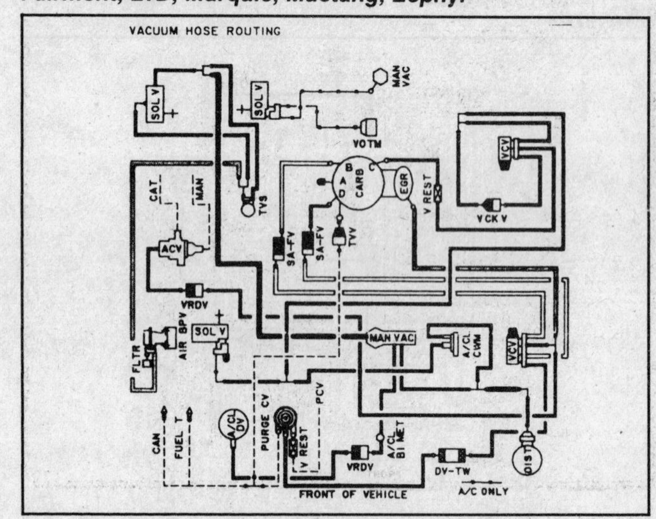

Fig. 12: 2.3L HSC; Typical Man. Trans. Calibration; 1984 Tempo, Topaz

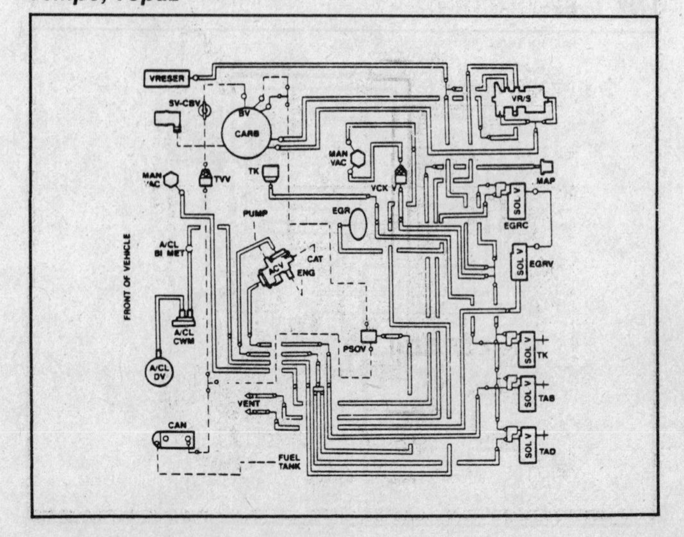

1983 FORD MOTOR CO. VACUUM DIAGRAMS (Cont.)

Fig. 13: 2.3L HSC; Typical Auto. Trans. Calibration; 1984 Tempo, Topaz

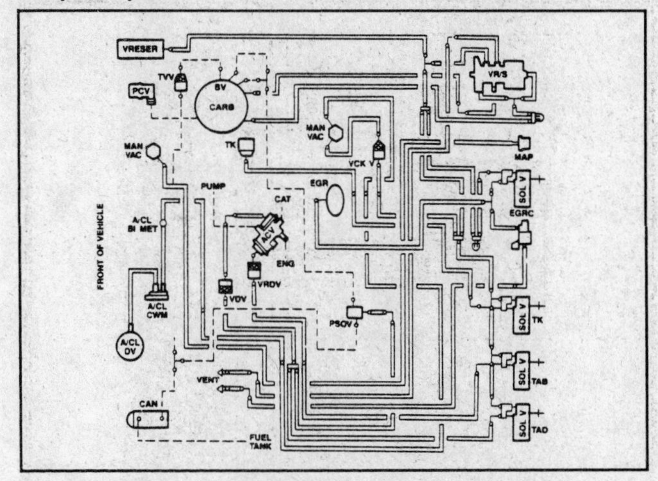

Fig. 14: 3.3L; Calibration 3-12A-R10; Federal; Capri, Fairmont, LTD, Marquis, Mustang, Zephyr

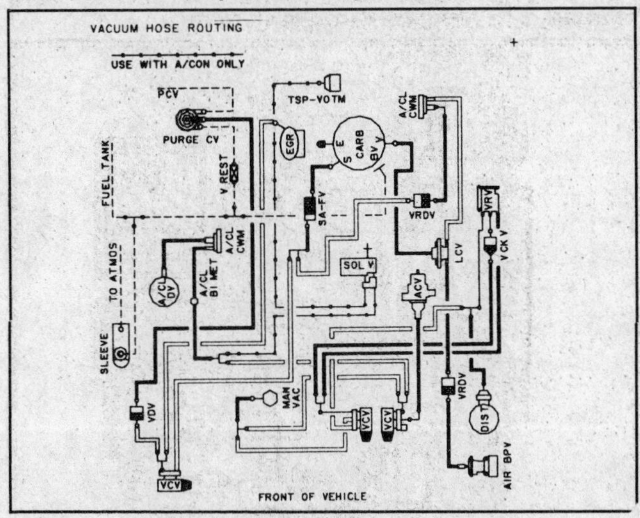

Fig. 15: 3.8L; Calibration 3-14B-R11; Federal; LTD, Marquis

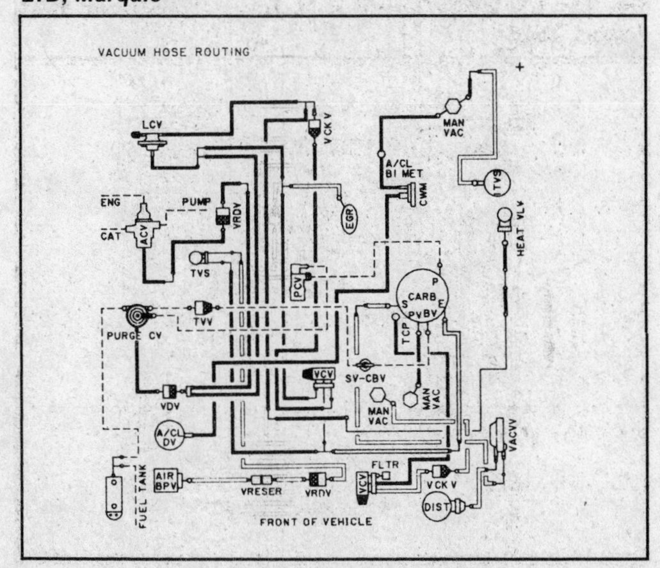

Fig. 16: 5.0L; Calibration 3-21A-R11; Exc. Calif.; Capri, Mustang

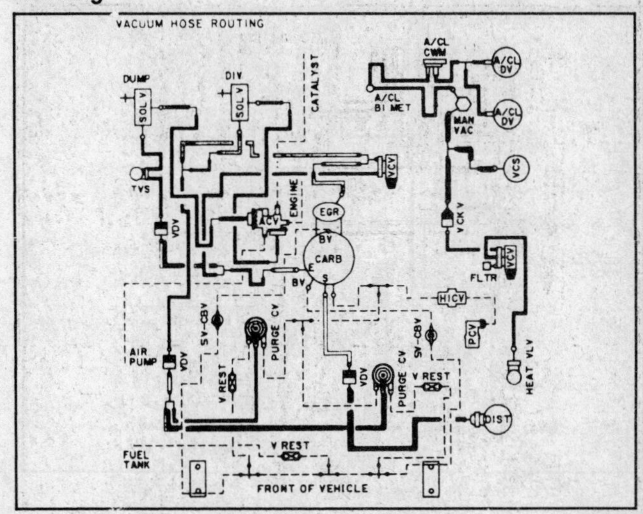

Fig. 17: 5.0L; Calibration 3-21A-R11; Exc. Calif.; Capri, Mustang

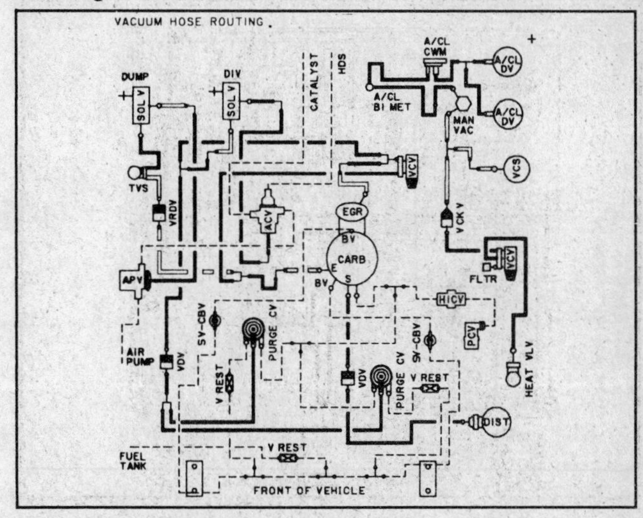

Fig. 18: 5.0L; Calibration 3-22D-R00; Exc. Hi. Alt.; Lincoln Continental (CFI)

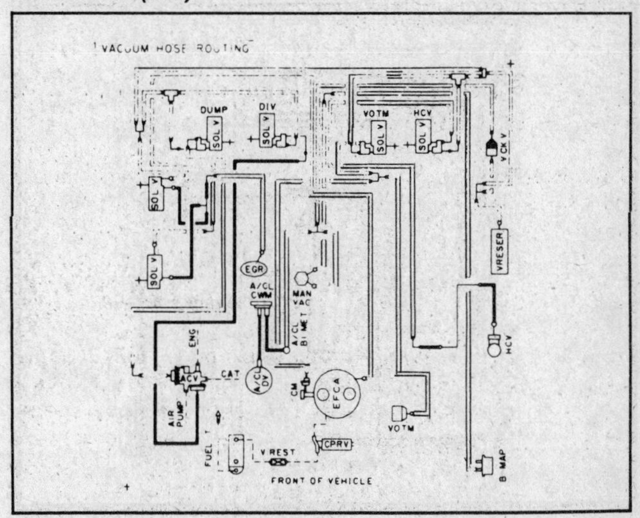

1983 FORD MOTOR CO. VACUUM DIAGRAMS (Cont.)

Fig. 19: 5.0L; Calibration 3-22D-R00; Exc. Hi. Alt.; Cougar, Thunderbird (CFI)

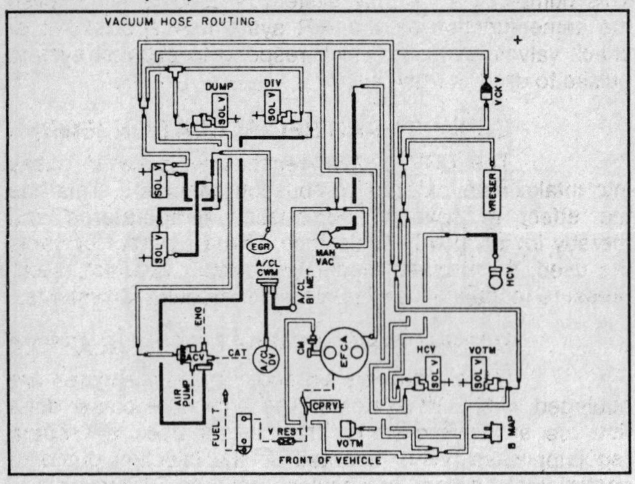

Fig. 20: 5.0L; Calibration 3-22W-R00; Hi. Alt.; Cougar, Thunderbird (CFI)

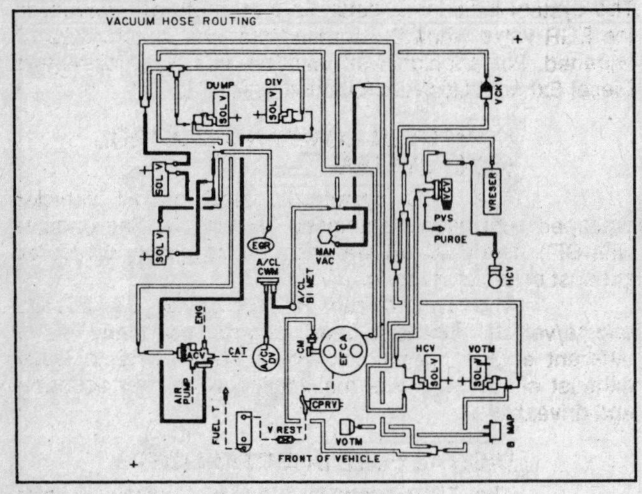

Fig. 21: 5.8L; Calibration 2-24P-R10; All; LTD & Marquis

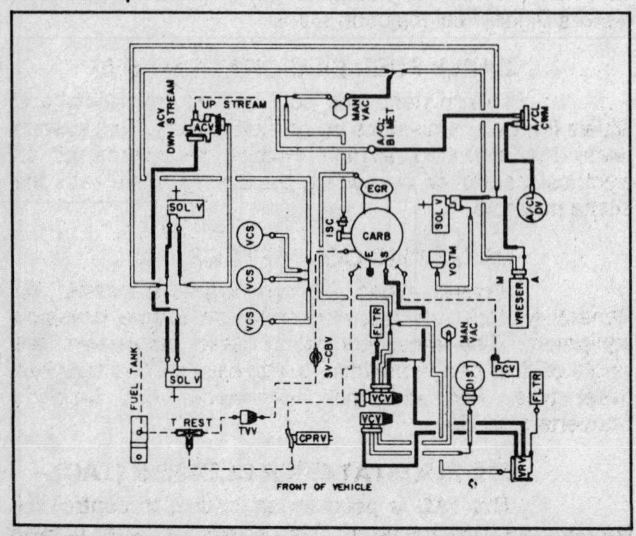

GENERAL MOTORS SYSTEMS & TUNE-UP PROCEDURES

DESCRIPTION

The following paragraphs describe emission control systems used on General Motors vehicles. More detailed articles describing each system appear later in this section.

HIGH ENERGY IGNITION (HEI) SYSTEM

The HEI system is used on all Federal 1.6L 4-cylinder engines. The HEI system consists of a distributor with an intregal electronic control module, battery, ignition coil, ignition switch, spark plugs and primary and secondary wiring.

The distributor combines the electronic control module, vacuum and centrifugal advance mechanisms, magnetic pick-up coil, timer core, rotor and distributor shaft into one unit.

HIGH ENERGY IGNITION-ELECTRONIC SPARK TIMING (HEI-EST)

The HEI-EST system provides a high voltage spark which allows the use of wide gap spark plugs to ignite a leaner air/fuel mixture. The system includes a distributor which contains a magnetic pick-up coil assembly, a special 7-terminal HEI module, and a built-in ignition coil.

The distributor does not contain either vacuum or centrifugal advance mechanisms. The HEI-EST system is used along with the Computer Command Control (CCC) system.

ELECTRONIC SPARK CONTROL (ESC) SYSTEM

The ESC system is used in conjunction with the HEI-EST system on 3.0L VIN E, 3.8L VIN A, 4.1L VIN 4, 5.0L VIN 7, and 5.7L VIN 8 engines. The ESC system retards ignition timing when detonation (spark knock) occurs. In addition to the HEI-EST components, ESC equipped vehicles have an ESC controller and a detonation sensor.

HALL EFFECT SYSTEM

This system is used in conjunction with the HEI-EST system on 2.5L VIN 2 and R 4-cylinder and 3.8L VIN 9 engines. The Hall Effect switch and shutter blades act as a second pick-up coil and timer core.

When the engine is in the cranking mode, the pick-up coil and timer core are used to send RPM signals to the electonic control module (ECM). When the engine is in the run mode, the Hall Effect switch and shutter blades perform this function.

AIR INJECTION REACTOR (AIR) SYSTEM

The AIR system uses an air pump to supply additional fresh air to the exhaust ports and/or the catalytic converter. The additional air helps complete combustion and lower hydrocarbon (HC) and carbon monoxide (CO) emissions. The system consists of an air pump, diverter valve, check valve, and various other valves and switches.

Some models use an air management system which diverts air between the exhaust ports and the catalytic converter based on engine operating conditions. These systems, controlled by the ECM, use an air switching valve. For additional information, see General Motors Air Injection Reactor System article.

PULSE AIR INJECTION REACTOR (PAIR)

This pumpless air supply system is used to accomplish the same function as the AIR system. A special set of check valves are used which respond to exhaust system pulses to draw in fresh air.

EXHAUST GAS RECIRCULATION (EGR)

The EGR system recirculates exhaust gases into intake manifold and combustion chambers. This has the effect of lowering combustion temperatures and thereby lowering NOx emissions. Three types of systems are used: the vacuum modulated (ported vacuum), back-pressure modulated, and pulse width modulated systems.

DIESEL EXHAUST GAS RECIRCULATION

General Motors V6 and V8 diesel engines are equipped with EGR systems. The 4-cylinder diesel does not use an EGR system. The system uses a vacuum regulator valve (VRV) mounted on the injection pump to control vacuum from the vacuum pump the EGR valve.

A response vacuum valve (RVV) is used between the VRV and the EGR valve to allow EGR valve to change position quickly as throttle position is changed. The system includes a solenoid that shuts off vacuum to the EGR valve when the torque converter clutch (TCC) is engaged. For additional information, see General Motors Diesel Exhaust Gas Recirculation article.

COMPUTER COMMAND CONTROL (CCC) SYSTEM

The CCC system is used on all vehicles equipped with gasoline engines (except Cadillac engines with DFI). The CCC system is an electronically controlled exhaust emission system.

The system can monitor up to 15 different engine/vehicle functions and control as many as 9 different engine operations. The system helps to lower exhaust emissions while maintaining good fuel economy and driveability.

DIGITAL FUEL INJECTION (DFI)

The DFI system is used on Cadillac vehicles equipped with 4.1L and 6.0L engines. This system includes computerized engine controls, fuel metering and emission control. For additional information, see General Motors Digital Fuel Injection article.

EARLY FUEL EVAPORATION (EFE)

This system aids cold engine driveability and allows for lower emissions on cold driveaway. This system heats the incoming air/fuel mixture by means of an electrical heater or by cycling exhaust gas beneath the intake manifold.

CATALYTIC CONVERTERS

Several types of converters are used on General Motors vehicles, depending on engine emission equipment. The most commonly used converters are single or dual bed monolithic, 3-way catalyst and dual bed pellet type. For additional information, see Catalytic Converters article.

THERMOSTATIC AIR CLEANER (TAC)

The TAC is used on all models to control the temperature of incoming air. This allows for better control

GENERAL MOTORS SYSTEMS & TUNE-UP PROCEDURES (Cont.)

of the air/fuel mixture during all engine operating temperatures. For additional information, see Thermostatic Air Cleaners article.

POSITIVE CRANKCASE VENTILATION (PCV)

The PCV system removes engine crankcase vapors which result from normal engine combustion. The vapors are drawn through a metered PCV valve and routed back to the intake manifold to be burned in the combustion chamber. For additional information, see Positive Crankcase Ventilation System article.

EVAPORATIVE EMISSION CONTROL

This system is used on all vehicles and is designed to keep fuel system vapors from escaping into the atmosphere. This closed system separates fuel vapors and routes them to the engine to be burned.

A carbon canister stores the vapors until the engine draws them in for burning. For additional information, see General Motors Evaporative Control System article.

GASOLINE ENGINE TUNE-UP SERVICE PROCEDURES

In addition to servicing of the individual emission systems, it is important that all ignition timing and carburetor adjustments are properly set.

Due to late changes and corrections, always refer to the Engine Tune-Up Decal in the engine compartment before performing tune-up procedures. In the event that specifications in this manual and decal specifications differ, always use the decal specifications.

IGNITION TIMING

NOTE: **Engines are equipped with a receptacle for a magnetic probe timing light, located 9.5° ATDC. Do not use this receptacle with a normal timing light.**

1.6L 4-Cyl.

1) Remove air cleaner assembly. If equipped, disconnect 4-wire EST connector at distributor. Disconnect and plug vacuum supply hose to thermactor system.

2) Disconnect and plug vacuum hose at EGR valve. Disconnect and plug canister purge hose and purge control hose at canister.

3) If equipped, disconnect and plug vacuum hose at distributor. Connect timing light to number 1 spark plug wire. Start engine and warm to normal operating temperature.

4) With engine at curb idle speed, loosen distributor hold down bolt and turn distributor housing to obtain specified timing.

5) Reconnect all disconnected vacuum hoses. Remove all test equipment. Reconnect 4-wire EST connector. Reinstall air cleaner assembly.

1.8L & 2.5L 4-Cyl.

1) Set parking brake and block drive wheels. Start engine and warm to normal operating temperature. Ensure that A/C and electric cooling fan are off.

2) Place transmission in Neutral (man. trans.) or "D" (auto. trans.). Ensure that "CHECK ENGINE" light is not on.

3) Locate diagnostic connector (left side of steering column under dash). Connect jumper wire across 2 terminals closest to column. "CHECK ENGINE" should now be flashing on and off in diagnostic mode. Connect an inductive pick-up timing light to number 1 spark plug wire. Check timing and adjust as necessary by turning distributor housing.

4) Remove ground from diagnostic connector. If "CHECK ENGINE" light remains on, clear trouble code from memory by removing ECM fuse from fuse block for 10 seconds.

2.0L 4-Cyl.

1) Setting ignition timing on this engine is accomplished using an averaging method that checks timing on all 4 cylinders at once. The COIL wire, instead of the number 1 spark plug wire, is used to trigger the timing light.

2) Start engine and warm to normal operating temperature. Connect an inductive timing light to the COIL wire (slide plastic cover back to gain access to coil wire).

3) Disconnect 4-wire EST connector at distributor. Start engine and aim timing light at timing tab. Timing is correct when the total apparent notch width is centered about the specified timing mark on the timing tab.

4) If timing is to specifications, stop engine and remove timing light. If timing is not to specifications, loosen distributor hold down clamp and rotate distributor until total apparent notch width is centered about the specified timing mark.

All V6 Engines Except 3.8L (VIN 9)

Check ignition timing with engine warm. Disconnect 4-wire connector at distributor. Set timing with engine idling.

3.8L V6 (VIN 9)

1) With engine off, place throttle on high step of fast idle cam. Disconnect and plug EGR valve hose. Start engine without touching throttle. Adjust fast idle to 1200 RPM and reconnect EGR vacuum hose.

2) With engine still at fast idle, find ALDL connector (below steering column under dashboard). Connect jumper across 2 terminals closest to steering column. DO NOT disconnect 4-wire connector at distributor. Set ignition timing, stop engine and disconnect jumper wire.

All V8 Engines

1) Place transmission in Neutral (man. trans.) or "P" (auto. trans.). On 4.1L engine, disconnect and plug vacuum line at automatic parking brake release. Disconnect Green reference signal connector.

2) On 5.0L VIN H and 6.0L engines, disconnect 4-wire EST connector at distributor. On 5.0L VIN S engine, place EST into by-pass mode by disconnecting single Tan/Black wire near right valve cover. On 5.0L VIN Y and VIN 9 engines, connect a jumper wire between 2 terminals closest to steering column in ALDL connector (near steering column below dashboard).

3) On all models, connect timing light to number 1 spark plug wire. Start engine and warm to normal operating temperature. Turn air conditioner off.

4) Adjust ignition timing by turning distributor housing. Recheck timing after tightening. Remove timing light and connect all wiring and vacuum hoses.

GENERAL MOTORS SYSTEMS & TUNE-UP PROCEDURES (Cont.)

IGNITION TIMING SPECIFICATIONS

Application	Degrees BTDC @ RPM
1.6L 4-Cyl.	
Federal	
Man. Trans.	
4-Speed	
With A/C	6 @ 800
Without A/C	8 @ 800
5-Speed	8 @ 950
Auto. Trans.	6 @ 700
Calif.	
Man. Trans.	6 @ 800
Auto. Trans.	6 @ 700
High Alt.	
Man. Trans.	
4-Speed	8 @ 800
5-Speed	8 @ 950
Auto. Trans.	6 @ 700
1.8L 4-Cyl.	8 @ 800
2.0L 4-Cyl.	0 @ 875
2.5L 4-Cyl. (VIN R)	
Man. Trans.	8 @ 850
Auto. Trans.	8 @ 750
2.5L 4-Cyl. (VIN 2)	
Man. Trans.	8 @ 900
Auto. Trans.	8 @ 650
2.8L V6	
Man. Trans.	10 @ 800
Auto. Trans.	10 @ 600
3.0L V6	15 @ 725
3.8L V6 (VIN 9)	0 @ 1200
3.8L V6 (VIN A & 8) & 4.1L V6	15 @ Idle
4.1L V8	10 @ Idle
5.0L V8 (VIN H)	6 @ Idle
5.0L V8 (VIN S)	6 @ Idle
5.0L V8 (VIN Y & 9)	20 @ 1100
5.7L V8	[1]
6.0L V8	10 @ Idle

[1] — Information not available from manufacturer.

Fig. 1: 1.6L 4-Cyl. Firing Order & Timing Marks

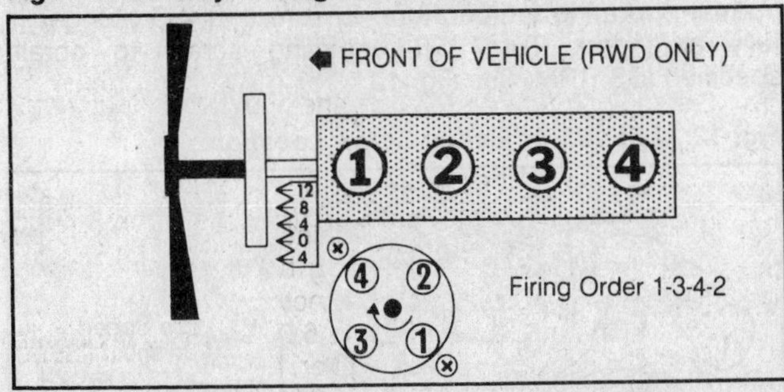

Fig. 2: 1.8L & 2.0L 4-Cyl. Firing Order & Timing Marks

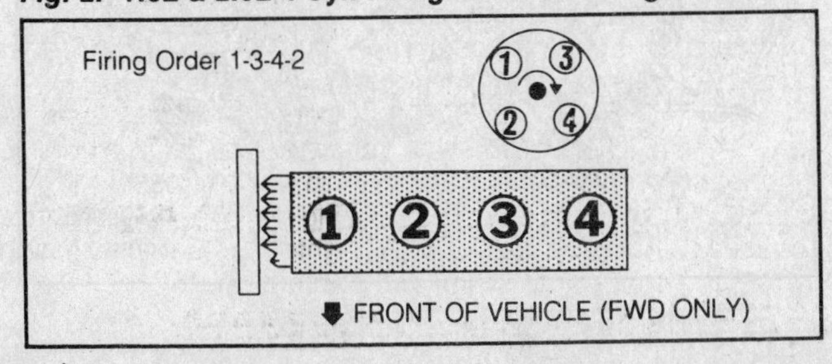

Fig. 3: 2.5L 4-Cyl. Firing Order & Timing Marks

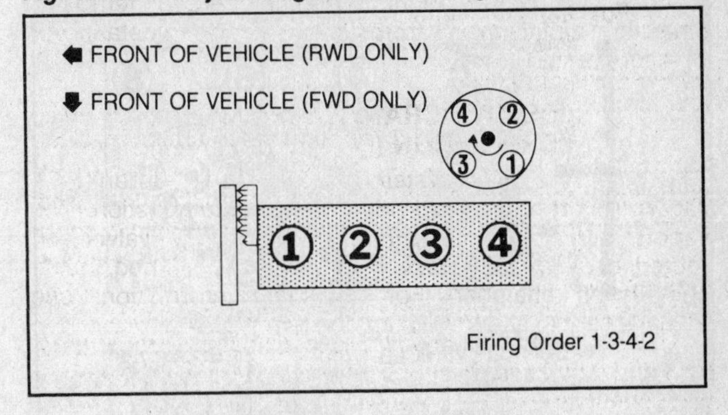

Fig. 4: 2.8L V6 Firing Order & Timing Marks

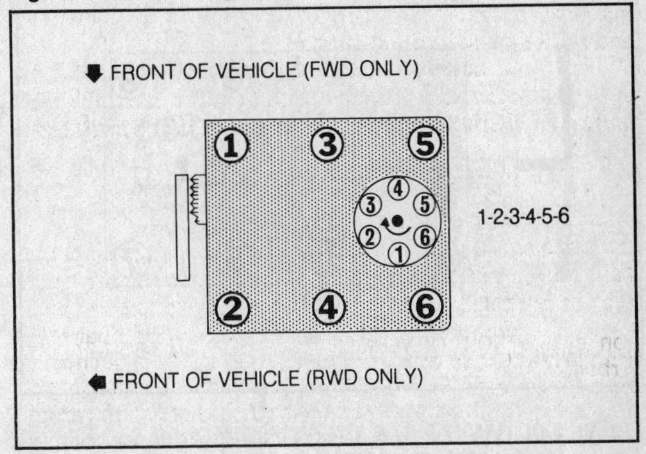

Fig. 5: 3.0L & 3.8L (VIN 9) V6 Firing Order & Timing Marks

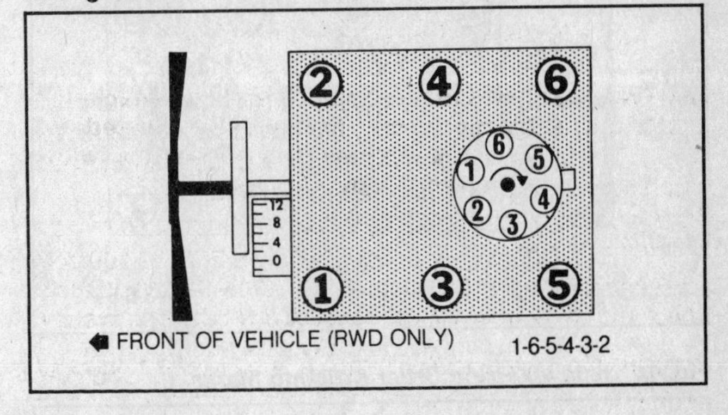

Fig. 6: 3.8L (VIN A & 8) & 4.1L V6 Firing Order & Timing Marks

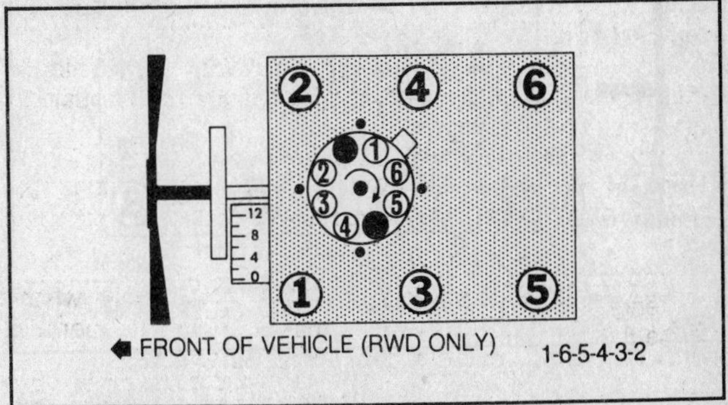

GENERAL MOTORS SYSTEMS & TUNE-UP PROCEDURES (Cont.)

Fig. 7: 4.1L V8 Firing Order & Timing Marks

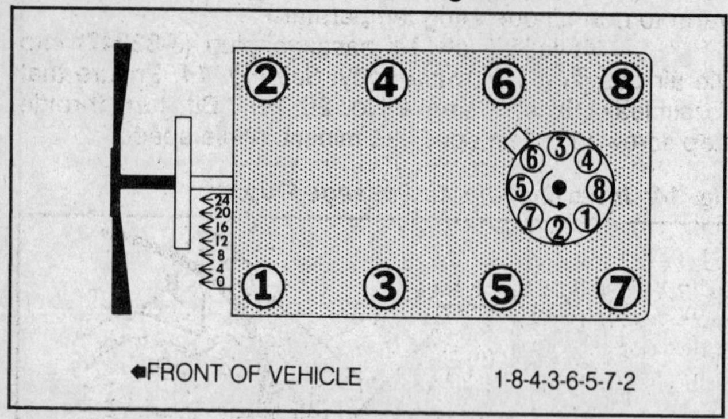

Fig. 8: 5.0L (VIN Y & 9) V8 Firing Order & Timing Marks

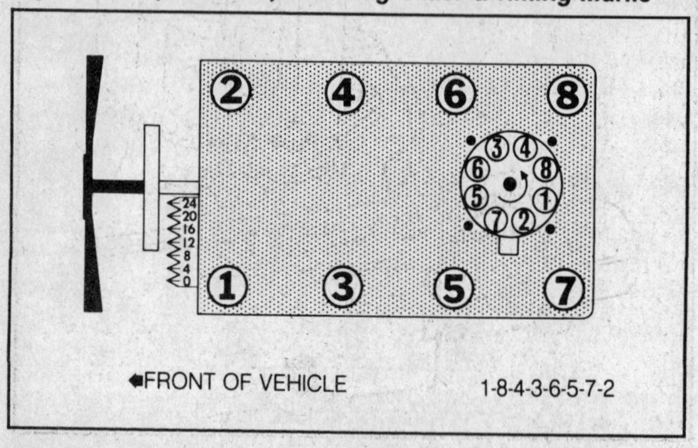

Fig. 9: 5.0L (VIN H & S) & 5.7L V8 Firing Order & Timing Marks

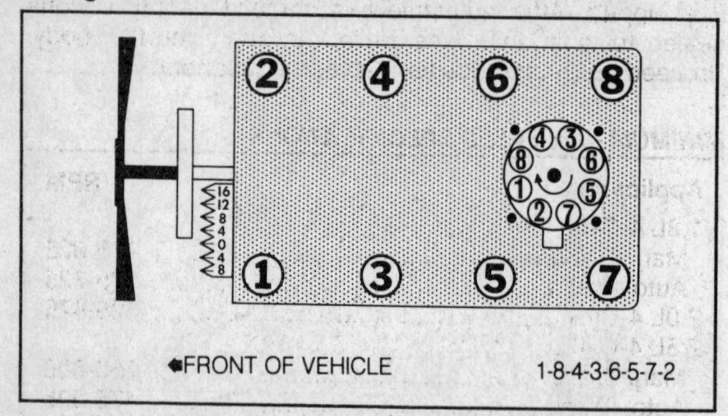

Fig. 10: 6.0L V8 Firing Order & Timing Marks

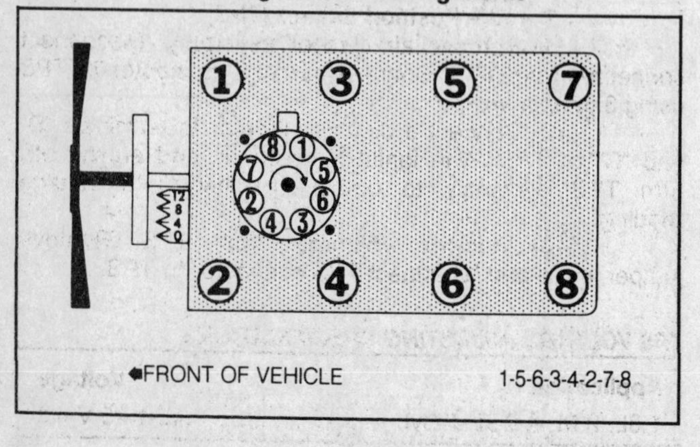

HOT (SLOW) IDLE RPM

1.6L 4-Cyl.

Curb Idle Speed

1) Set parking brake and block drive wheels. Ensure that ignition timing is properly set. Disconnect and plug vacuum hose at EGR valve. Disconnect and plug canister purge hose.

2) Disconnect and plug purge control hose at canister. Start engine and warm to normal operating temperature.

3) Place transmission in Neutral (man. trans.) or "D" (auto. trans.). Turn idle speed adjusting screw to obtain specified curb idle RPM. *See Fig. 11*. Remove plugs from all hoses and reconnect hoses to original locations.

Fig. 11: 1.6L Idle Speed Adjusting Screw Location

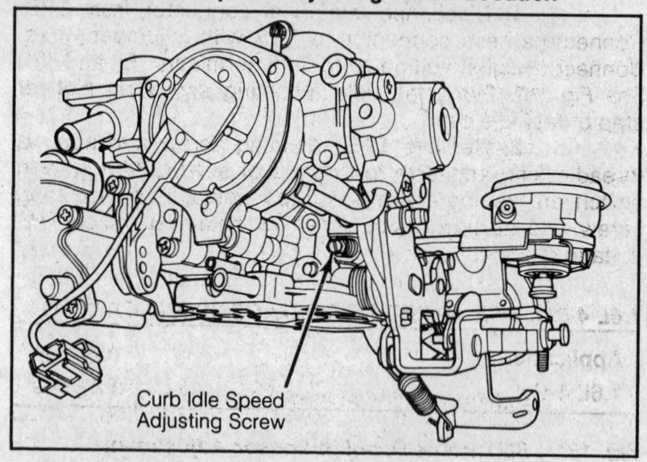

1.6L 4-Cyl.

Idle Speed Solenoid (ISS)

1) Set parking brake and block drive wheels. On models with A/C, disconnect electrical lead from A/C compressor and turn A/C control switch on.

2) On models without A/C, disconnect and plug vacuum hose at ISS. Apply enough vacuum to ISS to fully extend ISS plunger.

3) On all models, start engine and warm to normal operating temperature. Ensure that ISS plunger is fully extended. Turn ISS adjusting screw to obtain specified ISS RPM. *See Fig. 12*.

Fig. 12: 1.6L ISS Adjusting Screw Location

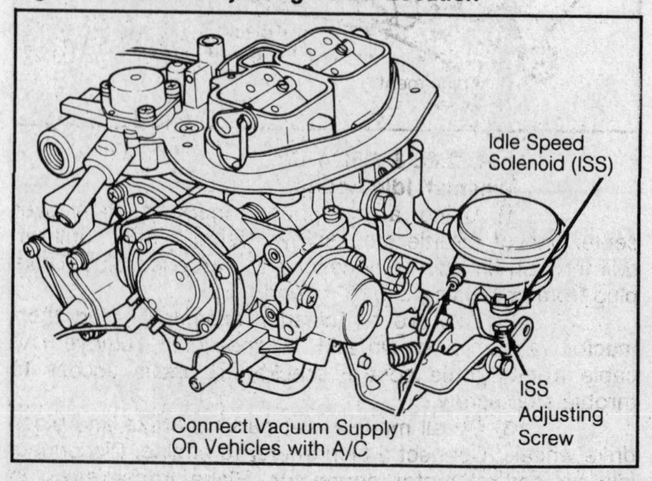

GENERAL MOTORS SYSTEMS & TUNE-UP PROCEDURES (Cont.)

1.6L 4-CYL. CURB IDLE & ISS IDLE SPECIFICATIONS

Application	Curb Idle RPM	ISS RPM
1.6L 4-Cyl.		
Federal & High Alt.		
Man. Trans.		
4-Speed	800	1150
5-Speed	950	1150
Auto. Trans.	700	875
Calif.		
Man. Trans.	800	1150
Auto. Trans.	700	875

1.6L 4-Cyl.
Throttle Position Sensor (TPS)

1) Disconnect electrical connector from TPS. Connect harness connector to TPS with 3 jumper wires. Connect a digital voltmeter to TPS terminals "B" and "C". *See Fig. 13.* Place fast idle adjusting screw on highest step of fast idle cam.

2) Remove TPS adjusting screw and apply a threadlocking adhesive to threads of screw. With ignition switch on, engine off and A/C off, install TPS adjusting screw and quickly adjust screw to obtain specified TPS voltage reading.

1.6L 4-CYL. TSP ADJUSTING VOLTAGE SPECIFICATIONS

Application	Voltage
1.6L 4-Cyl.	.92 Volts

Fig. 13: 1.6L Throttle Position Sensor Adjustment

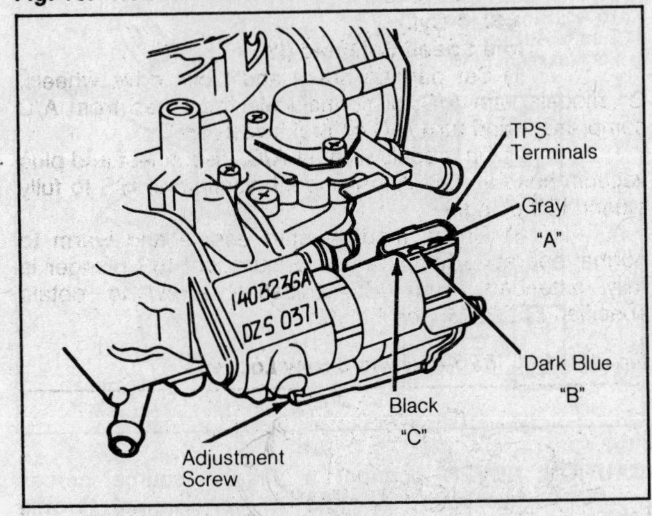

1.8L, 2.0L & 2.5L 4-Cyl.
Minimum Idle Speed

1) Using a pin punch, mark location over center line of throttle stop screw. Using a 5/32" drill bit, drill through throttle body casting to hardened plug. Drive plug from hole using a 1/16" punch.

2) Remove air cleaner assembly. Plug thermactor vacuum port. On 2.5L engines only, remove T.V. cable from throttle control bracket to obtain access to throttle stop screw.

3) On all models, set parking brake and block drive wheels. Connect a tachometer to engine. Disconnect idle air control motor connector. Place transmission in Neutral (man. trans.) or "P" (auto. trans.). Start engine and warm to normal operating temperature.

4) Install idle air passage plug (J-33047) into idle air passage of throttle body. *See Fig. 14.* Ensure that no air leaks exist. Using a No. 20 Torx Bit, turn throttle stop screw to obtain specified minimum idle speed.

Fig. 14: Installing Idle Air Passage Plug

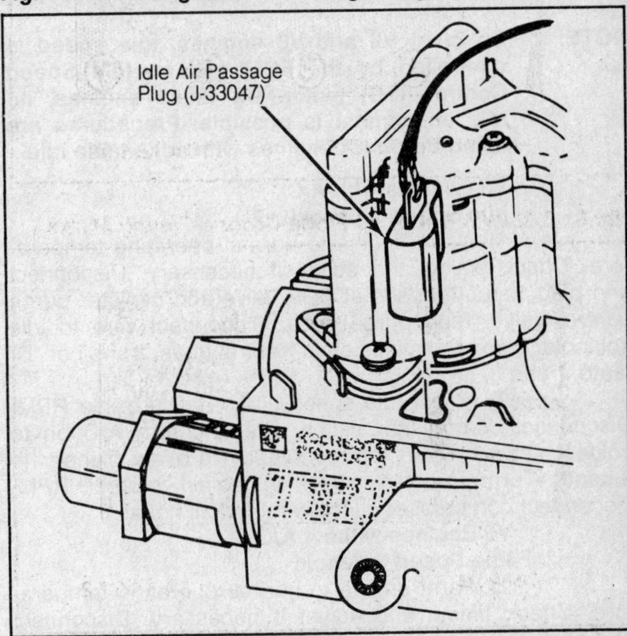

5) Remove tachometer from engine. Reconnect idle air control motor connector. Reinstall T.V. cable, if equipped. After adjustment is complete apply silicone sealer to hole that was drilled through throttle body. Proceed to Throttle Position Sensor adjustment.

MINIMUM IDLE SPEED SPECIFICATIONS

Application	RPM
1.8L 4-Cyl.	
Man. Trans.	775-825
Auto. Trans.	675-725
2.0L 4-Cyl.	625-675
2.5L 4-Cyl.	
Man. Trans.	750-800
Auto. Trans.	475-525

1.8L, 2.0L & 2.5L 4-Cyl.
Throttle Position Sensor (TPS)

1) Remove air cleaner assembly. Disconnect connector from TPS. Connect harness connector to TPS using 3 jumper wires.

2) Connect a digital voltmeter to terminals "B" and "C" of TPS. With ignition switch on and engine off, turn TPS assembly to obtain specified TPS voltage reading.

3) Remove voltmeter from TPS. Remove jumper wires and reconnect TPS connector to TPS.

TPS VOLTAGE ADJUSTING SPECIFICATIONS

Application	Voltage
1.8L, 2.0L & 2.5L 4-Cyl.	.45-1.25 Volts

1.8L, 2.0L & 2.5L 4-Cyl.
Idle Air Control Valve (IACV) Reset

If the idle speed remains abnormally high and will not regulate down, the IACV must be reset. To reset IACV, run engine until it reaches normal operating temperature and then drive vehicle at a speed of 40 MPH for a few moments to re-establish ECM-to-IACV reference point.

NOTE: **On most V6 and V8 engines, idle speed is controlled by the ECM and an Idle Speed Control (ISC) motor. On these engines, no idle adjustment is possible. Procedures are listed below for engines with adjustable idle.**

V6 Engines with A/C
Idle Speed Solenoid

1) Warm engine to normal operating temperature. Check timing and adjust if necessary. Disconnect and plug vacuum hoses at EGR valve and canister purge control valve. Plug purge hose. Disconnect wire to idle solenoid. Place transmission in Neutral (man. trans.) or "D" (auto. trans.).

2) Adjust idle speed screw to curb idle RPM. Disconnect compressor clutch wire and turn A/C on to coldest setting. Open throttle slightly to allow plunger to extend. Turn solenoid screw to obtain correct RPM. Reconnect compressor clutch wire and all hoses.

V6 Engines without A/C
Idle Speed Solenoid

1) Warm engine to normal operating temperature. Check timing and adjust if necessary. Disconnect and plug vacuum hoses at EGR valve and canister purge control valve. Plug purge hose. Disconnect wire to idle solenoid. Place transmission in Neutral (man. trans.) or "D" (auto. trans.).

2) Adjust idle speed screw to obtain curb idle RPM. Connect solenoid wire and open throttle to allow plunger to extend. Turn solenoid screw to obtain correct RPM. Reconnect hoses.

V6 CURB IDLE SPEED (RPM)

Application	Curb Idle	Solenoid Energized
2.8L V6 (VIN X)		
Man. Trans.	775	1100
Auto. Trans.	600	750
2.8L V6 (VIN L & Z)		
Man. Trans.	800	1100
Auto. Trans.	725	850
2.8L V6 (VIN 1)		
Man. Trans.	800	1000
Auto. Trans.	600	750
3.8L V6 (VIN A)		
Auto. Trans.	600	700

V6 Engines
Idle Speed Control Motor

1) Prior to making adjustments, check for an identification letter on ISC plunger. *See Fig. 15*. If no letter appears, remove plunger and measure length of plunger (distance "A" in fig. 4). Record measurement. Install plunger into ISC and position so that distance measured from back side of plunger to ISC is less than distance "B" listed in Idle Speed Control Plunger chart.

Fig. 15: Measuring V6 Engine Idle Speed Control Plunger

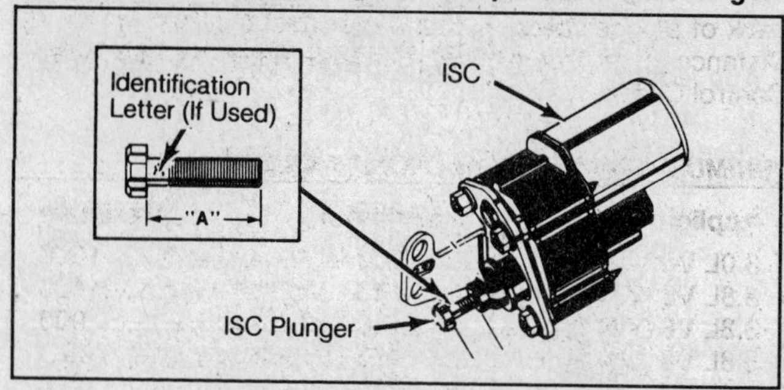

2) Place transmission in Neutral (man. trans.) or "P" (auto. trans.). Set brakes and block wheels. Connect tachometer to engine. Connect dwell meter to Mixture Control Solenoid lead. Set dwell meter in 6-cylinder scale. Turn A/C off (if equipped), start engine and run until engine enters "Closed Loop" operation (dwell meter needle starts to fluctuate). Stop engine.

CAUTION: **DO NOT disconnect or connect ISC connector with ignition "ON" or damage to ECM may result.**

3) Unplug ISC connector from motor. Retract plunger by applying 12 volts to terminal "C" and grounding terminal "D" of ISC motor. *See Fig. 16*. Do not leave 12 volts connected to the ISC motor any longer than necessary to retract plunger.

Fig. 16: Idle Speed Control Adjustment Connections

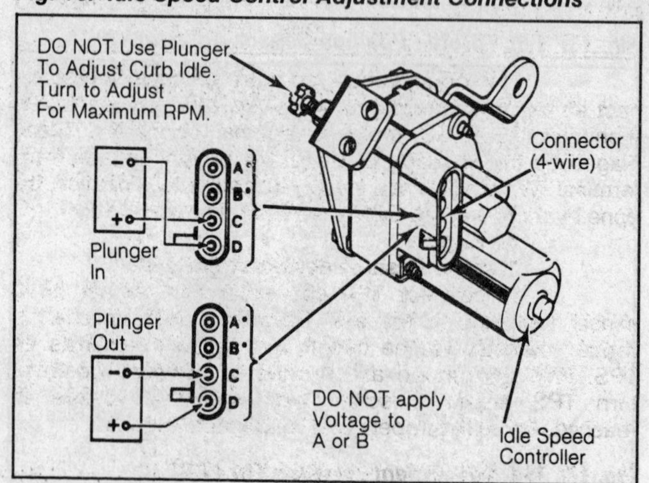

CAUTION: **NEVER connect a voltage source across terminals "A" and "B" or internal throttle contact switch will be damaged.**

4) Start engine and run until dwell meter starts to vary (Closed Loop operation), then place transmission in Neutral (man. trans.) or "D" (auto. trans.). Adjust carburetor slow idle screw until Minimum Authority RPM is obtained. With idle adjusted, place transmission in "P".

5) Extend ISC plunger by applying 12 volts to terminal "D" and grounding terminal "C" of ISC motor connector. *See Fig. 16*. Adjust plunger to obtain Maximum Authority RPM. Recheck adjustment RPM by applying voltage to extend plunger (plunger will ratchet at full extension).

GENERAL MOTORS SYSTEMS & TUNE-UP PROCEDURES (Cont.)

6) After adjustment, measure distance from back of plunger head to ISC motor (distance "B" in Fig. 4). Distance must not exceed distance listed in Idle Speed Control Chart.

MINIMUM & MAXIMUM AUTHORITY IDLE RPM

Application	Minimum	Maximum
3.0L V6	500	1300
3.8L V6 (VIN A)	450	900
3.8L V6 (VIN 8)	450	900
3.8L V6 (VIN 9)	475	750 [1]
4.1L V6	470	900

[1] — 800 RPM with A/C.

IDLE SPEED CONTROL PLUNGER SETTING

Identification Letter	Distance "A"	Distance "B"
None	9/16"	7/32"
None	41/64"	5/16"
X	47/64"	25/64"
A	49/64"	27/64"
Y	51/64"	15/32"
S	27/32"	1/2"
G	29/32"	37/64"
E	1"	43/64"
L	1 3/32"	3/4"
J	1 3/16"	27/32"
N	1 7/64"	59/64"
T	1 11/32"	1"

7) Retract plunger and turn engine off. Disconnect all test equipment and wires. Be sure ignition is off, then reconnect ISC motor 4-terminal connector. Clear diagnostic trouble code by removing battery voltage from terminal "R" of ECM for about 10 seconds. This can be done by removing the ECM fuse from the fuse block.

V6 Engine
Throttle Position Sensor Adjustment

Disconnect TPS connector and jumper all 3 sensor terminals to harness. Connect a high impedance digital voltmeter to the center and bottom terminals of TPS. With ignition on and throttle in specified position, turn TPS adjusting screw until specified voltage is reached. Remove jumpers and reconnect harness.

Fig. 17: TPS Adjustment Location For E2SE

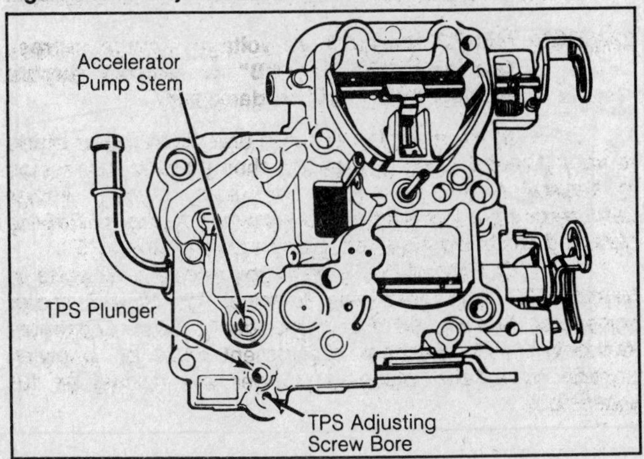

Fig. 18: TPS Adjustment Location For E2ME & E4ME

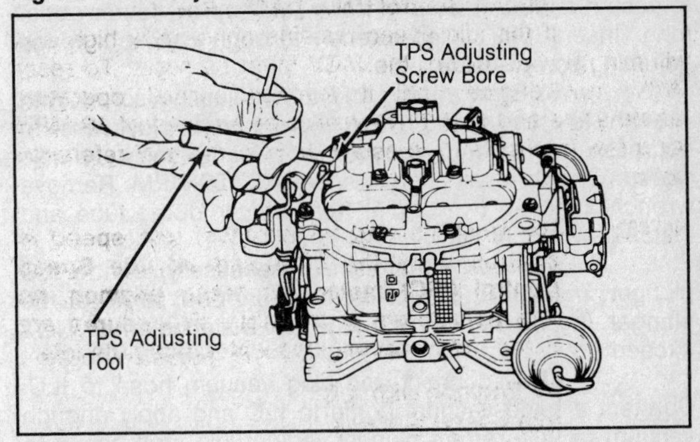

TPS ADJUSTMENT VOLTAGE

Application	Voltage	Throttle Position
2.8L	.26	Idle
3.0L	.42	Idle
3.8L (VIN 9)	.51	Idle
3.8L (VIN A & 8)	.77	Top Cam Step
4.1L	.97	Top Cam Step

5.0L V8 (VIN H) & 6.0L V8 (VIN 6)
Idle Speed (With Solenoid)

1) Warm engine to normal operating temperature and adjust timing. With A/C off, adjust idle speed screw to idle speed specifications.

2) Disconnect compressor clutch wire and turn A/C on. Open throttle slightly to allow plunger to extend. Turn solenoid plunger to obtain correct solenoid RPM. Reconnect compressor clutch wire.

IDLE SPEED (RPM)

Application	Curb Idle	Solenoid Energized
5.0L V8 (VIN H)		
Man. Trans.	700	800
Auto. Trans.	500	650
6.0L V8 (VIN 6)	[1]	450

[1] — Information not available from manufacturer.

5.0L V8 (VIN Y & 9)
Idle Speed (With Idle Load Compensator)

1) With transmission in "P", brakes set and wheels blocked, prepare vehicle for adjustments. Remove air cleaner and plug hose to thermal vacuum valve (TVV). Disconnect and plug hoses to EGR, canister purge port and idle load compensator (ILC).

2) Back out throttle stop screw 3 turns. With engine running and transmission selector in "D", adjust plunger to obtain specified plunger extended RPM. Hold jam nut on plunger to avoid damaging ILC.

3) Reconnect engine vacuum to ILC and observe idle speed. Idle speed should match "plunger retracted" RPM. If correct, proceed to step 7). If not, stop engine and remove ILC. Plug vacuum hose to ILC.

4) Remove rubber cap and metal plug from ILC center tube. Install ILC on carburetor and re-attach throttle return spring and other related parts removed during disassembly. Reconnect hose to ILC.

GENERAL MOTORS SYSTEMS & TUNE-UP PROCEDURES (Cont.)

5) Using a spare rubber cap with hole punched to accept a .090" Allen wrench, install cap on center outlet tube. Insert .090" Allen wrench through cap to engage adjusting screw inside tube.

6) Start engine and turn adjusting screw with wrench to obtain 500 RPM. Turn screw clockwise to decrease idle speed; counterclockwise to increase idle speed. One turn will change speed 75-100 RPM. Remove wrench and cap (with hole) from center outlet tube and install new rubber cap.

7) After adjustment (if necessary) of the ILC plunger, measure distance from the jam nut to tip of the plunger. *See Distance "B", Fig. 19.* Distance must NOT exceed 1".

8) Disconnect and plug vacuum hose to ILC. Connect a hand vacuum pump to ILC and apply enough vacuum to fully retract plunger. Adjust idle stop screw to obtain 500 RPM. Reconnect hoses and remove test equipment.

Fig. 19: Idle Load Compensator Adjustment

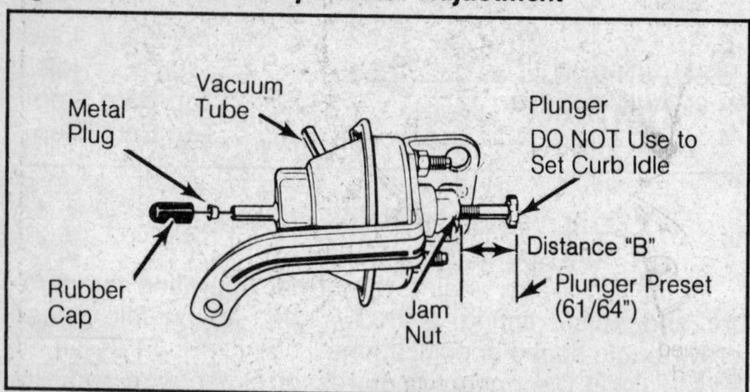

IDLE LOAD COMPENSATOR ADJUSTMENT (RPM)

Application	Plunger Retracted	Plunger Extended
5.0L (VIN Y & 9)	550	725

5.0L V8 (VIN H, Y & 9)
Throttle Position Sensor Adjustment

Disconnect TPS connector and jumper all 3 sensor terminals to harness. Connect a high impedance digital voltmeter to the center and bottom terminals of TPS. With ignition on and throttle in specified position, turn TPS adjusting screw until specified voltage is reached. Remove jumpers and reconnect harness.

TPS ADJUSTMENT VOLTAGE

Application	Voltage	Throttle Position
5.0L (VIN H)	.51	Idle
5.0L (VIN Y & 9)	.46	ILC retracted

NOTE: **On fuel injected engines, idle speed is controlled by ECM. Idle adjustment is necessary only when ISC or throttle body has been replaced. The procedure involves removal and disassembly of the throttle body. For throttle body removal and disassembly, refer to General Motors Electronic Fuel Injection or Digital Fuel Injection article.**

Fig. 20: TPS Adjustment Location For E4ME

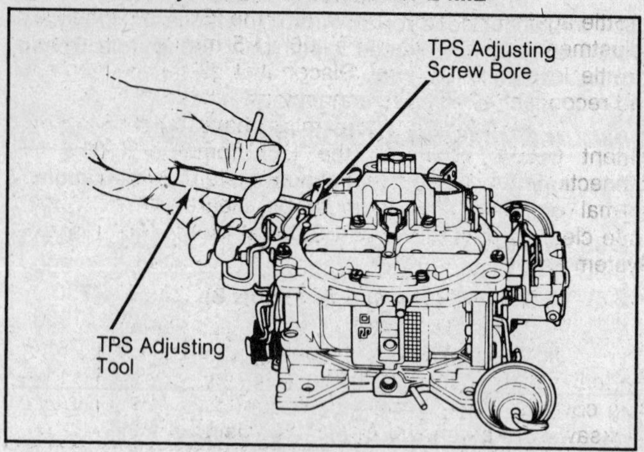

4.1L V8 & 6.0L V8 (VIN 9)
Curb Idle Speed

1) Remove air cleaner and warm engine to normal operating temperature. Turn air conditioner off. Check and adjust engine timing.

2) Turn off all electrical accessories, place steering wheel in center position and transmission selector in "P". With idle speed control (ISC) plunger fully retracted and not touching throttle lever, idle speed should be 450 RPM on 4.1L engine and as specified on Emission Control Decal for 6.0L engine.

3) Connect a digital voltmeter to the throttle position sensor (TPS) harness test point as follows: With ignition on and engine off, connect positive voltmeter lead to pin "A" (Dark Blue wire) and negative voltmeter lead to pin "B" (Black wire). Set voltmeter on 2 volt DC scale. With the throttle closed against the stop screw, voltmeter should read 1/10 of the system reference voltage.

4) Reference voltage (4.5-5.5 volts) can be measured at TPS pins "B" and "C". *Example: If reference voltage is about 5.2 volts, TPS voltage should be 0.52 volts.* If voltage is not to specifications, loosen TPS attaching screws and rotate TPS to obtain desired voltage. Recheck TPS voltage after retightening attaching screws.

Fig. 21: Test Point Location For Throttle Position Sensor Adjustment

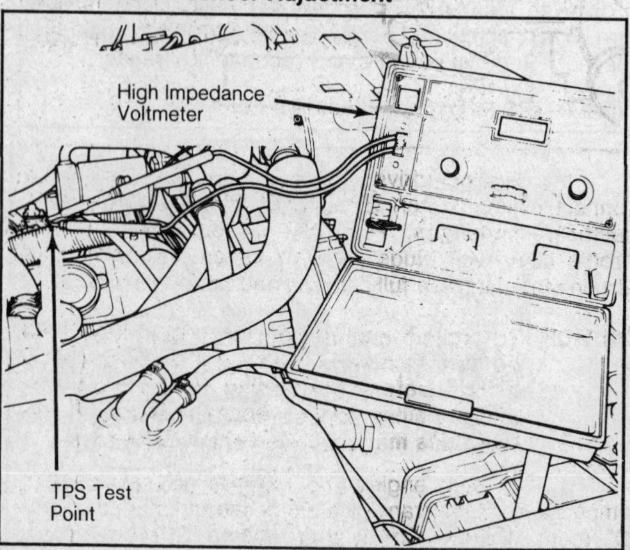

5) With ISC motor fully retracted and the throttle against the stop screw, turn the ISC motor plunger adjustment screw to obtain a .06" (1.5 mm) gap between throttle lever and plunger. Disconnect all test equipment and reconnect all harness connectors.

6) This procedure might have recorded intermittent trouble codes in the DFI computer. After all connections have been made and system is restored to normal operation, codes must be cleared. For trouble code clearing procedure, see General Motors DFI Control System article.

5.0L V8 (VIN S) & 5.7L (VIN 8)

Curb Idle Speed

1) Remove air cleaner and gaskets. Plug thermal vacuum port on rear of throttle body. Remove plug covering minimum air adjustment screw by making 2 hacksaw cuts as shown in *Fig. 22*. Using a small punch, knock out portion of casting cut by hacksaw. Hit in direction indicated by arrow 1. Knock out steel plug with small punch by hitting plug from direction indicated by arrow 2.

Fig. 22: Plug Removal for Minimum Air Adjustment Screw

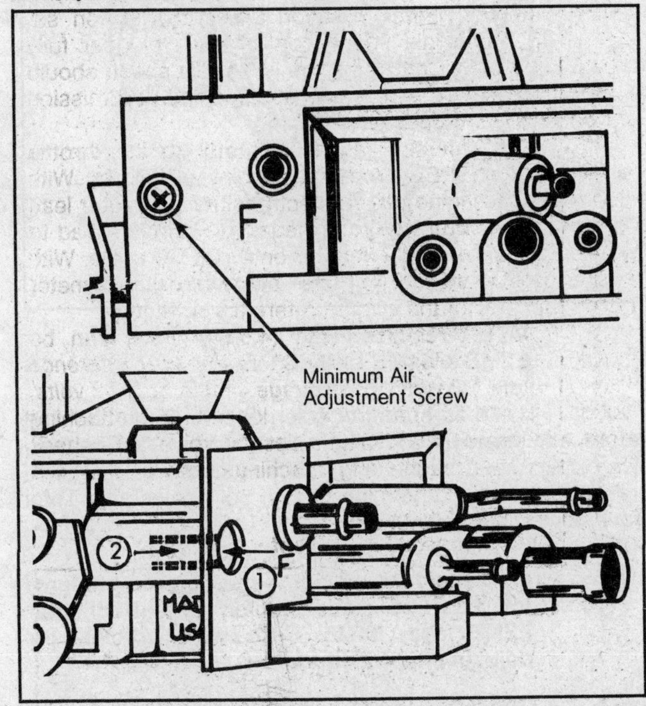

2) Block drive wheels and apply parking brake. Connect a tachometer. Disconnect Idle Air Control (IAC) electrical connectors. Plug idle air passages of each throttle body with plugs (J-33047 or equivalent), making certain that plugs are fully seated and no air leaks exist.

CAUTION: To prevent engine from running at high RPM, be sure ignition is "OFF" and transmission is in "N" before connecting IAC, or removing and installing idle air passage plugs. Failure to do this may result in vehicle movement.

3) Start engine and warm to normal operating temperature. Place transmission in Neutral (man. trans.) or "D" (auto. trans.). Check that engine RPM decreases below curb idle speed. If RPM does not decrease, check for vacuum leak. Remove cap from ported tube on rear throttle body and connect water manometer (vacuum gauge). Adjust minimum air adjustment screw to obtain about 6" water on manometer. Remove manometer and install cap on ported tube.

4) Remove cap from ported tube on front throttle body and connect manometer. Reading should again be about 6" water. If adjustment is required, locate idle balance screw on throttle linkage. *See Fig. 23*. If screw is welded, break weld and install new screw with thread sealing compound. Adjust screw to obtain about 6" water on manometer. Remove manometer and install cap on ported tube.

Fig. 23: Component Locations for 5.0L & 5.7L Fuel Injection System

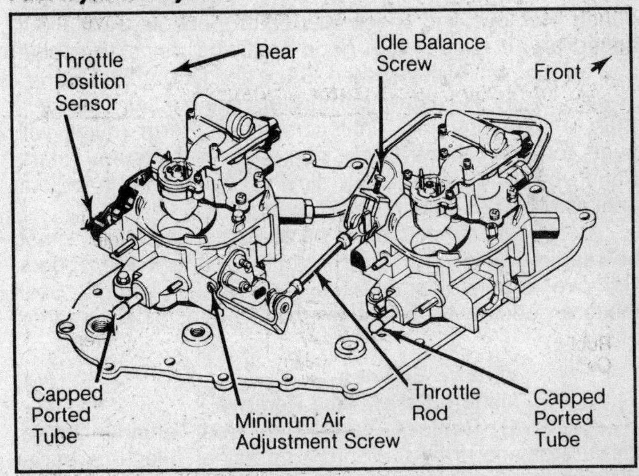

5) Adjust minimum air adjustment screw on rear unit to obtain 475 RPM. Turn ignition "OFF" and place transmission in "N". Remove idle air passage plugs and reconnect idle air control (IAC) assemblies. Start engine. Engine may run at high RPM but RPM will decrease when IAC assemblies close air passages. Stop engine when RPM decreases.

6) Check throttle position sensor (TPS) voltage. If adjustment is necessary, remove EGR valve and heat shield from engine. Using three 6" jumper wires, connect TPS harness to TPS. With ignition "ON" and engine stopped, use a digital voltmeter to measure the voltage present between the terminals marked "B" and "C" on TPS.

7) Loosen 2 TPS attaching screws and rotate throttle position sensor to obtain a voltage reading of .45-.60 volts. Tighten screws. Turn ignition "OFF", remove jumpers and reconnect TPS harness to TPS. Install EGR valve and heat shield to engine, using new gasket if necessary.

8) Install air cleaner gasket, connect vacuum line to throttle body and install air cleaner. Reset IAC motors by driving vehicle at 30 MPH.

IDLE MIXTURE ADJUSTMENT

NOTE: Idle mixture is controlled by the Electronic Control Module (ECM) on fuel injected engines. No adjustment is required or possible on these engines.

1.6L 4-Cyl.
Idle Mixture Adjustment

1) Engine must be idling at normal operating temperature. Set parking brake, block wheels, and disconnect canister purge hose. Connect tachometer and dwell meter to engine. Adjust idle speed and timing if necessary.

2) With transmission selector in Neutral (man. trans.) or "D" (auto. trans.), observe dwell reading (on 6-Cyl. scale). If dwell varies between 10-50°, mixture is correct. If dwell reading does not vary between 10-50°, proceed to step **3)**.

3) Remove carburetor and place upside down in a holding fixture. Break out a small piece of throttle body with a punch at the locator point (under idle mixture screw).

4) Drive out idle mixture screw plug with a punch. Remove and check idle mixture needle. Replace if necessary. If needle is in good condition, reinstall needle and turn in until lightly seated. Back needle out 2 turns.

5) Reinstall carburetor without air cleaner. Start engine and idle until completely warm (dwell will begin to vary). With transmission selector in Neutral (man. trans.) or "D" (auto. trans.), slowly turn needle in or out until dwell varies within 25-35° range.

6) If dwell cannot be adjusted, carburetor must be repaired. If dwell is set correctly, recheck idle speed. Remove test equipment and reconnect hoses. Seal mixture needle with silicone sealant. Reinstall air cleaner assembly.

V6 & V8 Engines
Mixture Screw Plug Removal

1) Remove carburetor from engine, invert carburetor and drain fuel into a container. Place carburetor on a holding fixture with manifold side up.

2) Use hacksaw to make 2 small cuts below mixture plugs on bottom of throttle body. Use flat punch or chisel to break out a piece of throttle body to gain access to plugs.

3) Use a punch to drive out plug. If hardened steel plug shatters, remove loose pieces.

4) Repeat steps **2)** and **3)** to remove remaining plug (if equipped).

V6 Engines with E2SE Carburetor
Idle Mixture Adjustment

1) Remove carburetor and remove mixture screw plug. Turn screw in until lightly seated, then back out 4 turns.

2) Remove vent stack screen. Turn part throttle lean mixture screw in until lightly seated and back out 2 1/2 turns. Reinstall carburetor without air cleaner.

3) Disconnect bowl vent line. Disconnect and plug vacuum hose at "T" in vent line (if used). Disconnect EGR valve and canister purge at carburetor and plug ports. Remove secondary vacuum break thermal vacuum switch from air cleaner, disconnect hot air valve hose from air cleaner, and plug switch. Leave all other hoses connected.

4) Connect tachometer to Brown connector and dwell meter to Green connector near carburetor. Set dwell meter on 6-cylinder setting. Run engine for at least 3 minutes or until dwell reading begins to vary.

5) Run engine at 3000 RPM and adjust lean mixture screw to achieve 35° dwell. Allow dwell to stabilize between adjustments. Return to idle.

6) Adjust idle mixture screw to obtain dwell reading of 25° while cooling fan is off. Allow readings to stabilize between adjustments. Disconnect mixture control solenoid while cooling fan is off and check for drop of at least 50 RPM.

7) Repeat 3000 RPM check and adjustment procedure if necessary. When dwell readings are correct, reconnect system hoses, replace vent screen, and remove test equipment.

Fig. 24: E2SE Lean Mixture Screw Location

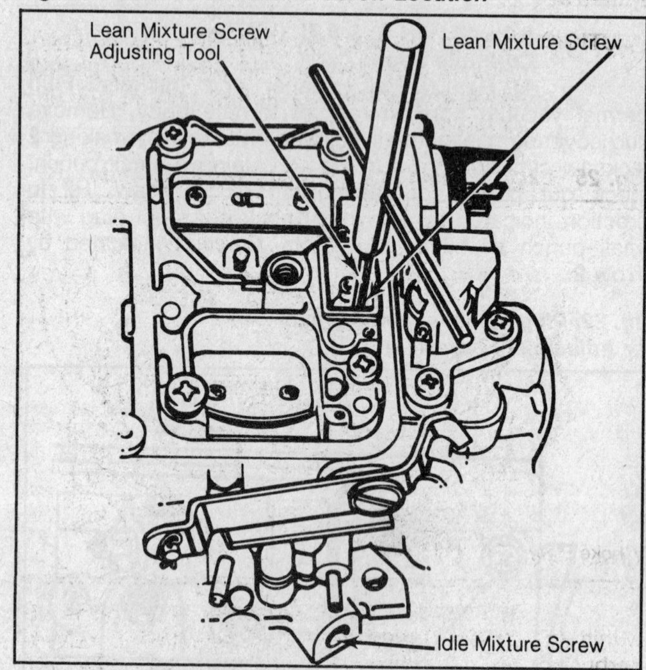

V6 & V8 Engines with
E2ME & E4ME Carburetors
Idle Mixture Adjustment

1) Mixture control solenoid should be checked before adjustment. Stop engine and remove air cleaner. Insert thin metal scale in "D" shaped hole in air horn. Press down to determine travel of solenoid. Total movement should be 1/16 - 3/16".

NOTE: **If solenoid movement is not correct, carburetor must be disassembled. See Rochester E2ME and E4ME Carburetor articles for adjustment procedures.**

2) To adjust idle air bleed valve, set parking brake and block drive wheels. Check ignition timing and adjust if necessary.

3) Connect tachometer to engine. Connect a dwell meter to lead wire from mixture control solenoid in carburetor, then set dwell meter on 6-cylinder scale. Start engine and run at idle until normal operating temperature is reached and a varying dwell is noted on dwell meter.

NOTE: **Engine must be run long enough to ensure that engine coolant sensor and oxygen sensor are at normal operating temperature.**

4) Adjust curb idle speed (on models with ISC or ILC, do not adjust). With engine idling in Neutral (man.

trans.) or "D" (auto. trans.), observe dwell reading. If dwell needle is moving within 10-50°, no adjustment is necessary. If needle is fixed at one point or outside this range, proceed with adjustment.

5) With engine stopped, cover carburetor air intakes and vents with tape. Drill rivet heads on idle air bleed plug (above primary bores). Remove plug and blow out metal chips and rivet pieces. Remove tape covering carburetor. Start engine, run until warm, and adjust idle air bleed valve with screwdriver until dwell varies within 25-35° range.

CAUTION: Perform this step carefully. The idle air bleed valve is very sensitive in controlling air/fuel ratios and should be turned only in 1/8 turn increments.

Fig. 25: E2ME & E4ME Idle Air Bleed Valve Location

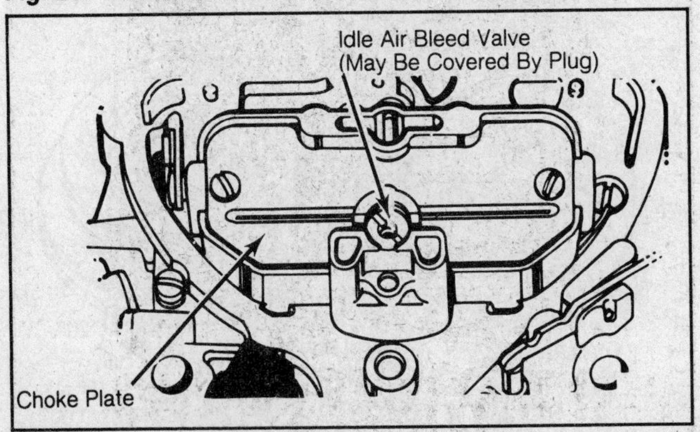

6) If dwell reading does not vary and is not within the 25-35° range after this adjustment, remove carburetor. Remove mixture needle plugs and adjust the idle mixture as follows:

7) Turn screws until lightly seated. Back out screws 3 turns. Reinstall carburetor and check dwell when engine is warm.

8) If dwell is below limits turn screws out in 1/8 turn increments. If above limits, turn screws in at 1/8 turn increments. Readjust air bleed valve to center dwell within limits. Reset idle speed if necessary. Remove all test equipment and reconnect all hoses.

COLD (FAST) IDLE RPM

NOTE: On fuel injected engines, fast idle speed is controlled by the Electronic Control Module. No adjustment is required or possible on these engines.

1.6L 4-Cyl.

1) Set parking brake and block drive wheels. Remove air cleaner assembly. Disconnect and plug vacuum hose at EGR valve.

2) Disconnect and plug canister purge hose and purge control hose at canister. Start engine and warm to normal operating temperature. Place transmission in Neutral (man. trans.) or "P" (auto. trans.).

3) Place fast idle screw on highest step of fast idle cam. Turn fast idle adjusting screw to obtain specified fast idle RPM. *See Fig. 26*. Unplug and reconnect all hoses. Reinstall air cleaner assembly.

Fig. 26: 1.6L Fast Idle Speed Adjusting Screw Location

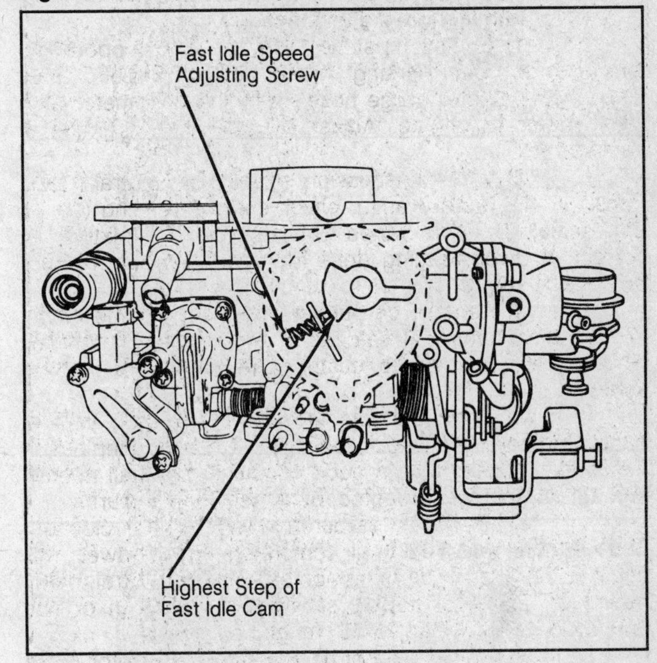

2.8L V6

Disconnect and plug vacuum hoses at EGR valve and canister purge valve. Plug purge hose. With engine at normal operating temperature, place fast idle screw on high step of cam. Set fast idle speed using fast idle screw. Reconnect hoses.

3.8L V6 (VIN 9)

With engine off, place throttle on high step of fast idle cam. Disconnect and plug EGR valve vacuum hose. Start engine without touching throttle and adjust fast idle speed.

All Other V6 Engines

With transmission in Neutral (man. trans.) or "P" (auto. trans.), place fast idle screw on high step of cam. Adjust fast idle.

All V8 Carbureted Engines

With engine at normal operating temperature, disconnect and plug vacuum hose at EGR valve. Position cam follower on high step of fast idle cam and turn fast idle screw to obtain specified fast idle RPM.

FAST IDLE SPEED (RPM)

Application	Man. Trans.	Auto. Trans.
1.6L 4-Cyl.	2500	2500
2.8L V6 (VIN X)	2500	2500
2.8L V6 (VIN L & Z)	2600	2700
2.8L V6 (VIN 1)	2600	2500
3.0L V6	2400 [1]	[1] 2400
3.8L V6 (VIN 9)		2200
3.8L V6 (VIN A & 8)		[2] 2200
4.1L V6		[2] 2200
5.0L V8	1800	2200
6.0L V8	[3]	[3]

[1] — Calif. is 2300 RPM.
[2] — FWD is 2100 RPM.
[3] — Information not available from manufacturer.

GENERAL MOTORS SYSTEMS & TUNE-UP PROCEDURES (Cont.)

DIESEL ENGINE TUNE-UP SERVICE PROCEDURES

Fig. 27: 1.8L Diesel Firing Order

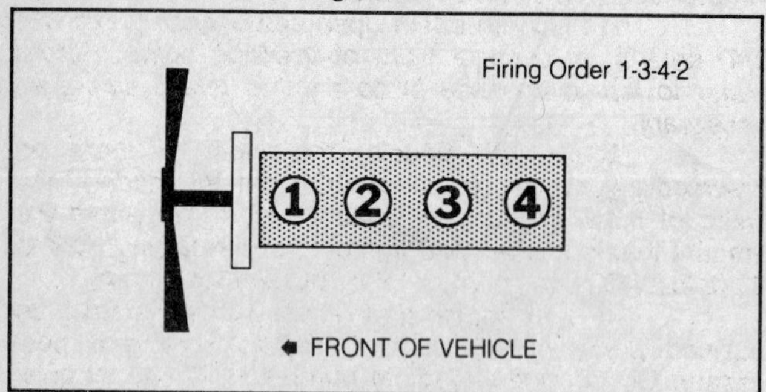

Fig. 28: 4.3L Diesel Firing Order

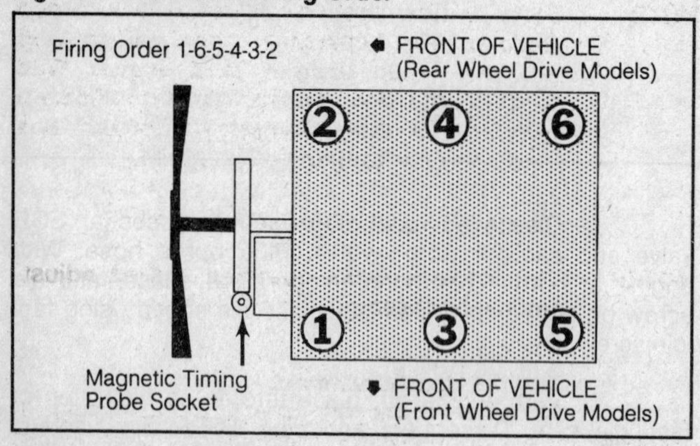

Fig. 29: 5.7L Diesel Firing Order

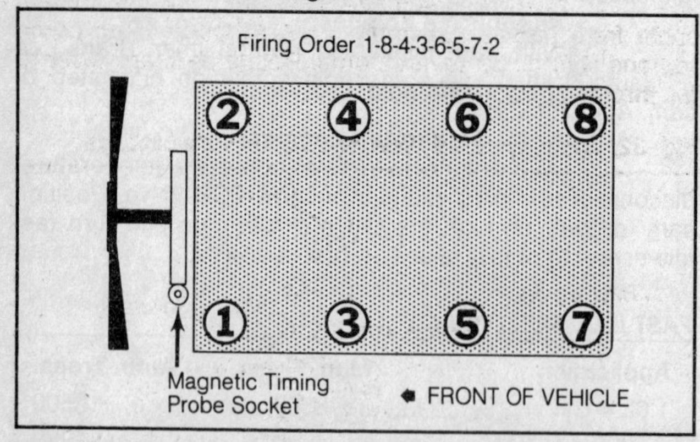

INJECTION TIMING

1.8L 4-Cyl.

Checking & Adjusting

1) Drain engine coolant. Remove fan shroud, radiator and coolant recovery bottle.

2) Remove upper dust cover. Disconnect necessary lines, hoses and electrical connections. Remove fuel filter at bracket. Remove fuel injection lines.

3) Rotate crankshaft until No. 1 piston reaches TDC of compression stroke. Remove upper timing belt cover. Check to make sure that timing belt is properly tensioned and that timing marks are aligned.

4) Remove camshaft cover. Check for alignment of slot on rear of camshaft-to-camshaft cover mounting surface using alignment tool (J-29761). Remove tool.

5) Remove injector lines. Remove distributor head screw and washer located in center of pump where injection lines connect to pump. Install static timing gauge (J-29763) and set lift at about .04" (1 mm) from plunger. Rotate crankshaft to bring No. 1 piston to 45-60° BTDC. Zero dial indicator.

6) The damper pulley has a series of notched lines on it. There are 4 notches on one side and 7 on the other. The 4 lines are used for static timing. Turn crankshaft in normal direction of travel until the 18° line is in alignment with pointer on dial indicator. *See Fig. 30.* Read dial indicator.

Fig. 30: Damper Pulley Alignment Notches

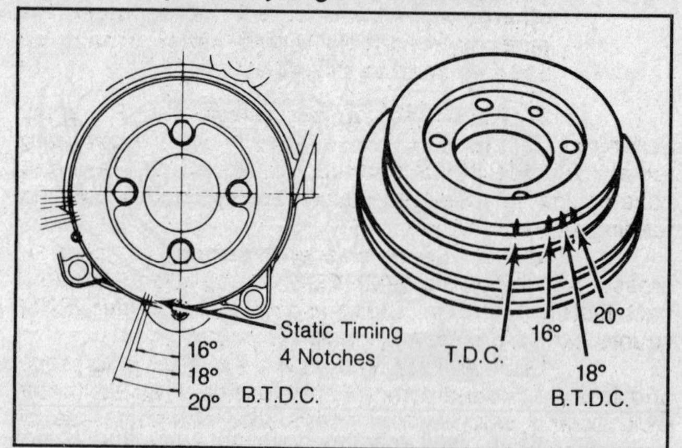

Only the group of 4 notches are used for static timing.

7) Standard reading should be .02" (.5 mm). If reading is not correct, turn crankshaft in normal direction of rotation. If reading on dial indicator deviates from specified range, hold crankshaft at 18° position and loosen 2 nuts on injection pump flange.

Fig. 31: Static Timing Setting

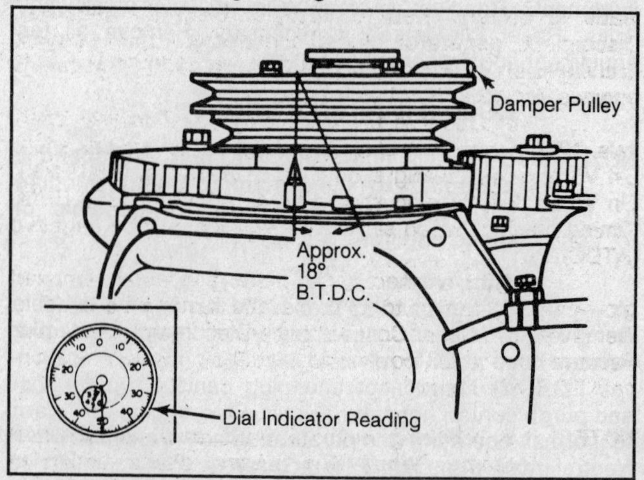

Dial indicator reading should be .02" (.5 mm).

8) Move injection pump to a point where proper dial indicator reading is reached and tighten pump flange nuts. Recheck reading and adjust as necessary.

9) Install distributor screw and washer in injection pump. Install cam cover, fuel injection lines and fuel filter. Connect necessary lines, hoses and electrical connectors. Install upper dust cover.

10) Install coolant recovery bottle, radiator, fan shroud and fill radiator with coolant. Adjust idle speeds.

4.3L V6 & 5.7L V8
Checking

NOTE: **1983 Diesel model timing adjustment must be made with a timing meter (J-33075 or equivalent). This meter picks up engine speed and crankshaft position from the crankshaft balancer using a luminosity signal through a glow plug probe to determine combustion timing. Engine malfunctions should be corrected before a timing adjustment is made. Timing mark alignment may be used in emergency situations, but for optimum engine operation the timing meter should be used as soon as possible.**

1) Place transmission selector in "P", apply parking brake and block drive wheels. Start engine and run at idle until fully warmed up. Shut off engine. Failure to have engine fully warmed up will result in incorrect timing reading and adjustments.

2) Remove air cleaner assembly and plug air crossover using cover (J-26996-1 or equivalent). Disconnect EGR valve hose. Clean engine probe holder (RPM counter) and crankshaft balancer rim.

3) Clean lens on both ends of glow plug probe and lens in photo-electric pick-up. Using a dulled toothpick, scrape carbon from combustion chamber side of glow plug probe. Retarded readings will result if probe is not clean.

4) Install RPM probe into crankshaft RPM counter (probe holder). Remove glow plug from cylinder No. 1 on V6 models or No. 3 on V8 models. Install glow plug probe into glow plug opening and tighten to 8 ft. lbs. (11 N.m).

5) Set timing meter offset selector to "A" (20) on V6 models or "B" (99.5) on V8 models. Connect meter leads to battery (Red to positive, Black to negative). Disconnect generator 2-lead connector. Start engine (transmission in "P") and adjust RPM to 1300 RPM on V6 engines and 1250 RPM on V8 engines.

6) Observe timing readings at 2 minute intervals. When readings stabilize, compare to specification. On V6 engines, timing should be 6° ATDC @ 1300 RPM. On V8 engines, timing should be 4° ATDC @ 1250 RPM. Timing reading, when set to specification, will be negative (ATDC).

7) Disconnect timing meter and install removed glow plug, tightening to 15 ft. lbs. (20 N.m) on V6 or 12 ft. lbs. (16 N.m) on V8. Connect generator 2-lead connector. Remove crossover cover and install air cleaner. Reconnect EGR valve hose.

NOTE: **A misfiring cylinder may result in incorrect timing. When this occurs, check timing in alternate cylinder. Timing can be checked in cylinder numbers 1 and 4 on V6 engines and numbers 2 and 3 on V8 engines. If a difference in timing exists between cylinders, time engine in both cylinders to determine which timing gives best engine performance.**

4.3L V6 & 5.7L V8
Adjusting

1) Shut off engine. Note position of marks on pump flange and pump intermediate adapter (V6) or pump adapter (V8). Loosen bolts or nuts holding pump to adapter until pump can be rotated.

2) Place an offset open end wrench (1" on V6, 3/4" on V8) on boss at front of injection pump. Rotate pump to left to advance or to right to retard timing as necessary.

3) On V6 models, the width of mark on intermediate adapter is about 2/3°. On V8 models, the width of mark on adapter is about 1°. Move pump the amount that is needed and tighten pump retaining nuts to 35 ft. lbs. (48 N.m) on V6 or 18 ft. lbs. (24 N.m) on V8.

4) Start engine and recheck timing reading as outlined previously. Reset and recheck timing if necessary. On V8 models, adjust pump rod. On all models, reset fast and curb idle speeds.

NOTE: **Sooty or dirty probes will result in retarded readings. The luminosity probe will soot up very fast when used in cold engine. Wild needle fluctuations on timing meter indicate a cylinder not firing properly. Correct this condition prior to timing adjustment.**

LINKAGE ADJUSTMENT

NOTE: **V6 linkage is cable operated and no adjustment is necessary.**

5.7L V8
Throttle Rod Adjustment

1) With engine off, check pump timing. If equipped with cruise control, remove clip from cruise control throttle rod. Disconnect rod from throttle lever.

2) Disconnect transmission T.V. or detent cable from throttle assembly. Loosen lock nut on pump rod and shorten by several turns. Rotate bellcrank lever to full throttle position and hold.

Fig. 32: Disassembled View of 5.7L Throttle Linkage

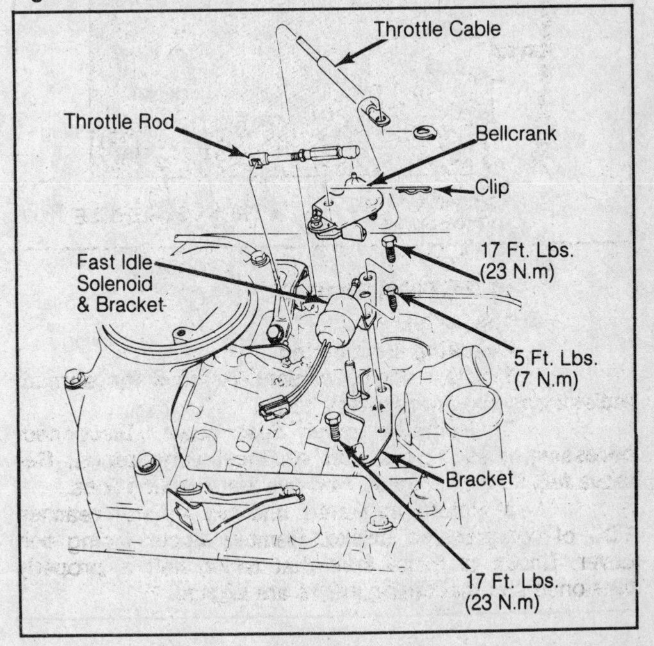

GENERAL MOTORS SYSTEMS & TUNE-UP PROCEDURES (Cont.)

3) Lengthen rod until injection pump lever just contacts full throttle stop. Release bellcrank assembly and tighten pump rod lock nut.

Fig. 33: Transmission T.V. or Detent Cable Adjustment

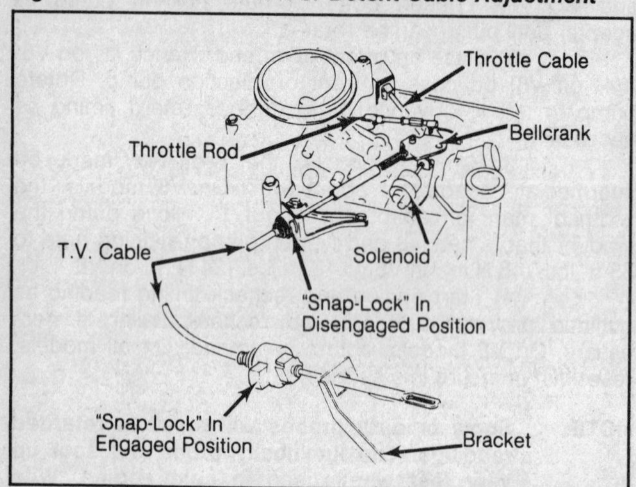

4) Reconnect transmission T.V. or detent cable. Depress and hold metal lock tab on upper end of cable. Move slider away from lever assembly until it stops against metal fitting. Release metal tab.

5) Install cruise control servo rod (if equipped). Rotate bellcrank lever assembly to full throttle stop and release lever assembly. Adjust vacuum regulator valve. See Vacuum Regulator Valve in this article. Adjust idle speed.

HOT (SLOW) IDLE RPM

1.8L 4-Cyl.

1) Set parking brake and block drive wheels. Place transmission in neutral and connect tachometer. Start and run engine until it reaches normal operating temperature.

Fig. 34: 1.8L Idle Adjustment Screw Locations

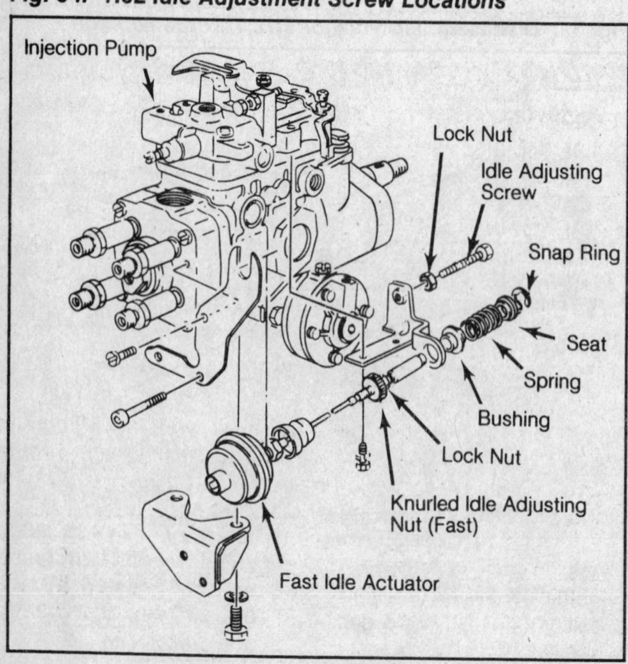

2) Loosen lock nut on idle speed adjusting screw. *See Fig. 34*. Turn adjusting screw to obtain specified slow idle speed RPM. Tighten lock nut. Stop engine and remove tachometer.

4.3L V6 & 5.7L V8

1) Set parking brake and block drive wheels. Place transmission in "P". On V8 engines, perform throttle linkage adjustment first, if required. See Throttle Linkage Adjustment in this article. Start and run engine until normal operating temperature is reached.

2) Stop engine and remove air cleaner. If equipped with cruise control, disconnect servo cable. Clean front cover RPM counter (probe holder) and crankshaft balancer rim. Connect magnetic pick-up tachometer (J-26925) into RPM counter. Connect meter leads to battery (Red to positive; Black to negative).

3) Disconnect 2-lead connector at alternator. On V6 engines, disconnect A/C compressor clutch lead at compressor, if equipped. Turn electrical accessories off. Start engine and place transmission in "D".

NOTE: **On some models, it will be necessary to disconnect the parking brake release vacuum line. This will enable the parking brake to remain engaged when the transmission is shifted into gear. Do not touch steering wheel or brake pedal during adjustment as load may alter engine speed.**

Fig. 35: 4.3L and 5.7L Roosa-Master Injection Pump Hot (Slow) Idle Adjustment Screw Location

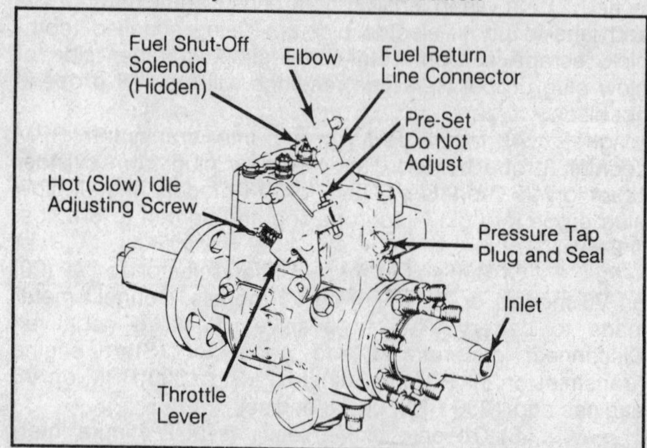

Fig. 36: 4.3L and 5.7L CAV Injection Pump Hot (Slow) Idle Adjustment Screw Location

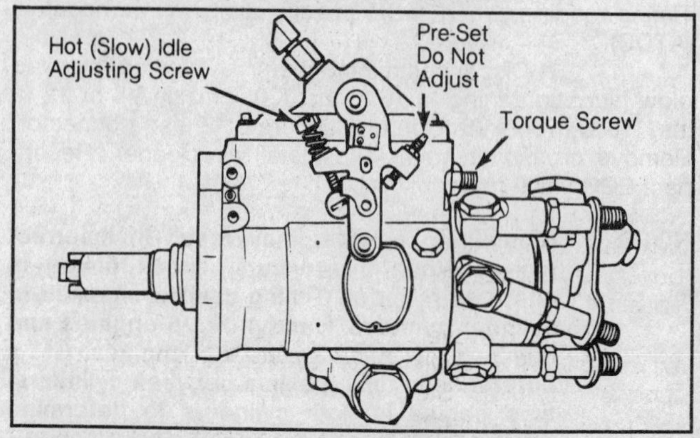

GENERAL MOTORS SYSTEMS & TUNE-UP PROCEDURES (Cont.)

4) Locate idle speed adjusting screw. *See Fig. 35 and/or Fig. 36*. Turn adjusting screw to obtain specified slow idle speed RPM.

5) Stop engine. Remove tachometer and reconnect 2-lead connector at alternator. Install air cleaner. If equipped with cruise control, adjust servo cable for minimum slack and install clip on servo stud. On V6 engines, connect A/C compressor clutch lead at compressor, if equipped.

HOT (SLOW) IDLE SPEED RPM

Application	Man. Trans.	Auto. Trans.
1.8L 4-Cyl.		
Federal	700	.....
Calif.	625	725
4.3L V6		
FWD	.....	675
RWD	.....	660
5.7L V8	.....	600

COLD (FAST) IDLE RPM

1.8L 4-Cyl.

1) Perform hot (slow) idle speed adjustment as previously outlined. Apply outside vacuum source to fast idle actuator on injection pump. *See Fig. 34*.

2) Start engine. Loosen lock nut on fast idle adjusting nut. *See Fig. 34*. Turn knurled adjusting nut to obtain specified fast idle speed RPM.

3) Tighten lock nut and recheck fast idle speed. Stop engine. Disconnect vacuum source and tachometer.

4.3L V6 & 5.7L V8

1) Perform hot (slow) idle speed adjustment as previously outlined. Disconnect fast idle cold advance (engine temperature) switch and install a jumper wire between connector terminals. Do not allow jumper wire to touch ground. *See Fig. 37*.

Fig. 37: 4.3L and 5.7L Fast Idle Cold Advance (Engine Temperature) Switch Locations

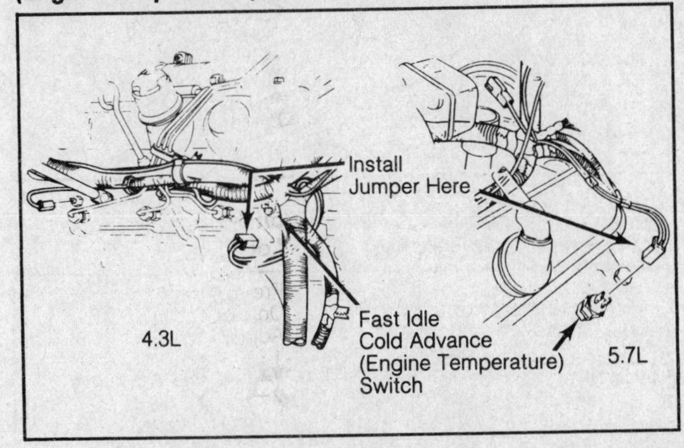

2) Start engine and check fast idle speed. Locate fast idle solenoid. *See Fig. 38 and/or Fig. 39*. Block drive wheels and place transmission in "D". Turn fast idle solenoid plunger to obtain specified fast idle speed RPM.

3) Remove jumper wire and reconnect connector at temperature switch. Recheck and readjust slow idle speed, if required. Stop engine and remove tachometer. Reconnect all components.

Fig. 38: Fast Idle Solenoid Location on 4.3L Engine

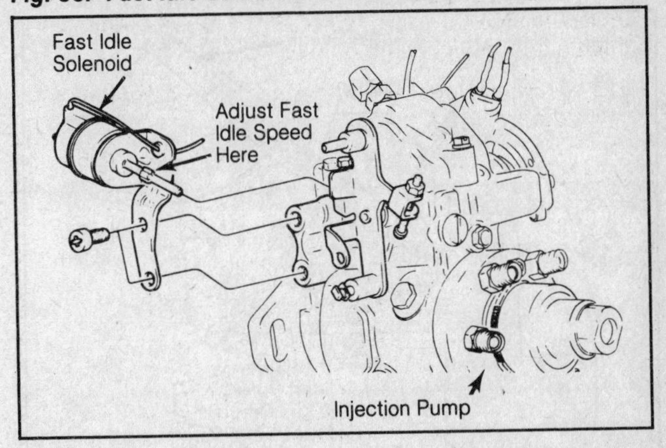

Fig. 39: Fast Idle Solenoid Location on 5.7L Engine

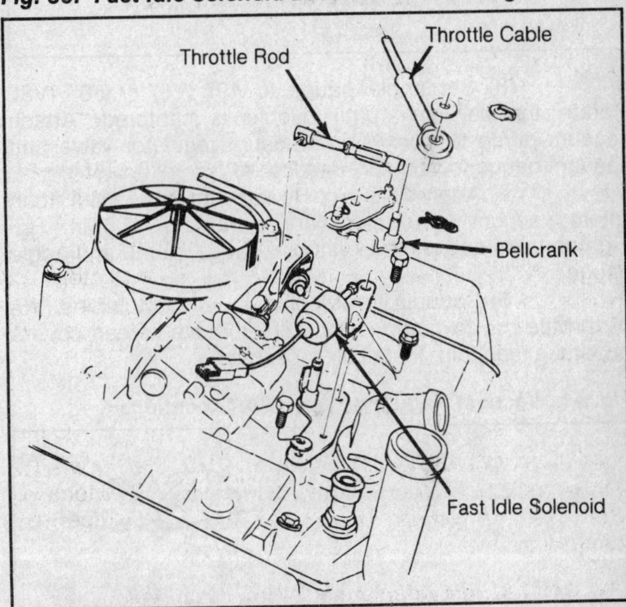

COLD (FAST) IDLE SPEED RPM

Application	Man. Trans.	Auto. Trans.
1.8L 4-Cyl.		
Federal	950	.....
Calif.	950	950
4.3L V6		
FWD	.....	775
RWD	.....	775
5.7L V8	.....	750

VACUUM REGULATOR VALVE

4.3L V6 & 5.7L V8

1) Remove air crossover and install screen covers over openings. On V6 models, disconnect throttle and T.V./detent cables from pump throttle lever. On V8 models, disconnect throttle rod from pump.

2) Loosen vacuum regulator valve-to-pump bolts. Install carburetor angle gauge to injection pump throttle lever. Rotate throttle lever to wide-open throttle position and set angle gauge to zero degrees, then center bubble.

GENERAL MOTORS SYSTEMS & TUNE-UP PROCEDURES (Cont.)

Fig. 40: Vacuum Regulator Valve Adjustment

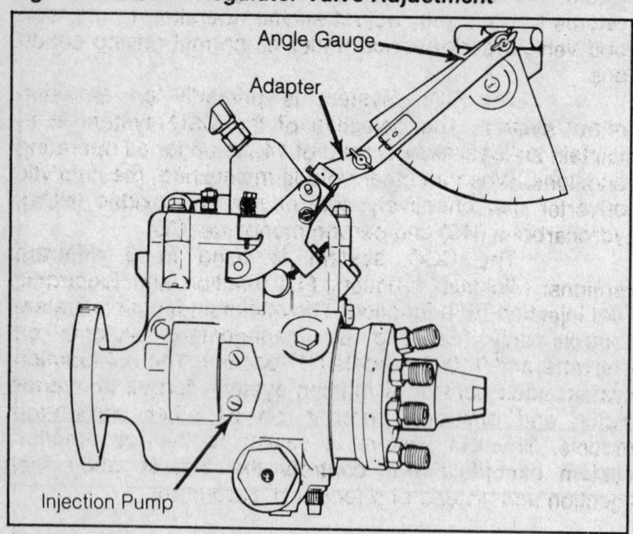

3) Set angle gauge to 49° (V6) or 58° (V8). Rotate throttle lever until bubble is centered. Attach vacuum pump to port "A" of vacuum regulator valve and vacuum gauge to port "B". *See Fig. 41.*

4) Apply 18-24 in. Hg vacuum to port "A", then rotate vacuum valve clockwise to obtain 10.6 in. Hg. Tighten bolts and remove vacuum gauge, pump and angle gauge.

5) Connect throttle and T.V./detent cables (V6) or throttle rod to pump lever (V8). Remove screen covers on intake manifold. Install air crossover.

Fig. 41: Vacuum Regulator Valve Port Locations

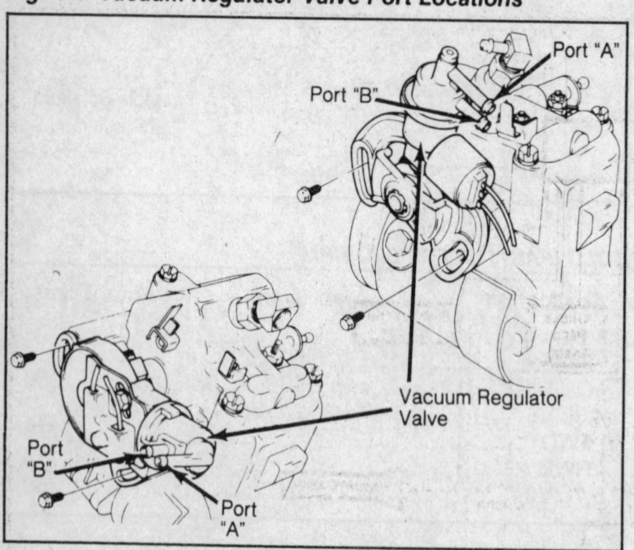

INJECTION PUMP HOUSING FUEL PRESSURE

4.3L V6 & 5.7L V8

1) Engine must be at normal operating temperature. Remove air crossover assembly and install screen covers over openings in intake manifold. Remove pressure tap plug or torque screw from injector pump. To remove torque screw, add a second nut. Back screw out with both nuts attached to prevent tampering with torque screw adjustment.

2) Place seal from pressure tap plug onto pressure tap adapter J-29382 and screw adapter into pump housing in place of plug. Connect a magnetic pick-up tachometer to engine. Screw pressure tap adapter J-28526 into pressure tap adapter J-29382.

3) Connect a low pressure gauge to adapter. Install magnetic pick-up tachometer. Start engine and run at 1000 RPM with transmission selector in "P". Pressure should be 8-12 psi (.56-.84 kg/cm²), with no more than 2 psi (.14 kg/cm²) fluctuation.

4) If pressure is zero, remove connector from housing pressure cold advance terminal. If pressure is still zero, remove injection pump cover and inspect solenoid operation. Free up solenoid if binding.

5) If pressure became normal when solenoid lead was disconnected, check operation of temperature switch on rear head bolt. Switch should open above 125°F (52°C), then close when temperature drops to 95°F (35°C).

6) If pressure is still low, replace or clean fuel return line connector assembly and return line. If pressure is too high, check fuel return system for restrictions. If fuel return line connector assembly is replaced, check injection timing.

7) Recheck pressure. If pressure is still not correct, remove injection pump for repair. Pump is not serviceable and must be exchanged for another unit.

8) Remove tachometer, pressure gauge and adapter. Install a NEW pressure tap plug seal on plug and/or torque screw. Install tap plug or torque screw into pump. Remove screened covers from manifold. Install air crossover assembly.

1983 Exhaust Emission Systems

GENERAL MOTORS COMPUTER COMMAND CONTROL

NOTE: **The Cadillac 4.1L V8 engine uses Cadillac's Digital Fuel Injection system. Any reference to 4.1L engine in this article refers only to the V6 engine.**

NOTE: **Most Computer Command Control (CCC) problems are the result of mechanical breakdowns, poor electrical connections, or damaged vacuum hoses. Before considering the CCC system as a possible source of problems, ignition high tension wires, fuel supply, electrical connections and vacuum hoses should be checked. Failure to do so may result in lost diagnostic time.**

NOTE: **This article will refer to various models by body style. "T" bodies —Chevette and T1000; "X" bodies — Citation, Omega, Phoenix and Skylark; "A" bodies — Century, Celebrity, Ciera and 6000; "F" bodies — Camaro and Firebird; "J" bodies — Cavalier, Cimarron, Firenza, J2000 and Skyhawk.**

DESCRIPTION

The Computer Command Control (CCC) system is an electronically controlled system that is used on all General Motors gasoline engines (except Cadillac with DFI). It monitors up to 10 engine/vehicle functions to control engine operation and lower exhaust emissions while maintaining good fuel economy and driveability. The Electronic Control Module (ECM) is the "brain" of the CCC system. The ECM can control as many as 9 engine-related systems to constantly adjust engine operation to maintain good vehicle performance under all normal driving conditions.

The CCC system is primarily an emission control system. The objective of the CCC system is to maintain an ideal air/fuel ratio of 14.7:1 under all operating conditions. When an ideal ratio is maintained, the catalytic converter can effectively control nitrogen oxides (NOx), hydrocarbons (HC) and carbon monoxide (CO).

The CCC system is used in 3 different versions: Minimum function, Full function and Electronic Fuel Injection (EFI) function. The minimum function system controls only fuel and air management systems on Chevette and T1000 models ("T" bodies). The full function system adds control of ignition system, torque converter clutch and emission controls on all other carbureted models. The EFI system is similar to the full function system except that it controls the throttle body fuel injection unit instead of a feedback carburetor.

OPERATION

The CCC system consists of the following subsystems: Fuel Control, Data Sensors, Electronic Control Module (ECM), Ignition Timing, Idle Speed Control (ISC) system (carbureted models), Idle Air Control (IAC) system (fuel injected models), Air Management, Emission Control, Torque Converter Clutch (TCC), Diagnostic System and Catalytic Converter. Not all subsystems are used on all models.

Fig. 1: Schematic of Computer Command Control System

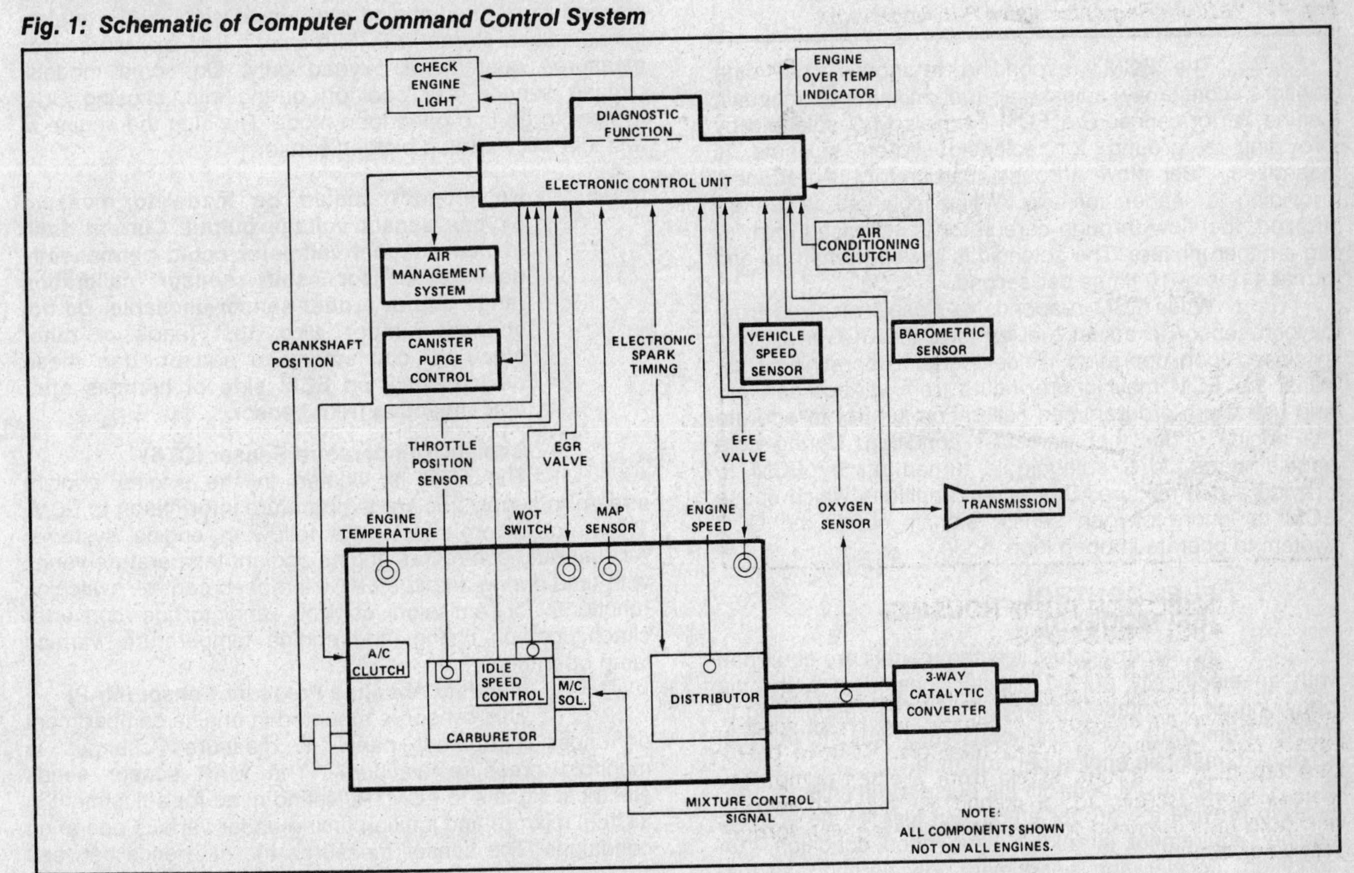

GENERAL MOTORS COMPUTER COMMAND CONTROL (Cont.)

FUEL CONTROL (CARB. MODELS)

All models are equipped with "feedback" carburetors which contain an electrically operated mixture control (M/C) solenoid. The M/C solenoid operates single or dual metering rods in float bowl. Metering rod(s) supplement fuel supplied to idle and main systems, varying air/fuel ratio within a pre-calibrated range. The M/C solenoid also controls air/fuel ratio through use of an idle air bleed circuit that operates in conjunction with metering rod(s).

Fig. 2: Sectional View of Mixture Control Solenoid

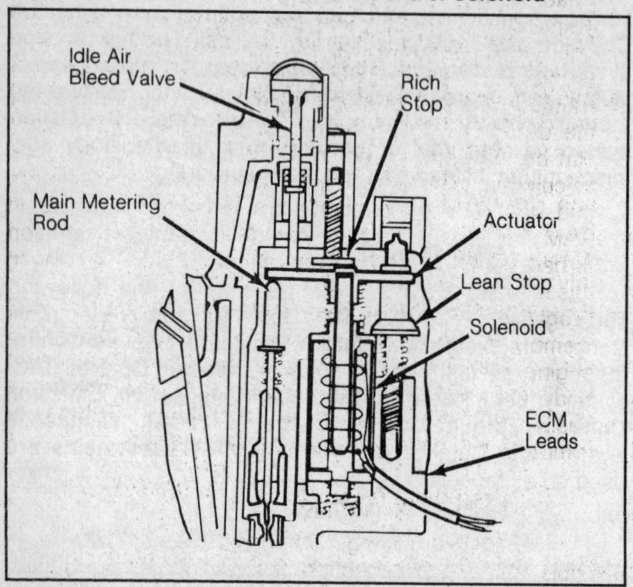

The ECM, responding to inputs from data sensors, constantly adjusts air/fuel mixture to maintain engine performance. The ECM controls M/C solenoid by providing a ground for solenoid. When solenoid is energized, fuel flow through carburetor is reduced, providing a leaner mixture. When solenoid is de-energized, fuel flow through carburetor is increased, providing a richer mixture. The solenoid is cycled (turned on and off) at a rate of 10 times per second.

When ECM responds to signals received from oxygen sensor to adjust fuel mixture, the CCC system is in closed loop operation. Under certain operating conditions, the ECM may ignore inputs from various sensors and use a pre-programmed calibration control to operate the engine under that particular condition. During cold engine starts, M/C solenoid is turned off by ECM to provide a rich mixture. Operating conditions which cause ECM to ignore oxygen sensor signals cause the CCC system to operate in open loop mode.

FUEL CONTROL (EFI MODELS)

All electronic fuel injected models are equipped with an electrically pulsed injector located in a throttle body unit on the intake manifold. The ECM, responding to inputs from data sensors, constantly adjusts air/fuel mixture to maintain engine performance.

The ECM controls the pulse width (injector "on" time) to provide the proper amount of fuel for the specific engine requirement (cranking, clear flood condition, run condition, acceleration enrichment, deceleration air/fuel ratio reduction and deceleration fuel cutoff). Increasing the injector pulse width, richens the air/fuel ratio. Decreasing the injector pulse width, leans the air/fuel ratio.

When the engine speed exceeds 600 RPM, the ECM operates in open loop mode. During open loop, ECM ignores oxygen sensor signals and calculates injector pulse width based upon coolant temperature and manifold vacuum. During open loop, the ECM monitors the following (values stored in ECM memory) to determine when closed loop mode of operation can be achieved: Oxygen sensor above 600°F (316°C), coolant temperature above predetermined value, predetermined elapsed time after engine start. When all of these conditions are met, the ECM will operate in closed loop mode. In closed loop, the ECM will issue injector pulses based upon oxygen sensor signals.

DATA SENSORS

Each sensor furnishes electrical impulses to ECM. The ECM computes ignition timing and fuel mixture ratio necessary to maintain proper engine operation. The function of each sensor is closely related to each of the other sensors. Minimum function systems use only coolant temperature, oxygen and throttle position sensors. Full function and EFI systems can use any or all of the sensors. Operation of each sensor is as follows:

Oxygen Sensor

This sensor is mounted in engine exhaust stream. It supplies a low voltage (under 1/2 volt) when fuel mixture is lean (too much oxygen) and a higher voltage (up to 1 volt) when fuel mixture is rich (not enough oxygen). The ECM will respond to oxygen sensor signals when it is hot (over 600°F/316°C), if engine coolant temperature and elapsed time after engine start have also met predetermined values stored in ECM memory. The oxygen sensor measures quantity of oxygen only. On some models, oxygen sensor may cool off during idle, causing CCC system to go into open loop mode. Running the engine at fast idle will warm up oxygen sensor.

NOTE: **No attempt should be made to measure oxygen sensor voltage output. Current drain of conventional voltmeter could permanently damage sensor, shift sensor calibration range and/or render sensor unusable. Do not connect jumper wire, test leads or other electrical connectors to sensor. Use these devices only on ECM side of harness after disconnecting from sensor.**

Coolant Temperature Sensor (CTS)

The CTS is located in the engine coolant stream to supply coolant temperature information to ECM. This information affects the following engine systems: Air/fuel ratio control (as engine coolant temperature varies with time during a cold start), idle speed control, switching functions for emission controls and torque converter clutch, ignition timing, and engine temperature warning lamp operation.

Manifold Absolute Pressure Sensor (MAP)

This sensor is mounted in engine compartment or under instrument panel. It measures changes in manifold pressure (vacuum). The MAP sensor sends electrical signals to ECM, reflecting need for adjustment in air/fuel mixture and ignition timing under various operating conditions. The sensor measures the difference between barometric pressure (outside air) and manifold pressure. A higher pressure (high voltage output) requires more fuel; a lower pressure (low voltage output) requires less fuel. The MAP sensor is not used on all engine applications. Some engines may use a special MAP sensor that also detects altitude changes.

Vacuum Sensor

Vehicles not equipped with a MAP sensor may be equipped with a vacuum sensor. The vacuum sensor also measures the difference between atmospheric pressure (outside air) and manifold pressure (vacuum).

Barometric Pressure Sensor (BARO)

This sensor is mounted on MAP sensor bracket. This sensor measures ambient or barometric pressures and signals ECM of pressure changes due to altitude and/or weather. This sensor may be used on engines equipped with MAP sensor.

Throttle Position Sensor (TPS)

This sensor is mounted on the carburetor or throttle body unit. The sensor is connected to throttle shaft and is controlled by throttle mechanism. The sensor, a variable resistor similar to fuel tank sending unit, signals ECM of changes in throttle blade position from closed to wide open throttle. At closed throttle position, TPS resistance is high and output voltage to ECM is low. As throttle is opened, resistance is decreased. At wide open throttle, output voltage to ECM is high (about 5 volts). The ECM uses this data to calculate fuel requirements based upon throttle position. Some engines may use a vacuum sensor or WOT switch instead of TPS.

Vehicle Speed Sensor (VSS)

This sensor is mounted behind the speedometer in instrument cluster. It provides a series of 8-volt pulses to ECM to indicate vehicle speed. The VSS is not used on all vehicles.

High Gear Switch

The high gear switch is mounted on automatic transmissions. This switch opens when transmission has shifted into high gear (3rd or 4th) and closes under all other conditions. High gear switch information is used for control of emission control components.

Park/Neutral Switch (P/N Switch)

This switch is connected to transmission gear selector. It is closed when selector is in "P" or "N" positions and open when selector is in gear. This switch is used for idle speed control and torque converter clutch operations.

Air Conditioner "ON" Switch (A/C "ON")

This switch is mounted in air conditioner compressor of some vehicles to signal ECM that air conditioner is operating. This switch supplies 12 volts when compressor is engaged and 0 volts when disengaged. This information is used by ECM to control idle speeds during air conditioner operation.

ELECTRONIC CONTROL MODULE (ECM)

The ECM is located in passenger compartment and controls all CCC system functions. The ECM consists of input/output devices, Central Processing Unit (CPU), power supply and memories. A brief description and operation of each component is as follows:

Input/Output Devices

These integral devices of ECM convert electrical signals received by data sensors and switches to digital signals for use by CPU.

Central Processing Unit (CPU)

Digital signals received by CPU are used to perform all mathematical computations and logic functions necessary to deliver proper air/fuel mixture. The CPU also calculates ignition timing and idle speed information. The CPU commands operation of emission control, closed loop fuel control and diagnostic system.

Power Supply

Main source of power for the ECM is from the battery, through the No. 1 ignition circuit.

Memories

The 3 types of memories in the ECM are: Read Only Memory (ROM), Random Access Memory (RAM) and Programmable Read Only Memory (PROM). Function of each memory is as follows:

- **Read Only Memory (ROM)** — The ROM is programmed information that can only be read by ECM. The ROM program cannot be changed. If battery voltage is removed, ROM information will be retained.
- **Random Access Memory (RAM)** — This memory is the decision making center for the CPU. Information can be read into or out of RAM memory; similar to a calculator. Data sensor information, diagnostic codes and results of calculations are temporarily stored in RAM memory. If battery voltage is removed (ignition turned off on "T" body cars), all information stored in this memory is lost.
- **Programmable Read Only Memory (PROM)** — This memory is factory-programmed information containing engine calibration data for each engine, transmission, body and rear axle ratio application. The PROM is easily removed from ECM. If battery voltage is removed, PROM information will be retained.

IGNITION TIMING

Ignition timing, controlled by the ECM, is possible only on full function and EFI systems. Ignition timing is controlled by 1 of 2 different systems: Electronic Spark Timing (EST) and Electronic Spark Timing with Electronic Spark Control (EST/ESC).

Electronic Spark Timing (EST)

The EST system consists of ECM and HEI distributor with 7 terminal HEI module. The EST distributor contains no vacuum or centrifugal advance mechanisms. The HEI distributor communicates to ECM through a 4-terminal connector which contains 4 circuits: Distributor reference circuit, by-pass circuit, EST circuit and ground circuit.

Whenever the pick-up coil signals HEI module to open the primary circuit, it also sends ignition timing signals to ECM through the reference line. When voltage on HEI by-pass line is less than 5 volts (engine cranking), HEI module switches to by-pass circuit.

In by-pass circuit, HEI module provides spark advance at base timing and disregards spark advance signal from ECM. When voltage on HEI by-pass circuit is 5 volts (engine running), HEI module accepts ignition timing signal from the ECM.

The ECM monitors engine speed through HEI reference line and monitors engine and vehicle operating conditions through data sensors and switches. From these parameters, ECM calculates proper spark advance and supplies signal to HEI distributor through EST line.

The ECM sends modified timing signals to distributor only when engine is running. No modified advance signal is sent to distributor when engine is being cranked. When distributor connector is unplugged, timing is controlled by the HEI distributor module.

GENERAL MOTORS COMPUTER COMMAND CONTROL (Cont.)

Fig. 3: HEI-EST Ignition System Including Relationship to ECM

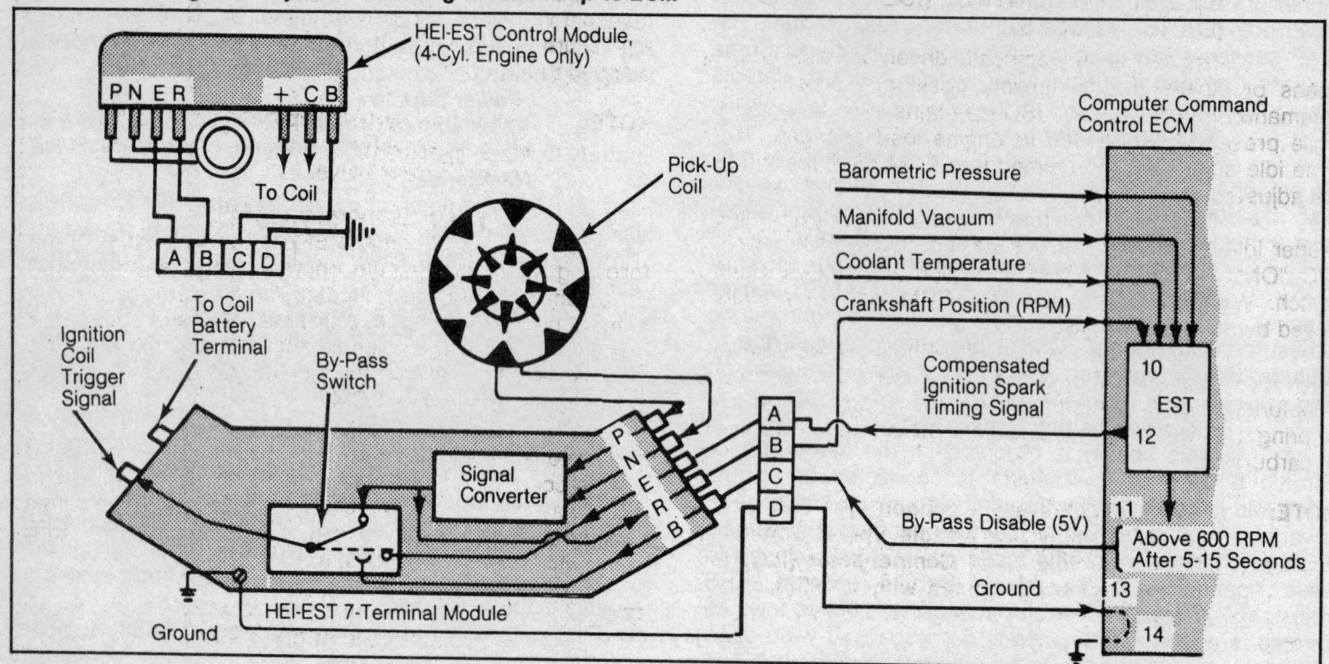

Terminal "R" of the HEI module provides the ECM with engine speed signal on all HEI-EST systems except 2.5L and 3.8L VIN 9 engines. The 2.5L and 3.8L VIN 9 engines are equipped with Hall Effect switch and shutter blades, in addition to the pick-up coil. Terminal "R" is not used with Hall Effect switch. The Hall Effect switch connects directly to the ECM and is not routed through the distributor module. On these engines, the Hall Effect switch provides the ECM with engine speed signals.

Fig. 4: HEI-EST System With Hall Effect Switch

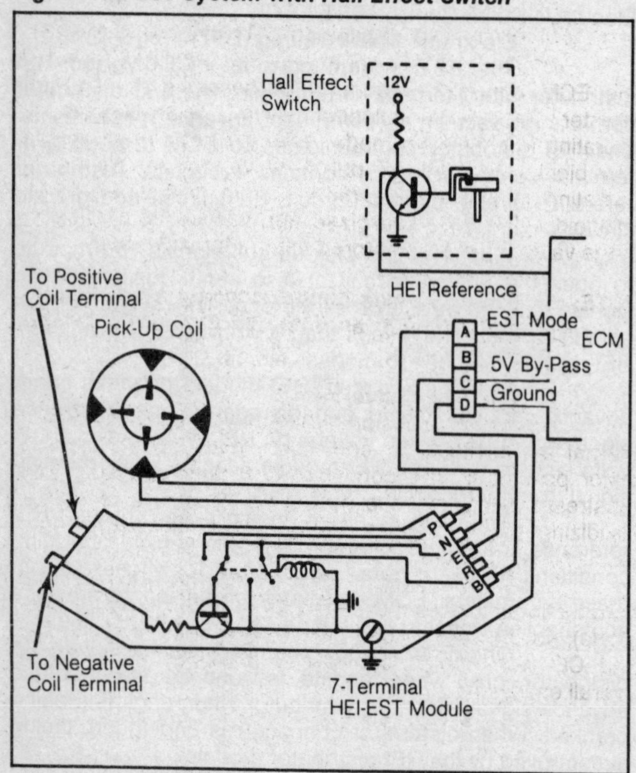

Electronic Spark Timing With Electronic Spark Control (EST/ESC)

There are 4 basic components of the ESC system: A detonation sensor, an HEI-EST distributor, an ESC controller, and the ECM. When detonation (engine knock) occurs, the detonation sensor sends an electrical signal to the ESC controller. The ESC controller amplifies this signal and transmits this signal to the ECM which then retards ignition timing. Timing will be retarded until the ECM no longer receives a signal from the detonation sensor, through the ESC controller. When detonation occurs, the ECM provides a predetermined amount of ignition timing retard until the ECM no longer receives a signal from the detonation sensor. The amount of retard is a function of degree of detonation.

The detonation sensor is mounted in engine block, behind intake manifold. The sensor detects presence (or absence) and intensity of detonation by vibration characteristics of engine. If sensor fails, no retard will occur.

Fig. 5: Electronic Spark Control (ESC) System

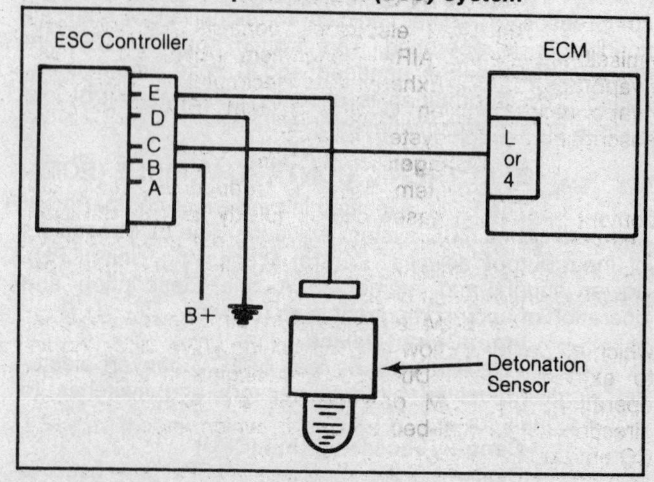

GENERAL MOTORS COMPUTER COMMAND CONTROL (Cont.)

IDLE SPEED CONTROL (ISC) (CARB. MODELS)

The ISC is an electrically driven actuator which opens or closes throttle (in idle position), according to commands from ECM. The ISC maintains low idle speeds while preventing stalls due to engine load changes. The base idle speed is programmed into ECM memory and is not adjustable.

The ECM monitors engine load to determine proper idle speed. To prevent stalling, the ECM monitors A/C "ON" switch, park-neutral switch and ISC throttle switch. With this information, the ECM will control idle speed by operating the ISC motor.

When engine is cold, ECM holds throttle valve open for longer period of time to provide faster warm-up. This function is by-passed when throttle is opened enough to bring TPS off its idle circuit. The ISC is located on side of carburetor.

NOTE: **Not all engines are equipped with ISC system. Some may use an Idle Speed Solenoid (ISS) or an Idle Load Compensator (ILC) to control engine idle speed without ECM commands.**

IDLE AIR CONTROL (IAC) (EFI MODELS)

The IAC valve is an electrically-driven actuator which changes the idle air flow around the throttle plate according to commands from the ECM. The IAC controls air flow in a similar manner as the ISC to maintain idle speeds while preventing stalls due to engine load changes.

IDLE SPEED MODULE (2.0L EFI ENGINE)

The 2.0L engine uses an idle speed module to help control engine idle speed. This module receives impulses from the power steering unit and A/C unit (if equipped). The module increases engine idle speed when power steering line pressure exceeds a predetermined value (such as turning steering wheel to a full lock position). If the vehicle is equipped with power steering, the ECM also disengages the A/C compressor clutch when the power steering line pressure exceeds the predetermined value.

EMISSION CONTROL

The ECM electrically controls the following emission systems: AIR Management (AIR), Early Fuel Evaporation (EFE), Exhaust Gas Recirculation (EGR) and Evaporative Emission Control System (EECS). A brief description of each system follows:

AIR Management System

This system helps to reduce HC and CO content in exhaust gases and to quickly heat up catalytic converter and oxygen sensor during cold engine operation. This is accomplished by injecting air into exhaust port of each cylinder when engine is cold.

The ECM energizes an air control solenoid which allows air to flow to air switching valve, directing air to exhaust ports. During warm engine (closed loop) operation, the ECM de-energizes air switching valve, directing air to dual-bed converter, which lowers HC and CO emissions.

If air control valve detects rapid increase in manifold vacuum (deceleration condition), or ECM detects any failure in CCC system, air is diverted to air cleaner or dumped to atmosphere.

NOTE: **Vehicles may use separate air switching and air control valves, integral control valves or an air diverter valve.**

Early Fuel Evaporation (EFE)

The ECM controls EFE system by either of the following methods: Vacuum operated valve and actuator, or ceramic heater grid located underneath carburetor primary bore. The vacuum operated valve and actuator is opened by a control solenoid mounted on valve cover. This solenoid controls vacuum to EFE valve by an electrical signal from the ECM.

The ceramic heater grid system is part of carburetor insulator. When ignition is turned on and engine coolant temperature is low, voltage is applied to EFE relay through ECM, energizing EFE heater. When coolant temperature increases, ECM de-energizes EFE relay, which shuts off voltage to EFE heater.

NOTE: **EFE may not be used on all vehicles. Some vehicles may incorporate EFE control through EGR or AIR system.**

Exhaust Gas Recirculation (EGR)

The ECM controls ported vacuum to EGR valve with an electrically operated solenoid valve. When engine is cold, solenoid is energized, blocking vacuum to EGR valve. When engine is warm, solenoid is de-energized and EGR operation is allowed.

NOTE: **Vehicles may use an integral EFE/EGR valve, TCC/EGR valve or an EFE/EGR/Canister Purge Valve.**

Evaporative Emission Control System (EECS)

This system controls vapor canister purging. The ECM controls vacuum to purge valve in charcoal canister through a solenoid valve. When engine is operating in open loop mode, solenoid valve is energized and blocks vacuum to purge valve. When engine is operating in closed loop mode above prescribed RPM, solenoid valve is de-energized and vacuum is applied to purge valve. This draws stored vapors into manifold.

NOTE: **Some vehicles control canister purge operation through an integral EFE/EGR/Canister Purge Valve.**

Catalytic Converter

Proper emission control is accomplished with a special 3-way catalytic converter which converts all 3 major pollutants. The converter is a dual-bed type. The "upstream" section of the converter contains a reducing-/oxidizing bed to reduce NOx while at the same time oxidizing HC and CO.

An air supply pipe from the AIR system introduces air between the dual beds (during closed loop mode), so the second bed can oxidize any remaining HC and CO with a high conversion efficiency to minimize overall emissions.

GENERAL MOTORS COMPUTER COMMAND CONTROL (Cont.)

TORQUE CONVERTER CLUTCH (TCC)

The ECM controls a solenoid (mounted on automatic transmission) to allow torque converter to directly connect engine to transmission, providing direct drive. When vehicle speed is high enough, ECM energizes TCC solenoid and engine is mechanically coupled to transmission.

When operating conditions indicate that transmission should operate as normal (during rapid acceleration or deceleration), solenoid is de-energized. The transmission also returns to normal automatic operation when brake pedal is depressed.

DIAGNOSTIC SYSTEM

NOTE: **A "CHECK ENGINE" lamp driver is installed in the wiring harness from ECM to the "CHECK ENGINE" lamp. This driver amplifies the power to the "CHECK ENGINE" lamp to reduce amperage draw on the battery.**

The ECM of the CCC system is equipped with a self-diagnostic system which detects system failures or abnormalities. When a malfunction occurs, ECM will light the Amber "CHECK ENGINE" lamp located on instrument panel. When malfunction is detected and lamp is turned on, a corresponding trouble code is stored in ECM memory. Malfunctions are recorded as "hard failures" or "intermittent failures".

- "Hard failures" cause "CHECK ENGINE" lamp to glow and remain on until malfunction is repaired. If the "CHECK ENGINE" lamp comes on and remains on during vehicle operation, cause of malfunction MUST be determined.
- "Intermittent failures" cause lamp to flicker or go out after 10 seconds when fault goes away. However, the associated trouble code will be retained in ECM memory. "Intermittent failures" may be sensor related. If a sensor fails, ECM will use a substitute value in its calculations to continue engine operation. In this condition, service is not mandatory; but loss of driveability may be encountered. If the related fault does not recur within 50 ignition cycles, related trouble code will be erased from ECM memory.

As a bulb and system check, the "CHECK ENGINE" lamp will glow when ignition switch is turned on and engine is not running. When engine is started, the lamp should go out after 1-4 seconds. If not, a malfunction has been detected in CCC system.

NOTE: **Trouble codes will be recorded at various operating times. Some codes require operation of that sensor or switch for 5 seconds; others require operation for 5 minutes or longer.**

TROUBLE SHOOTING (EFI MODELS ONLY)

NOTE: **Trouble shooting and diagnosis of EFI fuel systems should begin with determining fuel system pressure. Before performing any test on the EFI fuel system, pressure must be released from the system.**

FUEL SYSTEM PRESSURE TEST

1) Remove "FUEL PUMP" fuse from fuse block. Crank engine. Engine will start and run until fuel supply remaining in fuel lines is used. Engage starter again for about 3 seconds to ensure that all fuel is out of lines.

2) Remove air cleaner and plug thermal vacuum port on throttle body. Remove steel fuel line from throttle body unit (between front and rear throttle body units on dual unit systems). When removing fuel line, always use 2 wrenches. Install fuel pressure gauge.

3) Reinstall "FUEL PUMP" fuse in fuse block. Start engine and observe fuel pressure reading. If fuel pressure is not between 9 and 13 psi (.6-.9 kg/cm²), proceed to appropriate Fuel System Diagnostic chart. If fuel pressure is okay, proceed to step **4)**.

4) Depressurize fuel system as described in step **1)**. Remove fuel pressure gauge and reinstall fuel line. Reinstall "FUEL PUMP" fuse in fuse block. Turn ignition on and observe fuel system for leaks. If no leaks exist in fuel system, remove plug from throttle body thermal vacuum port. Reinstall air cleaner.

DIAGNOSIS & TESTING

DIAGNOSTIC TOOLS

1) The CCC system does not require special tools for diagnosis. A dwell meter, tachometer, test light, ohmmeter, digital voltmeter with 10 megohms impedance (minimum), vacuum pump, vacuum gauge and 6 jumper wires 6" long (1 wire with female connectors at both ends; 1 wire with male connectors at both ends; 4 wires with male and female connectors at opposite ends) are only tools necessary for diagnosis.

2) A test light, rather than a voltmeter, must be used when indicated by diagnostic chart.

3) A dwell meter is used to measure the time that mixture control solenoid is on or off. This indicates how the system is working and fuel mixture strength (rich or lean). The dwell meter is set for 6-cylinder scale on ALL carbureted engines, regardless of number of cylinders

4) Dwell meter is connected to Green connector located near the carburetor. This connector will not be connected to any circuit EXCEPT when you are testing with the dwell meter. Do not allow terminal wire to come in contact with any ground source, including rubber hoses.

NOTE: **If engine operation seems to change when dwell meter is connected to Green wire, remove dwell meter and use another type. A few brands are not compatible with CCC system.**

5) When engine is at operating temperature and idling, dwell meter needle will move up and down on scale, between 10-50°. This indicates closed loop operation. If the needle does not move, open loop operation is indicated.

CCC DIAGNOSIS

Diagnosis of the CCC system is done in the following order:

1) Ensure that all engine systems NOT related to the CCC are fully operational. Do not proceed with

GENERAL MOTORS COMPUTER COMMAND CONTROL (Cont.)

testing unless you are sure all other problems have been fixed.

2) Enter diagnostic mode and record trouble codes flashed by "CHECK ENGINE" light. Exit diagnostic mode.

3) Distinguish between "hard" or "intermittent" trouble codes.

4) If trouble codes were displayed, go to Diagnostic Circuit Check chart. Follow instructions given there.

5) If no trouble codes were recorded, go to Driver Complaint Sheet and follow instructions given there.

6) After any repairs are made, perform System Performance Check (carbureted models) or Field Service Mode Check (EFI models). Clear any trouble codes.

CAUTION: Minimum function systems ("T" cars) do not have "long-term" memory capability. All codes stored in the memory will be erased when ignition switch is turned off. Memory is operational only while engine is running and problem or malfunction exists.

The ECM stores component failure information for CCC system under a related trouble code which can be recalled for diagnosis and repair. When recalled, these codes will be displayed by flashes of "CHECK ENGINE" lamp. Codes are displayed starting with lowest numbered code. Only codes in which a related malfunction has occurred will be displayed.

NOTE: Example of trouble codes is as follows: "FLASH", "FLASH", "FLASH", pause, "FLASH", "FLASH" followed by a longer pause identifies trouble code "32". First series of flashes indicates first digit of trouble code; second series of flashes indicates second digit of trouble code.

Entering Diagnostic Mode

1) Turn ignition on (engine off). "CHECK ENGINE" lamp should glow. Locate Assembly Line Data Link (ALDL) connector attached to ECM wiring harness under instrument panel. Insert spade lug terminal across "TEST" terminal and "GROUND" terminal. *See Fig. 6.*

Fig. 6: ALDL Connector Terminal Locations

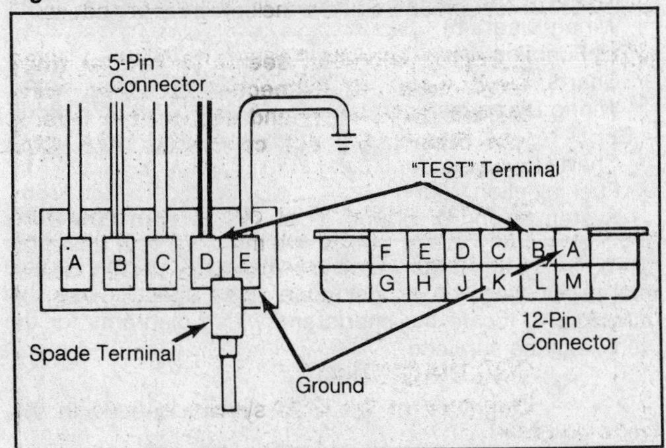

2) "CHECK ENGINE" lamp should flash code "12". Code "12" consists of "FLASH", pause, "FLASH", "FLASH" followed by a longer pause. Trouble code "12" will be repeated 2 more times, then if any trouble codes are stored in ECM memory, they will be displayed in same manner. This code is NOT stored in ECM memory.

3) Trouble codes will be displayed from lowest to highest numbered code (3 times each) and be repeated as long as the "TEST" terminal of ALDL connector is grounded.

CAUTION: Inserting lug in terminals of ALDL connector grounds "TEST" terminal lead. Do not ground ALDL connector before ignition is turned on or engine is started.

Clearing Trouble Codes

To clear memory of trouble codes, turn ignition on and ground "TEST" lead at ALDL connector. Turn ignition off and remove ECM fuse from fuse block for 10 seconds. Remove "TEST" lead ground.

Exiting Diagnostic Mode

To exit diagnostic mode, turn ignition off and remove spade lug terminal from ALDL connector.

NOTE: The terms "enter diagnostics" and "exit diagnostics" will be used periodically throughout this section. Follow the procedure for entering diagnostic mode when instructed to "enter diagnostics". Follow the procedure for exiting diagnostic mode when instructed to "exit diagnostics".

FAILURE CODE DETERMINATION

During any diagnostic procedure, "hard failure" codes MUST be distinguished from "intermittent failure" codes. Diagnostic charts CANNOT be used to analyze "intermittent failure" codes, except as noted under Diagnostic Procedure. To determine "hard failure" codes and "intermittent failure" codes, proceed as follows:

1) Turn ignition on and enter diagnostics. Read and record all stored trouble codes. Exit diagnostics and clear trouble codes.

NOTE: Trouble codes will be recorded on "T" cars only with engine running. Turning ignition off after any trouble codes have been set will erase all codes.

2) Apply parking brake and place transmission in Neutral (man. trans.) or "P" (auto. trans.). Block drive wheels. Start engine. "CHECK ENGINE" lamp should go out. Run warm engine at specified curb idle for 2 minutes and note "CHECK ENGINE" light.

NOTE: Grounding "TEST" terminal with engine running will force engine to operate in closed loop mode if engine is warm and oxygen sensor is hot. If "CHECK ENGINE" lamp does not glow while in closed loop, CCC system is operating properly.

3) If "CHECK ENGINE" lamp comes on, enter diagnostics, read and record trouble codes. This will reveal "hard failure" codes. Codes "13", "15", "24", "35", "44", "45" and "55" may require road test to reset "hard failure" after trouble codes were cleared.

GENERAL MOTORS COMPUTER COMMAND CONTROL (Cont.)

NOTE: **On EFI models only, "CHECK ENGINE" light will indicate operational mode of engine. In closed loop, the "CHECK ENGINE" light will flash at the rate of 1 flash every second. In open loop, the "CHECK ENGINE" light will flash at the rate of 2.5 flashes every second. See Field Service Mode Check chart.**

4) If "CHECK ENGINE" lamp does not come on, all stored trouble codes were "intermittent failures", except as noted under Diagnostic Procedure.

NOTE: **Trouble code "15" malfunction will only display after 5 minutes of engine operation. Trouble code "12" will display only during time of no reference pulses received by ECM; it will never be stored as a malfunction.**

DIAGNOSTIC PROCEDURE

The CCC system should be considered as a possible source of trouble on engine performance, fuel economy and exhaust emission complaints ONLY after normal checks (which apply to a vehicle without CCC) have been performed.

Diagnosis of CCC system consists of 3 types of initial checks: Diagnostic Circuit Check, Driver Complaint Check and System Performance Check/Field Service Mode Check. Any of these checks may lead to a chart for locating source of problem or indicate no problem on that check and refer to another check.

If there is no trouble in CCC system, all 3 checks will result in that conclusion. The checks and their procedures are as follows:

NOTE: **If vehicle exhibits performance problems and no codes are set, refer to System Performance Check/Field Service Mode Check. Components recorded by trouble codes generally do not cause performance problems when no codes are stored in ECM memory.**

Diagnostic Circuit Check

1) If complaint is "CHECK ENGINE" lamp related, this check will lead to most likely problem area, if malfunction exists. Enter diagnostics and record stored trouble codes. Begin diagnosis with lowest numbered code which is displayed and refer to appropriate trouble code chart.

2) If code "51" is displayed, refer to PROM removal and installation in this article for diagnosis of this code. If codes "54" or "55" are displayed with another code, always refer to diagnostic chart for code "54" or "55" first, then proceed to next lowest numbered code.

NOTE: **Any time codes "51", "54" or "55" are displayed with another code, start with "50-series" code first, then proceed to lowest numbered code.**

Driver Complaint Sheet

1) If complaint is not "CHECK ENGINE" lamp related, this check will lead to most likely problem area. However, first make checks that would normally be made for the complaint on a vehicle without CCC system.

2) Follow instructions in diagnostic chart and repair malfunction. After repair, perform System Performance Check/Field Service Mode Check.

System Performance Check (Carbureted Models Only)

1) This check verifies that CCC system is functioning correctly. This check should always be made after any repair on CCC system.

2) When performing this check, always engage parking brake and block DRIVE wheels. Parking brake on front-wheel drive models does not hold drive wheels. On engines equipped with Varajet carburetors (E2SE Model), remove bowl vent line at carburetor and plug hose at carburetor during check and reconnect it after the check is complete.

3) On some engines, the oxygen sensor will cool off after only a short period of time while engine is idling. This will cause engine to go into open loop. To restore closed loop mode, run engine at part throttle several minutes and accelerate from idle to part throttle several times.

Field Service Mode Check (EFI Models Only)

1) This test confirms proper operation of fuel system and verifies closed loop operation. Clear codes and perform this test after any repair is completed.

2) When performing this check, always engage parking brake and block DRIVE wheels. Parking brake on front-wheel drive models does not hold drive wheels.

3) On some engines, the oxygen sensor will cool off after only a short period of time while engine is idling. This will cause engine to go into open loop. To restore closed loop mode, run engine at part throttle several minutes and accelerate from idle to part throttle several times.

NOTE: **Although there are many charts connected with CCC diagnosis, only 2 charts are needed to prove the system is operating properly. Normally, only 3 charts are necessary to find a problem, if one exists.**

ORGANIZATION

GENERAL MOTORS CCC TROUBLE CHARTS

The large number of pages in this article makes locating the proper code chart difficult. Use this directory to locate the charts and wiring diagrams for the vehicle being serviced.

GENERAL MOTORS COMPUTER COMMAND CONTROL (Cont.)

MINIMUM FUNCTION ("T" CAR) ECM TROUBLE CODE IDENTIFICATION

Code	Circuit Affected
12	No reference pulses to ECM.
15	Open coolant sensor circuit.
21	Throttle position sensor circuit at wide open throttle.
44	Lean exhaust indication.
45	Rich exhaust indication.
51	Faulty PROM or improper PROM installation.

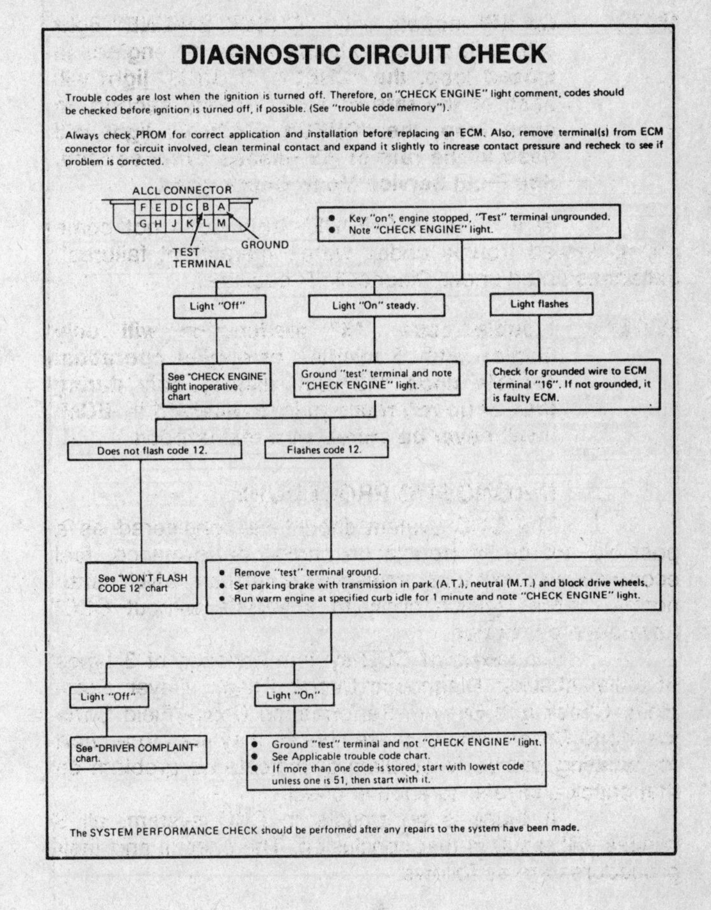

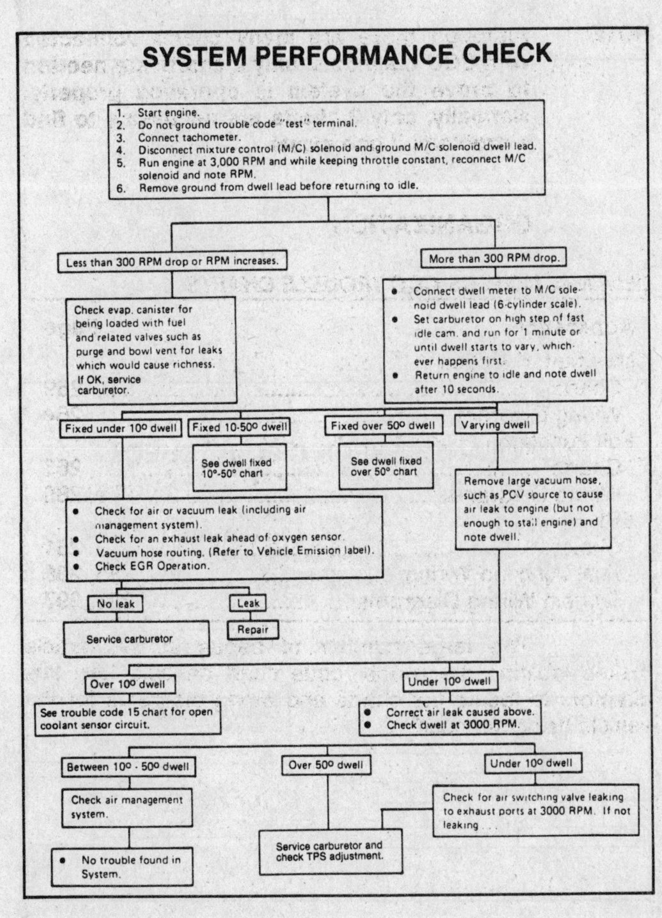

DRIVER COMPLAINT SHEET

ENGINE PERFORMANCE PROBLEM (ODOR, SURGE, FUEL ECONOMY . . .)
EMISSION PROBLEM

IF THE "CHECK ENGINE" LIGHT IS NOT ON, NORMAL CHECKS THAT WOULD BE PERFORMED ON CARS WITHOUT THE SYSTEM SHOULD BE DONE FIRST.

IF GENERATOR OR COOLANT LIGHT IS ON WITH THE "CHECK ENGINE" LIGHT, THEY SHOULD BE DIAGNOSED FIRST.

INSPECT FOR POOR CONNECTIONS AT COOLANT SENSOR, M/C SOLENOID, ETC., AND POOR OR LOOSE VACUUM HOSES AND CONNECTIONS. REPAIR AS NECESSARY.

- Intermittent "CHECK ENGINE" light but no trouble code stored.
  - Check for intermittent connection in circuit from:
    - Battery to ECM terminal "11".
    - ECM terminal "1" to engine ground.
    - ECM terminal "19" to distributor, including tach. filter.
  - Open diode across A/C compressor clutch.
- Poor Full Throttle Performance.
  See TPS Enrichment chart.
- Cold Operation Problem
  See Coolant Sensor Circuit check
- ALL OTHER COMPLAINTS
  Make SYSTEM PERFORMANCE CHECK on warm engine (Upper radiator hose hot).

GENERAL MOTORS COMPUTER COMMAND CONTROL (Cont.)

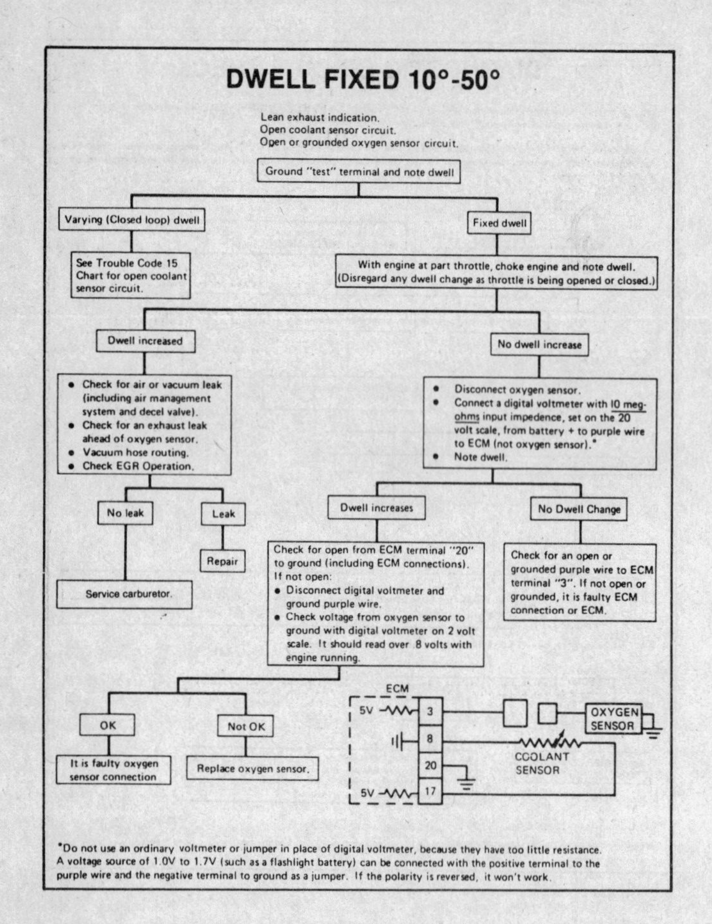

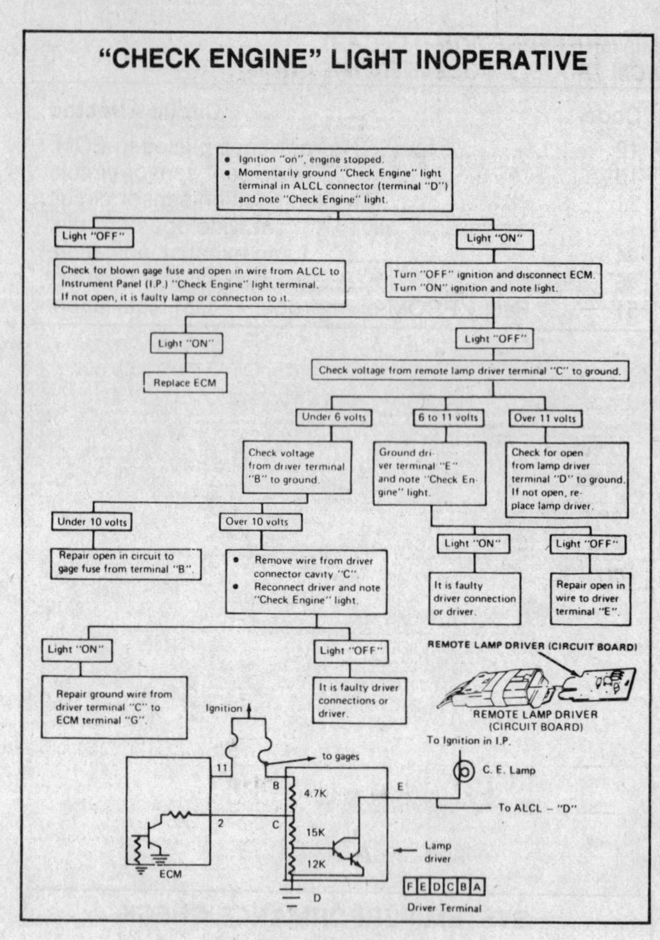

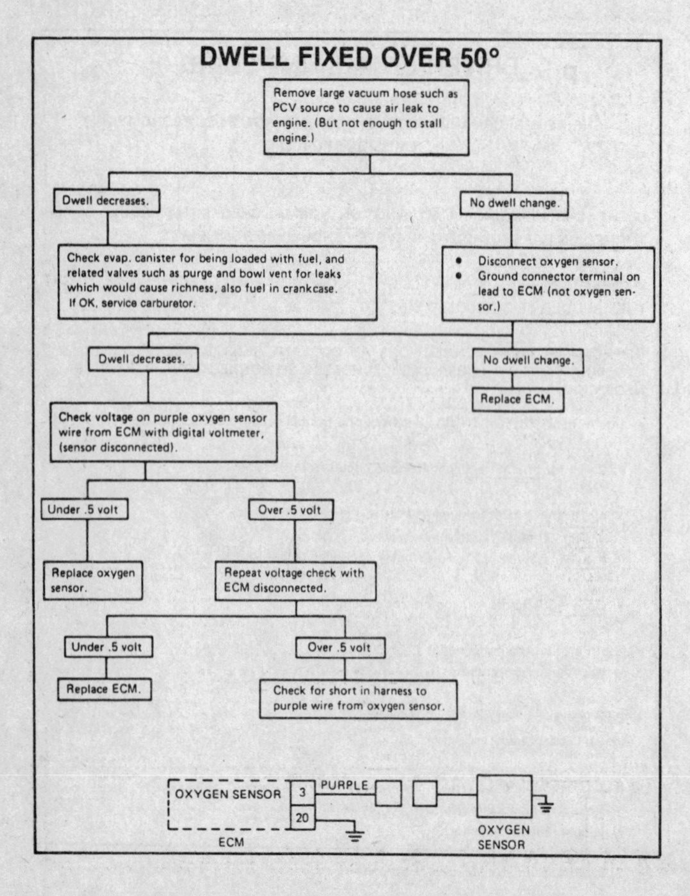

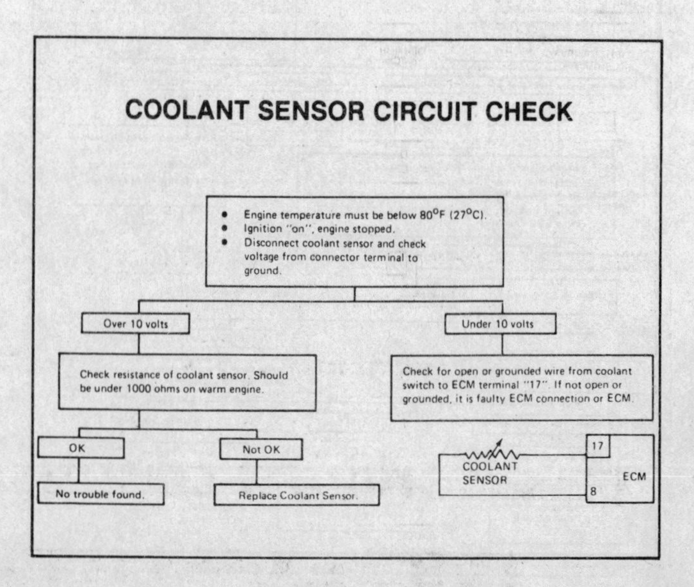

GENERAL MOTORS COMPUTER COMMAND CONTROL (Cont.)

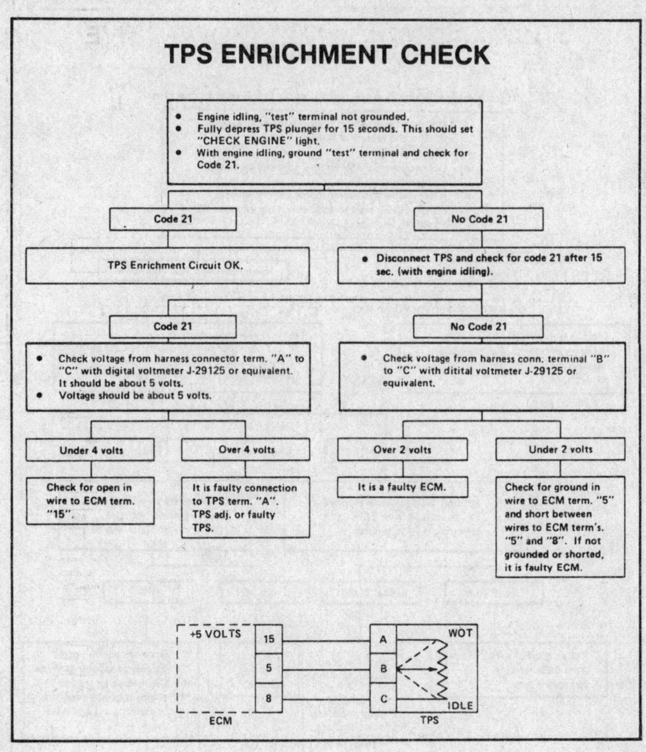

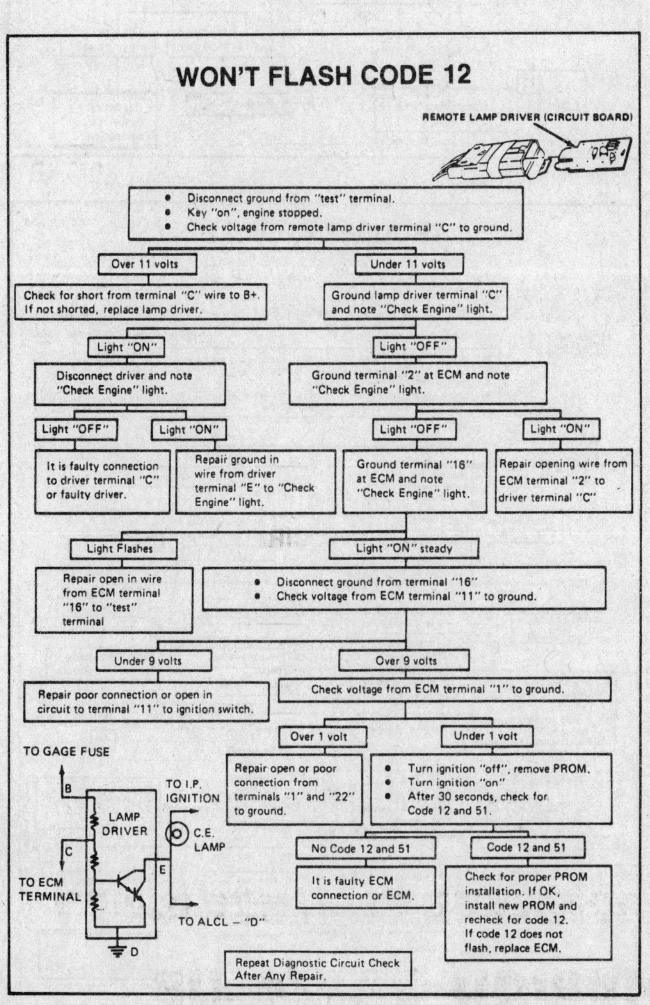

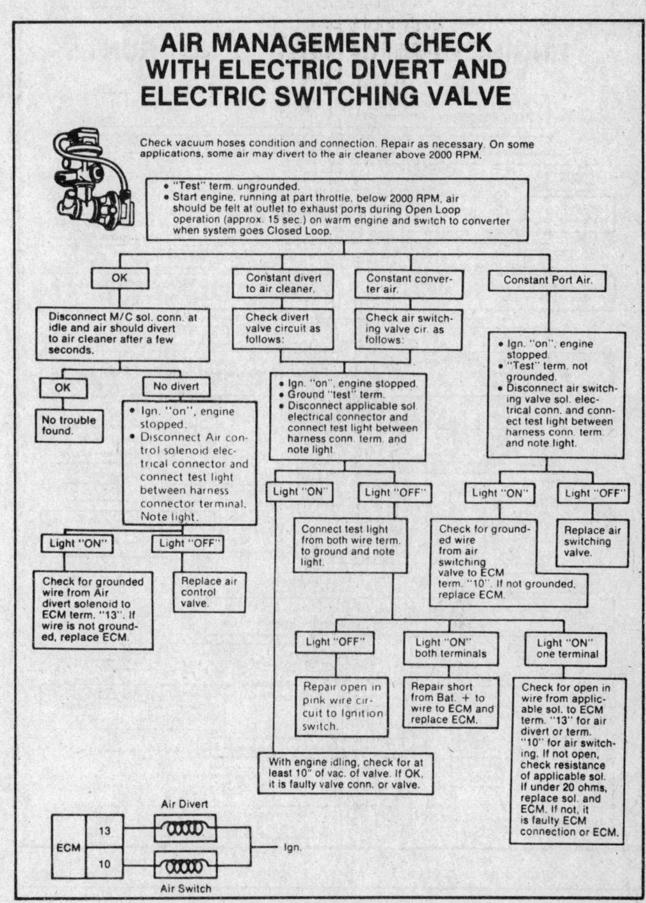

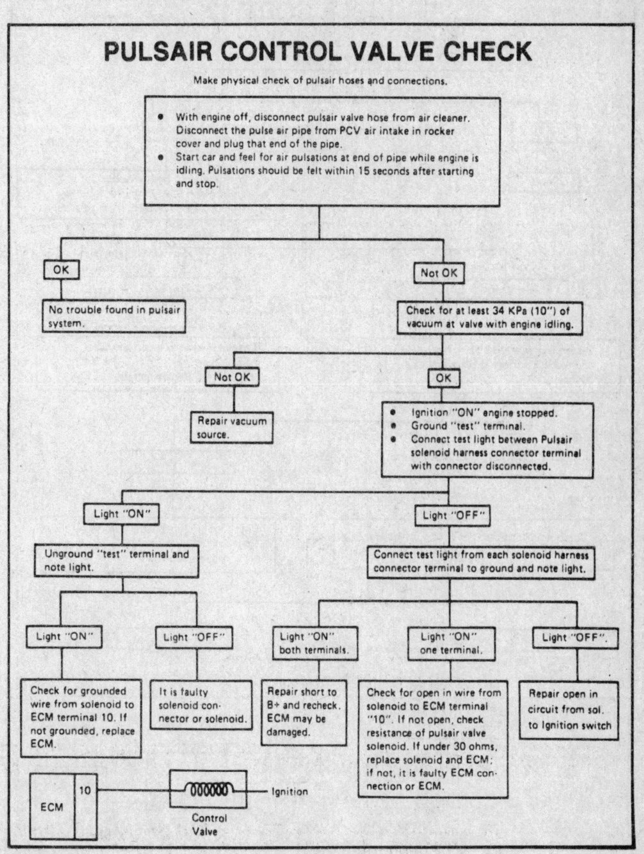

GENERAL MOTORS COMPUTER COMMAND CONTROL (Cont.)

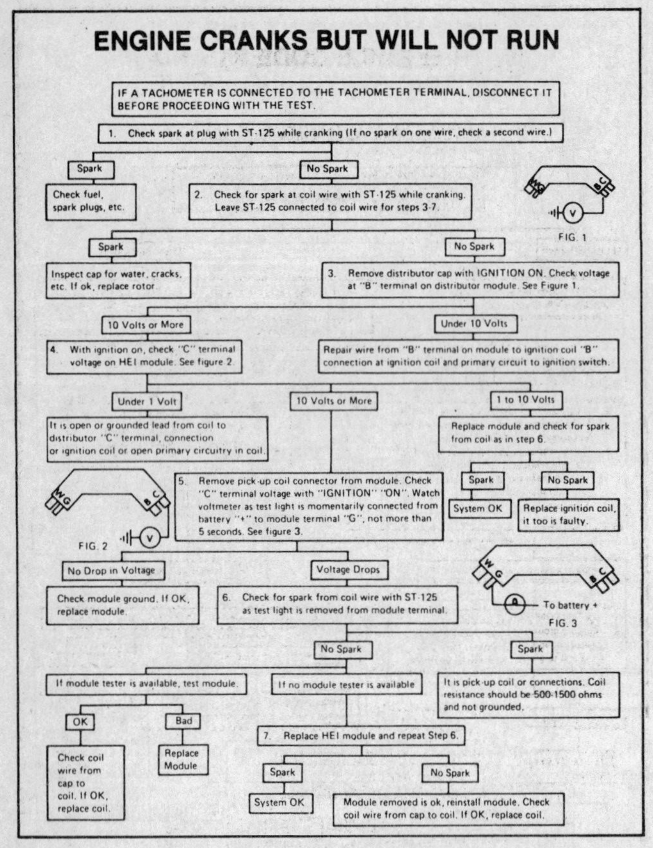

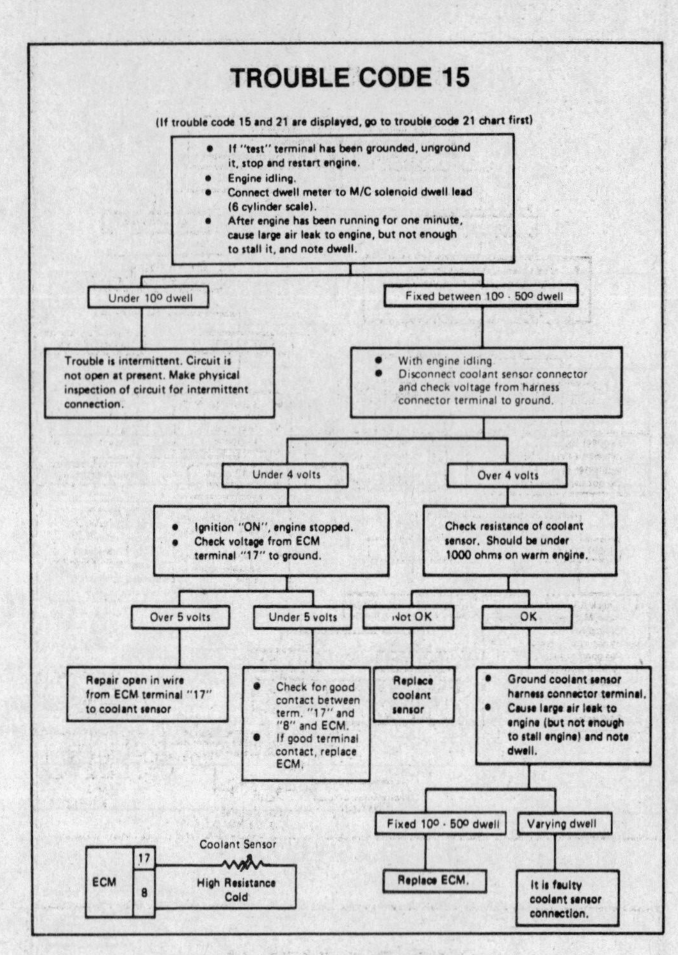

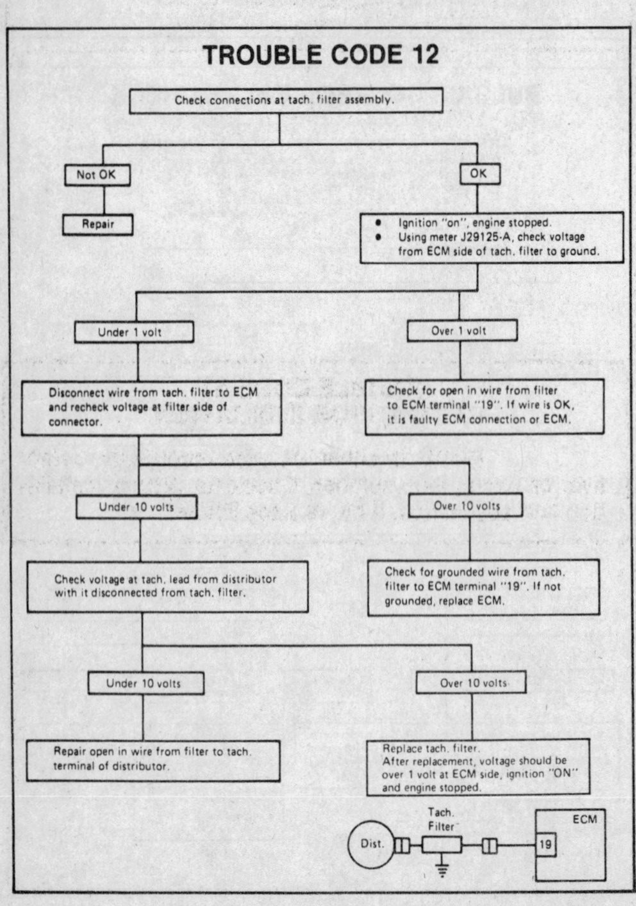

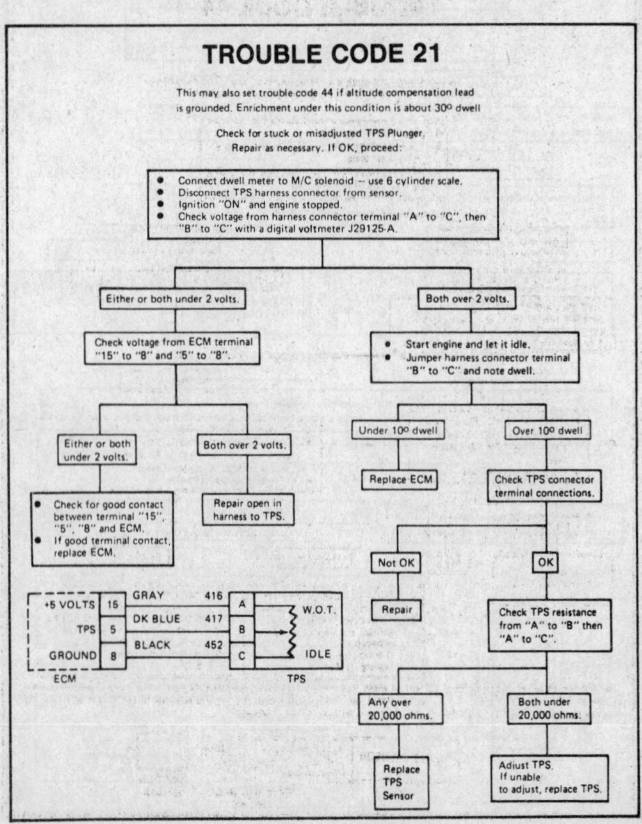

GENERAL MOTORS COMPUTER COMMAND CONTROL (Cont.)

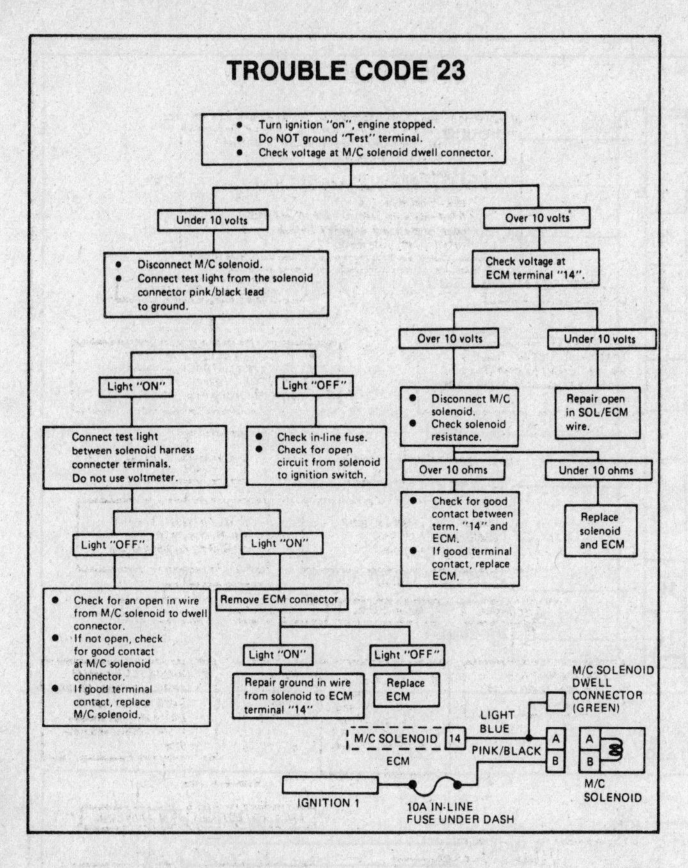

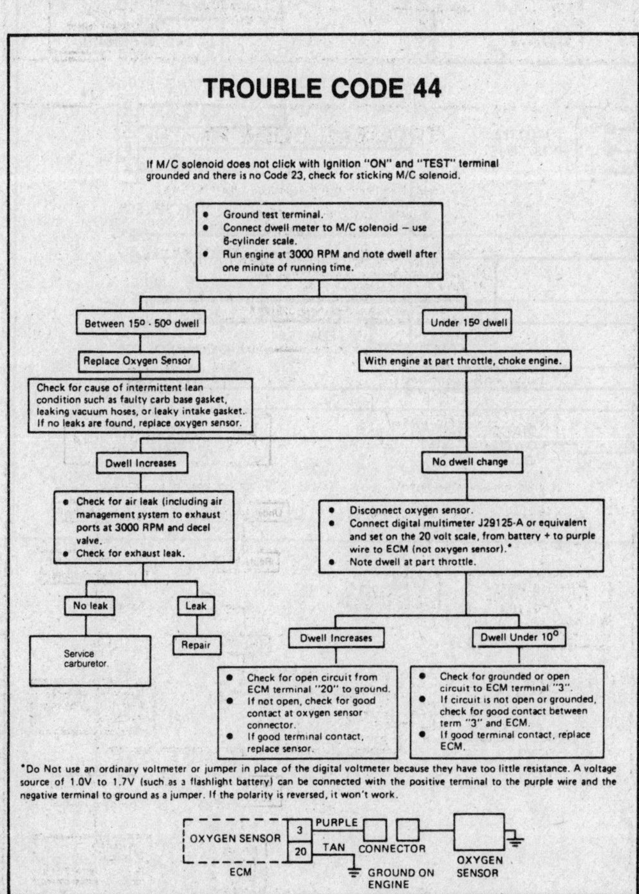

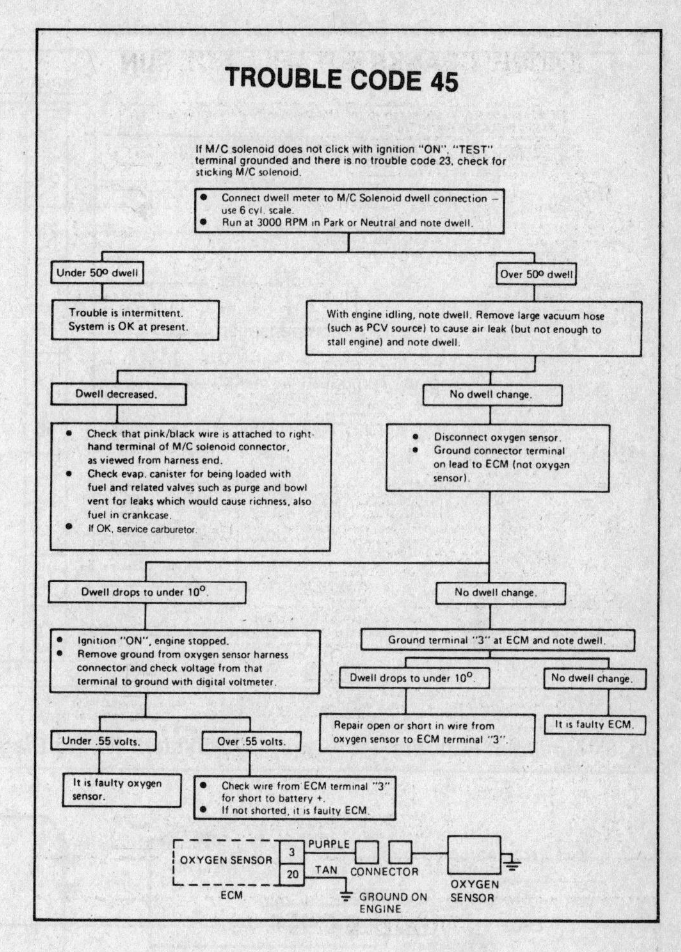

TROUBLE CODE 51
PROM ERROR INDICATION

PROM is either installed incorrectly, defective, or wrong part number. Check for proper installation and application. If ok, replace PROM.

GENERAL MOTORS COMPUTER COMMAND CONTROL (Cont.)

Fig 7: Minimum Function ECM terminal Identification

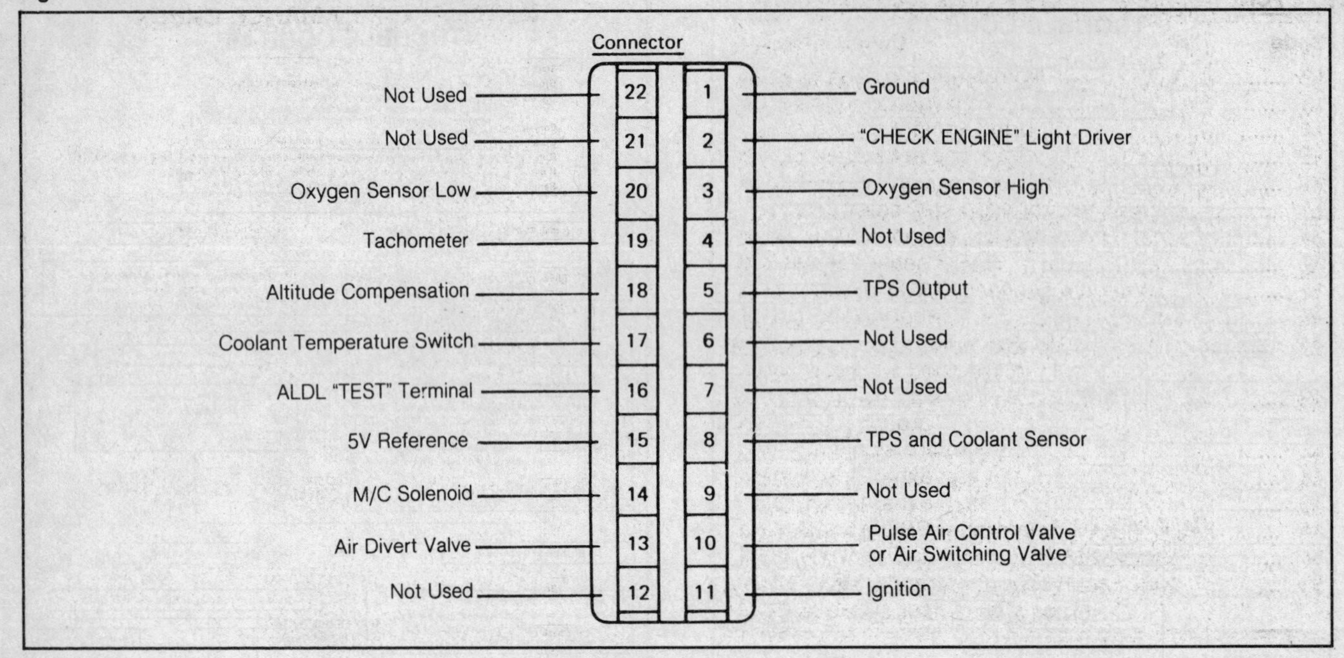

Fig. 8: Minimum Function ("T" Cars) CCC System Wiring Diagram

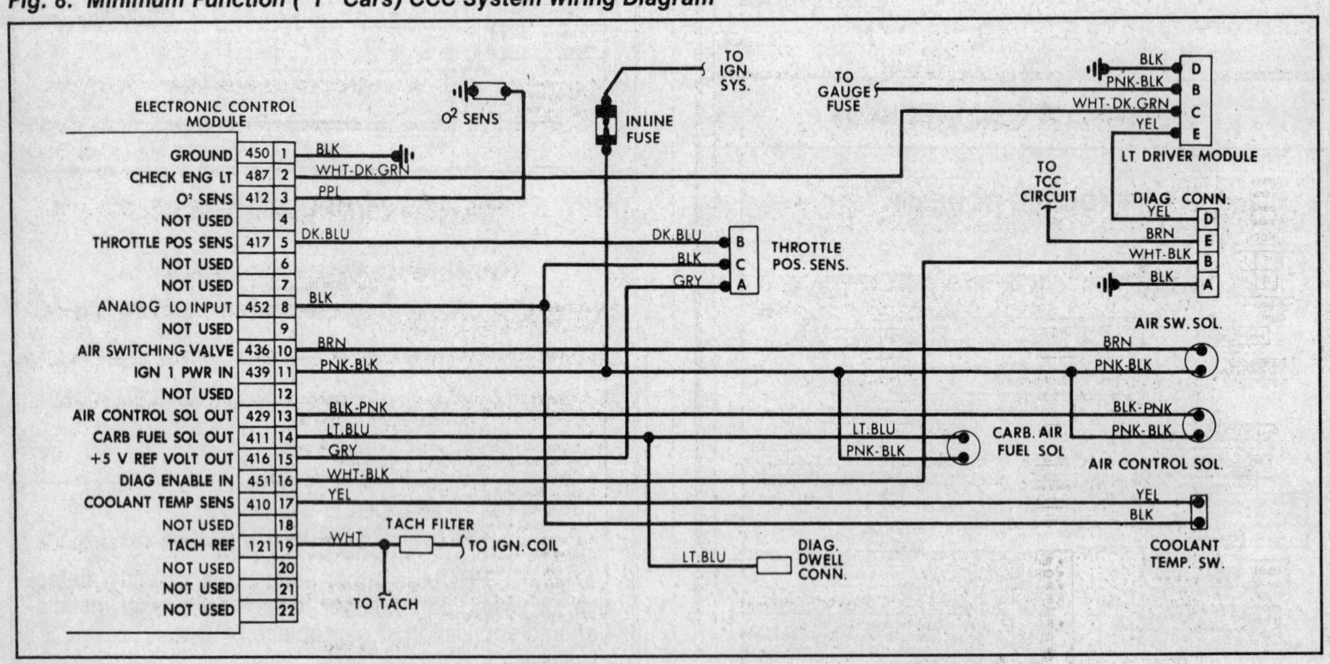

GENERAL MOTORS COMPUTER COMMAND CONTROL (Cont.)

FULL FUNCTION ECM TROUBLE CODE IDENTIFICATION

Code	Circuit Affected
12	No reference pulses to ECM.
13	Oxygen sensor circuit.
14	Shorted coolant sensor circuit.
15	Open coolant sensor circuit.
21	Throttle position sensor circuit.
23	Open or grounded M/C solenoid circuit.
24	Vehicle speed sensor circuit.
32	BARO sensor circuit low.
34	Vacuum sensor or MAP sensor circuit.
35	Shorted ISC circuit.
41	No distributor reference pulses at specified engine vacuum.
42	EST or EST by-pass circuit grounded or open.
43	ESC retard signal too long.
44	Lean exhaust indication.
45	Rich exhaust indication.
51	Faulty PROM or improper PROM installation.
54	Shorted M/C solenoid and/or faulty ECM.
55	Grounded voltage reference, high voltage on oxygen sensor circuit or ECM.

SYSTEM PERFORMANCE CHECK

1. Start engine.
2. Ground "test" term. (Must not be grounded before engine is started.)
3. Disconnect purge hose from canister and plug it.
4. Connect tachometer.
5. Disconnect Mixture Control (M/C) Solenoid and ground M/C Solenoid dwell term.
6. Run engine at 3,000 RPM and, while keeping throttle constant, reconnect M/C Solenoid and note RPM. If car is equipped with an electric cooling fan, it may lower RPM when it engages.
7. Remove ground from M/C Solenoid dwell term. before returning to idle.

Less than 100 RPM drop or RPM increases

- Check that pink wire is attached to righthand term. of M/C Solenoid Connector, as viewed from harness end (solenoid connected).
- Check evaporator canister for being loaded with fuel and related valves, such as purge and bowl vents for leaks which would cause richness. Also check for fuel in crankcase. If OK, service carburetor.

More than 100 RPM drop

- Connect dwell meter to M/C sol. dwell term. (6-cyl. scale).
- Set carb. on high step of fast idle cam. and run for one (1) minute or until dwell starts to vary, whichever happens first.
- Return engine to idle and note dwell.*

Fixed under 10° — See "DWELL FIXED UNDER 10° chart.

Fixed 10–50° — See "DWELL FIXED BETWEEN 10°-50° chart.

Fixed over 50° — See "DWELL FIXED OVER 50° chart.

Varying — Check dwell at 3,000 RPM

Between 10–50° — Check air management system. —
- No trouble found in the "System."
- Clear long term memory.**

Under 10° — Check air switching valve leaking to exhaust ports at 3000 RPM. If not leaking . . . . — Service carburetor. Check TPS adjustment.

Over 50° — Service carburetor. Check TPS adjustment.

* Oxygen sensors may cool off at idle and the dwell change from varying to fixed. If this happens, running the engine at fast idle will warm it up again.

** See Code(s) Clearing Procedure.

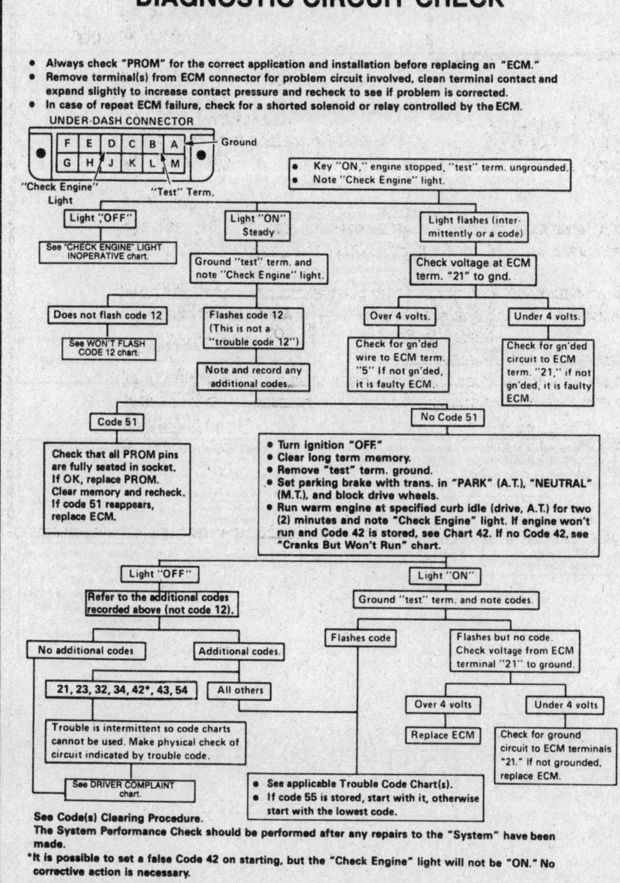

DRIVER COMPLAINT SHEET

ENGINE PERFORMANCE PROBLEM (ODOR, SURGE, FUEL ECONOMY . . .)
EMISSION PROBLEM

IF THE "CHECK ENGINE" LIGHT IS NOT ON, NORMAL CHECKS THAT WOULD BE PERFORMED ON VEHICLE WITHOUT THE SYSTEM SHOULD BE DONE FIRST.

IF GENERATOR OR COOLANT LIGHT IS ON WITH THE "CHECK ENGINE" LIGHT, THEY SHOULD BE DIAGNOSED FIRST.

INSPECT FOR POOR CONNECTIONS AT COOLANT SENSOR, M/C SOLENOID, ETC., AND POOR OR LOOSE VACUUM HOSES AND CONNECTIONS. REPAIR AS NECESSARY.

- **Intermittent "Check Engine" light but no trouble code stored.**
  - **Check for intermittent connection in circuit from:**
    - **Ignition coil to ground and arcing at spark plug wires or plugs.**
    - **Bat. to ECM Terms. 'C' and 'R.'**
    - **ECM Terms. 'A' and 'U' to engine ground.**
  - **Loss of trouble code (long-term) memory.**
    Grounding dwell lead for 10 seconds with "test" lead ungrounded should give Code 23 which should be retained after engine is stopped and ignition turned to "RUN" position.
    If it is not, ECM is defective.
  - **EST wires should be kept away from spark plug wires, distributor housing, coil and generator. Wires from ECM Term. 13 to dist. and the shield (if used) around EST wires should be a good ground.**
  - **Open diode across A/C compressor clutch.**
- **Stalling, Rough Idle, Dieseling or Improper Idle Speed.**
  See Idle Speed Control (ISC) Check.
- **Detonation (spark knock)**
  Check: ESC System Check, if applicable.
  MAP or Vacuum Sensor Output
  EGR Check.
  TPS Enrichment Operation.
  HEI Operation.
- **Poor Performance and/or Fuel Economy.**
  See EST Performance Check.
  See ESC System Check if applicable.
- **Poor Full Throttle Performance**
  Check TPS Enrichment Operation.
- **Intermittent No-start**
  - **Incorrect pick-up coil or ignition coil. See "Cranks, But Won't Run" chart.**
  - **Intermittent ground connections on ECM.**
- **ALL OTHER COMPLAINTS**
  Make System Peformance Check on warm engine (upper radiator hose hot).

The System Performance Check should be performed after any repairs to the system have been made.

GENERAL MOTORS COMPUTER COMMAND CONTROL (Cont.)

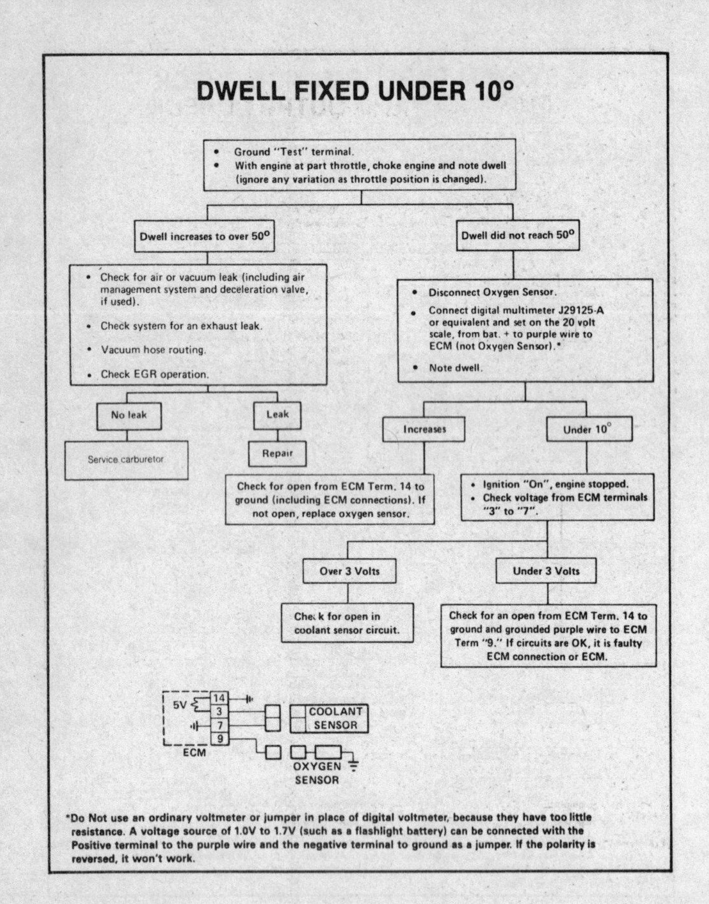

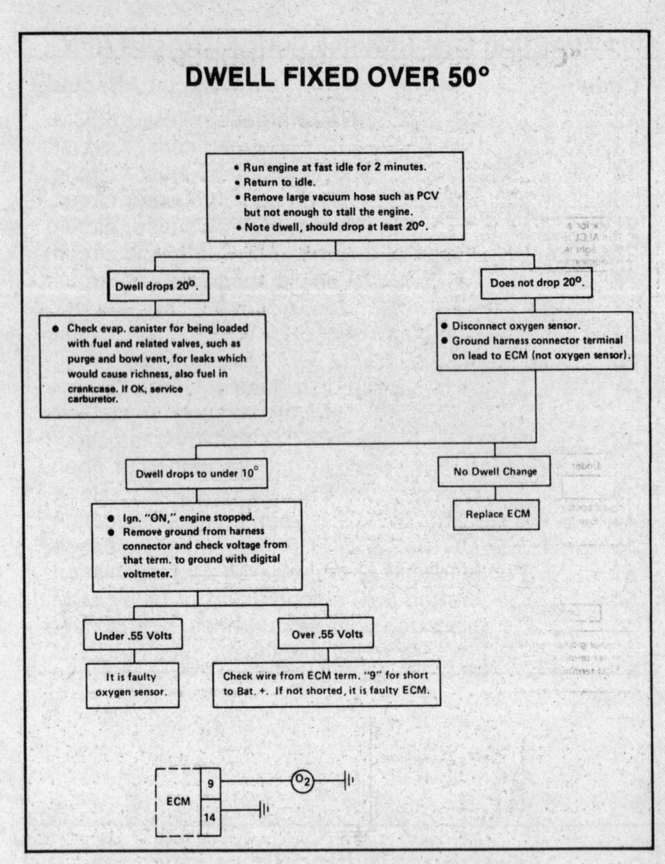

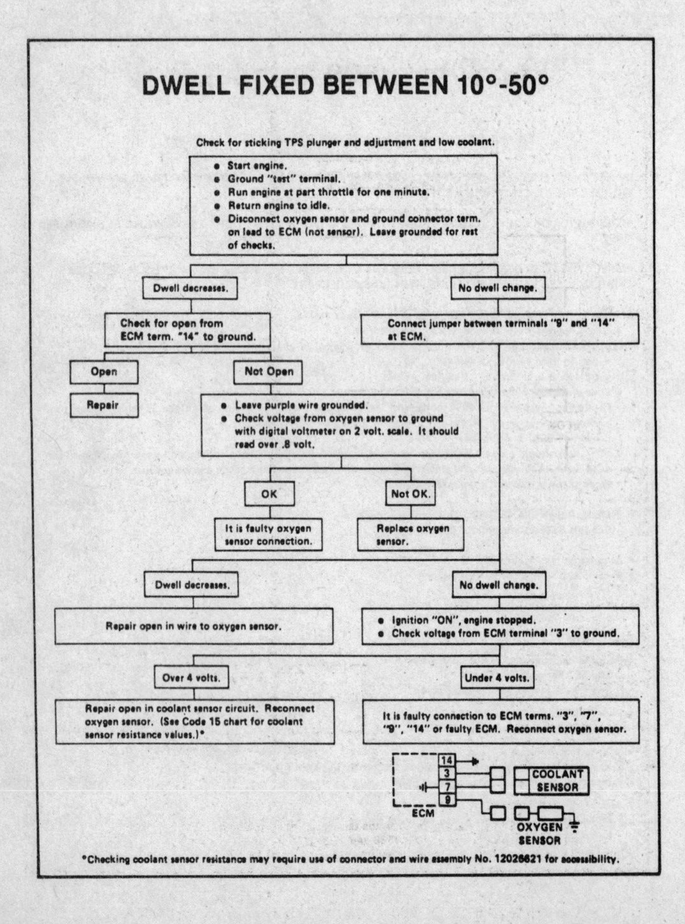

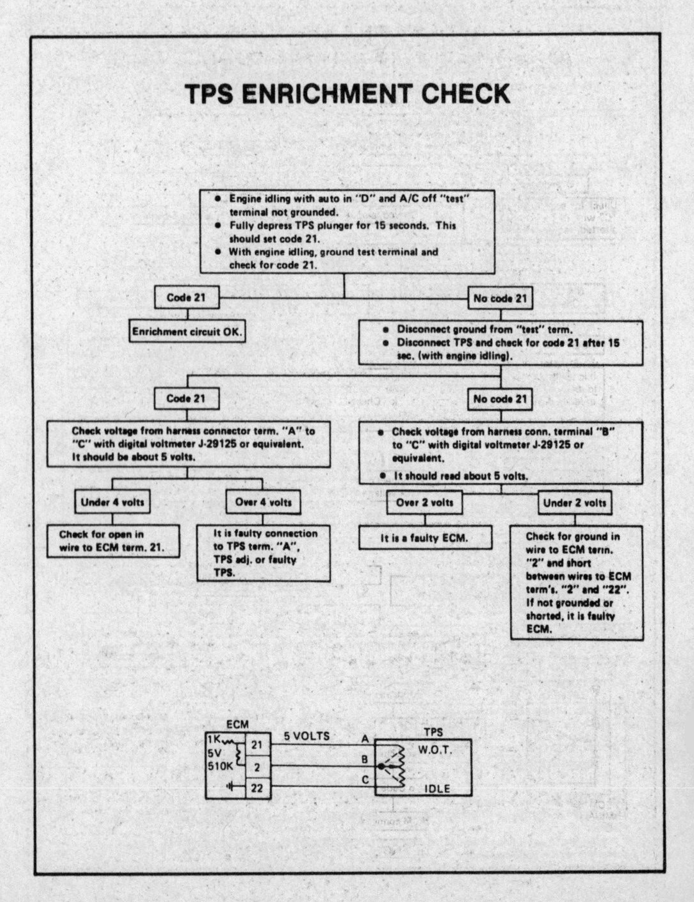

GENERAL MOTORS COMPUTER COMMAND CONTROL (Cont.)

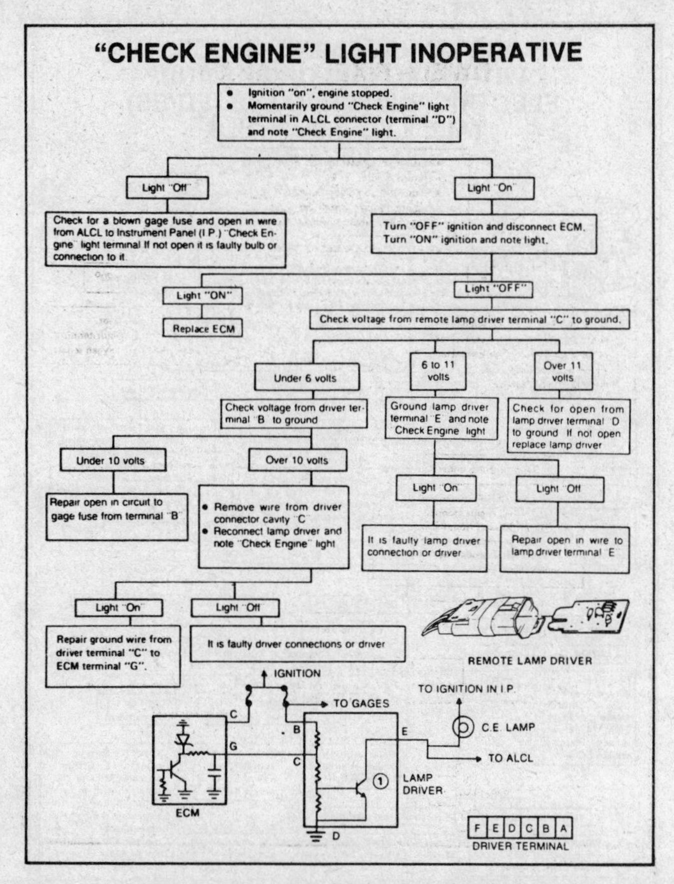

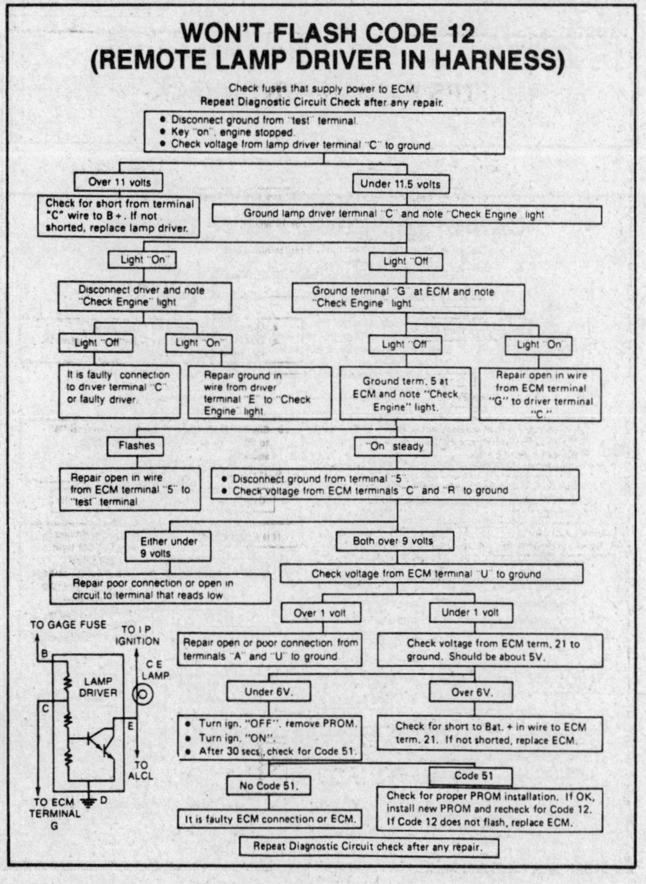

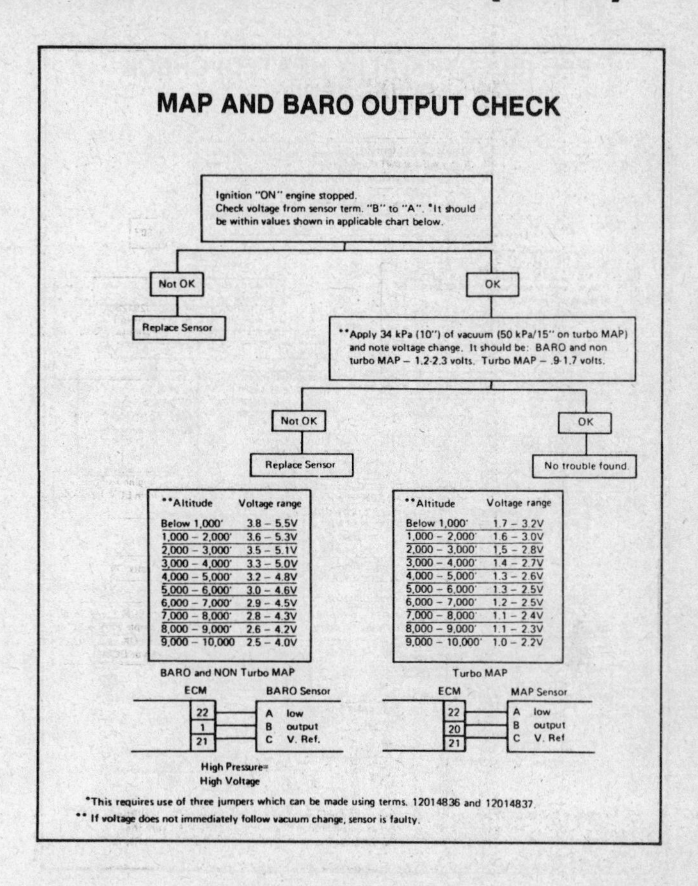

**Altitude	Voltage range
Below 1,000'	3.8 – 5.5V
1,000 – 2,000'	3.6 – 5.3V
2,000 – 3,000'	3.5 – 5.1V
3,000 – 4,000'	3.3 – 5.0V
4,000 – 5,000'	3.2 – 4.8V
5,000 – 6,000'	3.0 – 4.6V
6,000 – 7,000'	2.9 – 4.5V
7,000 – 8,000'	2.8 – 4.3V
8,000 – 9,000'	2.6 – 4.2V
9,000 – 10,000	2.5 – 4.0V

**Altitude	Voltage range
Below 1,000'	1.7 – 3.2V
1,000 – 2,000'	1.6 – 3.0V
2,000 – 3,000'	1.5 – 2.8V
3,000 – 4,000'	1.4 – 2.7V
4,000 – 5,000'	1.3 – 2.6V
5,000 – 6,000'	1.3 – 2.5V
6,000 – 7,000'	1.2 – 2.5V
7,000 – 8,000'	1.1 – 2.4V
8,000 – 9,000'	1.1 – 2.3V
9,000 – 10,000'	1.0 – 2.2V

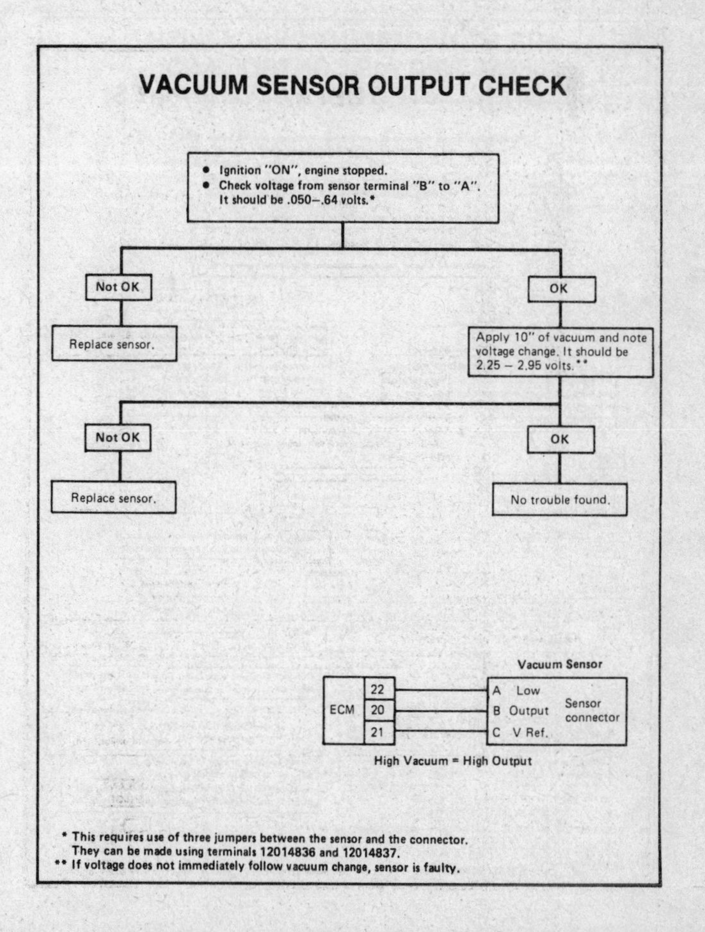

GENERAL MOTORS COMPUTER COMMAND CONTROL (Cont.)

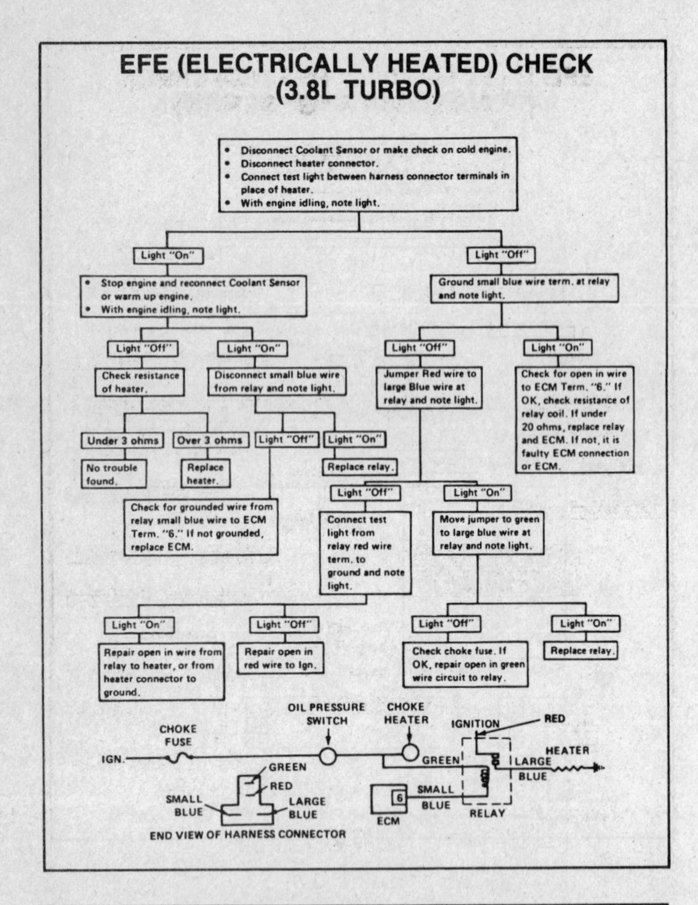

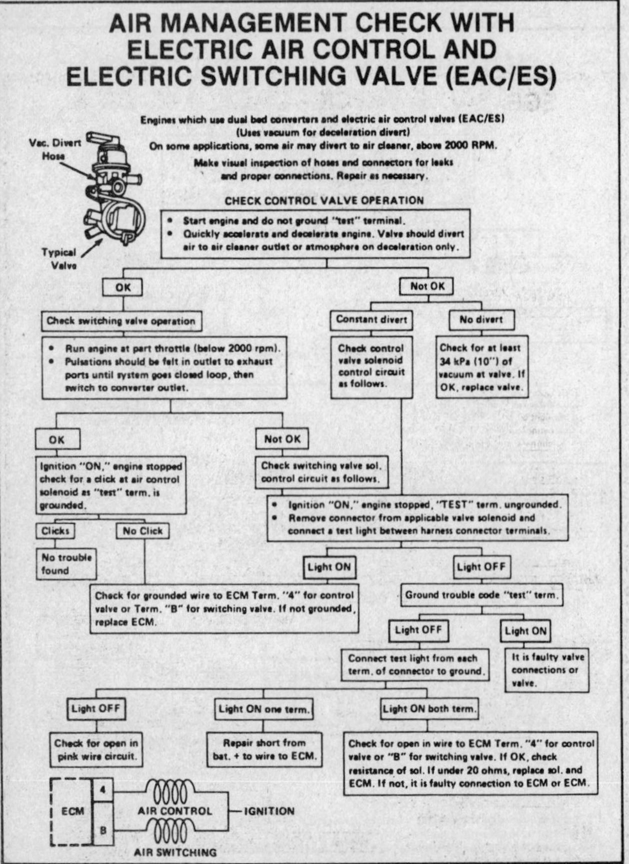

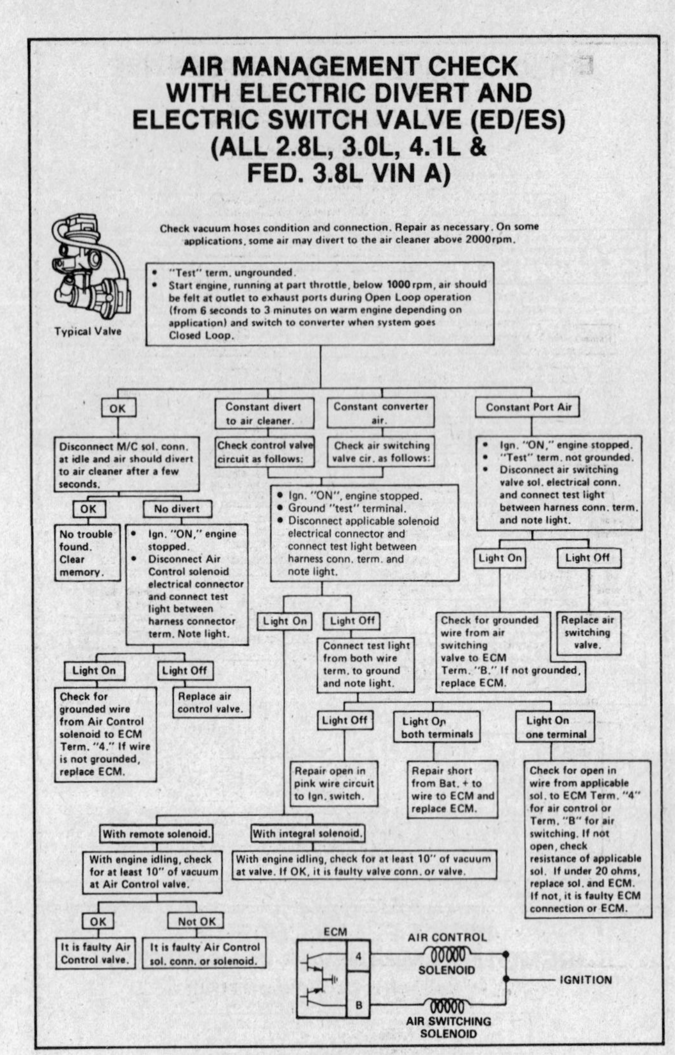

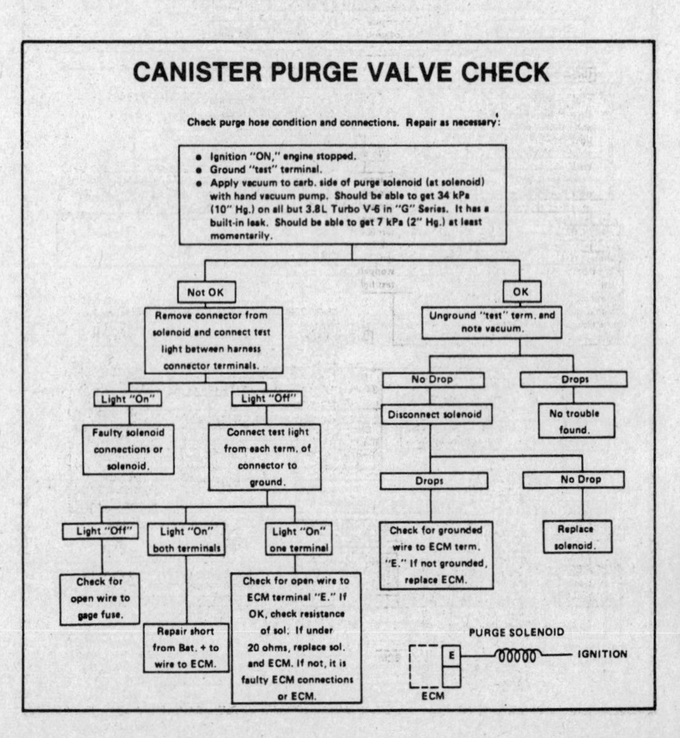

GENERAL MOTORS COMPUTER COMMAND CONTROL (Cont.)

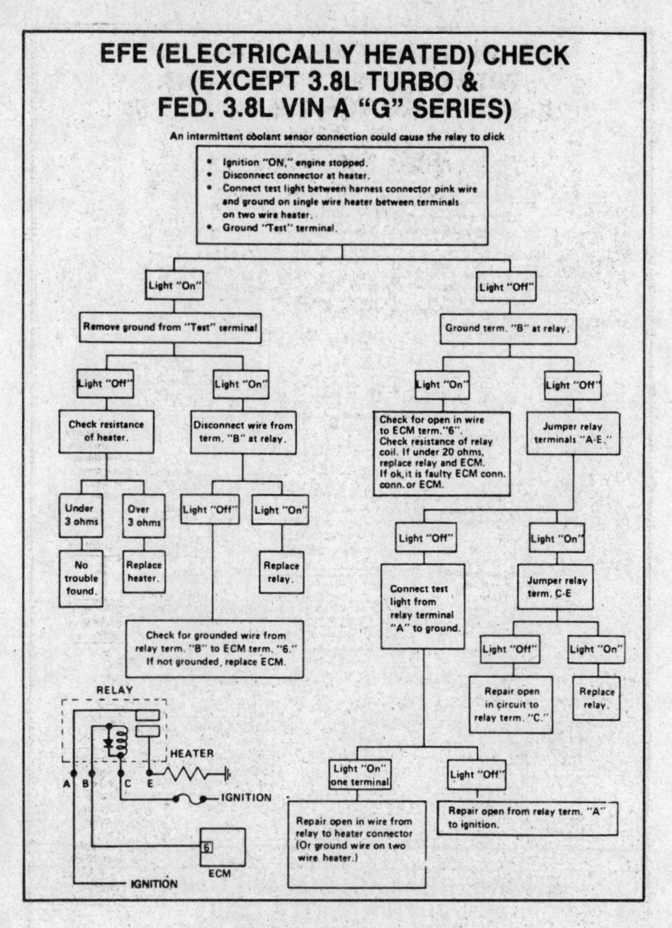

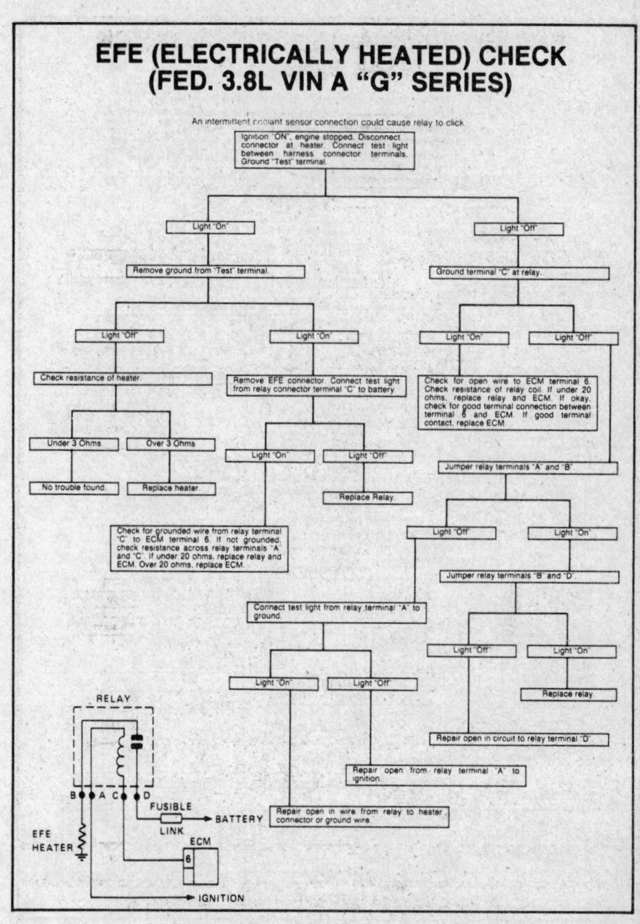

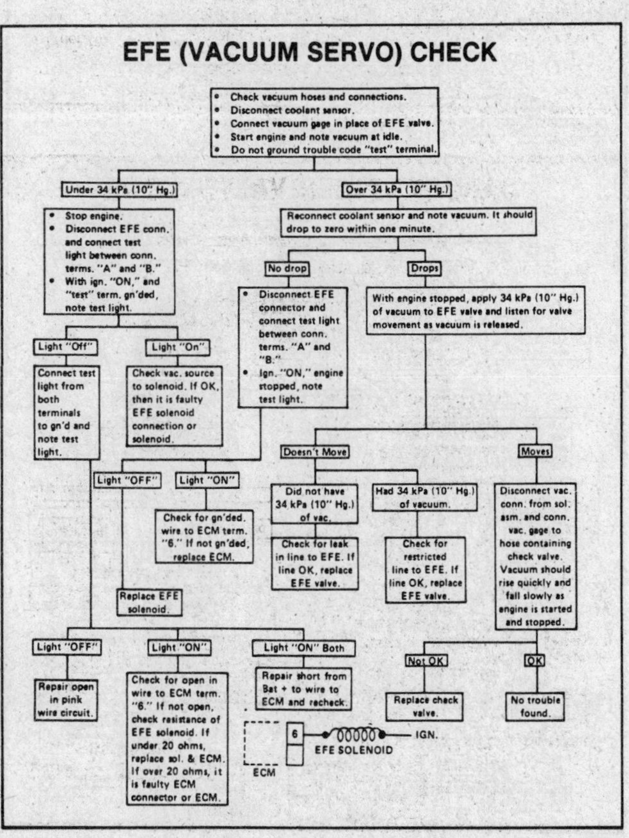

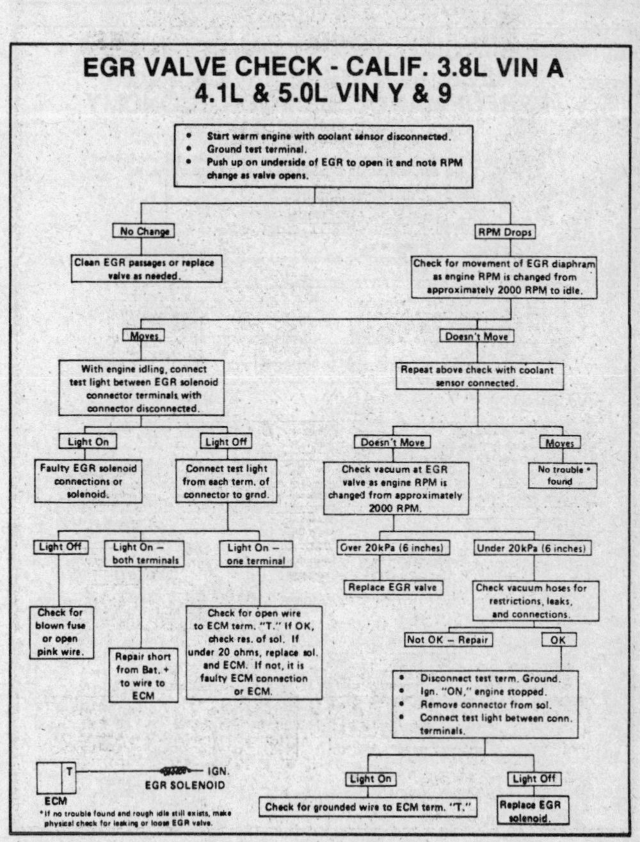

GENERAL MOTORS COMPUTER COMMAND CONTROL (Cont.)

ENGINE CRANKS, BUT WILL NOT RUN (WITH INTEGRAL COIL)

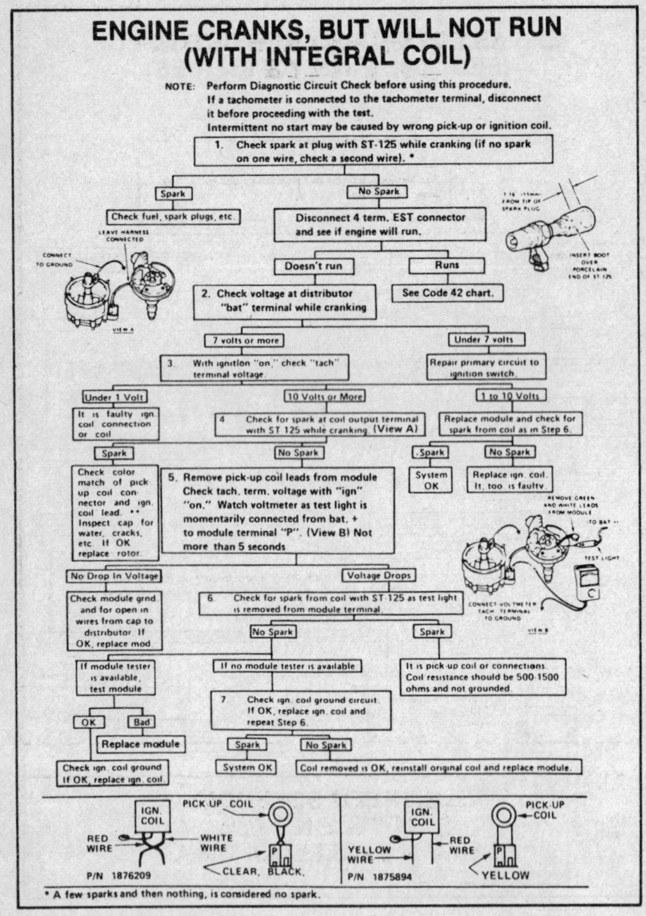

* A few sparks and then nothing, is considered no spark.

ELECTRIC DIVERTER VALVE CHECK CALIF. 3.8L VIN A, 5.0L VIN H ("B" &"G" BODIES) & 5.7L

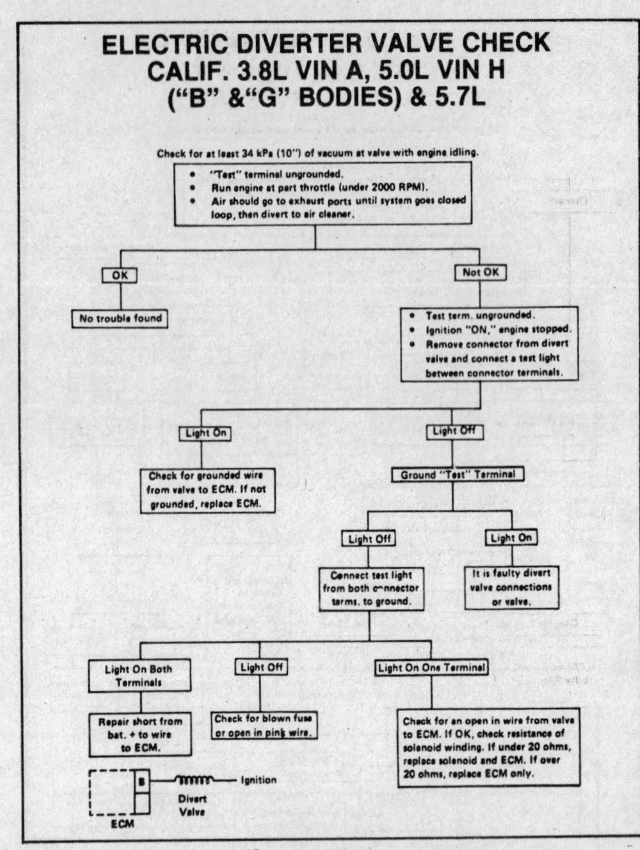

ELECTRONIC SPARK CONTROL (ESC) CHECK — ENGINE KNOCK, POOR PERFORMANCE, OR POOR ECONOMY (NO CODE 43)

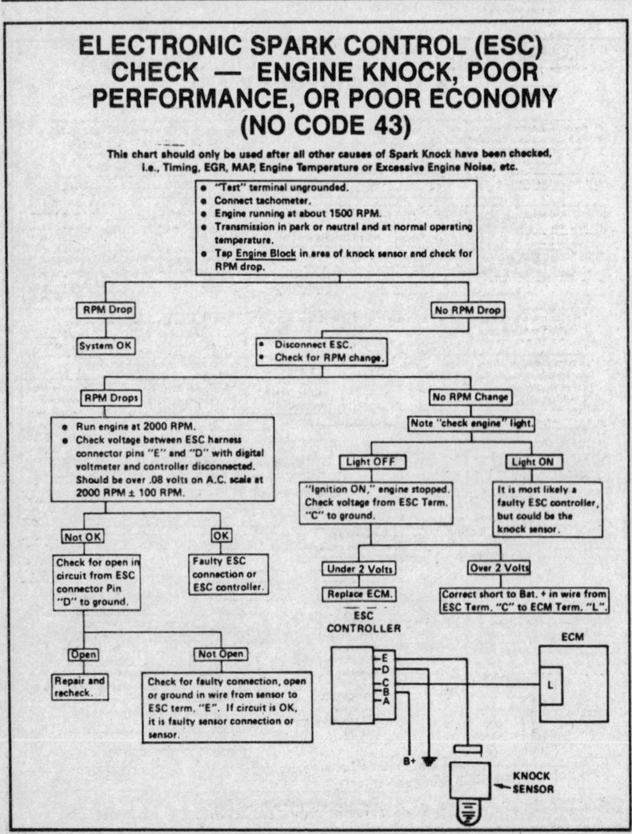

ENGINE CRANKS, BUT WILL NOT RUN (WITH REMOTE COIL)

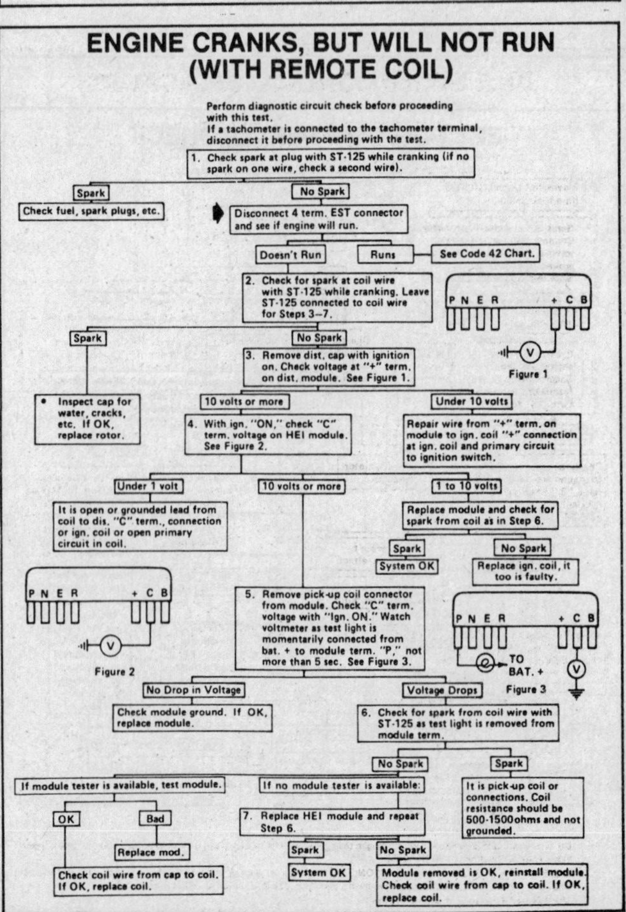

GENERAL MOTORS COMPUTER COMMAND CONTROL (Cont.)

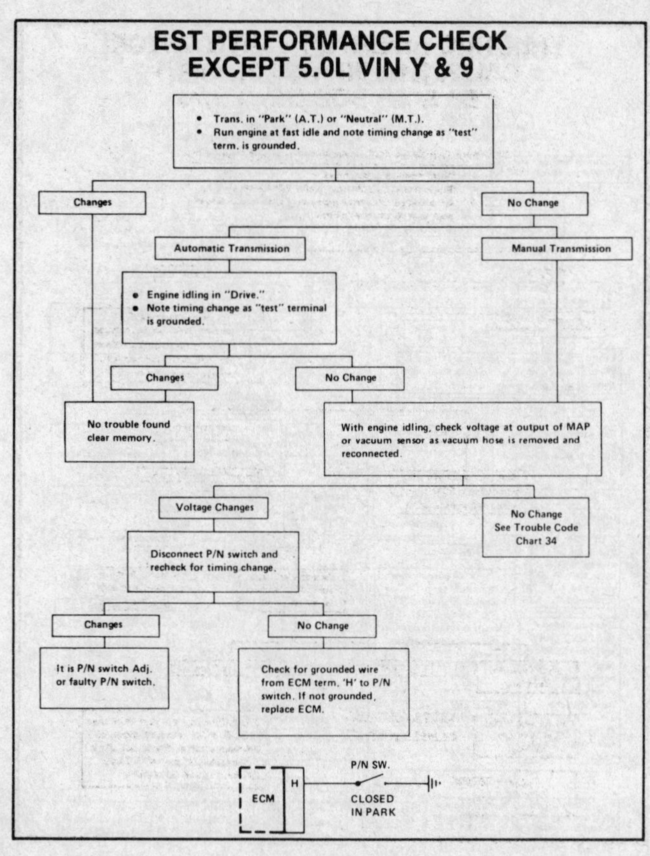

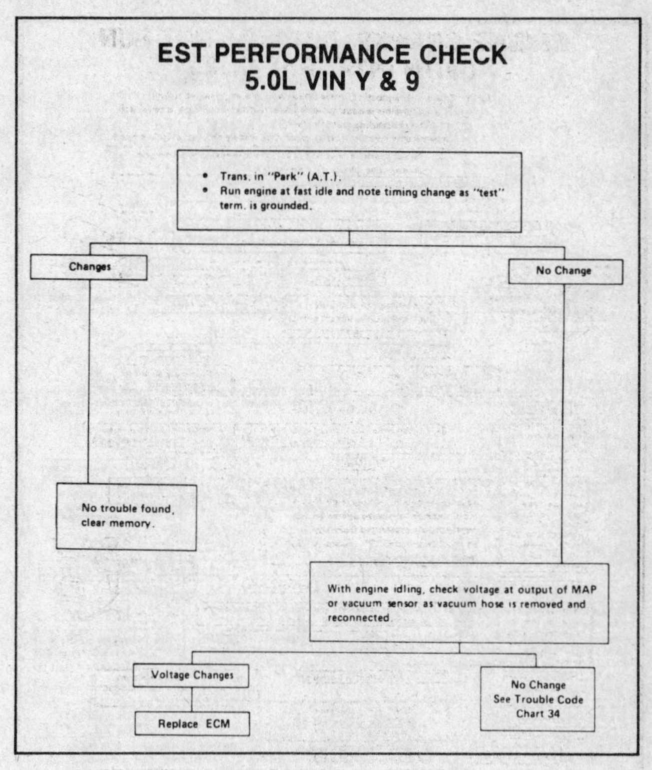

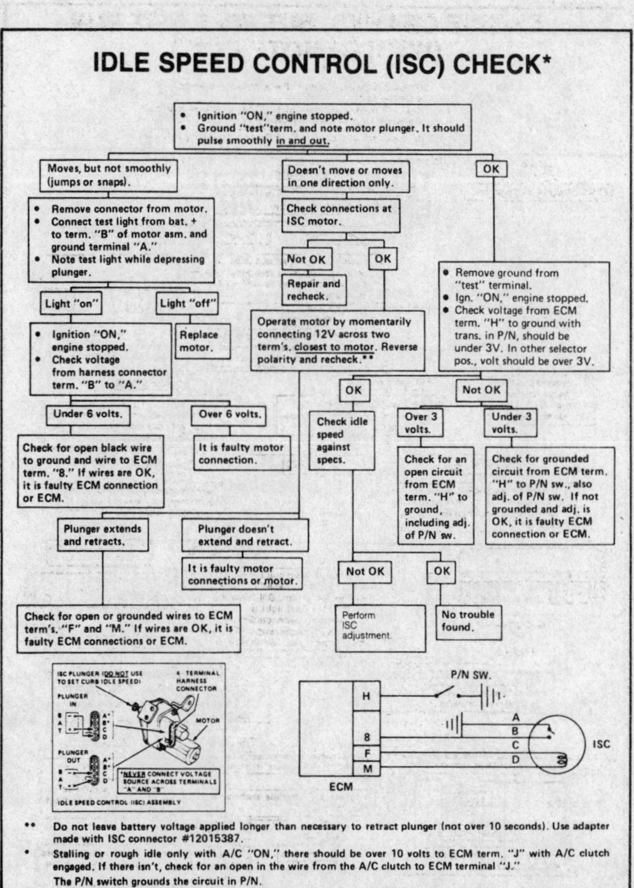

** Do not leave battery voltage applied longer than necessary to retract plunger (not over 10 seconds). Use adapter made with ISC connector #12015387.

* Stalling or rough idle only with A/C "ON," there should be over 10 volts to ECM term. "J" with A/C clutch engaged. If there isn't, check for an open in the wire from the A/C clutch to ECM terminal "J." The P/N switch grounds the circuit in P/N.

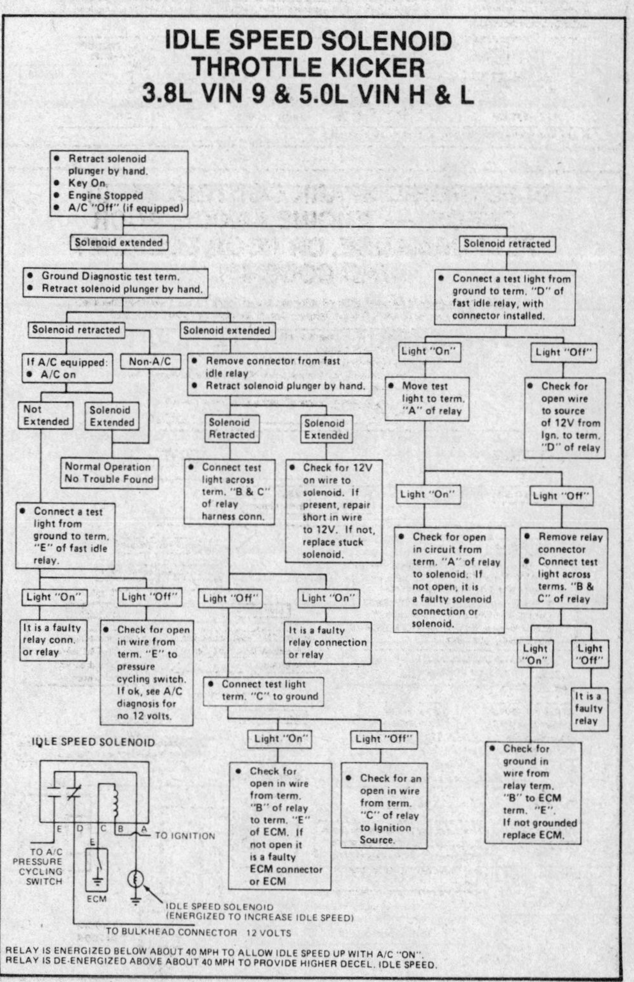

RELAY IS ENERGIZED BELOW ABOUT 40 MPH TO ALLOW IDLE SPEED UP WITH A/C "ON".
RELAY IS DE-ENERGIZED ABOVE ABOUT 40 MPH TO PROVIDE HIGHER DECEL. IDLE SPEED.

GENERAL MOTORS COMPUTER COMMAND CONTROL (Cont.)

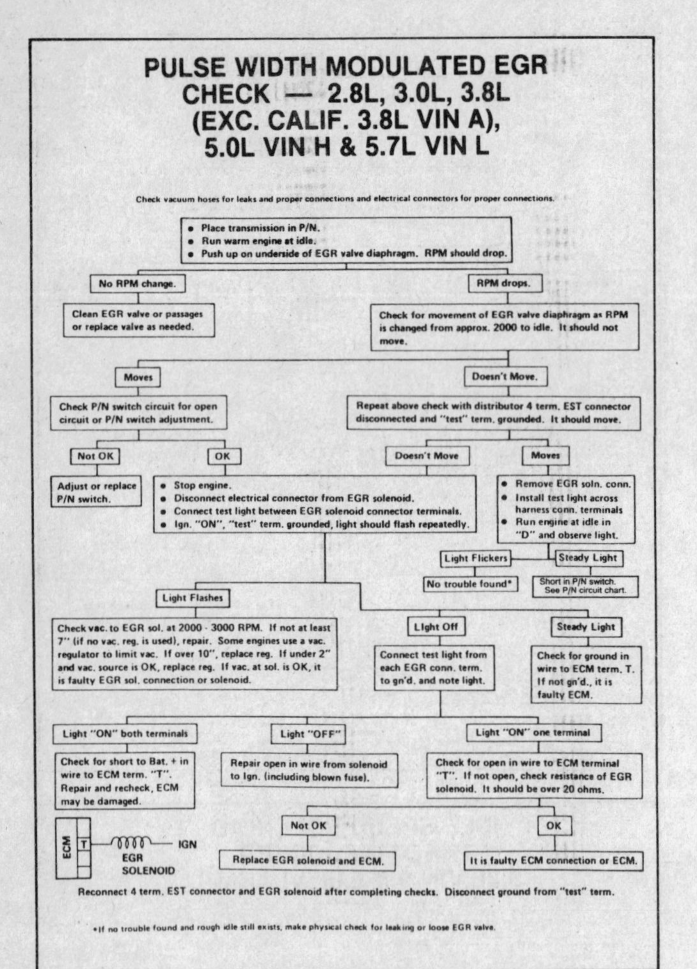

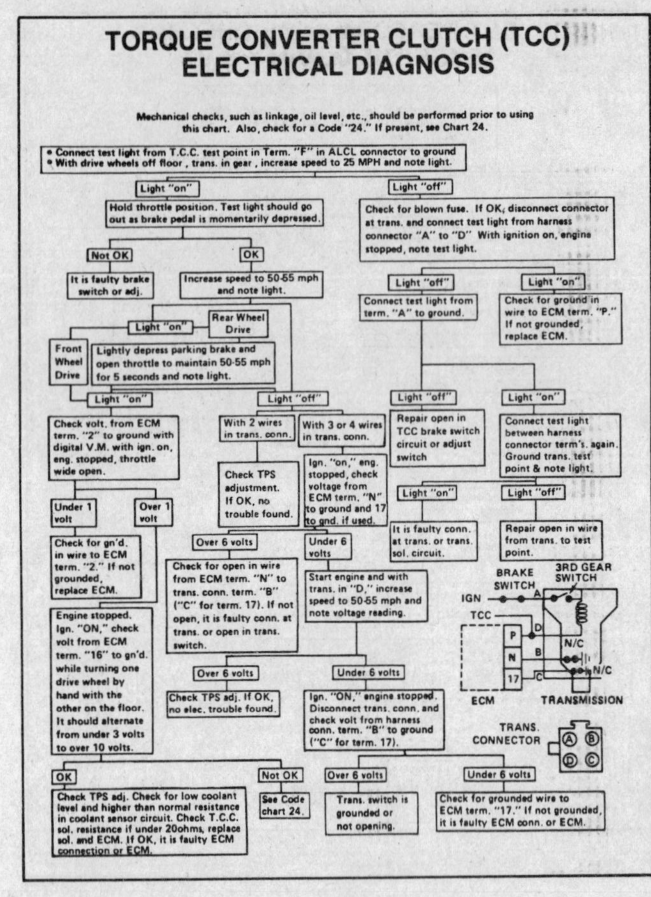

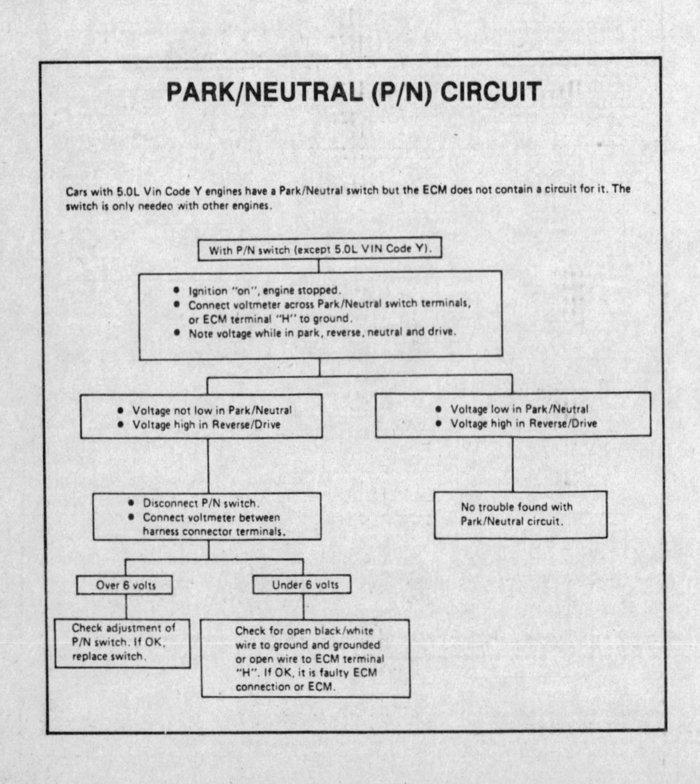

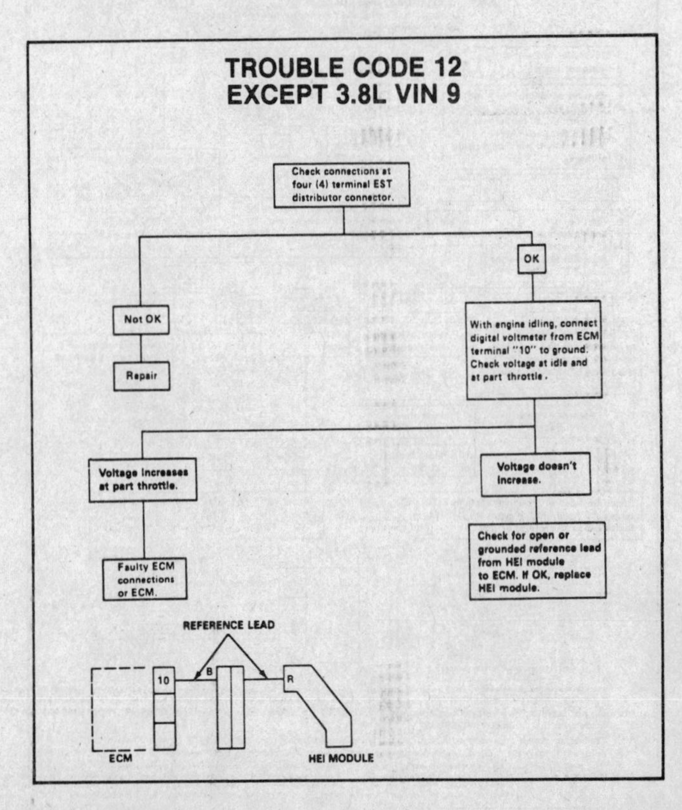

GENERAL MOTORS COMPUTER COMMAND CONTROL (Cont.)

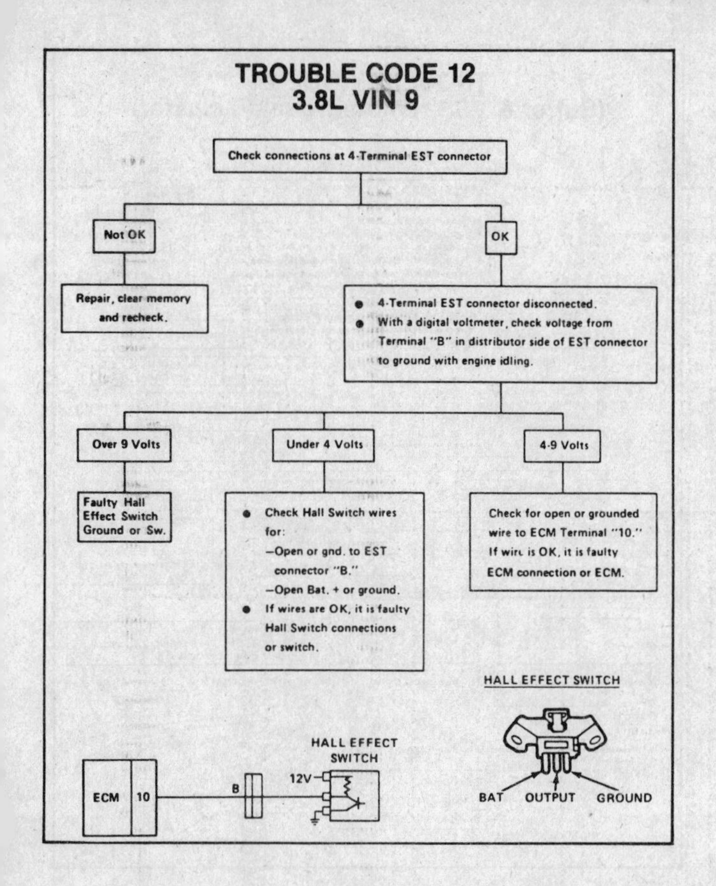

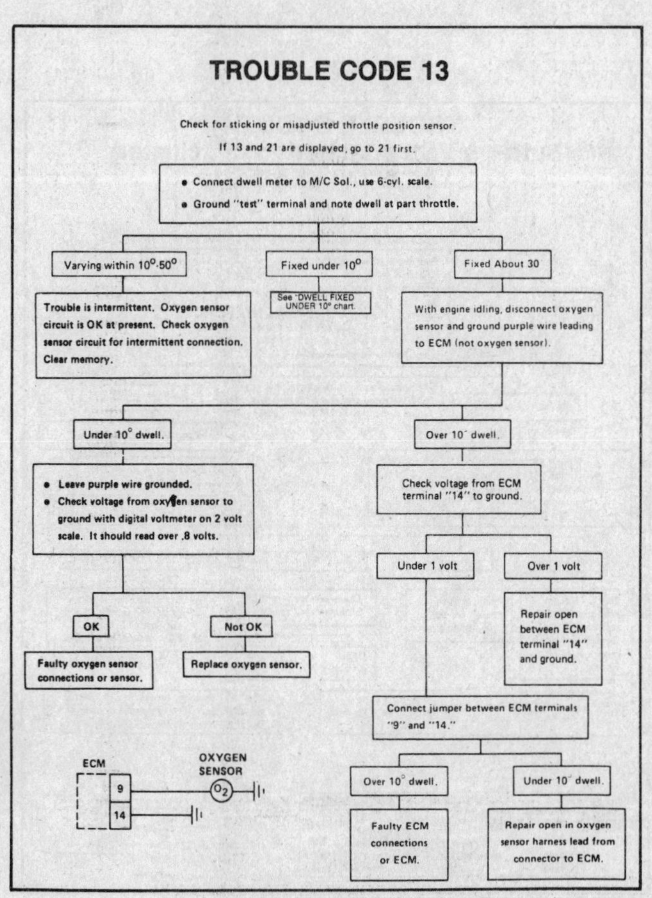

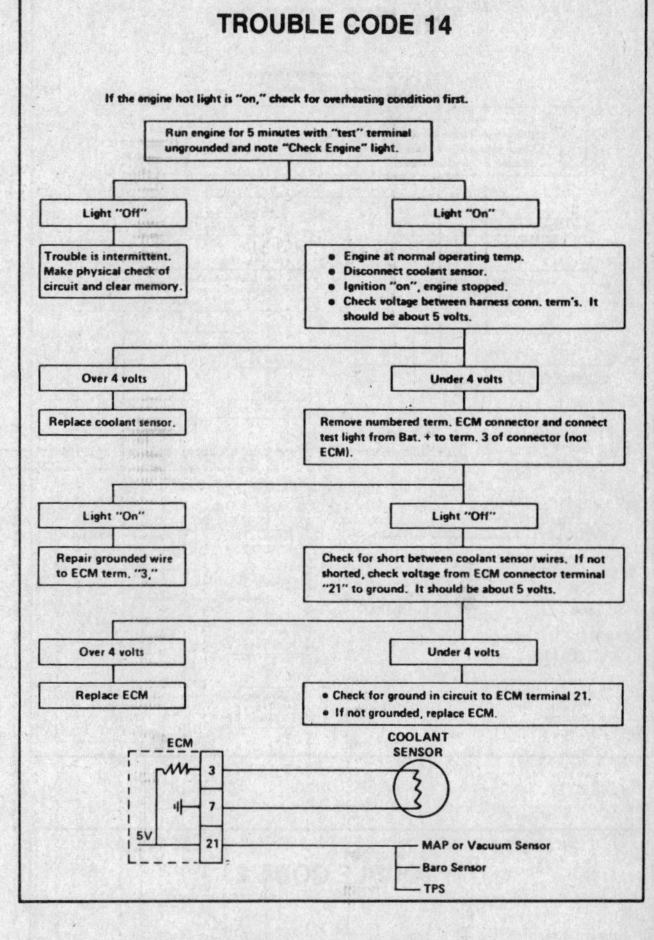

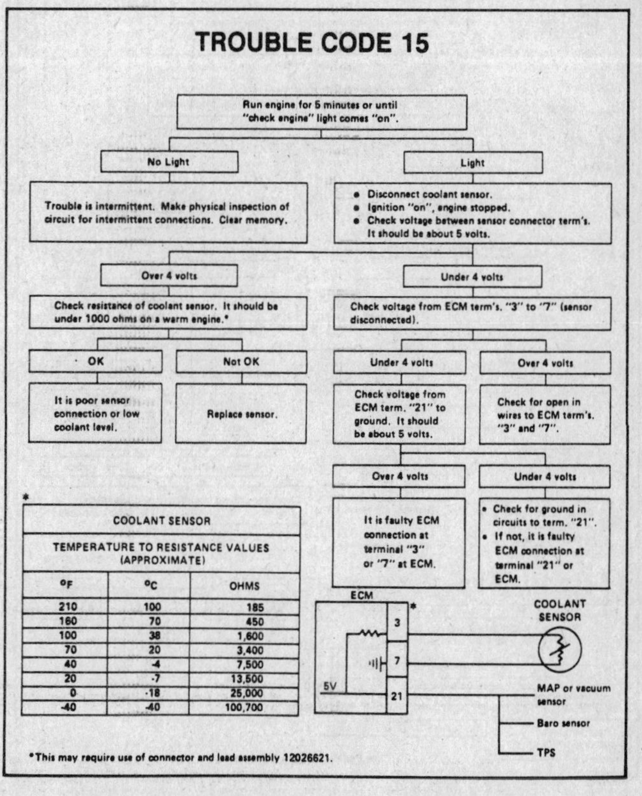

*

COOLANT SENSOR

TEMPERATURE TO RESISTANCE VALUES (APPROXIMATE)

°F	°C	OHMS
210	100	185
160	70	450
100	38	1,600
70	20	3,400
40	4	7,500
20	-7	13,500
0	-18	25,000
-40	-40	100,700

*This may require use of connector and lead assembly 12026621.

GENERAL MOTORS COMPUTER COMMAND CONTROL (Cont.)

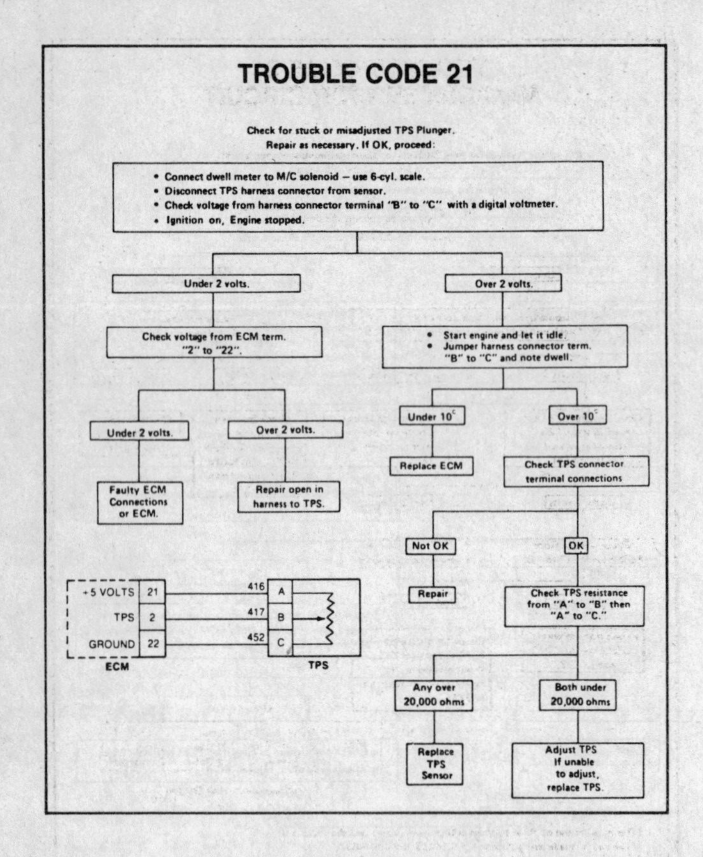

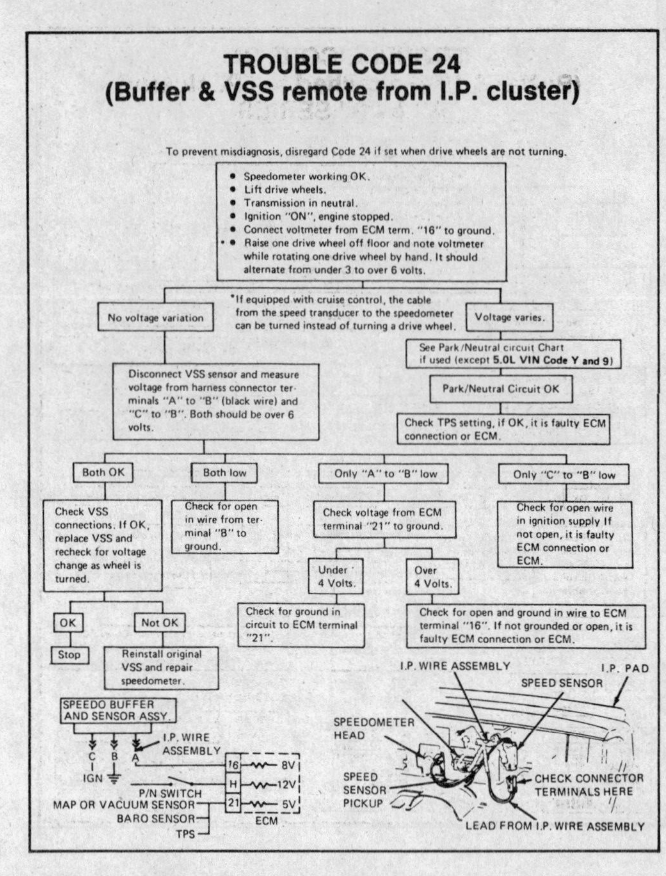

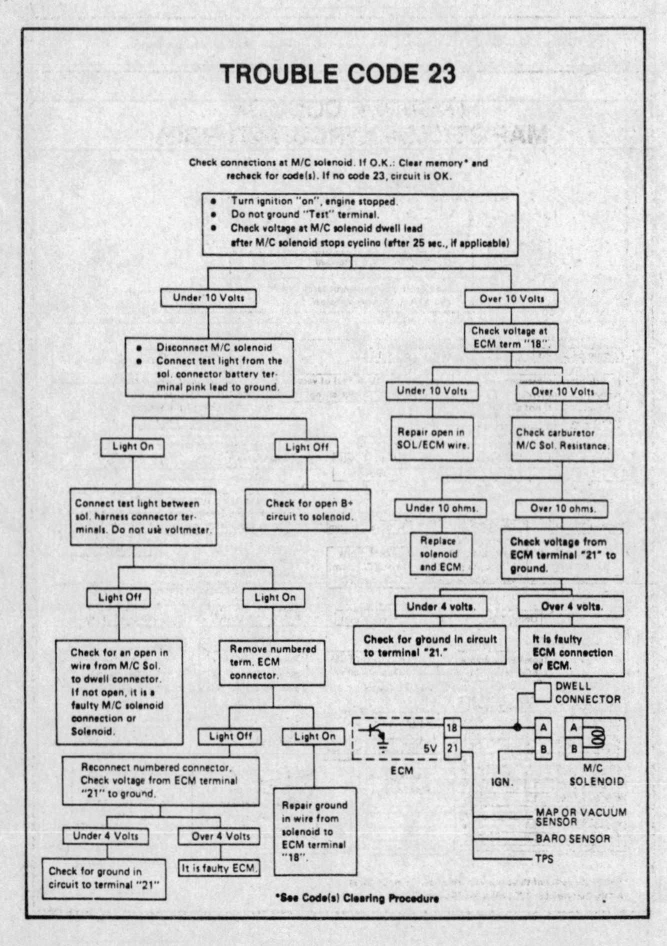

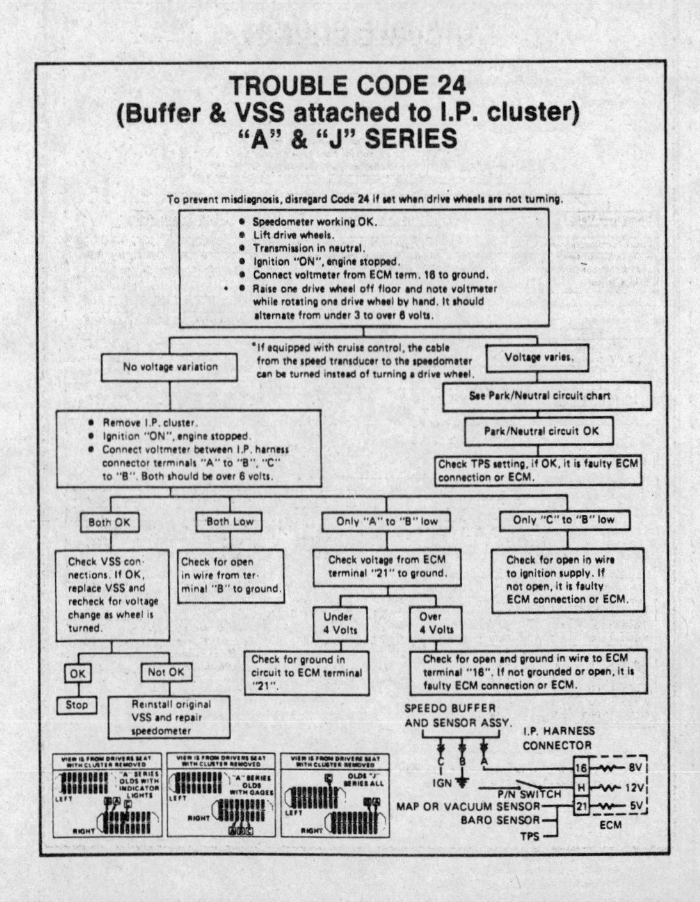

GENERAL MOTORS COMPUTER COMMAND CONTROL (Cont.)

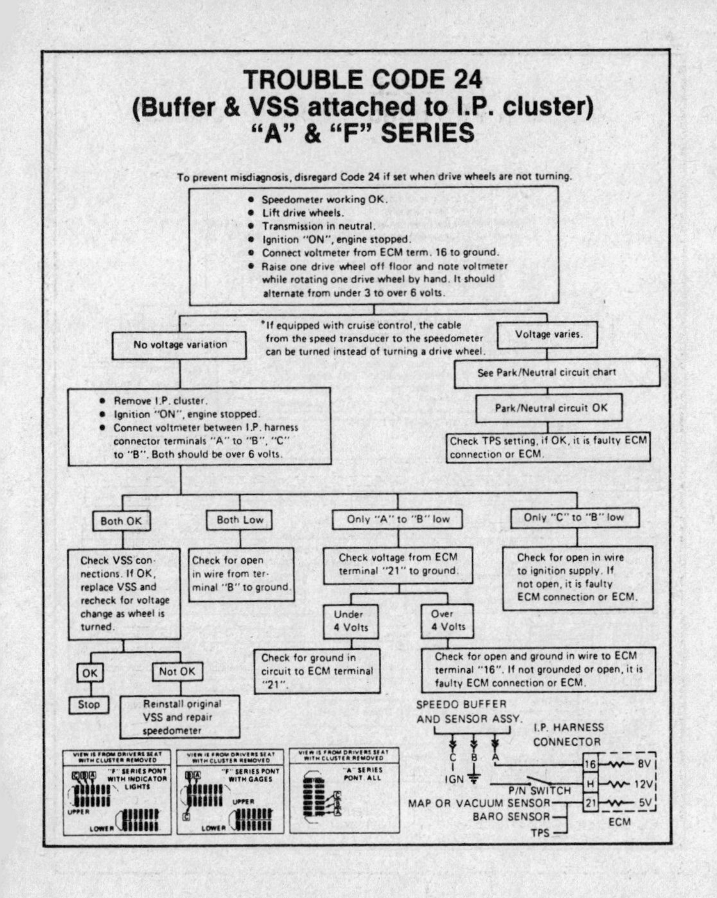

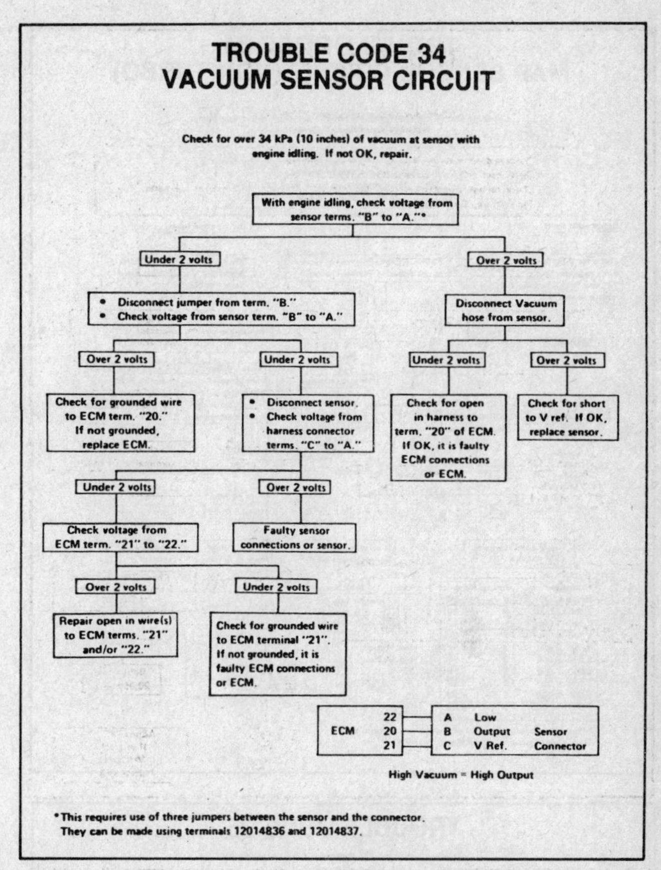

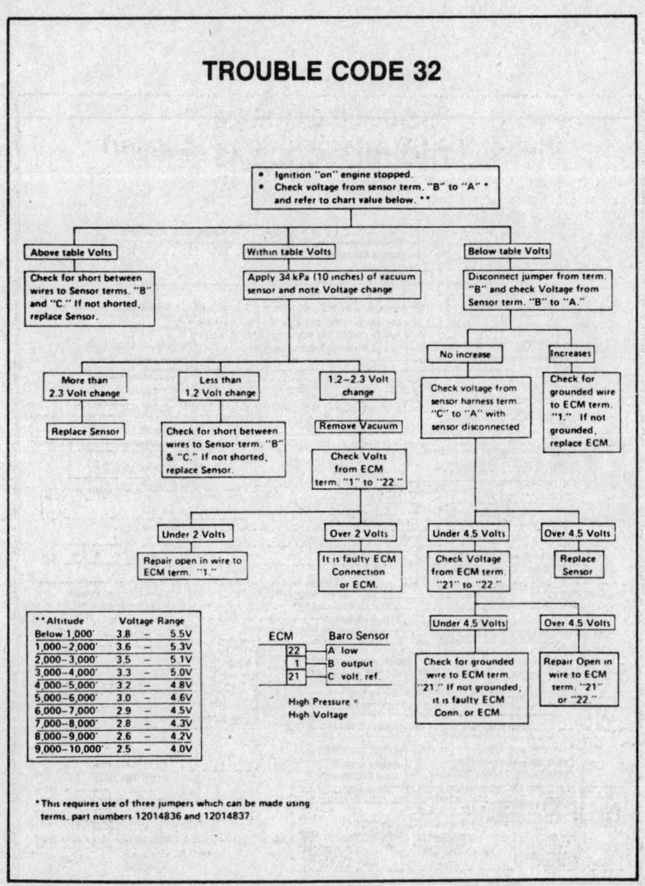

**Altitude	Voltage Range
Below 1,000'	3.8 – 5.5V
1,000–2,000'	3.6 – 5.3V
2,000–3,000'	3.5 – 5.1V
3,000–4,000'	3.3 – 5.0V
4,000–5,000'	3.2 – 4.8V
5,000–6,000'	3.0 – 4.6V
6,000–7,000'	2.9 – 4.5V
7,000–8,000'	2.8 – 4.3V
8,000–9,000'	2.6 – 4.2V
9,000–10,000'	2.5 – 4.0V

*This requires use of three jumpers which can be made using terms. part numbers 12014836 and 12014837.

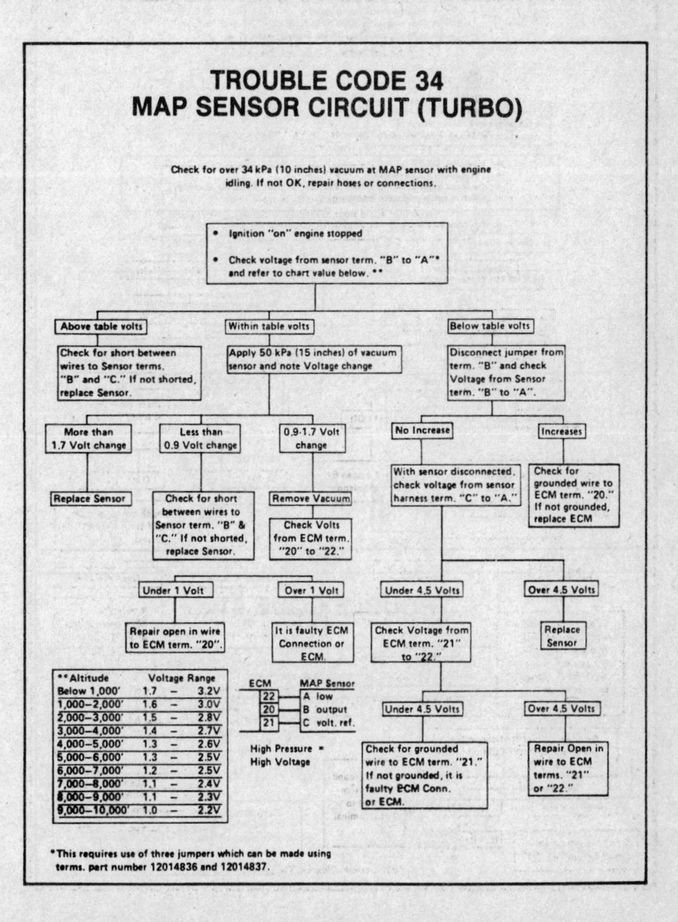

**Altitude	Voltage Range
Below 1,000'	1.7 – 3.2V
1,000–2,000'	1.6 – 3.0V
2,000–3,000'	1.5 – 2.8V
3,000–4,000'	1.4 – 2.7V
4,000–5,000'	1.3 – 2.6V
5,000–6,000'	1.3 – 2.5V
6,000–7,000'	1.2 – 2.5V
7,000–8,000'	1.1 – 2.4V
8,000–9,000'	1.1 – 2.3V
9,000–10,000'	1.0 – 2.2V

*This requires use of three jumpers which can be made using terms. part number 12014836 and 12014837.

GENERAL MOTORS COMPUTER COMMAND CONTROL (Cont.)

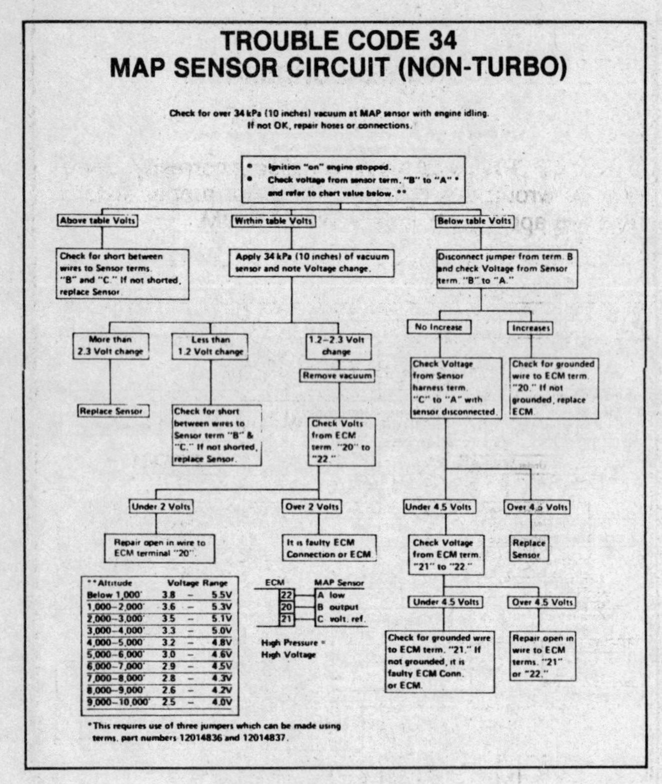

**Altitude	Voltage Range		
Below 1,000'	3.8	–	5.5V
1,000–2,000'	3.6	–	5.3V
2,000–3,000'	3.5	–	5.1V
3,000–4,000'	3.3	–	5.0V
4,000–5,000'	3.2	–	4.8V
5,000–6,000'	3.0	–	4.6V
6,000–7,000'	2.9	–	4.5V
7,000–8,000'	2.8	–	4.3V
8,000–9,000'	2.6	–	4.2V
9,000–10,000'	2.5	–	4.0V

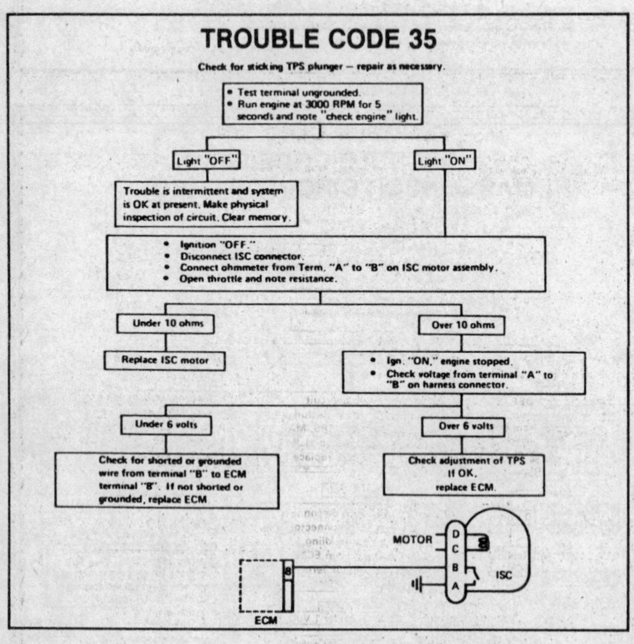

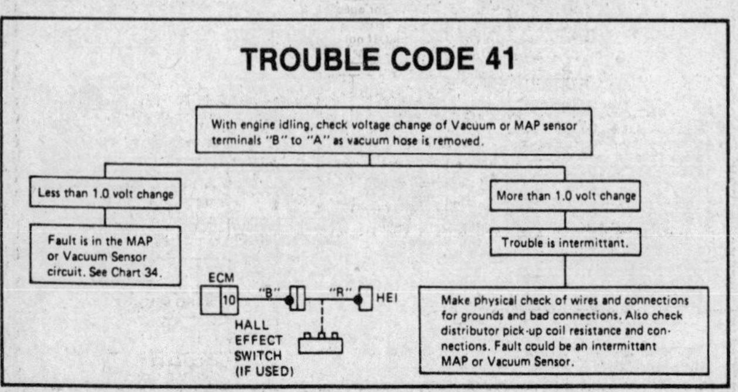

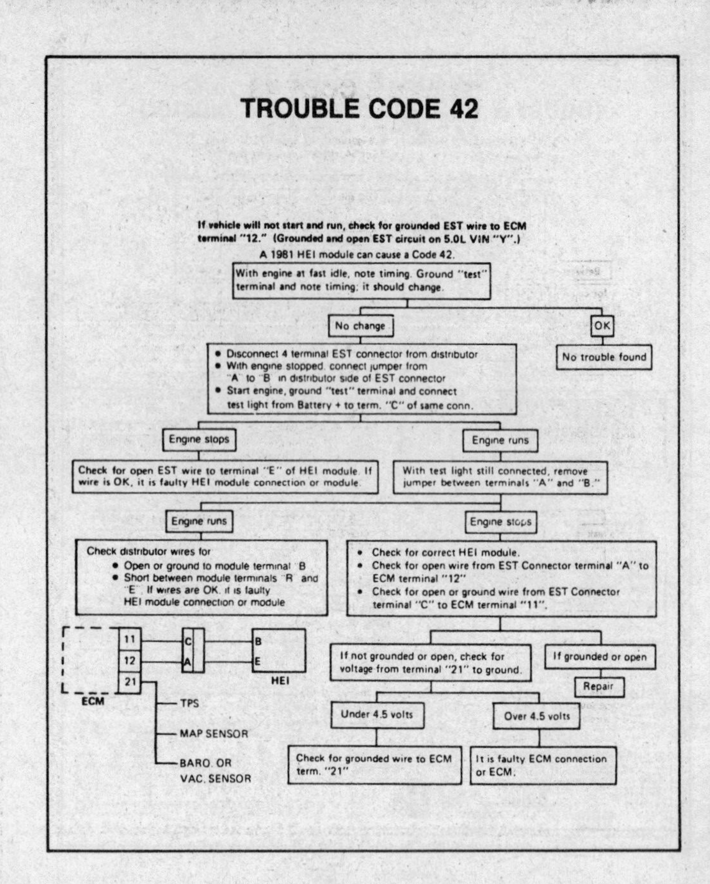

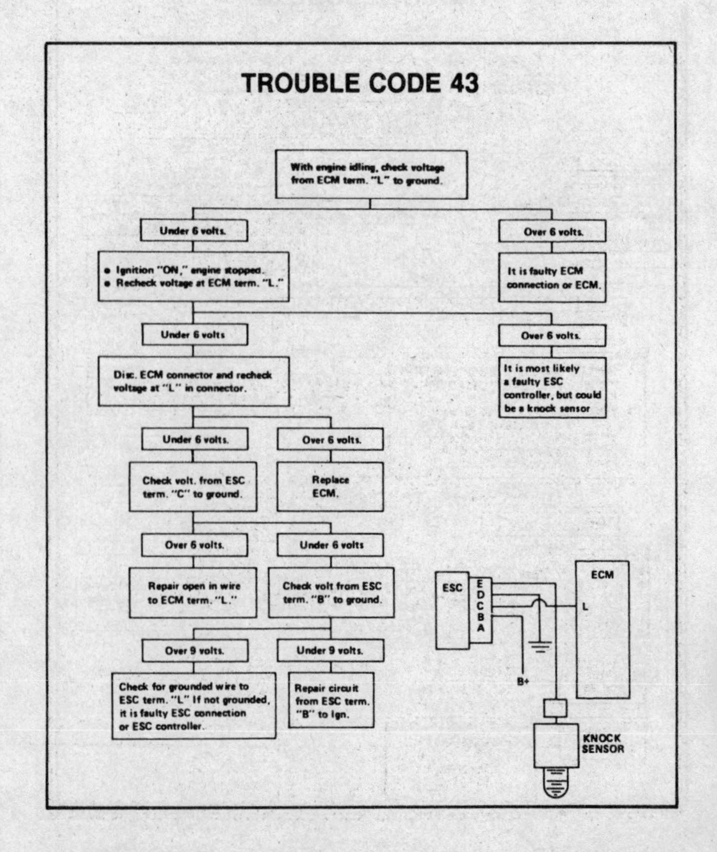

GENERAL MOTORS COMPUTER COMMAND CONTROL (Cont.)

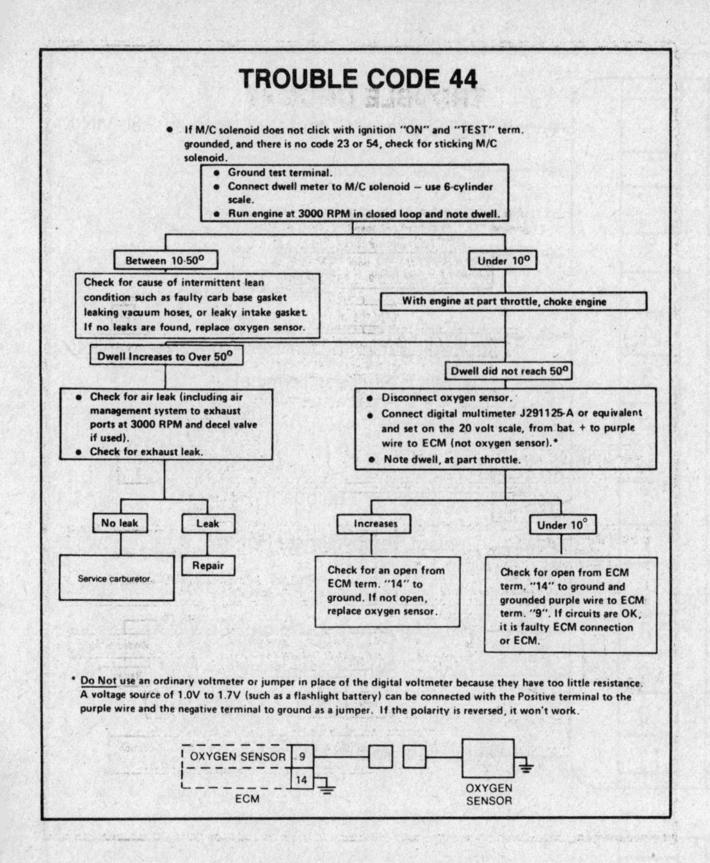

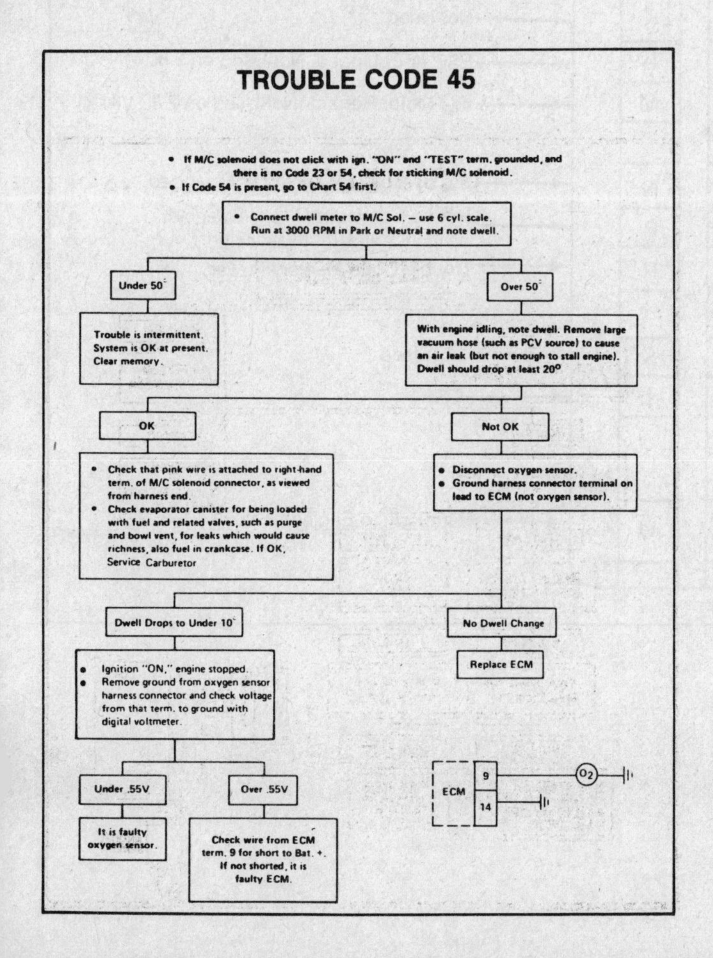

TROUBLE CODE 51

PROM is either installed incorrectly, defective, or wrong part number. Check for proper installation and application. If ok, replace PROM.

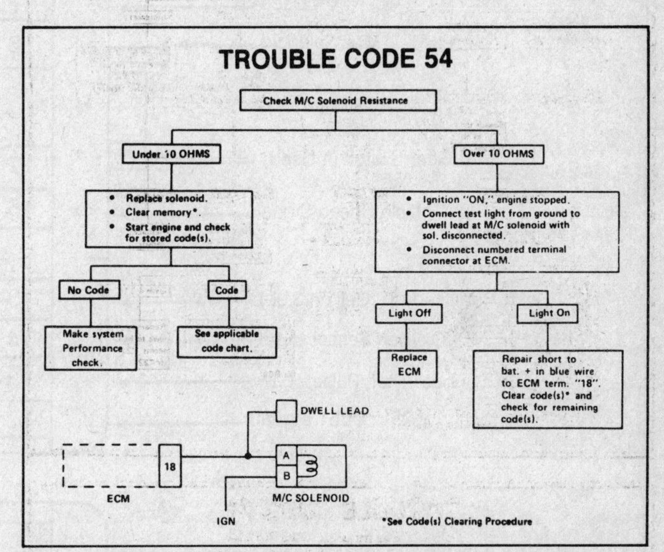

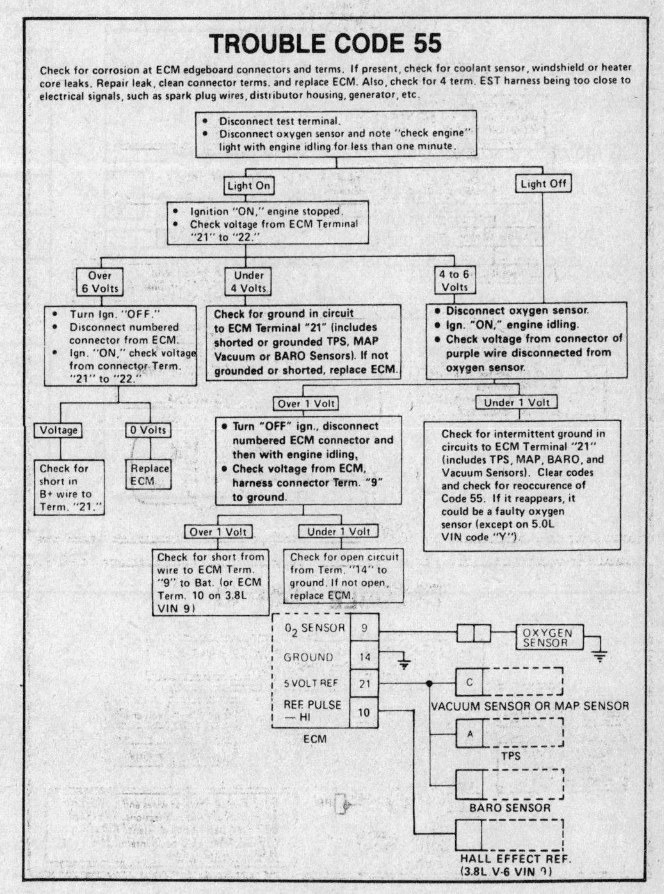

GENERAL MOTORS COMPUTER COMMAND CONTROL (Cont.)

Fig. 9: Full Function ECM Terminal Identification

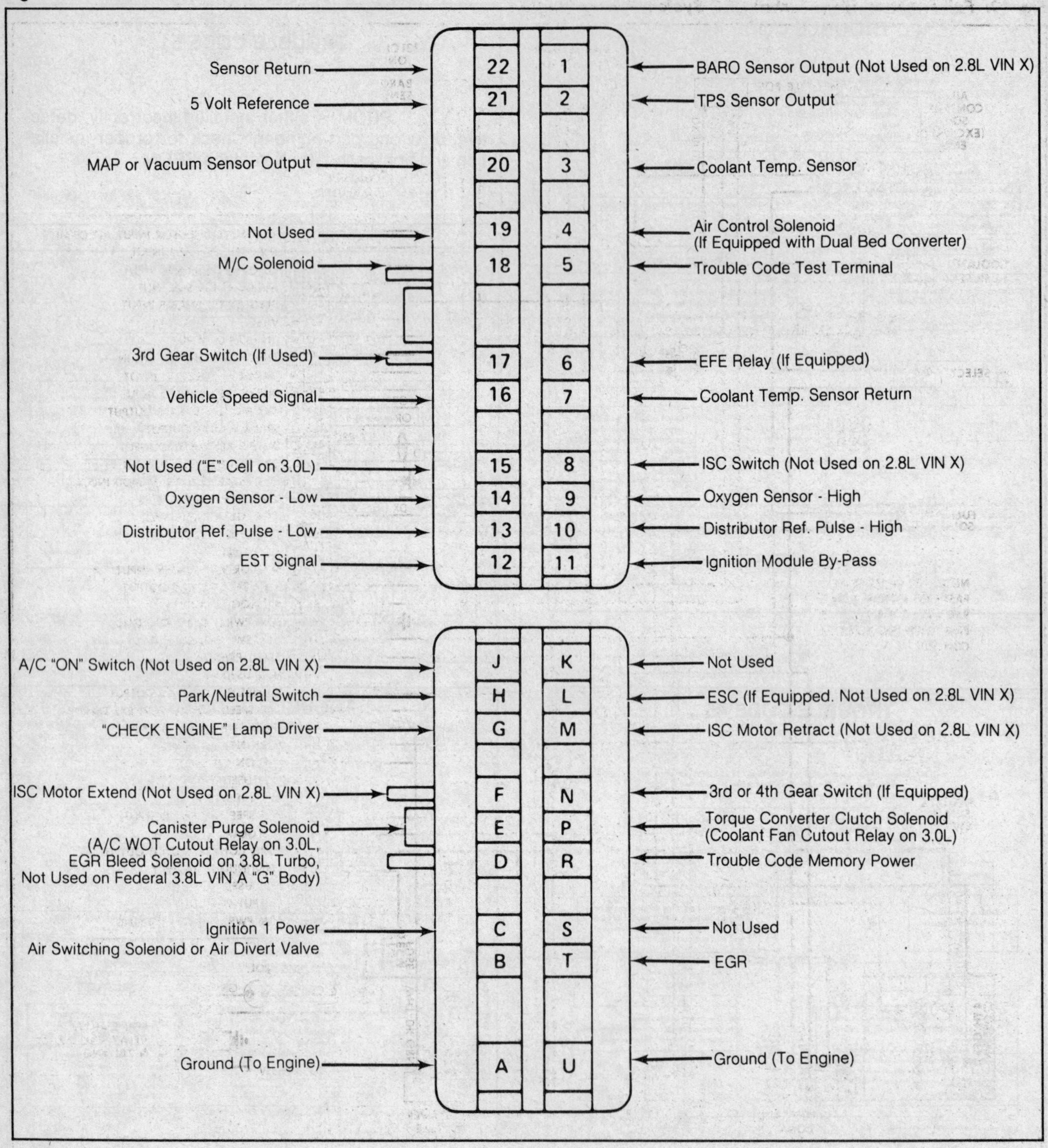

GENERAL MOTORS COMPUTER COMMAND CONTROL (Cont.)

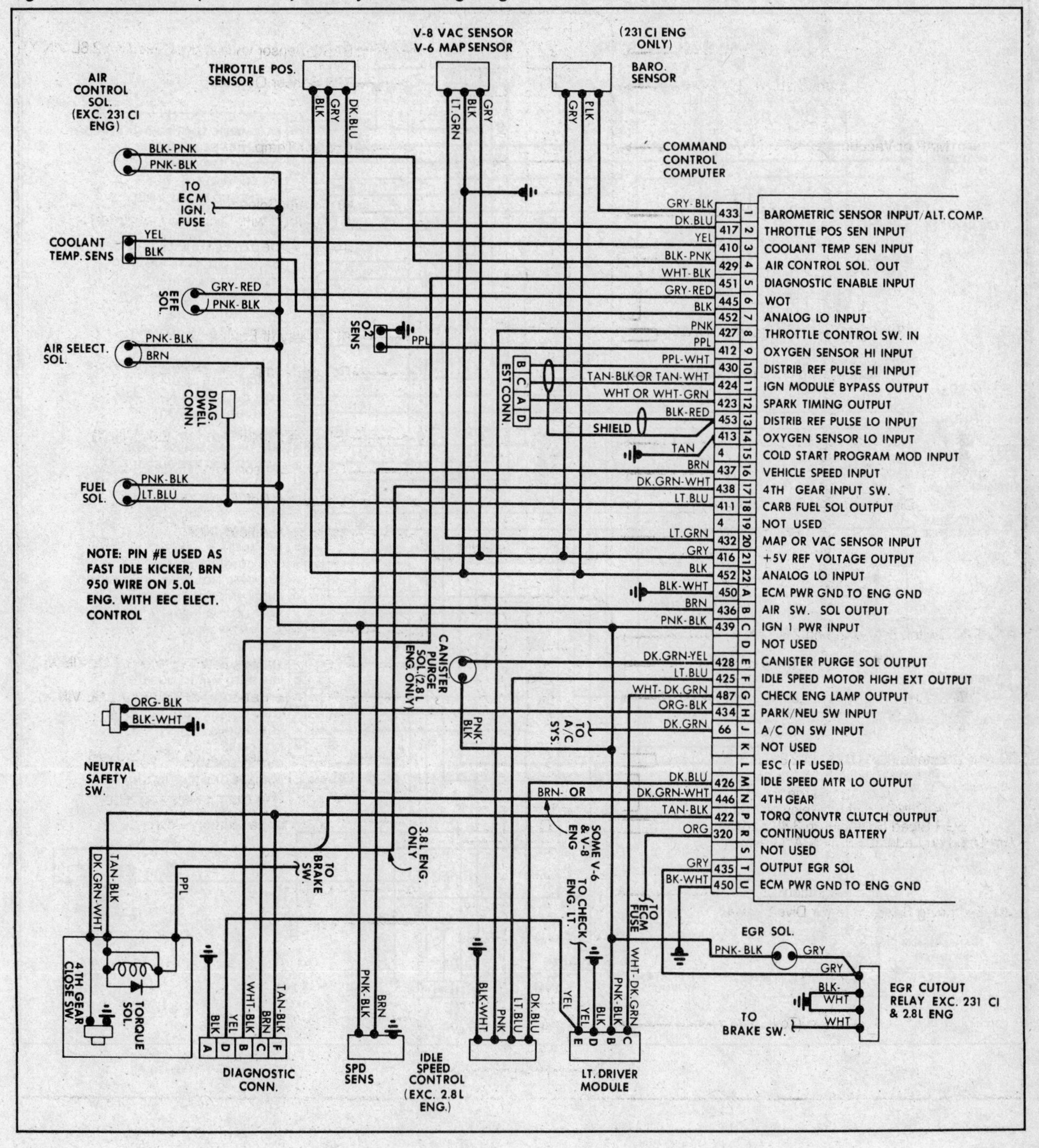

Fig. 10: Full Function (Exc. Turbo) CCC System Wiring Diagram

GENERAL MOTORS COMPUTER COMMAND CONTROL (Cont.)

Fig. 11: Full Function (Turbo) CCC System Wiring Diagram

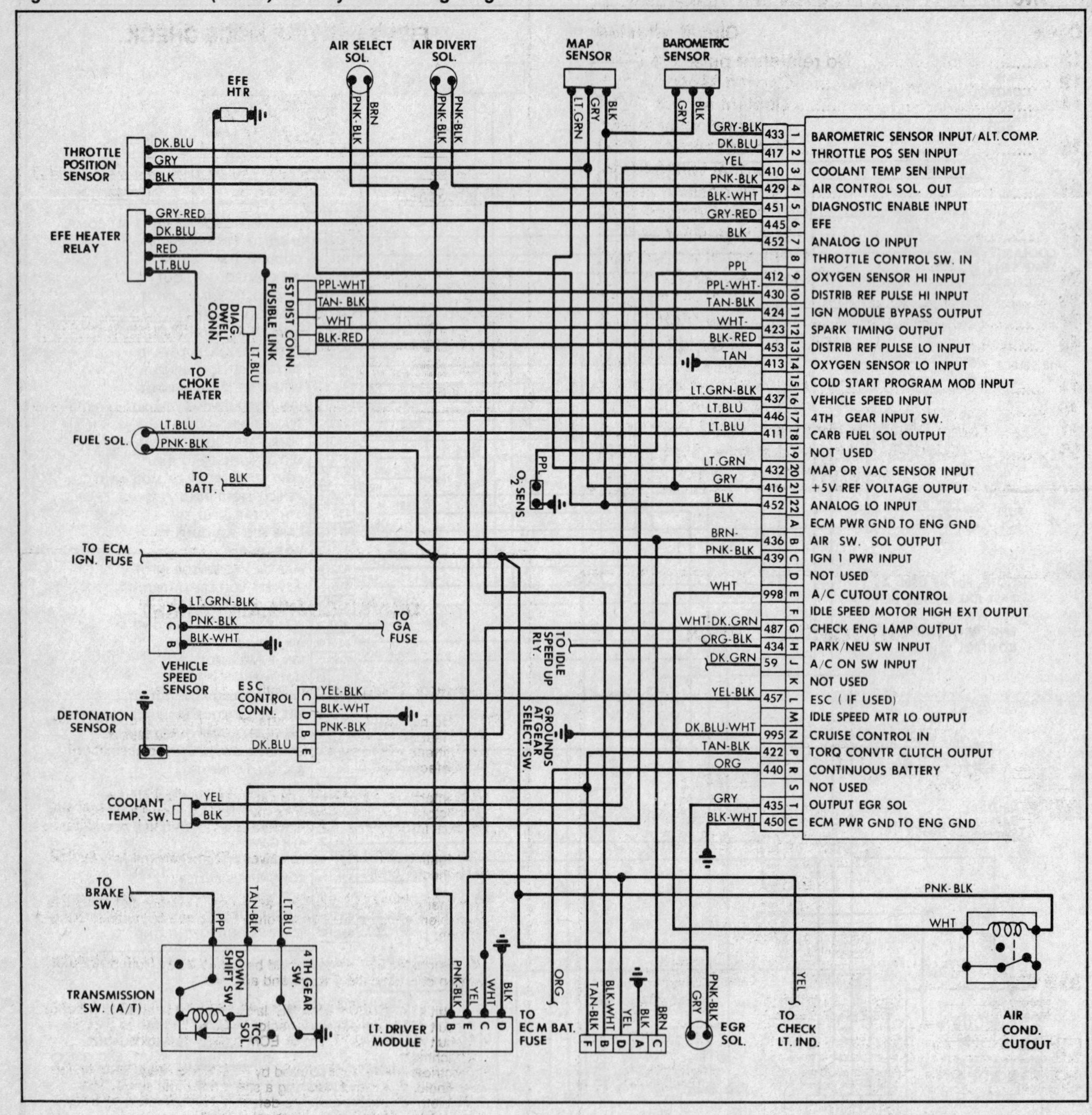

GENERAL MOTORS COMPUTER COMMAND CONTROL (Cont.)

EFI FUNCTION ECM TROUBLE CODE IDENTIFICATION

Code	Circuit Affected
12	No reference pulses to ECM.
13	Oxygen sensor circuit.
14	Coolant sensor circuit signal voltage low.
15	Coolant sensor circuit signal voltage high.
21	Throttle position sensor circuit signal voltage high.
22	Throttle position sensor circuit signal voltage low.
24	Vehicle speed sensor circuit.
33	High MAP signal.
34	Low MAP signal.
42	EST or EST by-pass circuit grounded or open.
44	Lean exhaust indication.
45	Rich exhaust indication.
51	Faulty PROM or improper PROM installation.
55	Grounded voltage reference, high voltage on oxygen sensor circuit or ECM.

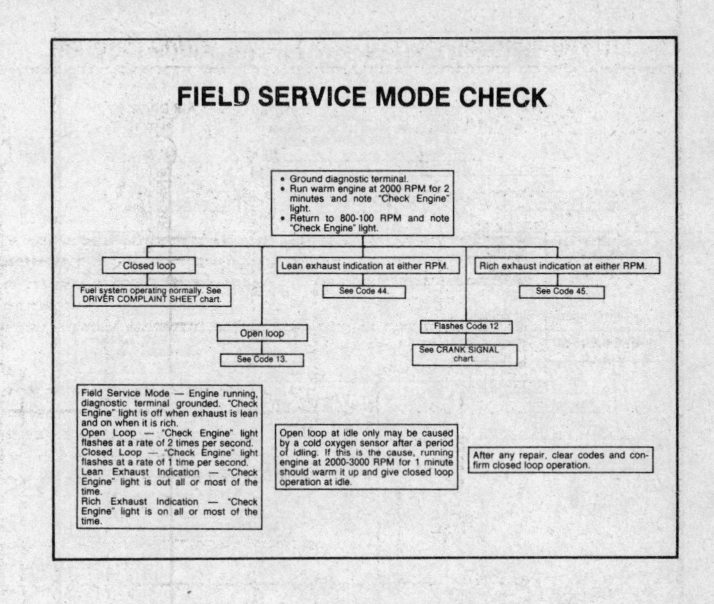

DIAGNOSTIC CIRCUIT CHECK

In case of repeat ECM failures, check resistance of solenoids and relays controlled by ECM.

- Ignition on. Engine stopped.
- Note "Check Engine" light.

No light → See NO "CHECK ENGINE" LIGHT chart.

Steady light → • Ground diagnostic terminal.

- **Does not flash code 12** → See WON'T FLASH CODE 12 chart.
- **Flashes code 12** → • Note and record any additional codes. See box with lowest code.
  - **Additional codes 13, 15, 24, 44, 45, 51 or 55.** → See code 51 or 55 first. Otherwise, start with lowest code.
  - **Additional codes 14, 21, 22, 33, 34, 42 or 43.** →
    - Engine at normal operating temperature. If engine cranks, but will not run, see Chart 4.
    - Ignition off, clear codes.
    - Diagnostic terminal not grounded.
    - Set parking brake and block drive wheels.
    - Place auto. trans. in "D", man. trans. in neutral.
    - Idle engine for one minute and note "Check Engine" light.
    - **On** → Stop engine → Additional codes recorded from above should be considered as intermittent.
    - **Off** → • Stop engine • Ground diagnostic terminal • Ignition on • Note codes → See applicable chart. If more than one code is stored, start with lowest code.
  - **No additional codes** → See FIELD SERVICE MODE CHECK chart.
- **Flashes code 51 or 55** → See code 51 or 55

Flashing light

- **Flashing code 12** → Check diagnostic circuit 451 for short to ground between ALCL connector and ECM. → Circuit 451 OK → Faulty ECM → In case of repeat ECM failures, check resistance of solenoids and relays controlled by ECM.
- **Erratic or intermittent at times.** → See DRIVER COMPLAINT SHEET chart.

ALCL CONNECTOR — Diagnostic Terminal (B), Ground (A); terminals F, E, D, C, B, A, G.

Fuel pump test terminal for F and J models. A and X models have terminal at engine compartment, left side.

DRIVER COMPLAINT SHEET

- Intermittent "CHECK ENGINE" light or stored codes.

NOTE: Do not use diagnostic charts for intermittent problems. The fault must be present to locate the problem. If the fault is intermittent, use of the charts may result in the replacement of non-defective parts.

Most intermittent problems are caused by faulty electrical connectors or wiring. Diagnosis must include a careful visual and physical inspection of the indicated circuit wiring and connectors.

Poor mating of the connector halves or terminals not fully seated in connector body.

Improperly formed or damaged terminals. All connector terminals in problem circuit should be carefully re-formed to increase contact tension.

HEI distributor EST wires should be routed away from distributor, ignition coil, secondary wires and alternator.

- Circuit 419 ("CHECK ENGINE" lamp to ECM) shorted to ground.
- Circuit 451 (diagnostic connector to ECM) shorted to ground.
- Circuit 450 and 450R, check ECM ground at engine block attachment.
- Electrical interference caused by a defective relay, ECM driven solenoid, or a switch causing a sharp electrical surge. The problem will occur when the defective component is operated.
- Improper installation of electrical options.
- Open A/C clutch diode.

- Stalling, rough or improper idle speed; see IDLE AIR CONTROL chart.
- Engine cranks but will not run; see ENGINE CRANKS BUT WILL NOT RUN chart.
- Hard starting, poor performance, driveability, or fuel econonmy; see POOR PERFORMANCE, NO STORED CODES chart.
- Detonation (spark knock)
  See ESC PERFORMANCE chart, if applicable.
  See EGR DIAGNOSIS chart.
- Poor engine performance with A/C on, problem in A/C, not CCC.

Following any repairs or adjustments, always clear codes and confirm closed loop operation and no "CHECK ENGINE" light.

GENERAL MOTORS COMPUTER COMMAND CONTROL (Cont.)

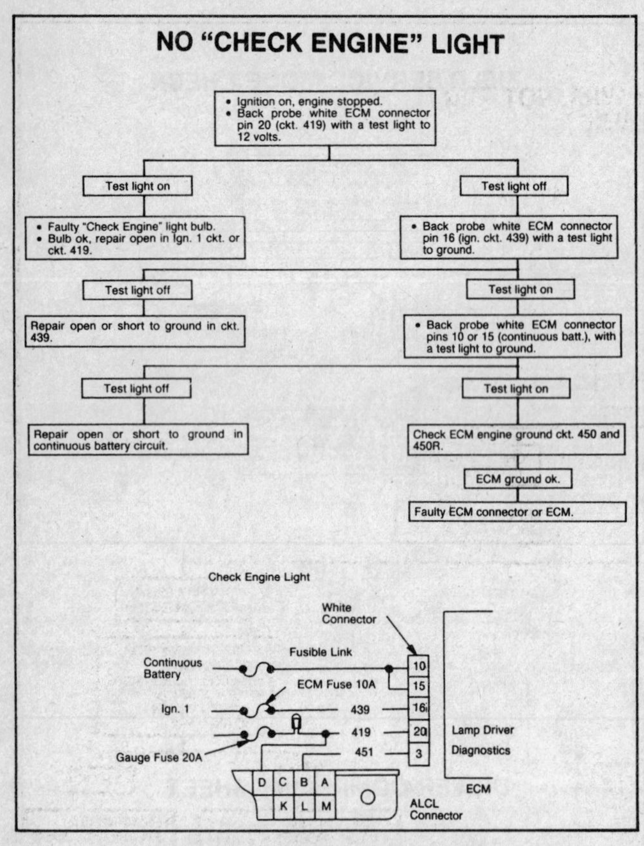

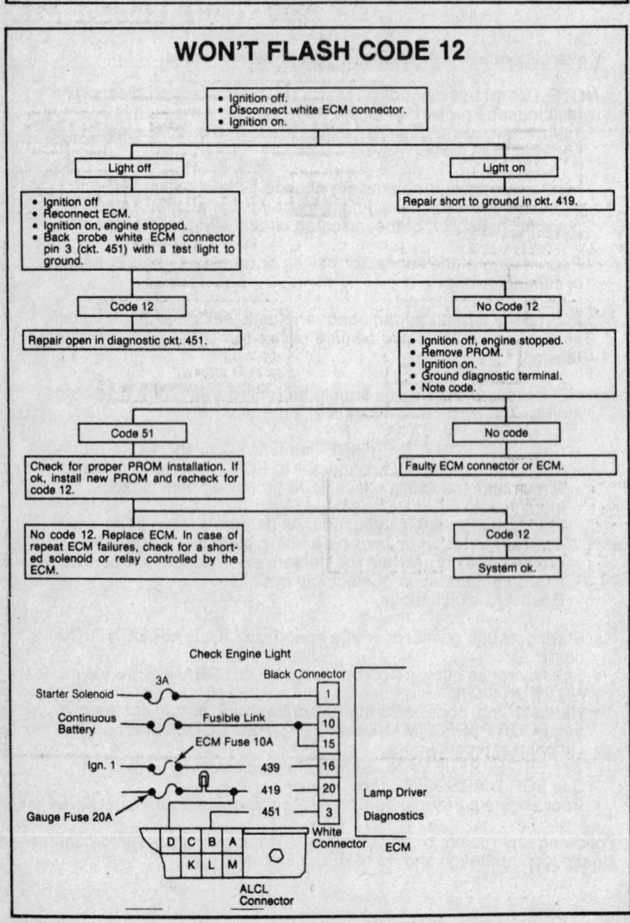

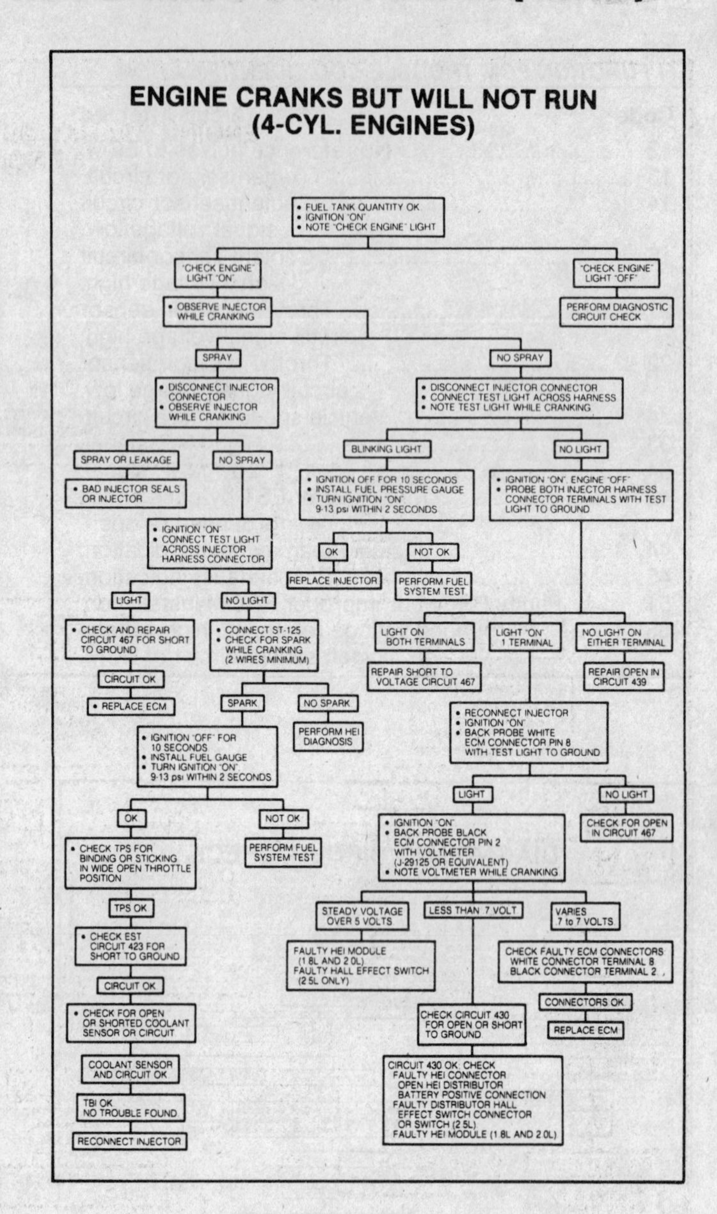

GENERAL MOTORS COMPUTER COMMAND CONTROL (Cont.)

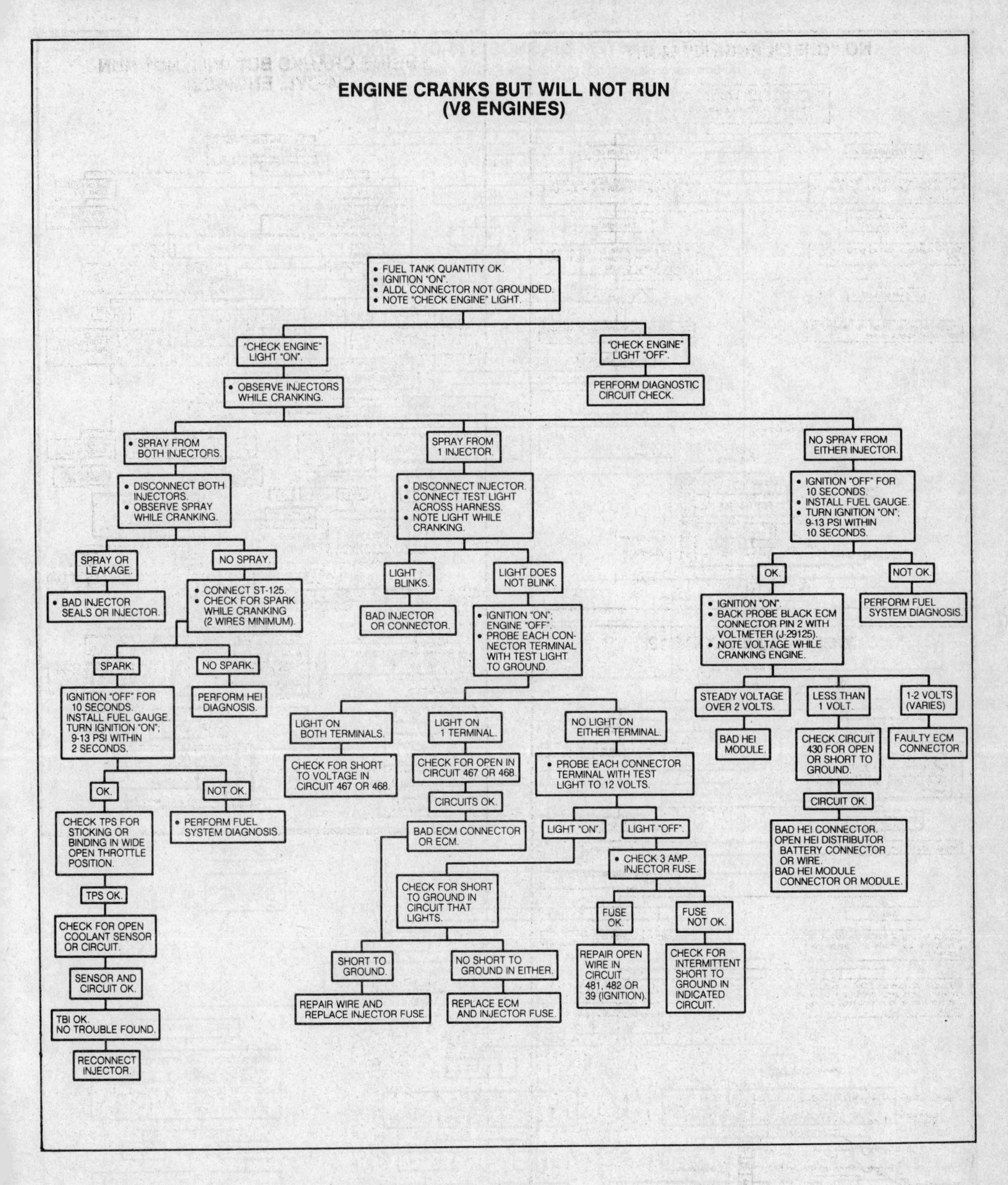

GENERAL MOTORS COMPUTER COMMAND CONTROL (Cont.)

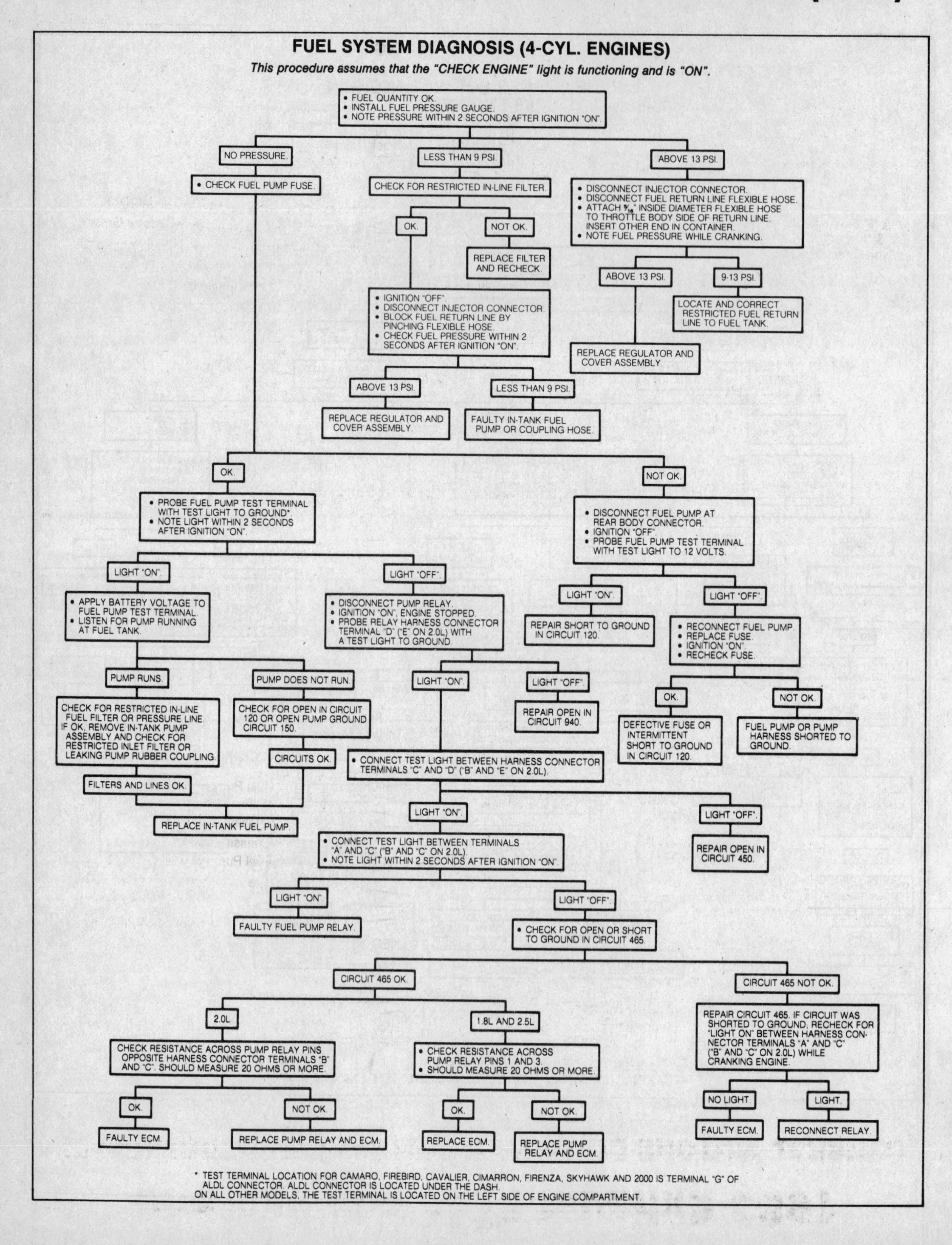

GENERAL MOTORS COMPUTER COMMAND CONTROL (Cont.)

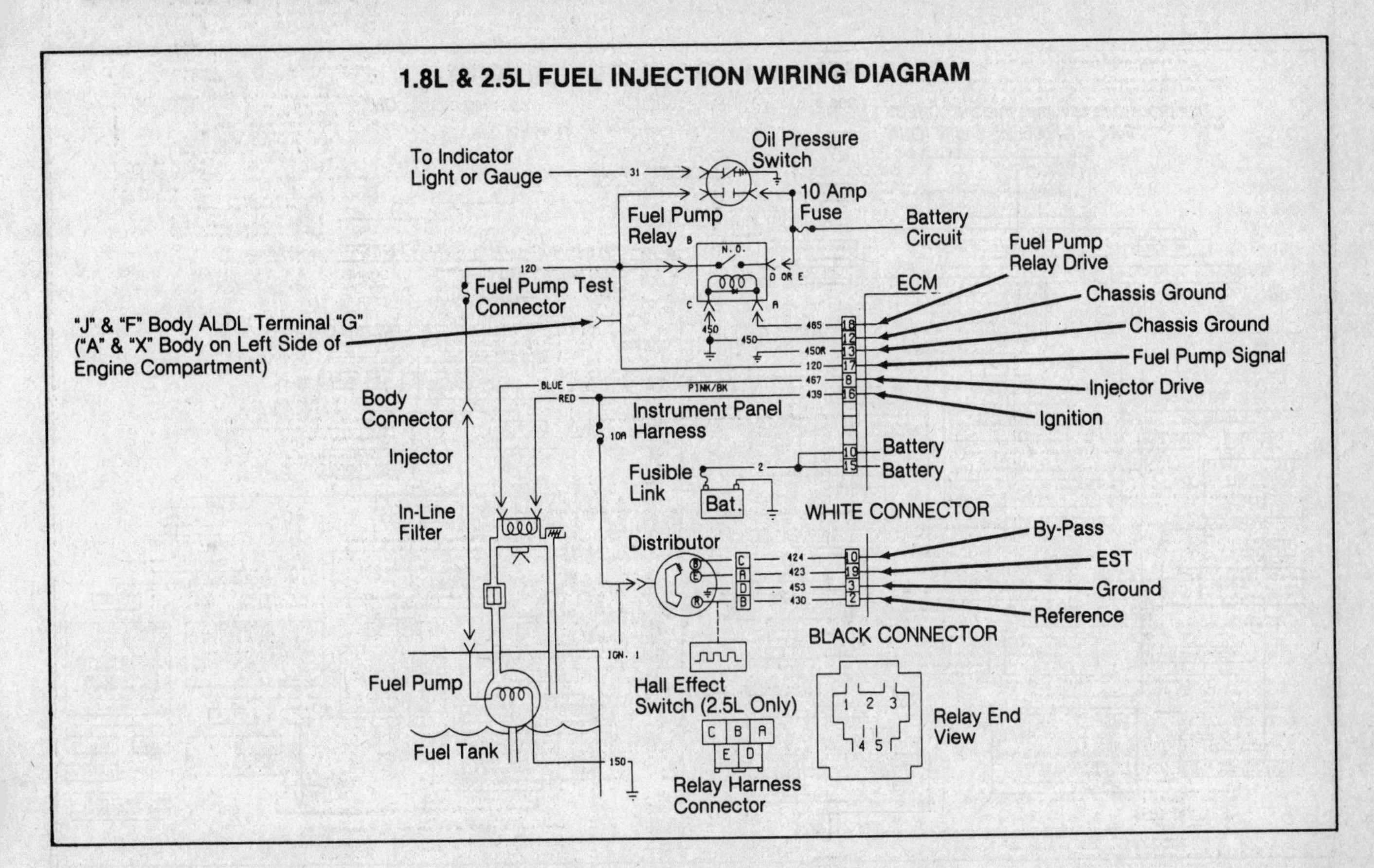

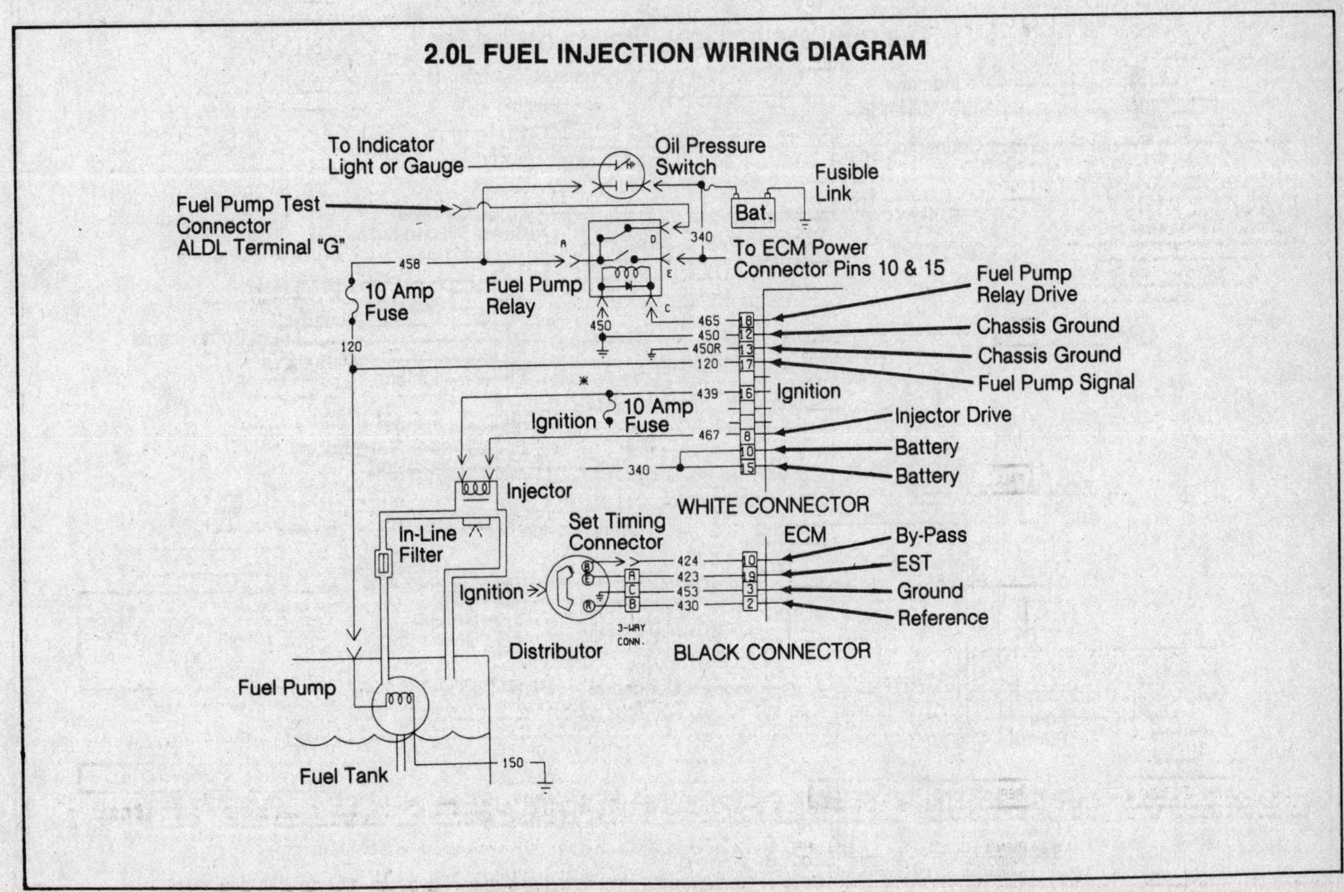

GENERAL MOTORS COMPUTER COMMAND CONTROL (Cont.)

FUEL SYSTEM DIAGNOSIS (V8 ENGINES)

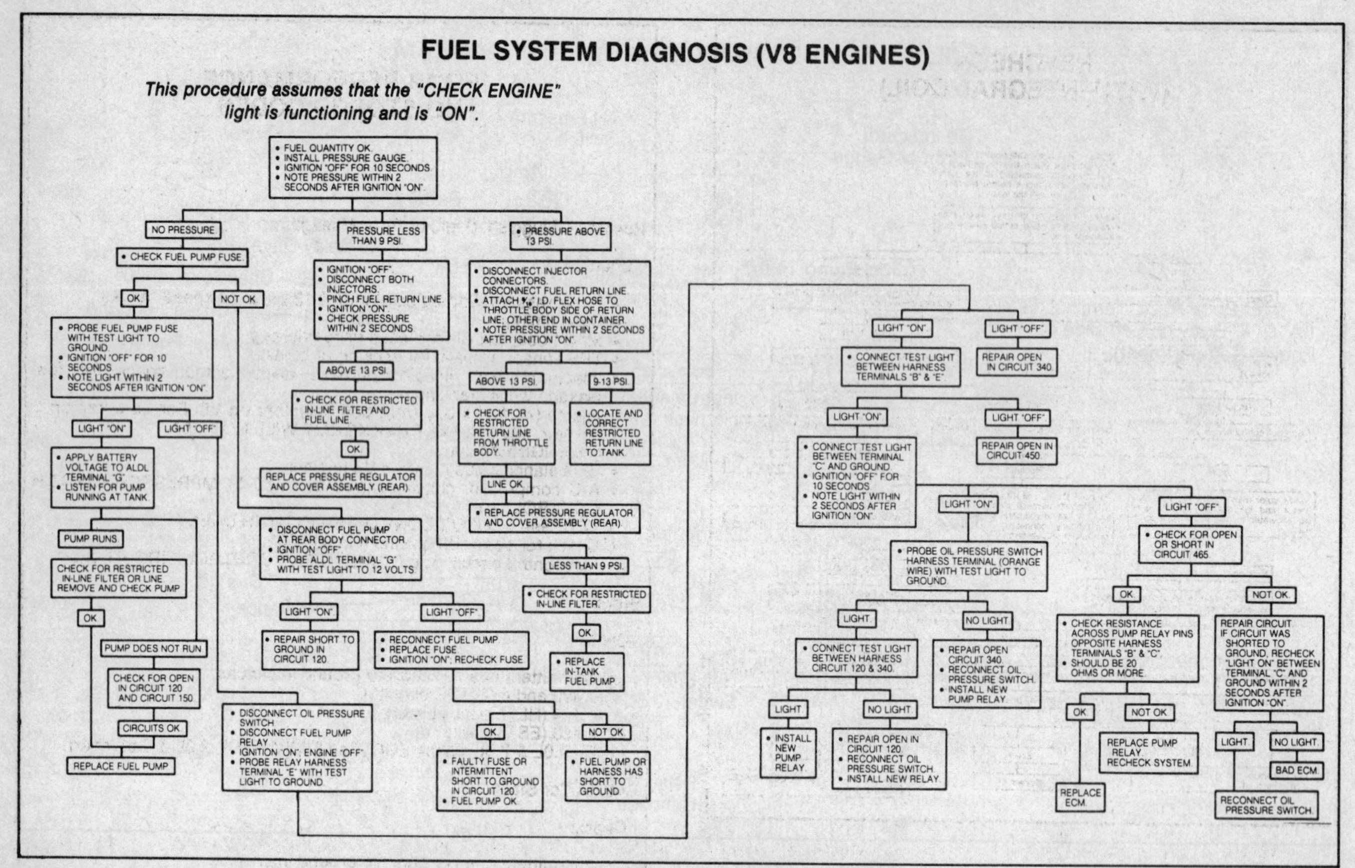

V8 FUEL INJECTION WIRING DIAGRAM

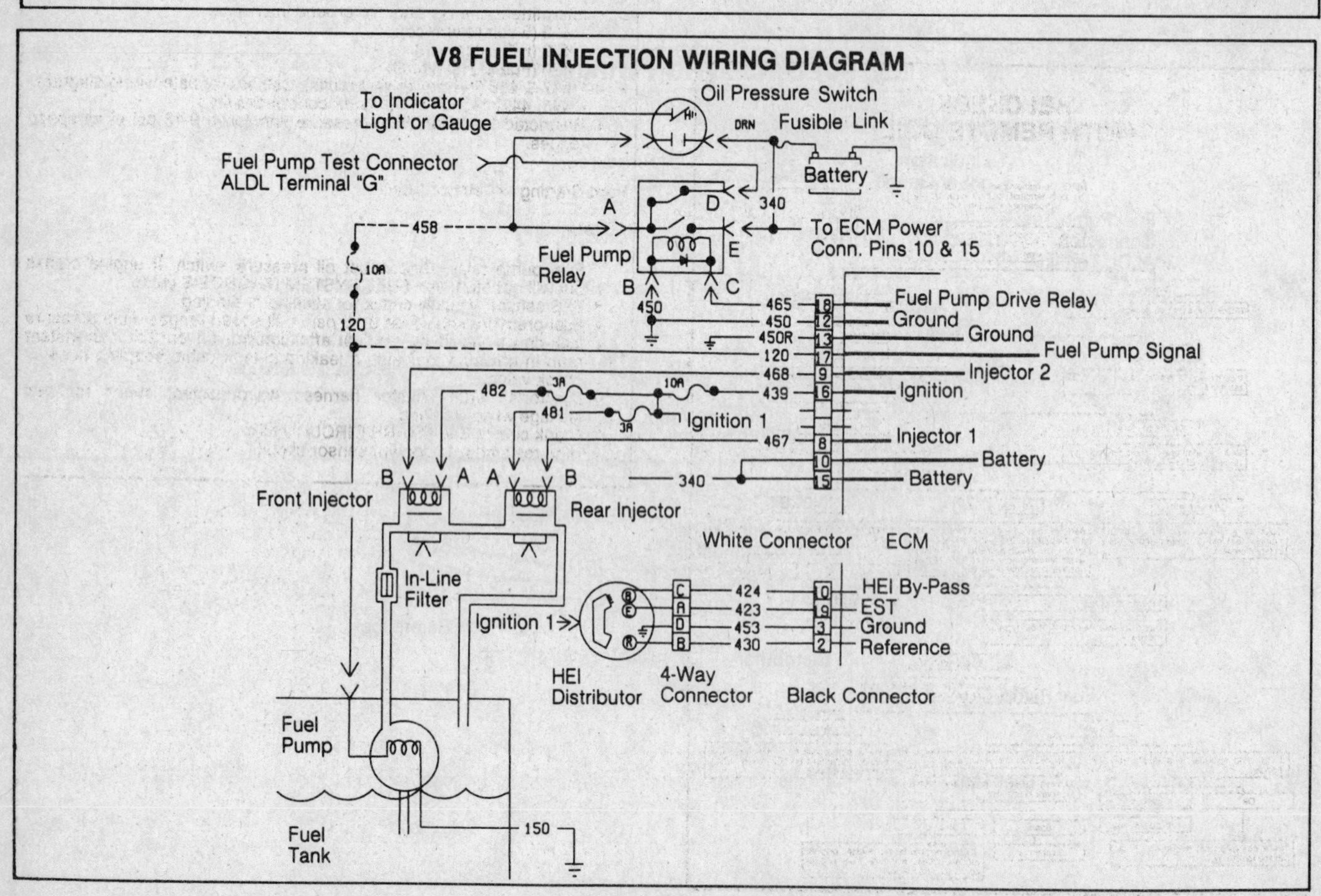

GENERAL MOTORS COMPUTER COMMAND CONTROL (Cont.)

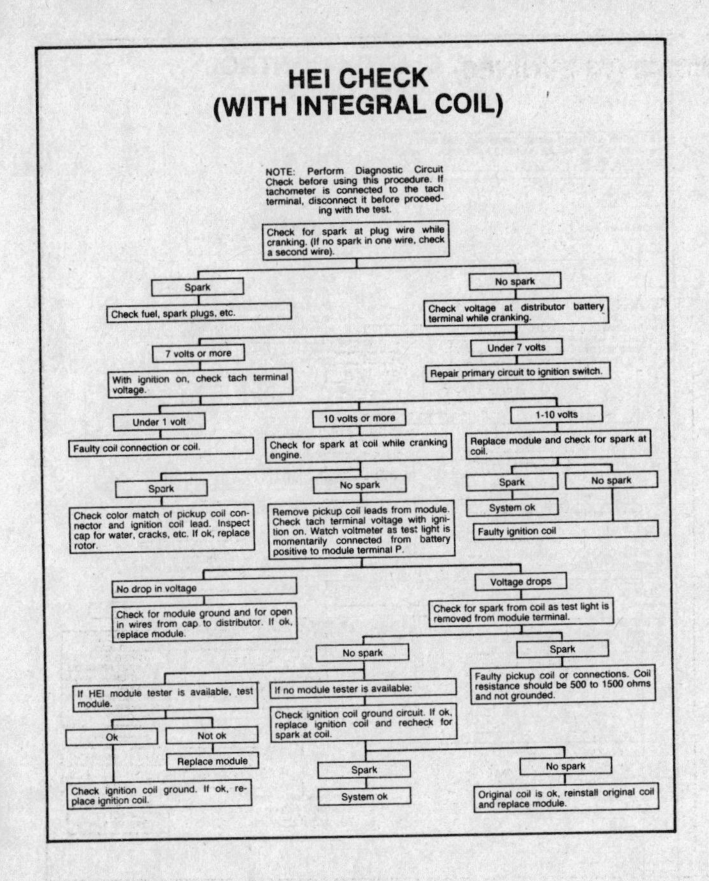

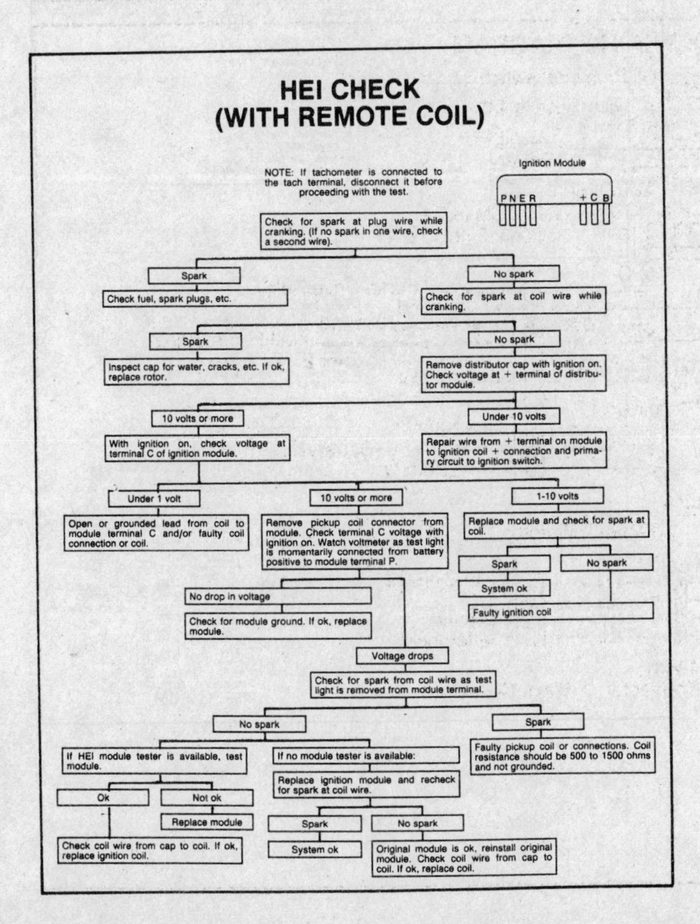

POOR PERFORMANCE
NO STORED CODES

Hesitates, Sluggish, Sags, or Poor Mileage

Check:

- Fuel pressure. Should be steady 9-13 psi at all speed ranges.
- Base timing.
- MAP hose; visually for leaks or restrictions.
- TPS sensor; visually for sticking or binding.
- Injector(s); with injector harness disconnected, check for fuel leakage while cranking.
- Injector(s); fuel srpay from both injectors on V8. For no spray on 1 injector, see ENGINE CRANKS BUT WILL NOT RUN (V8 ENGINES) chart.
- EFI balance adjustment on V8 engines.
- A/C compressor clutch control. See A/C COMPRESSOR CLUTCH CONTROL chart.
- TCC. See TORQUE CONVERTER CLUTCH chart.
- Check for open HEI ground (circuit 4530.
- Fan control circuit. See COOLING FAN CONTROL CIRCUIT chart.

Surge

Check:

- Intermittent open or short to ground in circuits:
  - 420 and 422 (TCC circuits).
  - 424 (HEI by-pass circuit).
  - 423 (EST circuit).
- On 2.0L & 2.5L, check EGR. See EGR CHECK 2.0L & 2.5L chart.

Cuts Out or Stalls

Check:

- Intermittent open or short to ground in circuits:
  - 416 (5 volt reference).
  - 430 (HEI reference).
  - 120 (Fuel pump circuit).
  - 467 & 468 (Injector drive circuits). See appropriate wiring diagram.
  - 441, 442, 443, or 444 (Idle air control circuits.)
- Restricted fuel filter. Fuel pressure should be 9-13 psi at all speed ranges.

Hard Starting — Hot or Cold

Check:

- Fuel pump relay. Disconnect oil pressure switch. If engine cranks but will not start, see FUEL SYSTEM DIAGNOSIS chart.
- TPS sensor. Visually check for sticking or binding.
- Fuel pressure should be 9-13 psi at all speed ranges. Fuel pressure leak-down should be gradual after ignition off on 2.5L. An instant drop in pressure indicates a leaking in-tank pump coupling hose or check valve.
- Injector(s). With injector harness disconnected, check for fuel leakage while cranking.
- Crank circuit. See CRANK CIRCUIT chart.
- High resistance in coolant sensor circuit.

GENERAL MOTORS COMPUTER COMMAND CONTROL (Cont.)

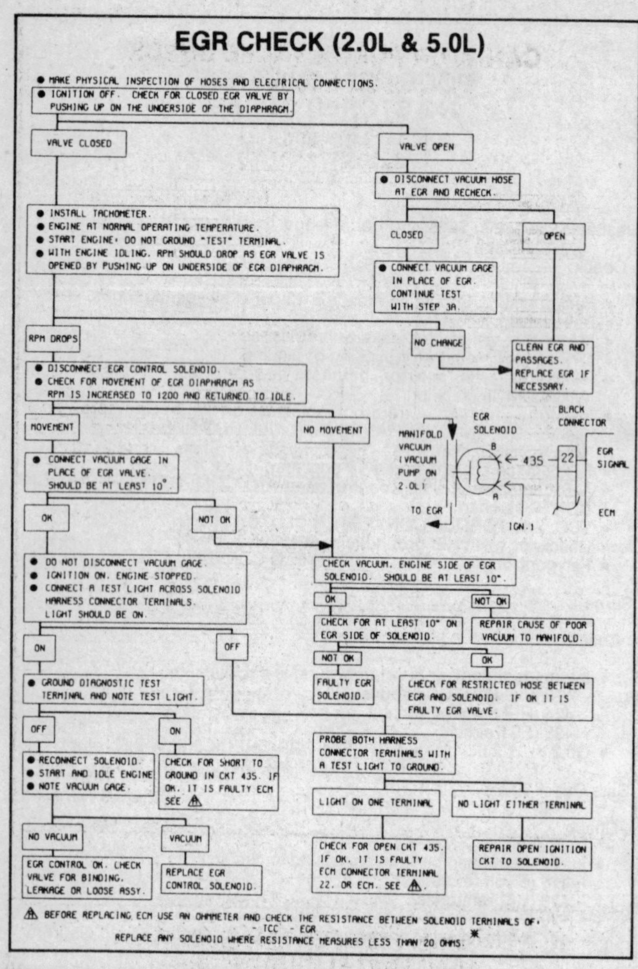

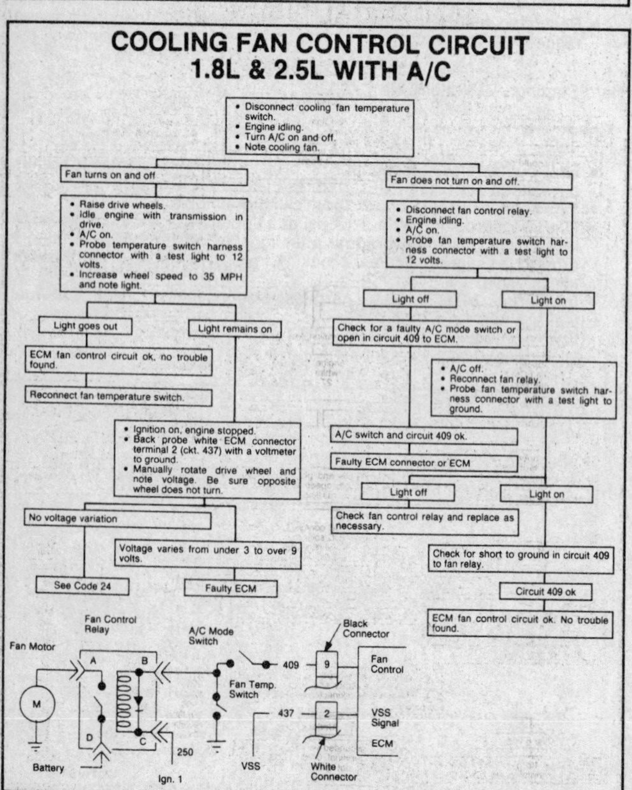

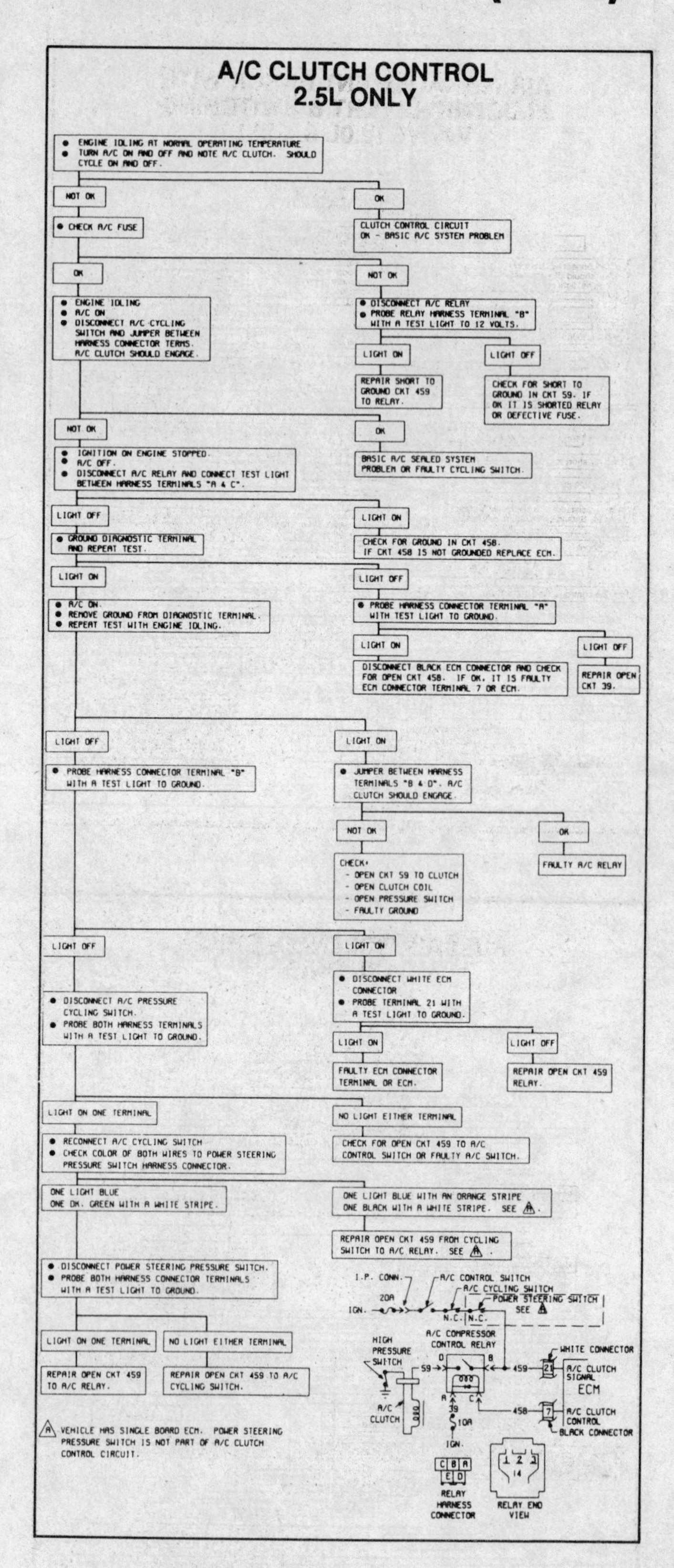

GENERAL MOTORS COMPUTER COMMAND CONTROL (Cont.)

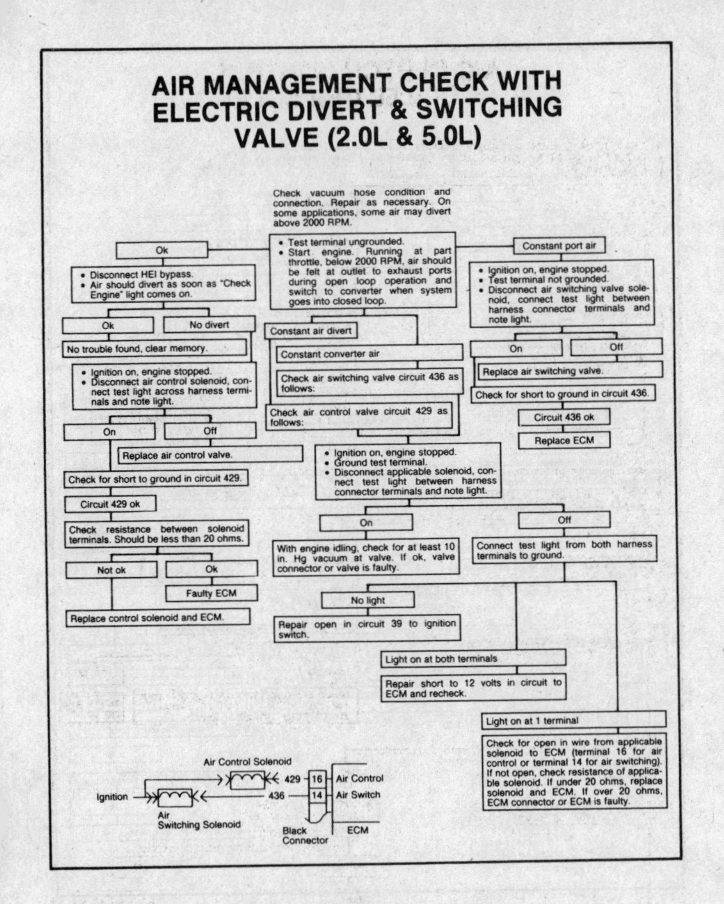

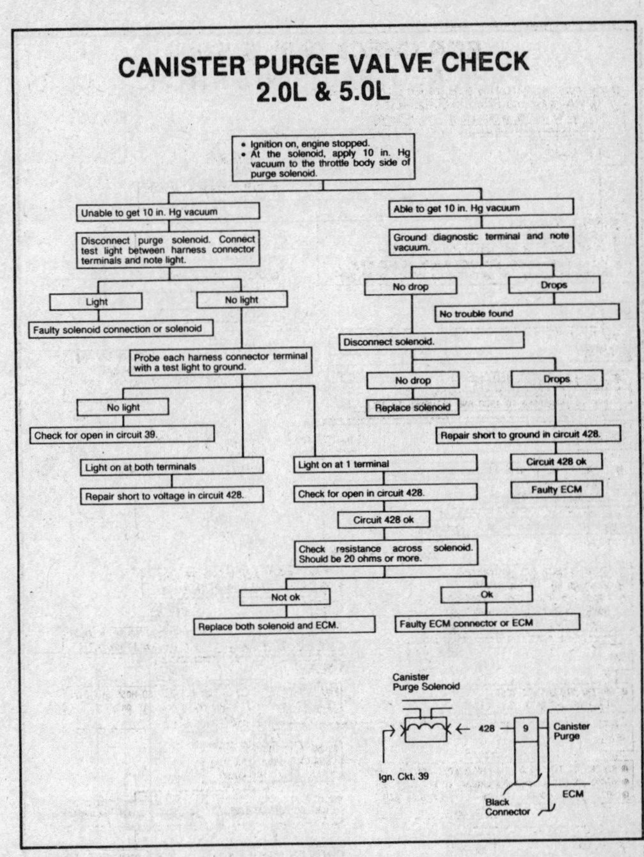

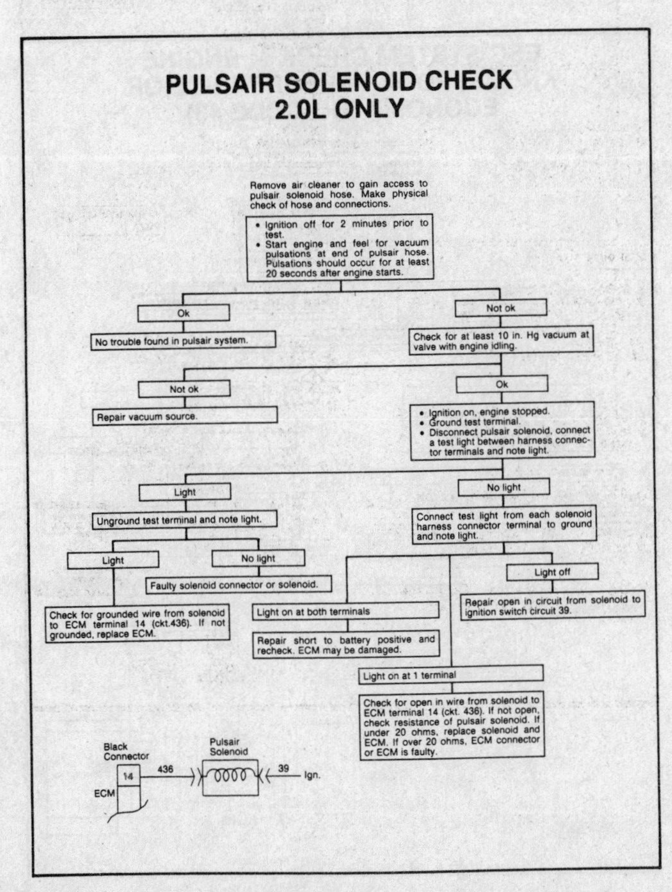

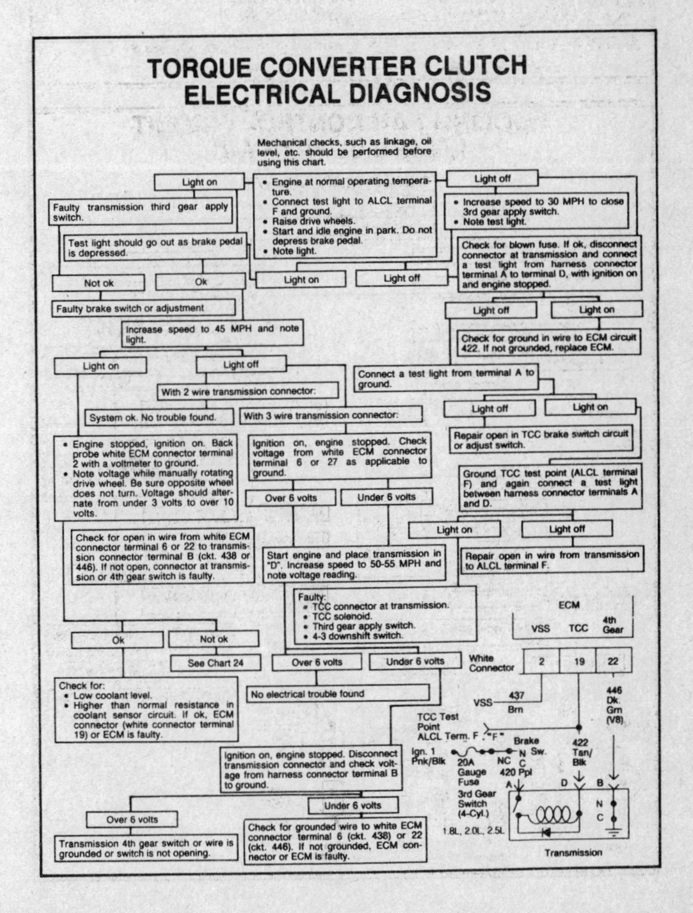

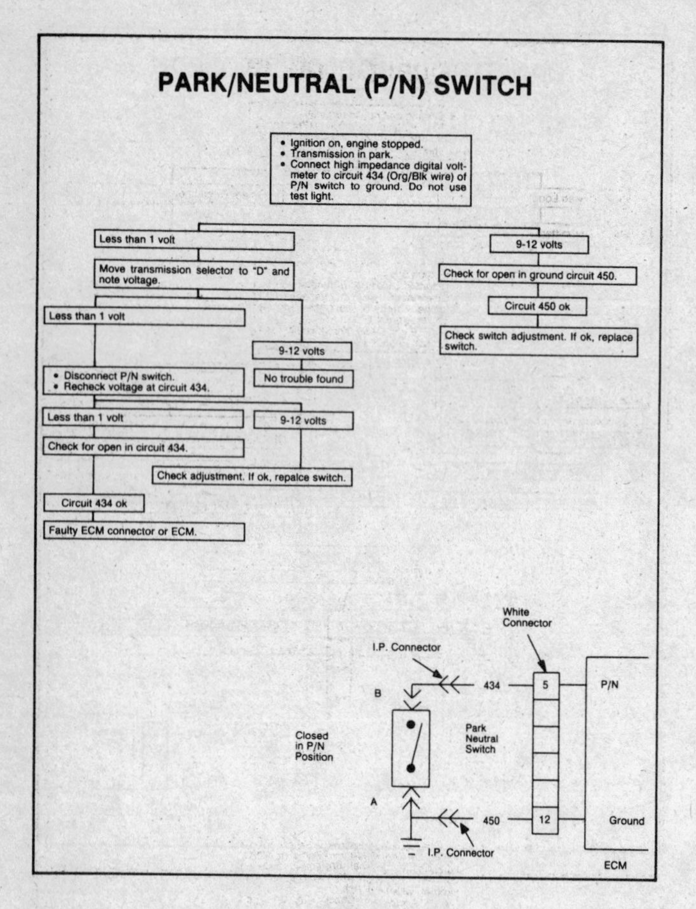
PARK/NEUTRAL (P/N) SWITCH
• Ignition on, engine stopped.
• Transmission in park.
• Connect high impedance digital voltmeter to circuit 434 (Org/Blk wire) of P/N switch to ground. Do not use test light.
Less than 1 volt
9-12 volts
Move transmission selector to "D" and note voltage.
Check for open in ground circuit 450.
Circuit 450 ok
Less than 1 volt
Check switch adjustment. If ok, replace switch.
9-12 volts
• Disconnect P/N switch.
• Recheck voltage at circuit 434.
No trouble found
Less than 1 volt
9-12 volts
Check for open in circuit 434.
Check adjustment. If ok, repalce switch.
Circuit 434 ok
Faulty ECM connector or ECM.
White Connector
I.P. Connector
434
5
P/N
B
Closed in P/N Position
Park Neutral Switch
A
450
12
Ground
I.P. Connector
ECM

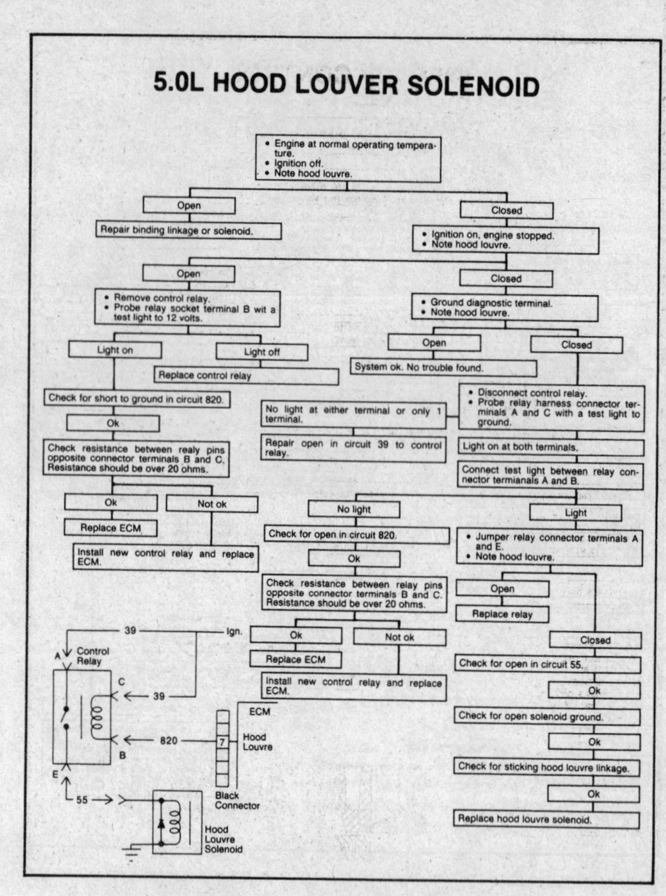
5.0L HOOD LOUVER SOLENOID
• Engine at normal operating temperature.
• Ignition off.
• Note hood louvre.
Open
Closed
Repair binding linkage or solenoid.
• Ignition on, engine stopped.
• Note hood louvre.
Open
Closed
• Remove control relay.
• Probe relay socket terminal B wit a test light to 12 volts.
• Ground diagnostic terminal.
• Note hood louvre.
Light on
Light off
Open
Closed
Replace control relay
System ok. No trouble found.
Check for short to ground in circuit 820.
No light at either terminal or only 1 terminal.
• Disconnect control relay.
• Probe relay harness connector terminals A and C with a test light to ground.
Ok
Repair open in circuit 39 to control relay.
Light on at both terminals.
Check resistance between realy pins opposite connector terminals B and C. Resistance should be over 20 ohms.
Connect test light between relay connector termianals A and B.
Ok
Not ok
No light
Light
Replace ECM
Check for open in circuit 820.
• Jumper relay connector terminals A and E.
• Note hood louvre.
Install new control relay and replace ECM.
Ok
Check resistance between relay pins opposite connector terminals B and C. Resistance should be over 20 ohms.
Open
Replace relay
39
Ign.
Ok
Not ok
Closed
Control Relay
Replace ECM
Check for open in circuit 55.
Install new control relay and replace ECM.
Ok
C
39
ECM
Check for open solenoid ground.
820
7
Hood Louvre
Ok
B
E
Check for sticking hood louvre linkage.
Black Connector
Ok
55
Replace hood louvre solenoid.
Hood Louvre Solenoid

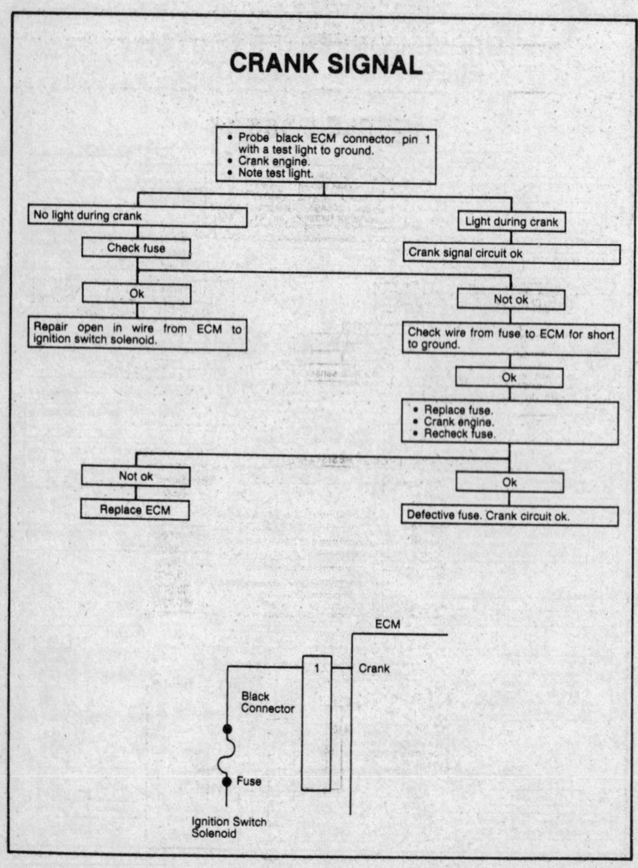
CRANK SIGNAL
• Probe black ECM connector pin 1 with a test light to ground.
• Crank engine.
• Note test light.
No light during crank
Light during crank
Check fuse
Crank signal circuit ok
Ok
Not ok
Repair open in wire from ECM to ignition switch solenoid.
Check wire from fuse to ECM for short to ground.
Ok
• Replace fuse.
• Crank engine.
• Recheck fuse.
Not ok
Ok
Replace ECM
Defective fuse. Crank circuit ok.
ECM
1
Crank
Black Connector
Fuse
Ignition Switch Solenoid

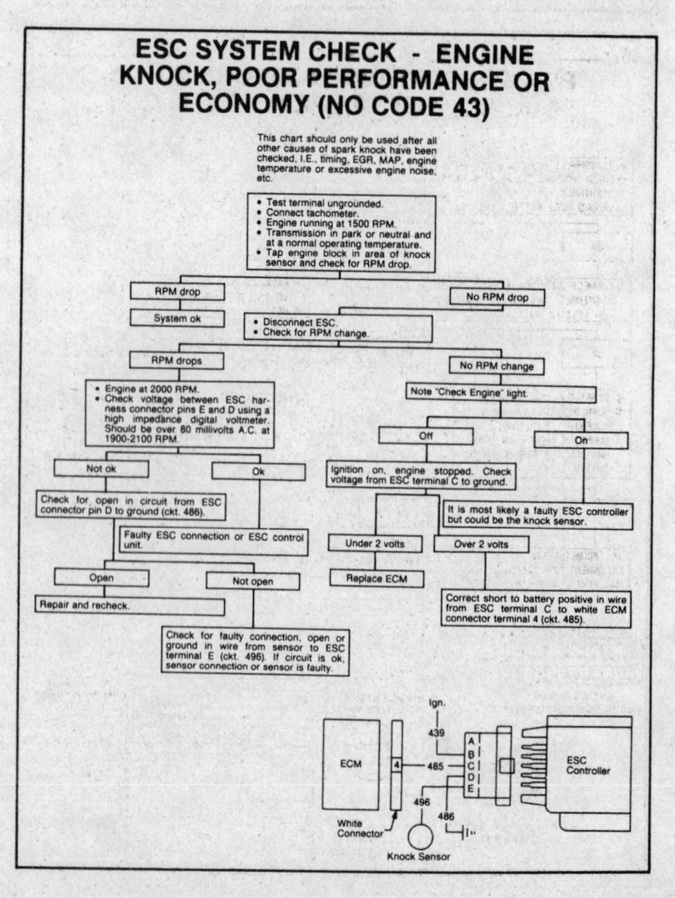
ESC SYSTEM CHECK - ENGINE KNOCK, POOR PERFORMANCE OR ECONOMY (NO CODE 43)
This chart should only be used after all other causes of spark knock have been checked, I.E., timing, EGR, MAP, engine temperature or excessive engine noise, etc.
• Test terminal ungrounded.
• Connect tachometer.
• Engine running at 1500 RPM.
• Transmission in park or neutral and at a normal operating temperature.
• Tap engine block in area of knock sensor and check for RPM drop.
RPM drop
No RPM drop
System ok
• Disconnect ESC.
• Check for RPM change.
RPM drops
No RPM change
Note "Check Engine" light.
• Engine at 2000 RPM.
• Check voltage between ESC harness connector pins E and D using a high impedance digital voltmeter. Should be over 80 millivolts A.C. at 1900-2100 RPM.
Off
On
Not ok
Ok
Ignition on, engine stopped. Check voltage from ESC terminal C to ground.
Check for open in circuit from ESC connector pin D to ground (ckt. 486).
It is most likely a faulty ESC controller but could be the knock sensor.
Faulty ESC connection or ESC control unit.
Under 2 volts
Over 2 volts
Open
Not open
Replace ECM
Repair and recheck.
Correct short to battery positive in wire from ESC terminal C to white ECM connector terminal 4 (ckt. 485).
Check for faulty connection, open or ground in wire from sensor to ESC terminal E (ckt. 496). If circuit is ok, sensor connection or sensor is faulty.
Ign.
439
ECM
4
485
A
B
C
D
E
ESC Controller
496
486
White Connector
Knock Sensor

GENERAL MOTORS COMPUTER COMMAND CONTROL (Cont.)

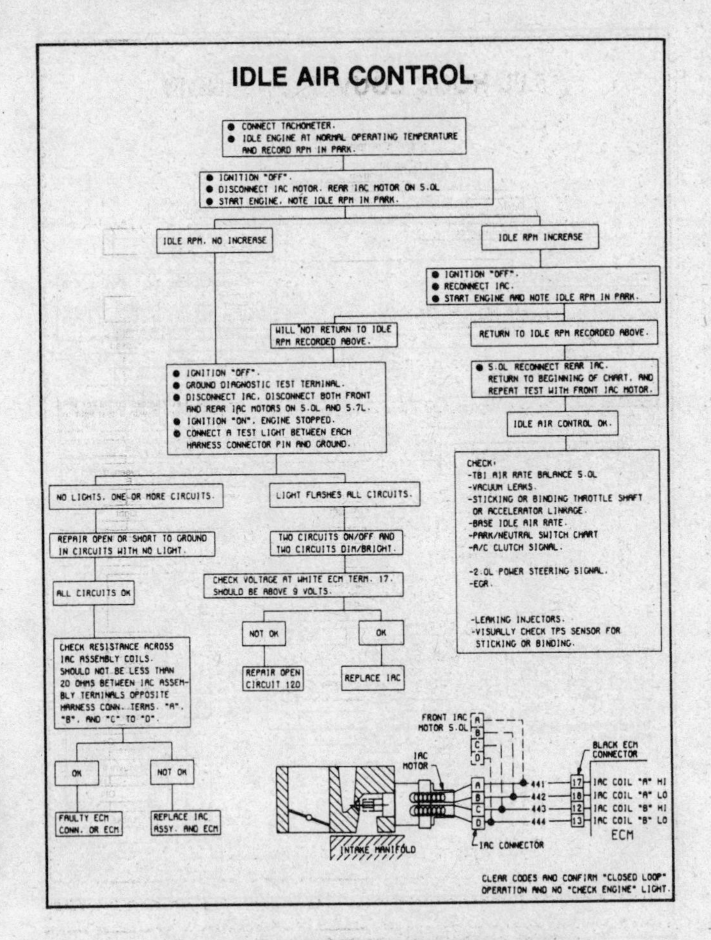

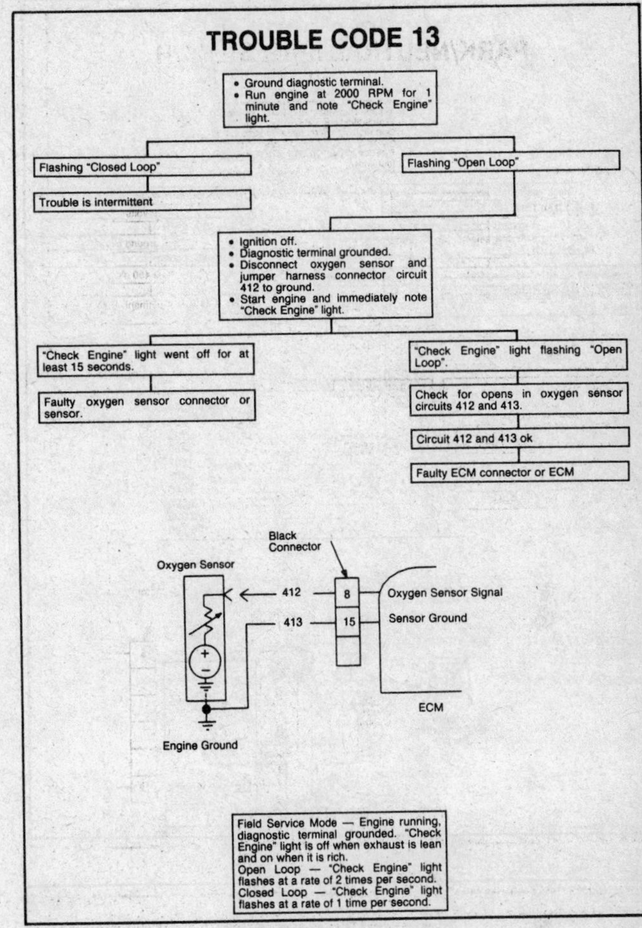

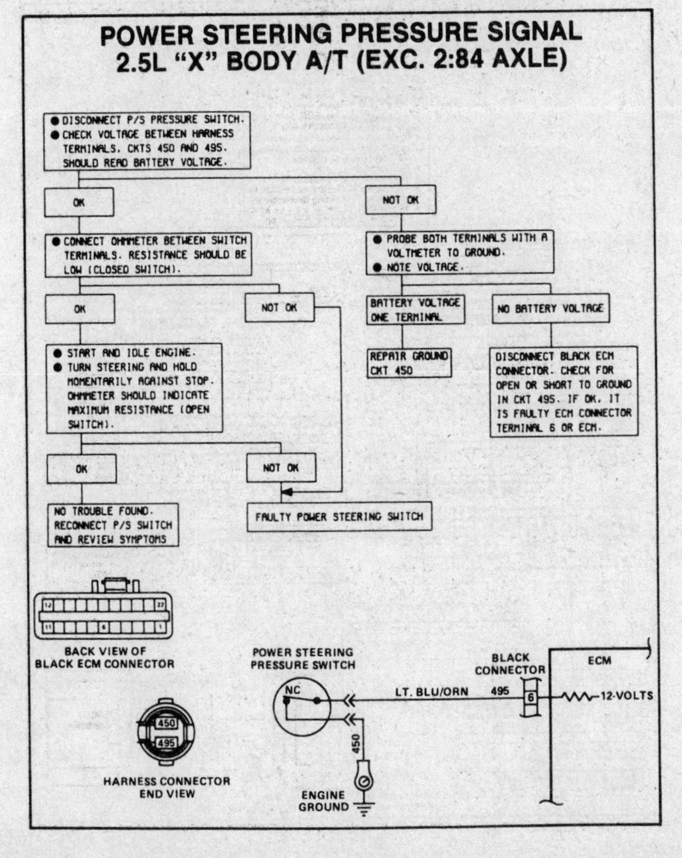

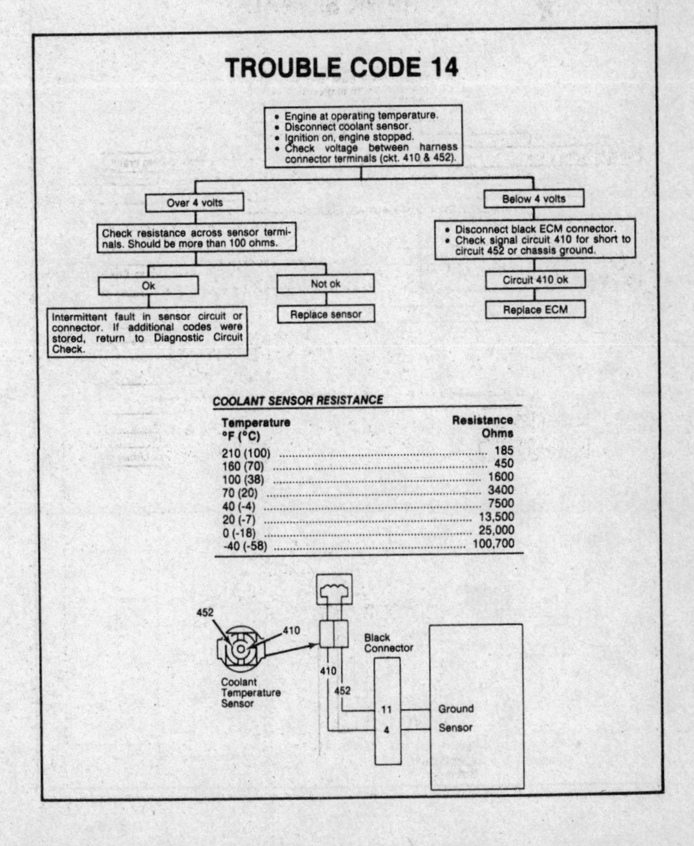

COOLANT SENSOR RESISTANCE

Temperature °F (°C)	Resistance Ohms
210 (100)	185
160 (70)	450
100 (38)	1600
70 (20)	3400
40 (-4)	7500
20 (-7)	13,500
0 (-18)	25,000
-40 (-58)	100,700

GENERAL MOTORS COMPUTER COMMAND CONTROL (Cont.)

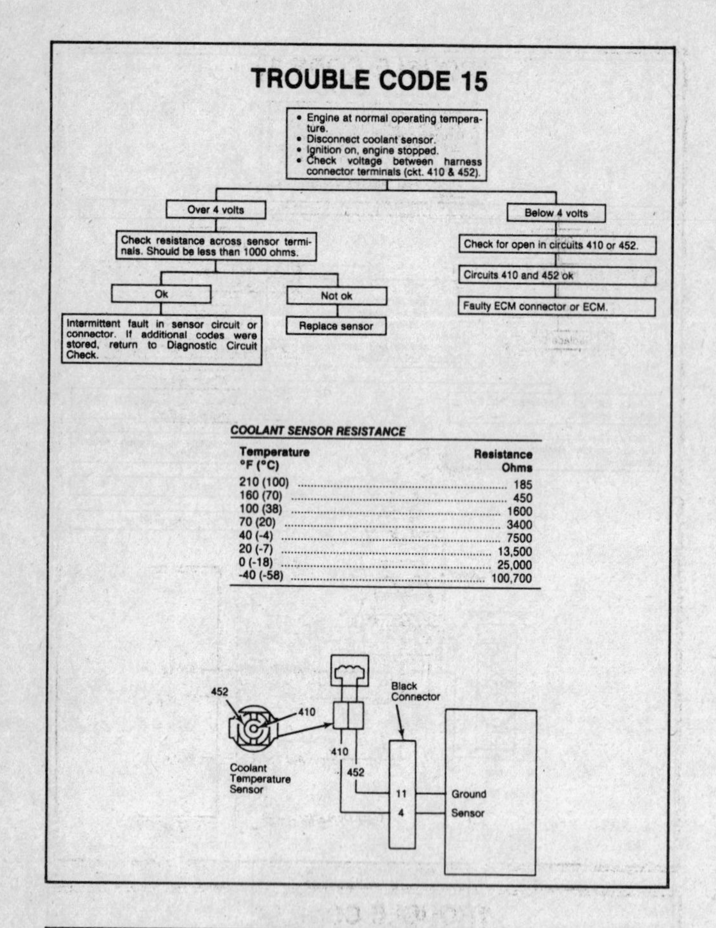

COOLANT SENSOR RESISTANCE

Temperature °F (°C)	Resistance Ohms
210 (100)	185
160 (70)	450
100 (38)	1600
70 (20)	3400
40 (-4)	7500
20 (-7)	13,500
0 (-18)	25,000
-40 (-58)	100,700

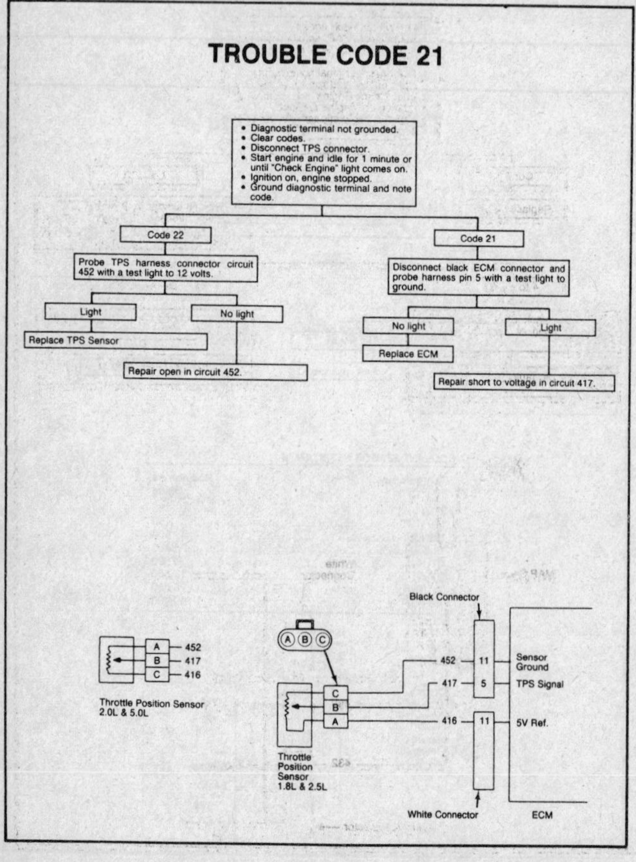

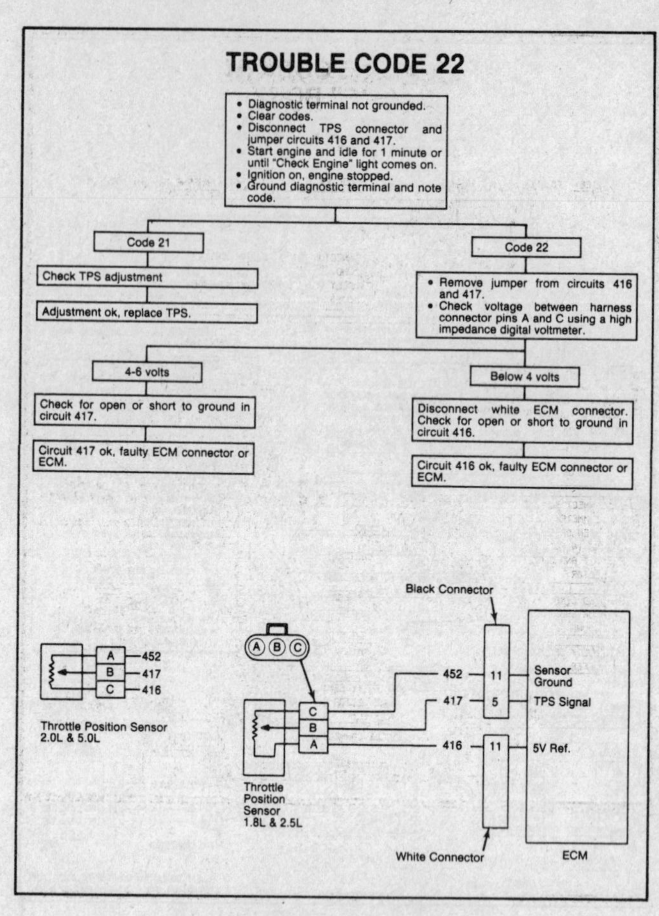

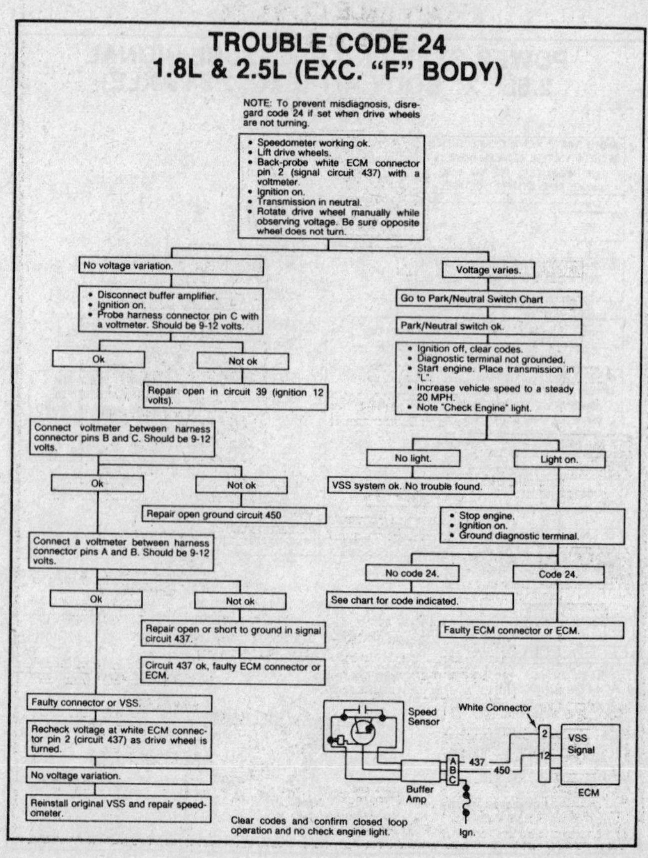

GENERAL MOTORS COMPUTER COMMAND CONTROL (Cont.)

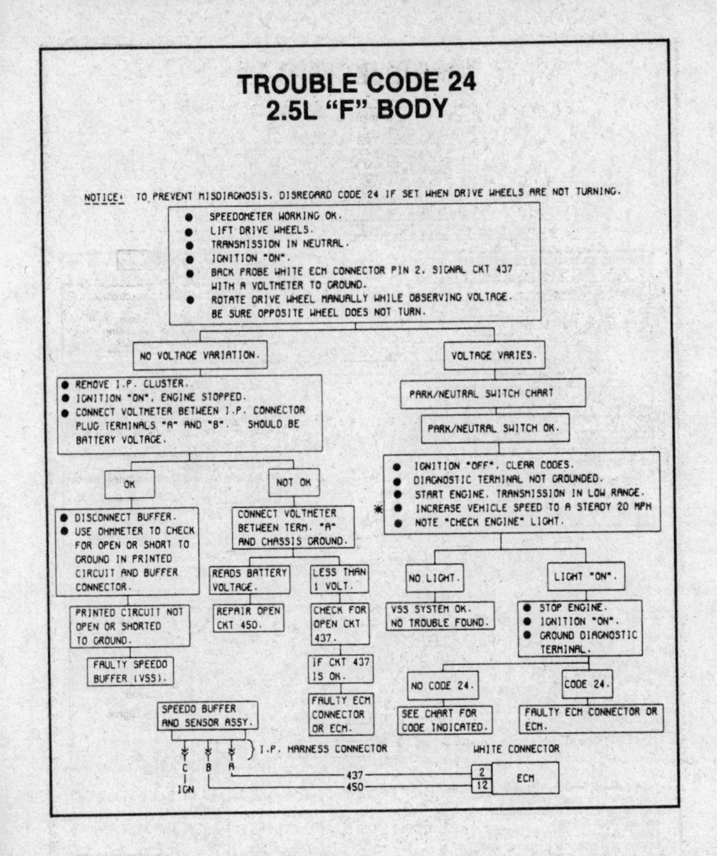

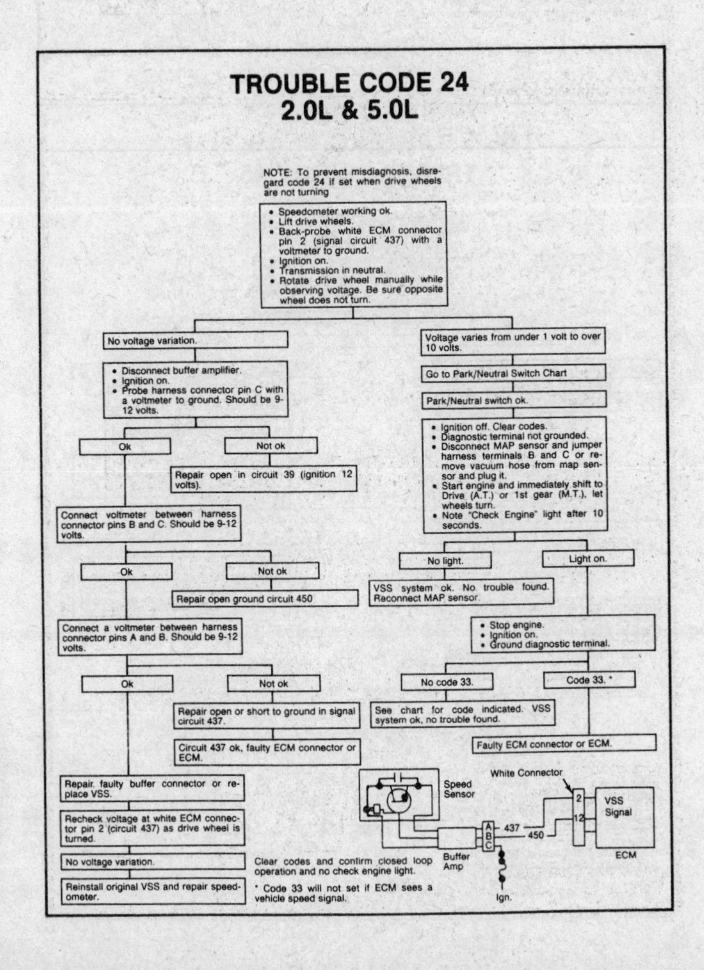

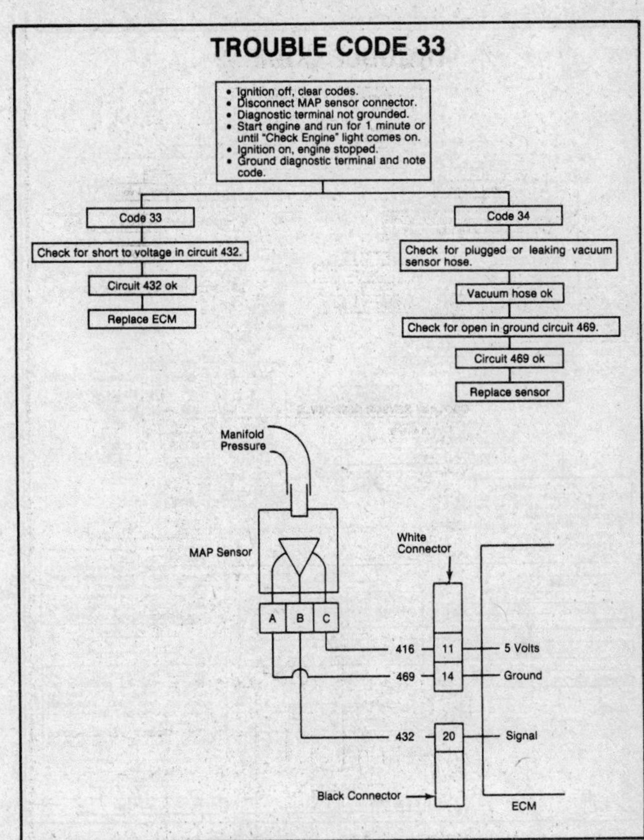

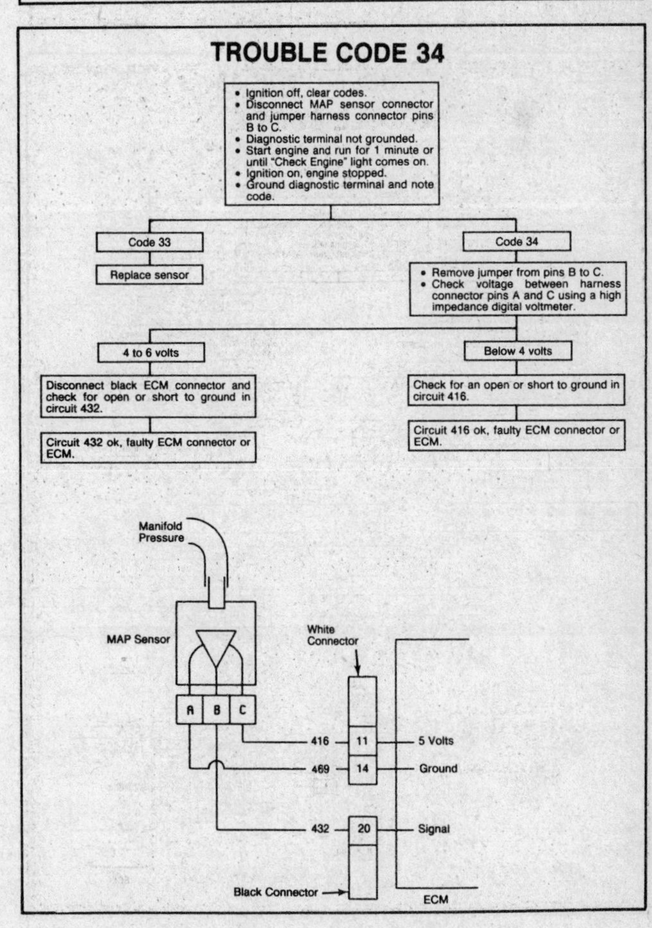

GENERAL MOTORS COMPUTER COMMAND CONTROL (Cont.)

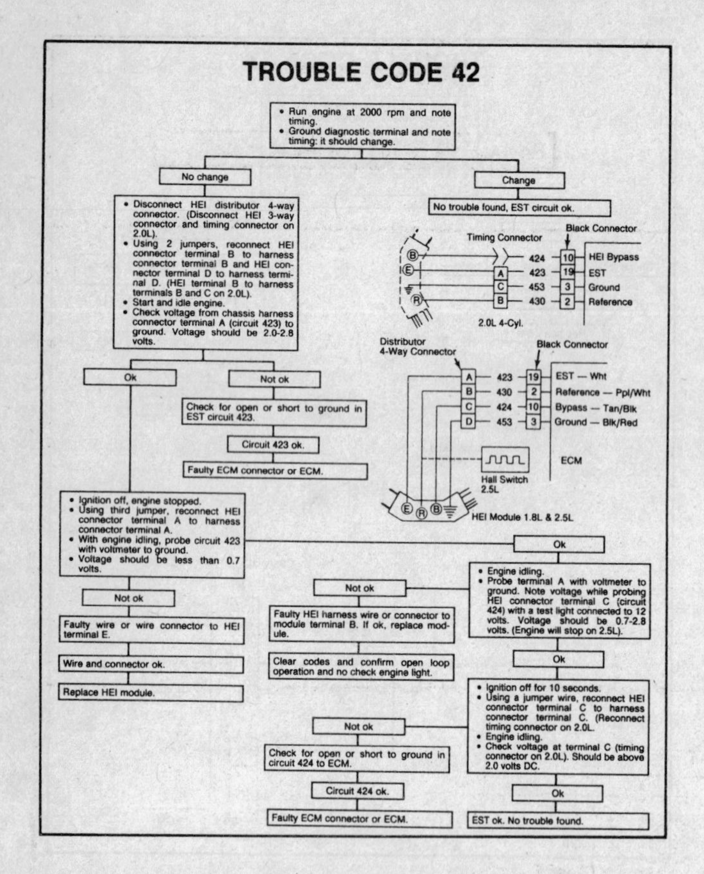

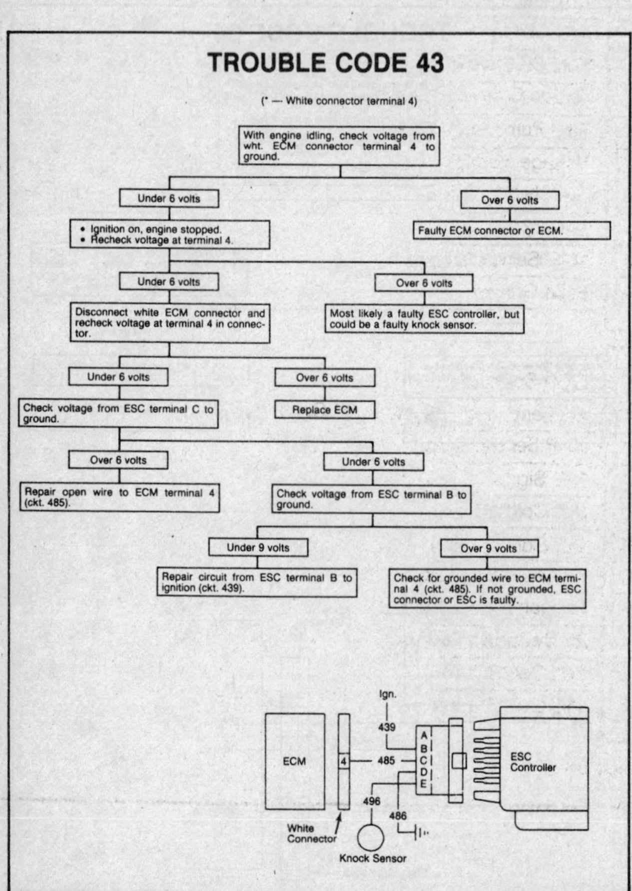

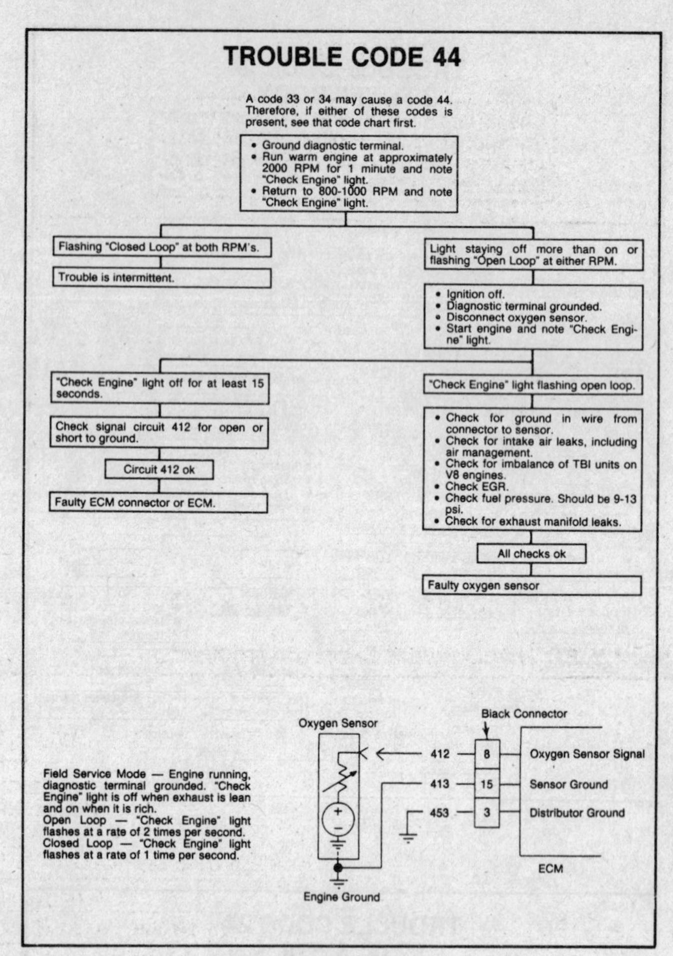

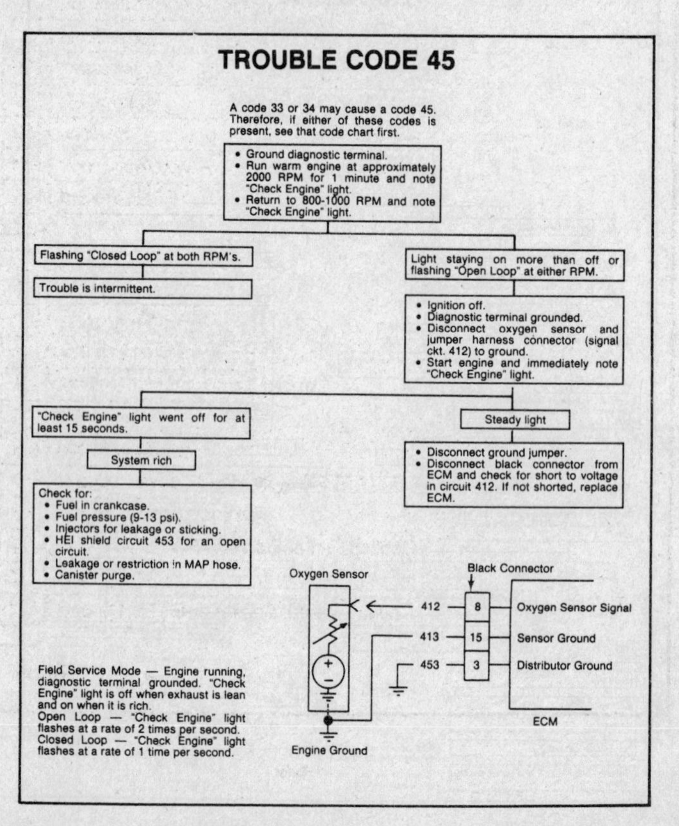

GENERAL MOTORS COMPUTER COMMAND CONTROL (Cont.)

TROUBLE CODE 51

Check that all pins are fully inserted in the socket. If ok, replace PROM, clear memory and recheck. If code 51 reappears, replace ECM.

TROUBLE CODE 55

Replace Electronic Control Module.

Fig. 12: EFI Function ECM Terminal Identification

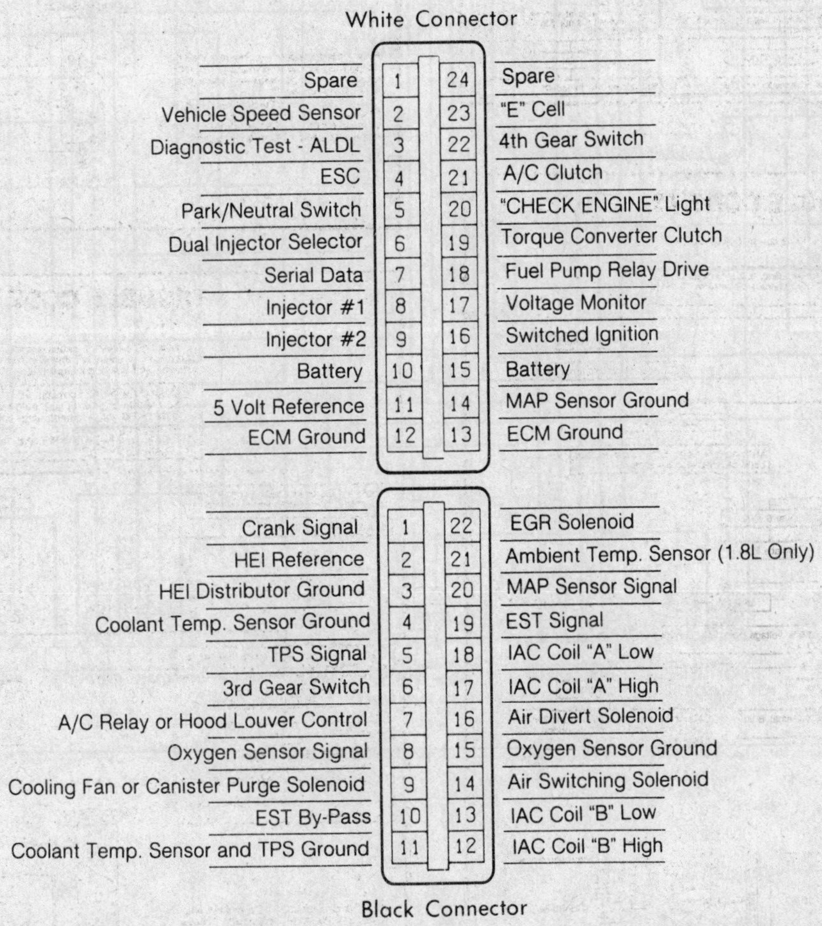

White Connector

Function	Pin	Pin	Function
Spare	1	24	Spare
Vehicle Speed Sensor	2	23	"E" Cell
Diagnostic Test - ALDL	3	22	4th Gear Switch
ESC	4	21	A/C Clutch
Park/Neutral Switch	5	20	"CHECK ENGINE" Light
Dual Injector Selector	6	19	Torque Converter Clutch
Serial Data	7	18	Fuel Pump Relay Drive
Injector #1	8	17	Voltage Monitor
Injector #2	9	16	Switched Ignition
Battery	10	15	Battery
5 Volt Reference	11	14	MAP Sensor Ground
ECM Ground	12	13	ECM Ground

Function	Pin	Pin	Function
Crank Signal	1	22	EGR Solenoid
HEI Reference	2	21	Ambient Temp. Sensor (1.8L Only)
HEI Distributor Ground	3	20	MAP Sensor Signal
Coolant Temp. Sensor Ground	4	19	EST Signal
TPS Signal	5	18	IAC Coil "A" Low
3rd Gear Switch	6	17	IAC Coil "A" High
A/C Relay or Hood Louver Control	7	16	Air Divert Solenoid
Oxygen Sensor Signal	8	15	Oxygen Sensor Ground
Cooling Fan or Canister Purge Solenoid	9	14	Air Switching Solenoid
EST By-Pass	10	13	IAC Coil "B" Low
Coolant Temp. Sensor and TPS Ground	11	12	IAC Coil "B" High

Black Connector

GENERAL MOTORS COMPUTER COMMAND CONTROL (Cont.)

Fig. 13: EFI Function (Exc. 5.0L) CCC System Wiring Diagram

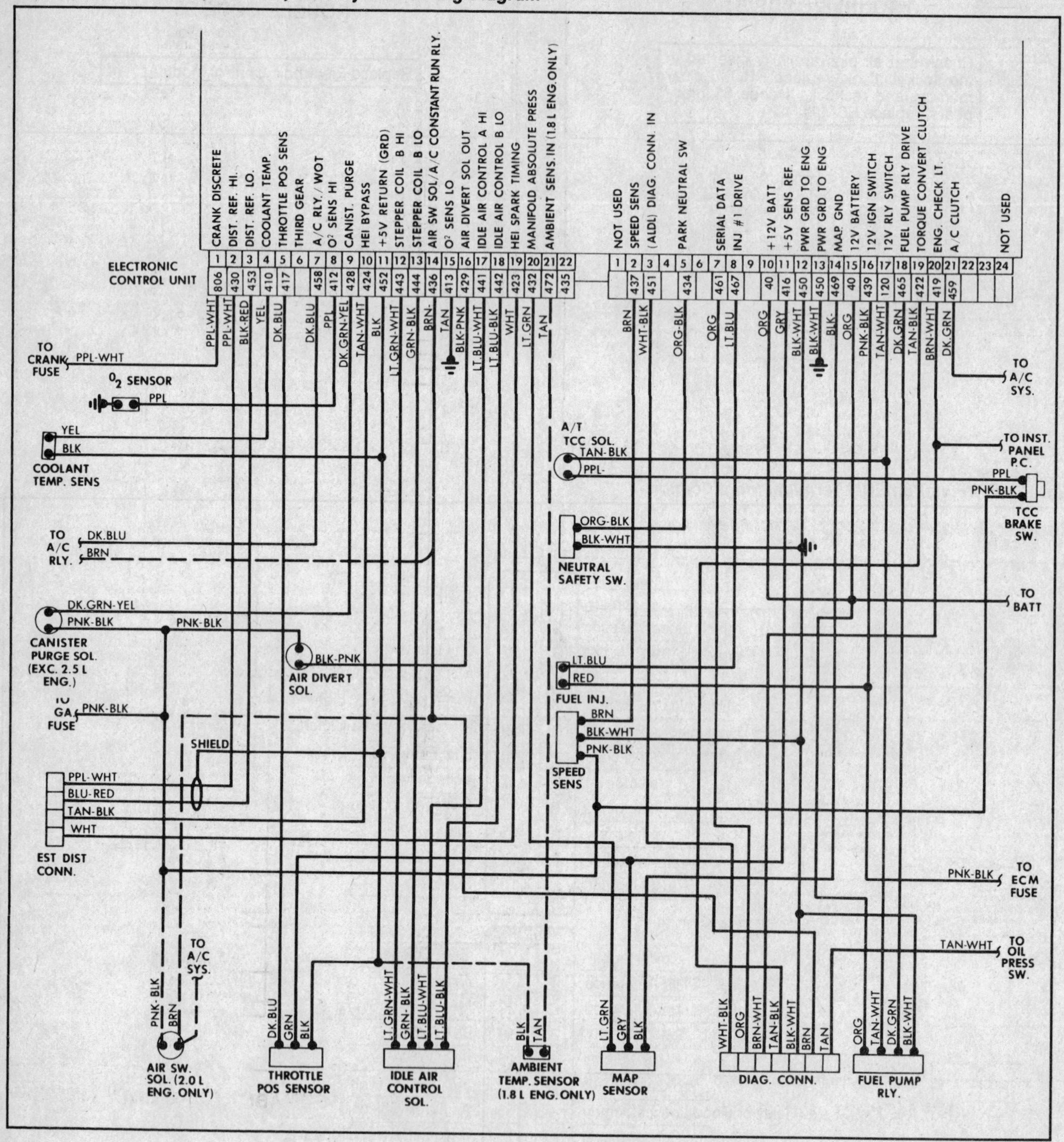

GENERAL MOTORS COMPUTER COMMAND CONTROL (Cont.)

Fig. 14: EFI Function (5.0L) CCC System Wiring Diagram

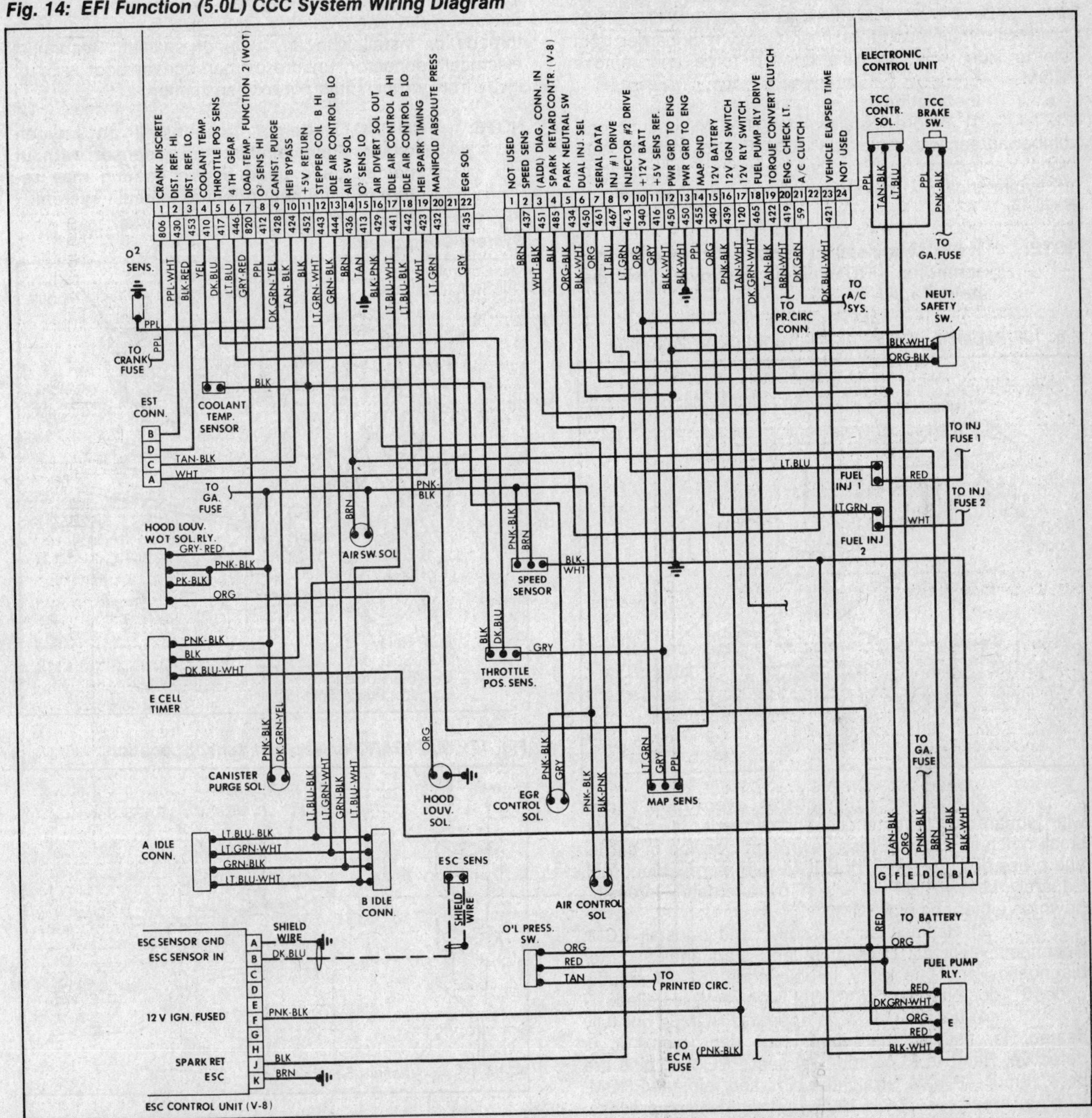

REMOVAL & INSTALLATION

ELECTRONIC CONTROL MODULE (ECM)

Removal & Installation

The ECM may be located at right side kick panel, glove compartment area or center console area. Remove ECM mounting hardware. Disconnect electrical connectors and ground strap. Remove ECM. To install ECM, reverse removal procedure and ensure ground strap is securely attached.

PROGRAMMABLE READ ONLY MEMORY (PROM)

Removal

1) Remove ECM as previously described. Remove sheet metal screw holding access cover closed and remove access cover. Using a small flat tip screwdriver, place blade at PROM carrier reference end between edge of opening in case and underside of protruding lip of carrier. Apply prying force and force side of carrier up as far as possible. Repeat procedure on other reference end lip.

GENERAL MOTORS COMPUTER COMMAND CONTROL (Cont.)

2) Using prying force explained in step **1)**, force opposite end of carrier up as far as possible. Grasp carrier with thumb and forefinger. Gently rock carrier from side to side while applying upward force and remove PROM.

Installation

1) Before installing new PROM, ensure part number agrees with removed PROM. Ensure molded "half-round" depression of PROM is at same end as "squared-off" symmetrical end of carrier and that PROM is centered in carrier.

NOTE: If PROM is installed backwards and ignition is turned on, PROM will be destroyed and must be replaced.

Fig. 15: Replacing PROM In Electronic Control Module

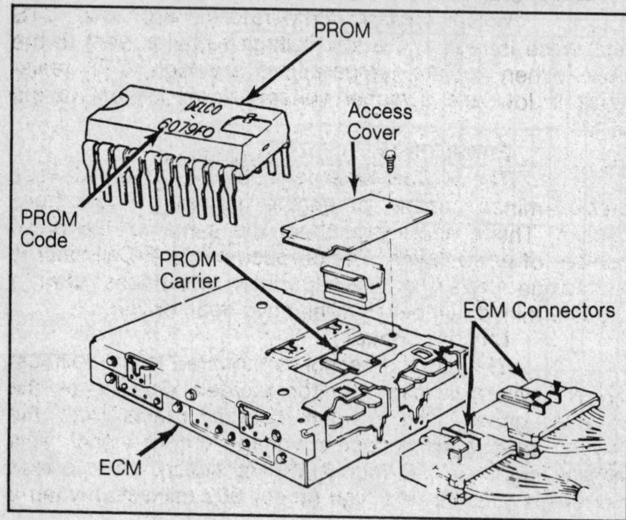

2) Position carrier squarely over PROM socket with "squared-off" symmetrical end of carrier aligned with small notch in socket. Press down firmly on top of carrier and press down on body of PROM with narrow blunt tool. Squarely seat PROM in socket by alternately pressing down on either end of PROM.

3) Replace access cover and reinstall ECM. Reconnect electrical connectors and start engine. Enter diagnostics and check for trouble code "51". If trouble code "51" does not appear, PROM is correctly installed.

4) If code "51" does appear, PROM is not fully seated, is installed backward, has bent pins, or is defective. Remove ECM and fully seat PROM. If pins are bent, remove PROM, straighten pins and reinstall PROM. If pins break or crack during straightening process, replace PROM. If PROM is installed backward, replace PROM.

OXYGEN SENSOR

Removal

Raise and support vehicle (if required). Disconnect electrical connector at harness. Spray threads of oxygen sensor with penetrating oil and allow to soak for 5 minutes. Carefully remove oxygen sensor. Oxygen sensor may be difficult to remove when engine temperature is below 120°F (45°C). Excessive force may damage threads in exhaust manifold or pipe.

Installation

Install new oxygen sensor and torque to 30 ft. lbs. (41 N.m). When installing new oxygen sensor, do not remove glass bead coating (anti-seize compound) from threads or install with any type of sealant. Reconnect electrical connector. Ensure oxygen sensor boot is 5/16" away from wrench fitting of oxygen sensor.

NOTE: DO NOT attempt to reinstall an oxygen sensor. Reinstallation of a sensor without special glass bead thread coating may require replacement of entire exhaust system

Fig. 16: Location of Carbureted CCC System Components

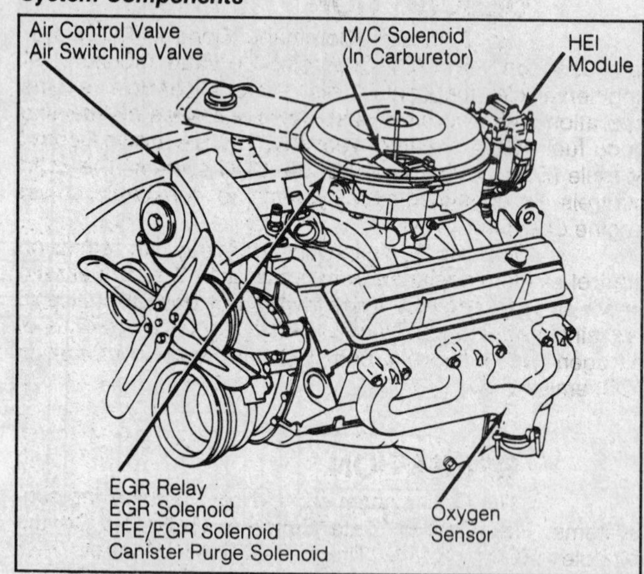

Fig. 17: MAP/BARO or Vacuum Sensor Location

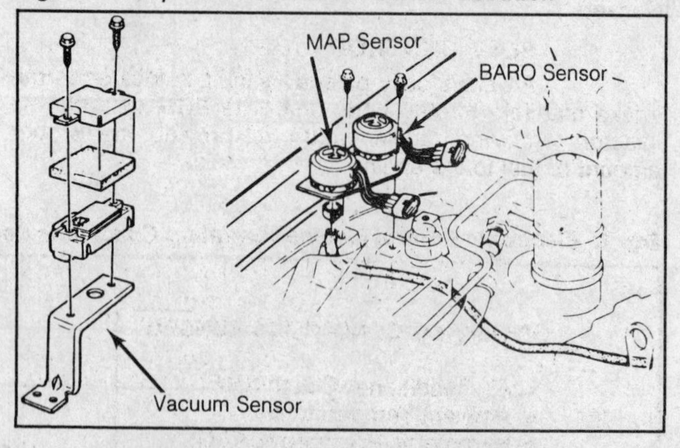

THROTTLE POSITION SENSOR (TPS)

Removal and installation requires removal of carburetor or throttle body unit.

TORQUE CONVERTER CLUTCH SOLENOID (TCC), HIGH GEAR SWITCH

Removal and installation requires disassembly of transmission.

NOTE: Removal and installation of any solenoids switches or sensors not listed is done by disconnecting wiring and removing device. Install device and reconnect wiring.

1984 CORVETTE COMPUTER COMMAND CONTROL

NOTE: Most Computer Command Control (CCC) problems are the result of mechanical breakdowns, poor electrical connections or damaged vacuum hoses. Before considering the CCC system as a possible cause of problems, ignition high tension wires, fuel supply, electrical connections and vacuum hoses should be checked. Failure to do so may result in lost diagnostic time.

DESCRIPTION

The Computer Command Control (CCC) system used on the 1984 Chevrolet Corvette monitors 14 engine/vehicle functions. This system controls engine operation and lowers exhaust emissions while maintaining good fuel economy and driveability. The Electronic Control Module (ECM) is the "brain" of the CCC system. The ECM controls 12 engine related systems to constantly adjust engine operation.

The CCC system is primarily an emission control system, designed to maintain a 14.7:1 air/fuel ratio under all operating conditions. When the ideal air/fuel ratio is maintained, the catalytic converter can control oxides of nitrogen (NOx), hydrocarbon (HC), and carbon monoxide (CO) emissions.

OPERATION

The CCC system consists of the following subsystems: Fuel Control, Data Sensors, Electronic Control Module (ECM), Spark Timing, Idle Air Control (IAC) system, Air Management, Emission Control, Torque Converter Clutch (TCC), Diagnostic System and Catalytic Converter.

FUEL CONTROL

An electrically pulsed injector is located in the intake manifold throttle body unit. The ECM controls the injector "on" time (pulse width) to provide the proper amount of fuel to the engine.

DATA SENSORS

Each sensor furnishes electronic impulses to the ECM. The ECM computes spark timing and air/fuel mixture ratio for proper engine operation.

Air Conditioner "ON" Switch

The air conditioner "ON" switch is mounted in the air conditioner compressor. This switch signals the ECM when the air conditioner compressor clutch is engaged. The ECM uses this signal to adjust idle speed when the air conditioner compressor clutch is engaged.

Coolant Temperature Sensor (CTS)

The CTS is located in the coolant stream to supply coolant temperature information to the ECM. The ECM sends a 5 volt signal to the CTS. This 5 volt signal is then reduced by the CTS and sends a voltage signal back to the ECM. The ECM then measures this voltage to determine engine coolant temperature.

When coolant temperatures are low, CTS resistance is high and a low voltage signal is sent to the ECM. When coolant temperatures are high, CTS resistance is low and a higher voltage signal is sent to the ECM.

E-Cell Timer

The E-Cell timer signals the ECM when a predetermined number of engine operating hours have passed. These hours are about the same as the given number of miles driven. The purpose of the E-Cell timer is to change certain engine operating conditions after a predetermined number of miles have been driven.

Oxygen Sensor

The oxygen sensor is mounted in the exhaust system where it can monitor oxygen content of the exhaust gases. The oxygen content reacts with the oxygen sensor to produce a voltage output signal. This voltage signal is low (about 100 millivolts) when a lean mixture is present and high (about 900 millivolts) when a rich mixture is present.

When the ECM reads the voltage signal from the oxygen sensor, the ECM will alter commands to the injector to produce either a leaner or richer mixture. The oxygen sensor does not function until its temperature reaches 600°F (316°C).

Fig. 1: Electronic Control Module Operating Conditions Sensed & Systems Controlled

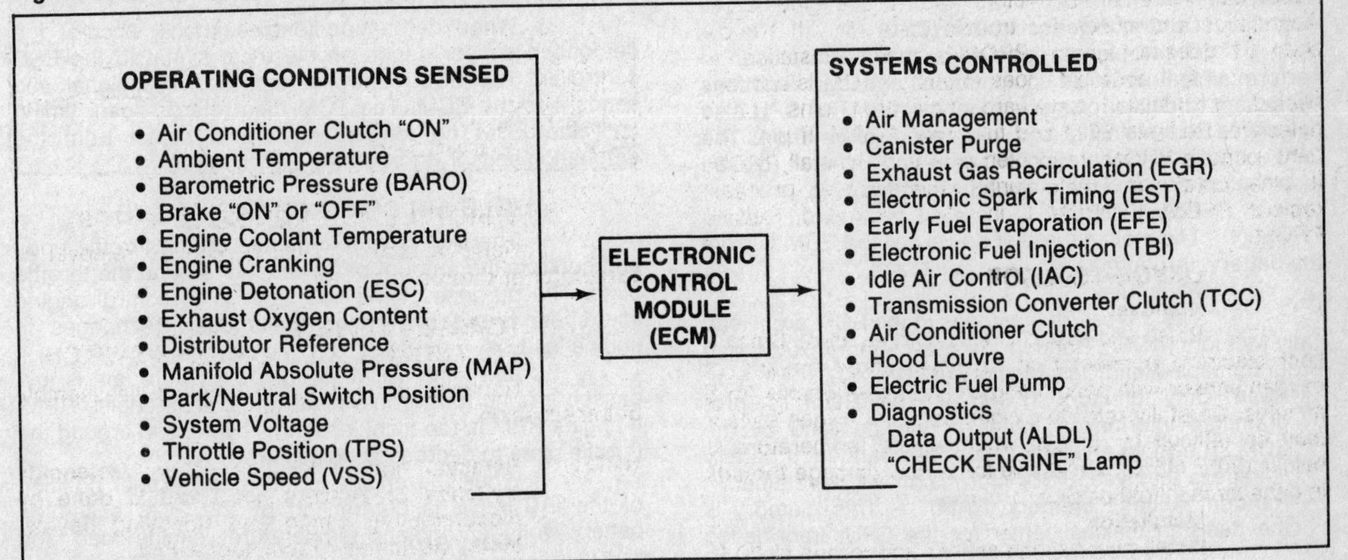

1984 CORVETTE COMPUTER COMMAND CONTROL (Cont.)

CAUTION: **Do not attempt to measure oxygen sensor output voltage. Current drain of voltmeter could damage the oxygen sensor. Do not connect any wiring or test equipment to the oxygen sensor.**

Manifold Absolute Pressure Sensor (MAP)

The MAP sensor measures changes in manifold pressure. Changes in manifold pressure can result from engine load and speed changes. The MAP sensor converts these changes in manifold pressure into a voltage output signal. These signals are then sent to the ECM. The ECM can monitor these signals and adjust air/fuel ratio and ignition timing under various operating conditions.

Park/Neutral Switch

This switch is connected to the transmission gear selector. The switch indicates when the transmsision is in Neutral or Park. Information from the park/neutral switch is used for ignition timing control, the torque converter clutch and idle air control valve operation.

Throttle Position Sensor (TPS)

The TPS is a potentiometer that is connected to the throttle shaft on the TBI unit. The TPS has 3 wires connected to it; one is connected to a 5 volt supply voltage from the ECM, one is connected to ground and the other is connected to the ECM to send voltage signals according to throttle position. The voltage signal from the TPS varies from closed throttle to wide open throttle.

Vehicle Speed Sensor (VSS)

The VSS is mounted behind the speedometer. The VSS supplies information on vehicle speed to the ECM. This sensor produces a series of 8 volt pulses (about 2000 per mile) to the ECM. The ECM counts the amount of pulses to determine vehicle speed.

ELECTRONIC CONTROL MODULE (ECM)

The ECM is located in the passenger compartment behind the right side of the instrument panel. The ECM consists of input/output devices, Central Processing Unit (CPU), power supply and memories.

Input/Output Devices

These devices are an integral part of the ECM. They convert electrical signals, received by the ECM from the various engine sensors, into digital signals for use by the CPU.

Central Processing Unit (CPU)

Digital signals recieved by the CPU are used to perform all mathematical computations and logic functions necessary to deliver proper air fuel mixture. The CPU also calculates spark timing and idle speed information. The CPU commands operation of emission control, closed loop fuel control and the diagnostic system.

Power Supply

The main source of power for the ECM is from the battery, through the ignition circuit.

Memories

The 3 types of memories in the ECM are: Read Only Memory (ROM), Random Access Memory (RAM) and Programmable Read Only Memory (PROM).

- **Read Only Memory (ROM)** — The ROM is programmed information that can only be read by the ECM. The ROM program cannot be changed. If battery voltage is removed, ROM information will be retained.
- **Random Access Memory (RAM)** — This memory is the decision making center for the CPU. Information can be read into or out of the RAM memory, similar to a calculator. Data sensor information, diagnostic codes and results of calculations are temporarily stored in the RAM memory. If battery voltage is removed from the ECM, all information stored in the memory is lost.
- **Programmable Read Only Memory (PROM)** — This memory is factory programmed information containing engine calibration data for each engine, transmission, vehicle weight and rear axle ratio application. The PROM can be carefully removed from the ECM. If battery voltage is removed, PROM information will be retained.

IGNITION TIMING

The 1984 Corvette is equipped with a High Energy Ignition system with Electronic Spark Timing (HEI-EST). The distributor contains a 7-terminal HEI-EST control module. The distributor is connected to the EST system by means of a 4-wire connector, leading to the external electronic control module (ECM).

When engine speed reaches 600 RPM or more (about 5-15 seconds after starting), the ECM transmits a constant 5 volt signal to the distributor HEI-EST module. This changes the position of the by-pass switch in the HEI-EST module.

When this occurs, the pick-up coil's RPM signals can no longer flow directly to the ignition coil as this circuit is now open. Instead the RPM signals are converted in the distributor module and routed to the ECM.

The Programmable Read Only Memory (PROM) portion of the ECM carries the basic spark advance curve based on engine RPM. Spark timing is calculated by the ECM whenever an ignition pulse is present.

Spark advance information is only sent to the distributor when the engine is running (not during cranking). Engine sensor values are used by the ECM to modify the PROM information, increasing or decreasing spark advance to achieve maximum performance with minimum emissions.

An Electronic Spark Control (ESC) system is also used. There are 4 basic components to the ESC system: A detonation sensor, an HEI-EST distributor, an ESC controller, and the ECM.

When detonation (engine knock) occurs, the detonation sensor sends an electrical signal to the ESC controller. The ESC controller amplifies this signal and sends it to the ECM. The ECM then retards spark timing until the ECM no longer receives a signal from the detonation sensor, through the ESC controller.

IDLE AIR CONTROL (IAC) VALVE

The IAC valve is mounted on the throttle body and controls the amount of by-pass air around the throttle plate. The purpose of the IAC valve is to control engine idle speed while preventing stalls due to changes in engine load.

If engine RPM is too low, more air is by-passed around the throttle plate to increase engine RPM. If engine RPM is too high, less air is by-passed around the throttle plate to decrease engine RPM.

When the engine is idling, the proper position of the IAC valve is determined by the ECM based on battery voltage, coolant temperature, engine load and

1984 CORVETTE COMPUTER COMMAND CONTROL (Cont.)

engine RPM. If the IAC valve is disconnected or connected with the engine running, the IAC valve has to be reset. Reset of the IAC is accomplished by driving the vehicle over 35 MPH with the circuit properly connected.

EMISSION CONTROL

The ECM electrically controls the following emission control systems: The Air Injection Reaction (AIR) system, the Exhaust Gas Recirculation (EGR) system and the Evaporative Emission Control System (EECS).

Air Injection Reaction (AIR)

This system helps to reduce hydrocarbon (HC) and carbon monoxide (CO) exhaust emissions. This system is also used to quickly heat up the catalytic converter and oxygen sensor during cold engine operation. This is accomplished by injecting air into the exhaust port or catalytic converter.

When the ECM energizes the air control valve, air is allowed to flow to the air switching valve. The air switching valve then directs this air to the exhaust port. During warm engine operation (closed loop), the ECM de-energizes the air control valve. This causes the air switching valve to direct air to the catalytic converter.

If the air control valve detects a rapid decrease in manifold vacuum (deceleration condition), or ECM detects any failure in the CCC system, air is diverted to the air cleaner or is dumped to the atmosphere.

Exhaust Gas Recirculation

The ECM controls ported vacuum to the EGR valve with an electrically operated solenoid valve. The ECM uses information from the coolant temperature sensor, the throttle position sensor and the manifold absolute pressure sensor to determine vacuum solenoid operation.

During cold engine operation and at idle, the solenoid valve is grounded by the ECM. This blocks vacuum to the EGR valve. During warm engine operation and off idle speeds, the solenoid is not grounded and vacuum is allowed to flow to the EGR valve.

Evaporative Emission Control System (EECS)

This system controls purging of the vapor canister. The ECM controls vacuum to the purge valve using a solenoid valve. When the engine is operating in the open loop mode, the solenoid valve is energized. This blocks off vacuum to the purge valve.

When the engine is operating in the open loop mode above a preset RPM, the solenoid valve is de-energized. This allows vacuum to be applied to the purge valve. When vacuum is applied to the purge valve, fuel vapors are then drawn into the intake manifold for burning.

Catalytic Converter

The 3-way catalytic converter with a dual bed is used to reduce exhaust emissions. This type of converter can reduce hydrocarbons (HC), carbon monoxide (CO) and oxides of nitrogen (NOx).

The upstream section of the converter contains a reducing/oxidizing bed to reduce NOx while at the same time oxidizing HC and CO. An air supply pipe from the AIR system injects air between the beds of the converter. This is so the second converter bed can oxidize any remaining HC and CO to efficiently reduce exhaust emissions.

TORQUE CONVERTER CLUTCH (TCC)

The ECM controls a solenoid mounted in the transmission to allow the torque converter to directly connect the engine to the transmission. When vehicle speed is high enough, the ECM energizes the TCC solenoid and the engine is mechanically connected to the transmission.

When operating conditions indicate that the transmission should operate as normal, the TCC solenoid is de-energized. This allows the transmission to return to normal automatic operation. The transmission will also return to normal automatic operation when the brake pedal is depressed.

DIAGNOSTIC SYSTEM

The ECM of the CCC system is equipped with a self-diagnostic system which detects system failures or abnormalities. When a malfunction occurs, the ECM will light the Amber "CHECK ENGINE" lamp located on the instrument panel. When the malfunction is detected and the lamp is turned on, a corresponding trouble code will be stored in the ECM memory. Malfunctions are recorded as "hard failures" or as "intermittent failures".

- "Hard failures" cause the "CHECK ENGINE" lamp to glow and remain on until the malfunction is repaired. If the "CHECK ENGINE" lamp comes on and remains on during vehicle operation, the cause of the malfunction must be determined.
- "Intermittent failures" cause the "CHECK ENGINE" lamp to flicker or go out after about 10 seconds when the fault goes away. However, the corresponding trouble code will be retained in the ECM memory. "Intermittent failures" may be sensor related. If a sensor fails, the ECM will use a substitute value in its calculations to continue engine operation. In this condition, service is not mandatory; but loss of good driveability may be encountered. If the related fault does not reoccur within 50 engine restarts, the related touble code will be erased from the ECM memory.

As a bulb and system check, the "CHECK ENGINE" lamp will glow when the ignition switch is turned on and the engine is not running. When the engine is started, the lamp should go out. If not, a malfunction has been detected in the CCC system.

TROUBLE SHOOTING

NOTE: **Trouble shooting and diagnosis of the fuel system should begin with determining fuel system pressure. Before performing any test on the fuel system, pressure must be released from the system.**

FUEL SYSTEM PRESSURE TEST

1) Remove "FUEL PUMP" fuse from fuse block. Crank engine. Engine will start and run until fuel supply remaining in fuel lines is used. Engage the starter again for about 3 seconds to ensure that all fuel is out of lines.

2) Remove air cleaner and plug thermal vacuum port on throttle body. Remove steel fuel line from between front and rear throttle body units. When removing fuel line, always use 2 wrenches. Install fuel pressure gauge (J-29658 or equivalent) between throttle body units.

3) Reinstall "FUEL PUMP" fuse in fuse block. Start engine and observe fuel pressure reading. If fuel pressure is not between 9 and 13 psi (.6-.9 kg/cm²), proceed to Fuel System Diagnosis chart. If fuel pressure is okay, proceed to step **4)**.

1984 CORVETTE COMPUTER COMMAND CONTROL (Cont.)

4) Depressurize fuel system as described in step **1)**. Remove fuel pressure gauge and reinstall steel fuel line between throttle bodies. Reinstall "FUEL PUMP" fuse in fuse block. Start engine and watch for fuel system leaks. Remove plug from throttle body thermal vacuum port and reinstall air cleaner.

INTERMITTENT "CHECK ENGINE" LIGHT

Symptom Definition

"CHECK ENGINE" light come on at all times, but does not stay on. A stored code may or may not exist.

Possible Cause & Correction

- Check for poor mating of one connector to another. Terminals may not be fully seated. Check for improperly formed or damaged terminals. Check wire to terminal connections.
- Check for poor connection from ignition coil to ground or arcing at spark plug wires or plugs.
- Check wire from "CHECK ENGINE" light to ECM for short to ground.
- Check for poor connections in wires from ECM terminals 12 and 13 to engine ground.
- Check for loss of the trouble code memory. To check this, disconnect TPS and run engine at idle until "CHECK ENGINE" light comes on. Code 22 should be stored and retained in memory when ignition is turned off. If not, ECM is faulty.
- Check for electrical system interference caused by a defective relay or a ECM driven solenoid or switch. They can cause a sharp electrical surge. This type of problem will normally occur when faulty component is operated.
- Check for improper installation of electrical accessories such as auxiliary lights or 2-way radios.
- Make sure that EST wires are kept away from spark plug wires, distributor wires, distributor housing, ignition coil and generator. Make sure that wire from ECM Black connector terminal 3 is connected to a good ground.
- Check for open diodes across air conditioner compressor clutch.

HARD START

Symptom Definition

Engine cranks okay but does not start for a long time. Engine eventually starts and runs okay.

Possible Cause & Correction

- Check fuel pump relay. To do this, disconnect oil pressure switch. If engine starts, relay is okay. If engine does not start, proceed to Fuel System Diagnosis chart.
- Check that TPS is not sticking or binding.
- Check for a leaking injector. To do this, disconnect injector electrical connector at injector. Crank engine and watch for fuel leakage.
- Check that resistance of coolant sensor circuit or coolant sensor is not too high.
- Check ignition system for a worn distributor shaft, bare or shorted wires, incorrect pick-up coil resistance, loose ignition coil ground or moisture in distributor cap.
- Remove spark plugs and check for wet plugs, cracks, improper gap, burned electrodes or heavy carbon deposits.
- Check for correct fuel pressure of 9-13 psi in all speed ranges.

STALLS AFTER STARTING

Symptom Definition

Engine starts okay but dies after brief idle, dies as soon as any load is placed on engine (such as turning on air conditioner or engaging transmission), or on initial driveaway.

Possible Cause & Correction

- Make sure that hot air tube is connected to air cleaner.
- Check for proper operation of thermostatic air cleaner.
- Check for proper operation of idle air control (IAC) system.
- Check PCV valve for proper operation by placing finger over inlet hole in valve. Valve should snap back. If not, replace valve.
- Check EGR system for proper operation using EGR Check chart.
- If stall occurs when air conditioner is turned on, check for air conditioner clutch signal to ECM terminal 21. Voltage at terminal 21 of ECM should be battery voltage when air conditioner compressor clutch is engaged.
- Check for an overcharged air conditioner system.
- Check for plugged or restricted fuel lines.
- Check for a weak spark from ignition coil.

HESITATION, SAG OR STUMBLE

Symptom Definition

Momentary lack of responce when accelerator is pushed down. Can occur at all vehicle speeds. Usually occurs when taking off from a stop.

Possible Cause & Correction

- Check for proper operation of thermostatic air cleaner damper door.
- Check that fuel pressure is steady at 9-13 psi in all speed ranges. Also check for contaminated fuel.
- Check for leaks or restrictions in vacuum hose to MAP sensor.
- Check for fouled spark plugs.
- Check that PROM in vehicle is correct PROM for that vehicle. Check with local dealer for latest PROM application information.
- Check for a binding or sticking TPS.
- Make sure that initial ignition timing is properly set.
- Make sure that ECM controlled idle speed is correct.
- Check EGR system for proper operation.
- Disconnect fuel injector electrical connectors. Crank engine and check for injector leaks. Check for fuel spray from both injectors. If spray from only 1 injector, proceed to Engine Cranks But Will Not Run chart. Also check injector balance.
- Check for an open in the HEI ground circuit.
- Check canister purge system for proper operation.

VEHICLE SURGES

Symptom Definition

Engine power varies under steady throttle or cruise. Feels like vehicle speeds up and slows down without changing position of accelerator pedal.

Possible Cause & Correction

- Check operation of thermostatic air cleaner damper door.
- Check that park/neutral switch is properly adjusted.
- Check for intermittent open or short to ground in torque converter clutch or HEI by-pass circuits.
- Check for proper operation of EGR system. See EGR Check chart.

1984 CORVETTE COMPUTER COMMAND CONTROL (Cont.)

- Check for proper operation of Electronic Spark Control (ESC) system. See Electronic Spark Control System Check chart.
- Make sure that initial ignition ignition timing is properly set.
- Check in-line fuel filter. Replace if dirty or clogged.
- Check fuel tank for water. Also check that fuel system pressure is 9-13 psi at all engine speeds.
- Remove spark plugs and check for wet plugs, cracks, improper gap, burned electrodes or heavy carbon deposits. Also check condition of distributor cap, rotor and spark plug wires.

LACK OF POWER OR SLUGGISH

Symptom Definition

Engine delivers less power than expected. Little or no increase in speed when accelerator is pushed down farther.

Possible Cause & Correction

- Check that air filter is not plugged. Replace if neceesary.
- Check for proper operation of thermostatic air cleaner damper door.
- Check for a plugged or dirty fuel filter.
- Make sure that initial ignition timing is properly set.
- Check Electronic Spark Control (ESC) system for excessive retard. See Electronic Spark Control System Check chart.
- Check for restricted fuel filter or incorrect fuel pressure.
- Make sure that EGR valve is not open all the time.
- Check exhaust system for restrictions, such as a damaged or collapsed pipe, muffler or catalytic converter.
- Check engine valve timing and compression.
- Check engine for a worn camshaft.

ENGINE BACKFIRES

Symptom Definition

Fuel ignites in intake manifold or in exhaust system making a loud popping noise.

Possible Cause & Correction

- Check for proper valve timing.
- Check for fuel or water in vacuum hose to MAP sensor. Also check for restricted hose.
- Check engine for sticking or leaking valves.
- Check output voltage of ignition coil.
- Check for crossfire between spark plugs, distributor cap and spark plug wires.
- Check for an intermittent ignition system problem.
- Make sure that initial ignition timing is properly set.

POOR FUEL ECONOMY

Symptom Definition

Fuel economy, as measured by an actual road test, is noticeably lower than expected. Fuel economy is noticeably lower than was on this vehicle at one time.

Possible Cause & Correction

- Check for proper operation of thermostatic air cleaner damper door. Also check for a clogged air filter.
- Make sure that odometer is properly calibrated.
- Make sure that initial ignition timing is properly set.
- Remove spark plugs and check for wet plugs, cracks, improper gap, burned electrodes or heavy carbon deposits.
- Check engine compression.
- Check for proper operation of torque converter clutch. See Torque Converter Clutch Electrical Diagnosis chart.
- Check for dragging brakes.

DETONATION/SPARK KNOCK

Symptom Definition

A mild to severe ping, usually worse under acceleration. The engine makes sharp metallic knocks that change with amount of acceleration.

Possible Cause & Correction

- Check for obvious overheating problems.
- Make sure that initial ignition timing is properly set.
- Make sure that EGR valve is opening and not staying closed all of the time.
- Make sure that Electronic Spark Control (ESC) system is operating properly. See Electronic Spark Control System Check chart.
- Check for restriction or fuel in vacuum hose to MAP sensor. Also check for low output from MAP sensor.
- Make sure that fuel system pressure is 9-13 psi in all speed ranges.
- Remove carbon from engine with top engine cleaner.
- Make sure that the correct PROM is installed in ECM.
- Check for leaking valve guide seals.
- Make sure that torque converter clutch is operating properly. See Torque Converter Clutch Electrical Diagnosis chart.
- Check for incorrect basic engine parts such as camshaft, cylinder heads and pistons.

ROUGH, UNSTABLE OR INCORRECT IDLE

Symptom Definition

Engine runs unevenly at idle. If bad enough vehicle will shake. Idle may vary in RPM. Engine idles at incorrect RPM.

Possible Cause & Correction

- Make sure that throttle linkage is not sticking or binding.
- Make sure that initial ignition timing is properly set.
- Check engine idle speed, both base idle and ECM idle.
- Check idle air control (IAC) system. See Idle Air Control System chart.
- Check for proper operation of EGR system. See EGR Check chart.
- Check park/neutral switch circuit. Also make sure that park/neutral switch is properly adjusted.
- If rough idle only occurs when engine is hot, check PCV valve for proper operation, check evaporative emission control system, check for proper spark plug gap and check engine compression.

ENGINE WILL NOT IDLE

Symptom Definition

Engine starts okay but will not run at idle speeds. Engine will run if accelerator is held at part throttle.

Possible Cause & Correction

- Problem is most likely in idle air control (IAC) system. See Idle Air Control System chart.

ENGINE DIESELING/RUN-ON

Symptom Definition

Engine continues to run after ignition is turned off but runs very rough. If engine runs smoothly, check ignition switch.

1984 CORVETTE COMPUTER COMMAND CONTROL (Cont.)

Possible Cause & Correction

- Problem is most likely leaking injectors.

EXCESSIVE EXHAUST EMISSION (ODORS)

Symptom Definition

Vehicle fails emission test. Vehicle may also have excessive "rotton egg" smell (hydrogen sulfide) being emitted from exhaust pipe.

Possible Cause & Correction

- If emission test shows excessive carbon monoxide (CO) and hydrocarbon emissions and also has excessive odor being emitted, check all systems and components that could cause the engine to run rich.
- If emission test shows excessive oxides of nitrogen emissions, check all systems and components that could cause the engine to run lean or to run too hot.

DIAGNOSIS & TESTING

DIAGNOSTIC TOOLS

The CCC system does not require special tools for diagnosis. A tachometer, test light, ohmmeter, digital voltmeter with 10 megohms impedance (minimum), vacuum pump, vacuum gauge and 6 jumper wires 6" long (1 wire with female connectors at both ends; 1 wire with male connector at both ends; 4 wires with male and female connectors at opposite ends) are the only tools necessary for diagnosis.

A test light, rather than a voltmeter, must be used when indicated by a diagnostic chart.

CCC DIAGNOSIS

Diagnosis of the CCC system should be performed in the following order:

1) Make sure that all engine systems not related to the CCC system are operating properly. Do not proceed with testing unless all other problems have been repaired.

2) Enter diagnostic mode and record trouble codes flashed by "CHECK ENGINE" light. Exit diagnostic mode.

3) Distiguish between "hard" or "intermittent" trouble codes.

4) If trouble codes were displayed, proceed to Diagnostic Circuit Check chart. Follow all instructions given in that chart.

5) If no trouble codes were displayed, proceed to System Performance Check and Trouble Shooting.

The ECM stores component failure information for CCC system under a related trouble code which can be recalled for diagnosis and repair. When recalled, these codes will be displayed by flashes of the "CHECK ENGINE" light. Trouble codes are displayed starting with the lowest numbered code. The only codes that will be displayed are those in which a related malfunction has occured.

NOTE: **Example of trouble codes is as follows: "FLASH", "FLASH", pause, "FLASH", "FLASH", "FLASH", "FLASH" followed by a longer pause identifies trouble code "24". The first series of flashes indicates first digit of trouble code; second series of flashes indicates second digit of trouble code.**

Entering Diagnostic Mode

1) Turn ignition switch on but do not start engine. "CHECK ENGINE" light should glow. Locate assembly line data link (ALDL) connector attached to ECM wiring harness under instrument panel. Insert spade lug terminal across "TEST" terminal and "GROUND" terminal. *See Fig. 2.*

Fig. 2: ALDL Connector Terminal Locations

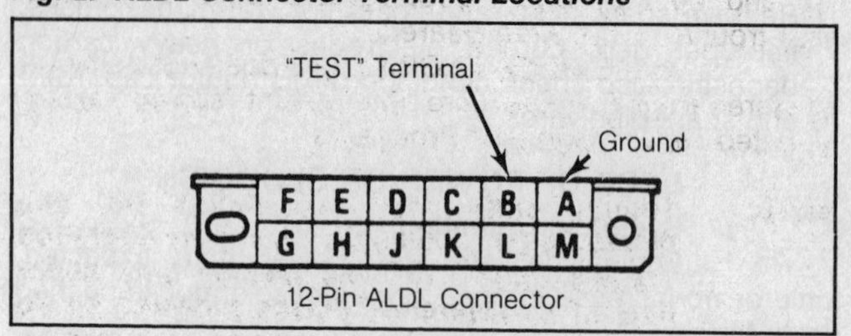

2) "CHECK ENGINE" light should flash code "12". Code "12" consists of "FLASH", pause, "FLASH", "FLASH" followed by a longer pause. Trouble Code "12" wil be repeated 2 more times, then if any trouble codes are stored in the ECM memory, they will be displayed in the same manner.

3) Trouble codes will be displayed from lowest to highest numbered codes (3 times each) and be repeated as long as the "TEST" terminal of the ALDL connector is grounded.

CAUTION: **Inserting spade lug in terminals of ALDL connector grounds "TEST" terminal lead. Do not ground ALDL connector before ignition is turned on or engine is started.**

Clearing Trouble Codes

To clear memory of trouble codes, turn ignition switch on and ground "TEST" lead at ALDL connector. Turn ignition switch off and remove ECM fuse from fuse block for 10 seconds. Remove "TEST" lead ground.

Exiting Diagnostic Mode

To exit diagnostic mode, turn ignition switch off and remove spade lug terminal from ALDL connector.

NOTE: **The terms "enter diagnostics" and "exit diagnostics" will be used periodically throughout this section. Follow the procedure for entering diagnostic mode when instructed to "enter diagnostics". Follow the procedure for exiting diagnostic mode when instructed to "exit diagnostics".**

FIALURE CODE DETERMINATION

During any diagnostic procedure, "hard failure" codes MUST be distiguished from "intermittent failure" codes. Diagnostic charts cannot be used to analyze "intermittent failure" codes, except as noted under Diagnostic Procedure. To determine "hard failure" codes and "intermittent failure" codes, proceed as follows:

1) Turn ignition switch on and enter diagnostics. Read and record all stored trouble codes. Exit diagnostics and clear trouble codes.

2) Apply parking brake and place transmission in Neutral (man. trans.) or "P" (auto. trans.). Block drive wheels and start engine. "CHECK ENGINE" should go out. Run warm engine at specified curb idle for 2 minutes and note "CHECK ENGINE" light.

1984 CORVETTE COMPUTER COMMAND CONTROL (Cont.)

NOTE: Grounding "TEST" terminal with engine running will force engine to run in closed loop mode if engine is warm and oxygen sensor is hot.

3) If "CHECK ENGINE" light comes on, enter diagnostics and read and record trouble codes. This will reveal "hard failure" codes. Codes "13", "15", "24", "44", "45" and "55" may require a road test to reset "hard failure" after trouble codes were cleared.

4) If "CHECK ENGINE" light does not come on, all stored trouble codes were "intermittent failures", except as noted under Diagnostic Procedure.

NOTE: Trouble code "15" malfunction will only display after 5 minutes of engine operation. Trouble code "12" will display only during time of no reference pulses received by the ECM; it will never be stored as a malfunction.

DIAGNOSTIC PROCEDURE

The CCC system should be considered as a source of trouble on engine performance, fuel economy and exhaust emission complaints only after normal checks (which would apply to a vehicle without CCC) have been performed.

Diagnosis of the CCC system consists of 2 initial checks: Diagnostic Circuit Check and Field Service Mode Check. Either of these checks may lead to a chart for locating a source of a problem or indicate no problem on that check and refer to another check.

If there is no trouble in the CCC system, both checks will result in that conclusion.

Field Service Mode Check

NOTE: This test confirms proper operation of fuel system and verifies closed loop operation. Clear codes and perform this test after any repair is completed.

If the "TEST" terminal is grounded with the engine running, the system will enter the field service mode. In this mode the "CHECK ENGINE" light will indicate whether the system is in open or closed loop. Open loop is indicated by the "CHECK ENGINE" flashing about 2 1/2 times per second. In the closed loop mode, the light will stay out most of the time if the systen is too lean. It will stay on most of the time when the system is too rich.

Fig. 3: Electronic Control Module Connector Terminal Identification

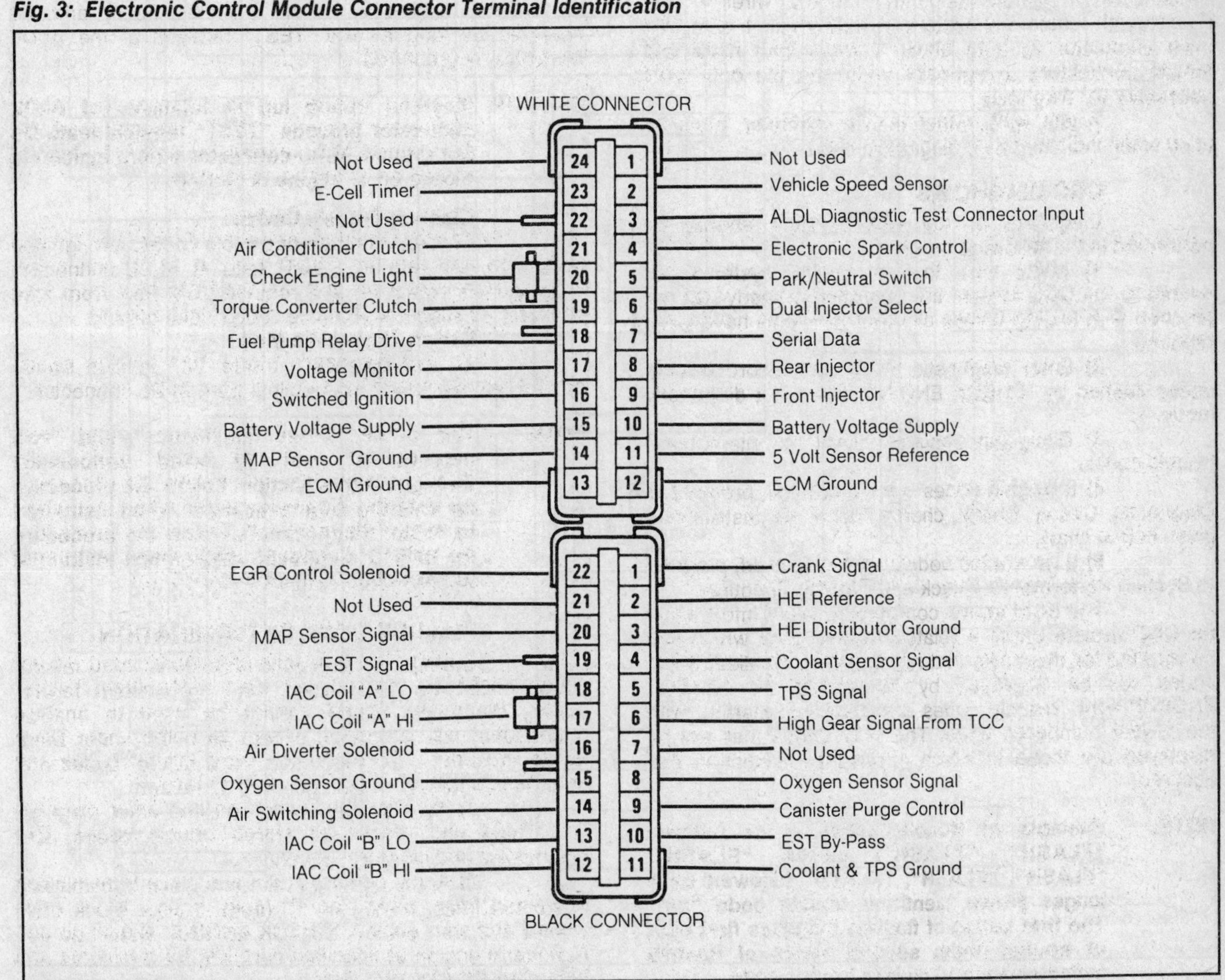

1984 CORVETTE COMPUTER COMMAND CONTROL (Cont.)

Fig. 4: 1984 Corvette Computer Command Control System Wiring Diagram

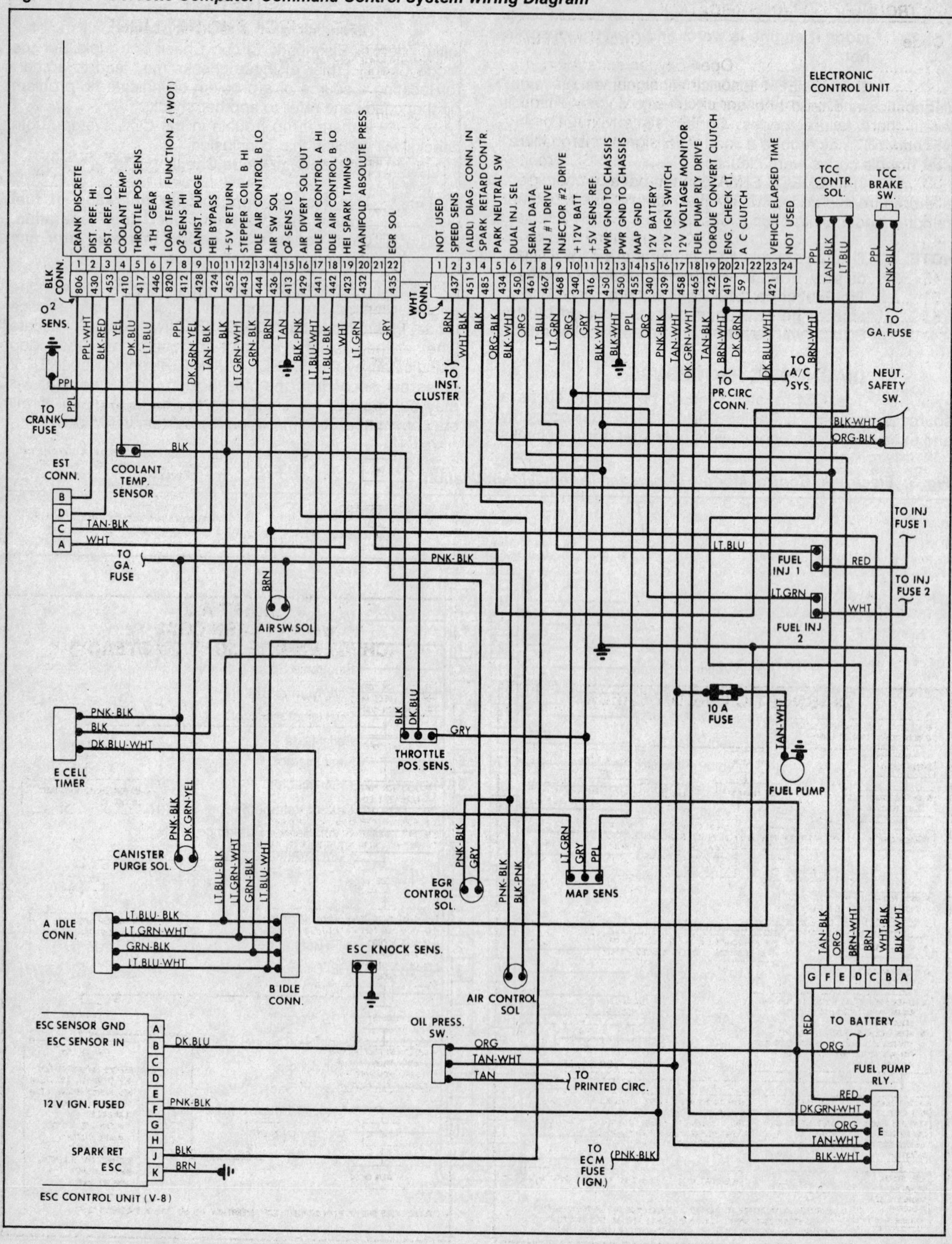

1984 CORVETTE COMPUTER COMMAND CONTROL (Cont.)

ECM TROUBLE CODE IDENTIFICATION

Code	Circuit Affected
13	Open oxygen sensor circuit.
14	Coolant sensor circuit signal voltage low.
15	Coolant sensor circuit signal voltage high.
21	TPS signal voltage high.
22	TPS signal voltage low.
24	VSS circuit.
33	MAP sensor voltage too high.
34	MAP sensor voltage too low.
42	EST circuit.
43	ESC retard signal too low.
44	Lean oxygen sensor value.
45	Rich oxygen sensor value.
51	Faulty PROM, PROM installation or ECM.
55	Faulty ECM.

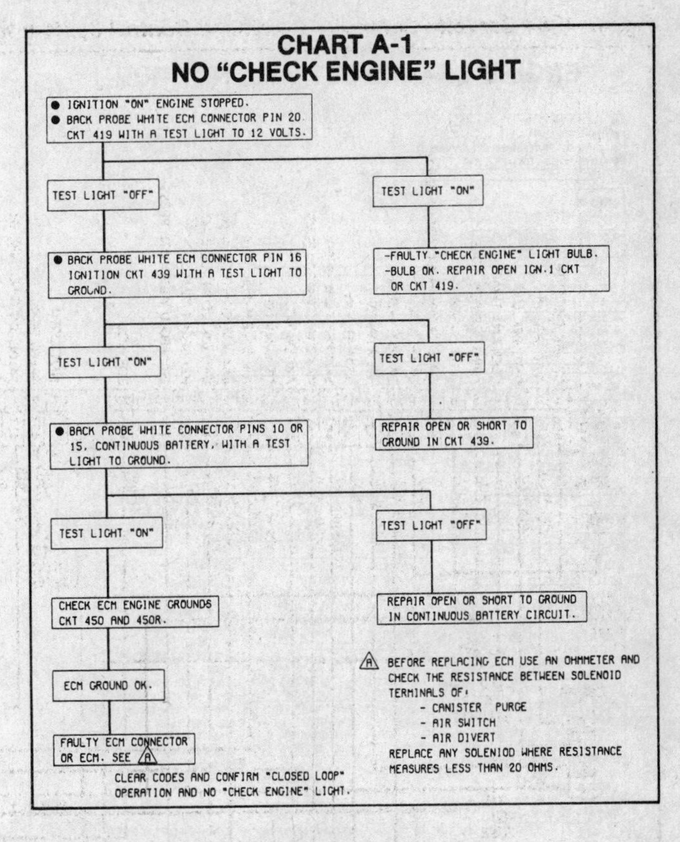

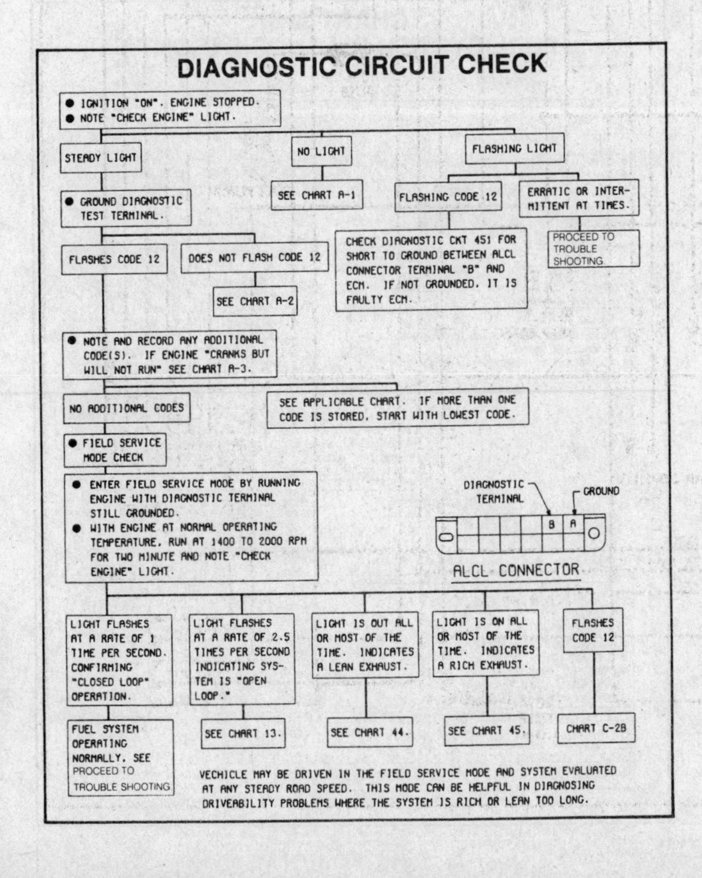

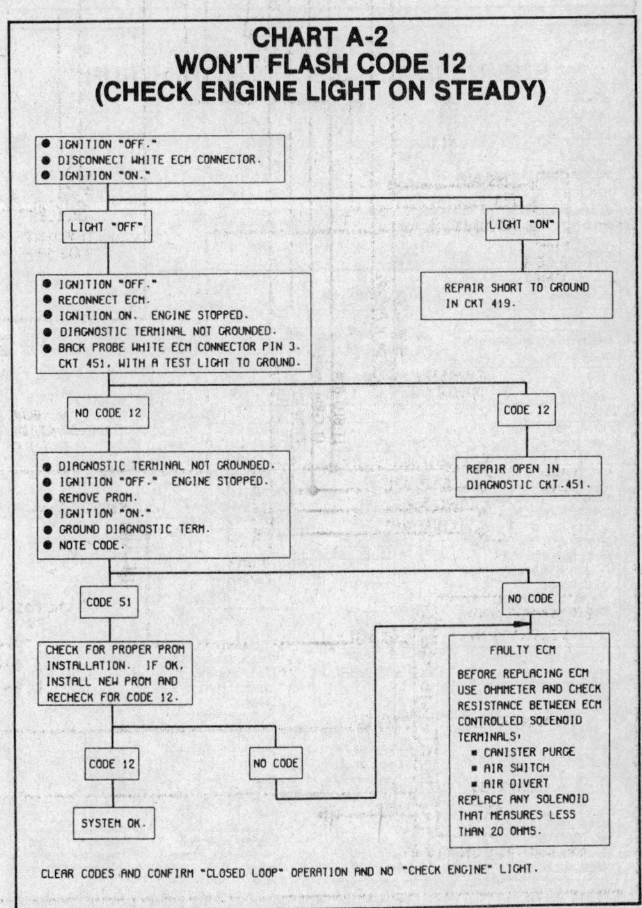

1984 CORVETTE COMPUTER COMMAND CONTROL (Cont.)

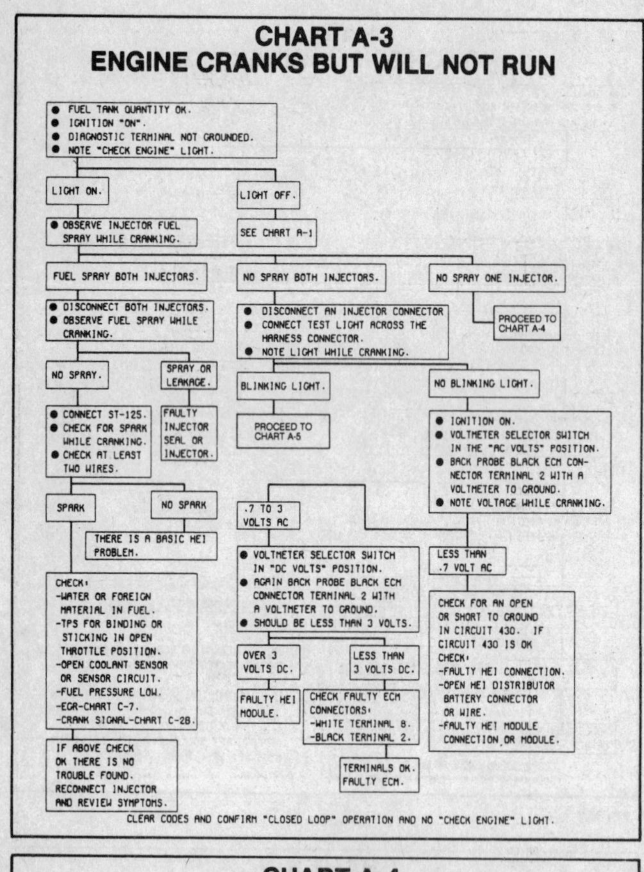

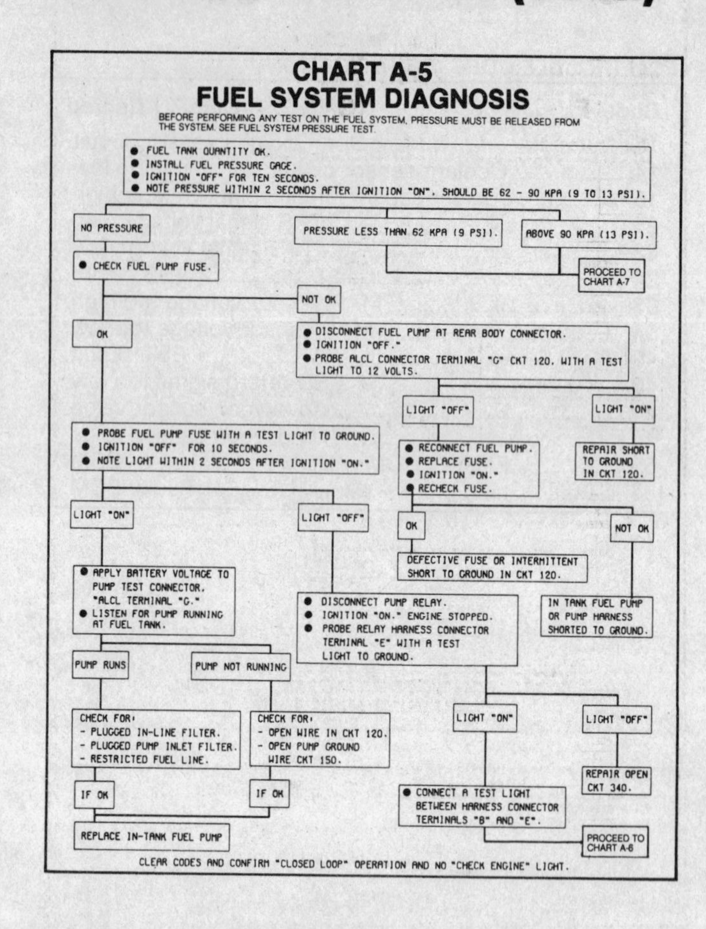

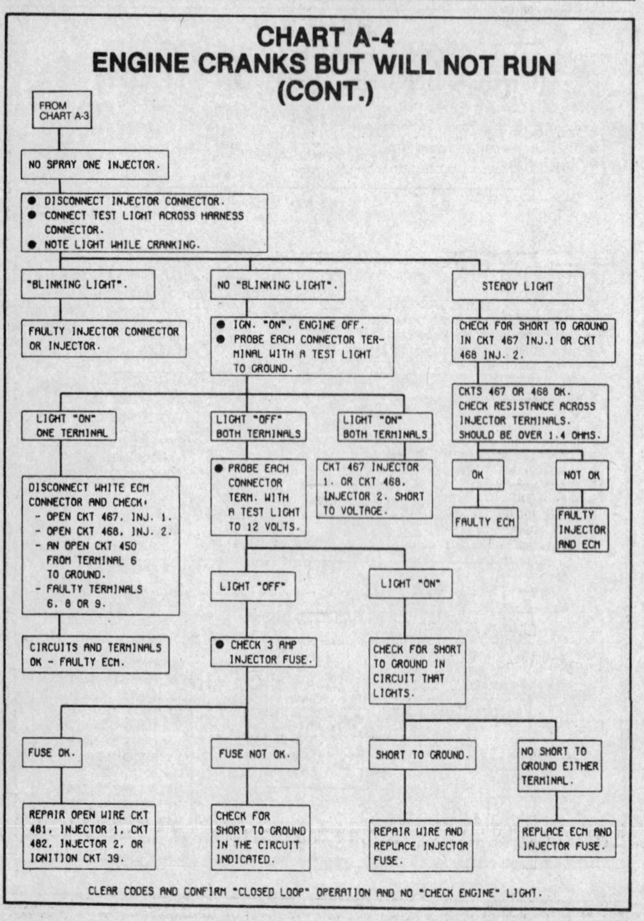

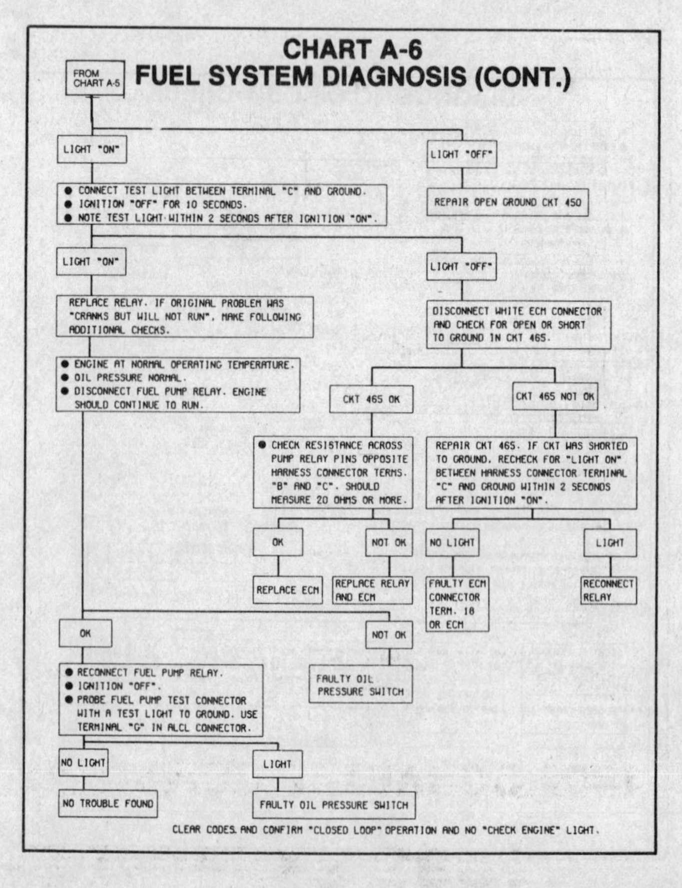

1984 CORVETTE COMPUTER COMMAND CONTROL (Cont.)

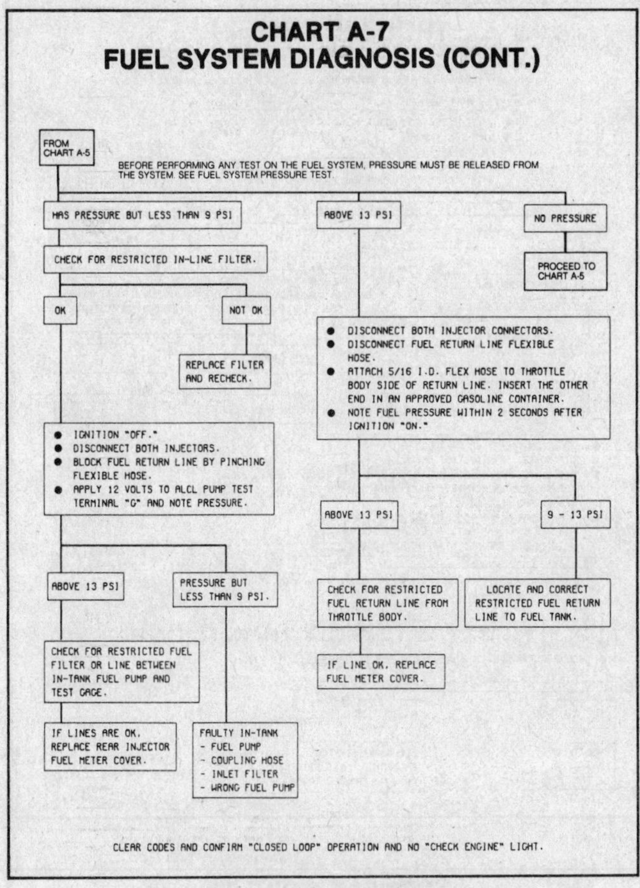

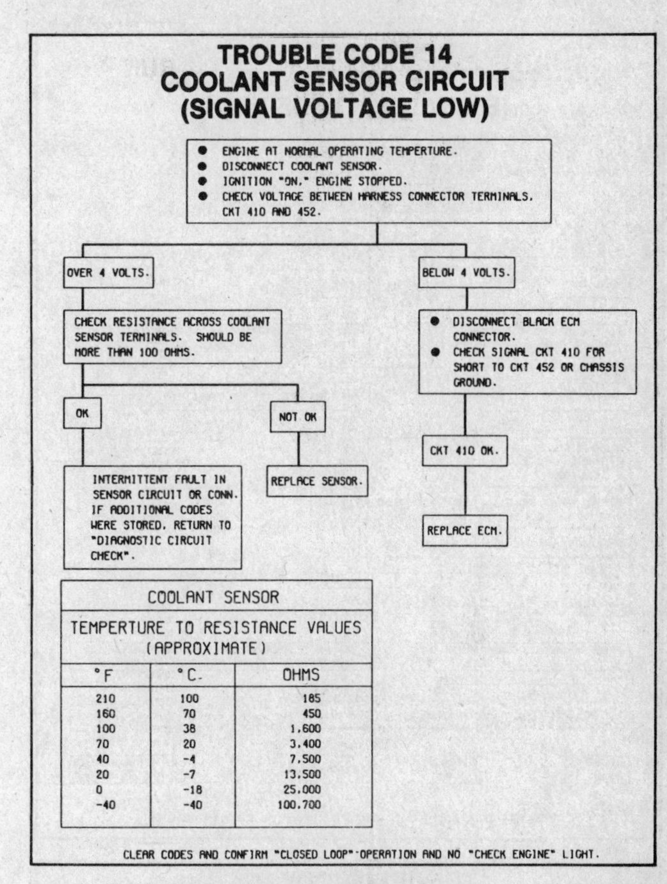

COOLANT SENSOR

TEMPERTURE TO RESISTANCE VALUES (APPROXIMATE)

°F	°C	OHMS
210	100	185
160	70	450
100	38	1,600
70	20	3,400
40	-4	7,500
20	-7	13,500
0	-18	25,000
-40	-40	100,700

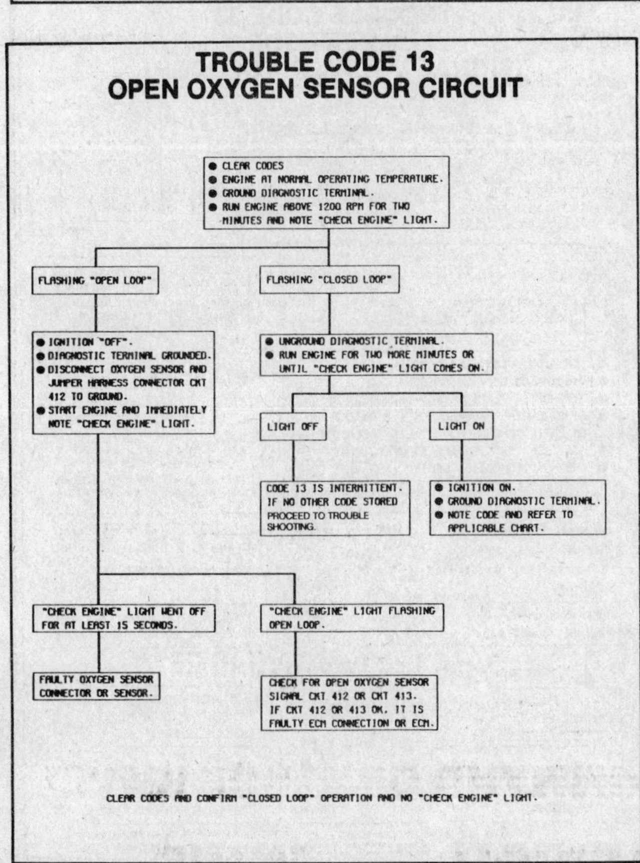

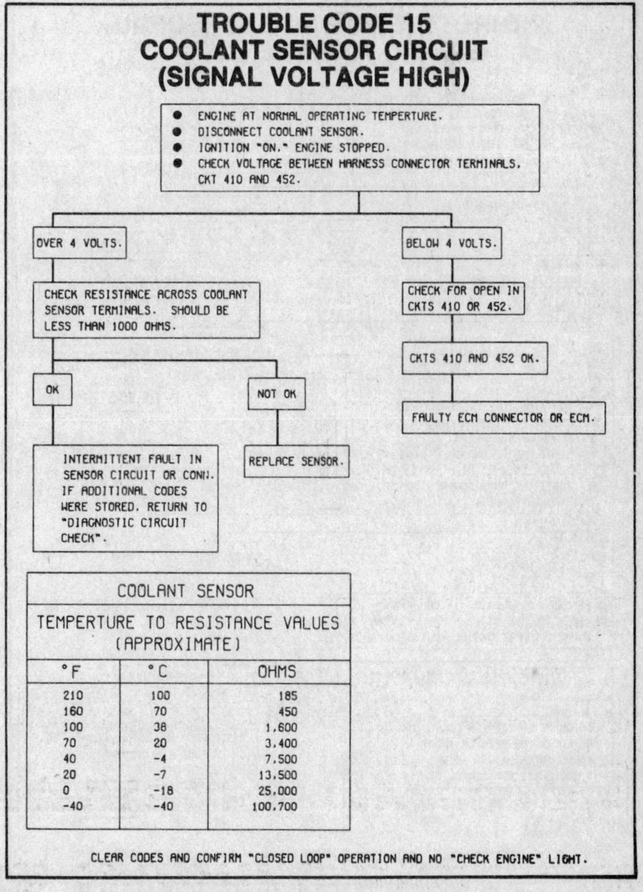

COOLANT SENSOR

TEMPERTURE TO RESISTANCE VALUES (APPROXIMATE)

°F	°C	OHMS
210	100	185
160	70	450
100	38	1,600
70	20	3,400
40	-4	7,500
20	-7	13,500
0	-18	25,000
-40	-40	100,700

1984 CORVETTE COMPUTER COMMAND CONTROL (Cont.)

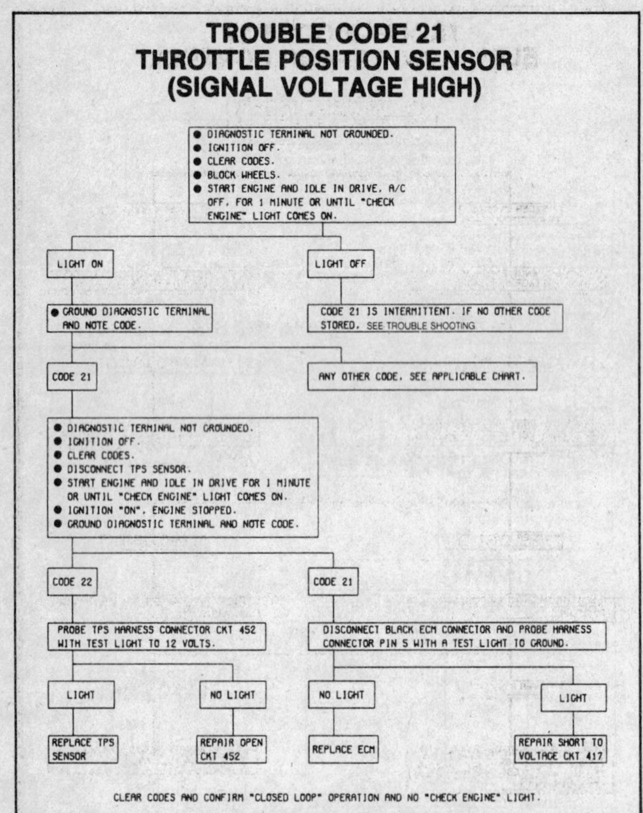

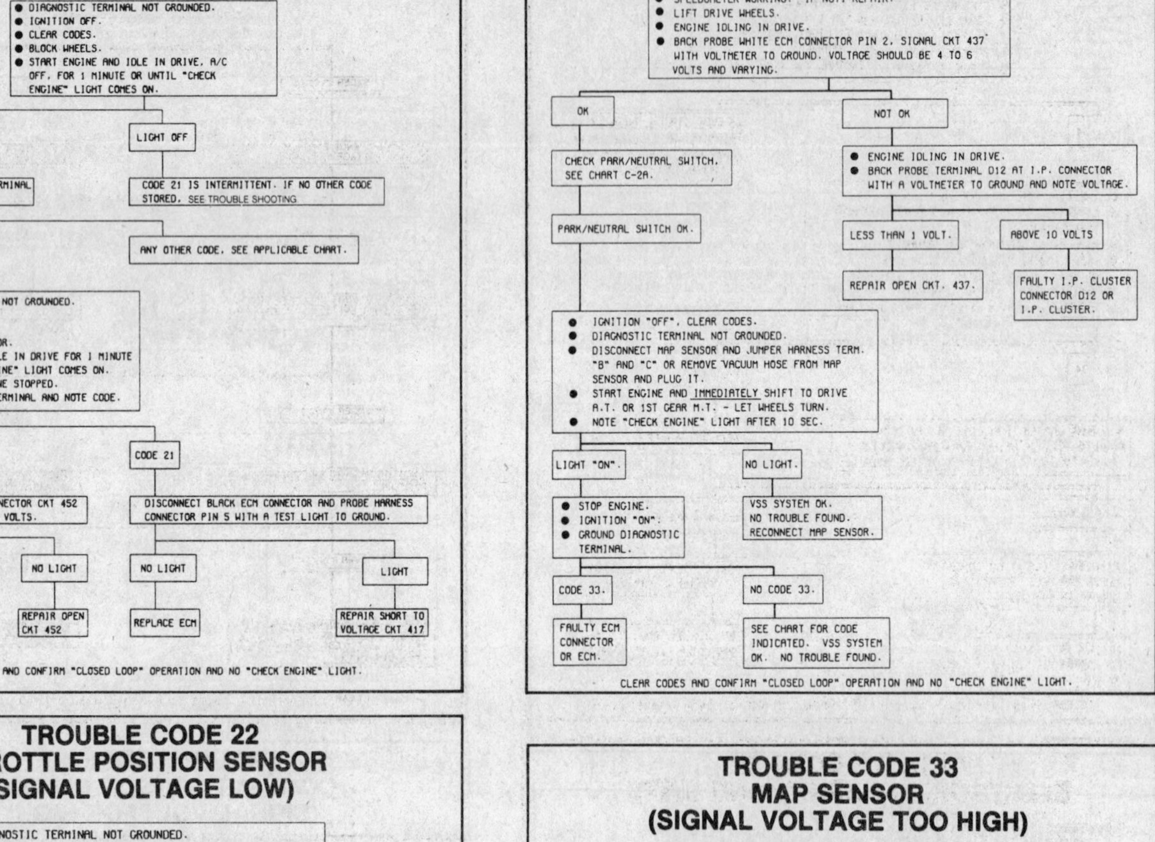

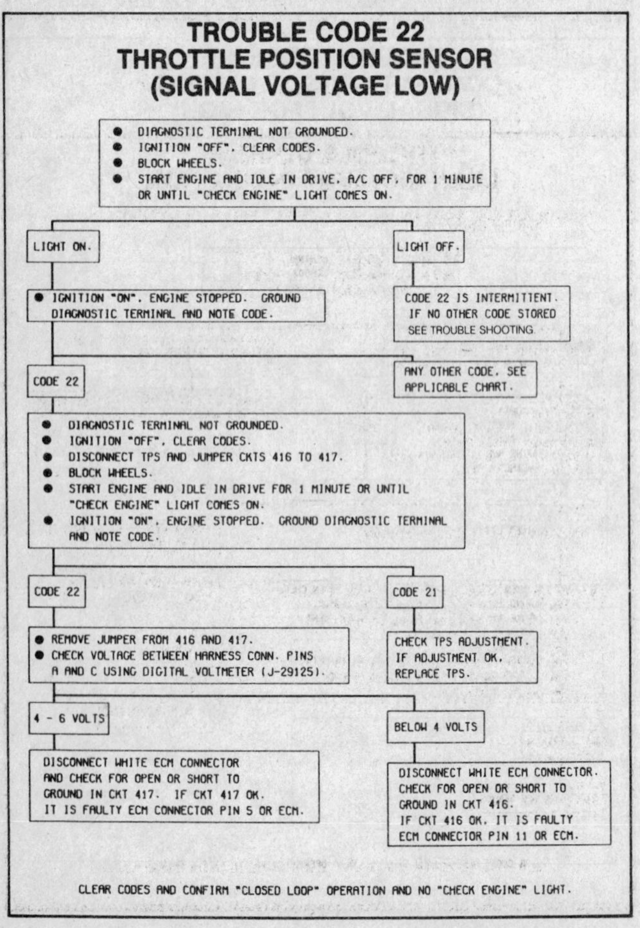

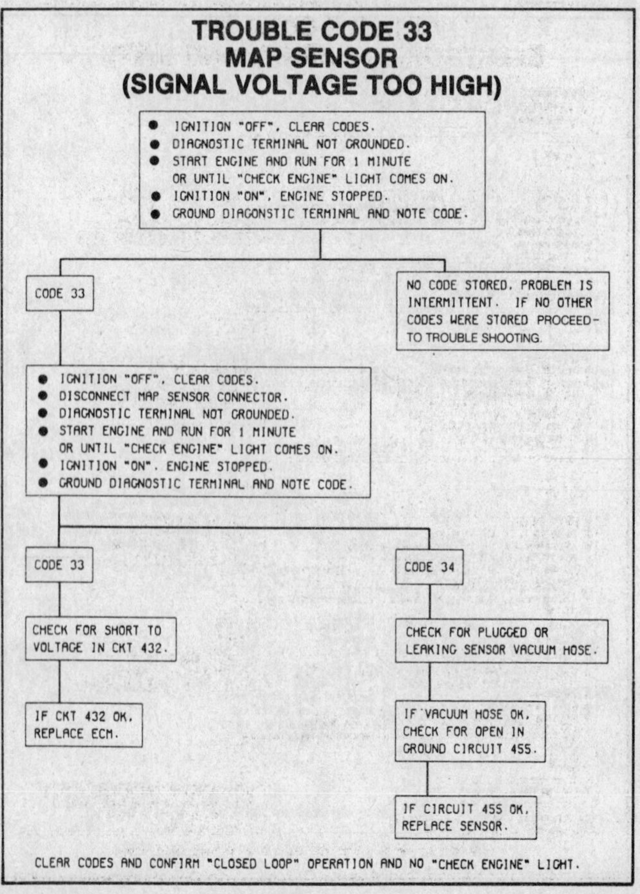

1984 CORVETTE COMPUTER COMMAND CONTROL (Cont.)

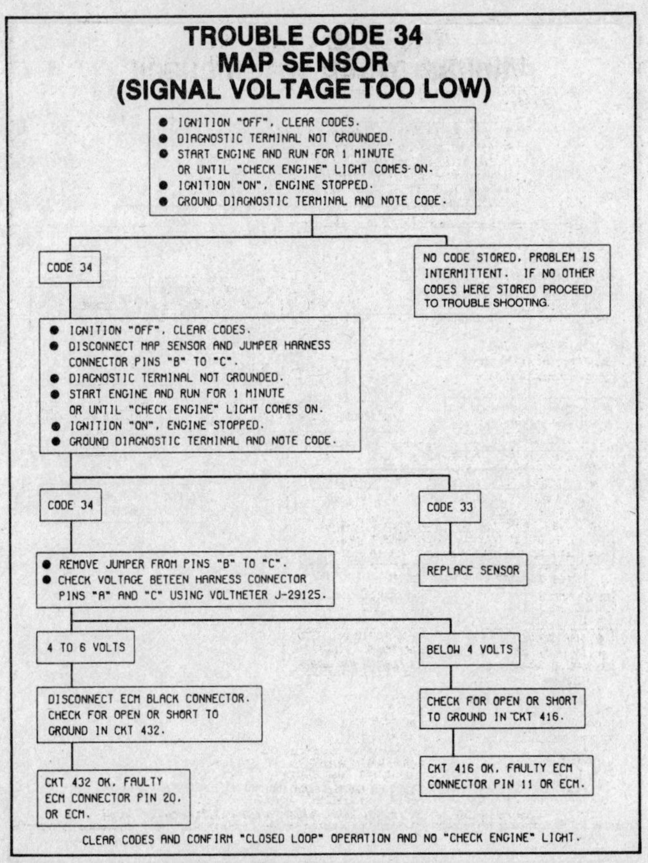

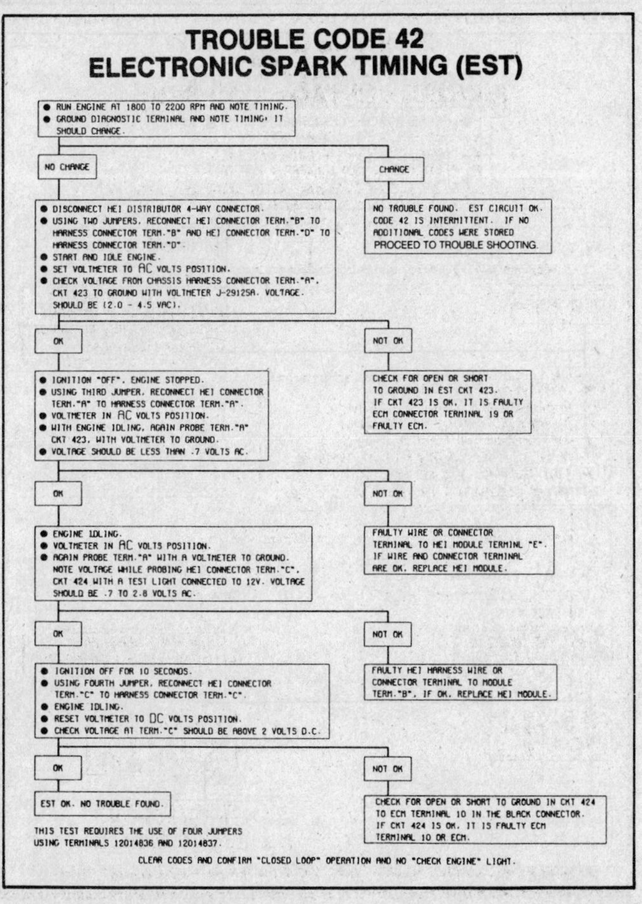

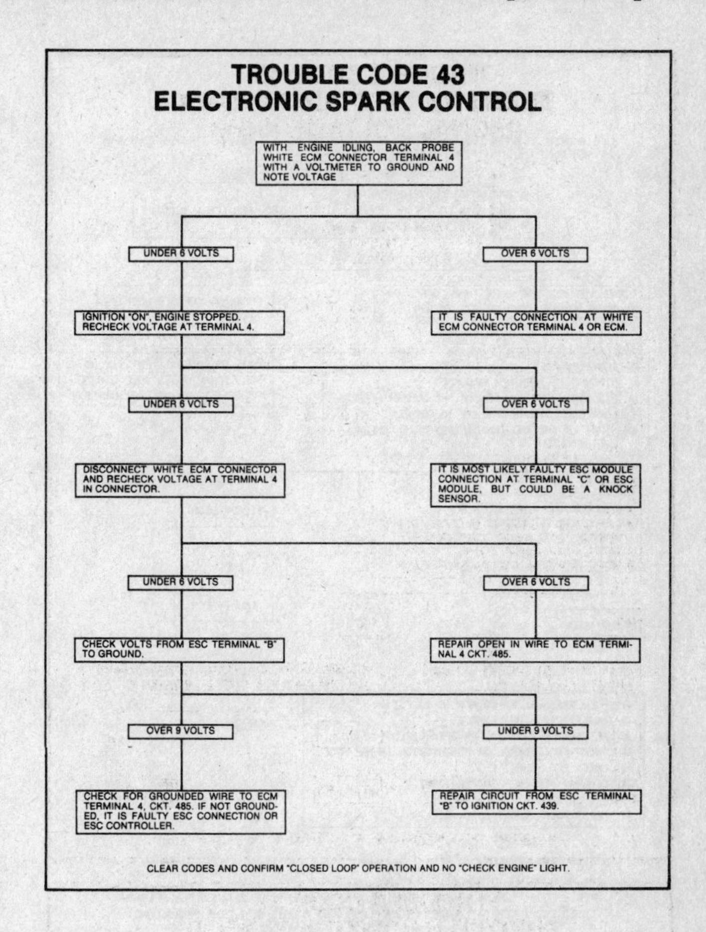

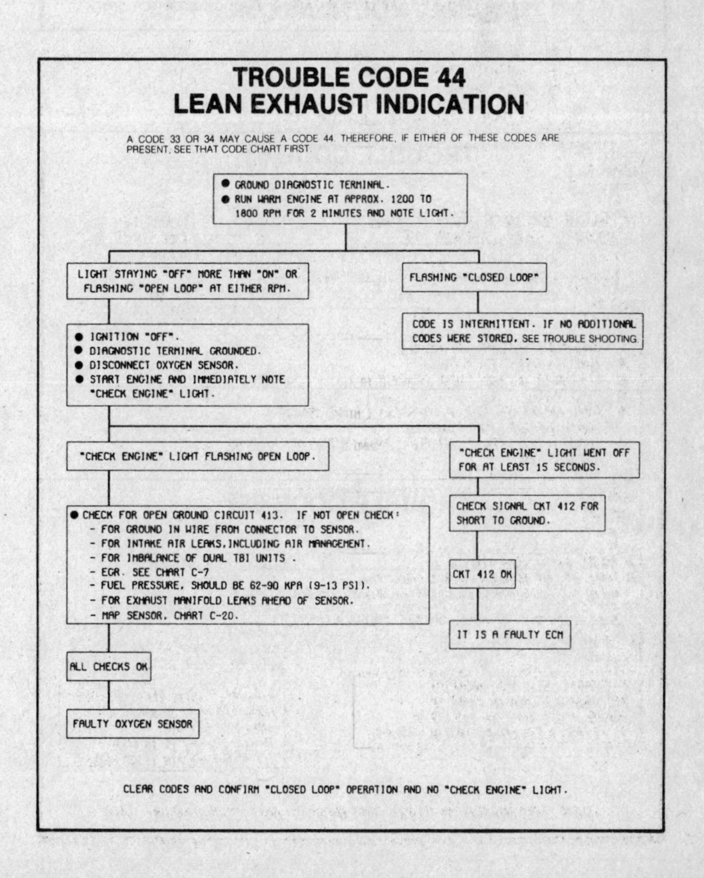

1984 CORVETTE COMPUTER COMMAND CONTROL (Cont.)

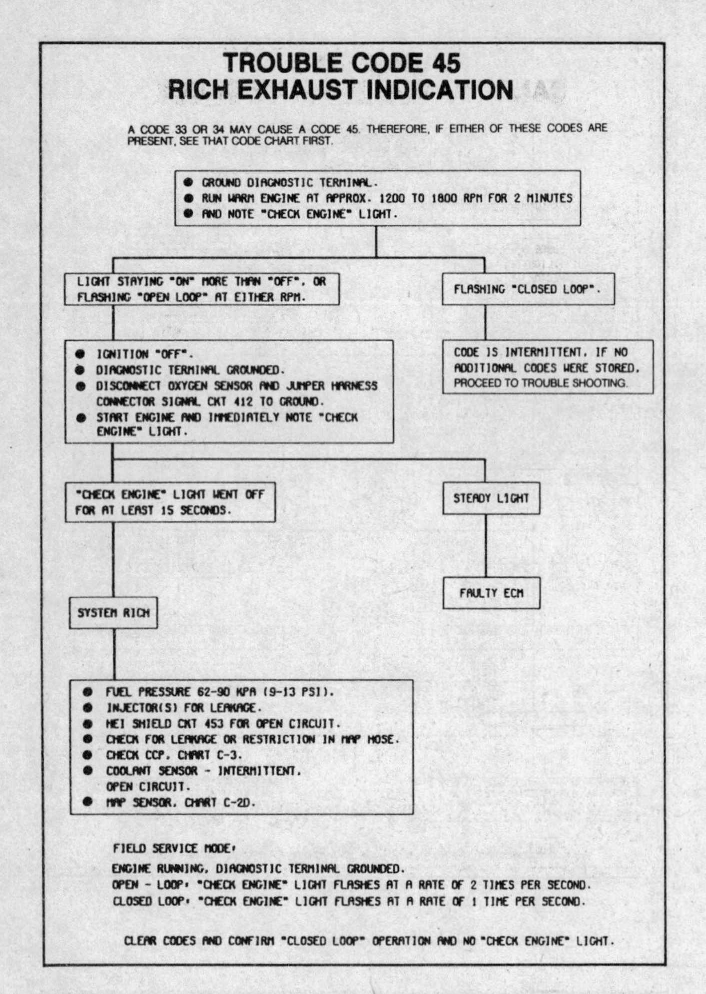

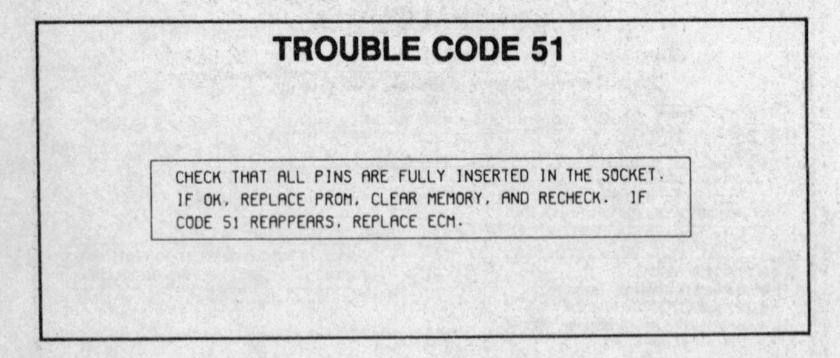

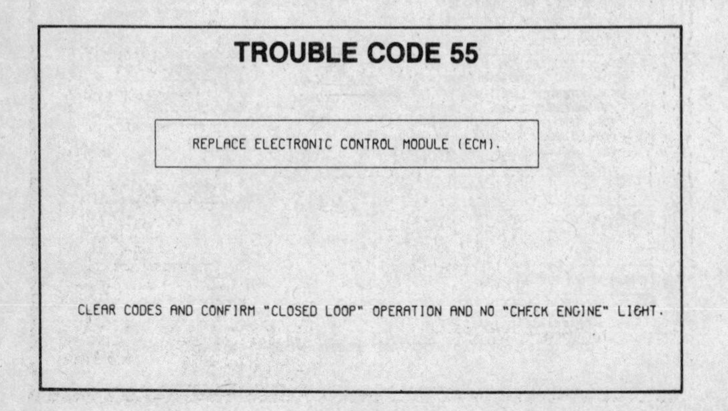

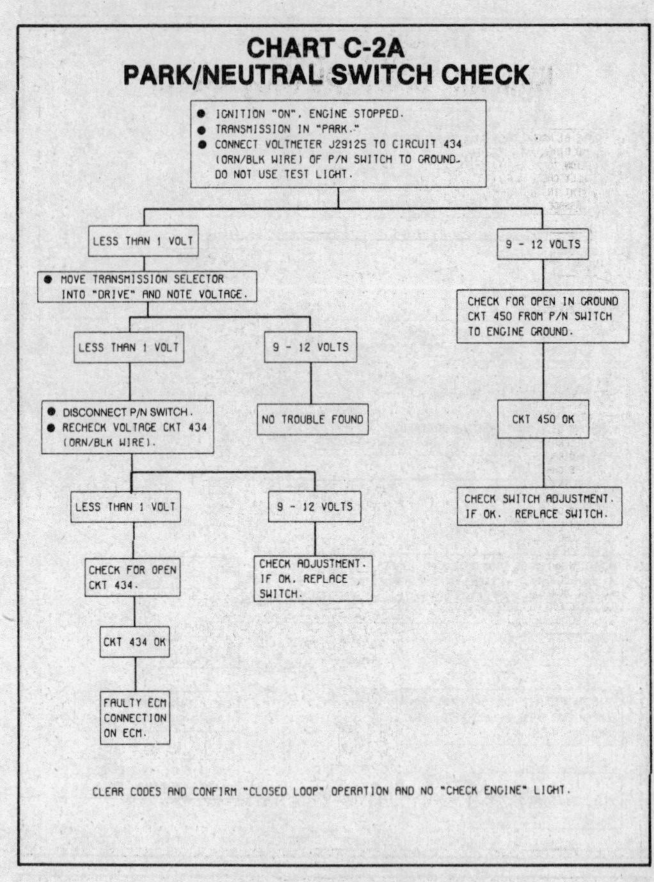

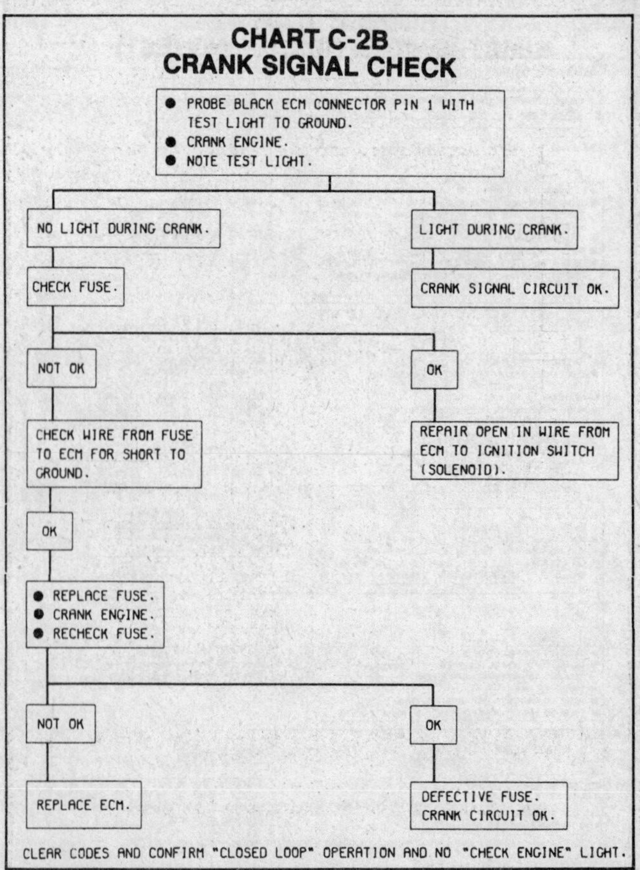

1984 CORVETTE COMPUTER COMMAND CONTROL (Cont.)

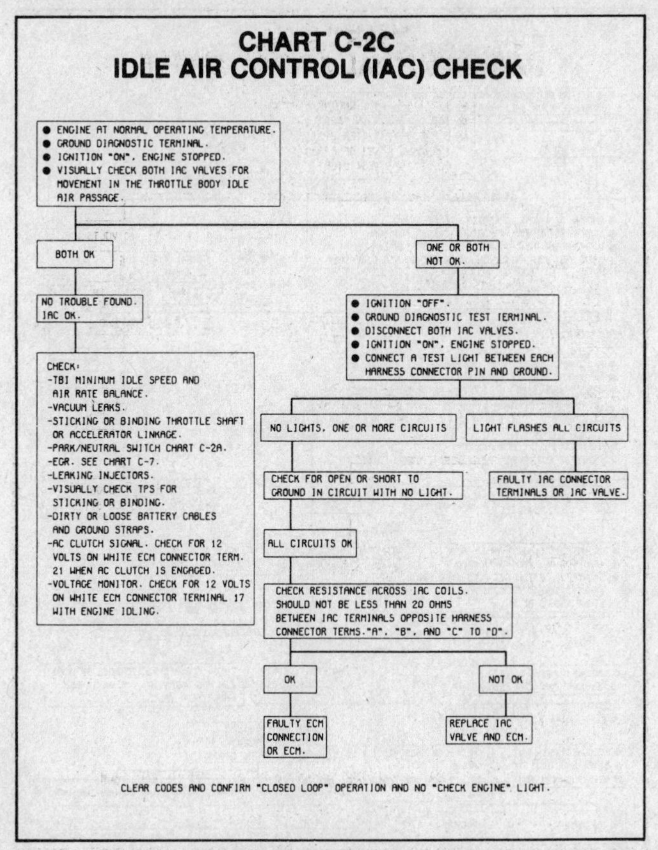

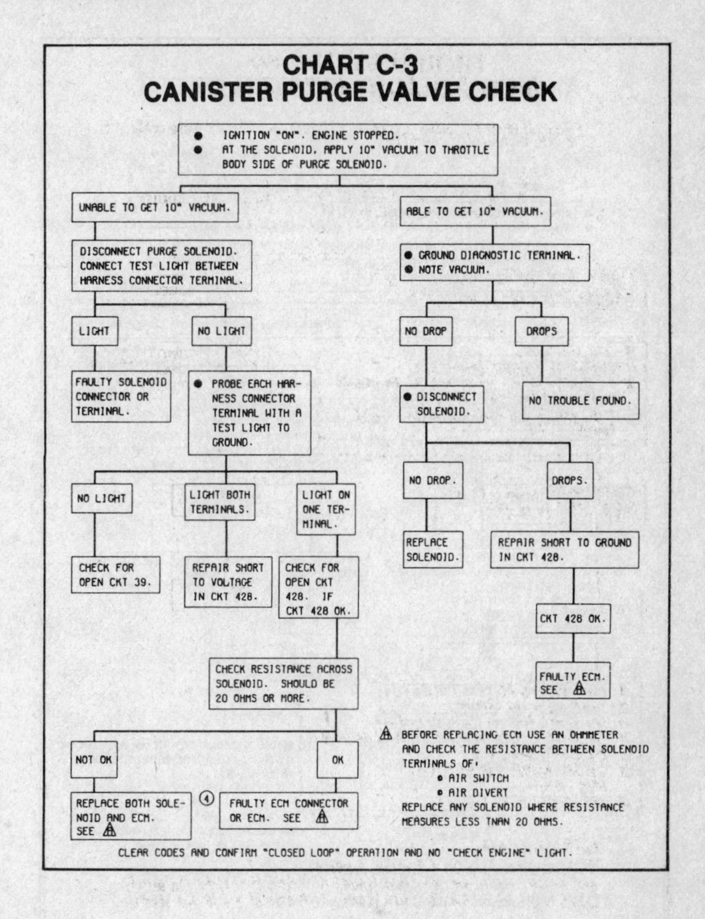

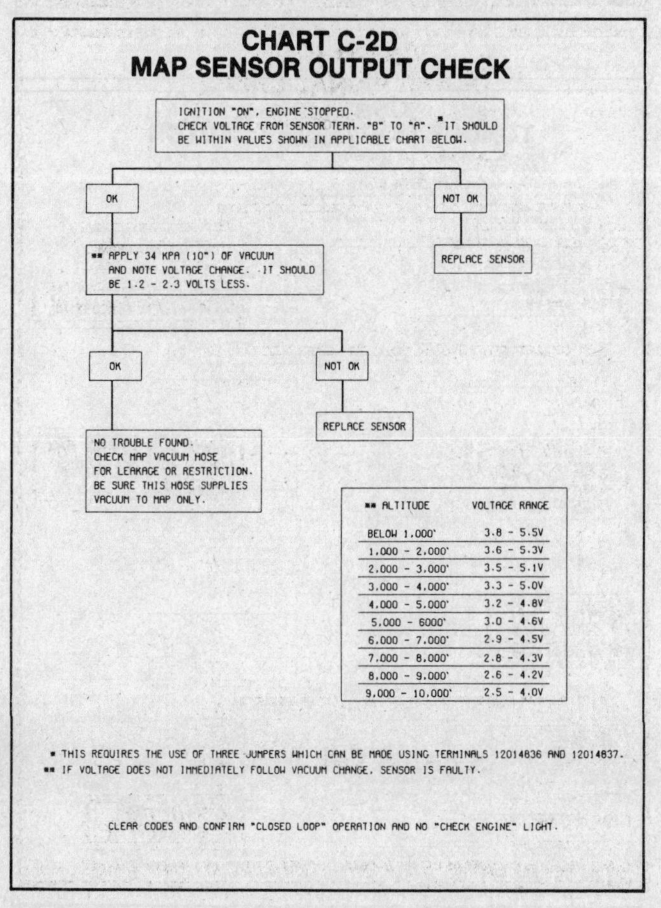

** ALTITUDE	VOLTAGE RANGE
BELOW 1,000'	3.8 - 5.5V
1,000 - 2,000'	3.6 - 5.3V
2,000 - 3,000'	3.5 - 5.1V
3,000 - 4,000'	3.3 - 5.0V
4,000 - 5,000'	3.2 - 4.8V
5,000 - 6000'	3.0 - 4.6V
6,000 - 7,000'	2.9 - 4.5V
7,000 - 8,000'	2.8 - 4.3V
8,000 - 9,000'	2.6 - 4.2V
9,000 - 10,000'	2.5 - 4.0V

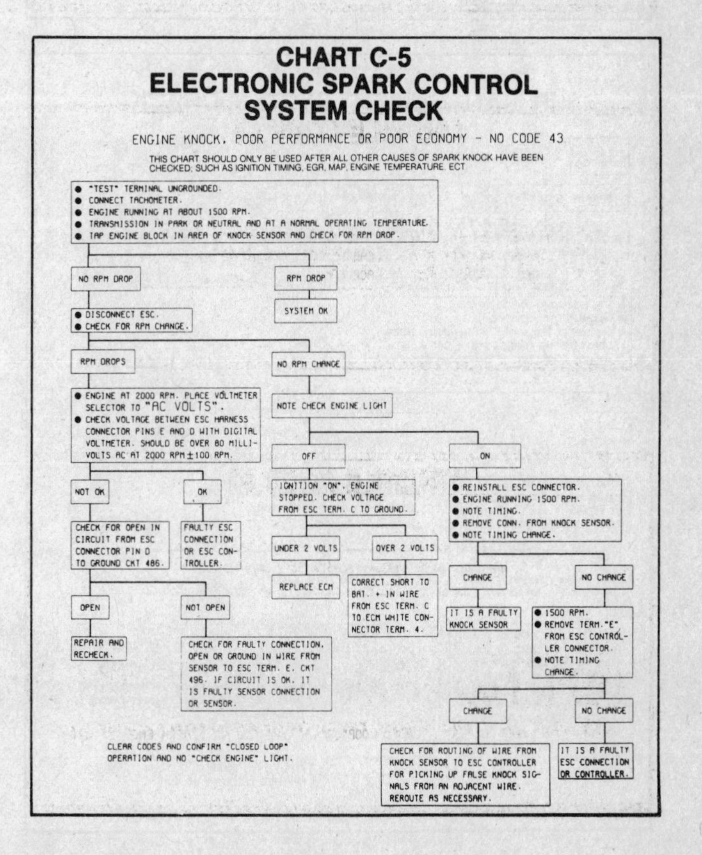

1984 CORVETTE COMPUTER COMMAND CONTROL (Cont.)

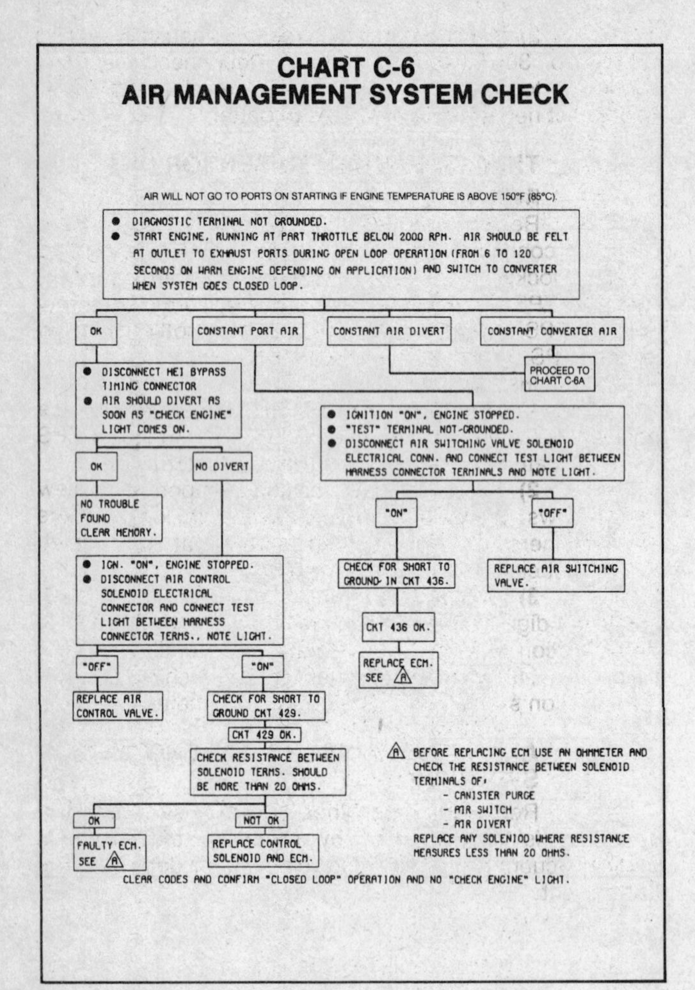

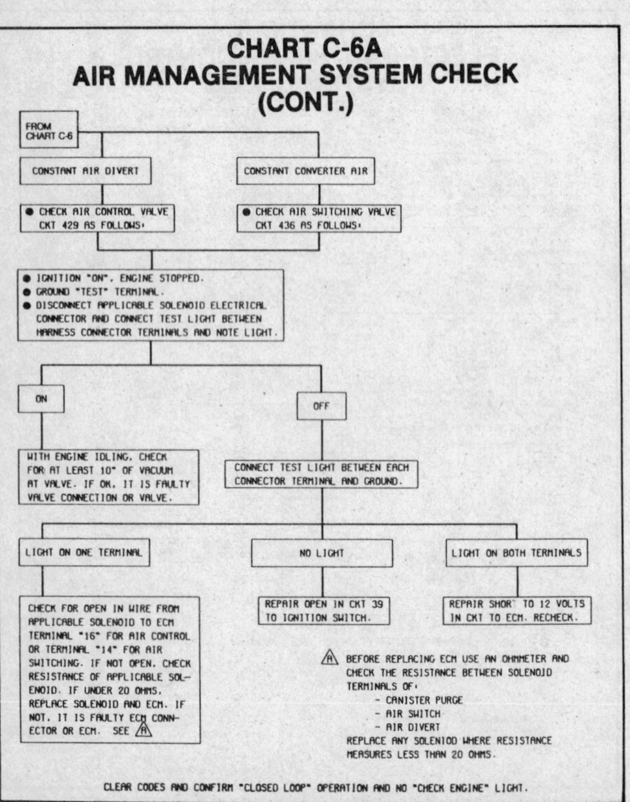

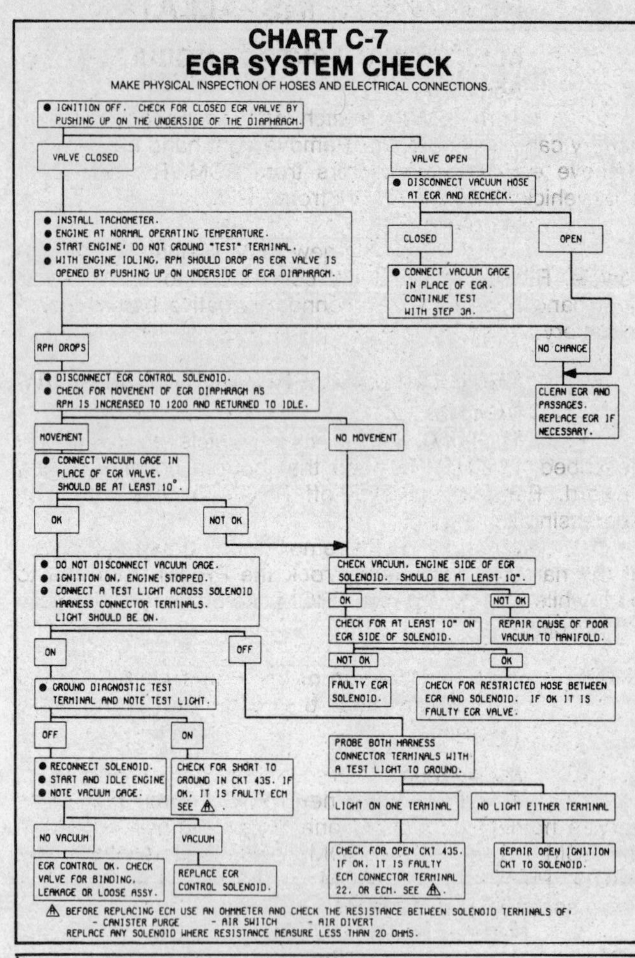

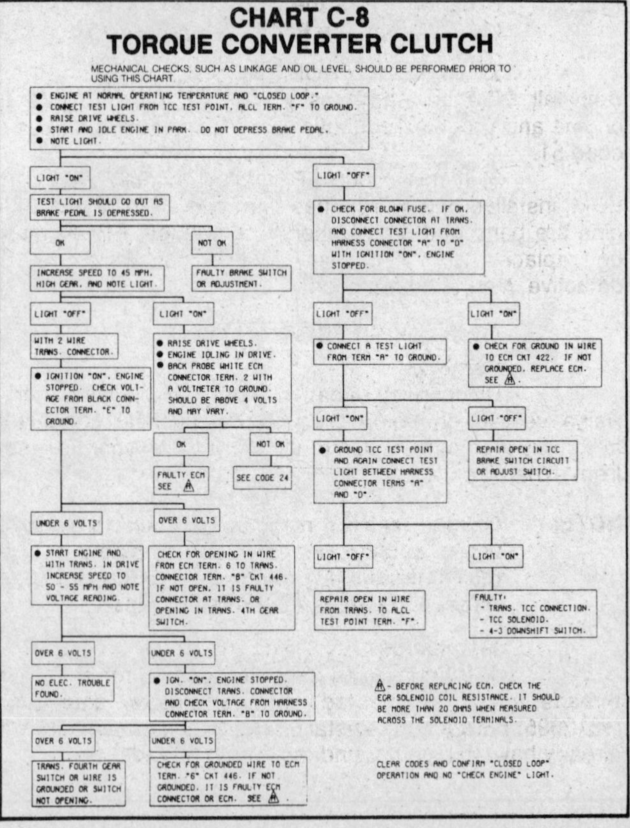

1984 CORVETTE COMPUTER COMMAND CONTROL (Cont.)

REMOVAL & INSTALLATION

ELECTRONIC CONTROL MODULE (ECM)

Removal

Turn ignition switch off. Disconnect negative battery cable from battery. Remove right hand hush panel. Remove electrical connectors from ECM. Remove ECM from vehicle. Remove PROM from ECM.

Installation

Install PROM on new ECM. Reinstall ECM into vehicle. Reconnect electrical connectors to ECM. Install right hand hush panel. Reconnect negative battery cable to battery.

PROGRAMMABLE READ ONLY MEMORY

Removal

1) Remove ECM from vehicle as previously described. Position ECM so that bottom cover is facing upward. Remove the slide-off PROM access cover by depressing locking tab.

2) Using PROM removal tool, grasp the PROM at the narrow ends. Gently rock the PROM from end to end while pulling up on PROM. Remove PROM from PROM carrier.

NOTE: **Note the location of the reference notches in the PROM and the ECM for reassembly reference.**

Installation

1) Check that new PROM has the same service number as the old one. Place the new PROM in the ECM. Position the PROM carrier squarely over the PROM. Press on the PROM carrier until the PROM is firmly seated in the ECM.

NOTE: **Make sure that the reference notches in both the ECM and the PROM are properly aligned.**

2) Reinstall PROM access cover on ECM. Reinstall ECM in vehicle as previously described. Start engine and ground diagnostic test lead. Watch for trouble code 51.

3) If this occurs, PROM is not fully seated in ECM, installed backwards, has bent pins or is defective. If pins are bend and crack when straightened, PROM must be replaced. If PROM is installed backwards or is defective, it must be replaced.

OXYGEN SENSOR

Removal

Disconnect negative battery cable at battery. Raise vehicle on hoist. Disconnect electrical connector from oxygen sensor. Carefully remove oxygen sensor from exhaust pipe.

NOTE: **Oxygen sensor may be difficult to remove when engine temperature is below 120°F (49°C). Excessive removal force may damage threads in exhaust manifold or pipe.**

Installation

1) Whenever an oxygen sensor is removed, it's threads must be coated with anti-seize compound (5613695) before it is reinstalled. New oxygen sensors will already have this compound applied to threads.

2) Install oxygen sensor in exhaust pipe and tighten to 30 ft. lbs. (41 N.m). Reconnect electrical connector to oxygen sensor. Lower vehicle from hoist. Reconnect negative battery cable to battery.

THROTTLE POSITION SENSOR (TPS)

Removal

Remove air cleaner assembly. Disconnect electrical connector from TPS. Remove 2 TPS attaching screws, lockwashers and retainers. Discard screws. Remove TPS. It may be necessary to remove screw holding TPS actuator lever to end of throttle shaft to remove TPS.

Installation

1) With throttle valve in normal closed idle position, install TPS on throttle body. Make sure that TPS lever is located above tang on throttle actuator lever.

2) Apply a thread locking compound to new TPS screws. Install new TPS screws with lockwashers and retainers. Do not tighten screws at this point. Reconnect electrical connector to TPS.

3) Without removing connector from TPS, connect a digital voltmeter to terminals "A" and "B" of TPS. Turn ignition switch "ON". Rotate TPS until voltmeter reading is .45-.60 volts. Tighten TPS attaching screws. Turn ignition switch "OFF" and remove voltmeter.

ALL OTHER SENSORS, SOLENOIDS & SWITCHES

Removal of all other sensors, switches and solenoids is accomplished by removing the electrical and/or vacuum connectors and removing or detaching the component.

GENERAL MOTORS DFI CONTROL SYSTEM

DESCRIPTION

The Digital Fuel Injection (DFI) system combines engine control, fuel metering and emission monitoring into a computer-controlled system. The Electronic Control Module (ECM) is the "brain" of the DFI system. The ECM is a digital electronic computer which receives and processes engine data, computes and interprets engine information and sends instructions to various components. It provides fuel efficient operation with reduced exhaust emissions.

OPERATION

The DFI system consists of the following subassemblies: Fuel delivery, air induction, data sensors, Electronic Control Module (ECM), Electronic Spark Timing (EST), Idle Speed Control (ISC), emission controls, closed loop fuel control, cruise control, diagnostic system, catalytic converter and Torque Converter Clutch (TCC).

FUEL DELIVERY

Fuel delivery system consists of an electric in-tank fuel pump (integral part of fuel sending unit), fuel filter, fuel pressure regulator, fuel injectors and fuel lines. Fuel is supplied to engine through 2 electronically pulsed (timed) injector valves located in throttle body on top of intake manifold. The ECM controls the amount of fuel metered through injectors based upon engine demand information.

AIR INDUCTION

The air induction system consists of a throttle body and intake manifold. Air for combustion enters throttle body and is distributed to each cylinder through intake manifold. Throttle body contains a special distribution skirt below each injector to improve fuel distribution. Air flow rate is controlled by throttle valves which are connected to accelerator linkage. Idle speed is determined by position of throttle valves and is controlled by Idle Speed Control (ISC).

Fig. 1: Diagram of DFI Components

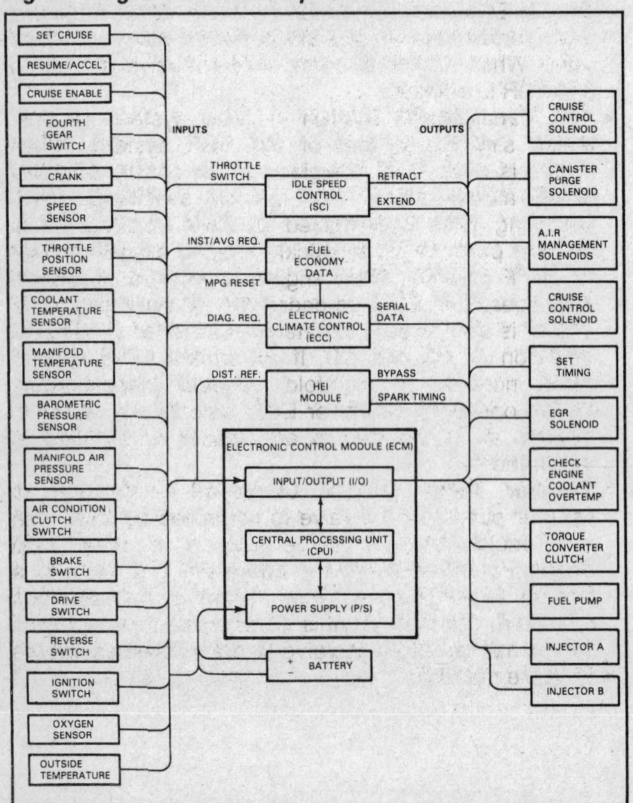

DATA SENSORS

Each sensor furnishes electrical impulses to ECM. Using these impulses, the ECM computes spark timing and fuel delivery rate necessary to maintain desired air/fuel mixture, thus controlling amount of fuel delivered to engine. Data sensors are interrelated to each other as illustrated in *Fig. 1.* Sensor operation is as follows:

Manifold Air Temperature Sensor (MAT)

This sensor is mounted in intake manifold directly in front of throttle body. The MAT sensor measures air/fuel mixture temperature in intake manifold. Sensor resistance changes as air temperature changes. The ECM receives this change in signal and adjusts injector pulse accordingly. Low temperature produces high resistance.

Coolant Temperature Sensor (CTS)

The CTS is located in the left front corner of the intake manifold. This sensor provides information to ECM which is used for fuel enrichment, ignition timing, EGR operation, canister purge control, air management, early fuel evaporation control and closed loop fuel control.

Manifold Absolute Pressure Sensor (MAP)

MAP sensor is mounted under instrument panel near right side A/C outlet. A hose from throttle body to MAP sensor provides vacuum signal. Sensor monitors changes in intake manifold pressure which result from engine load, speed and barometric pressure variations. As intake manifold pressure increases, additional fuel is required by engine. The MAP sends this information to ECM and ECM increases injector pulse width (time injector is open). As pressure decreases, pulse width is decreased.

Barometric Pressure Sensor (BARO)

The BARO sensor is mounted on MAP sensor bracket. This sensor measures ambient or barometric pressures and signals ECM on pressure changes due to altitude and/or weather.

Throttle Position Sensor (TPS)

TPS sensor is mounted on side of throttle body and is connected directly to throttle shaft. This unit senses throttle movement and position of throttle, then transmits appropriate electrical signals to ECM. The ECM processes these signals to operate the ISC and to supply fuel enrichment.

Vehicle Speed Sensor (VSS)

Vehicle speed sensor informs ECM of vehicle speed. Speed sensor produces a weak signal which is amplified by a buffer amplifier. Speed sensor and buffer amplifier are mounted behind speedometer cluster. The ECM uses vehicle speed sensor signals for logic required to operate fuel economy data panel, integral cruise control and ISC.

Oxygen Sensor

The oxygen sensor used in DFI is a closed-end Zirconia sensor placed in the exhaust gas stream. This sensor produces a very weak voltage which varies with oxygen content of exhaust gases. As oxygen content of

GENERAL MOTORS DFI CONTROL SYSTEM

exhaust gases increases, a leaner mixture is indicated by low voltage output. As oxygen content decreases, a richer mixture is indicated by higher voltage output. The ECM corrects air/fuel ratio according to signals received from oxygen sensor.

NOTE: **No attempt should be made to measure oxygen sensor voltage output. Current drain of conventional voltmeter could permanently damage sensor, shift sensor calibration range and/or render sensor unusable. Do not connect jumper wire, test leads or other electrical connectors to sensor.**

Engine Speed Sensor

The engine speed signal comes from a 7-terminal HEI module in distributor. Pulses from distributor are sent to ECM where time between pulses is used to calculate engine speed. The ECM adds spark advance modifications to signal and sends this signal back to distributor.

ELECTRONIC CONTROL MODULE (ECM)

The ECM monitors and controls all DFI system functions. The ECM consists of input/output devices, Central Processing Unit (CPU), power supply and memories. A brief description and operation of each component is as follows:

Input/Output Devices

These integral devices of ECM convert electrical signals received by data sensors and switches to digital signals for use by CPU.

Central Processing Unit (CPU)

Digital signals received by CPU are used to perform all mathematical computations and logic functions necessary to deliver proper air/fuel mixture. The CPU also calculates spark timing and idle speed information. The CPU commands operation of emission controls, closed loop fuel control, cruise control, diagnostic system and modulated displacement (1981 6.0L engine only).

Power Supply

Main source of power for the ECM is from the battery, through the No. 1 ignition circuit.

Memories

The 3 types of memory in the ECM are: Read Only Memory (ROM), Random Access Memory (RAM) and Programmable Read Only Memory (PROM). Function of each memory is as follows:

- **Read Only Memory (ROM)** — The ROM is programmed information that can only be read by ECM. The ROM program cannot be changed. If battery voltage is removed, ROM information will be retained.
- **Random Access Memory (RAM)** — This memory is the scratch pad for the CPU. Information can be read into or out of RAM memory, similar to a calculator. Data sensor information, diagnostic codes and results of calculations are temporarily stored in RAM memory. If battery voltage is removed, all information stored in this memory is lost.
- **Programmable Read Only Memory (PROM)** — Two factory-programmed units make up this memory. They contain calibration information about each engine, transmission, body and rear axle ratio combination. If battery voltage is lost, PROM information is retained. The PROM's can be easily replaced if necessary.

ELECTRONIC SPARK TIMING (EST)

The EST system consists of ECM and modified HEI distributor with 7-terminal HEI module. The HEI distributor communicates to ECM through a 4-terminal connector which contains 4 circuits: Distributor reference circuit, by-pass circuit, EST circuit and ground circuit.

Whenever pick-up coil signals HEI module to open primary circuit, it also sends spark timing signals to ECM through the reference line. When voltage on HEI by-pass line is 0 volts (engine cranking), HEI module switches to by-pass circuit. In by-pass circuit, HEI module provides spark advance at base timing and disregards spark advance signal from ECM. When voltage on HEI by-pass circuit is 5 volts (engine running), HEI module accepts spark timing signal provided by ECM.

The ECM monitors engine speed through the HEI reference line and engine operating conditions through data sensors. From these parameters, ECM calculates proper spark advance and supplies signals to HEI distributor through the EST line.

IDLE SPEED CONTROL (ISC)

The ISC is an electrically driven actuator which changes throttle valve angle (in idle position) according to commands from ECM. This function is by-passed when throttle is opened enough to bring TPS off its idle circuit. When engine is cold, ECM holds throttle valve open for longer period of time to provide faster warm-up. ISC is located on side of throttle body.

EMISSION CONTROLS

The ECM controls operation of EGR system, AIR management system and canister purge control operation. Description of each system is as follows:

- **EGR System** — Signals received from coolant sensor provide ECM with engine temperature. When engine is cold, ported vacuum to EGR is closed with a solenoid valve. When engine is warm, solenoid valve is opened and EGR is allowed.
- **AIR Management System** — This system is controlled similarly to that of the EGR system. When engine is cold, ECM energizes an air control solenoid which allows air to flow to air switching valve. Switching valve is energized by ECM to direct air to exhaust ports to aid in quickly heating oxygen sensor to 600°F (316°C). When engine is warm or in closed loop operation, ECM de-energizes air switching valve and air is sent directly to catalytic converter to assist in oxidation of HC and CO. If air control valve detects rapid increase in manifold vacuum (deceleration), certain operating modes or ECM detects any failure in system, air is diverted to air cleaner or dumped to atmosphere.
- **Canister Purge Control Operation** — Vacuum to canister purge control valve is controlled by ECM with a solenoid valve. When engine is in open loop operation, solenoid valve is energized and vacuum is blocked to purge valve. When system is in closed loop operation, solenoid valve is de-energized and vacuum can be applied to purge valve to draw collected vapors to intake manifold.

GENERAL MOTORS DFI CONTROL SYSTEM (Cont.)

CLOSED LOOP FUEL CONTROL

Closed loop fuel control maintains an air/fuel ratio of 14.7:1. Oxygen sensor monitors oxygen content of exhaust gases, sending information to ECM. The ECM then corrects air/fuel mixture for deviations from ideal ratio.

CRUISE CONTROL

The ECM receives input signals from cruise control engagement switches, instrument panel switch, brake release switch, drive switch and speed sensor. The ECM processes cruise control inputs together with DFI engine control inputs and transmits command signals to vacuum control solenoid valve and power unit solenoid valve to control vehicle speed.

TORQUE CONVERTER CLUTCH (TCC)

The torque converter clutch is controlled by ECM via an electrical solenoid mounted in the transmission. At a specific speed, the ECM energizes the solenoid and the torque converter is mechanically coupled to the engine. Under specific operating conditions (when normal fluid coupling is required) the solenoid is de-energized.

CATALYTIC CONVERTER

Proper emission control is accomplished with a special 3-way catalytic converter; that is, it converts all 3 major pollutants (CO, HC and NOx). The converter contains pellets coated with platinum and palladium (California vehicles have additional coating of rodium).

The 3-way catalytic converter used in the DFI system is a dual-bed converter. The "upstream" section of the converter contains a reducing/oxidizing bed to reduce NOx while at the same time oxidizing CO and HC. An air supply pipe from the AIR pump introduces an extra amount of air between the dual beds (during closed loop mode), so the second bed can oxidize any remaining CO and HC with a high conversion efficiency to minimize overall emissions.

DIAGNOSTIC SYSTEM

The ECM of the DFI control system has a built-in diagnostic system to constantly monitor engine/vehicle performance and operation. The diagnostic system consists of 4 tests: Engine malfunction tests, switch tests, engine data displays and output cycling tests. Description of each test is as follows:

Engine Malfunction Test

This test is constantly performed by ECM to detect system failures or malfunctions. When a malfunction occurs, ECM will light the "SERVICE NOW/SOON" light(s). When a malfunction occurs and lamp is turned on, a corresponding trouble code is stored in ECM memory. Malfunctions are recorded as "hard failures" or "intermittent failures".

- "Hard failures" cause "SERVICE NOW/SOON" light(s) to glow and remain on until malfunction is repaired. If the "SERVICE NOW/SOON" light(s) comes on and remains on during vehicle operation, cause of malfunction MUST be determined.
- "Intermittent failures" cause "SERVICE NOW/SOON" light(s) to flicker or go out after malfunction clears. "Intermittent failures" may be sensor related. If a senosr fails, ECM will use a substitute value in its calculations to continue engine operation. In this condition, service is not mandatory; but loss of driveability may be encountered. If the related sensor malfunction does not recur within 50 ignition cycles, related trouble code will be erased from ECM memory.

Switch Test

This series of tests checks operation of various switches which provide input to ECM. During this operation, specific switches are cycled and ECM analyzes the action to determine if switches are operating properly.

Engine Data Displays

This is a series of checks which display important engine data information. This information may be compared to that information received from a properly operating engine for analysis.

Output Cycling Tests

This series of tests causes ECM to cycle various output devices on and off. During this test, operation of engine control solenoids and lamps may be checked by using command signals from ECM.

As a lamp and system check, "SERVICE NOW/SOON" light(s) should glow when ignition is turned on and go out 1-4 seconds after engine has started. If not, ECM has detected fault in system.

NOTE: **The tests which comprise the diagnostic system should be performed in the sequence given to diagnosis any failure in the shortest period of time.**

DIAGNOSIS & TESTING

The ECM stores component failure information for DFI system under a related trouble code which can be recalled for diagnosis and repair. When recalled, these codes will be displayed on Electrical Climate Control (ECC) panel starting with lowest numbered code. Only codes in which a related malfunction has occurred will be displayed. When system is displaying in diagnostic mode, Fuel Data Display panel will show no readings.

NOTE: **The terms "enter diagnostics" and "exit diagnostics" will be used periodically throughout this section. Follow the procedure for entering diagnostic mode when instructed to "enter diagnostics". Follow the procedure for exiting diagnostic mode when instructed to "exit diagnostics".**

ENTERING DIAGNOSTIC MODE

Turn ignition on. Depress "OFF" and "WARMER" buttons on ECC panel simultaneously and hold buttons until ".." appears on digital display panel. Release buttons and code "-1.8.8" should appear, indicating beginning of diagnostic readout. Trouble codes will be displayed beginning with lowest numbered code and be repeated a second time. After second time, trouble code ".7.0" will appear, indicating ECM is ready for next diagnostic feature. If no codes are stored, "-1.8.8" will appear for longer period of time, then code ".7.0" will appear. *See Fig. 2.*

NOTE: **Trouble code ".7.0" is a decision point. When this code is displayed, either select diagnostic feature e.g., switch test, engine data display, etc., or clear codes and then exit diagnostic mode.**

GENERAL MOTORS DFI CONTROL SYSTEM (Cont.)

Fig. 2: Trouble Code "-1.8.8" Displayed on ECC Panel

CLEARING TROUBLE CODES

Trouble codes stored in ECM memory may be cleared (erased) by entering diagnostic mode and then depressing "OFF" and "HI" buttons at the same time. Hold buttons until ".0.0" is displayed. Release buttons and code ".7.0" should appear.

EXITING DIAGNOSTIC MODE

Depress any ECC function keys except "LO" or "OUTSIDE TEMP". Exiting may also be completed by turning ignition switch "OFF" for 10 seconds. This will take ECC panel out of diagnostic mode, but will not clear any trouble codes. Original temperature setting should appear on ECC panel.

STATUS LIGHT DISPLAY

While in diagnostic mode, the lights above the ECC control head function buttons indicate status of various operating modes. The different modes of operation are indicated by the light being either on or off. The lights and their respective mode are as follows:

"OFF" Button

This light will be on when the ECM is operating in closed loop mode of operation. The light should come on after coolant temperature and oxygen sensors have reached normal operating temperature. The light is off when the ECM is operating in open loop mode.

"ECON" Button

This light will be on when the oxygen sensor signal indicates a rich exhaust mixture (not enough oxygen). The light will be off when the signal indicates a lean mixture (too much oxygen). This light should flicker on and off during warm steady throttle operation. This verifies that the oxygen sensor is providing signals to the ECM and that the ECM is in closed loop operation.

"LO" Button

This light will be on whenever the throttle switch is closed. The light will be off whenever the throttle is applied.

"AUTO" Button

This light will be on when the ECM is commanding the torque converter clutch (TCC) to engage. The light only indicates if the TCC is engaged or disengaged (light off) by the ECM. Actual TCC operation depends upon the integrity of the TCC system.

"HI" Button

This light will be on whenever the 4th gear switch is open (actual 4th gear operation). The light should be off at all other times.

"OUTSIDE TEMP"

This light will be on when the ECC (A/C) compressor clutch is engaged. The light will be off when the compressor is disengaged. Depressing this button while in diagnostic mode causes the compressor to be engaged and disengaged. The light only indicates whether the compressor clutch is operating. Actual compressor operation depends on compressor cycling switch and system integrity.

ENGINE MALFUNCTION TEST PROCEDURE

During any diagnostic procedure, "hard failure" codes MUST be distinguished from "intermittent failure" codes. Diagnostic charts CANNOT be used to analyze "intermittent failure" codes, except as noted under Diagnostic Procedure. To determine "hard failure" codes and "intermittent failure" codes, proceed as follows:

1) Enter diagnostics. ECC will display trouble codes beginning with lowest numbered code. Each code will be displayed for 2 seconds until the highest code present has been displayed. Record all codes. Then, "-1.8.8" will appear.

2) Display procedure will repeat twice. On the 3rd pass through the display, "hard failure" codes ONLY, will be displayed. Record all codes again. Any codes which appeared during the 1st and 2nd passes but not during the 3rd, are "intermittent failures". If no codes are displayed during the 3rd pass, there are no "hard failures", and the "SERVICE NOW/SOON" light(s) should have been out before entering diagnostics.

3) The 3rd pass ends with "-1.8.8" display. When trouble code sequence is completed, ".7.0" will display. If a code "51" is present, it must be diagnosed before further testing can begin. As long as "51" is displayed, no other diagnostic features are possible.

4) Begin diagnosis with the lowest numbered code, unless codes "51" and/or "16" are present. If codes "51" or "16" are shown, begin diagnosis with code "51", then proceed to code "16" since these codes may have an effect on setting of other codes. If no trouble codes are present, ECC will display "-1.8.8" for 2 seconds and then ".7.0".

NOTE: **If vehicle exibits performance problems and no codes are set, refer to the performance charts. Components recorded by trouble codes generally do not cause performance problems when no codes are stored.**

5) If "intermittent failures" "13", "20", "30", "33", "39", "44" or "45" appear, use diagnostic chart for corresponding "hard failure" code.

NOTE: **After diagnosing trouble codes; switch tests, engine data displays and output cycling tests can be used to isolate "intermittent failures". DO NOT perform any adjustment or repairs on any component until malfunction has been positively located.**

SWITCH TEST PROCEDURE

1) Enter diagnostics and with code ".7.0" displayed, depress and release brake pedal. This will start switch test procedure and code ".7.1" will be displayed.

NOTE: **Each test action must be performed within 10 seconds after codes appear on display panel or ECM will store code as failure and proceed to next code.**

2) With code ".7.1" displayed, depress and release brake pedal again. Code ".7.2" should appear. With code ".7.2" displayed, depress throttle to wide open

GENERAL MOTORS DFI CONTROL SYSTEM (Cont.)

position and slowly release. This checks throttle switch for proper operation. Code ".7.3" should appear.

3) With code ".7.3" displayed, shift transmission into "D" then back to "N". This checks operation of the drive switch. Code ".7.4" should appear. With code ".7.4" displayed, shift transmission to "R" and back to "P". This checks operation of the reverse switch. Code ".7.5" should appear.

4) With code ".7.5" displayed, switch cruise control on then off. This controls operation of the cruise control switch. Code ".7.6" should appear. With code ".7.6" displayed, switch cruise control on, then depress and release "Set/Coast" button. This checks operation of the "Set/Coast" switch. Code ".7.7" should appear. With code ".7.7" displayed, switch cruise control on, then depress and release "Resume/Acceleration" switch. This checks operation of the "Resume/Acceleration" switch. Code ".7.8" should appear.

NOTE: **To pass codes ".7.5", ".7.6" and ".7.7" on vehicles without cruise control, allow codes to appear for 10 seconds each, then proceed with step 5).** Codes will cycle through ECM and be processed as failures.

5) With code ".7.8" displayed, depress and release "Instant/Average" button on fuel data panel. This checks operation of the "Instant/Average" switch. Code ".7.9" should appear. With code ".7.9" displayed, depress and release "Reset" button on fuel panel. This checks operation of the "Reset" switch. Code ".8.0" should appear.

Fig. 3: Fuel Data Panel

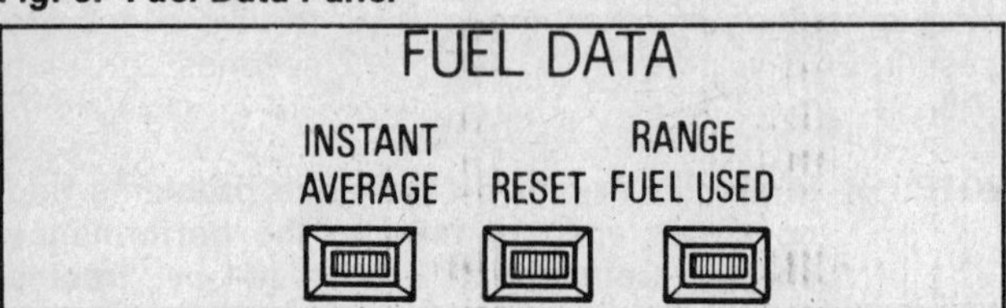

6) With code ".8.0" displayed, push "Outside Temp" button twice. This test checks ECM's ability to recognize and process air conditioning clutch signal. This test may require engine running with A/C operating in "Auto" mode with temperature selection set at 60°F (16°C).

7) When switch tests are completed, ECM will display codes which did not pass test. Each code will appear beginning with lowest code. Codes will not disappear until affected switch circuit is repaired and retested. After switch tests are completed, ECC will display code ".0.0" and return to code ".7.0". Code ".0.0" indicates all switch circuits are operating properly. Remember that ".0.0" will never be obtained on vehicles without cruise control.

ENGINE DATA DISPLAY PROCEDURE

1) Enter diagnostics and with code ".7.0" displayed, press "Reset" button on fuel data panel. Code ".9.0" should appear. If code ".9.0" does not appear, refer to switch test code ".7.9".

2) Engine data display shows values of 13 parameters monitored by ECM. Parameter numbers .0.1-.1.3 will be displayed for 1 second on ECC panel, followed by a numerical value. The parameter value will be displayed for 9 seconds. Each parameter and value will be **repeated until manually advanced to next parameter.**

3) To advance display parameter, depress "Instant/Average" button on fuel data panel. To return to previously displayed parameter, depress "Reset" button. After last parameter is displayed, code "9.5" should appear. Engine data display may be cleared at anytime, by pressing "Off" and "High" buttons on ECC panel simultaneously. Code "7.0" should appear.

4) Engine data display information can be used to compare information of engine to that of properly functioning engine for diagnosis of malfunctions. Parameters read and values displayed are as follows:

ENGINE DATA PARAMETERS

Display	Parameter
.0.1	Throttle angle displayed in degrees.
.0.2	MAP value in kilopascals (kPa).
.0.3	BARO value in kilopascals (kPa).
.0.4	Coolant temperature in °C.
.0.5	Manifold air temperature in °C.
.0.6	Injector Pulse width displayed in milliseconds. Decimal point will appear between 2 digits.
.0.7	Oxygen sensor voltage is displayed in volts. Decimal point will appear between 2 digits.
.0.8	Spark advance in degrees (2 digits).
.0.9	Ignition cycle value is number of times ignition has been cycled since trouble code was last set.
.1.0	Battery voltage. Decimal point will appear before last digit.
.1.1	Engine RPM (divided by 10). Engine speed over 2000 RPM is displayed as "199" (actual 1990) since this is the highest number the ECC can display.
.1.2	Vehicle speed in MPH.
.1.3	PROM identification number (up to 3 digits). To ensure correct PROM is installed.

OUTPUT CYCLING TESTS PROCEDURE

1) This test procedure can be activated in either of the following methods: Enter diagnostics and with code ".7.0" displayed on ECC panel, depress "Instant/Average" button on fuel data panel. If code ".9.5" does not appear, refer to switch test code ".7.8". The other method is to depress "Instant/Average" button while in Engine Data Display, with parameter ".1.3" displayed.

2) The output cycling test turns ECM's outputs on and off. To enter output cycling tests, start engine. Turn engine off and within 2 seconds, turn ignition on. Enter diagnostics and display code ".9.5" on ECC panel. Depress accelerator pedal to wide open throttle position and release pedal. Code ".9.6" should appear. If ".9.6" does not appear, refer to switch test ".7.2".

3) Turn cruise contol instrument panel switch on. Cruise control outputs will cycle. Output cycling tests will automatically end after 2 minutes. After cycling output is complete, display should switch from code ".9.6" back to code ".9.5". Additional output cycling may be obtained by pressing and releasing the throttle switch.

FIXED SPARK MODE PROCEDURE

1) Purpose of test is to verify proper adjustment of spark timing. In this test procedure, the ECM commands a fixed spark advance of 20° and prevents EGR operation when the following conditions are met: **Engine running and warm, code ".9.5" displayed on ECC**

GENERAL MOTORS DFI CONTROL SYSTEM (Cont.)

panel, engine speed under 900 RPM, and transmission in "P".

2) This procedure can be activated in 1 of the following methods: Enter diagnostics and with code ".7.0" displayed on ECC panel, depress "Instant/Average" button on fuel data panel. Code ".9.5" should appear. If the code does not appear, refer to code ".7.8" of the switch test. The other method is to depress the "Instant/Average" button on fuel data panel while in Engine Data Display, with parameter ".1.3" displayed.

1983 PROGRAMMED ECM TROUBLE CODES

Code	Circuit Affected
12	No tach signal.
13	Oxygen sensor not ready.
14	Shorted coolant sensor circuit.
15	Open coolant sensor circuit.
16	Generator voltage out of range.
18	Open crank signal circuit.
19	Shorted fuel pump circuit.
20	Open fuel pump circuit.
21	Shorted TPS circuit.
22	Open TPS circuit.
23	EST/By-pass circuit problem.
24	Speed sensor circuit problem.
26	Shorted throttle switch circuit.
27	Open throttle switch circuit.
28	Open 4th gear circuit.
29	Shorted 4th gear circuit.
30	ISC circuit problem.
31	Shorted MAP sensor circuit.
32	Open MAP sensor circuit.
33	MAP/BARO sensor correlation.
34	MAP signal too high.
35	Shorted BARO sensor circuit.
36	Open BARO sensor circuit.
37	Shorted MAT sensor circuit.
38	Open MAT sensor circuit.
39	TCC engagement problem.
44	Lean exhaust signal.
45	Rich exhaust signal.
51	PROM error.
52	ECM memory reset indicator.
60	Transmission not in "DRIVE".
63	Car speed exceeds maximum limit.
64	Car exceeds maximum acceleration limit.
65	Coolant temperature exceeds maximum limit.
66	Engine RPM exceeds maximum limit.
67	Shorted "SET" or "RESUME" circuit.
.7.0	System ready for further tests.
.7.1	Cruise control brake circuit test.
.7.2	Throttle switch circuit test.
.7.3	Drive (ADL) circuit test.
.7.4	Reverse circuit test.
.7.5	Cruise "ON/OFF" circuit test.
.7.6	"SET/COAST" circuit test.
.7.7	"RESUME/ACCELERATION" circuit test.
.7.8	"INSTANT/AVERAGE" circuit test.
.7.9	"RESET" circuit test.
.8.0	A/C clutch circuit test.
1.8.8	Display check.
.9.0	System ready to display engine data.
.9.5	System ready for output cycling or in fixed spark mode.
.9.6	Output cycling.
.0.0	All diagnostics complete.

3) As long as the conditions in step **1)** are met and the HEI system is working properly (no code "23" set), a timing light can be used to verify that ignition timing is correctly adjusted. If ignition timing is not within 20° ± 2° BTDC, the base timing of 10° BTDC should be adjusted accordingly.

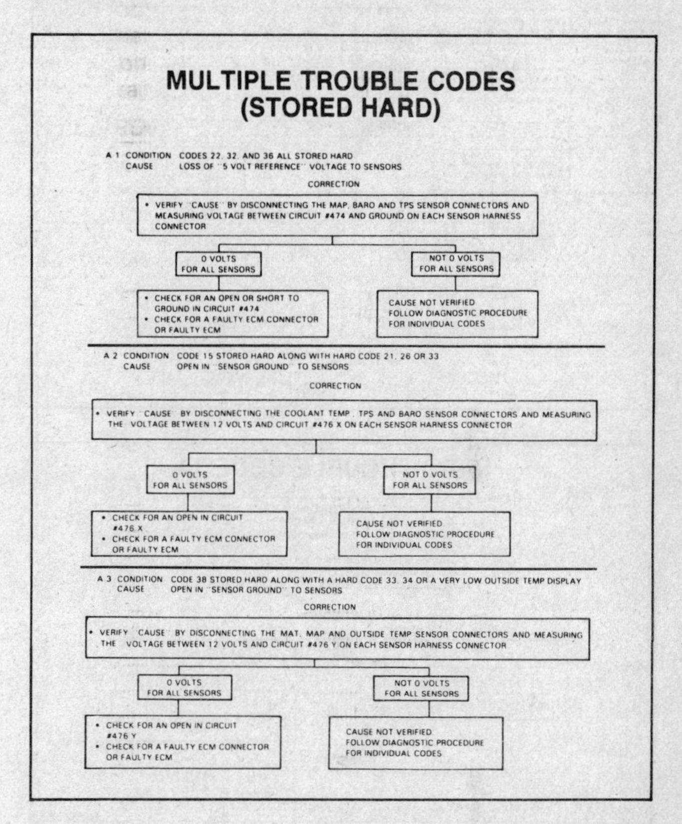

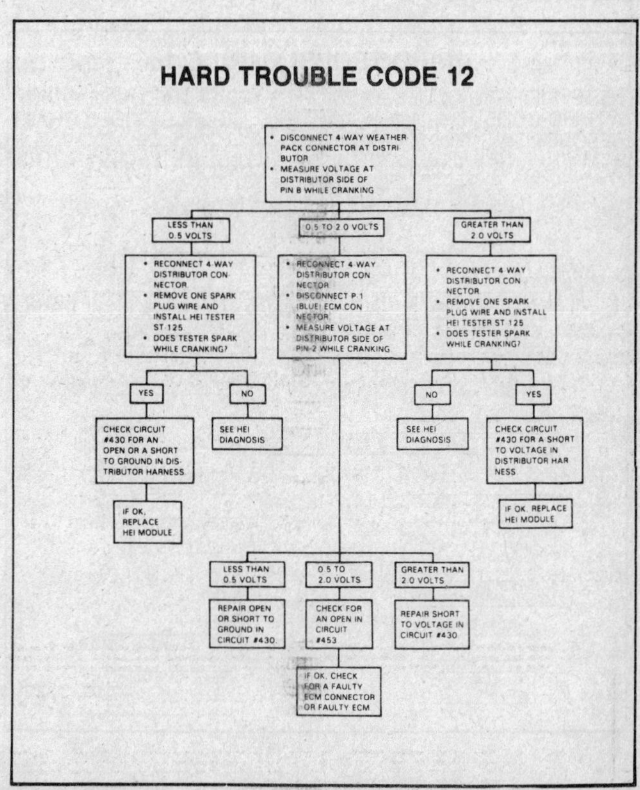

GENERAL MOTORS DFI CONTROL SYSTEM (Cont.)

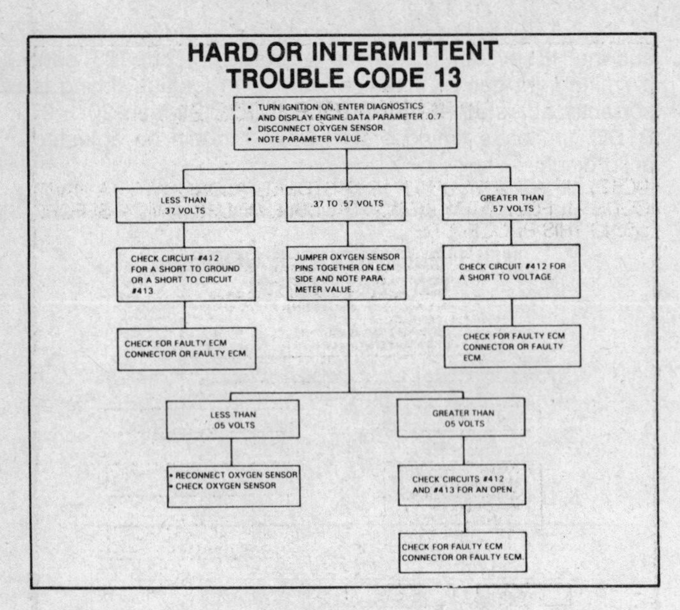

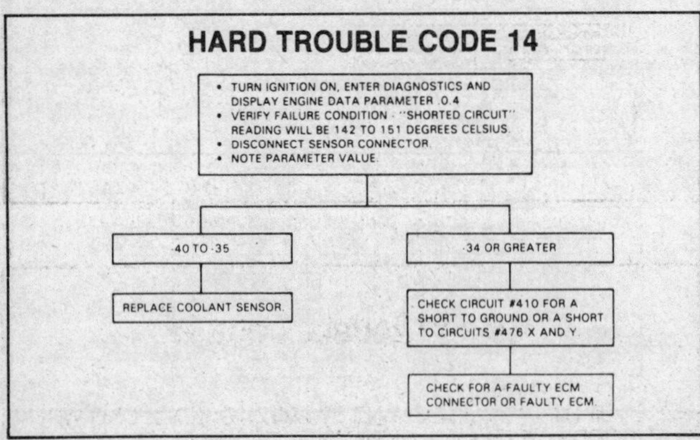

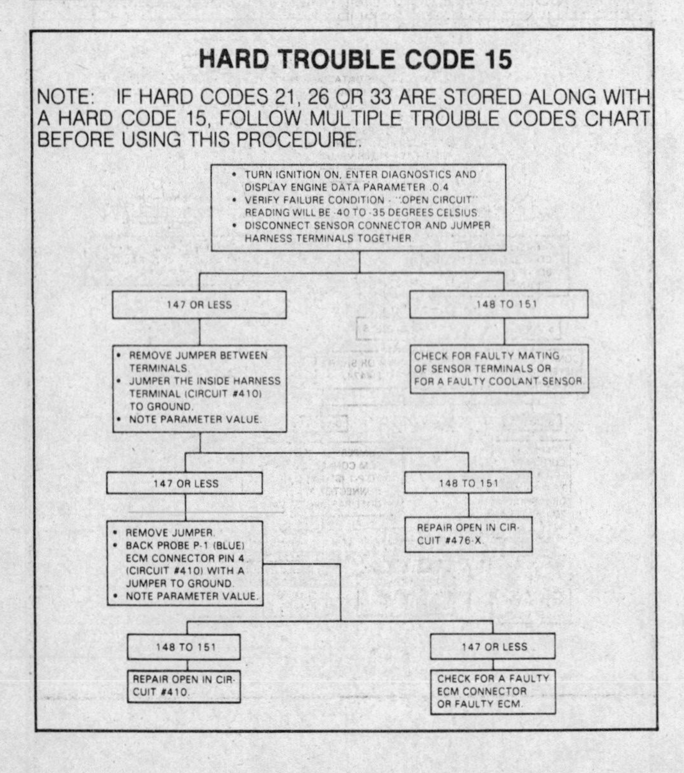

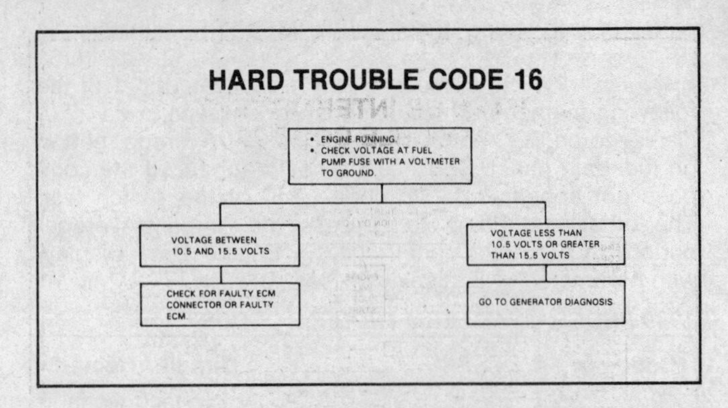

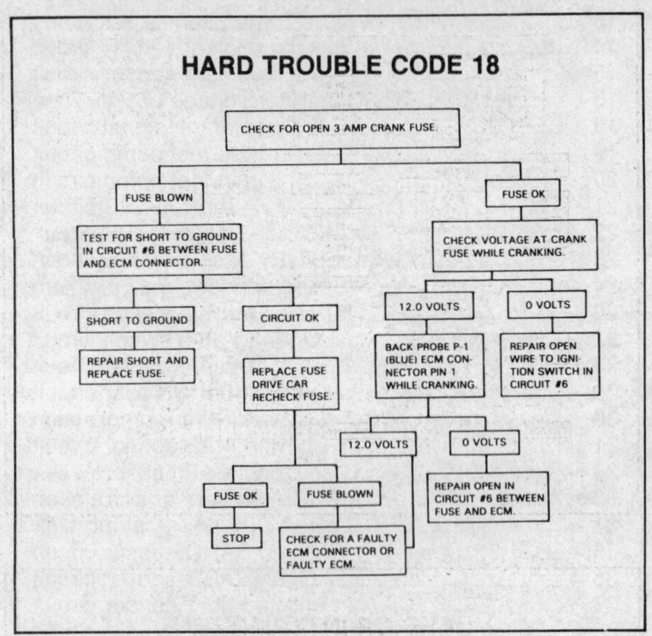

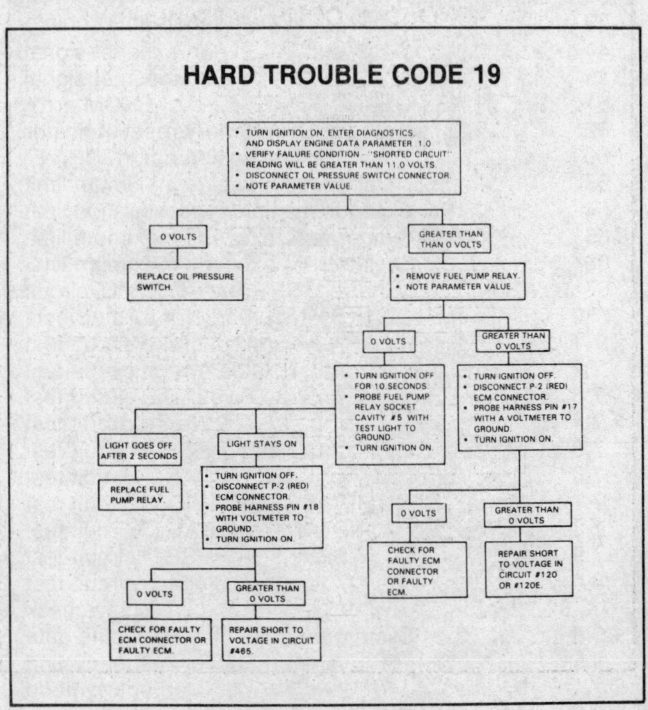

GENERAL MOTORS DFI CONTROL SYSTEM (Cont.)

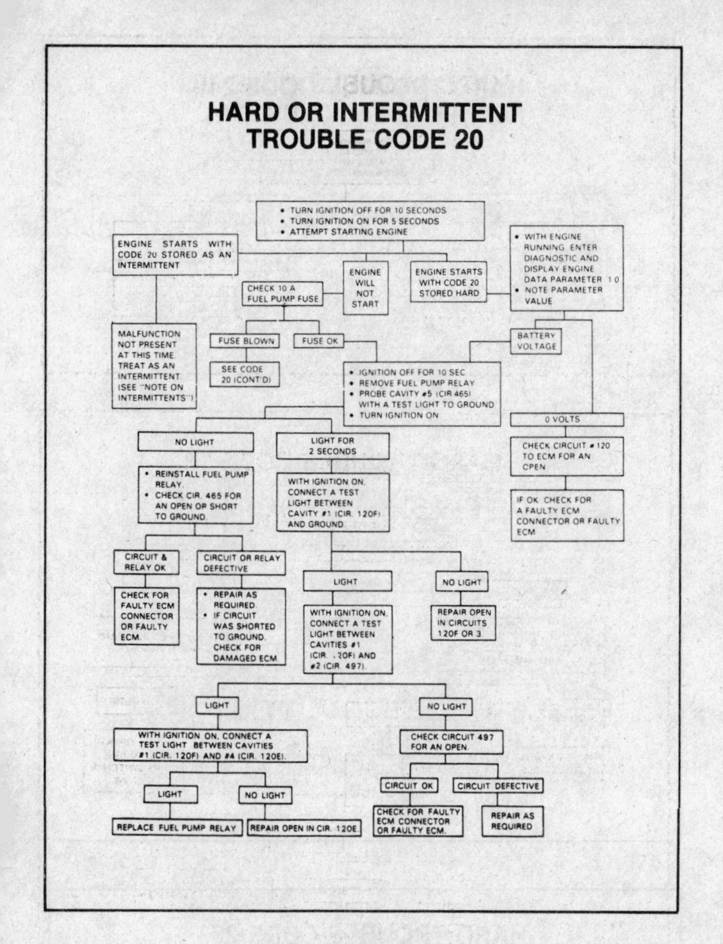

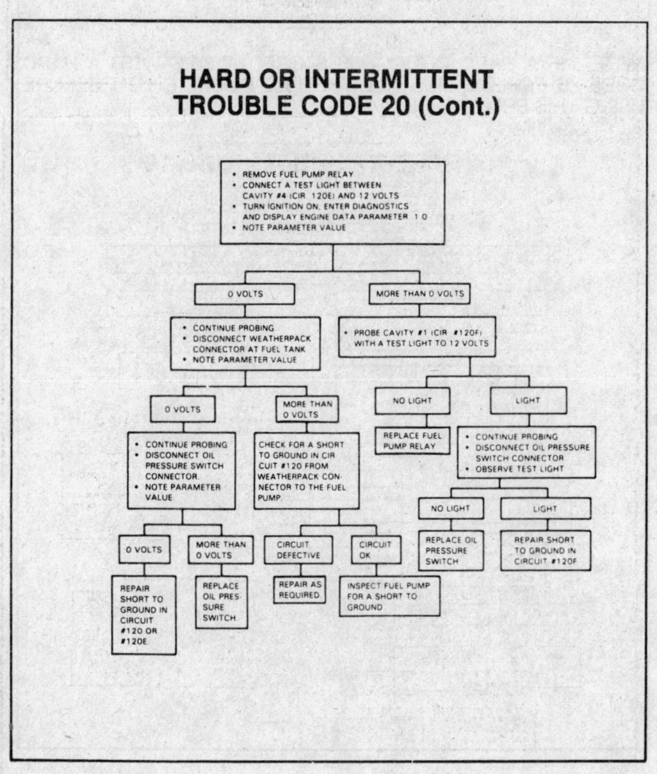

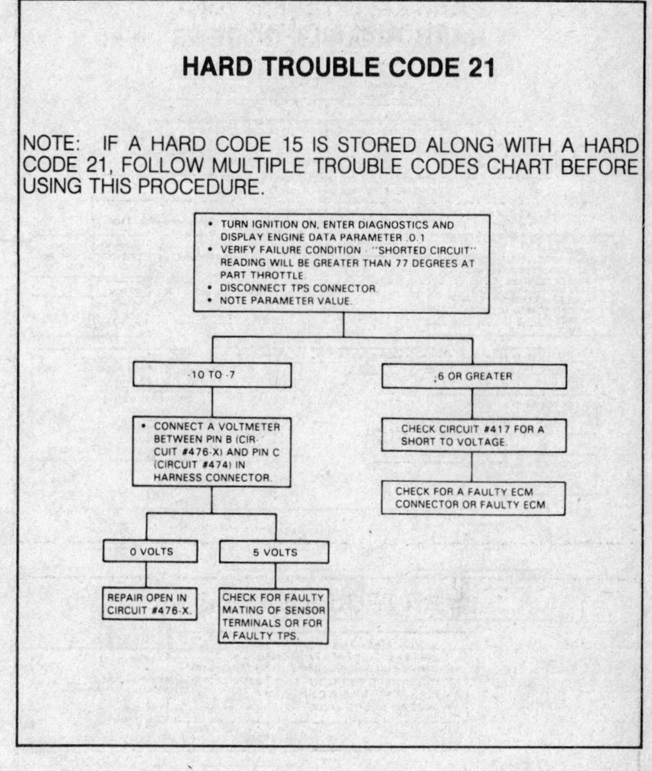

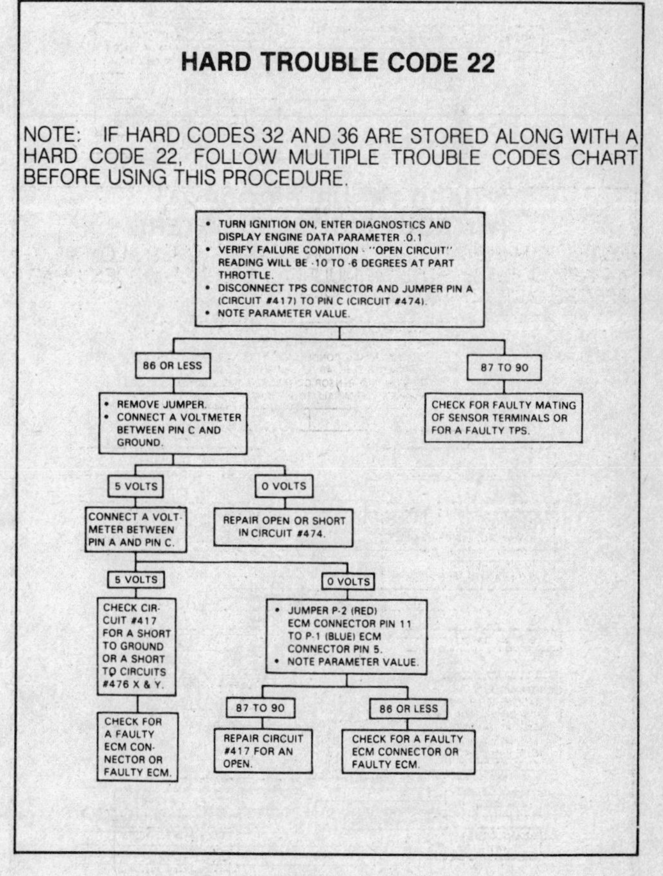

GENERAL MOTORS DFI CONTROL SYSTEM (Cont.)

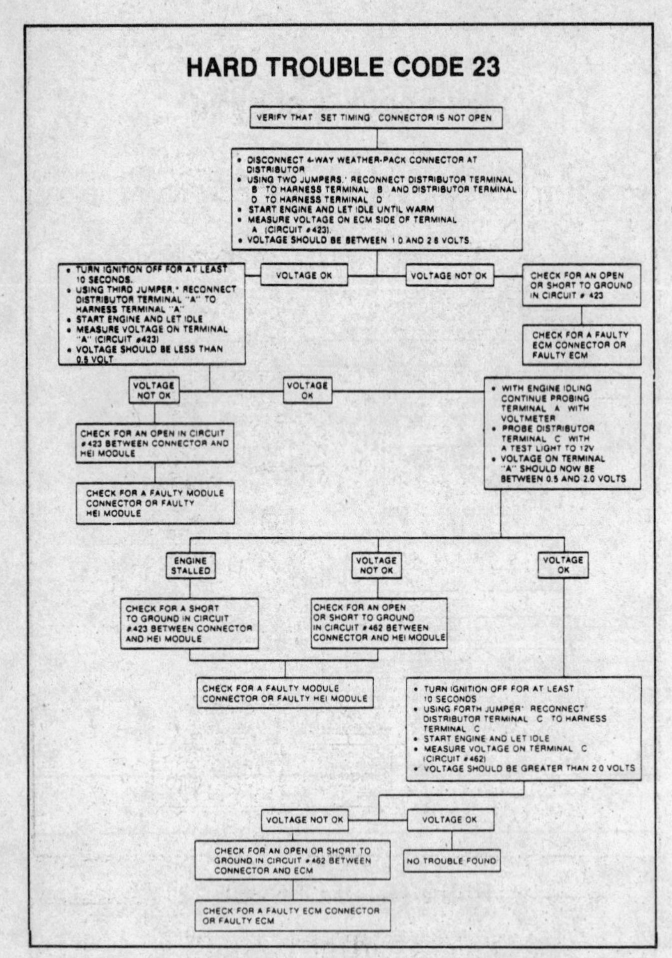

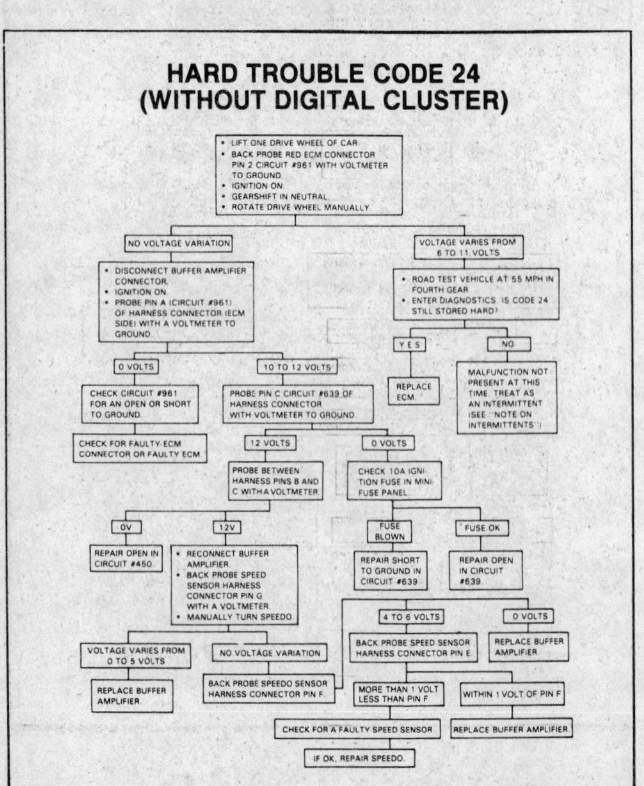

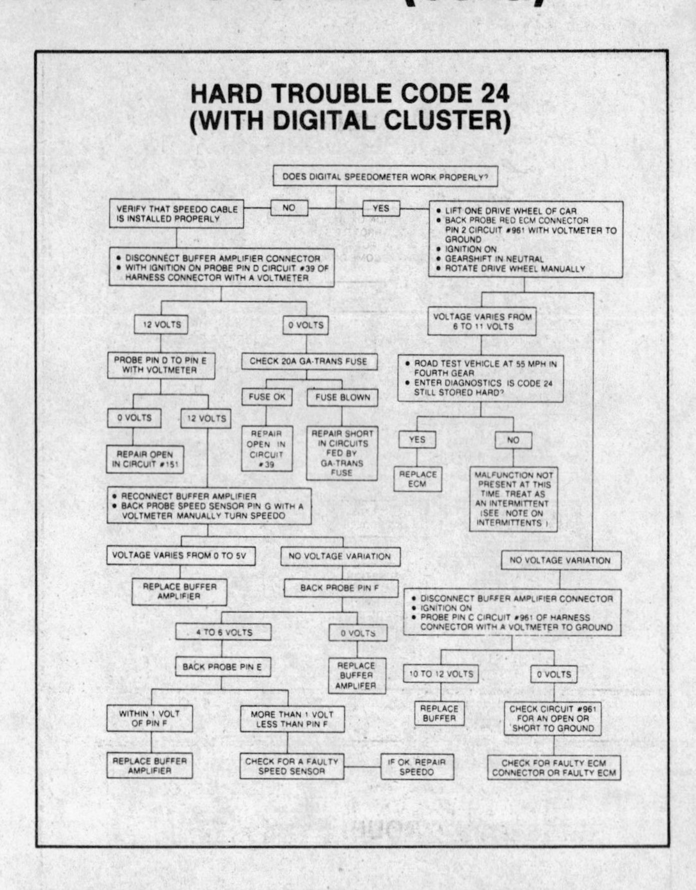

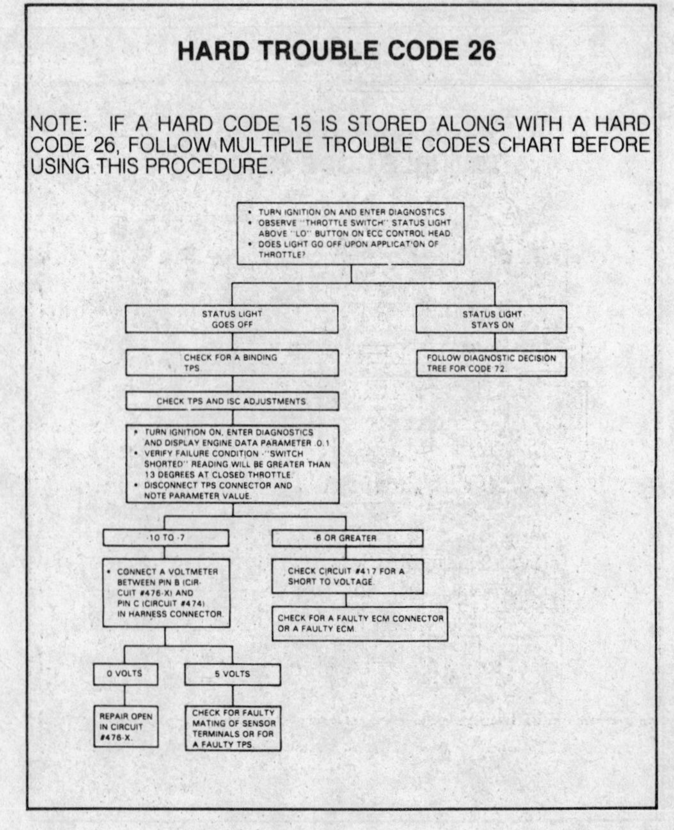

GENERAL MOTORS DFI CONTROL SYSTEM (Cont.)

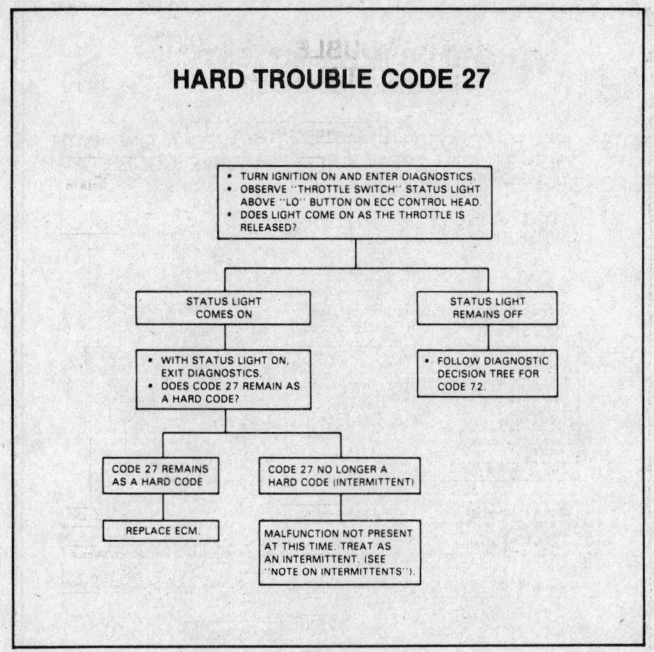

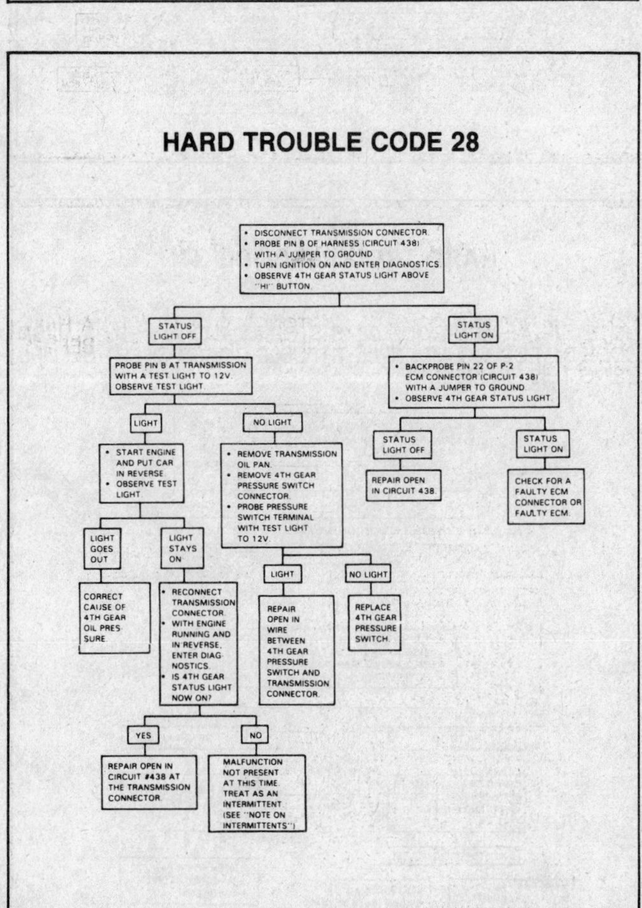

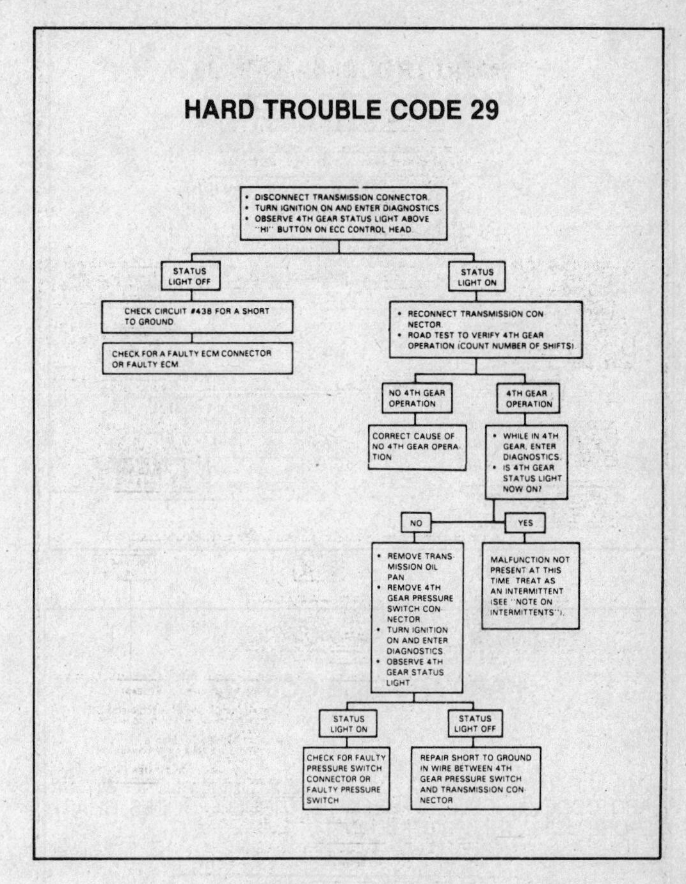

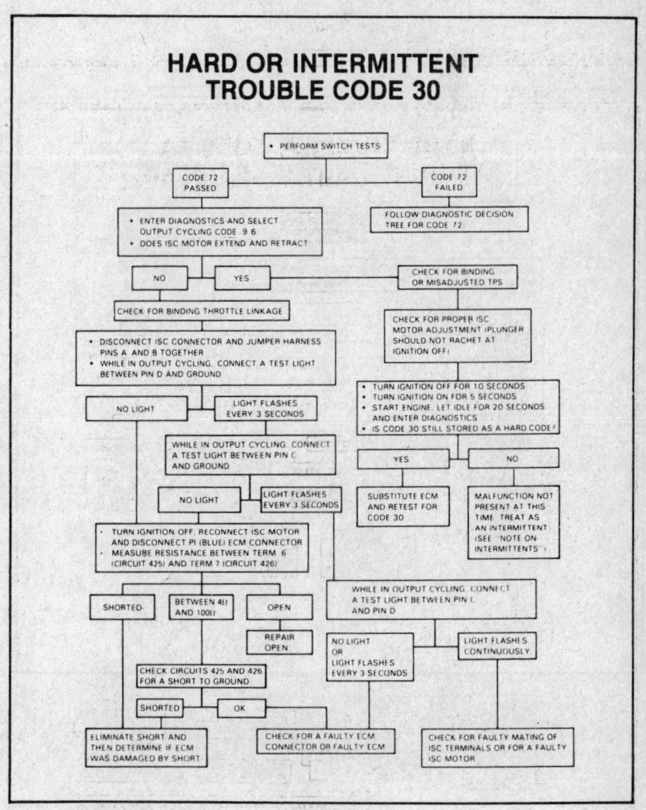

GENERAL MOTORS DFI CONTROL SYSTEM (Cont.)

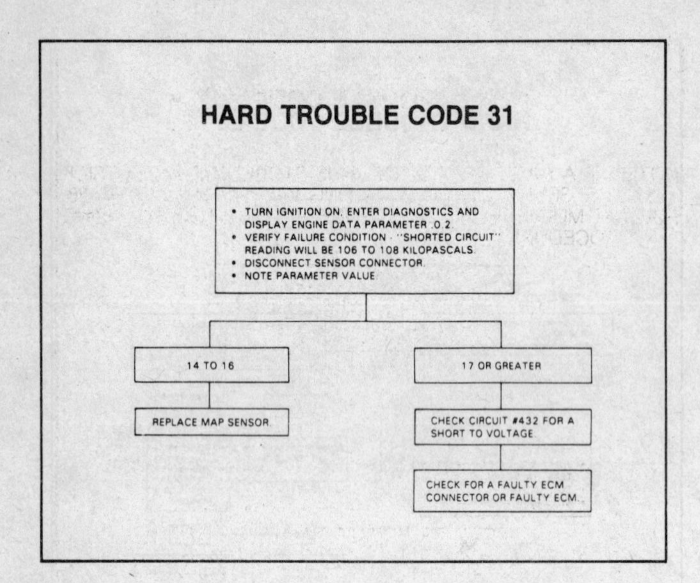

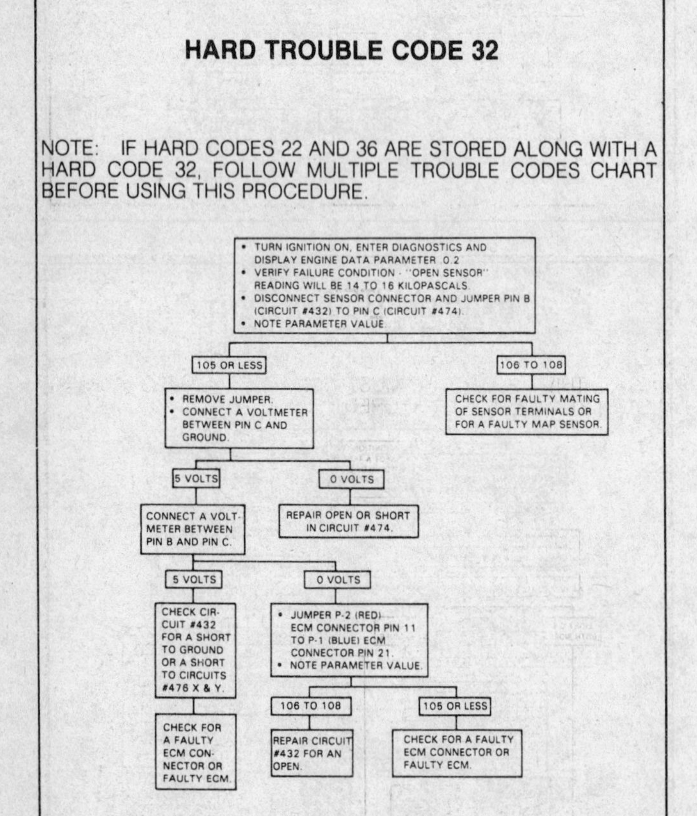

HARD OR INTERMITTENT TROUBLE CODE 33

NOTE: IF A HARD CODE 15 OR 38 IS STORED ALONG WITH A HARD CODE 33, FOLLOW MULTIPLE TROUBLE CODES CHART BEFORE USING THIS PROCEDURE.

• CLEAR CODES AND TURN IGNITION OFF FOR 10 SECONDS.
• TURN IGNITION ON FOR 10 SECONDS AND ENTER DIAGNOSTICS.
• READ STORED CODES.

CODE 33 STORED AS AN INTERMITTENT

• DISCONNECT MAP AND BARO SENSORS.
• OBSERVE ENGINE DATA PARAMETER .0.2 AS THE MAP SENSOR IS RECONNECTED.
• OBSERVE ENGINE DATA PARAMETER .0.3 AS THE BARO SENSOR IS RECONNECTED.

MAP DISPLAYED INTERMEDIATE VALUES BEFORE REACHING MAXIMUM — REPLACE MAP SENSOR

BARO DISPLAYED INTERMEDIATE VALUES BEFORE REACHING MAXIMUM — REPLACE BARO SENSOR

BOTH SENSORS WENT IMMEDIATELY TO MAXIMUM VALUE — SUBSTITUTE ECM AND RETEST FOR CODE 33

CODE 33 NO LONGER STORED

MALFUNCTION NOT PRESENT AT THIS TIME. TREAT AS AN INTERMITTENT (SEE "NOTE ON INTERMITTENTS").

CODE 33 STORED AS A HARD FAILURE

• DISPLAY ENGINE DATA PARAMETERS .0.2 AND .0.3 AND RECORD VALUES.
• VERIFY FAILURE CONDITION - "CORRELATION" READINGS WILL DIFFER BY 2 OR MORE KPA.
• JUMPER PIN A OF MAP SENSOR TO PIN A OF BARO SENSOR AND NOTE PARAMETER VALUES.

MAP MOVED CLOSER TO BARO — REPAIR OPEN IN CIRCUIT #476-Y

BARO MOVED CLOSER TO MAP — REPAIR OPEN IN CIRCUIT #476-X

NO CHANGE

• OBTAIN A REPLACEMENT MAP OR BARO SENSOR AND CONNECT TO APPROPRIATE HARNESS.
• COMPARE THIS SENSOR'S PARAMETER VALUE TO THOSE RECORDED PREVIOUSLY.

CLOSER TO MAP — REPLACE BARO SENSOR

CLOSER TO BARO — REPLACE MAP SENSOR

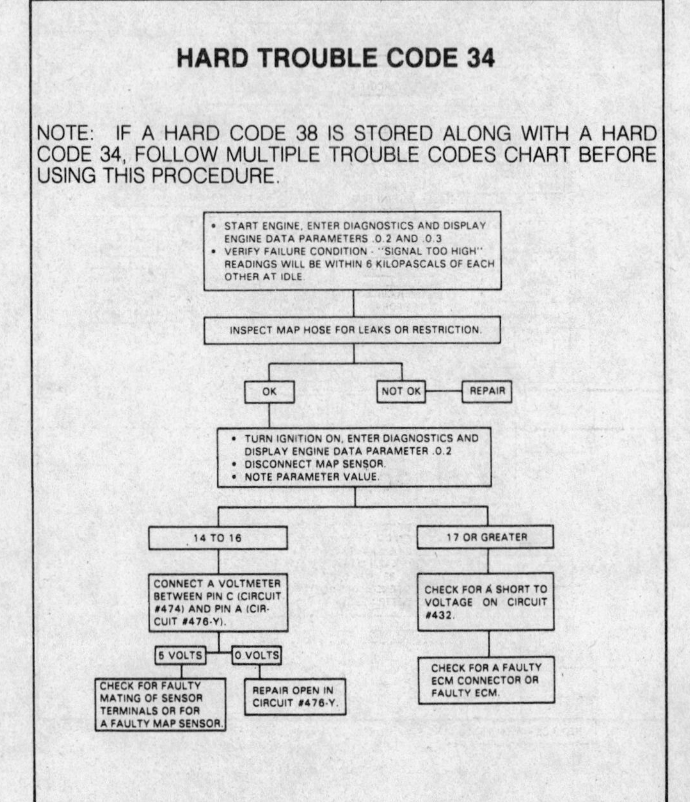

GENERAL MOTORS DFI CONTROL SYSTEM (Cont.)

HARD TROUBLE CODE 35

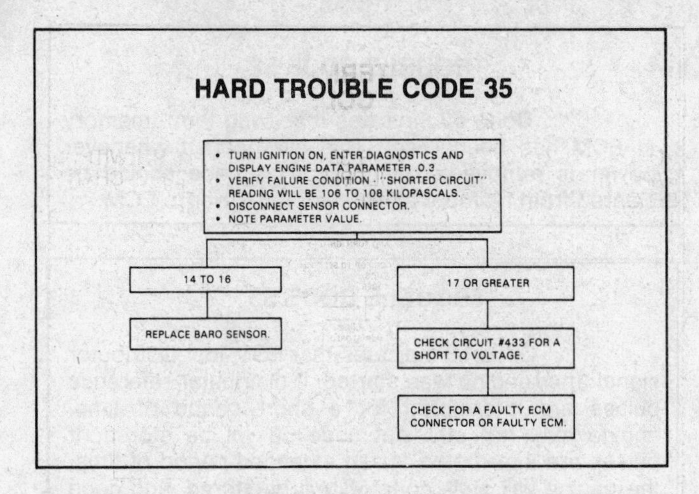

HARD TROUBLE CODE 36

NOTE: IF HARD CODES 22 AND 32 ARE STORED ALONG WITH A HARD CODE 36, FOLLOW MULTIPLE TROUBLE CODES CHART BEFORE USING THIS PROCEDURE.

- TURN IGNITION ON, ENTER DIAGNOSTICS AND DISPLAY ENGINE DATA PARAMETER .0.3
- VERIFY FAILURE CONDITION - "OPEN SENSOR" READING WILL BE 14 TO 52 KILOPASCALS.
- DISCONNECT SENSOR CONNECTOR AND JUMPER PIN B (CIRCUIT #433) TO PIN C (CIRCUIT #474).
- NOTE PARAMETER VALUE.

105 OR LESS

- REMOVE JUMPER.
- CONNECT A VOLTMETER BETWEEN PIN C AND GROUND.

5 VOLTS

CONNECT A VOLTMETER BETWEEN PIN B AND PIN C.

5 VOLTS

CHECK CIRCUIT #433 FOR A SHORT TO GROUND OR A SHORT TO CIRCUITS #476 X & Y.

CHECK FOR A FAULTY ECM CONNECTOR OR FAULTY ECM.

0 VOLTS

- JUMPER P-2 (RED) ECM CONNECTOR PIN 11 TO P-3 (ORN) ECM CONNECTOR PIN 9.
- NOTE PARAMETER VALUE.

106 TO 108

REPAIR CIRCUIT #433 FOR AN OPEN.

105 OR LESS

CHECK FOR A FAULTY ECM CONNECTOR OR FAULTY ECM.

0 VOLTS

REPAIR OPEN OR SHORT IN CIRCUIT #474.

106 TO 108

CHECK FOR FAULTY MATING OF SENSOR TERMINALS OR FOR A FAULTY BARO SENSOR.

HARD TROUBLE CODE 37

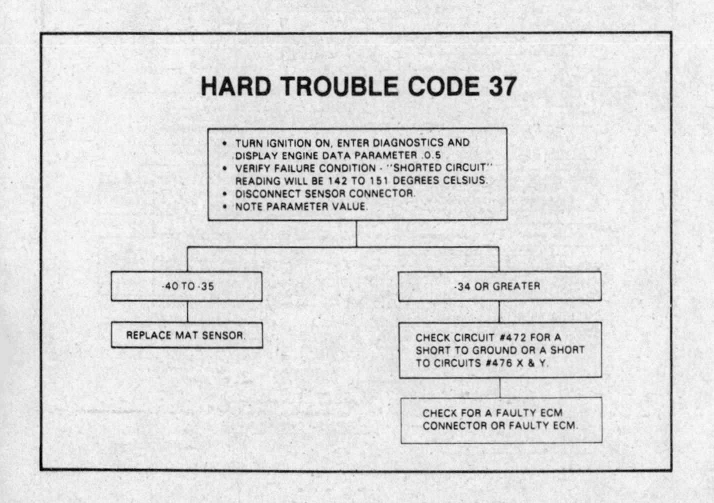

HARD TROUBLE CODE 38

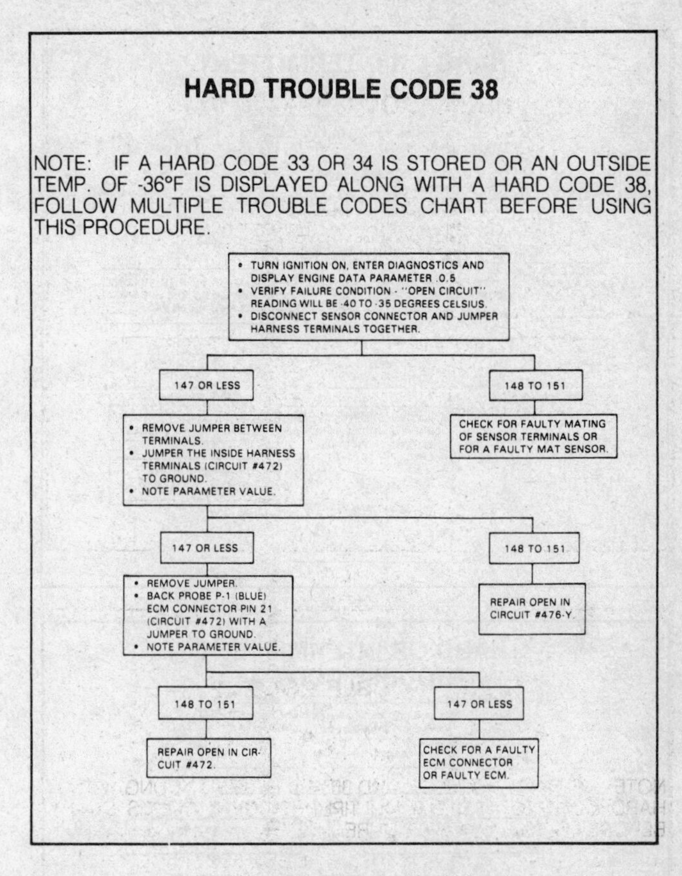

HARD OR INTERMITTENT TROUBLE CODE 39

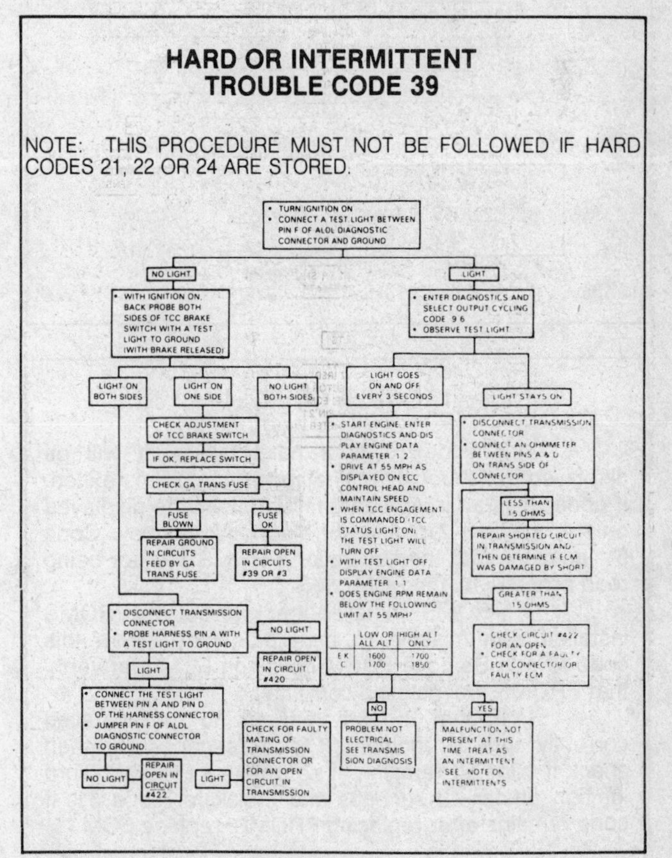

GENERAL MOTORS DFI CONTROL SYSTEM (Cont.)

HARD OR INTERMITTENT TROUBLE CODE 44

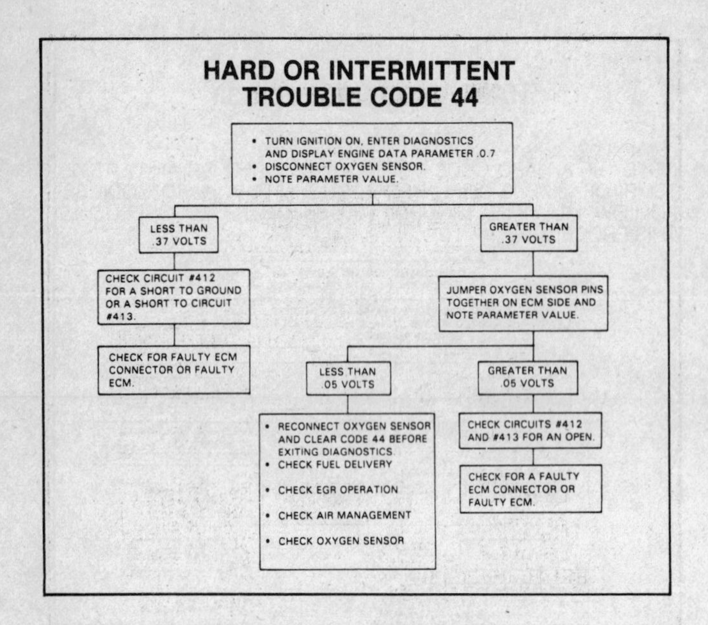

HARD OR INTERMITTENT TROUBLE CODE 45

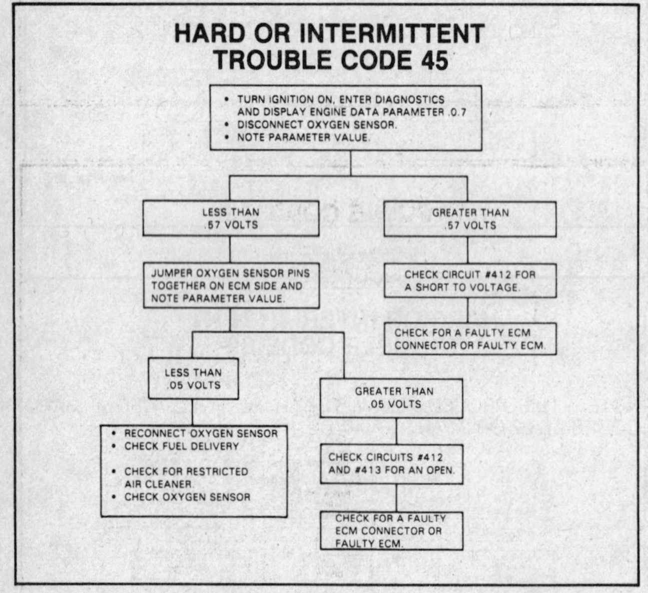

TROUBLE CODE 51

If code 51 is a hard failure, it will be displayed continuously until diagnostic mode is exited. If code 51 is an intermittant failure, it will be displayed only in the first 2 passes of diagnostic display. Code 51 indicates that the calibration PROMS are not being read properly by the ECM.

PROMS installed backwards or PROMS installed with missing or bent pins may cause this code to set. Remove PROM cover on ECM and verify that PROMS are installed correctly.

If the PROMS appear to be installed correctly, turn the ignition off for 10 seconds and then check if code 51 remains. If so, replace PROMS. Turn ignition off for 10 seconds and check for code 51. If code remains after replacing PROMS, replace ECM.

TROUBLE CODE 52

Code 52 indicates that "long term" memory in ECM has been reset. This will happen whenever power is removed from ECM. This code should be cleared from memory after restoring power to ECM.

TROUBLE CODE 53

Code 53 indicates that ECM lost distributor signal after engine was started. If distributor reference pulses are interrupted for a short period of time, engine may not stall but code 53 wil be stored. If pulses are interrupted for an extended period of time, the engine will stall, code 53 will be stored, and code 12 will be set upon attempting to restart.

If code 53 is stored but does not result in a no start condition, it should be treated as an intermittent code 12.

TROUBLE CODE 60

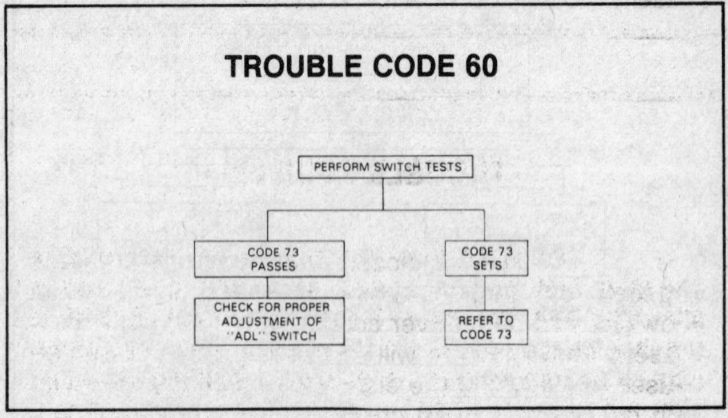

TROUBLE CODE 63

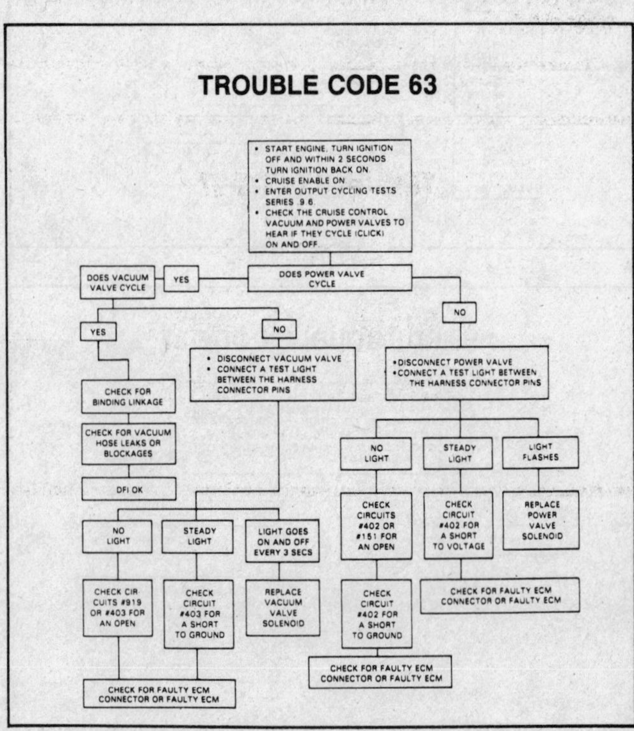

GENERAL MOTORS DFI CONTROL SYSTEM (Cont.)

TROUBLE CODE 64

Code 64 indicates that cruise control was engaged and vehicle acceleration exceeded the preset rate which was programmed into the ECM. If the condition which set code 64 is present, cruise control will disengage. Code 64 could be caused by icy or wet pavement.

TROUBLE CODE 65

Code 65 indicates that cruise control was engaged and coolant temperature exceeded a maximum limit. If the condition which set code 65 is present, cruise control will disengage.

TROUBLE CODE 66

Code 66 indicates that cruise control was engaged and engine speed exceeded a maximum allowable limit. Whenever condition that set code 66 is present, cruise control will disengage. Code 66 can be caused by removing the engine load (shifting transmission out of gear) when cruise control is engaged and operating.

TROUBLE CODE 67

PERFORM SWITCH TEST

CODE 76 AND CODE 77 PASS → DFI OK

CODE 76 OR CODE 77 SET → REFER TO THE APPROPRIATE CHART

TROUBLE CODE .7.1

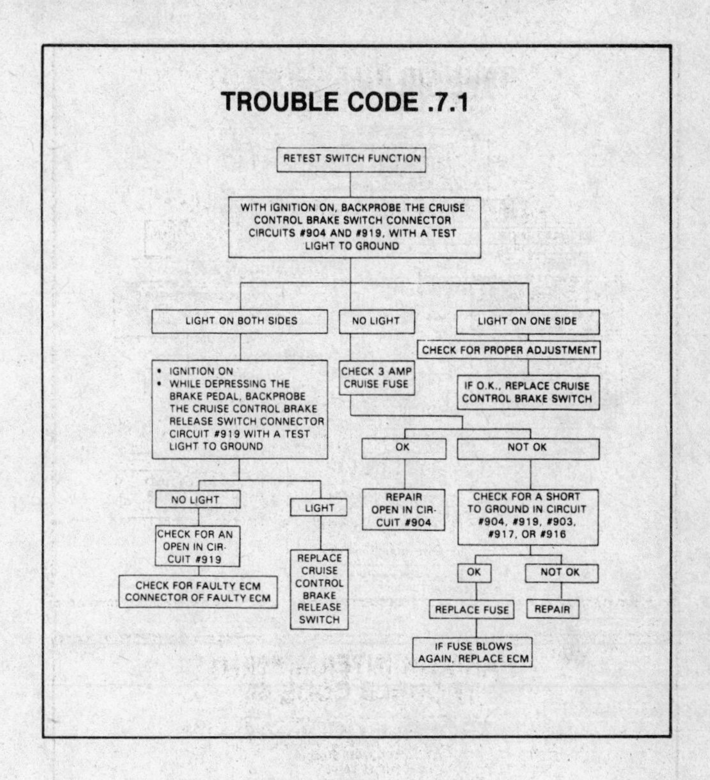

TROUBLE CODE .7.2

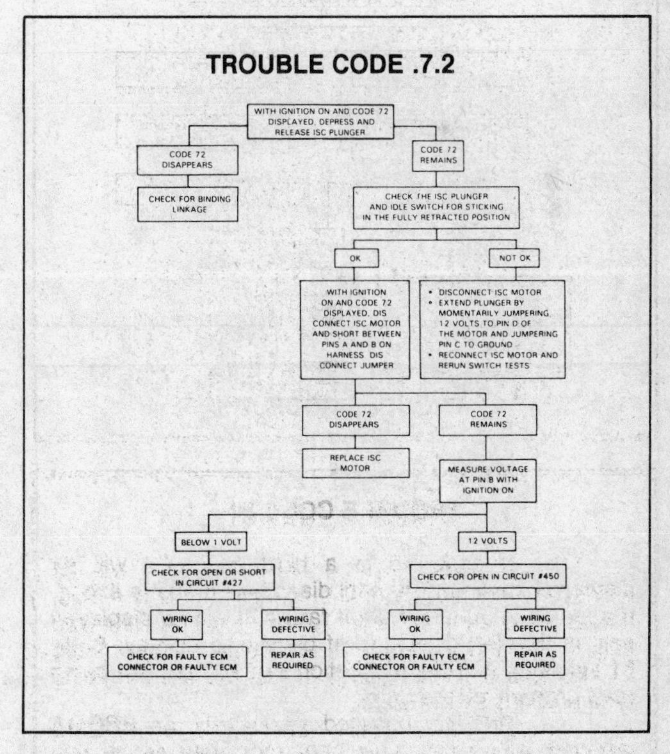

GENERAL MOTORS DFI CONTROL SYSTEM (Cont.)

TROUBLE CODE .7.3

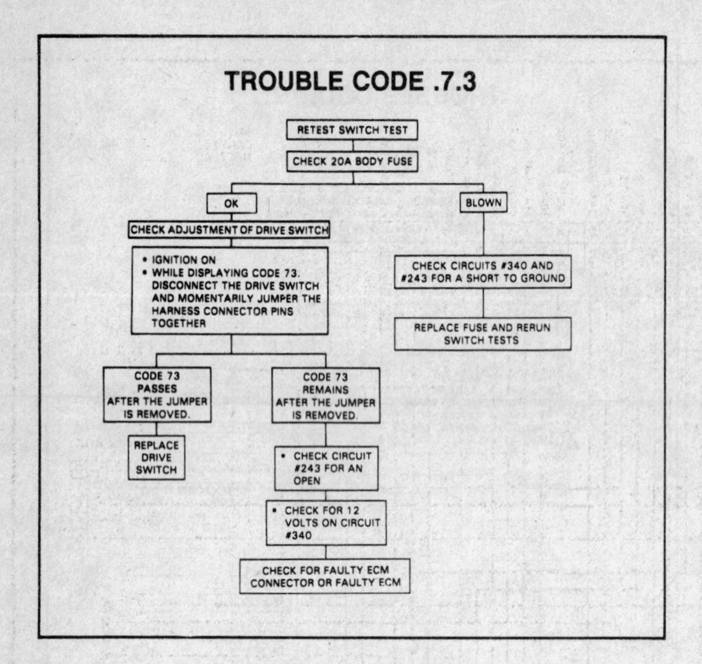

TROUBLE CODE .7.4

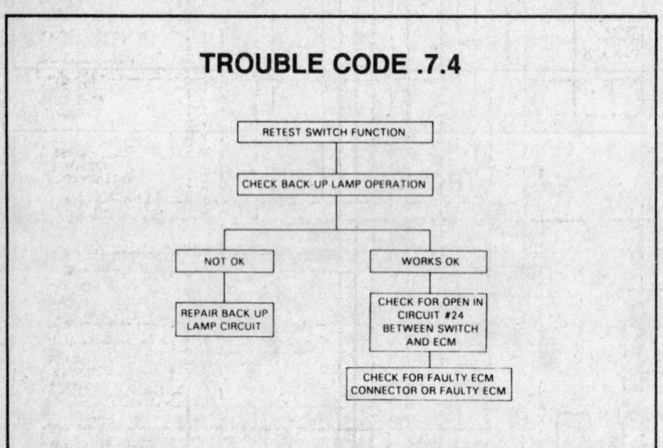

TROUBLE CODE .7.5

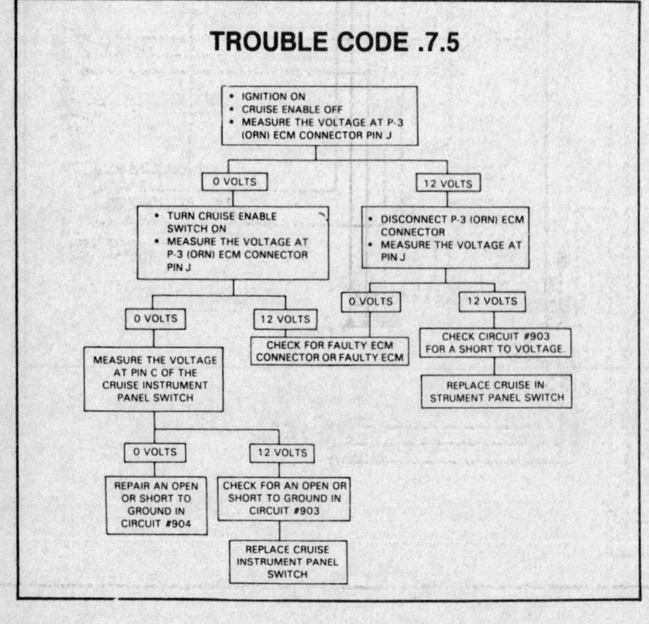

TROUBLE CODE .7.6

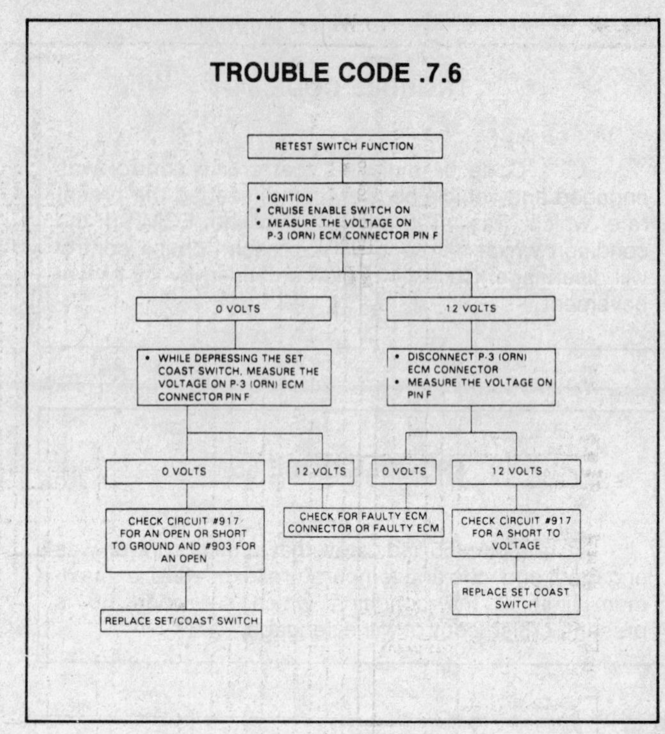

TROUBLE CODE .7.7

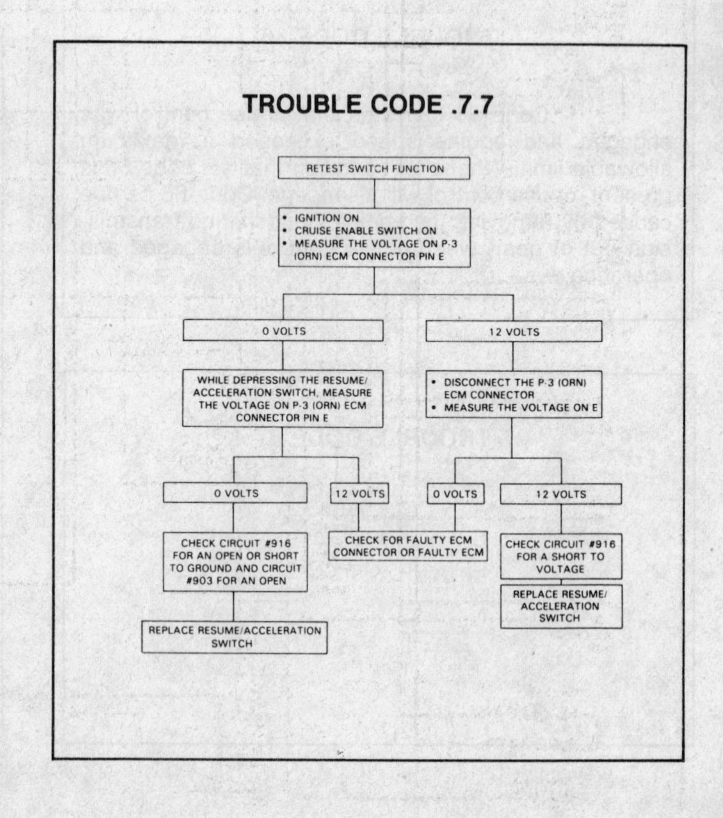

GENERAL MOTORS DFI CONTROL SYSTEM (Cont.)

Fig. 4: DFI Control System Wiring Diagram

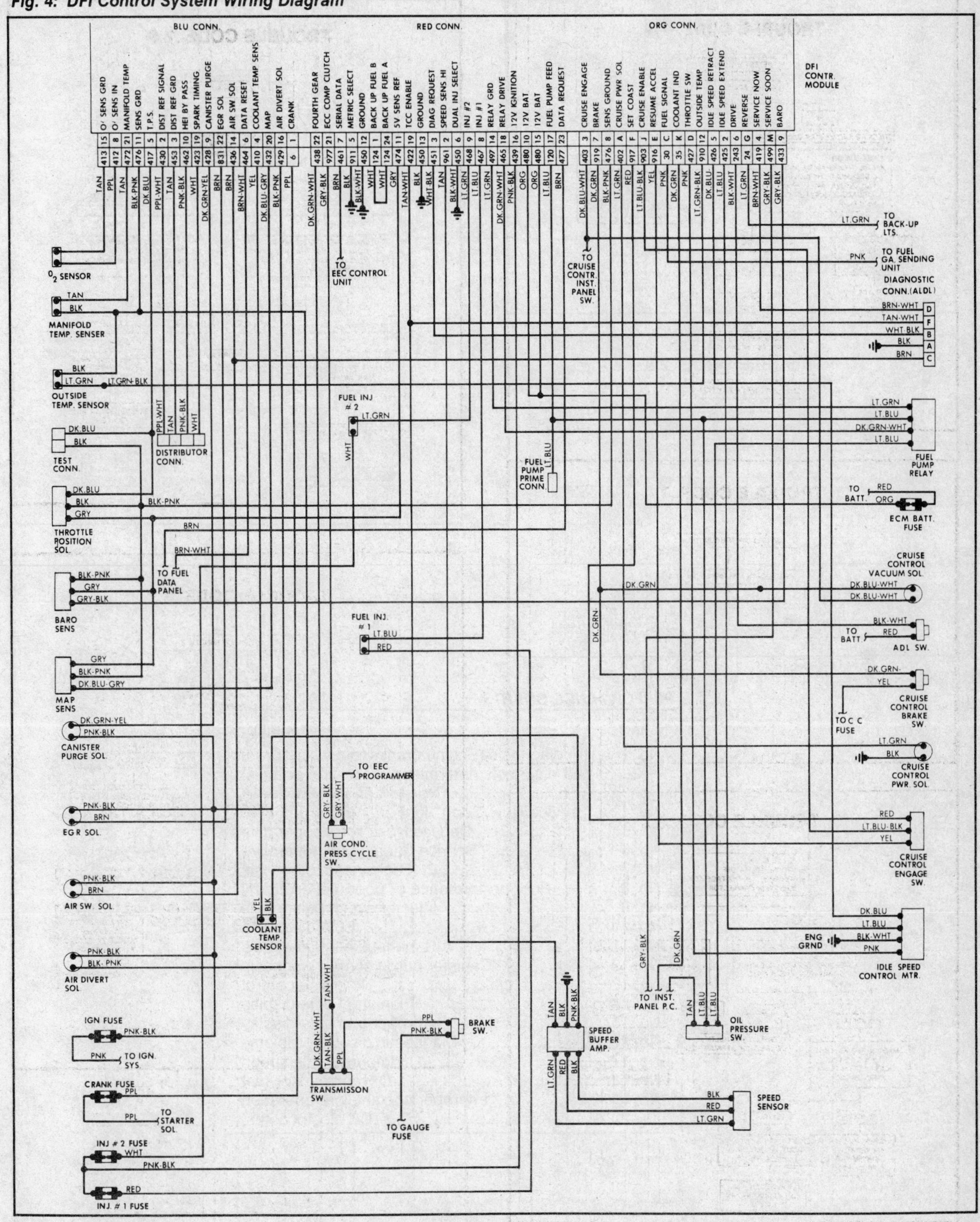

GENERAL MOTORS DFI CONTROL SYSTEM (Cont.)

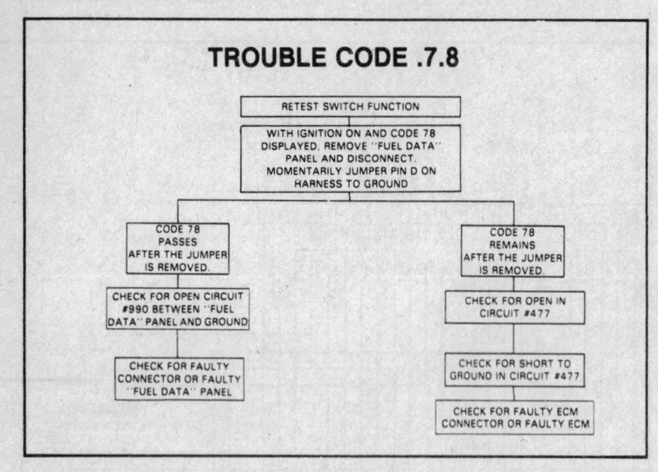

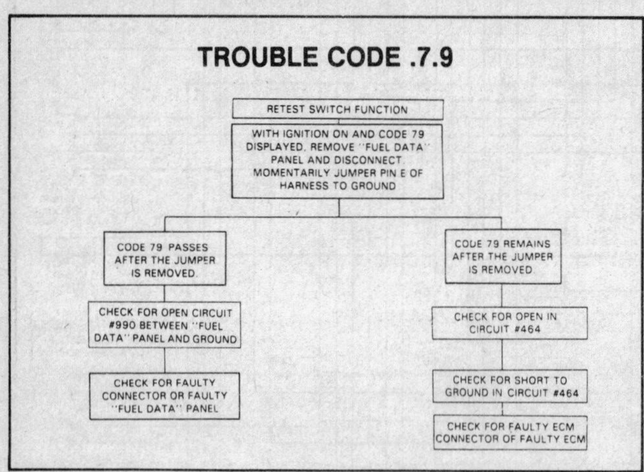

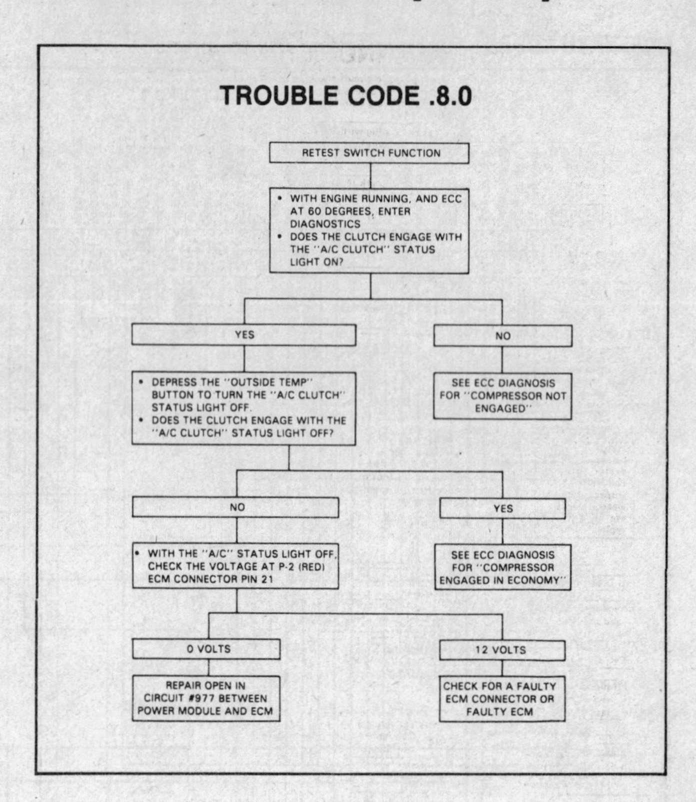

PERFORMANCE CHARTS

Chart	Condition
No. 1	HEI diagnosis (Engine cranks, but will not run).
No.2	HEI diagnosis (Intermittent operation or miss).
No. 3	No start or stall after start.
No. 4	"Service Now/Soon" light on, no "Hard codes".
No. 5	"Service Now" light inoperative.
No. 6	"Service Soon" light inoperative.
No. 7	Fuel system diagnosis.
No. 8	Poor performance or poor fuel economy.
No. 9	Injector system diagnosis.
No. 10	EGR diagnosis.
No. 11	AIR management diagnosis.
No. 12	Canister purge control diagnosis.
No. 13	No cruise control.
No. 14	Blank fuel data display.
No. 15	Improper fuel data display.
No. 16	Diagnostic display problems.
No. 17	Improper idle speed.
No. 18	Oxygen sensor test.
No. 19	Improper coolant light operation.
No. 20	TCC electrical test.

1983 Exhaust Emission Systems

GENERAL MOTORS DFI CONTROL SYSTEM (Cont.)

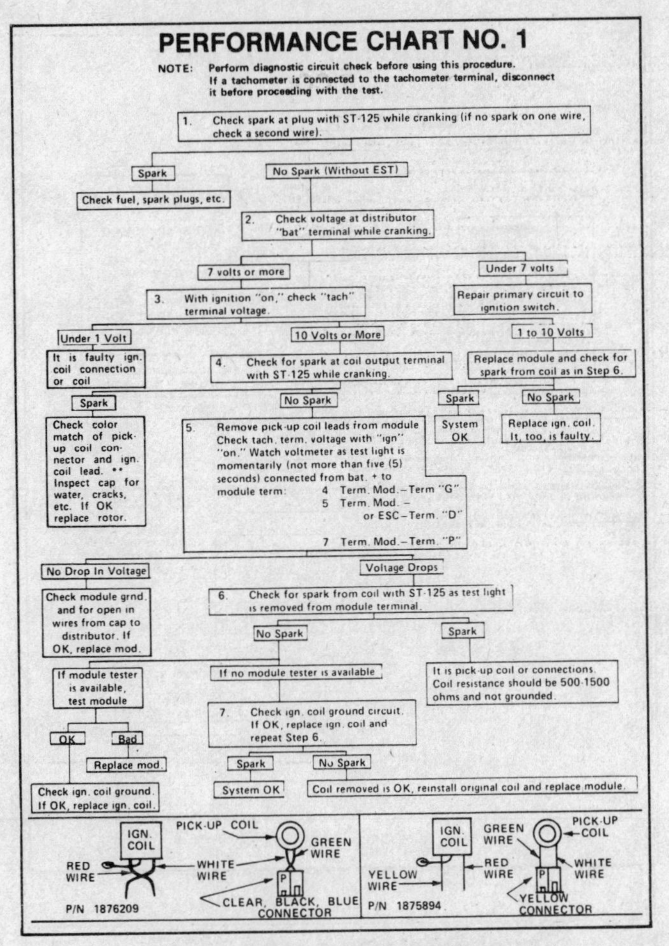

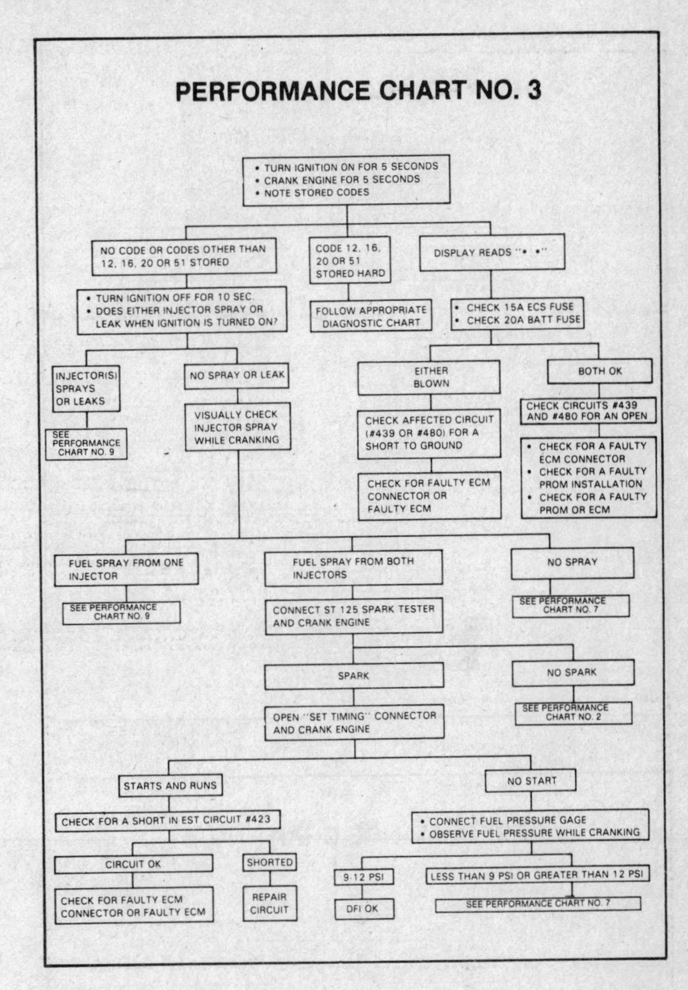

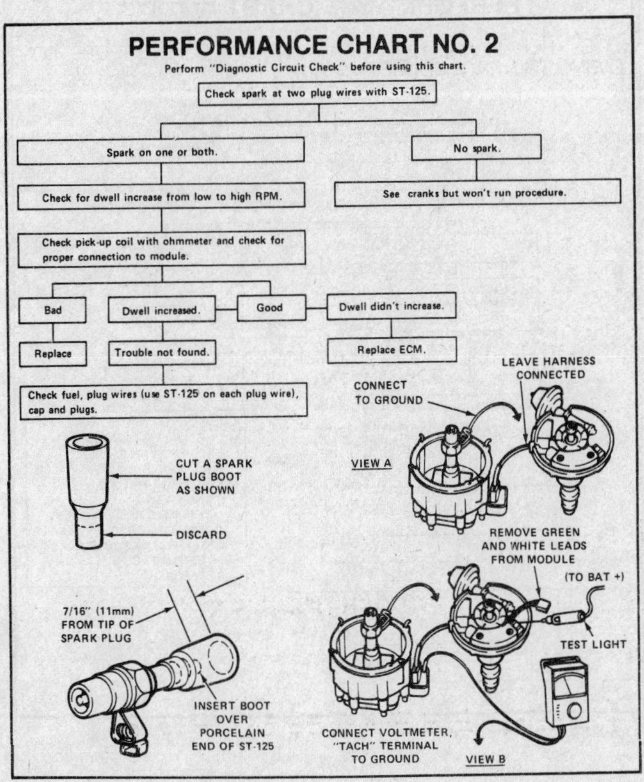

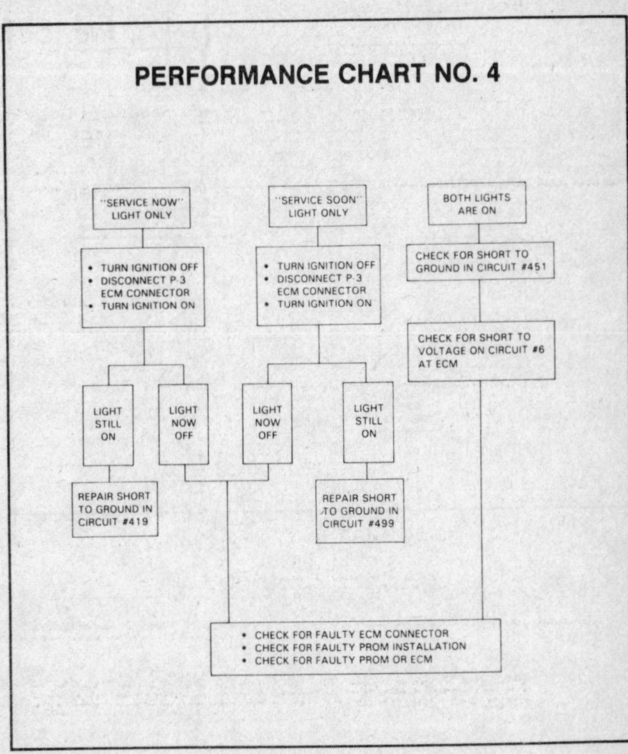

GENERAL MOTORS DFI CONTROL SYSTEM (Cont.)

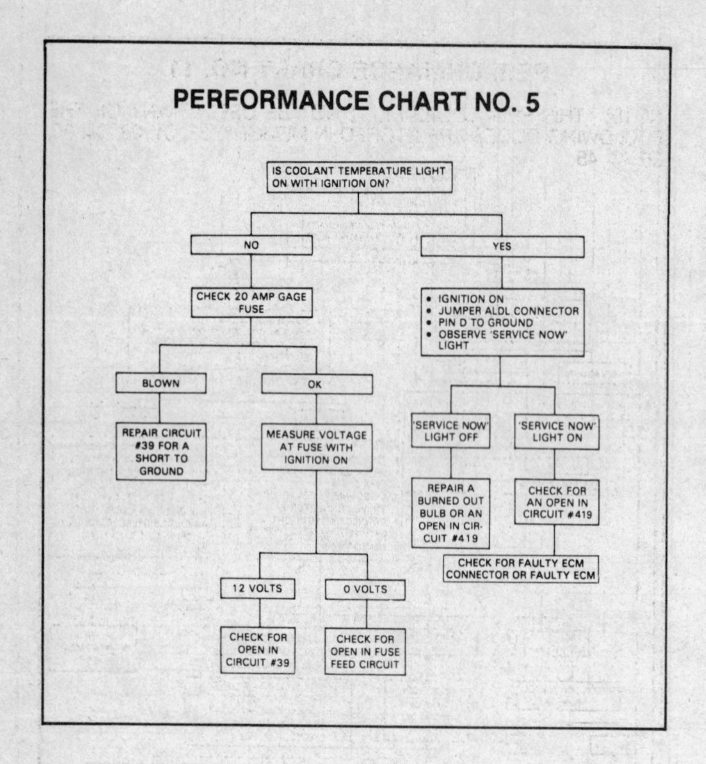

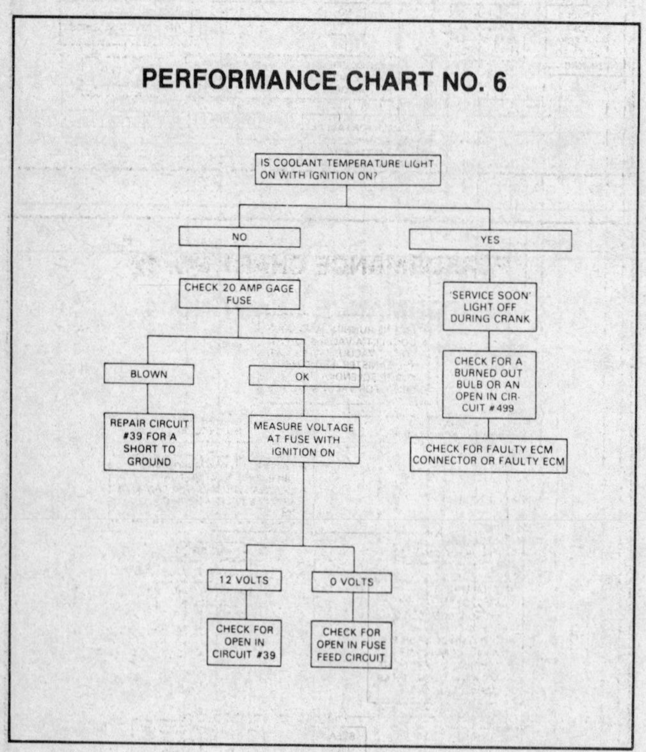

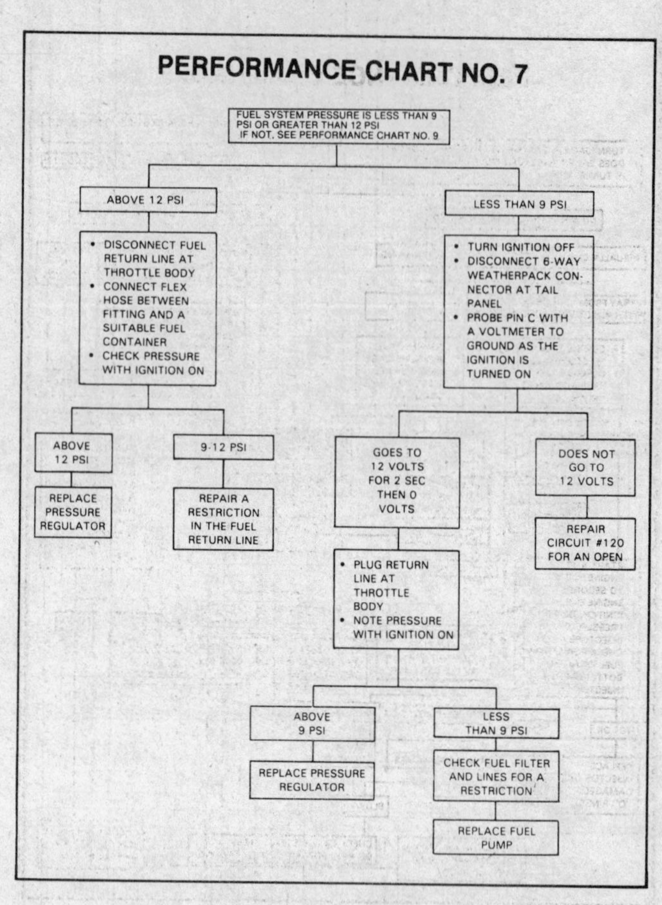

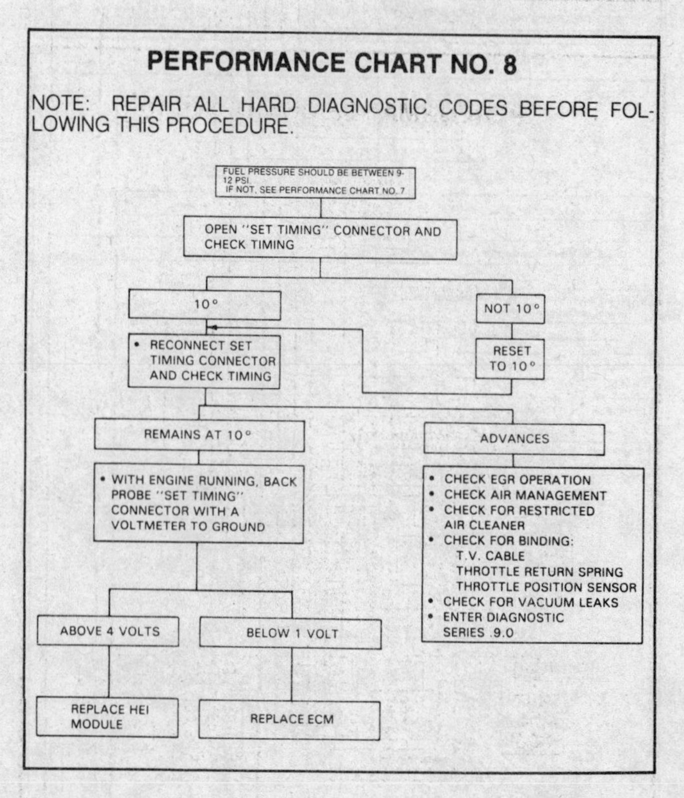

GENERAL MOTORS DFI CONTROL SYSTEM (Cont.)

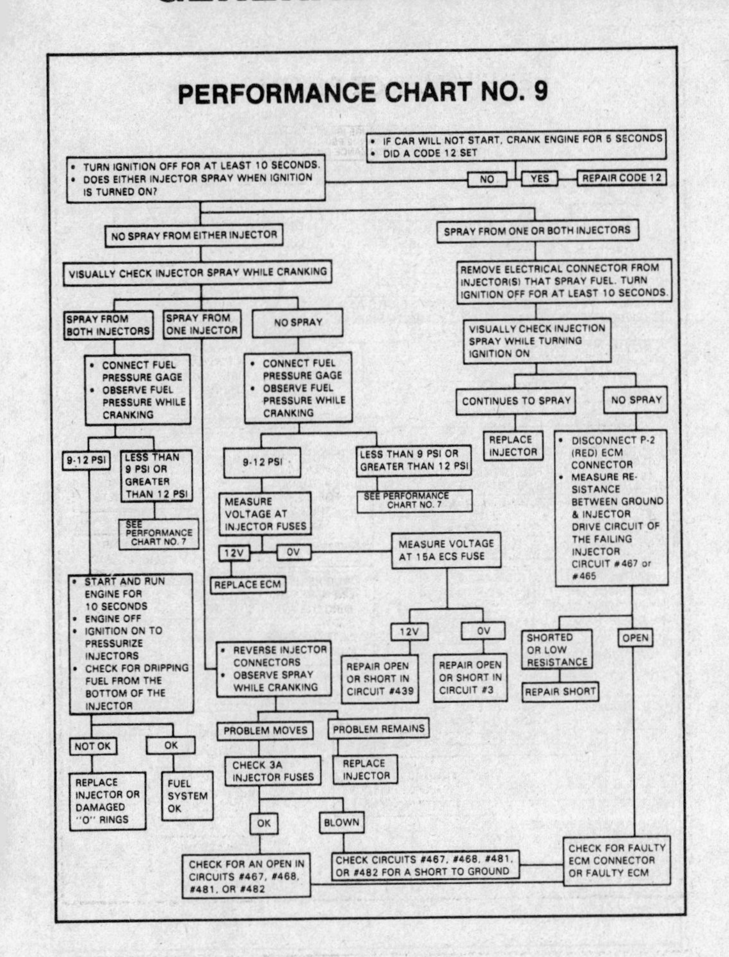

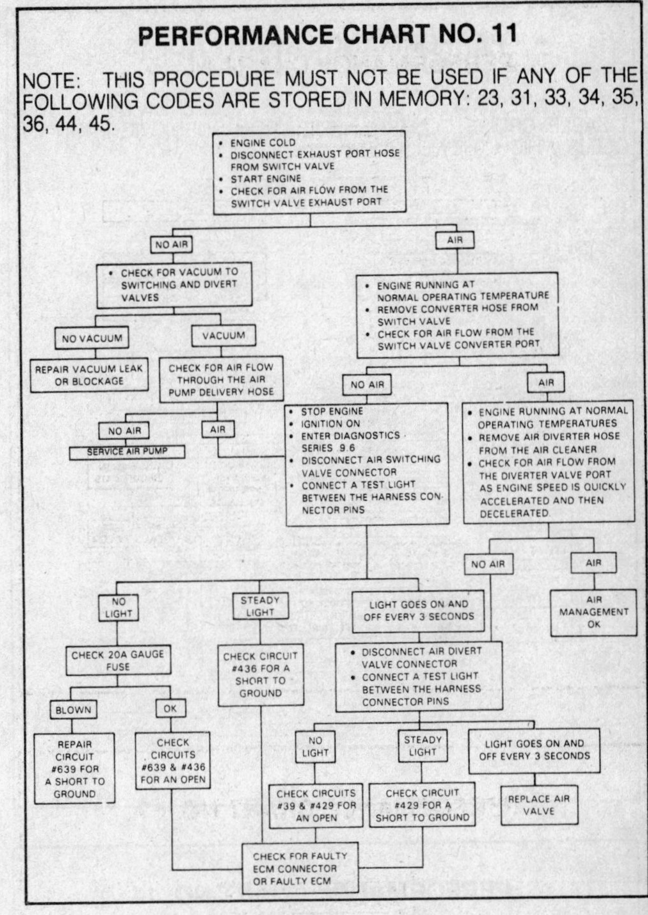

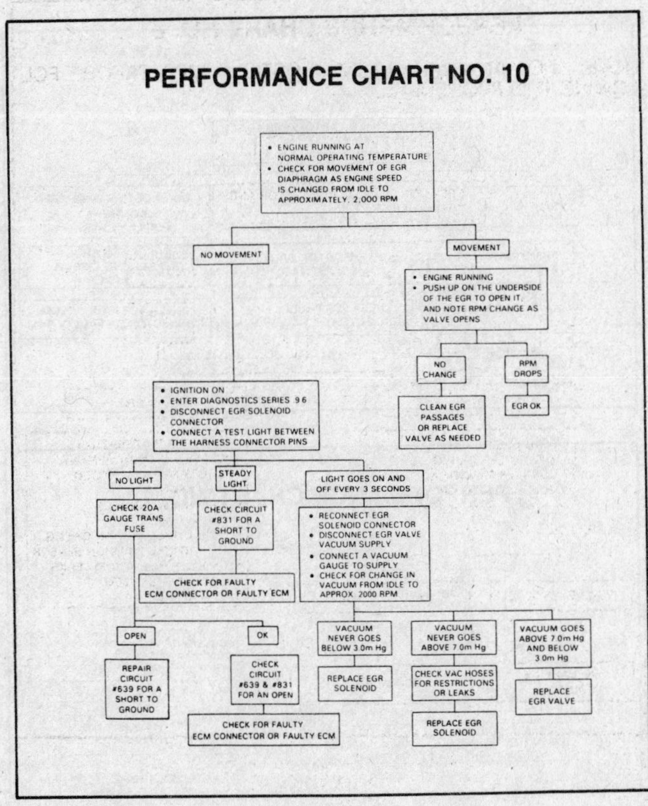

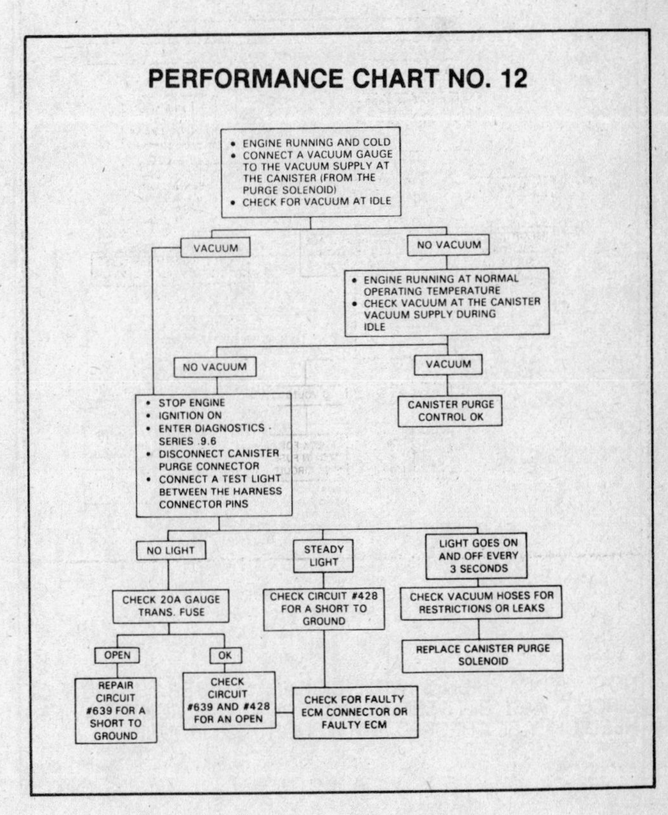

GENERAL MOTORS DFI CONTROL SYSTEM (Cont.)

PERFORMANCE CHART NO. 13

NOTE: INTERMITTENT SETTINGS OF CODES 24 OR 67 WILL DISABLE CRUISE CONTROL OPERATION DURING IGNITION CYCLE IN WHICH THEY OCCUR.

ENTER DIAGNOSTICS AND NOTE CODES

NO HARD CODES SET

PERFORM SWITCH TESTS DIAGNOSE AND REPAIR AS REQUIRED

- START ENGINE. TURN IGNITION OFF AND WITHIN 2 SECONDS TURN IGNITION BACK ON
- CRUISE ENABLE ON
- ENTER OUTPUT CYCLING TESTS SERIES 9.6
- CHECK THE CRUISE CONTROL VACUUM AND POWER VALVES TO HEAR IF THEY CYCLE (CLICK) ON AND OFF

HARD CODES SET

FOLLOW APPROPRIATE DIAGNOSIS CHART

DOES POWER VALVE CYCLE

YES

DOES VACUUM VALVE CYCLE

YES

CHECK FOR BINDING CRUISE LINKAGE

REPAIR VACUUM HOSE LEAKS OR BLOCKAGES

DFI OK

NO

- DISCONNECT VACUUM VALVE
- CONNECT A TEST LIGHT BETWEEN THE HARNESS CONNECTOR PINS

NO LIGHT

CHECK CIRCUITS #919 OR #403 FOR AN OPEN

STEADY LIGHT

CHECK CIRCUIT #403 FOR A SHORT TO GROUND

LIGHT GOES ON AND OFF EVERY 3 SECONDS

REPLACE VACUUM VALVE SOLENOID

NO

- DISCONNECT POWER VALVE
- CONNECT A TEST LIGHT BETWEEN THE HARNESS CONNECTOR PINS

NO LIGHT

CHECK CIRCUITS #402 OR #151 FOR AN OPEN

CHECK CIRCUIT #402 FOR A SHORT TO GROUND

STEADY LIGHT

CHECK CIRCUIT #402 FOR A SHORT TO VOLTAGE

LIGHT FLASHES

REPLACE POWER VALVE SOLENOID

CHECK FOR FAULTY ECM CONNECTOR OR FAULTY ECM

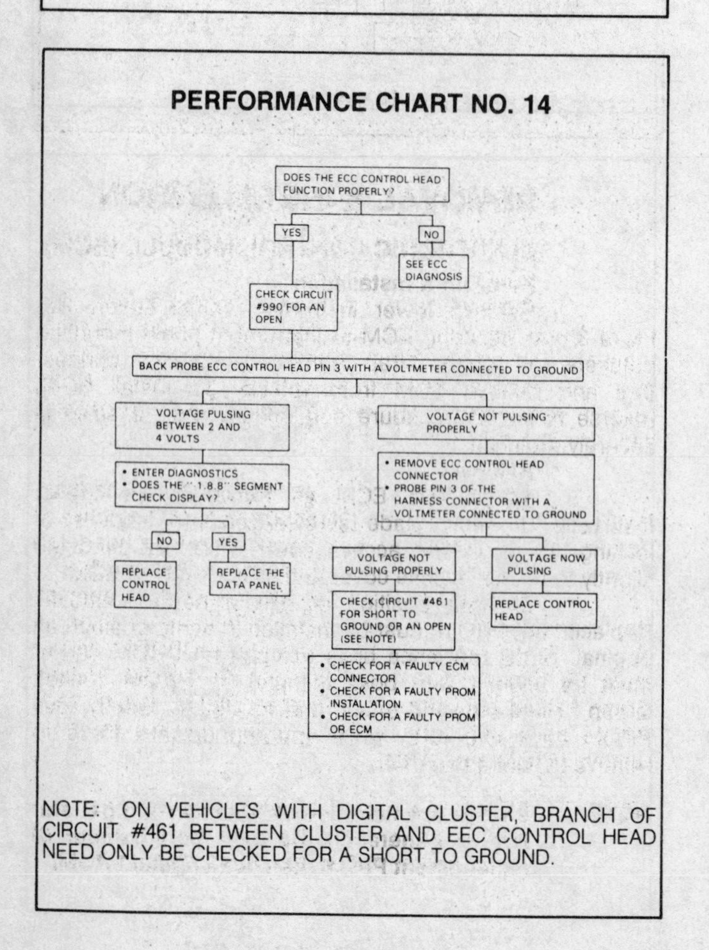

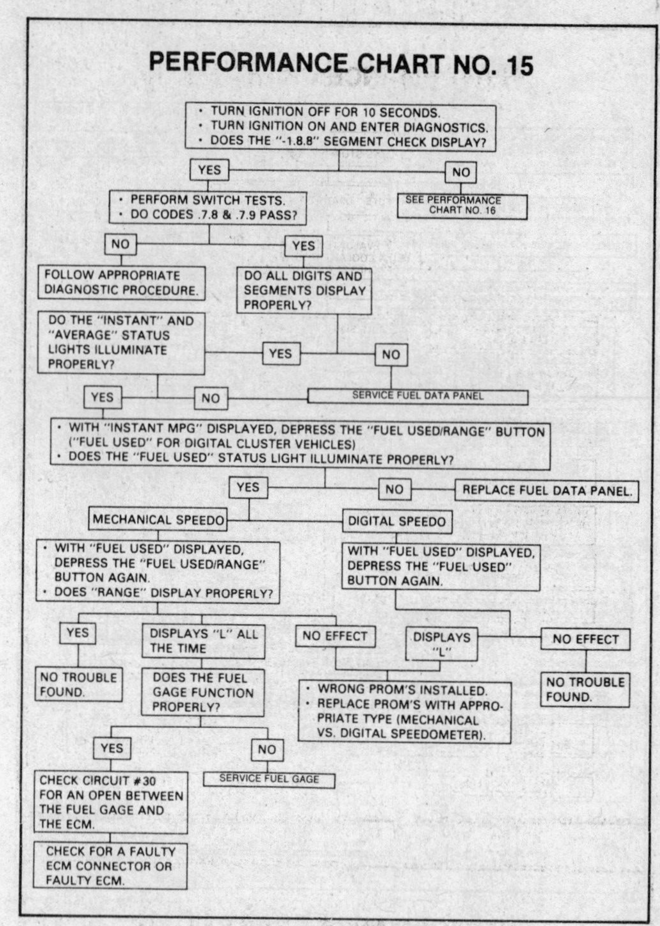

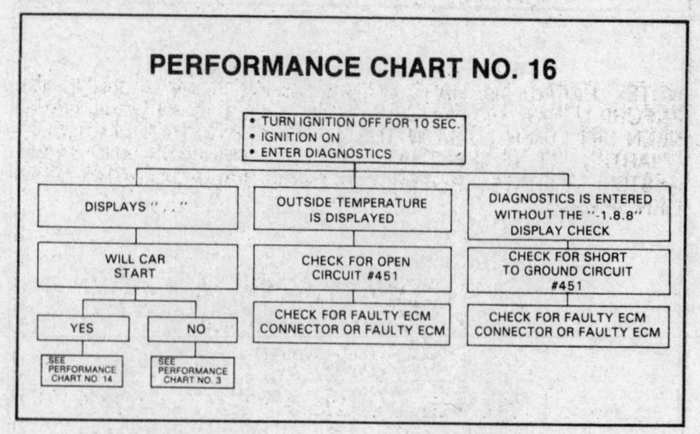

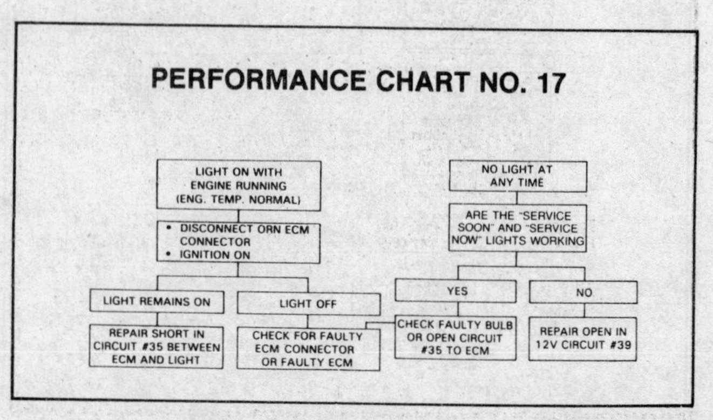

GENERAL MOTORS DFI CONTROL SYSTEM (Cont.)

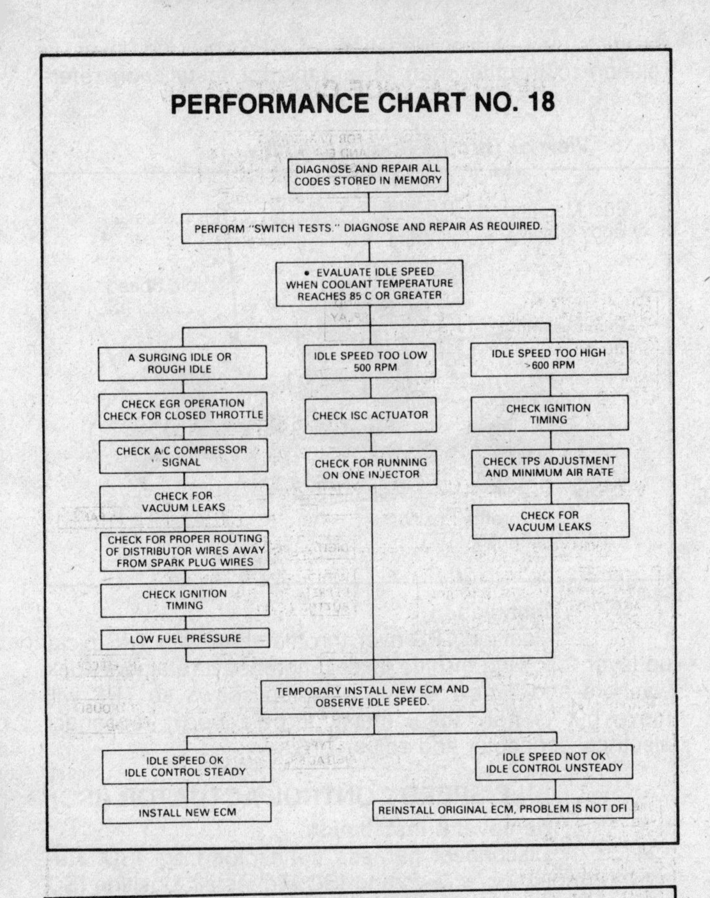

PERFORMANCE CHART NO. 19

NOTE: REPAIR ALL HARD CODES, OTHER THAN 13, 44 OR 45, BEFORE USING THIS PROCEDURE. IF CODES 13, 44 OR 45 HAVE BEEN SET, THEN FOLLOW THE APPROPRIATE TROUBLE CODE CHART(S) TO VERIFY THAT THE ECM, HARNESS AND FUEL SYSTEM OPERATE PROPERLY BEFORE REPLACING THE OXYGEN SENSOR.

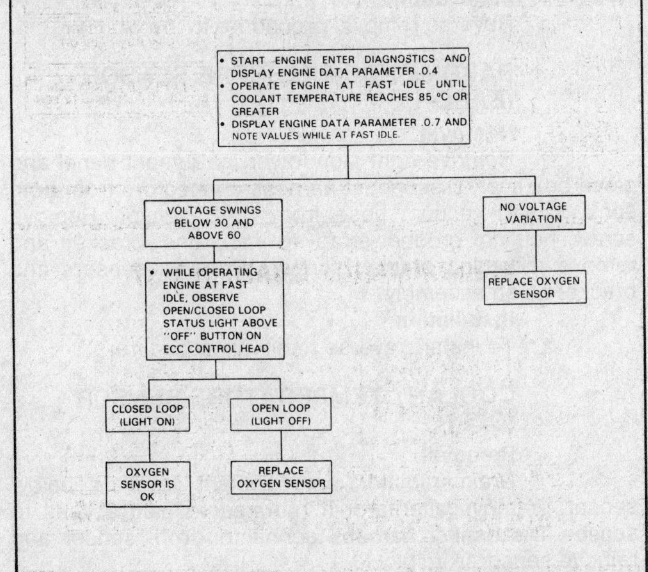

PERFORMANCE CHART NO. 20

NOTE: THIS PROCEDURE MUST NOT BE USED IF ANY OF THE FOLLOWING CODES ARE STORED IN MEMORY: 21, 22, 24, 28, 29, 33, 35, or 36.

• TURN IGNITION ON.
• CONNECT A TEST LIGHT BETWEEN PIN F OF ALDL DIAGNOSTIC CONNECTOR AND GROUND.

NO LIGHT

LIGHT

• WITH IGNITION ON, BACK PROBE BOTH SIDES OF TCC BRAKE SWITCH WITH A TEST LIGHT TO GROUND (WITH BRAKE RELEASED)

• ENTER DIAGNOSTICS AND SELECT OUTPUT CYCLING CODE .9.6
• OBSERVE TEST LIGHT.

LIGHT ON BOTH SIDES

LIGHT ON ONE SIDE

NO LIGHT BOTH SIDES

LIGHT GOES ON AND OFF EVERY 3 SECONDS

LIGHT STAYS ON

CHECK ADJUSTMENT OF TCC BRAKE SWITCH.

IF OK, REPLACE SWITCH.

TCC ELECTRICAL SYSTEM OK

• DISCONNECT TRANSMISSION CONNECTOR.
• CONNECT AN OHMMETER BETWEEN PINS A & D ON TRANS SIDE OF CONNECTOR.

• DISCONNECT TRANSMISSION CONNECTOR
• PROBE HARNESS PIN A WITH A TEST LIGHT TO GROUND.

CHECK GA-TRANS FUSE.

FUSE BLOWN

FUSE OK

LESS THAN 15 OHMS

REPAIR SHORTED CIRCUIT IN TRANSMISSION AND THEN DETERMINE IF ECM WAS DAMAGED BY SHORT.

NO LIGHT

LIGHT

REPAIR OPEN IN CIRCUIT #420

REPAIR GROUND IN CIRCUITS FEED BY GA TRANS FUSE.

REPAIR OPEN IN CIRCUITS #39 OR #3.

GREATER THAN 15 OHMS

CONNECT THE TEST LIGHT BETWEEN PIN A AND PIN D OF HARNESS CONNECTOR

• CHECK CIRCUIT #422 FOR AN OPEN.
• CHECK FOR A FAULTY ECM CONNECTOR OR FAULTY ECM.

NO LIGHT

LIGHT

JUMPER PIN F AND ALDL DIAGNOSTIC CONNECTOR TO GROUND

DISCONNECT P-2 (RED) ECM CONNECTOR

LIGHT REMAINS OFF

LIGHT COMES ON

LIGHT REMAINS ON

LIGHT GOES OFF

REPAIR OPEN IN CIRCUIT #422

CHECK FOR AN OPEN OR SHORT TO GROUND IN TRANSMISSION.

REPAIR CIRCUIT #422 FOR A SHORT TO GROUND

CHECK FOR A FAULTY ECM CONNECTOR OR FAULTY ECM

CHECK FOR FAUTLY MATING OF TRANSMISSION CONNECTOR TERMINALS

REFER TO: TRANSMISSION CIRCUIT

REMOVAL & INSTALLATION

ELECTRONIC CONTROL MODULE (ECM)

Removal & Installation

Remove lower instrument panel cover. Remove 3 nuts securing ECM to instrument panel mounting brackets and ground strap. Remove 3 electrical connectors and remove ECM from vehicle. To install ECM, reverse removal procedure and ensure ground strap is securely attached.

Removal

1) Remove ECM as previously described. Insert tip of small blade screwdriver into keyhole of locking tab on PROM access cover. Carefully bend tab slightly to unlock access cover and slide cover off ECM.

2) Note position of PROM before removal. Replacement PROM must be installed in same position as original. Small reference boss (dimple) on PROM carrier must be aligned with boss (dimple) on PROM socket. Grasp PROM between thumb and forefinger. Gently rock PROM back and forth while applying upward force to remove PROM and carrier.

NOTE: **PROMs are not interchangeable from generation to generation. Be sure part number of replacement PROM matches original PROM.**

GENERAL MOTORS DFI CONTROL SYSTEM (Cont.)

Installation

1) Place PROM in carrier upside down on flat surface with pins facing up. Using a narrow blunt tool, press PROM body down on both sides of retainer bar so top of PROM is flush with top of carrier. *See Fig. 5.*

Fig. 5: Installing PROM into Electronic Control Module

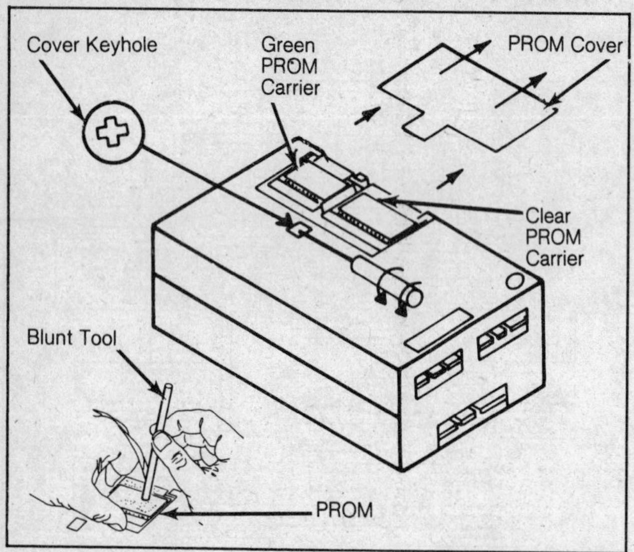

2) Position PROM carrier squarely over PROM socket in ECM. Firmly press down on top of carrier. While holding carrier down, press body of PROM down with a blunt tool. Alternately pressing down on either end will securely seat PROM.

3) Install access cover on ECM and ensure it locks in place. Install ECM in vehicle. Start engine, enter diagnostics and check for code "51". If code "51" does not appear, PROM installation is correct. If code "51" is displayed, PROM is not fully seated, installed backwards, has bent pins or is defective.

4) If pins are bent, straighten pins and reinstall PROM. If pins break or crack during straightening process, replace PROM. If PROM is installed backwards, replace PROM.

FUEL DATA DISPLAY

Removal & Installation

Remove center instrument panel applique. Remove 2 fuel data display mounting screws and pull display out of instrument panel. Disconnect electrical connector. To install, reverse removal procedure.

THROTTLE POSITION SENSOR (TPS)

NOTE: **DO NOT remove TPS unless all diagnosis confirms that TPS requires adjustment or repair.**

Removal

1) Remove TPS electrical connector. Remove air cleaner and throttle body assembly. Turn throttle body upside down and support assembly to prevent damage to injector connectors. Using a 5/16" drill bit, drill completely through both TPS access holes in base of throttle body to remove spot welds holding screws in place.

2) Remove and discard TPS attaching screws. Remove lock washers and retainers. Remove TPS from throttle body, noting location of TPS pick-up lever in relation to throttle shaft lever tang for installation reference.

Fig. 6: View of Throttle Body Assembly

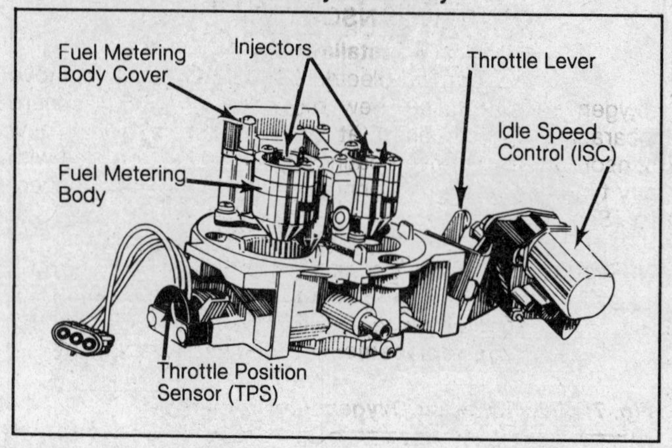

Installation

Position TPS over throttle shaft with TPS pick-up lever following throttle lever tang. Install retainers, lock washers and 2 new screws. Tighten scews so TPS will move but is not loose. Install throttle body, reconnect electrical connector and adjust TPS.

IDLE SPEED CONTROL ACTUATOR (ISC)

Removal & Installation

Disconnect harness connector from ISC. Remove 2 mounting screws and ISC. To install, position ISC on left side of throttle body. Install mounting screws and adjust ISC.

MANIFOLD ABSOLUTE PRESSURE SENSOR (MAP)

Removal

Remove instrument panel lower cover. Disconnect MAP vacuum hose and electrical connector. Remove screw securing MAP sensor to MAP/BARO bracket and remove sensor.

Installation

Reverse removal procedure to install.

BAROMETRIC PRESSURE SENSOR (BARO)

Removal

Remove right side lower instrument panel and glove box liner. Disconnect harness connectors from both sensors and vacuum hose from MAP sensor. Remove screw holding ground strap to mounting bracket and remove mounting bracket screws. Remove sensors and bracket as an assembly.

Installation

To install, reverse removal procedure.

COOLANT TEMPERATURE SENSOR (CTS)

Removal

Drain radiator until coolant level is below sensor. Remove alternator if required to gain access to sensor. Disconnect harness connector from sensor and remove sensor from block.

GENERAL MOTORS DFI CONTROL SYSTEM (Cont.)

Installation

Apply non-hardening sealer to threads of sensor and install sensor. Reconnect harness connect and install alternator (if removed). Refill radiator.

OXYGEN SENSOR

Removal & Installation

Disconnect electrical connector and remove oxygen sensor. Install new oxygen sensor and ensure clearance is maintained at boot. When installing new sensor, do not remove coating from threads or install with any type of sealant. Reconnect electrical harness connector. *See Fig. 7.*

NOTE: DO NOT attempt to reinstall an oxygen sensor. Reinstallation of a sensor without the special glass bead thread coating may require replacement of exhaust system.

Fig. 7: View Showing Oxygen Sensor Location

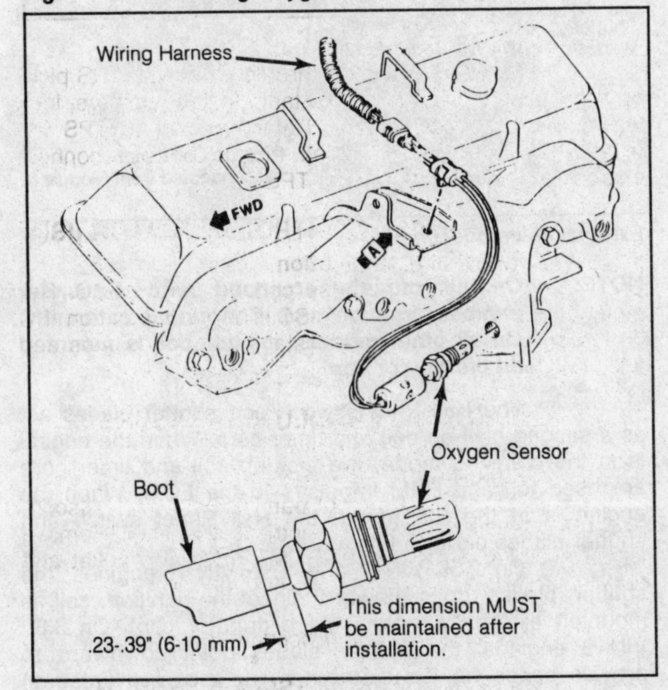

1983 Exhaust Emission Systems

DELCO-REMY
ELECTRONIC SPARK TIMING (EST) IGNITION

All General Motors Models Except Federal 1.6L

DESCRIPTION

The Delco-Remy High Energy Ignition system with Electronic Spark Timing (HEI-EST) is used on most General Motors vehicles equipped with gasoline engines. The 3.0L VIN E, 3.8L VIN A, 4.1L VIN 4, 5.0L VIN 7 and 5.7L VIN 8 engines also use the Electronic Spark Control (ESC) system to retard timing when detonation occurs.

The Delco-Remy HEI-EST system, a part of all General Motors Computer Command Control systems, is designed to provide optimum performance through electronic control of air/fuel ratios, spark timing, air management and idle speed.

The distributor has neither vacuum nor centrifugal advance mechanisms. *See Figs. 1 and 2*. The distributor contains a 7-terminal HEI-EST control module, a timer core, pick-up coil, radio noise suppression capacitor and, on most models, an integrally mounted ignition coil, located under the distributor cap's coil cover. Distributors on vehicles equipped with 2.5L VIN 2, 2.5L VIN R and 3.8L VIN 9 engines also contain a Hall Effect switch and shutter blades.

Fig. 1: Disassembled View of HEI-EST Distributor

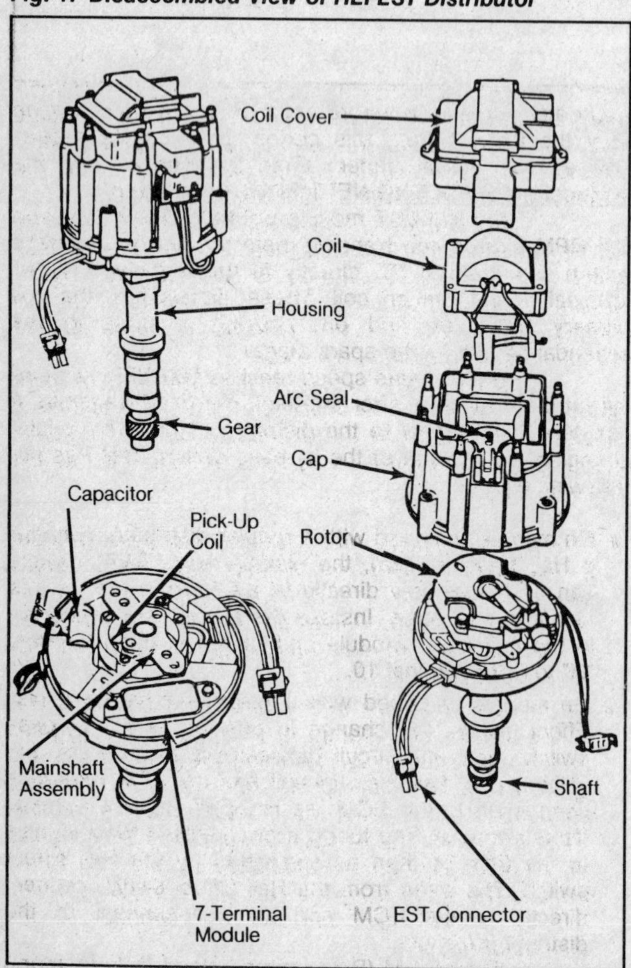

Integral coil model shown.

Fig. 2: HEI-EST Distributor with Hall Effect Switch

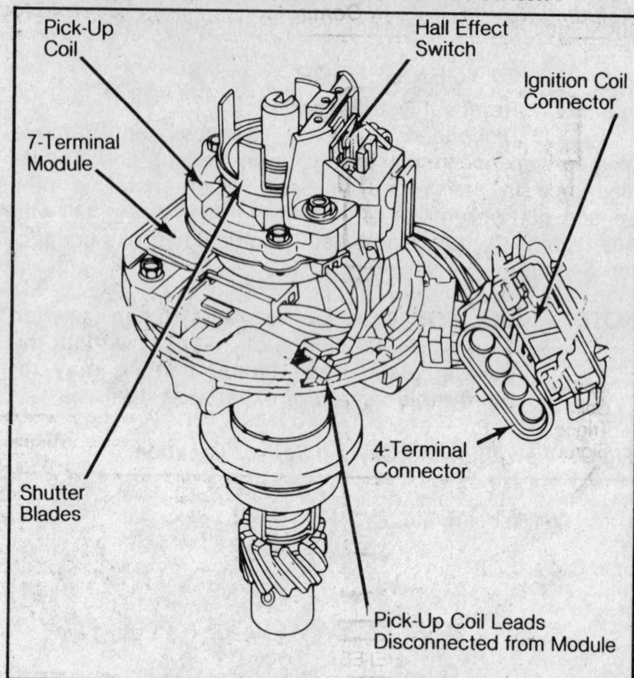

External coil model shown.

NOTE: On all models equipped with 4-cylinder engines, ignition coil is mounted externally. On all other models, ignition coil is mounted on distributor cap.

The Hall Effect switch and shutter blades act as a second pick-up coil and timer core. When the engine is in the cranking mode, the pick-up coil and timer core are used to send RPM impulses to the ECM. When the engine is in the run mode, the Hall Effect switch and shutter blades perform this function.

On 2.5L VIN 2 and 2.5L VIN R engines, the shutter blades point upward since the ignition coil is mounted externally (not in the distributor cap). On 3.8L VIN 9 engines, the shutter blades point downward to provide space for the distributor cap mounted (integral) ignition coil. The number of shutter blades must equal the number of cylinders in the engine being used.

The distributor is connected to the EST system by means of a 4-wire connector, leading to the external electronic control module (ECM). The ECM (not the distributor HEI-EST module) receives voltage signals from a number of sensors. A typical system could be provided signals from oxygen, engine coolant temperature, throttle position, barometric pressure and manifold absolute pressure sensors, as well as the distributor pick-up coil and Hall Effect switch (if equipped).

CAUTION: Few components are interchangeable between HEI-EST and HEI distributors used on various engines. Be sure that the correct part is used, as similar appearance does not mean identical design or operation.

DELCO-REMY
ELECTRONIC SPARK TIMING (EST) IGNITION (Cont.)

Fig. 3: Schematic of HEI-EST Ignition System Including Relationship to Computer Command Control Electronic Control Module

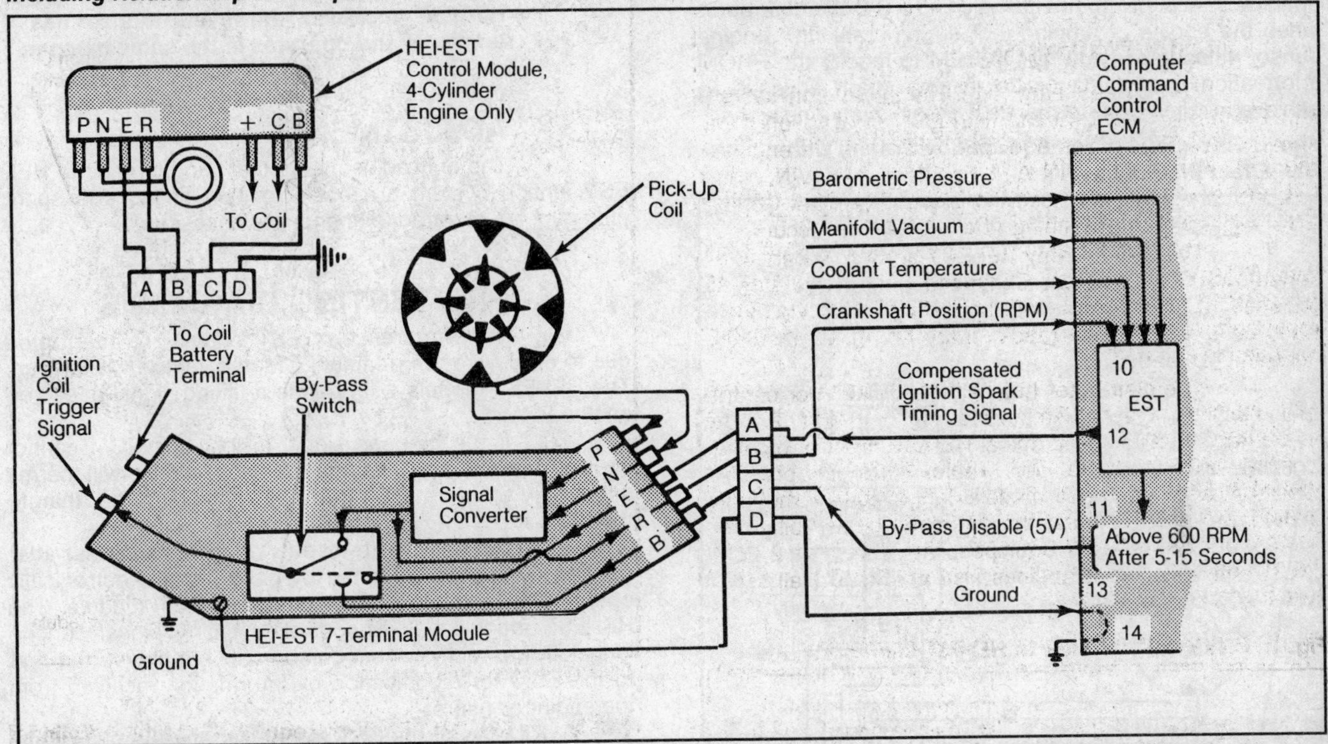

There are 4 basic components to the ESC system: A detonation sensor, an HEI-EST distributor, an ESC controller, and the ECM. When detonation (engine knock) occurs, the detonation sensor sends an electrical signal to the ESC controller. The ESC controller amplifies this signal and transmits it to the ECM which then retards the spark timing until the ECM no longer receives a signal from the detonation sensor, through the ESC controller.

Fig. 4: Schematic of Electronic Spark Control System

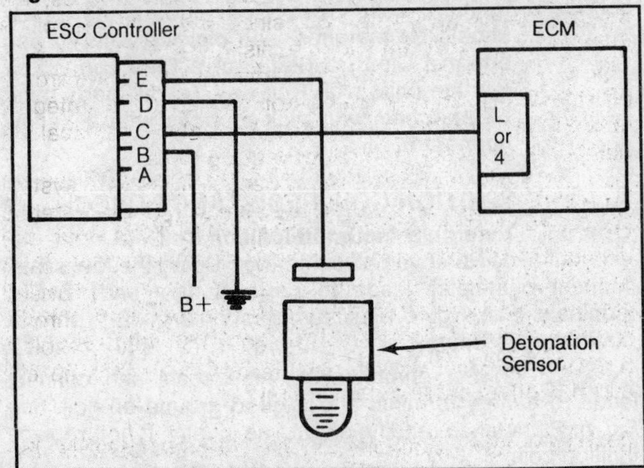

OPERATION

During cranking or in event of EST ECM failure, a by-pass signal from ECM terminal 11 to the HEI-EST module terminal "B" is either absent or low. *See Fig. 3.* This notifies the HEI-EST module to take over control of spark advance and to ignore any EST information coming from the ECM. During this period, poor engine performance may result under some conditions, but the diagnostic "CHECK ENGINE" light will not come on.

The HEI-EST module will then convert pick-up coil RPM signals and transmit them through the by-pass switch and terminal "C" directly to the negative "TACH" terminal of the ignition coil. These signals turn the coil primary circuit on and off, causing a surge in the secondary that fires the spark plugs.

When engine speed reaches 600 RPM or more (about 5-15 seconds after starting), the ECM transmits a constant 5-volt signal to the distributor HEI-EST module, changing the position of the by-pass switch. This has the following effect:

- On models equipped with a regular distributor (without a Hall Effect switch), the pick-up coil's RPM signals can no longer flow directly to the ignition coil as this circuit is now open. Instead the signals are converted in the distributor module and routed through terminal "R" to ECM terminal 10.
- On models equipped with a distributor having a Hall Effect switch, the change in position of the by-pass switch opens the circuit between the pick-up coil and ignition coil. The pick-up coil has no RPM reference connection to the ECM, as HEI-EST module terminal "R" is not used. The function of supplying RPM signals to the ECM is then accomplished by the Hall Effect switch. The wires from the Hall Effect switch connect directly to the ECM and do not connect to the distributor module.

The PROM (Programmed Read Only Memory) portion of the ECM carries the basic spark advance curve

DELCO-REMY
ELECTRONIC SPARK TIMING (EST) IGNITION (Cont.)

based on engine RPM. Spark Timing is calculated by the ECM whenever an ignition pulse is present, however, spark advance information is only SENT TO the distributor when the engine is running (not during cranking). Engine sensor values are used by the ECM to modify the PROM information, increasing or decreasing spark advance to achieve maximum performance with minimum emissions.

Fig. 5: Schematic of HEI-EST Ignition System with Hall Effect Distributor

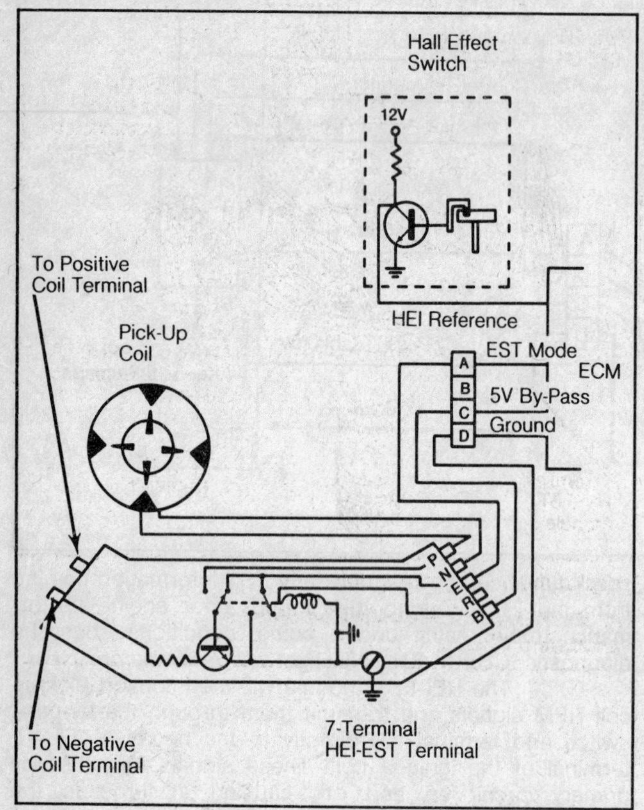

The coolant temperature sensor advances spark on a cold engine and reduces advance as the engine reaches normal operating temperature. If the engine is too hot, spark is retarded to prevent detonation.

During light throttle operation, the throttle switch allows for additional advance. Additional adjustment results from input from coolant temperature, engine RPM and manifold absolute pressure (MAP) sensors. When MAP is low, spark is at maximum advance.

As load increases and pressure increases, spark timing is retarded to allow the engine to maintain its proper performance and emission level.

After computation of all information from the various sensors, a compensated ignition spark timing signal is sent through the HEI-EST module's terminal "E", the by-pass switch, and terminal "C", to the ignition coil negative terminal. Each time the signal is flashed on and off, the coil's primary circuit is turned on and off. As this occurs, a voltage surge occurs in the secondary that fires the spark plugs.

The ECM is continually computing sensor information to maintain efficient engine performance with low emission levels, doing so under varying engine conditions.

NOTE: The shape of the HEI-EST module used on 4-cylinder engines differs from those of other HEI-EST modules. However, it also has 7 terminals and operates in the same manner.

ADJUSTMENTS

The only adjustments that can be made to HEI-EST igntion system are basic ignition timing and spark plug gap. No other adjustments are necessary.

PRE-TESTING DIAGNOSIS

If the reference or EST signals are interrupted due to open wires or a faulty ECM, the vehicle will still run. The HEI-EST module will provide a timing signal based on engine RPM.

If the by-pass signal is lost, the ECM cannot control spark timing, as the by-pass switch will permit direct flow of information to the ignition coil rather than to the ECM.

Normally, a few seconds (5-15 seconds) after starting a warm engine, the by-pass signal electronically operates a by-pass switch in the HEI-EST module. The HEI-EST module's RPM-controlled timing signal can no longer flow directly to the ignition coil, but is diverted first to the ECM for modification by information received from the engine sensors.

Loss of the EST signal with the by-pass signal "ON", however, will stop the engine, because the HEI-EST module is no longer sending signals directly to the ignition coil, but to the ECM, and any loss of the EST signal cuts all flow to the coil. If an attempt is made to restart the vehicle, the engine will run for a few seconds and then stop when the by-pass signal comes back on.

TESTING

NOTE: Ignition coils with Red and White leads should be matched with pick-up coils having either a Clear, a Black, or a Blue connector. Ignition coils with Red and Yellow leads must be matched with pick-up coils with a Yellow connector.

IGNITION COIL RESISTANCE CHECK

Externally Mounted Ignition Coil

1) Remove coil connector. Using the low scale, connect ohmmeter leads to coil's battery and "TACH" terminals. *See Fig. 6*. Resistance should be 0-1 ohm. If not, replace ignition coil.

2) Set ohmmeter to high scale and connect leads to battery terminal and a good ground on coil. *See Fig. 6*. Resistance reading should be infinity. If not, replace ignition coil.

3) With ohmmeter still set in high range, connect leads to "TACH" terminal and to secondary terminal. *See Fig. 6*. Resistance should be 6,000-30,000 ohms. If not, replace ignition coil.

1983 Exhaust Emission Systems

DELCO-REMY
ELECTRONIC SPARK TIMING (EST) IGNITION (Cont.)

Fig. 6: Ignition Coil Resistance Test Points

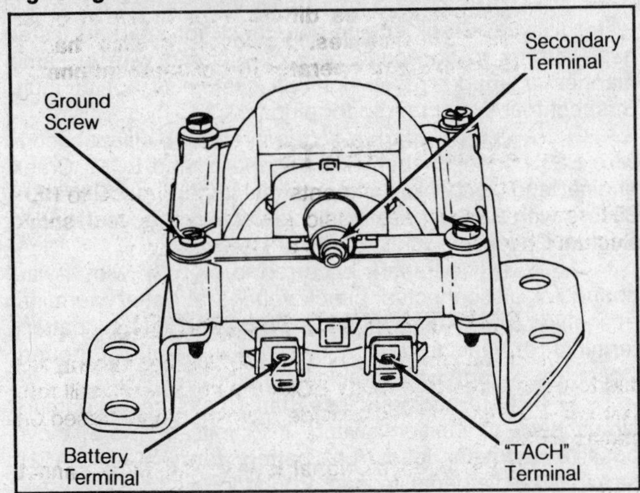

Externally mounted ignition coil.

Integrally Mounted Ignition Coil (In Distributor Cap)

1) Turn ignition switch "OFF". Remove distributor cap and coil assembly. *See Fig. 7.* Set ohmmeter in low scale. Connect leads to coil's battery and "TACH" terminals. Resistance should be 0-1 ohm. If not, replace ignition coil.

Fig. 7: Ignition Coil Resistance Test Points

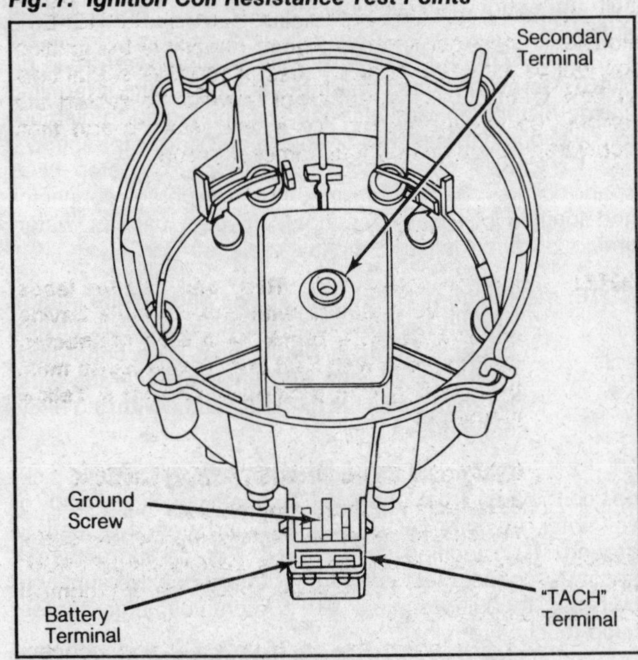

Integral mounted ignition coil.

2) Set ohmmeter in high scale. Connect one ohmmeter lead to coil secondary terminal. Connect other ohmmeter lead to "TACH" terminal and then to ground terminal. *See Fig. 7.*

3) If one reading is infinity and other is 6,000-30,000 ohms, ignition coil is okay. If resistance reading in BOTH instances is infinity, replace ignition coil.

DISTRIBUTOR PICK-UP COIL SHORT AND RESISTANCE CHECKS

1) Disconnect pick-up coil leads from HEI-EST module terminals "N" and "P" (usually a Green and a White

Fig. 8: Distributor Pick-Up Coil Short & Resistance Checks

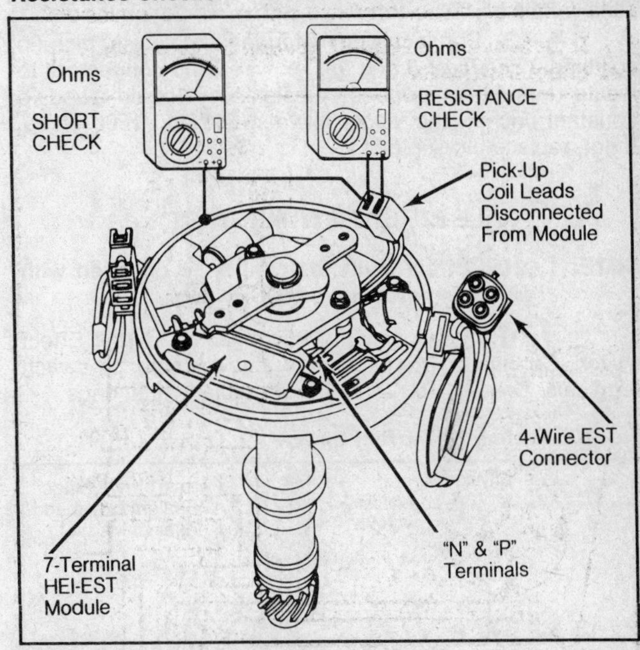

Integral mounted ignition coil.

Fig. 9: Distributor Pick-Up Coil Short & Resistance Checks

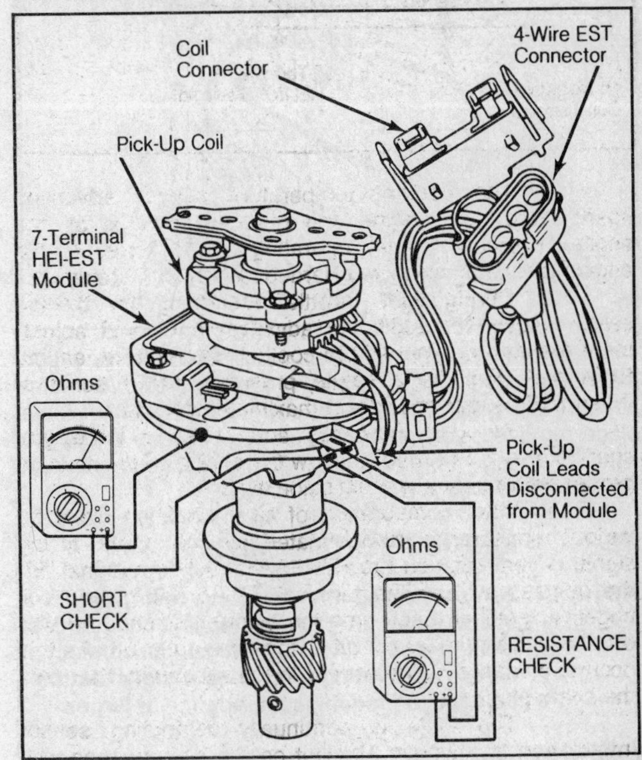

Externally mounted ignition coil.

DELCO-REMY
ELECTRONIC SPARK TIMING (EST) IGNITION (Cont.)

wire). To check for shorted pick-up coil, set ohmmeter in middle range.

2) Connect one lead to either pick-up coil lead and other lead to distributor housing. Flex pick-up coil leads by hand to check for intermittent shorts. *See Figs. 8 and 9*. Reading should be infinite at all times. If not, replace pick-up coil.

3) Connect ohmmeter leads to both pick-up coil leads. *See Figs. 8 and 9*. Flex wires and connectors to locate intermittent opens. Resistance should read a constant unchanging value between 500 and 1500 ohms. If not, replace pick-up coil.

HALL EFFECT SWITCH TEST

NOTE: **Hall Effect switches cannot be checked with an ohmmeter like a pick-up coil.**

1) Disconnect 3-wire connector at Hall Effect switch. Connect a 12 volt battery and voltmeter to switch terminals. *See Fig. 10*. Carefully note polarity markings.

Fig. 10: Testing Hall Effect Switch

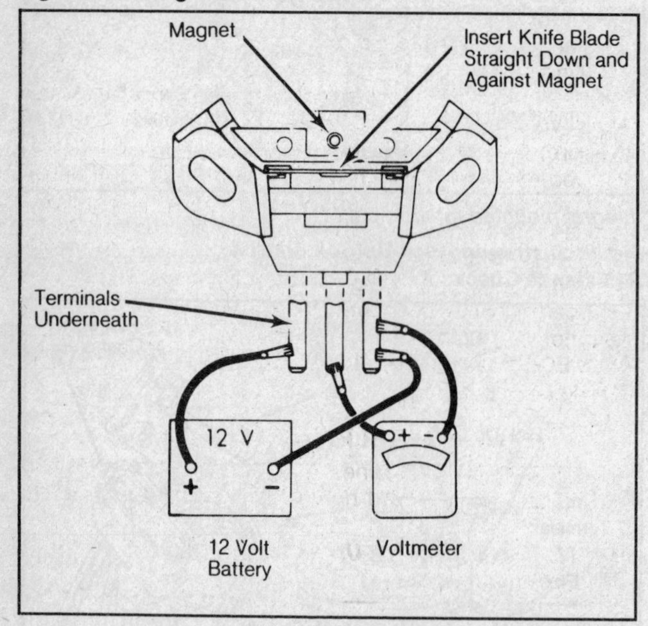

2) Insert knife blade straight down between magnet and Hall Effect switch. *See Fig. 10*. Voltmeter should read within 0.5 volts of battery voltage. With knife blade removed, voltmeter should read between 0 and 0.5 volts. If voltage readings are not as described, replace Hall Effect switch.

IGNITION SYSTEM CHECK

NOTE: **Before making the following tests, obtain a spark tester. If tachometer is connected to ignition coil "TACH" terminal, disconnect it before performing tests. Use a digital voltmeter with 10 megohms impedance or larger.**

CAUTION: **When removing a spark plug wire from a spark plug, twist boot on spark plug and pull on boot NOT on wire to remove.**

Integrally Mounted Ignition Coil

1) Remove a spark plug wire and attach spark tester to wire. Crank engine and check for spark at tester gap. If there is no spark, check a second wire in same manner. If sparks result, ignition system is not at fault. Suspect fuel system or spark plugs.

2) If no spark resulted in step **1)**, disconnect 4-wire EST connector between distributor and ECM. Crank engine and recheck for spark at tester gap. If spark occurs with EST connector disconnected, proceed to EST System Check.

3) If no spark occurred in step **2)**, with 4-wire connector disconnected, check voltage at battery terminal of ignition coil. Attach positive voltmeter lead to battery terminal of ignition coil and negative lead to ground. Check for voltage while cranking engine.

4) If reading is less than 7 volts, repair primary circuit back to ignition switch. If 7 volts or more, move positive voltmeter lead from battery terminal to "TACH" terminal. Leave negative lead grounded.

5) If reading is under 1 volt, ignition coil connection or ignition coil is defective. Repair or replace as necessary. If 10 volts or more is registered on voltmeter, proceed to step **7)**. If voltmeter reading is 1-10 volts, proceed to step **6)**.

6) If voltage reading on "TACH" terminal was 1-10 volts, replace distributor HEI-EST module and check for spark, following procedure outlined in steps **7)**, **9)**, and **11)**. However, if a spark results in step **11)**, ignition system is okay following module replacement. If there is still no spark, replace ignition coil also, as it too is defective.

7) If in step **5)**, 10 volts or more were read on "TACH" terminal, attach spark tester to coil output terminal (inside distributor cap) with cap still connected to distributor by wiring harness. Crank engine and check for spark.

8) If no spark occurs, proceed to step **9)**. If spark occurs, check color match of pick-up coil connector and ignition coil lead (see note). Inspect cap for water, cracks or other damage. If okay, replace rotor.

NOTE: **Ignition coils with Red and White leads should be matched with pick-up coils having either a Clear, a Black, or a Blue connector. Ignition coils with Red and Yellow leads must be matched with pick-up coils with a Yellow connector.**

9) If no spark occurred in step **7)**, remove pick-up coil leads from module. Connect positive lead of voltmeter to coil "TACH" terminal and negative lead to ground. Turn ignition switch "ON". For no more than 5 seconds, connect test lamp from battery positive supply to HEI-EST module terminal "P". Watch voltmeter as test lamp touches terminal.

10) If voltage drops, proceed to step **11)**. If voltage does not drop, check module ground screw. Also check for open in wires from distributor cap (coil) to distributor. If okay, replace HEI-EST module.

11) If voltage dropped in step **10)**, check for spark at tester gap (still attached to coil output terminal) when test light is removed from module terminal. If spark occurred, either pick-up coil or its connections are defective. Perform Distributor Pick-Up Coil Short and

DELCO-REMY
ELECTRONIC SPARK TIMING (EST) IGNITION (Cont.)

Resistance Check if not done previously. Resistance should be 500-1500 ohms.

12) If distributor module tester is available, check HEI-EST module. If okay, check ignition coil ground. If ground is okay, replace ignition coil. If module is defective, replace.

13) If no module tester is available, check ignition coil ground circuit. If okay, replace ignition coil and repeat steps **7)**, **9)**, and **11)**. If spark results, system is okay. If no spark results, original ignition coil is okay. Reinstall original ignition coil and replace HEI-EST module.

Externally Mounted Ignition Coil

1) Remove a spark plug wire and connect a spark tester to it. Check for spark while cranking engine. If no spark results, check for spark at another wire. If spark results, problem is in fuel system or spark plugs. If no spark occurs, proceed to step **2)**.

2) If no spark occured in step **1)**, remove the secondary ignition coil wire from the distributor cap. Connect spark tester to end of wire. Check for spark while cranking engine. If no spark occurs, proceed to step **3)**. If spark occurs, check distributor cap for water or cracks. If okay, replace rotor.

3) Remove distributor cap but leave it connected to distributor with wiring harness. Connect negative voltmeter lead to ground and positive lead to HEI-EST module terminal "+". Turn ignition switch "ON". If voltage is 10 volts or more, proceed to step **4)**. If voltage is less than 10 volts, repair wire from terminal "+" to ignition coil and primary circuit to ignition switch.

4) If voltage was 10 volts or more in step **3)**, leave ignition switch "ON" and negative voltmeter lead grounded. Connect positive lead to HEI-EST module terminal "C". If voltage is under 1 volt, check for open or grounded lead from ignition coil to terminal "C", ignition coil connections or for an open primary circuit in ignition coil.

5) If voltage was 10 volts or more, proceed to step **6)**. If voltage was 1-10 volts, replace HEI-EST module and check for spark from ignition coil as described in step **7)**. If sparks occur, system is operating properly. If no sparks occur, replace ignition coil as it too is defective.

6) If voltage was 10 volts or more in step **4)**, remove pick-up coil connector from HEI-EST module. Connect negative voltmeter lead to ground and positive lead to HEI-EST module terminal "C". Turn ignition switch "ON". Momentarily connect a test light between battery voltage and HEI-EST module terminal "P" while observing voltmeter.

7) If voltage does not drop, check HEI-EST module ground. If okay, replace HEI-EST module. If voltage does drop, use a spark tester and check for spark at end of coil wire as test light is removed from HEI-EST module terminal "P". If spark does not occur, proceed to step **8)**. If spark does occur, check pick-up coil and its connections. Also make sure pick-up coil is not grounded.

8) If distributor module tester is available, check HEI-EST module. If okay, check secondary wire from distributor cap to ignition coil. If okay, replace ignition coil. If module is defective, replace. If no distributor module tester is available, replace the HEI-EST module and repeat step **7)**.

9) If spark occurs, system is operating properly. If no spark occurs, HEI-EST module removed is okay. Reinstall original module and check secondary wire from distributor cap to ignition coil. If okay, replace ignition coil.

INTERMITTENT OPERATION CHECK

1) Connect spark tester to 2 different spark plug wires. If no spark, perform Ignition System Check. If spark on either or both wires, check for dwell increase from low to high RPM.

2) Check pick-up coil and Hall Effect switch (if equipped). Replace, if faulty. If pick-up coil and Hall Effect switch are good and dwell did not increase, replace HEI-EST module. If good, but dwell did increase, check fuel system, spark plug wires, distributor cap and spark plugs.

EST EMISSION SYSTEM CHECK

1) With shift lever in "P" (auto. trans.) or Neutral (man. trans.), run engine at fast idle and note timing change as test terminal is grounded. If timing changes, system is operating properly.

2) If timing does not change on vehicles equipped with manual transmissions, proceed to step **3)**. If timing does not change on vehicles equipped with automatic transmissions, let engine return to idle and place transmission in "D". Note timing change as test terminal is grounded. If timing changes, system is operating properly.

3) If no change in timing occurs (all models), check voltage at output of MAP (Manifold Absolute Pressure) sensor or vacuum sensor as vacuum hose is removed and reinstalled. If no change occurs, problem is in the vacuum or MAP sensor circuit. If voltage output changes, proceed to step **4)**.

4) Disconnect park/neutral switch and recheck for timing change. If timing changes, problem is either an improperly adjusted or faulty park/neutral switch. If timing does not change, check for grounded wire from terminal "H" of ECM to park/neutral switch. If wire is not grounded, replace ECM.

BY-PASS OR FAULTY EST CHECK

1) With engine at fast idle, check timing. Ground test terminal and note if timing changes. If timing

Fig. 11: Test Light Hook-Up for Checking EST Emission System

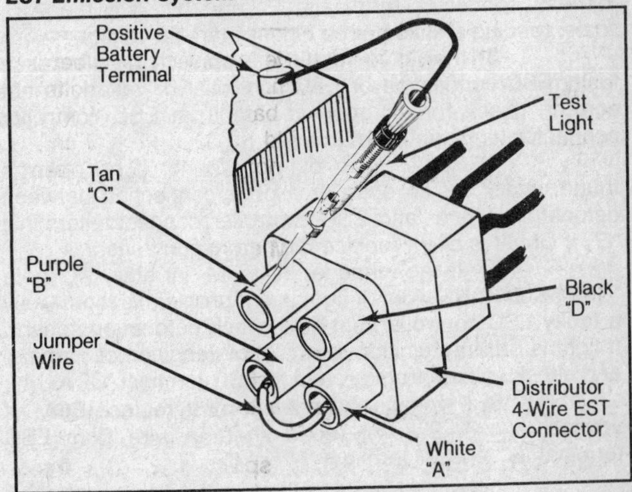

DELCO-REMY ELECTRONIC SPARK TIMING (EST) IGNITION (Cont.)

does change, system is operating properly. If timing does not change, stop engine and disconnect 4-wire EST connector from distributor.

2) Connect a jumper wire from terminal "A" to "B" on distributor side of EST connector. *See Fig. 11.* Start engine, ground test terminal and connect test light from battery positive terminal to terminal "C" of EST connector.

3) If engine stops, check for open wire from EST terminal "E" to ECM. If wire is okay, replace either HEI-EST connector or module. If engine runs, remove jumper wire from terminals "A" and "B" while leaving test light connected. If engine runs, proceed to step **4)**. If engine stops, proceed to step **5)**.

4) If engine continued to run in step **3)**, check distributor wires for open or ground to HEI-EST module terminal "B" or short between module terminals "R" and "E". If wires are okay, repair faulty HEI-EST module connection or replace HEI-EST module.

5) If engine stopped in step **3)**, check for open wire from EST connector terminal "A" to ECM connector terminal "12". Also check for open or grounded wire from EST connector terminal "C" to ECM connector terminal "11". If wires are okay, replace faulty ECM connector or ECM.

NOTE: **ECM connector terminal numbers may vary between models.**

ESC PERFORMANCE CHECK

NOTE: **Perform these checks only after checking other causes of engine detonation, such as ignition timing, MAP, lack of EGR, or engine temperature.**

1) Connect tachometer to engine and run at fast idle speed (about 1500 RPM). Place shift lever in "P" (auto. trans.) or Neutral (man. trans.). With engine at normal operating temperature, tap engine block in area of detonation sensor. If engine RPM drops, system is operating properly.

2) If RPM did not drop, disconnect ESC controller and check for RPM change. If no change in RPM, proceed to step **5)**. If RPM drops, run engine at 2000 RPM. Connect a digital voltmeter between ESC harness connector terminals "E" and "D". On the A.C. scale, reading should not be higher than .08 volts.

3) If voltage reading is correct, problem is a fualty ESC connection or ESC controller. If voltage is not correct, check for an open in wire from ESC controller connector terminal "D" to ground.

4) Repair if an open is found. If no open is found, check for an open or a poor connection between detonation sensor and ESC controller connector terminal "E". If circuit is okay, replace the detonation sensor.

5) If no change in RPM in step **2)**, note "CHECK ENGINE" light. If light is on, problem is most likely a faulty ESC controller, but also check detonation sensor. If light is off, turn ignition switch "ON" (engine not running) and check voltage from ground to ESC terminal "C".

6) If voltage is under 2 volts, replace ECM. If voltage is over 2 volts, repair short in wire from ESC terminal "C" to ECM terminal "L" or "4".

OVERHAUL

NOTE: **When distributor is removed from 1.6L engine, the fuel pump and fuel pump rod MUST be removed first.**

DISASSEMBLY

1) On distributors with integral ignition coils, detach 4-wire EST connector and wiring connector from cap and turn 4 latches. Remove cap and coil assembly from lower housing. To remove coil, remove coil cover attaching screws, cover, and coil attaching screws. Lift coil with leads from cap.

2) Remove coil arc seal and clean cap with soft cloth, checking for cracks or other damage.

3) On vehicles with external coils, remove coil connector and disconnect 4-wire EST connector. Turn 2 latches and lift off distributor cap.

4) On all models, remove rotor and disconnect pick-up coil leads from HEI-EST module. *See Fig. 1.* Remove Hall Effect switch (if equipped) by removing 2 attaching screws. Mark distributor shaft and gear for later reassembly. Drive out roll pin and remove distributor shaft.

5) On models with integral coil, remove magnetic shield. Then remove retaining "C" washer, pick-up coil, magnet and pole piece. Remove 2 module attaching screws and capacitor screw. Lift module, capacitor and harness assembly from distributor housing. Disconnect wiring harness from module.

REASSEMBLY

Assemble in reverse order, noting the following. Wipe distributor housing and module clean and apply silicone grease between module and housing. Spin shaft to be sure timer core external teeth do not strike pole piece internal teeth.

GENERAL MOTORS AIR INJECTION REACTOR SYSTEM

DESCRIPTION

The Air Injection Reactor (A.I.R.) system is used on all engines except some 2.0L 4-cylinder engines. This system is designed to reduce hydrocarbons (HC) and carbon monoxide (CO) emissions.

This is accomplished by injecting air into either the exhaust port of the cylinder head, exhaust manifold or catalytic converter. The A.I.R. system operates at all times and will by-pass air only for a short period of time during deceleration and at high speeds.

The air management valve performs the by-pass and diverter function. The check valve protects the air pump from damage by preventing a backflow of exhaust gases.

Fig. 1: Schematic of a Typical Air Management System

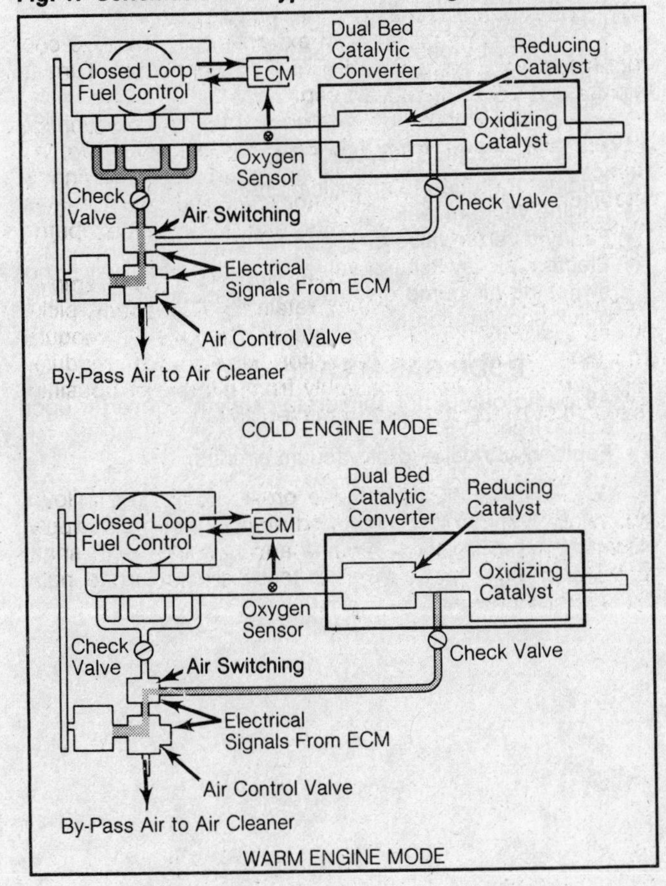

OPERATION

AIR PUMP

The air pump is a belt driven type vane pump, located at the front of the engine. The pump supplies clean air to the A.I.R. system.

The system uses air from the air pump to cause further oxidation (burning) of HC and CO before these gases are discharged from the tailpipe.

DECELERATION VALVE

This valve is used on some engines to prevent backfiring in the exhaust system during deceleration. This valve is normally closed, but opens when sudden deceleration increases vacuum to a point of overcoming internal spring pressure.

This allows additional air into the intake manifold to prevent overly rich mixtures from entering the combustion chambers. Air trapped in the chamber above the vacuum diaphragm will bleed, at a calibrated rate, through the delay valve portion of the integral check and delay valve.

This reducing vacuum acts on the diaphragm. When the vacuum load on the diaphragm matches spring load, the valve assembly closes. This shuts off air to the intake manifold.

DIVERTER VALVE

The diverter valve is also used to prevent backfire in the exhaust system during sudden deceleration. The valve senses sudden increases in intake manifold vacuum causing the valve to open. This allows air from the air pump to pass, through the valve and silencer, to the atmosphere.

A pressure relief valve controls pressure within the system by diverting excess pump outlet air (developed at higher engine speeds) to the atmosphere through the silencer.

CHECK VALVE

The check valve prevents the backflow of exhaust gases into the air distribution system. The valve prevents backflow when the air pump by-passes at high speeds, extreme engine loads, or in case the air pump malfunctions.

ELECTRIC AIR CONTROL VALVE

This valve combines 3 separate functions into a single valve. It provides normal diverter valve function and pressure relief by diverting air into the engine air cleaner when system pressure exceeds a predetermined value.

Since the valve utilizes a solenoid, the valve can be electrically controlled to divert air under any desired operating mode.

When the solenoid is energized, the valve will perform like a standard diverter valve. When the solenoid is de-energized, the solenoid causes air to divert during all operating modes.

ELECTRIC AIR SWITCHING VALVE

The air switching valve is a spring actuated 2-way valve. This valve is located in series between the air control valve and the exhaust system.

When the solenoid is de-energized, a vacuum is applied to the diaphragm chamber to provide air flow to the exhaust ports.

When the solenoid is energized, vacuum to the diaphragm chamber is blocked and the chamber is vented to the atmosphere. This allows the spring to open the port to the catalytic converter and close the port to the engine.

ELECTRIC AIR CONTROL/ ELECTRIC AIR SWITCHING VALVE

The electric air control/electric air switching valve (EAC/EAS) combines both diverter function and the air switching function into one integral valve.

In addition to normal diverter valve function, this valve can be electronically controlled to provide divert air under any driving mode.

GENERAL MOTORS AIR INJECTION REACTOR SYSTEM (Cont.)

The second section of the valve can be electronically controlled to provide the air switching function. This is to provide direction for air not diverted to the air cleaner.

Fig. 2: Sectional View of EAC/EAS Valve

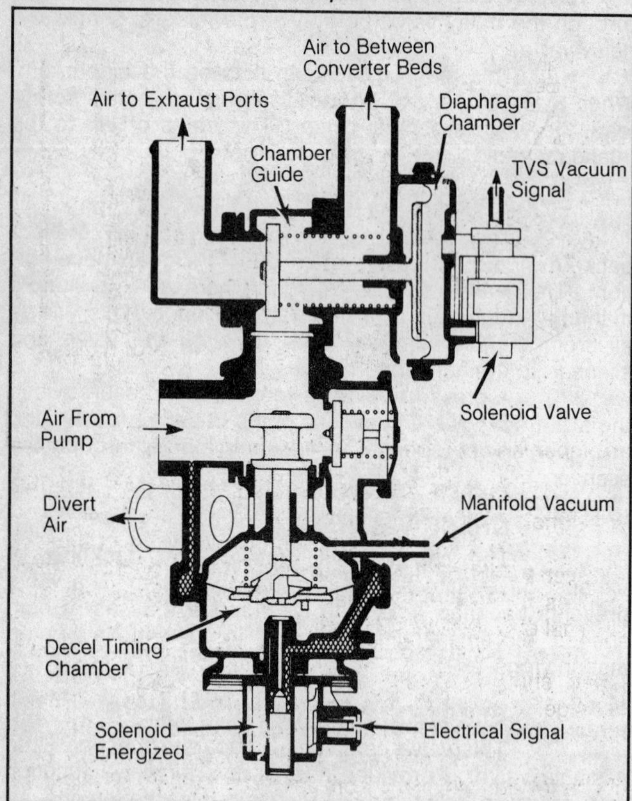

TESTING

NOTE: **For Air Management System Function Check, Electric Air Control/Electric Air Switching Valve check and Electric Diverter Valve check, see Diagnostic Charts in General Motors Computer Command Control article.**

CHECK VALVE

1) Inspect check valve whenever working on A.I.R. system. If pump was inoperative and had signs of exhaust gases reaching pump, a failed check valve would be indicated.

2) After detaching valve, blow though it in direction of flow to cylinder head, then attempt to suck back through direction of flow. Replace valve if it allows airflow against direction of flow.

AIR PUMP

1) Accelerate engine to approximately 1500 RPM and observe air flow from hoses. If airflow increases as engine is accelerated, pump is operating properly. If it does not increase, or is not present, proceed to next step.

2) Check for proper pump belt tension, leaky valves, seized pump, improperly routed hoses or disconnected hoses.

NOTE: **Do not oil air pump. The air pump system is not completely noiseless.**

TROUBLE SHOOTING

EXCESSIVE NOISE

- Loose drive belt.
- Seized air pump.
- Leaking hose or hoses.
- Diverter and/or by-pass valve failure.
- Loose pump mounting bolts.
- Internal pump damage.

NO AIR SUPPLY

- Loose drive belt.
- Leak in hoses or tubing.
- Diverter or by-pass valve failure.
- Check valve failure.
- Internal pump malfunction.

EXHAUST BACKFIRE

- Engine not tuned to specifications.
- Engine vacuum leaks.
- Faulty diverter valve or check valve.
- Electric air switching valve or air control valve not switching air pump discharge to air cleaner on start or quick deceleration.

POOR GAS MILAGE

- Air pump output not shifting to catalytic converter upon signal from TVS.
- Faulty electrical and/or vacuum circuits.

GENERAL MOTORS PULSE AIR INJECTION REACTOR

DESCRIPTION

The Pulse Air Injection Reactor (PAIR) system is used on some 2.0L 4-cylinder engines.

This system is a non-pump type air injection system. This system uses engine exhaust pulses to draw fresh air into the exhaust system.

This helps to further oxidize hydrocarbon (HC) and carbon monoxide (CO) emissions. A single pulse air valve with 4 check valves, 1 for each exhaust port, is used.

Fig. 1: Pulse Air Injection Reactor System Used on Some 2.0L 4-Cylinder Engines

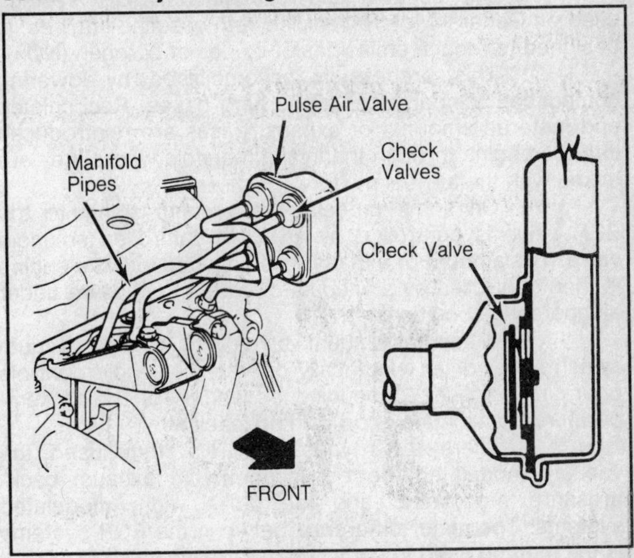

OPERATION

Each one of the check valves in the pulse air valve is connected to an exhaust port. The firing of the engine creates a pulsating flow of exhaust gases.

When positive exhaust pressure is felt, the check valve will be forced closed and no exhaust gas will flow past the valve into the fresh air supply line.

With negative exhaust pressure (vacuum), the check valve will open and fresh air will be drawn in and mixed with the exhaust gases. During high engine RPM, such as under heavy acceleration, the check valve will remain closed.

Air supply to the pulse air system is controlled by an electric and vacuum shut-off valve operated by the Computer Command Control (CCC) system.

When the engine starts and is operating in the open loop mode, the valve is energized and the fresh air line is opened.

When the CCC switches into the closed loop mode, the valve is de-energized and the fresh air line is closed.

A deceleration valve is used to prevent backfiring in the exhaust system during deceleration and to reduce emissions of unburned hydrocarbons.

TESTING

PULSE AIR SOLENOID CHECK

1) Remove air cleaner to gain access to pulse air solenoid hose. Make sure that hose is properly connected. Turn ignition off for 2 minutes.

2) Start engine and feel for vacuum pulsations at end of pulse air hose. Pulsations should occur for at least 20 seconds after engine starts.

3) If pulsations are felt as described, pulse air system is operating properly. If pulsations are not felt or do not last for at least 20 seconds, check for at least 10 in. Hg vacuum at pulse air solenoid with engine idling.

4) If there is not at least 10 in. Hg vacuum, repair vacuum hose(s). If vacuum is okay, turn ignition switch on without starting engine.

5) Ground test terminal of assembly line data link (ALDL) inside vehicle. Connect test light between pulse air solenoid connector terminals with connector disconnected.

6) If test light does not come on, proceed to step **9)**. If test light does come on, proceed to step **7)**.

7) Remove ground from test terminal of ALDL while watching test light. If light stays on, check for a grounded wire from pulse air solenoid to electonic control module (ECM) terminal 14. If there is no ground in the circuit, replace ECM.

8) If the test light went out in step **7)**, solenoid or solenoid connector is defective.

9) If the test light did not come on in step **6)**, connect a test light between ground and each solenoid harness connector terminal. If test light comes on at 1 terminal only, proceed to step **11)**.

10) If test light comes on at both terminals, repair short in power feed wire. Also check ECM for damage. If test light did not come on at either terminal, repair open in circuit from solenoid to ignition switch.

11) If test light came on at 1 terminal only, check for an open wire from solenoid to ECM terminal 14. If wire is okay, check resistance of pulse air solenoid.

12) If resistance is under 20 ohms, replace solenoid and ECM. If resistance is over 20 ohms, repair ECM connector or replace ECM.

GENERAL MOTORS EXHAUST GAS RECIRCULATION

DESCRIPTION

The exhaust gas recirculation (EGR) system, used on General Motors vehicles with gasoline engines, is designed to reduce emissions of oxides of nitrogen (NOx).

This process is accomplished by lowering combustion temperatures of burning gases. Recirculated and metered amounts of exhaust gases are reintroduced into the engine through the intake manifold where they are mixed with the air/fuel mixture.

On some models, the vacuum signal to the EGR valve is controlled by an ECM controlled solenoid valve. The amount of exhaust gas admitted into the engine is then controlled by a vacuum operated EGR valve under all operating conditions.

A thermal vacuum valve (TVV), thermal vacuum switch (TVS) or an electrically operated solenoid controls operating vacuum, depending on engine operating temperature, to maintain good cold driveability.

There are 3 types of EGR systems used, the vacuum modulated (ported vacuum), the exhaust back-pressure modulated, and the pulse width modulated systems. The major difference between the EGR systems is the method used to control how far each valve opens.

OPERATION

VACUUM MODULATED (PORTED VACUUM) EGR SYSTEM

With this system, the amount of exhaust gas admitted into the intake manifold depends on a vacuum signal (ported vacuum), controlled by throttle position.

When the throttle is closed (at idle or deceleration), there is no vacuum signal to the EGR valve because the EGR vacuum port is above the closed throttle valve. As the throttle valve is opened, a ported vacuum signal is supplied to the EGR valve, admitting exhaust gas into the intake manifold.

Fig. 1: Cutaway View of Vacuum Modulated & Pulse Width Modulated EGR Valve

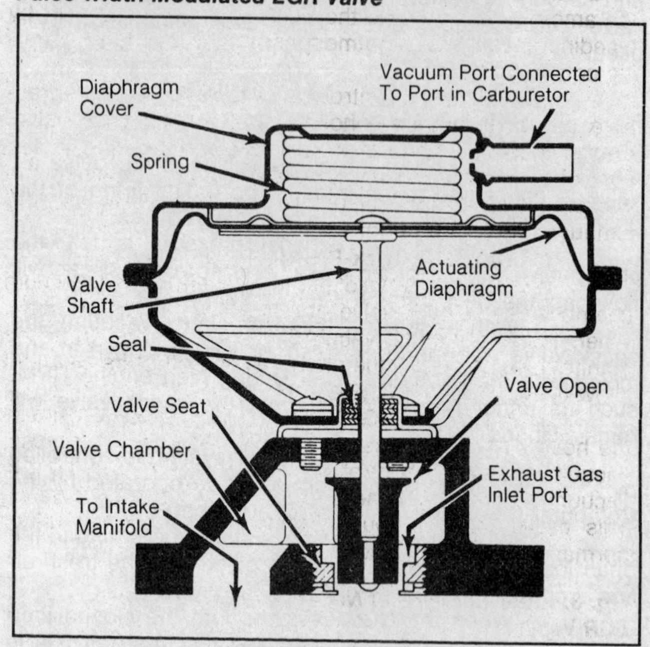

Fig. 2: Cutaway View of Positive Back-Pressure EGR Valve

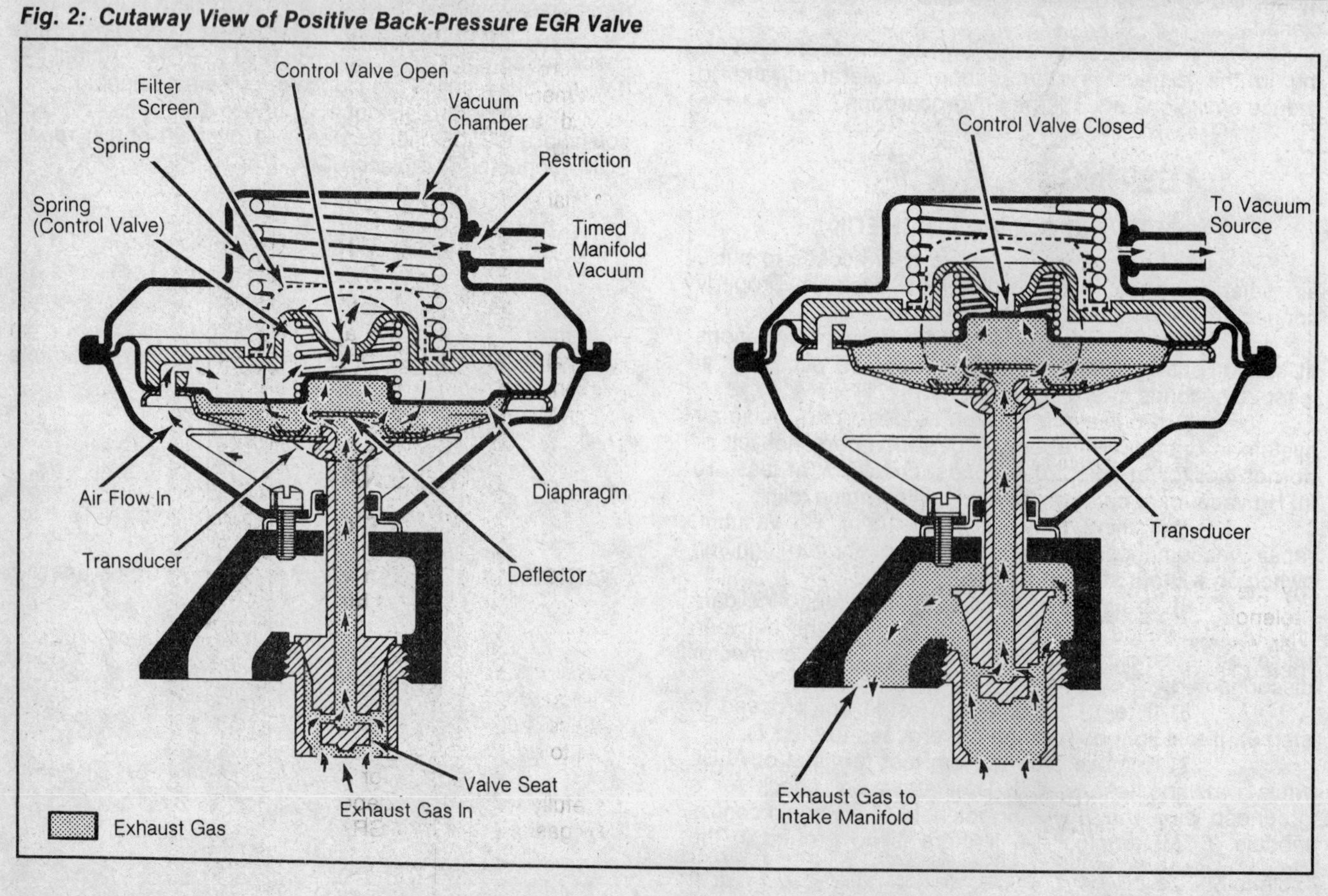

GENERAL MOTORS EXHAUST GAS RECIRCULATION (Cont.)

EXHAUST BACK-PRESSURE MODULATED EGR SYSTEM

Two types of back-pressure EGR valves are used, either a positive or negative back-pressure valve. Operation of these 2 systems is as follows:

Positive Back Pressure EGR Valve

A control valve, located in the EGR valve, acts as a vacuum regulator valve. The control valve controls the amount of vacuum to the EGR diaphragm chamber by bleeding vacuum to the atmosphere during certain operating conditions.

When the control valve receives a back-pressure signal, through the hollow shaft of the EGR valve, pressure on the bottom of the control valve closes the control valve. When the control valve closes, the maximum vacuum signal is applied directly to the EGR valve allowing exhaust gas recirculation.

Negative Back-Pressure EGR Valve

If there is little or no vacuum in the vacuum chamber of the EGR valve, the EGR valve will not open. When there is enough vacuum in the chamber, from the manifold vacuum port, the pintle will rise off of its seat and allow the EGR valve to open.

When the EGR valve opens, back-pressure in the hollow shaft decreases. As back-pressure decreases, vacuum opens the control valve and bleeds EGR control vacuum to the atmosphere, thus closing the EGR valve. This cycle occurs about 40 times every second under normal operating conditions.

Fig. 3: Cutaway View of Negative Back-Pressure EGR Valve

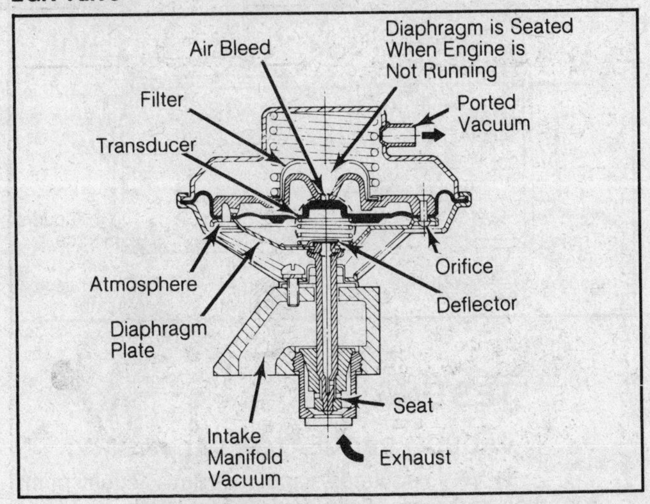

PULSE WIDTH MODULATED EGR SYSTEM

This type of EGR system is controlled entirely by the ECM. The ECM controls the flow rate through a solenoid. The solenoid is pulsed at a rate up to 32 times per second. The ECM uses a ported vacuum signal to determine the flow rate signal to the solenoid.

TESTING

POSITIVE BACK-PRESSURE EGR VALVE

1) Disconnect electrical connector from EGR solenoid. Place transmission in Neutral (man. trans.) or "P" (auto. trans.). Set parking brake and block drive wheels. Connect tachometer to engine.

2) Make sure that fast idle speed is set to specified RPM. With engine at normal operating temperature, place fast idle screw on highest step of fast idle cam.

3) Disconnect and plug vacuum hose at EGR valve. As vacuum hose is removed, watch for downward movement of diaphragm. This should be accompanied by an increase in engine speed.

4) Reconnect vacuum hose. Diaphragm should move upward and engine speed should decrease.

5) If engine speed change and diaphragm movement are noticed with vacuum hose removed or installed, EGR valve is operating properly. Reconnect electrical connector to EGR solenoid.

6) If engine speed and diaphragm movement did not occur, remove EGR valve from engine. Connect a vacuum pump to EGR valve and apply a constant vacuum of 10 in. Hg (.7 kg/cm²). EGR valve should not open. If EGR valve does open, replace it.

7) With vacuum still applied to EGR valve, direct a 15 psi air pressure stream directly into valve seat. EGR valve should open fully. If not, EGR valve should be cleaned.

VACUUM MODULATED & NEGATIVE BACK-PRESSURE EGR VALVE

1) Turn engine off. Disconnect vacuum hose from EGR valve. Place finger underneath valve and push up to depress valve diaphragm. With diaphragm depressed, plug vacuum port on EGR valve.

2) Diaphragm should take over 20 seconds to return to its seated position. If diaphragm takes less than 20 seconds to return to its seat, replace EGR valve.

3) Again depress diaphragm and plug vacuum port. Immediately start engine and watch for diaphragm movement. Diaphragm is operating properly if diaphragm moved to seated position during cranking and initial starting.

4) If diaphragm did not move during cranking or initial starting, EGR valve should be cleaned.

PULSE WIDTH MODULATED EGR VALVE

For testing of Pulse Width Modulated EGR system and valve, see appropriate diagnostic chart in General Motors Computer Command Control article in this section.

MAINTENANCE

EGR VALVE CLEANING

CAUTION: Do not clean valve in solvents or degreaser. Do not sand blast valve.

1) Remove EGR valve and discard gasket. Lightly tap sides and end of valve. Shake valve to remove any loose deposits. Buff exhaust deposits from mounting surface with wire wheel. Visually inspect valve seating area to ensure that it is clean.

2) Inspect for exhaust deposits in valve outlet. Carefully remove any deposits with a screwdriver. Using a new gasket, reinstall EGR valve.

GENERAL MOTORS DIESEL EXHAUST GAS RECIRCULATION

DESCRIPTION & OPERATION

NOTE: The following information applies to V6 and V8 diesel engines only. The 1.8L diesel does not use an EGR system.

To lower the formation of oxides of nitrogen (NOx), it is necessary to reduce combustion chamber temperatures. This is accomplished by introducing exhaust gases into the combustion chambers.

V6 ENGINES

On V6 diesel engines, vacuum from the vacuum pump is modulated by the vacuum regulator valve (VRV) mounted on the injection pump. Vacuum is highest at idle and decreases to zero at wide open throttle. The EGR valve is designed to open to its maximum at idle and close at wide open throttle.

The amount of EGR valve opening is further modulated by a vacuum modulator valve (VMV). The VMV allows for an increase in vacuum to the EGR valve as throttle is closed, up to the switching point of the VMV.

A response vacuum reducer (RVR) valve is used between the VRV and the torque converter clutch (TCC) operated solenoid. The RVR is used to allow EGR and exhaust pressure regulator (EPR) valves to change position quickly as throttle position is changed.

A solenoid is placed between the RVR and VMV that blocks vacuum to the EGR valve whenever the torque converter clutch is applied.

V8 ENGINES

On V8 diesel engines, vacuum from the vacuum pump is modulated by the vacuum regulator valve (VRV) mounted on the injection pump. Vacuum is highest at idle and decreases to zero at wide open throttle. The EGR valve is therefore fully open at idle and closed at wide open throttle.

A response vacuum reducer (RVR) is used between the VRV and EGR valves to allow EGR valve to change position quickly as throttle position is changed. A solenoid in the system shuts off vacuum to the EGR valve when the torque converter clutch (TCC) is engaged.

Fig. 1: General Motors V6 & V8 Diesel Engine EGR Valve Mounting Location

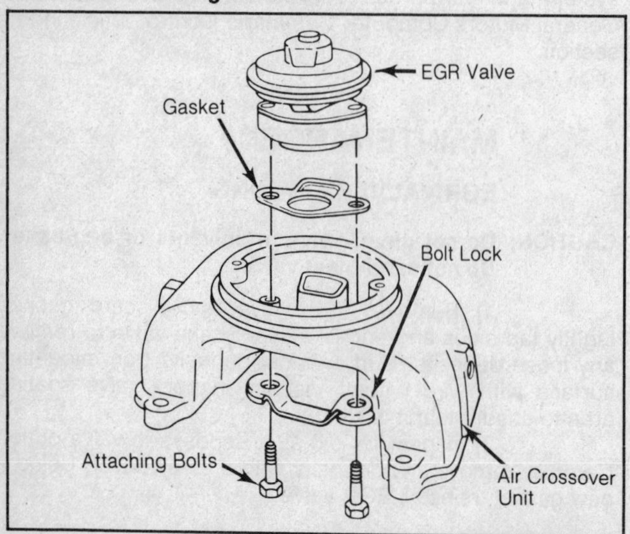

Fig. 2: General Motors V6 Diesel EGR System Vacuum Diagram

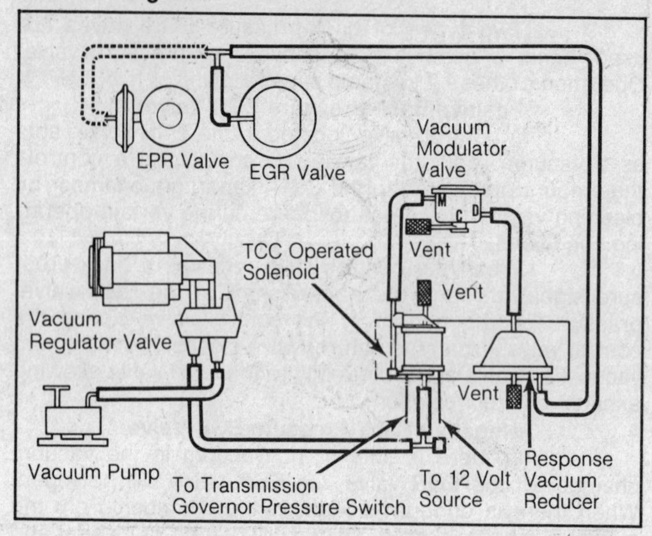

Fig. 3: General Motors V8 Diesel EGR System Vacuum Diagram

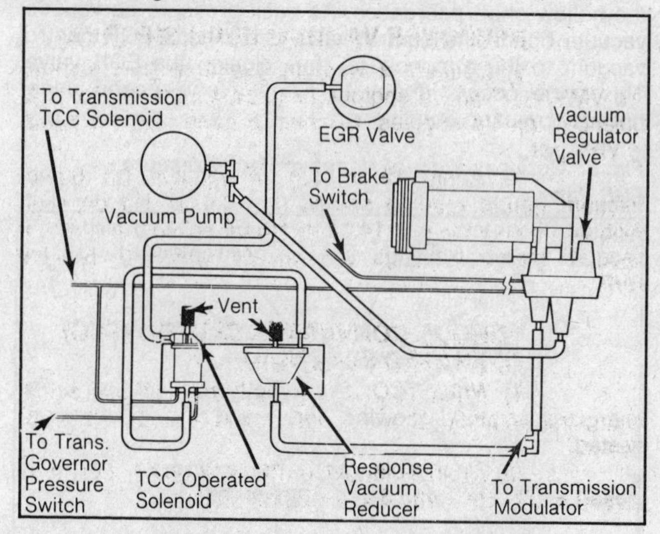

TESTING

VACUUM REGULATOR VALVE (VRV)

1) VRV regulates vacuum from vacuum pump in proportion to throttle angle. Vacuum from vacuum pump is supplied to port "A" and vacuum at port "B" is reduced as throttle is opened. *See Fig. 4*.

2) Vacuum at port "B" should be 15 in. Hg at closed throttle, 6 in. Hg at half throttle and 0 in. Hg at wide open throttle.

EXHAUST GAS RECIRCULATION (EGR) VALVE

1) On V6 engines, gradually apply vacuum to vacuum port on EGR valve. EGR valve should be fully open at 12 in. Hg and closed below 7.5 in. Hg.

2) On V8 engines, gradually apply vacuum to vacuum port on EGR valve. EGR valve should be fully open at 9.5-10.5 in. Hg and closed below 6 in. Hg.

GENERAL MOTORS DIESEL EXHAUST GAS RECIRCULATION (Cont.)

Fig. 4: Vacuum Regulator Valve Used On V6 & V8 Diesel Engines

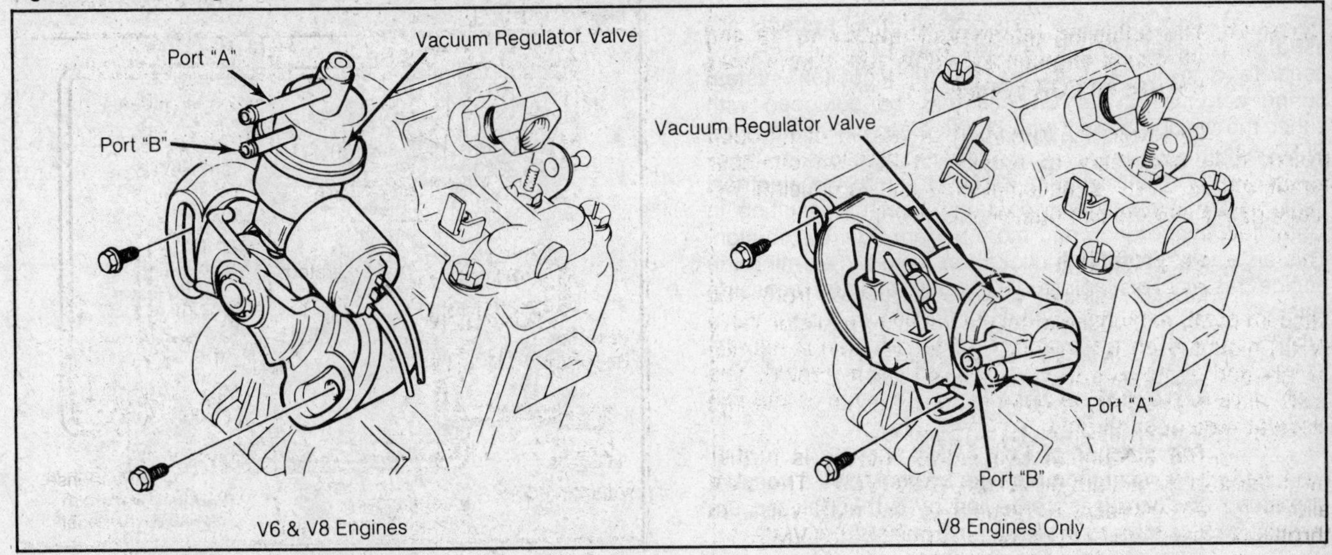

3) If either valve does not operate as described in steps **1)** and **2)**, replace EGR valve.

RESPONSE VACUUM REDUCER (RVR)

1) Connect a vacuum gauge to port marked "To VMV/VLV" on V6 engines or to port marked "To TCC Solenoid" on V8 engines. Connect a hand vacuum pump to VRV port.

2) Apply 15 in. Hg of vacuum on pump. Vacuum gauge reading should be 12.5 in. Hg on High Altitude V8 engines and 14.25 in. Hg on all other models. If vacuum gauge readings are not as specified, replace RVR.

TORQUE CONVERTER CLUTCH (TCC) OPERATED SOLENOID

1) When TCC is engaged, an electrical signal energizes solenoid allowing port 1 and 2 to be interconnected.

2) When solenoid is not energized, port 1 is closed and ports 2 and 3 are interconnected.

VACUUM MODULATOR VALVE (VMV)

1) Block drive wheels and apply parking brake. Place transmission in "P". Start engine and run at slow idle. Connect vacuum gauge to hose that connects to port marked "M".

2) There should be at least 14 in. Hg of vacuum. If not, check vacuum pump, VRV, solenoid and connecting hoses.

3) Reconnect vacuum hose to port "M". Connect vacuum gauge to port "D" on VMV. Vacuum reading should be 13 in. Hg. If not, replace VMV.

GENERAL MOTORS EARLY FUEL EVAPORATION (EFE) SYSTEM

DESCRIPTION

Two Early Fuel Evaporation (EFE) systems are used on General Motors vehicles. The EFE systems are used to provide heat to the engine induction system during cold driveaway. Engines may be equipped with either the vacuum servo type or the electrical heater type EFE system.

Both the vacuum servo type and the electrical heater type systems provide rapid heating, resulting in faster fuel evaporation and more uniform fuel distribution. This also helps to reduce choke "on" time by warming the engine faster. This helps in reducing exhaust emission levels.

OPERATION

VACUUM SERVO TYPE

The vacuum servo type system uses a vacuum operated valve which is controlled by a thermal vacuum switch (TVS) or a thermal vacuum valve (TVV).

During cold engine operation, the system provides an increase in the exhaust gas flow under the intake manifold. Either the TVS or TVV pass vacuum to the EFE valve when the engine coolant temperature is below the calibration value programmed into the ECM or carried by the TVS or TVV.

Fig. 1: Typical Vacuum Servo Type EFE System

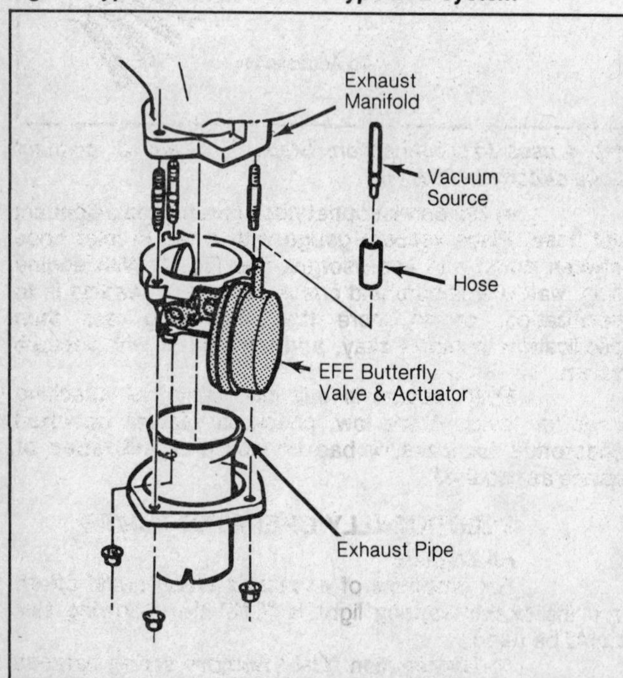

ELECTRICAL HEATER TYPE

The electrical heater type system uses a ceramic heater grid under the primary bore of the carburetor as an integral part of the carburetor insulator and gasket. *See Fig. 2.*

When engine coolant temperature is below a given value, electrical current is supplied to the heater through an electrical relay controlled by the ECM.

Fig. 2: Typical Electrical Heater Type EFE System

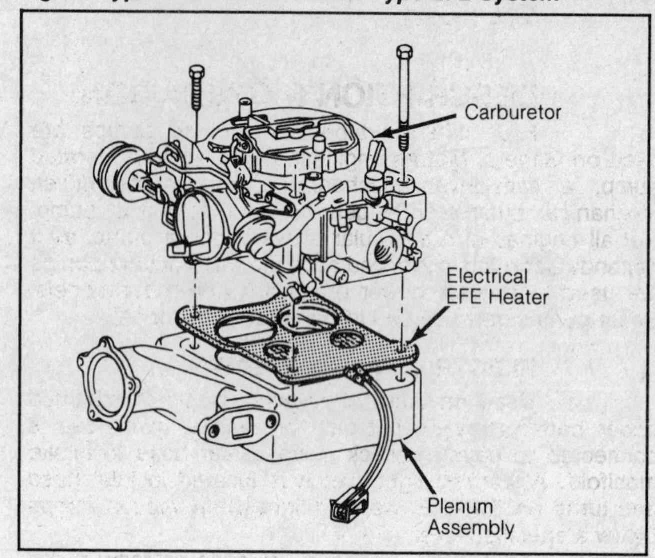

TESTING

VACUUM SERVO QUICK CHECK

NOTE: Before performing EFE test, allow engine coolant temperature to cool to below 40°F (4°C).

1) Locate EFE valve and note position of actuator arm. On some V8 engines, EFE valve actuator arm is protected by a 2-piece metal cover, which must be removed and then replaced after service has been performed.

2) Valve should close when engine is started cold. Actuator link will be pulled into diaphragm housing. If valve does not close, stop engine and remove vacuum hose from EFE valve.

3) Using a hand vacuum pump, apply at least 10 in. Hg of vacuum. Valve should close and remain closed for at least 20 seconds without applying additional vacuum. Replace valve if leakdown time is less than 20 seconds.

4) If valve does not close, lubricate valve with manifold heat valve lubricant (1050422). Replace valve if necessary. If valve did not close when vacuum was applied and valve is not seized, vacuum diaphragm is defective. Replace EFE valve.

5) If valve closed, problem is not in EFE valve. Check for loose, kinked, pinched or plugged vacuum hoses or connections. Also check EFE-TVE, EFE-TVV or EFE solenoids.

VACUUM SERVO SYSTEM CHECK

For Vacuum Servo System Check, see appropriate diagnostic chart in General Motors Computer Command Control article.

ELECTRICAL HEATER SYSTEM CHECK

For Electrical Heater System Check, see appropriate diagnostic chart in General Motors Computer Command Control article.

GENERAL MOTORS VACUUM PUMPS

2.0L, 2.5L, 2.8L, 3.0L, 4.1L, 4.3L Diesel, 5.7L Diesel

DESCRIPTION & OPERATION

Four different types of vacuum pumps are used on General Motors engines; an electrically-operated pump, a cam-driven mechanical pump, a belt-driven mechanical pump and a gear-driven mechanical pump. Not all engines of a particular size will use a pump, as it depends upon the model and accessories. Vacuum pumps are used to operate power brake units on most models. Some pumps may be used to operate accessories.

ELECTRIC VACUUM PUMPS

Used on 2.8L V6 engines, pump is mounted under battery tray on left side of vehicle. Inlet hose is connected to booster check valve, outlet hose to intake manifold. A warning light switch is located in inlet hose and turns on "BRAKE" warning light when vacuum drops below a specified level.

A charcoal filter in outlet hose protects pump from vapors. Pump has an internal switch in controller to activate pump when power brake vacuum drops below 13-15.7 in. Hg. Pump can only be operated with ignition key in "RUN" position.

CAM-DRIVEN MECHANICAL PUMP

The cam-driven pump is used on 2.0L and 2.5L 4-cylinder engines. Pump is installed on lower part of engine block behind oil filter. Pump is actuated by camshaft lobe acting on a spring-loaded diaphragm within pump.

BELT-DRIVEN MECHANICAL PUMP

The belt-driven pump is used on 3.0L, 4.1L and 4.3L V6 engines. The pump has a pulley attached which turns a shaft inside the pump that operates a cam, which in turn operates a spring-loaded diaphragm within the pump. On 4.1L and 4.3L engines, a warning light switch is located in inlet hose and turns on "BRAKE" warning light when vacuum drops below a specified level. Pump is serviced as an assembly only, and on 3.0L engines, the pulley must not be re-used once removed from pump.

GEAR-DRIVEN MECHANICAL PUMP

The gear-driven pump is used on 5.7L diesel engines and operates the EGR system, heater and air conditioning, transmission modulator and cruise control (if equipped), as well as power brakes. It is driven by a cam inside the drive assembly to which it mounts. Drive housing assembly has a drive gear on lower end which meshes with cam gear in engine. Drive gear causes cam in drive housing to rotate. Drive gear also powers engine oil pump.

DIAGNOSIS & TESTING

CAM & BELT-DRIVEN PUMPS

All Engines

For problems of excessive brake pedal effort, or if the brake warning light is "ON," the following diagnosis should be used.

1) Remove vacuum hoses from inlet port. Remove hose from outlet port on all except 4.3L. Plug openings. Install vacuum gauge to inlet port. Block drive wheels, apply parking brake and place auto. trans. in "PARK," man. trans. in Neutral.

2) Start engine and operate at idle while watching vacuum gauge. After 30 seconds, gauge should read at least 15 in. Hg on 2.5L, 20 in. Hg on Camaro and Firebird or 21 in. Hg on all others. If okay, check for vacuum leaks in other parts of system. If reading is incorrect, proceed as follows:

3) Check gauge connection for leaks. If belt-driven type pump, check for proper belt tension. Check idle RPM. Again check vacuum reading. If okay, proceed to next step. If not okay, replace vacuum pump.

Fig. 1: Cam and Belt-Driven Vacuum Pump Test Connections

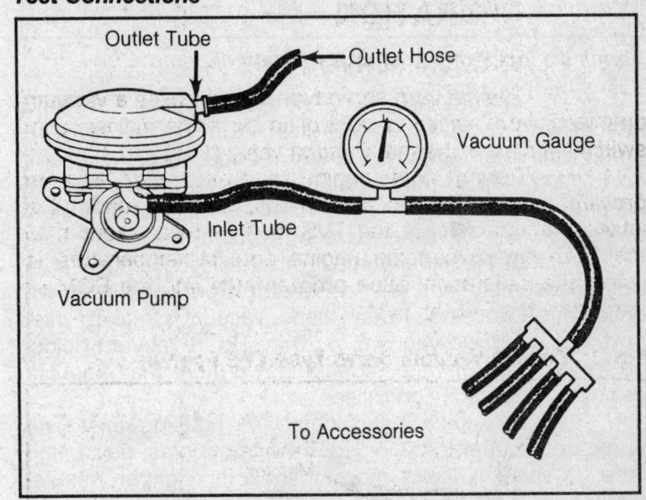

Step 4 uses this connection. Steps 1, 2, and 3, connect gauge directly to inlet port.

4) Reconnect outlet hose (if removed). Connect inlet hose. Place vacuum gauge with a tee in inlet hose between pump and accessories. *See Fig. 1.* With engine idling, wait one minute and check vacuum. If reading is to specification, or no more than 3 in. Hg less than specification, pump is okay, and fault is not with vacuum system.

5) If vacuum is still low, check all attaching hoses for leaks. If still low, check all vacuum operated accessories for leaks or bad connections and repair or replace as required.

ELECTRICALLY OPERATED PUMPS

All Engines

For problems of excessive brake pedal effort, or if the brake warning light is "ON," the following test should be used.

1) Turn ignition "ON." Remove wiring harness from motor and check for 12 volts at terminals "A" and "B." Check for good ground at terminal "D." *See Fig. 2.* If 12 volts not present or ground not good, repair as required. If okay proceed as follows:

2) Connect 12 volts to terminals "A" and "B." Ground terminal "D." If pump does not operate, go to next step. If pump operates, go to step **4)**.

3) Remove vacuum pump from vehicle. Check for stuck brush, shorted brush or broken wires in controller. If defects are found, repair as required. If no defects, replace controller.

GENERAL MOTORS VACUUM PUMPS (Cont.)

Fig. 2: Electric Vacuum Pump Connector Terminals

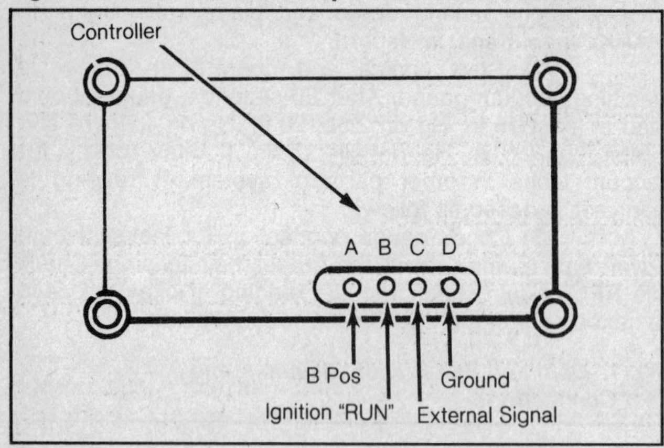

Terminals located on controller portion of pump

4) Turn ignition "OFF." Remove inlet hose and attach hand vacuum pump to inlet. Turn ignition "ON." If pump runs intermittently and will not hold steady vacuum, go to next step. If pump runs, then shuts off within 5-10 seconds when vacuum reads 10-15 in. hg, pump is okay and a leak exists in other parts of system.

5) Remove pump from vehicle. Remove controller assembly and tee connector from inlet hose-to-outlet hose housing. Attach hand vacuum pump to inlet port and pump up vacuum to 20 in. Hg. If vacuum holds, go to next step. If vacuum leaks down more than 2 in. Hg per minute, replace controller.

6) Attach hand pump to housing inlet and pump up vacuum to 20 in. Hg. If vacuum holds, go to next step. If vacuum leaks more than 2 in. Hg per minute, replace umbrella valve.

7) Plug pump inlet port, attach hand pump to outlet port and pump up vacuum to 20 in. Hg. If vacuum holds, pump is okay and no further checks are required. If vacuum does leaks more than 2 in. Hg per minute, check outlet housing bonnet and recrimp if necessary. If vacuum holds, pump is okay. If vacuum still does not hold, replace piston assembly inside bonnet.

If the vacuum pump runs continuously, the following checks should be performed.

1) Check all attaching hoses for leaks. Repair as required. With ignition "OFF," remove inlet hose from pump and connect hand vacuum pump to inlet. Turn ignition "ON." With 10 in. Hg applied, if pump continues to run, replace controller.

2) If pump shuts off when vacuum reaches 10-15 in. Hg, drop vacuum back to less than 10 in. Hg. Pump should run until vacuum reaches 10 in. Hg then shut off after 5-10 seconds. If so, pump is okay.

REMOVAL & INSTALLATION

ELECTRIC PUMPS

Removal & Installation

Raise vehicle and remove splash shield on left side. Disconnect hoses at vacuum pump. Disconnect electrical connections at pump. Remove 3 nuts securing pump to mounting bracket. Remove pump. To install, reverse removal procedures.

Fig. 3: Electric Vacuum Pump Mounting

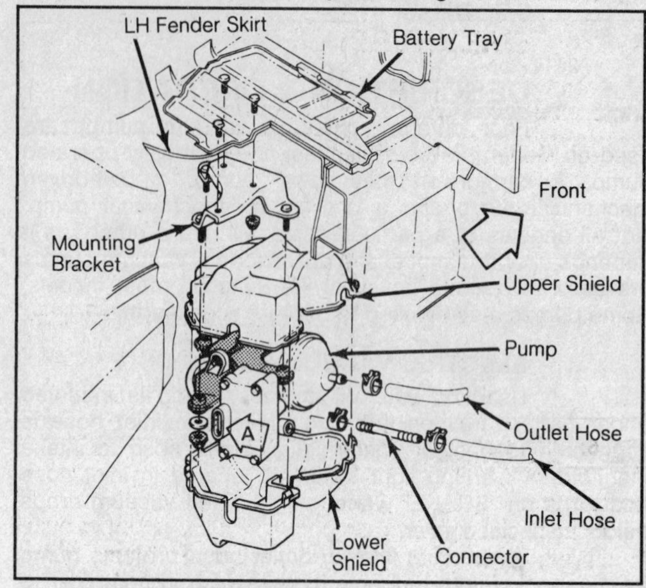

Used on some 2.8L V6 engines

CAM-DRIVEN PUMPS

Removal

Remove vacuum hoses from inlet and outlet ports of pump. Remove attaching fasteners mounting pump to engine. Remove gasket.

Installation

Inspect mounting surface for damage. Lubricate pump lever. Inspect cam eccentric for wear. Fit pump to mounting surface making sure gasket is installed correctly. Install fasteners and tighten. Check pump operation.

Fig. 4: Cam-Driven Vacuum Pump Mounting

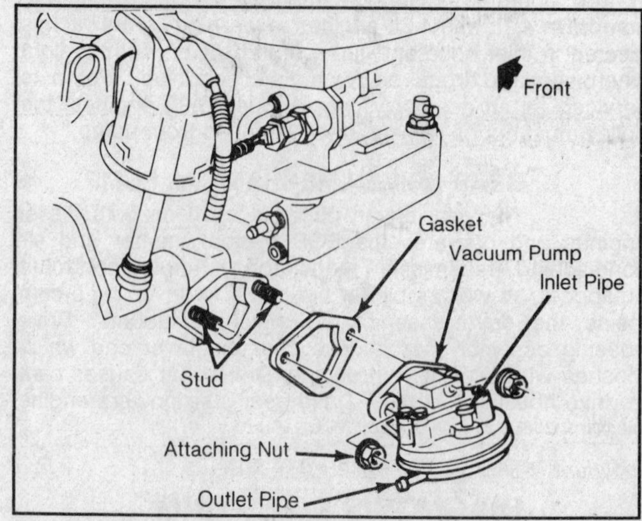

2.0L engine shown; 2.5L similar

BELT-DRIVEN PUMPS

Removal & Installation

Loosen belt tension. Remove pump-to-mounting bracket attaching bolts and remove pump from vehicle. To install, reverse removal procedure.

GENERAL MOTORS VACUUM PUMPS (Cont.)

Fig. 5: 3.0L Belt-Driven Pump Mounting

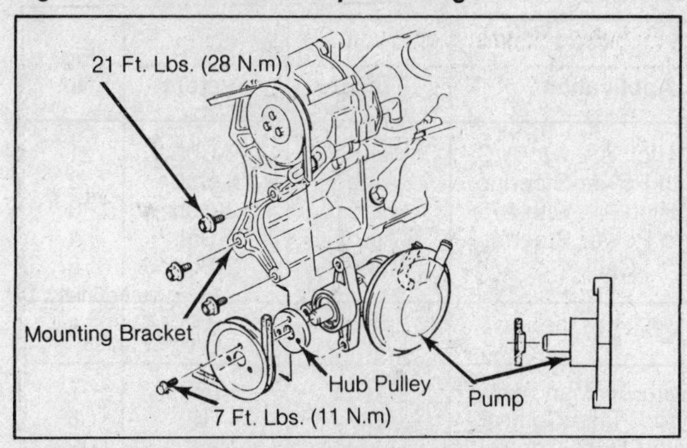

Fig. 6: 4.3L Belt-Driven Pump Mounting

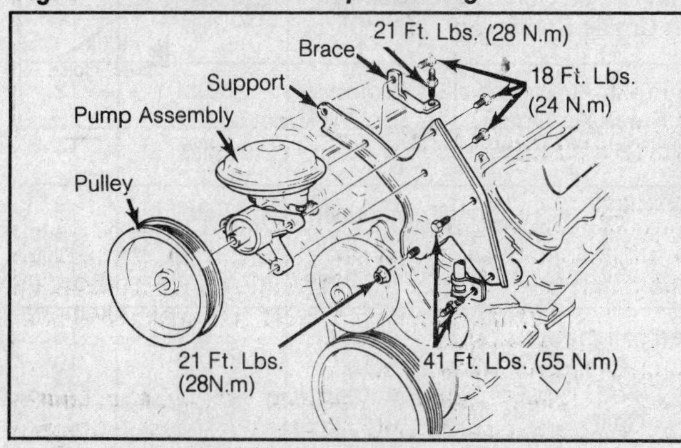

Engine without A/C shown, with A/C similar.

GEAR-DRIVEN PUMPS

Removal & Installation

Loosen hold-down clamp bolt. Grasp vacuum pump and gently remove it from engine. To install, apply lubricant to "O" ring and reinstall in engine. Tighten hold-down bolt.

Fig. 7: Gear-Driven Pump Mounting

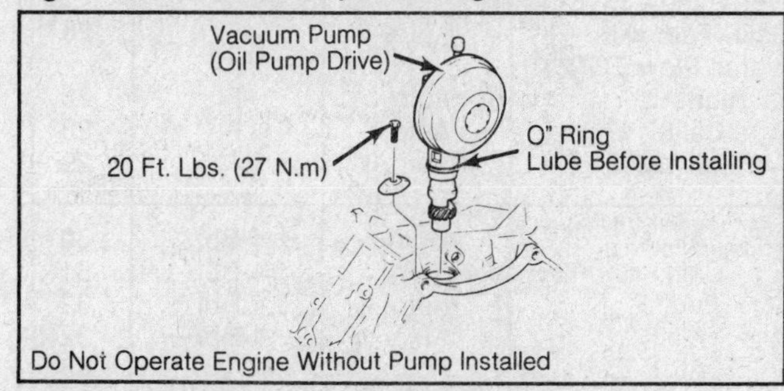

Apply lubricant to "O" ring before installing.

OVERHAUL

ELECTRIC PUMPS

Controller Assembly

Disassembly

1) Remove tie bolts holding together body, pump housing and rear housing. Remove rear housing. Do not damage tee connector. Remove self-tapping screws holding controller to rear housing.

Fig. 8: Exploded View of Electric Vacuum Pump

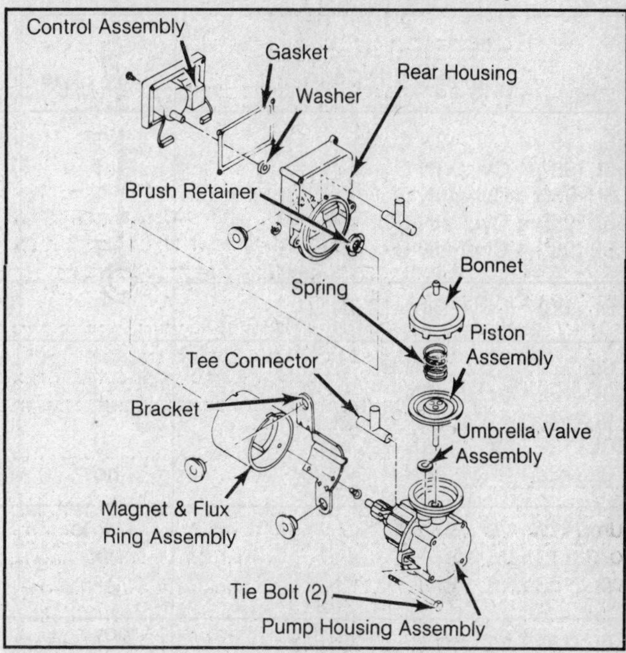

Housings are serviced as complete assemblies only.

2) Detach brushes from brush holder and remove controller. Remove old gasket.

Reassembly

1) Replace controller assembly, using new gasket and washer. Ensure that both brushes are located in brush holder cavity of rear housing. Install brush springs, placing one end in slots above spring access holes.

2) Place brushes in brush channel being sure that shunts are routed properly. Place brush retainer in preassembly position and return the spring to load condition. Install rear housing. Install tie bolts holding body pump housing and rear housing together.

Piston Assembly

Disassembly

Uncrimp tabs on bonnet. Pump housing and bonnet must be held together during disassembly due to spring load on bonnet. Remove bonnet and spring. Lift piston assembly out of pump housing. Remove and replace umbrella valve assembly.

Reassembly

Replace piston assembly and spring. Place bonnet on spring and compress. Crimp tabs on bonnet, allowing no tolerance for movement between bonnet and pump housing assembly.

TIGHTENING SPECIFICATIONS

Application	Ft. Lbs. (N.m)
Pump Attaching Nuts or Bolts	
2.0L & 2.5L Engine	15 (20)
3.0L Engine	20 (27)
4.3L Engine	
Mounting Nuts	21 (28)
Front Bracket Bolts	41 (55)
Rear Bracket Bolts	18-21 (24-28)
Pulley-to-Hub Bolts 3.0L	7 (9)
Gear-Driven Pump Hold-Down Bolt	20 (27)
Electric Pump-to-Bracket	6 (8)

1983 GENERAL MOTORS VACUUM DIAGRAMS

1983 GENERAL MOTORS VACUUM DIAGRAM REFERENCE CHART

Engine & VIN Code	Body Style	Application	Trans.	Fuel System	Fig. No.
1.6L (98") 4 Cyl., VIN C	T	Fed., High Alt. w/o A/C	Manual	2-Bbl.	1
1.6L (98") 4 Cyl., VIN C	T	All with Power Steering	Auto.	2-Bbl.	2
1.6L (98") 4 Cyl., VIN C	T	Fed., High Alt. with A/C	Manual	2-Bbl.	3
1.6L (98") 4 Cyl., VIN C	T	All w/o Power Steering	Auto.	2-Bbl.	4
1.6L (98") 4 Cyl., VIN C	T	Calif.	Manual	2-Bbl.	5
1.8L (112") 4 Cyl. Diesel, VIN D	T	All	Both	FI	6
2.0L (122") 4 Cyl., VIN P	J	Fed. with Air Man. Valve	Manual	TBI	7
2.0L (122") 4 Cyl., VIN P	J	All w/o Cruise Control	Auto.	TBI	8
2.0L (122") 4 Cyl., VIN P	J	All with Cruise Control	Auto.	TBI	9
2.0L (122") 4 Cyl., VIN P	J	Calif. with Cruise Control	Manual	TBI	10
2.0L (122") 4 Cyl., VIN P	J	All w/o Cruise Control	Manual	TBI	11
2.8L (173") V6, VIN X & Z	A, X	All w/o Fresh Air Option	Both	2-Bbl.	12
2.8L (173") V6, VIN Z	X	All with Fresh Air Option	Both	2-Bbl.	13
2.8L (173") V6, VIN 1	F	All	Both	2-Bbl.	14
3.0L (181") V6, VIN E	A	All	Manual	2-Bbl.	15
3.0L (181") V6, VIN E	A	All	4-Spd. Auto.	2-Bbl.	16
3.0L (181") V6, VIN E	A	All	3-Spd. Auto.	2-Bbl.	17
3.8L (229") V6, VIN 9	B, G	Fed., High Alt.	Auto.	2-Bbl.	18
3.8L (231") V6, VIN 8	G	All	Auto.	2-Bbl.	19
3.8L (231") V6, VIN 8	E	Fed.	Auto.	2-Bbl.	20
3.8L (231") V6, VIN A	B, G	Calif.	Auto.	2-Bbl.	21
3.8L (231") V6, VIN A	B, G	Fed.	Auto.	2-Bbl.	22
4.1L (250") V8, VIN 8	C, E, K	All	Auto.	DFI	23
4.1L (252") V6, VIN 4	B, C	Calif.	Auto.	2-Bbl.	24
4.1L (252") V6, VIN 4	B, C	Fed. with Vacuum Pump	Auto.	2-Bbl.	24
4.1L (252") V6, VIN 4	B	Fed. w/o Vacuum Pump	Auto.	2-Bbl.	25
4.1L (252") V6, VIN 4	E	Calif., Fed.	Auto.	2-Bbl.	26
4.3L (262") V6 Diesel, VIN T	A	Calif./Fed. without Reverse Flow EGR	Auto.	FI	27
4.3L (262") V6 Diesel, VIN T	A	Calif./Fed. with Reverse Flow EGR	Auto.	FI	28
4.3L (262") V6 Diesel, VIN T	A	High Alt.	Auto.	FI	28
4.3L (262") V6 Diesel, VIN V	G	Calif.	Auto.	FI	28
4.3L (262") V6 Diesel, VIN V	G	All Exc. Calif.	Auto.	FI	29
5.0L (305") V8, VIN H	F	All	Both	4-Bbl.	30
5.0L (305") V8, VIN H	B, G	Calif.	Auto.	4-Bbl.	31
5.0L (305") V8, VIN H	G	Fed.	Auto.	4-Bbl.	32
5.0L (305") V8, VIN 7	G	All	Auto.	4-Bbl.	32
5.0L (305") V8, VIN S	F	All	Auto.	TBI	33
5.0L (307") V8, VIN 9	G	All Hurst Olds	Auto.	4-Bbl.	34
5.0L (307") V8, VIN 9	G	All Exc. Hurst Olds	Auto.	4-Bbl.	35
5.0L (307") V8, VIN 9	B, C, E	All	Auto.	4-Bbl.	35
5.7L (350") V8, VIN 6	B	Fed.	Auto.	4-Bbl.	36
5.7L (350") V8, VIN 8	Y	All	Auto.	TBI	37
6.0L (368") V8, VIN 6	Z	Fed.	Auto.	4-Bbl.	38
6.0L (368") V8, VIN 9	D	Fed.	Auto.	DFI	39

NOTE: Vacuum diagrams not available for 1.8L 4-Cyl. VIN 0, 2.5L VIN R & 2, 5.0L VIN Y & 5.7L VIN N

1983 GENERAL MOTORS VACUUM DIAGRAMS (Cont.)

MODEL IDENTIFICATION

Reference will be made to body style codes for GM cars in the vacuum diagrams index. Refer to the table below for identification of these body style codes.

GENERAL MOTORS BODY CODE IDENTIFICATION

Body Code	GM Division	Model Name
A	Buick	Century
A	Chevrolet	Celebrity
A	Oldsmobile	Ciera
A	Pontiac	6000
B	Buick	LeSabre
B	Chevrolet	Caprice Classic, Impala
B	Oldsmobile	Delta 88
C	Buick	Electra
C	Cadillac	DeVille, Fleetwood
C	Oldsmobile	Ninety-Eight
D	Cadillac	Fleetwood Limousine
E	Buick	Riviera
E	Cadillac	Eldorado
E	Oldsmobile	Toronado
F	Chevrolet	Camaro
F	Pontiac	Firebird
G	Buick	Regal
G	Chevrolet	Malibu, Monte Carlo
G	Oldsmobile	Cutlass
G	Pontiac	Bonneville, Grand Prix
J	Buick	Skyhawk
J	Cadillac	Cimarron
J	Chevrolet	Cavalier
J	Oldsmobile	Firenza
J	Pontiac	2000
K	Cadillac	Seville
T	Chevrolet	Chevette
T	Pontiac	1000
X	Buick	Skylark
X	Chevrolet	Citation
X	Oldsmobile	Omega
X	Pontiac	Phoenix
Y	Chevrolet	Corvette

Fig. 1: 1.6L (98") 4 Cyl. 2-Bbl.
VIN C, Fed. & High Alt. Man. Trans.

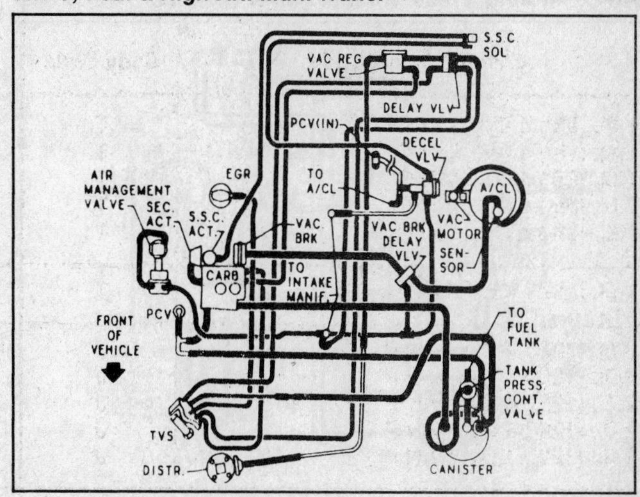

Fig. 2: 1.6L (98") 4 Cyl. 2-Bbl.
VIN C, All with Auto. Trans. & Pwr. Steering

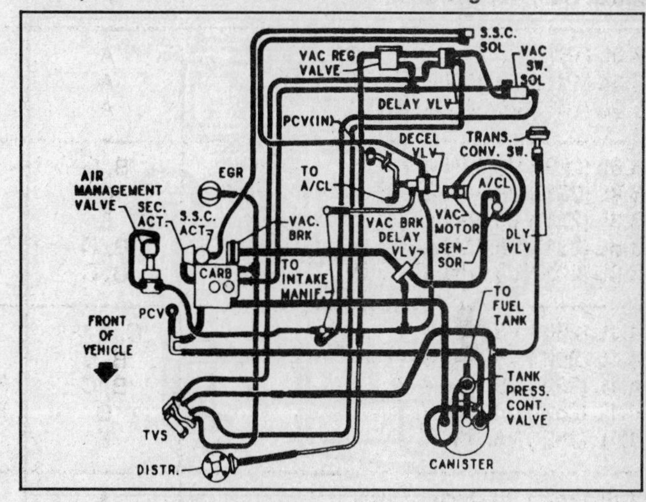

Fig. 3: 1.6L (98") 4 Cyl. 2-Bbl.
VIN C, Fed. & High Alt. Man. Trans. with Air

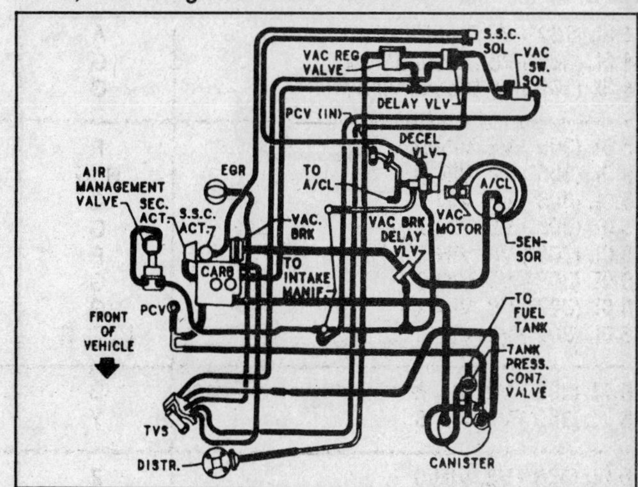

1983 GENERAL MOTORS VACUUM DIAGRAMS (Cont.)

Fig. 4: 1.6L (98") 4 Cyl. 2-Bbl.
VIN C, All Auto. Trans. without Power Steering

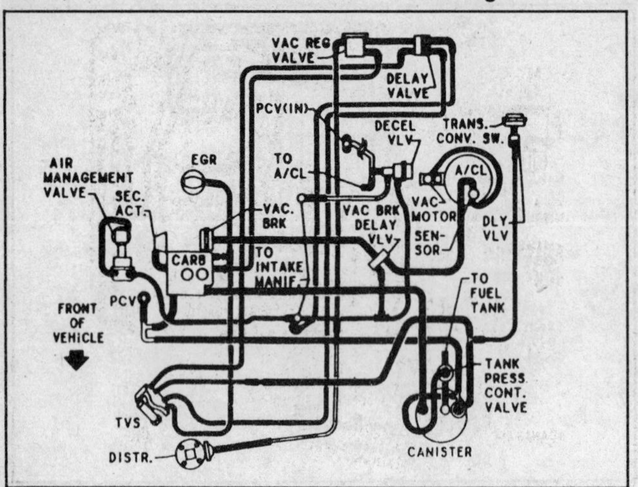

Fig. 5: 1.6L (98") 4 Cyl. 2-Bbl.
VIN C, Calif. Man. Trans.

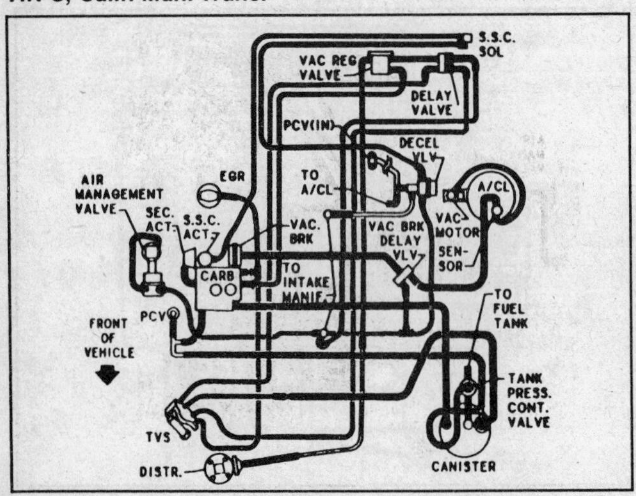

Fig. 6: 1.8L (122") 4 Cyl. Diesel
VIN D, All Models

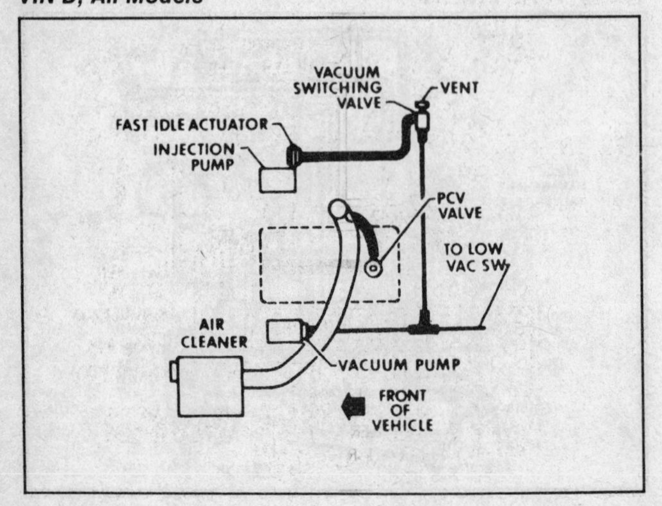

Fig. 7: 2.0L (122") 4 Cyl. TBI
VIN P, Fed. Man. Trans. with Air Management Valve

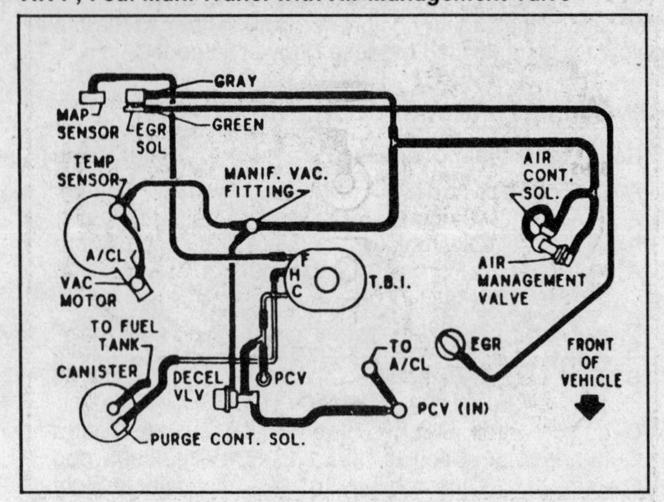

Fig. 8: 2.0L (122") 4 Cyl. TBI
VIN P, All Auto. Trans. without Cruise Control

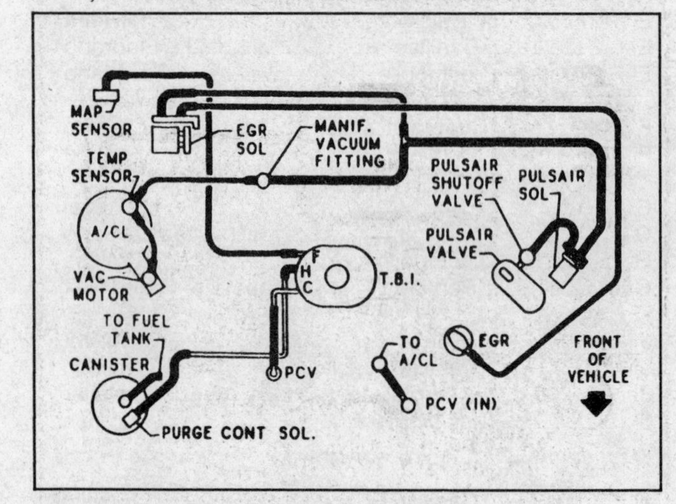

Fig. 9: 2.0L (122") 4 Cyl. TBI
VIN P, All Auto. Trans. with Cruise Control

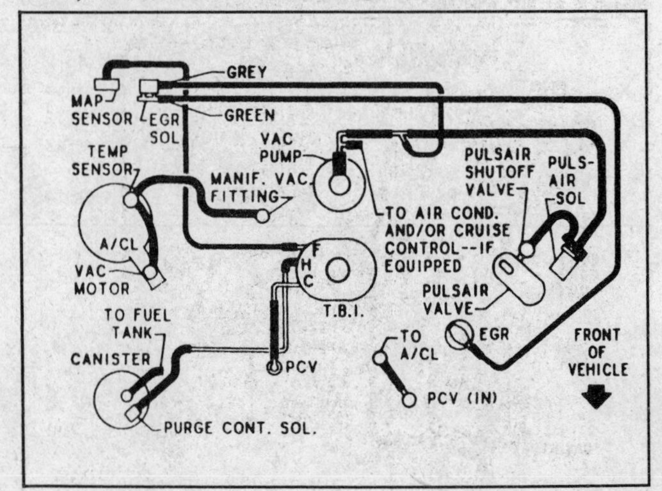

1983 GENERAL MOTORS VACUUM DIAGRAMS (Cont.)

Fig. 10: 2.0L (122") 4 Cyl. TBI
VIN P, Calif. Man. Trans. with Cruise Control

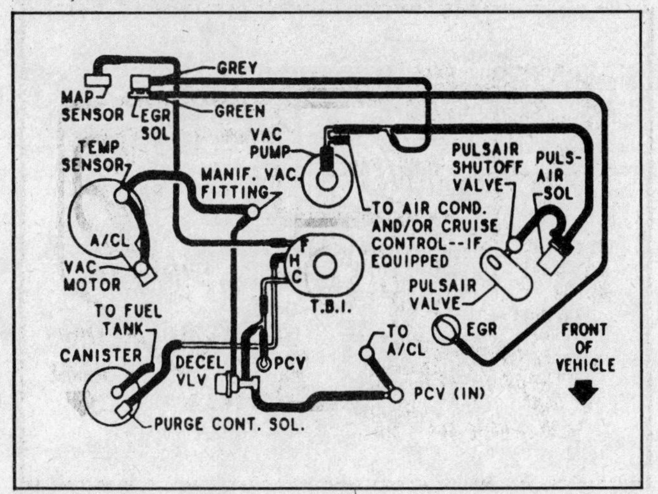

Fig. 11: 2.0L (122") 4 Cyl. TBI
VIN P, All Man. Trans. without Cruise Control

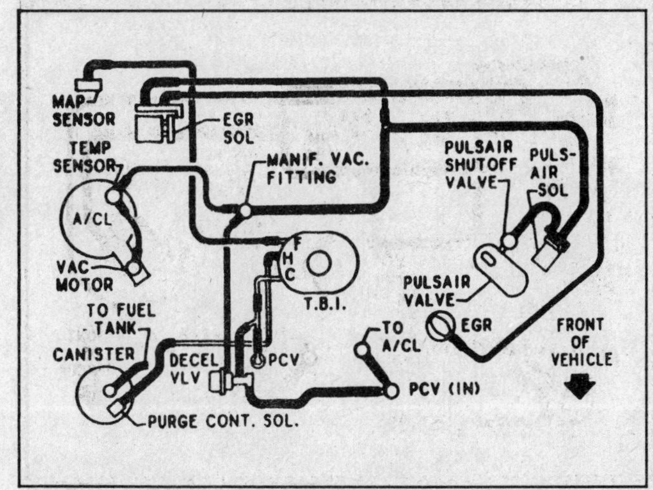

Fig. 12: 2.8L (173") V6 2-Bbl.
VIN X & Z, All without Fresh Air Option

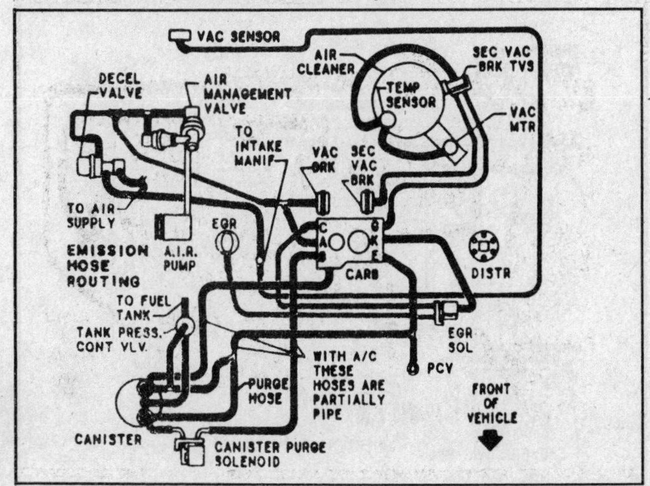

Fig. 13: 2.8L (173") V6 2-Bbl.
VIN Z, All with Fresh Air Option

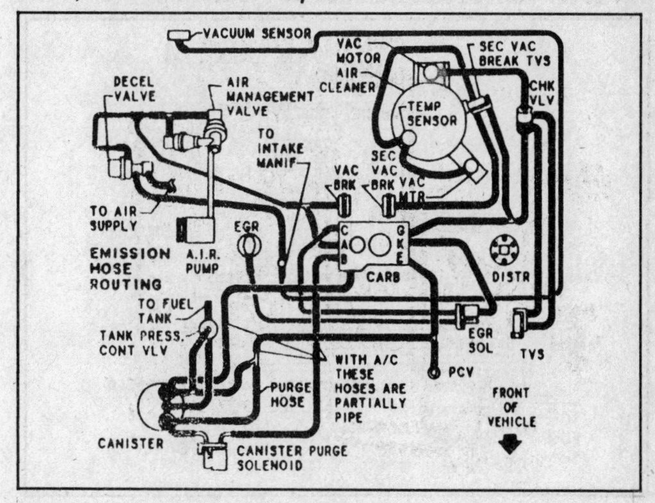

Fig. 14: 2.8L (173") V6 2-Bbl.
VIN 1, All Models

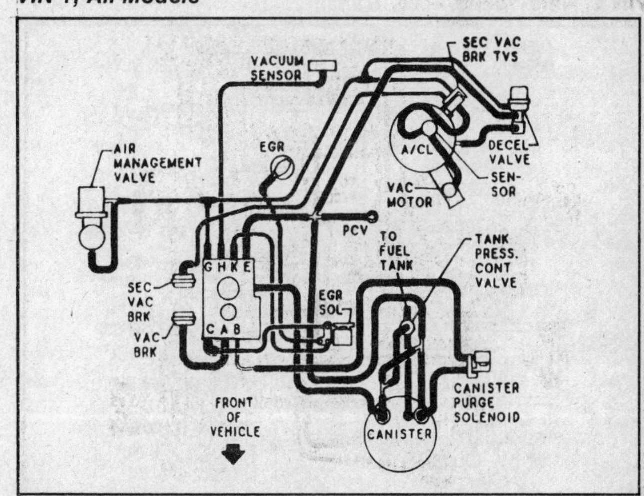

Fig. 15: 3.0L (181") V6 2-Bbl.
VIN E, All Man. Trans.

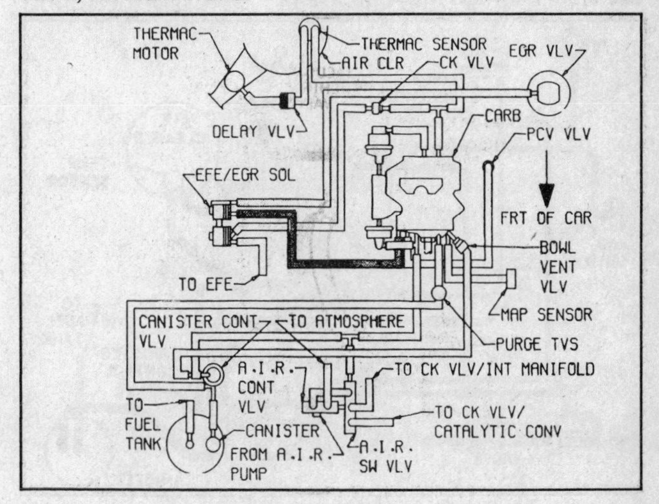

1983 Exhaust Emission Systems

1983 GENERAL MOTORS VACUUM DIAGRAMS (Cont.)

Fig. 16: 3.0L (181") V6 2-Bbl.
VIN E, All 4-Speed Auto. Trans.

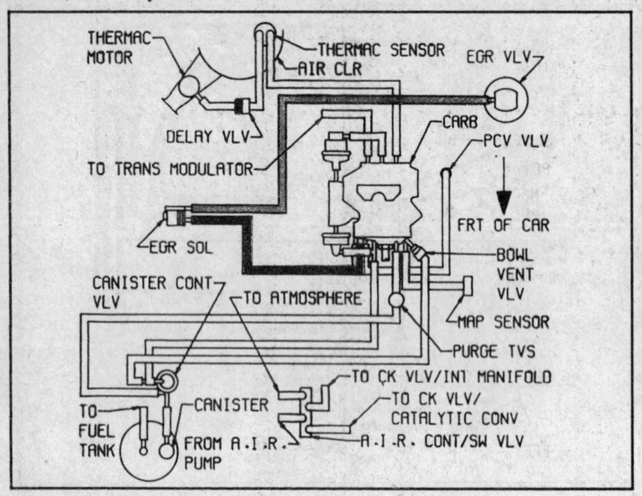

Fig. 17: 3.0L (181") V6 2-Bbl.
VIN E, All 3-Speed Auto. Trans.

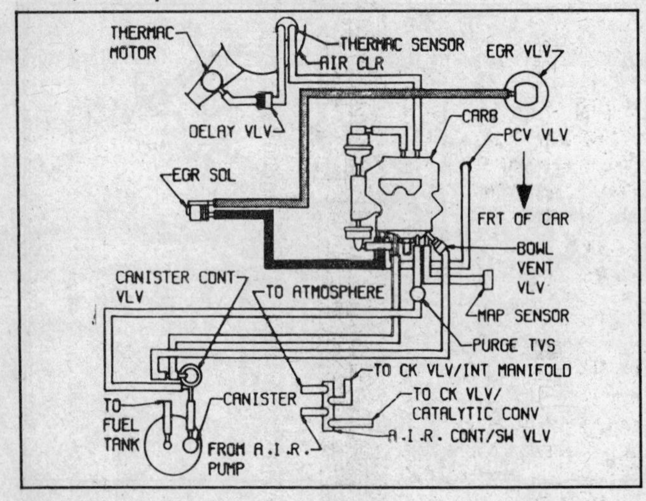

Fig. 18: 3.8L (229") V6 2-Bbl.
VIN 9, Fed. & High Alt. Auto. Trans.

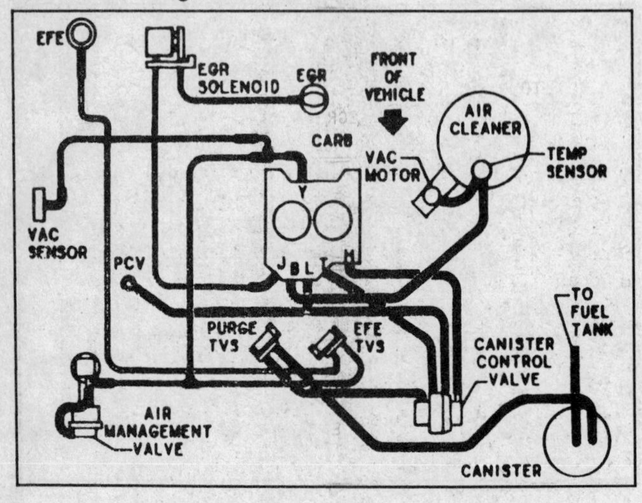

Fig. 19: 3.8L (231") V6 2-Bbl.
VIN 8, All G Body Auto. Trans.

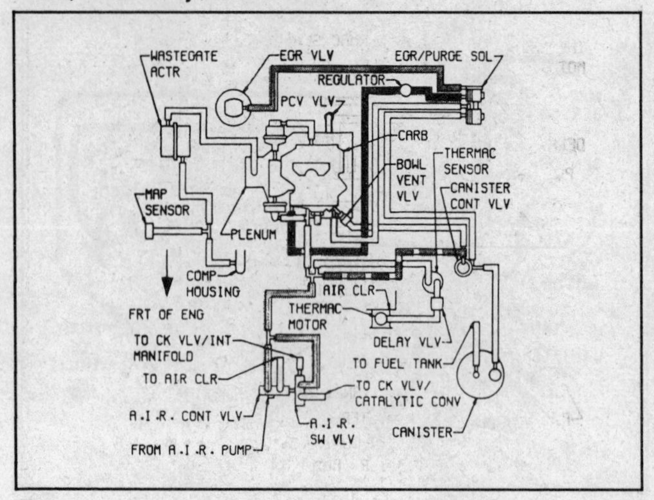

Fig. 20: 3.8L (231") V6 2-Bbl.
VIN 8, Fed. E Body Auto. Trans.

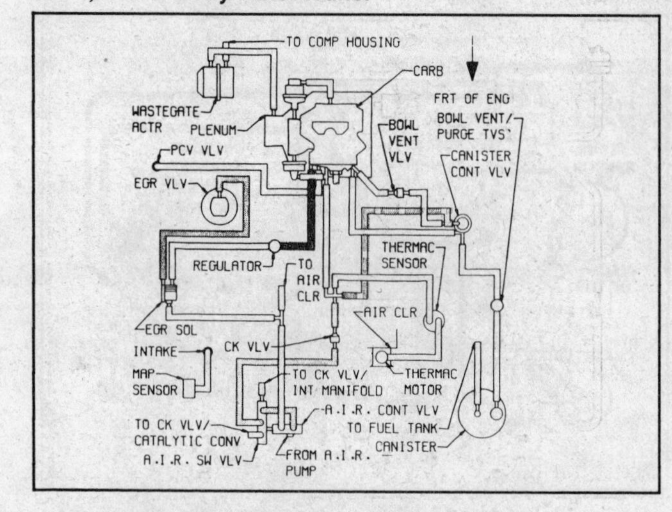

Fig. 21: 3.8L (231") V6 2-Bbl.
VIN A, Calif. Auto. Trans.

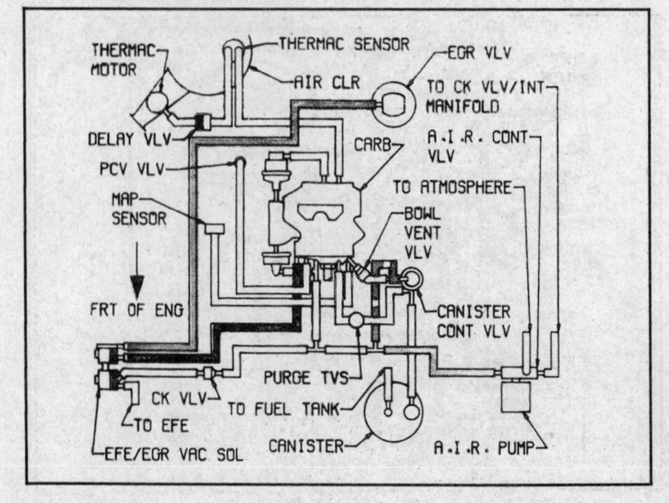

1983 GENERAL MOTORS VACUUM DIAGRAMS (Cont.)

Fig. 22: 3.8L (231") V6 2-Bbl.
VIN A, Fed. Auto. Trans.

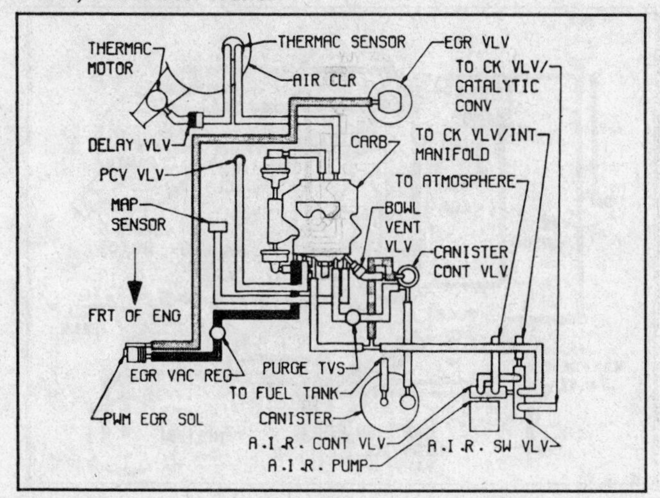

Fig. 23: 4.1L (250") V8 DFI
VIN 8, All Auto. Trans.

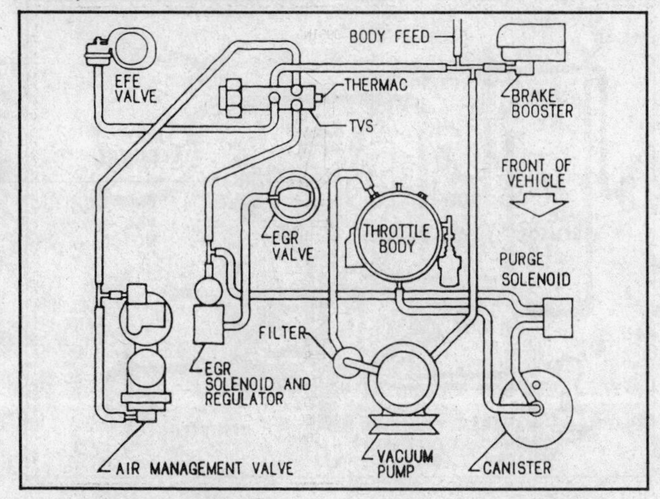

Fig. 24: 4.1L (252") V6 2-Bbl.
VIN 4, Calif. & Fed. Auto. Trans. with Vacuum Pump

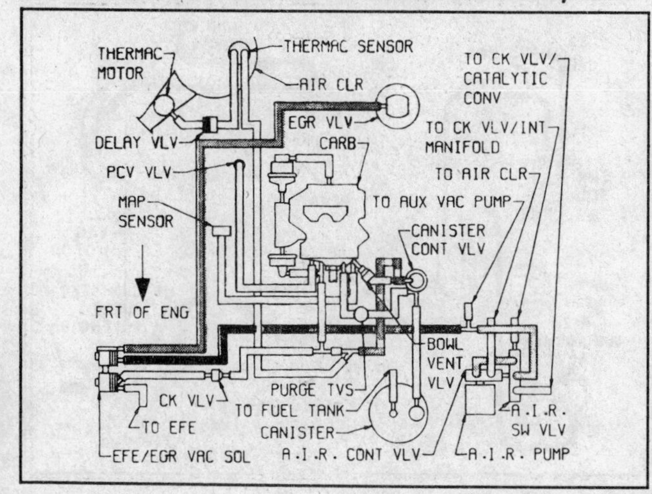

Fig. 25: 4.1L (252") V6 2-Bbl.
VIN 4, Fed. Auto. Trans. without Vacuum Pump

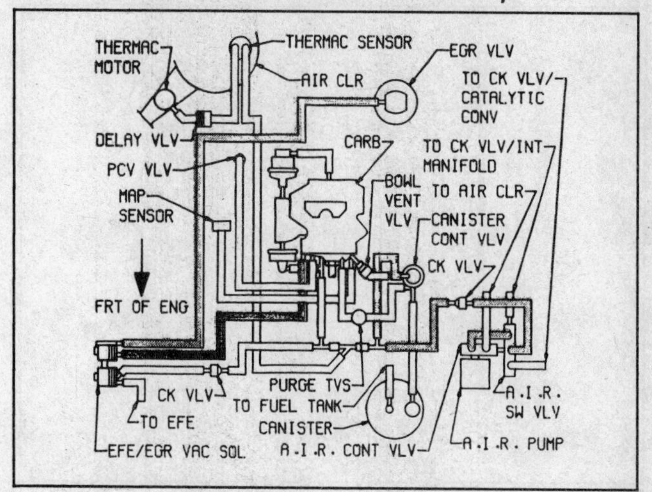

Fig. 26: 4.1L (252") V6 2-Bbl.
VIN 4, Calif. & Fed. E Body Auto. Trans.

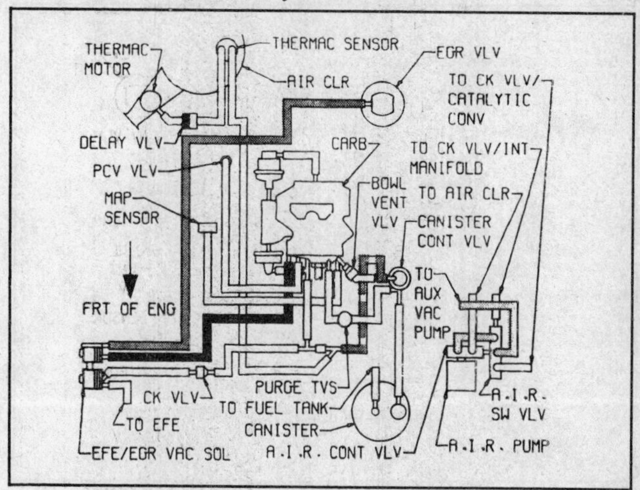

Fig. 27: 4.3L (262") V6 Diesel
VIN T, Calif. & Fed. Auto. Trans. w/o Reverse Flow EGR

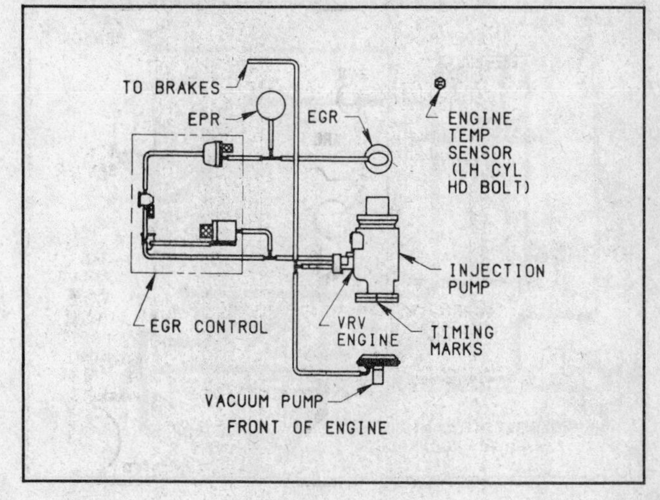

1983 GENERAL MOTORS VACUUM DIAGRAMS (Cont.)

Fig. 28: 4.3L (262") V6 Diesel
VIN T & V, All Auto. Trans. with Reverse Flow EGR

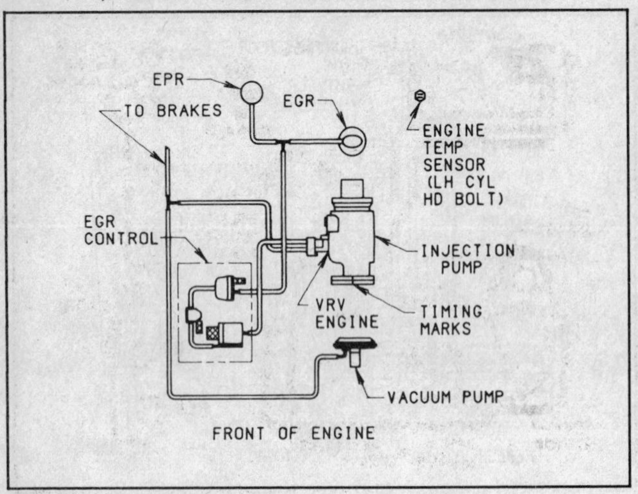

Fig. 31: 5.0L (305") V8 4-Bbl.
VIN H, Calif. Auto. Trans.

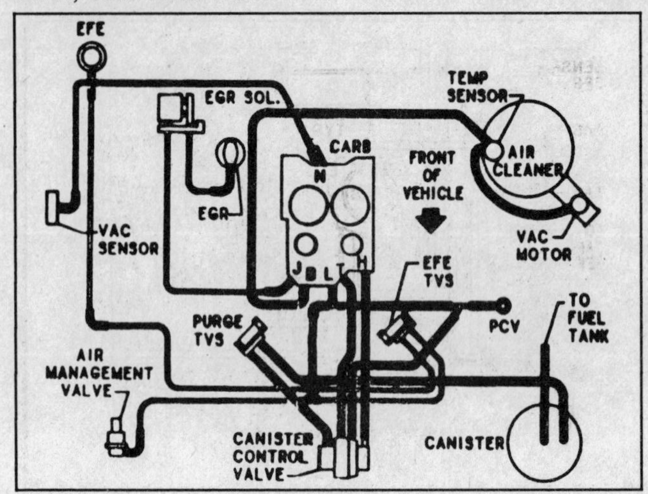

Fig. 29: 4.3L (262") V6 Diesel
VIN V, Fed. & High Alt. Auto. Trans.

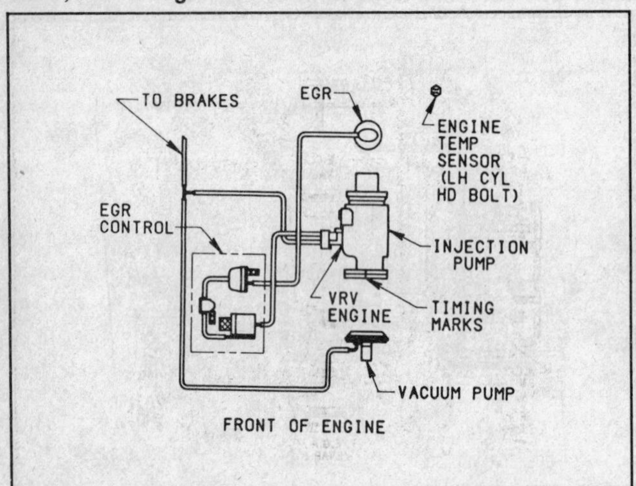

Fig. 32: 5.0L (305") V8 4-Bbl.
VIN H & 7, All Auto. Trans. except Calif. G Body

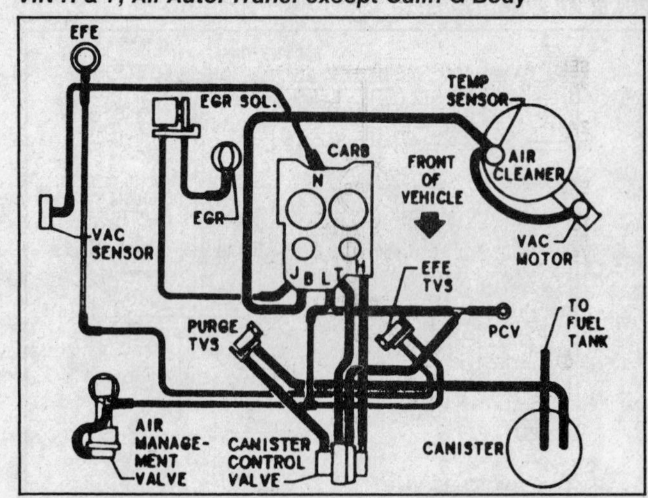

Fig. 30: 5.0L (305") V8 4-Bbl.
VIN H, All F Body Auto. & Man. Trans.

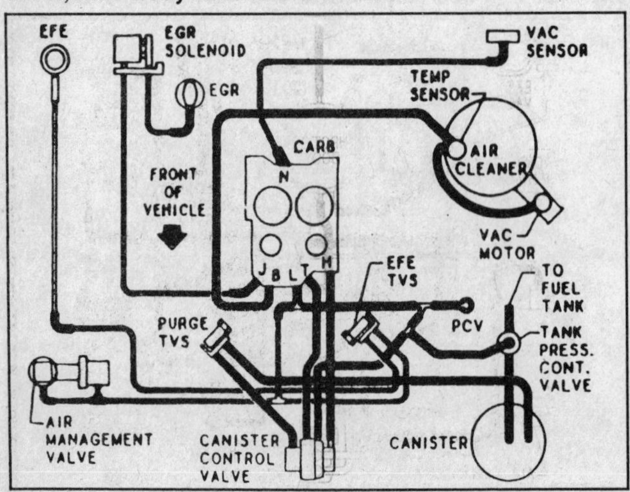

Fig. 33: 5.0L (305") V8 TBI
VIN S, All Auto. Trans.

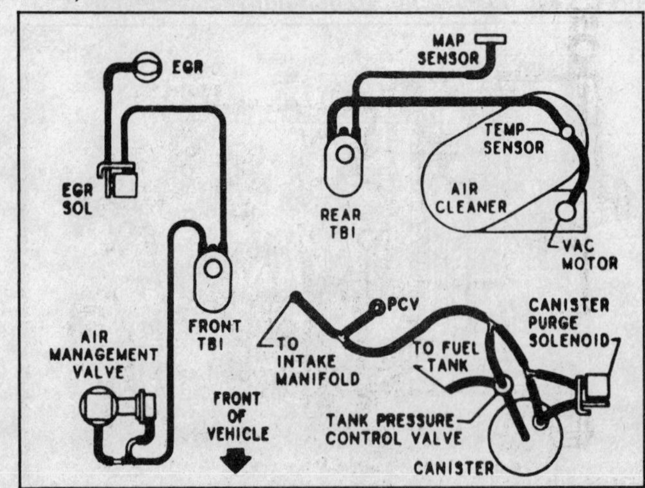

1983 GENERAL MOTORS VACUUM DIAGRAMS (Cont.)

Fig. 34: 5.0L (307") V8 4-Bbl.
VIN 9, All Hurst Olds Auto. Trans.

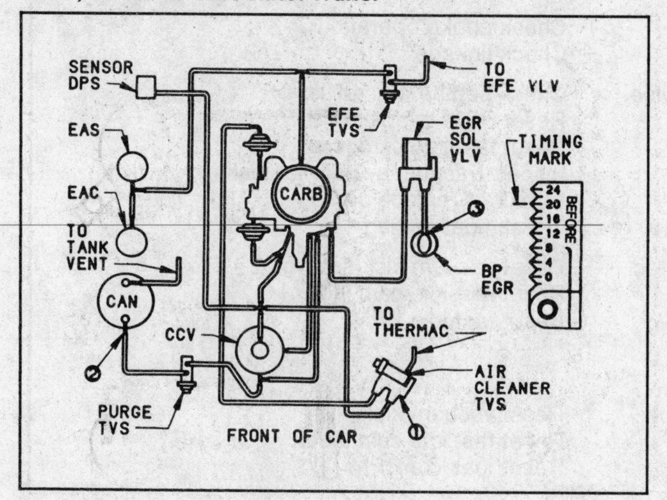

Fig. 35: 5.0L (307") V8 4-Bbl.
VIN 9, All Auto. Trans. except Hurst Olds

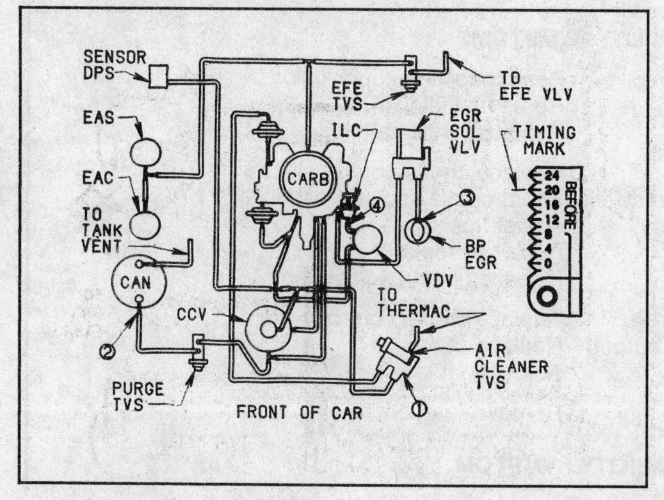

Fig. 36: 5.7L (350") V8 4-Bbl.
VIN 6, Fed. Auto. Trans.

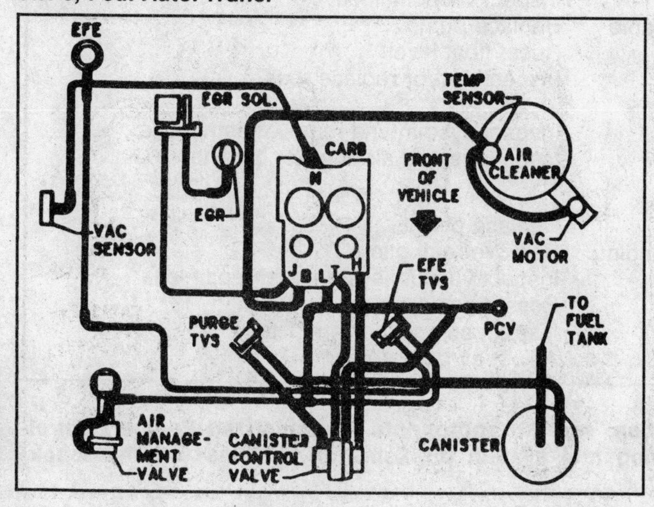

Fig. 37: 5.7L (350") TBI
VIN 8, All Auto. Trans.

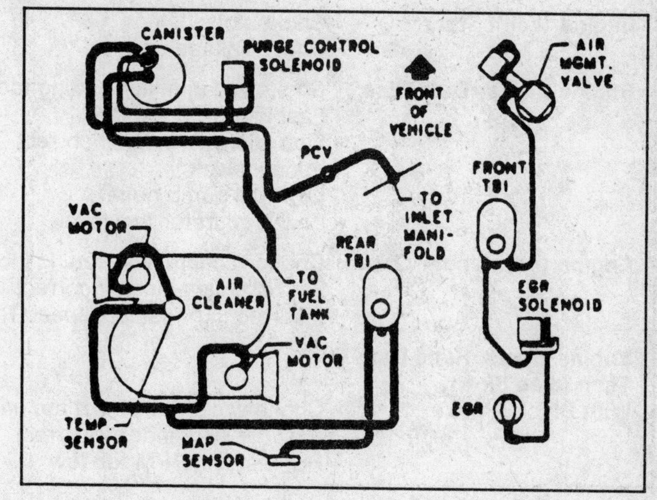

Fig. 38: 6.0L (368") V8 4-Bbl.
VIN 6, Fed. Auto. Trans.

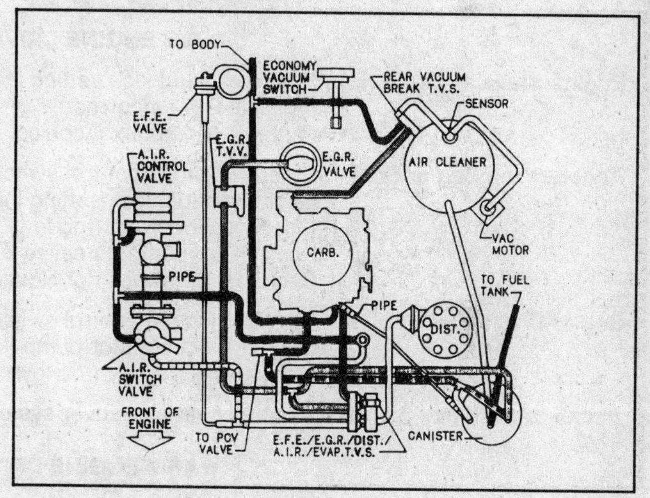

Fig. 39: 6.0L (368") V8 DFI
VIN 9, Fed. Auto. Trans.

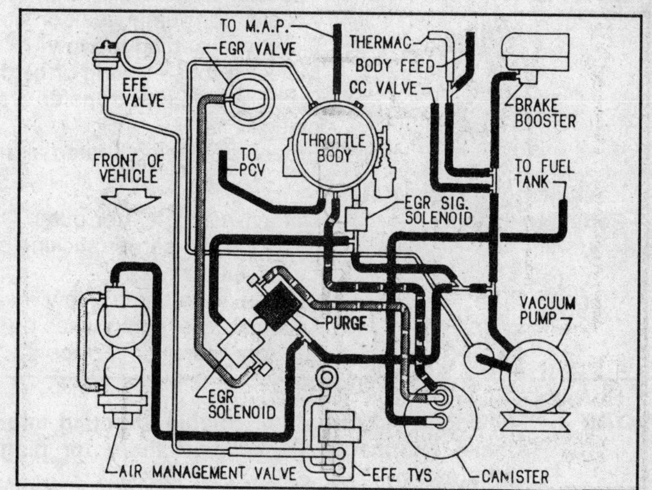

1983 Fuel Systems

CARBURETOR TROUBLE SHOOTING

CONDITION	POSSIBLE CAUSE	CORRECTION
Engine Won't Start	Choke not closing	Check choke operation
	Choke linkage bent	Check linkage
Engine Starts, Then Dies	Choke vacuum kick setting too wide	Check setting and adjust
	Fast idle RPM too low	Reset RPM to specification
	Fast idle cam index incorrect	Reset fast idle cam index
	Vacuum leak	Inspect vacuum system for leaks
	Low fuel pump outlet	Repair or replace pump
	Low carburetor fuel level	Check float setting
Engine Quits Under Load	Choke vacuum kick setting incorrect	Reset vacuum kick setting
	Fast idle cam index incorrect	Reset fast idle cam index
	Incorrect hot fast idle speed RPM	Reset fast idle RPM
Engine Starts, Runs Up, Then Idles Slowly With Black Smoke	Choke vacuum kick set too narrow	Reset vacuum kick
	Fast idle cam index incorrect	Reset fast idle cam index
	Hot fast idle RPM too low	Reset fast idle RPM
HOT STARTING SYMPTOMS		
Engine Won't Start	Engine flooded	Allow fuel to evaporate
COLD ENGINE DRIVEABILITY SYMPTOMS		
Engine Stalls in Gear	Choke vacuum kick setting incorrect	Reset choke vacuum kick
	Fast idle RPM incorrect	Reset fast idle RPM
	Fast idle cam index incorrect	Reset fast idle cam index
Acceleration Sag or Stall	Defective choke control switch	Replace choke control switch
	Choke vacuum kick setting incorrect	Reset choke vacuum kick
	Float level incorrect (too low)	Adjust float level
	Accelerator pump defective	Repair or replace pump
	Secondary throttles not closed	Inspect lockout adjustment
Sag or Stall After Warmup	Defective choke control switch	Replace choke control switch
	Defective accelerator pump (low output)	Replace pump
	Float level incorrect (too low)	Adjust float level
Backfiring & Black Smoke	Plugged heat crossover system	Remove restriction
WARM ENGINE DRIVEABILITY SYMPTOM		
Hesitation With Small Amount of Gas Pedal Movement	Vacuum leak	Inspect vacuum lines
	Accelerator pump weak or inoperable	Replace pump
	Float level setting too low	Reset float level
	Metering rods sticking or binding	Inspect and/or replace rods
	Carburetor idle or transfer system plugged	Inspect system and remove restrictions
	Frozen or binding heated air inlet	Inspect heated air door for binding
Hesitation With Heavy Gas Pedal Movement	Defective accelerator pump	Replace pump
	Metering rod carrier sticking or binding	Remove restriction
	Large vacuum leak	Inspect vacuum system and repair leak
	Float level setting too low	Reset float level
	Defective fuel pump, lines or filter	Inspect pump, lines and filter
	Air door setting incorrect	Adjust air door setting

NOTE: **For additional carburetor trouble shooting information, see the appropriate Computerized Engine Control article. Information is provided there for diagnosing fuel system problems on vehicles with feedback carburetors.**

DIESEL FUEL INJECTION TROUBLE SHOOTING

CONDITION	POSSIBLE CAUSE	CORRECTION
Engine Won't Start	No voltage to fuel solenoid	Check electrical connections
	Faulty glow plugs or glow plug controls	Check and/or replace glow plugs or controller
	Plugged fuel return system	Remove restrictions
	No fuel to nozzles	Inspect fuel delivery system
	No fuel to injecton pump	Inspect fuel delivery system
	Clogged fuel tank filter	Replace filter
	Incorrect or contaminated fuel	Remove and replace fuel
	Incorrect pump timing	Reset pump timing
Engine Stalls at Idle	Incorrect slow idle adjustment	Reset idle adjustment
	Faulty fast idle solenoid	Replace solenoid
	Plugged fuel return system	Remove restrictions
	Glow plugs turn off too soon	Check glow plug system
	Incorrect pump timing	Check and reset timing
	Limited fuel to injection pump	Check fuel delivery system
	Air in injection lines to nozzles	Check line fittings
	Incorrect or contaminated fuel	Remove and replace fuel
	Faulty injection pump	Remove and replace pump
	Fuel solenoid closes in RUN position	Check solenoid operation
Engine Starts, Idles Rough WITHOUT Unusual Noise or Smoke	Incorrect slow idle adjustment	Reset slow idle adjustment
	Leaking injection line	Check fittings and/or replace line
	Plugged fuel return line	Remove restrictions
	Air in lines to nozzles	Check line fittings
	Air in injection pump	Check pump fittings and pump operation
	Faulty nozzle	Replace nozzle
	Improper or contaminated fuel	Remove and replace fuel
	Uneven fuel distribution	Check fuel delivery system
Engine Starts and Idles WITH Excessive Noise and/or Smoke	Incorrect pump timing	Reset injection pump timing
	Air in injection lines to nozzles	Check fittings on lines
	Faulty nozzle	Replace nozzle
	Improperly installed high pressure lines	Remove and reinstall properly
Engine Idles Okay but Misfires Above Idle	Plugged fuel filter	Remove restrictions and/or replace filter
	Incorrect pump timing	Reset injection pump timing
	Incorrect or contaminated fuel	Remove and replace fuel
Engine Will Not Idle	Linkage binding or misadjusted	Remove binding and readjust linkage
	Defective injection pump	Replace injection pump
Fuel Leaks With No Other Engine Malfunction	Loose or broken fuel line or connection	Check all fuel line fittings and correct
	Internal seal leak in injection pump	Remove and replace injection pump
Low Engine Power	Restricted air intake	Remove restrictions
	Plugged fuel filter	Remove restriction and/or replace filter
	Restricted fuel return system	Remove restrictions
	Restricted tank-to-pump fuel supply	Check fuel delivery system
	Incorrect or contaminated fuel	Remove and replace fuel
	Restricted fuel tank filter	Replace filter
	Nozzle or glow plug compression leaks	Check fittings and replace as required
	Plugged nozzle	Remove restriction and/or replace nozzle
"Rapping" Noise From One or More Cylinders	Air in fuel system	Check fuel delivery system for leaks
	Air in high pressure lines	Check fittings for leaks
	Nozzle sticking in open position	Inspect nozzle and/or replace
	Low nozzle opening pressure	Check nozzle operation
	Filter in nozzle broken or loose	Remove and replace filter

1983 Fuel Systems

DIESEL FUEL INJECTION TROUBLE SHOOTING (Cont.)

CONDITION	POSSIBLE CAUSE	CORRECTION
Excessive Combustion Noise With Black Smoke	Incorrect pump timing	Reset injection pump timing
	Incorrect pump housing pressure	Check pump for internal leaks
	Defective injection pump	Replace injection pump
Engine Will Not Shut Off With Key	Injection pump fuel solenoid does not return to off position	Check solenoid operation

NOTE: For Gasoline Fuel Injection Trouble Shooting, see the appropriate Fuel Injection article under the individual manufacturer. Also see the appropriate Computerized Engine Control article.

TURBOCHARGER TROUBLE SHOOTING

CONDITION	POSSIBLE CAUSE	CORRECTION
Engine Detonation	Malfunction in spark advance or retard system	Check distributor and ignition
	EGR system defect	Check EGR system
	Carburetor/throttle body or turbocharger air inlet restrictions	Remove restrictions
	Actuator allows too much boost	Check boost pressure and adjust
	Defect in carburetor/throttle body power system	Inspect and repair carburetor/throttle body
	Internal turbocharger defect	Replace turbocharger
Low Engine Power	Air inlet restriction	Remove restriction in inlet
	Exhaust system restriction	Remove restriction
	Malfunction in spark advance or retard system	Check distributor and ignition, see ELECTRICAL
	EFE system defect (GM only)	Check EFE system operation
	EGR system defect	Check EGR system
Engine Noise	EFE system defect (GM only)	Check EFE system
	Loose exhaust system or leak	Check exhaust mounting and connections
	AIR system defect	Check AIR system
	Restricted turbocharger oil supply	Check oil delivery system
Engine Surges	ESC malfunction	Check ESC system
	Defective vacuum switch	Replace defective switch
	EGR system defect	Check EGR system
	Loose turbocharger bolts on compressor side	Check mounting bolts and tighten
Excessive Oil Consumption (Blue Exhaust Smoke)	Leak at turbocharger oil inlet	Check fittings and repair
	Turbocharger oil drain hose leaks or stopped up	Check drain hose for restrictions or loose fittings
	Turbocharger seals leaking	Replace seals

1983 Carter Carburetors

CARTER YFA & YFA FEEDBACK SINGLE BARREL

CARBURETOR APPLICATION

FORD MOTOR CO. CARBURETOR NO.

Application	Part No.
2.3L Engine	
Man. Trans.	
Federal	
Capri & Mustang	
4-Speed	
With A/C	E3ZE-9510-LA
Without A/C	E3ZE-9510-MA
5-Speed	
With A/C	E3ZE-9510-UB
Without A/C	E3ZE-9510-TC
Fairmont, LTD, Marquis & Zephyr	
With A/C	E3ZE-9510-VA
Without A/C	E3ZE-9510-YA
California	
With A/C	E3ZE-9510-VA
Without A/C	E3ZE-9510-YA
High Altitude	
With A/C	E3ZE-9510-ADA
Without A/C	E3ZE-9510-AEA
Auto. Trans.	
Federal	
With A/C	E3ZE-9510-ASA
Without A/C	E3ZE-9510-ATA
California	
With A/C	E3ZE-9510-ACA
Without A/C	E3ZE-9510-ABA

CARBURETOR IDENTIFICATION

A carburetor identification tag is attached to carburetor. Tag contains part number prefix and suffix, design change code, if any, and assembly date code, including year, month and day. To obtain replacement parts, it is necessary to know identification number prefix and suffix, and in some instances, the design change code.

Fig. 1: Ford Motor Co. Carburetor Identification Tag

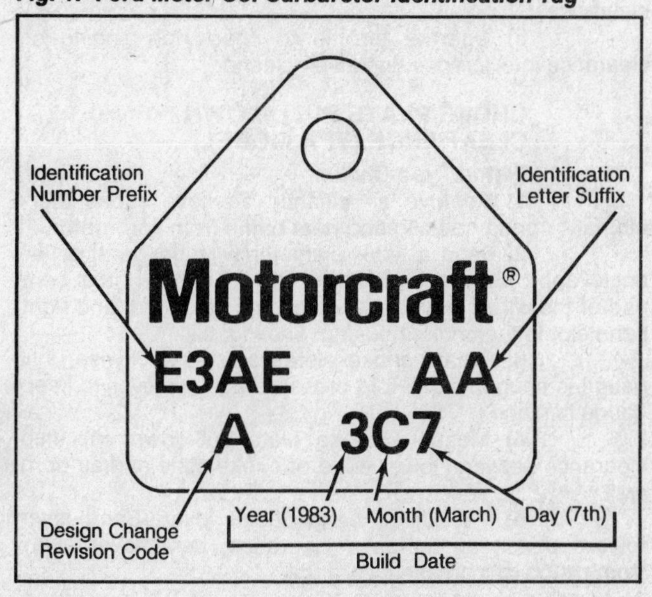

DESCRIPTION

Carter YFA and YFA Feedback carburetors are made up of 3 main assemblies: air horn, main body and throttle body. YFA carburetors have an adjustment limiting vacuum diaphragm type automatic choke with an electric assist choke cap. The electric choke adds a high mileage economy application to the carburetor. The main body contains a temperature compensated accelerator pump which has a thermostatic disc designed to open and close within a specified range.

The YFA Feedback carburetor differs from the YFA in its addition of a feedback solenoid attached to the air horn assembly. This solenoid is used to meter air into both the idle and main circuits for improved engine performance. A Microprocessor Control Unit (MCU) senses various engine needs and supplies feedback fuel as required by forcing air into fuel bowl, and in turn, more fuel into carburetor air stream.

ADJUSTMENTS

NOTE: **For on-vehicle adjustments, see TUNE-UP PROCEDURES article.**

FLOAT LEVEL

1) Remove air cleaner assembly. Remove air horn and gasket from top of carburetor.

2) Turn air horn assembly upside-down. Measure distance between top of float at free end and gasket surface of air horn.

NOTE: **Do not apply pressure against needle when adjusting float.**

3) Bend float arm as necessary to obtain correct clearance. DO NOT bend tab at end of float arm as this will stop float travel to bottom of fuel bowl when empty.

4) When adjustment is completed, reinstall air horn and new gasket. Start engine and check for fuel leaks. Install air cleaner.

Fig. 2: Float Level Adjustment

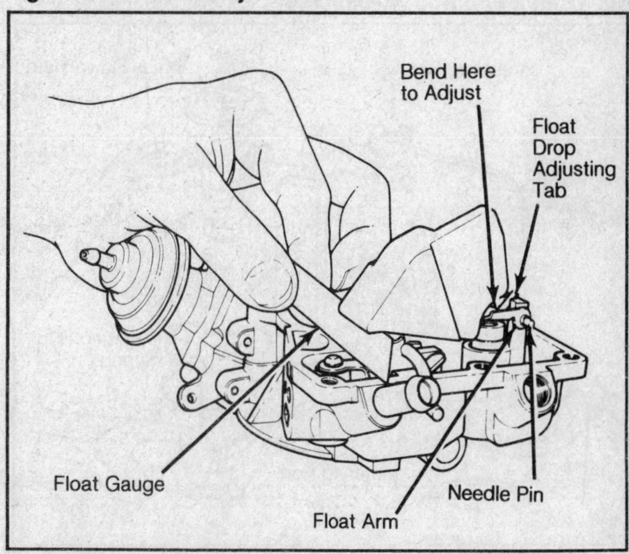

Bend float arm to adjust.

CARTER YFA & YFA FEEDBACK SINGLE BARREL (Cont.)

FLOAT DROP

1) Remove air cleaner, carburetor air horn and gasket from top of carburetor.

2) Hold air horn in upright position. Allow float to hang free. Using specified gauge, measure minimum clearance from tip of float to bottom of air horn casting. *See Fig. 3.*

Fig. 3: Float Drop Adjustment

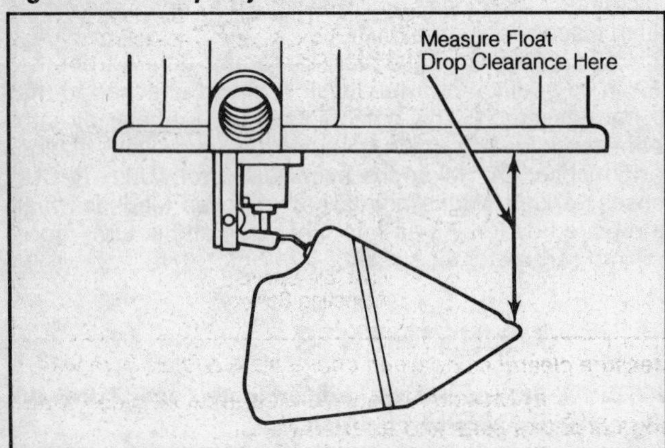

Bend tab at end of float arm to adjust.

3) Bend tab at end of float arm to adjust. After completing adjustment, install air horn and a new gasket on carburetor. Start engine and check for fuel leaks. Install air cleaner.

METERING ROD

1) Remove air cleaner, air horn and gasket from carburetor.

2) Using a side cutter, remove the tamper proof cup covering the closed plate adjusting screw. Back out adjusting screw until it is clear of the casting.

3) Press down on top of pump diaphragm shaft until assembly bottoms. While holding diaphragm assembly in this position, turn rod adjustment screw counterclockwise until metering rod gently bottoms in body casting. *See Fig. 4.*

Fig. 4: Metering Rod Adjustment

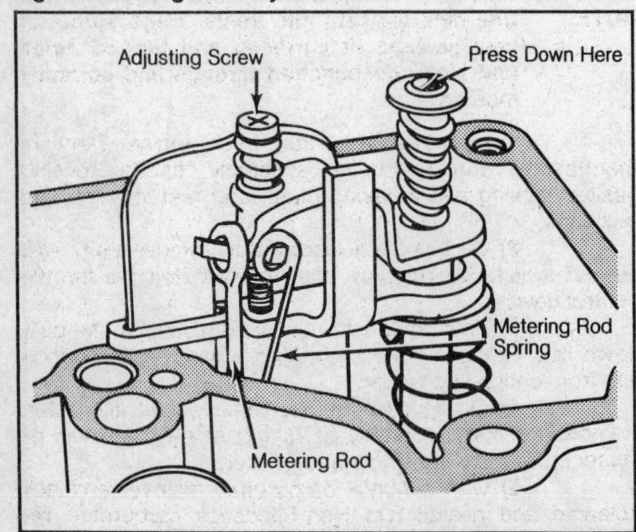

Before adjusting, press down on pump diaphragm shaft.

4) Now turn metering rod adjustment screw clockwise (IN) one turn for final adjustment. Install air horn and new gasket on carburetor.

5) Turn adjusting screw clockwise until it contacts the casting, then one additional turn clockwise. Install a new tamper proof cup. Install air cleaner.

CHOKE UNLOADER (DECHOKE)

1) Remove air cleaner. Hold throttle valve in fully open position and press choke valve toward closed position.

2) Measure clearance between lower edge of choke valve and air horn wall.

3) Adjust by bending arm on choke lever of throttle lever. *See Fig. 5.*

Fig. 5: Choke Unloader (Dechoke) Adjustment

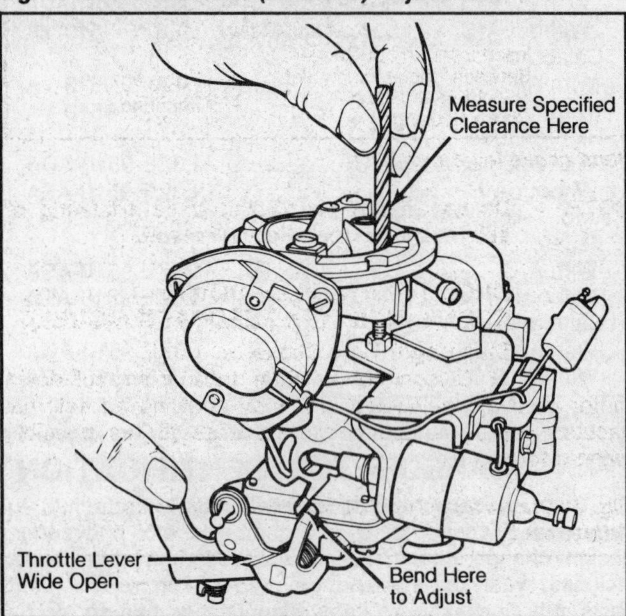

Adjust by bending choke lever arm of throttle lever.

4) Bend arm upward to increase clearance; bend downward, away from fast idle cam, to decrease clearance.

5) Operate throttle to check for binding or clearance interference. Install air cleaner.

CHOKE PLATE PULL-DOWN CLEARANCE (YFA MODEL)

Piston Type Choke

1) Remove air cleaner. Remove choke thermostatic spring housing and heat baffle from carburetor.

2) Bend a .026" diameter wire gauge at a 90° angle approximately 1/8" from one end. Insert the bent end of the wire gauge between choke piston slot and right hand slot in the choke housing. *See Fig. 6.*

3) Rotate choke piston counterclockwise until gauge is snug in slot. Hold pressure against lever to keep gauge in place.

4) Measure choke plate pull-down specified clearance between lower edge of choke plate and air horn wall.

5) To adjust, bend choke lever. Bend lever toward piston to decrease clearance; bend lever away from piston to increase clearance.

CARTER YFA & YFA FEEDBACK SINGLE BARREL (Cont.)

Fig. 6: Piston Type Choke Plate Pull-Down Adjustment

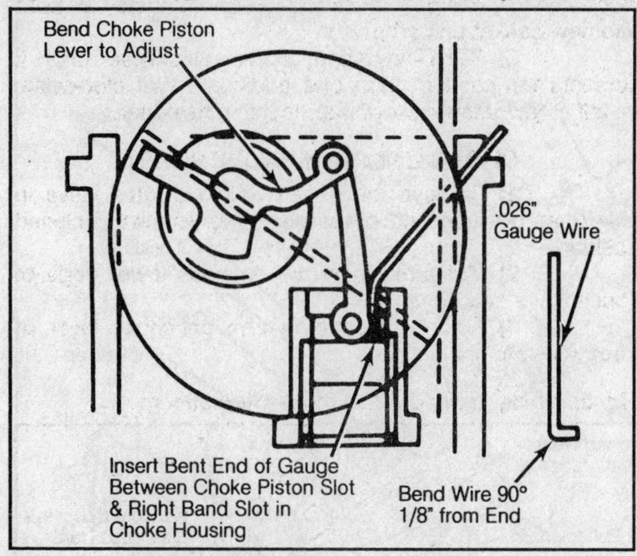

Bend choke lever to adjust.

NOTE: **Do not distort piston link while adjusting or erratic choke operation will result.**

CHOKE PLATE PULL-DOWN CLEARANCE (YFA FEEDBACK MODEL)

Diaphragm Type Choke

1) Disconnect vacuum tube from pull-down motor. Activate pull-down motor by applying an external vacuum source. Close choke plate as far as possible without forcing it.

Fig. 7: Diaphragm Type Choke Plate Pull-Down Adjustment

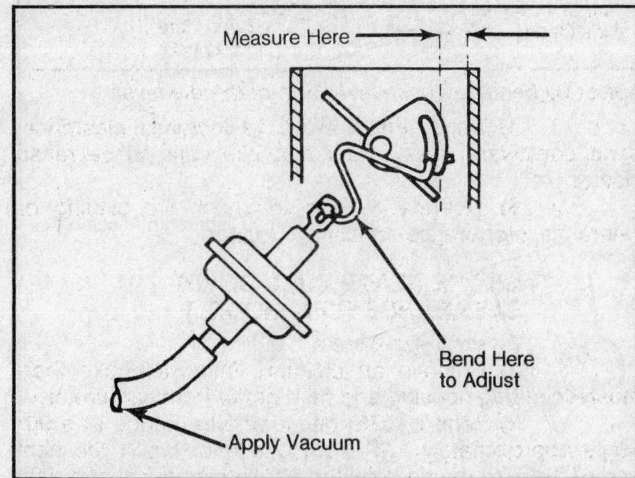

Bend choke diaphragm link to adjust.

2) Using specified drill, check clearance between lower edge of choke plate and air horn wall. To adjust, bend choke diaphragm link as required. Reconnect pull-down motor vacuum tube.

FAST IDLE CAM POSITION

1) Place fast idle speed screw on kickdown step of fast idle cam, against shoulder of highest step. *See Fig. 8.*

Fig. 8: Fast Idle Cam Position

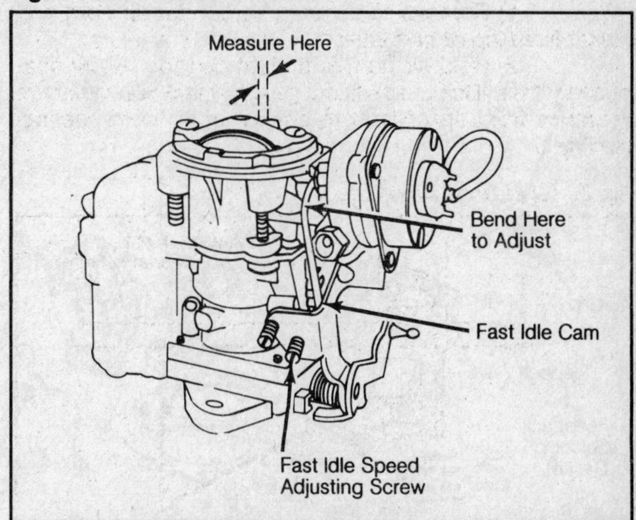

Measure clearance between choke plate and air horn wall.

2) Measure specified clearance between lower edge of choke plate and air horn wall.

3) If clearance is not to specification, adjust by bending fast idle cam link.

AUTOMATIC CHOKE

NOTE: **Although automatic choke is of tamper-proof design, these steps are used if automatic choke is damaged or when carburetor is rebuilt.**

Loosen choke thermostat cover. Remove 2 rivets and retaining screw. Rotate cover assembly in "Rich" or "Lean" direction to align reference mark on cover with specified scale graduation on housing. Install new rivets and screw, and tighten.

OVERHAUL

DISASSEMBLY

NOTE: **Use new gaskets and seals. Make sure that new gaskets fit correctly and that all holes and slots are punched through and correctly located.**

1) Remove carburetor from engine. Remove thermostatic spring housing assembly, spring housing gasket, locking and indexing plate, and fast idle link and bushings.

2) On Feedback carburetor, remove WOT A/C cut-out switch, if equipped, and bracket. Remove throttle control device.

3) Remove 2 screws disconnecting choke pull-down link. Remove pulldown motor assembly. Disengage link from choke shaft lever.

4) On all carburetors, remove fuel filler inlet. Remove air horn assembly attaching screws, solevac or solenoid, air horn assembly and gasket.

5) On Feedback carburetor, remove feedback solenoid and gasket. On Non-Feedback carburetor, remove wire clip retaining the link that joins the fast idle choke lever to fast idle cam and remove link.

1983 Carter Carburetors

CARTER YFA & YFA FEEDBACK SINGLE BARREL (Cont.)

Fig. 9: Exploded View of Carter Model YFA 1-Barrel Feedback Carburetor (YFA Similar)

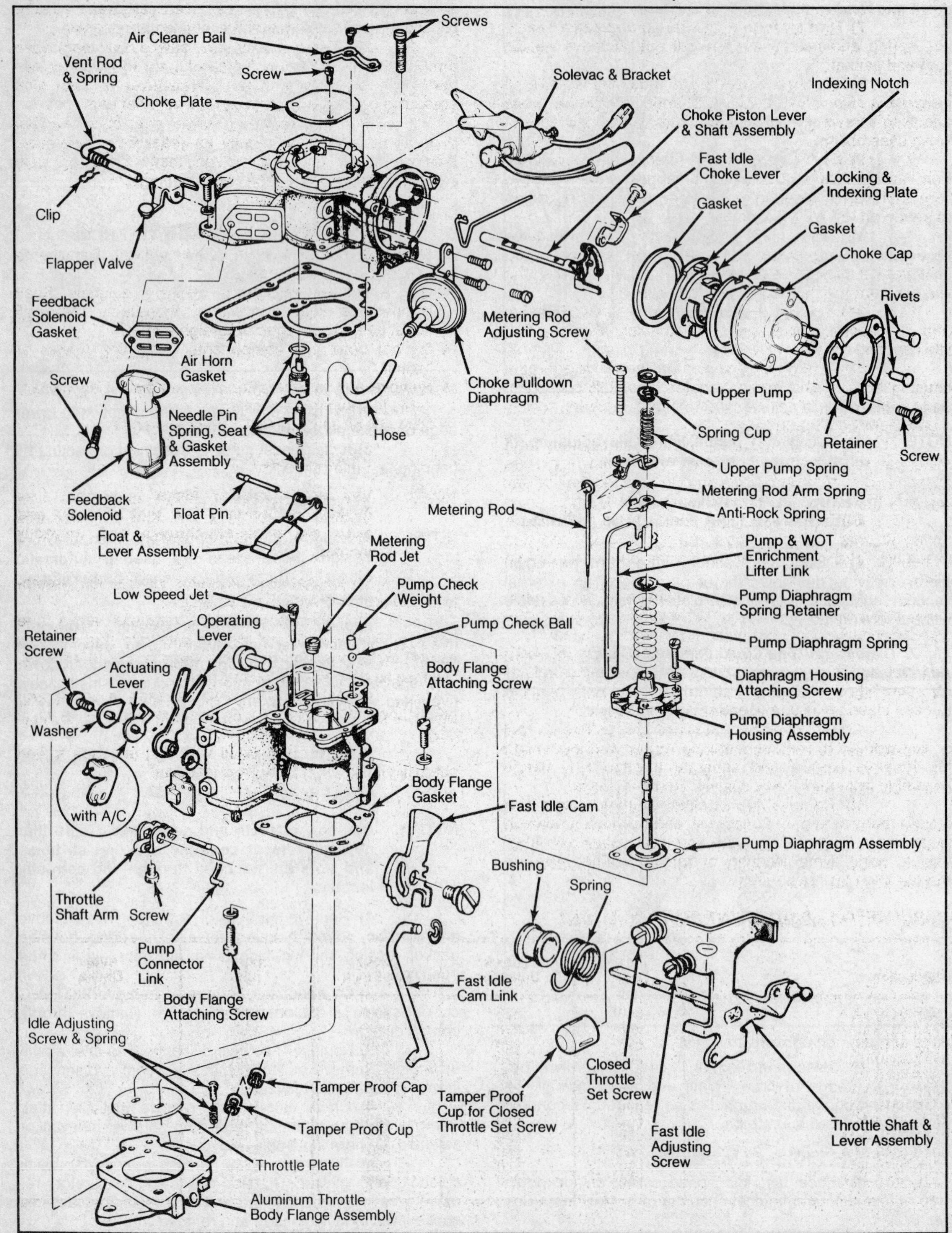

CARTER YFA & YFA FEEDBACK SINGLE BARREL (Cont.)

6) On all carburetors, turn air horn upside-down and remove float pin, float and lever assembly.

7) Turn air horn right-side-up and catch needle pin, spring and needle as they fall out. Remove needle seat and gasket.

8) Remove choke plate attaching screws. If necessary, file staked (burred) ends of choke plate attaching screws and remove. Be sure to use new screws when assembling.

9) On all carburetors, remove spring retainer from mechanical fuel bowl vent flapper valve. Remove vent shaft rod and spring and flapper valve. Note position of spring on rod for reassembly.

10) Turn main body upside-down and catch accelerator pump check ball and weight. Remove bowl vent lever screw in end of throttle shaft. Remove spring washer, vent rod, actuating lever and clip.

11) Loosen throttle shaft arm screw. Remove arm and accelerator pump connector link. Remove fast idle cam and screw.

12) Remove accelerator pump diaphragm housing screws and pump transfer tube. Lift out pump diaphragm assembly, pump lifter link and metering rod as a unit. Remove lifter link seal.

13) Disengage metering rod arm spring from metering rod. Remove metering rod from rod arm assembly. For reassembly, be sure to note location of any washers that were used for shimming either spring.

14) Compress upper pump spring and remove spring retainer. Remove upper spring, metering rod arm assembly, and pump lifter link from pump diaphragm shaft.

15) Compress pump diaphragm spring. Remove pump diaphragm spring retainer, spring and pump diaphragm assembly from pump diaphragm housing.

16) On Feedback carburetor, using a sharp punch or awl, remove temperature compensated accelerator pump bleed valve plug from outside main body casting. Loosen bleed valve screw and remove valve.

17) On all carburetors, use proper size jet tool or screwdriver to remove metering rod jet and low speed jet. Remove screws and separate throttle body flange assembly from main body casting. Remove gasket.

18) Remove throttle plate retaining screws. File staked (burred) ends if necessary, and use new screws at reassembly. Slide throttle shaft and lever assembly out of throttle body. Note location of torsion spring ends on throttle shaft for reassembly.

19) Remove idle mixture screw adjustment limiting cap and cup as follows: Invert carburetor assembly and tape all vacuum and fuel connection openings.

20) Using a hacksaw, saw a slot lengthwise through thickness of cup. Be careful not to touch throttle body with saw blade. Insert screwdriver in new slot, spreading outer cup enough to remove inner cap.

21) After removing limiter cap, count number of turns to lightly seat needle for reassembly reference. Remove screw and cup. Clean metal shavings from carburetor and remove tape from openings.

CLEANING & INSPECTION

- Do not immerse air horn in any solvent. Damage to vent shaft seal could result.
- Use a regular carburetor cleaning solution. Soak components long enough to thoroughly clean all surfaces and passages of foreign matter.
- Do not soak any components containing rubber or leather.
- Remove any residue after cleaning by rinsing components in a suitable solvent.
- Blow out all passages with compressed air.

REASSEMBLY

NOTE: **Use new gaskets. Make sure that new gaskets fit correctly and that all holes and slots are punched through and correctly located.**

To reassemble carburetor, reverse disassembly procedures and note the following:

1) If throttle valve was removed, make sure notch in throttle valve is aligned with idle port in body flange. Make sure throttle plate does not bind or stick. Restake or peen throttle plate screws.

2) Make sure vacuum passage in accelerator pump housing is aligned with vacuum passage in main body.

3) Make sure bowl vent rod engages forked actuating lever when air horn is installed.

CARBURETOR ADJUSTMENT SPECIFICATIONS

Application	Float Level	Choke Unloader	Choke Pull-Down	Fast Idle	Auto. Choke
E3ZE-9510-LA	.650"	.220"	.260"	.140"	.....
E3ZE-9510-MA	.650"	.220"	.260"	.140"	.....
E3ZE-9510-TC	.650"	.220"	.240"	.140"	.....
E3ZE-9510-UB	.650"	.220"	.240"	.140"	.....
E3ZE-9510-VA	.650"	.220"	.260"	.140"	.....
E3ZE-9510-YA	.650"	.220"	.260"	.140"	.....
E3ZE-9510-ABA	.650"	.220"	.260"	.140"	.....
E3ZE-9510-ACA	.650"	.220"	.260"	.140"	.....
E3ZE-9510-ADA	.650"	.220"	.260"	.140"	.....
E3ZE-9510-AEA	.650"	.220"	.260"	.140"	.....
E3ZE-9510-ASA	.650"	.220"	.260"	.160"	.....
E3ZE-9510-ATA	.650"	.220"	.260"	.160"	.....

1983 Carter Carburetors

CARTER BBD 2-BARREL

CARBURETOR APPLICATION

AMERICAN MOTORS CARBURETOR NO.

Application	Part. No.
4.2L Engine	
With High Altitude	
Man. Trans.	8367
Auto. Trans.	8362
Without High Altitude	
Man. Trans.	8364
Auto. Trans.	8360

CHRYSLER CORP. (CARTER) CARBURETOR NO.

Application	Part No.
5.2L Engine	BBD-8291S

CARBURETOR IDENTIFICATION

Carter carburetor number is stamped on a tag attached to carburetor by 1 air horn screw. *See Fig. 1.*

Fig. 1: Carter Model BBD Carburetor I.D. Tag

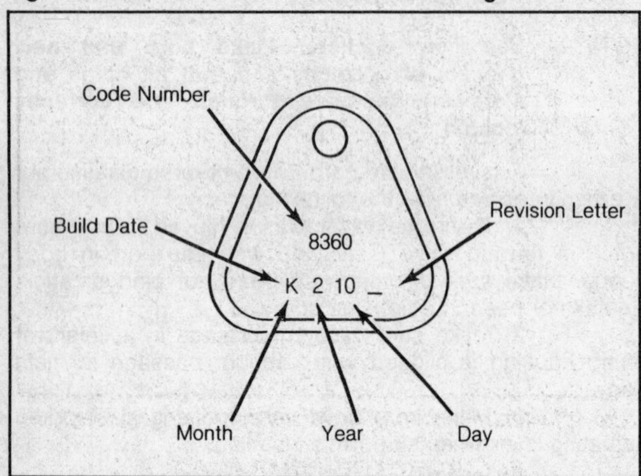

DESCRIPTION

The model BBD carburetor is a 2-barrel downdraft type, incorporating 3 basic fuel metering systems. The idle system provides mixture for idle and low speed operation. The accelerator pump system provides additional fuel for acceleration. The main metering system provides a more economical mixture for normal driving.

The carburetor is also equipped with a fuel inlet system which supplies a constant amount of fuel to provide sufficient fuel to the metering circuits for all engine operating conditions. The choke system (electrically assisted on Chrysler Corp. vehicles) provides temporary enrichment of the air/fuel mixture to aid in starting and running a cold engine.

Chrysler models are equipped with a duty cycle solenoid that is controlled by a Spark Control Computer. The solenoid is used to alter the main air/fuel mixture, in response to commands from an oxygen sensor and is located on rear of carburetor main body.

American Motors models are equipped with an electronically controlled stepper motor which controls air flow through metered air bleeds located in each main fuel metering circuit.

Both manufacturers equip the BBD carburetor with idle speed control systems which maintain idle speed on vehicles equipped with A/C and other accessories.

CAUTION: The idle speed control circuit is an integral part of the CEC system and cannot be serviced separately.

ADJUSTMENTS

NOTE: For on-vehicle adjustments, see TUNE-UP PROCEDURES article.

FLOAT LEVEL

American Motors

1) Remove air horn. Apply light pressure to float arm, gently seating needle in seat and raising float. *See Fig. 2.*

Fig. 2: American Motors Float Level Adjustment

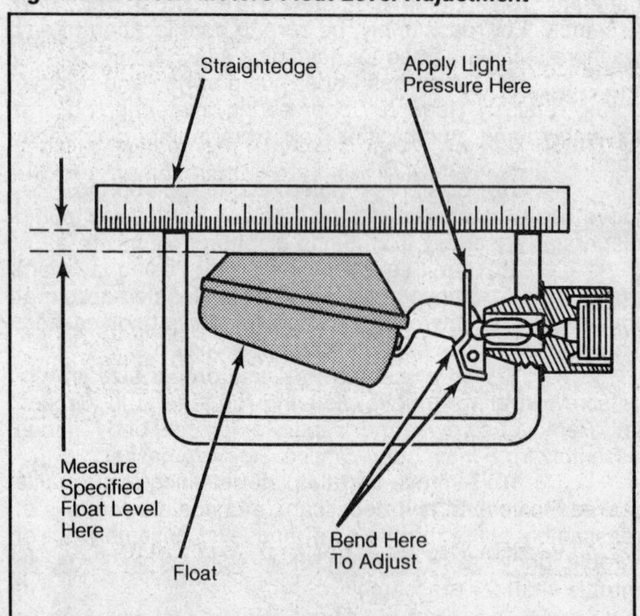

Bend tang to adjust.

2) Place a straightedge across main body. Measure float level specified clearance between top edge of float and bottom of straightedge.

3) To adjust, bend float tang to obtain specified clearance. Float tang is portion of float that contacts end of float needle valve.

CAUTION: Do not adjust float while tang is resting against needle. Damage to synthetic tip of needle may occur.

Chrysler Corp.

1) Remove air horn. Turn main body upside down. Catch accelerator pump check ball as it falls out. Hold float pin retainer in with finger. Weight of float should be closing float needle. *See Fig.3.*

CARTER BBD 2-BARREL (Cont.)

Fig. 3: Chrysler Corp. Float Level Adjustment

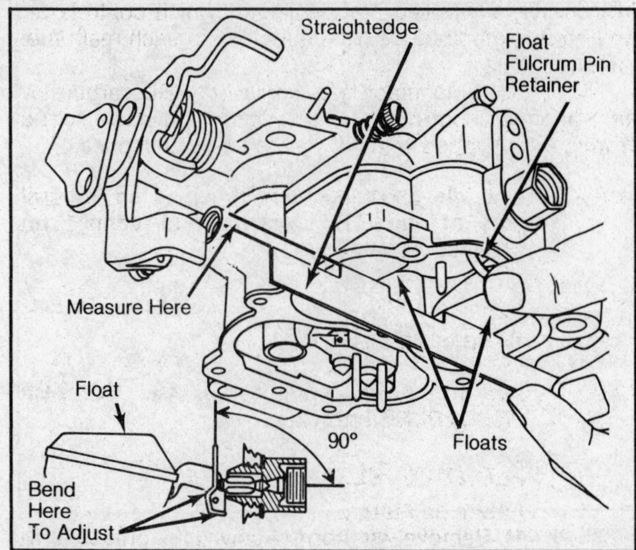

Bend tang to adjust.

2) Place a straightedge across main body. Measure float level specified clearance between straightedge and crown of each float.

3) To adjust, bend float tang to obtain specified clearance. Float tang is portion of float that contacts end of float needle valve.

CAUTION: Do not adjust while tang is resting against needle. Damage to synthetic tip of needle may occur.

VACUUM STEP-UP PISTON GAP QUALIFICATION

NOTE: This adjustment is required if step-up piston is removed or if piston lifter position is changed on actuating rod. This adjustment positions piston in a "mean" or centered position.

1) Remove step-up piston cover plate and gasket. Remove lifter lock screw and piston.

Fig. 4: Vacuum Step-Up Piston Gap Qualification

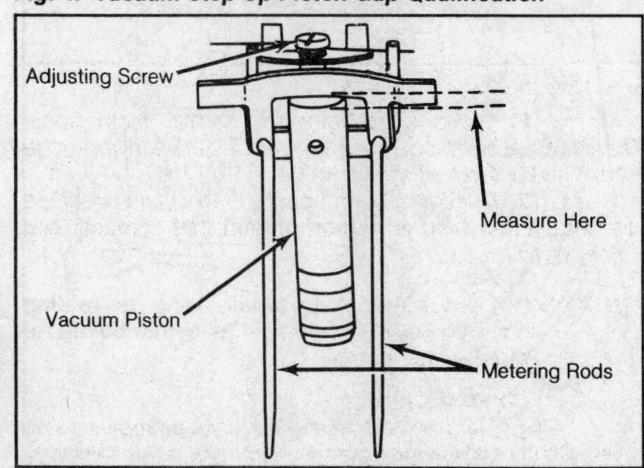

This adjustment positions piston in a "mean" or centered position.

2) Measure piston gap as shown in *Fig. 4*. If not to specifications, adjust Allen head screw on top of piston.

3) Turning screw clockwise makes mixture richer. Turning screw counterclockwise makes mixture leaner.

VACUUM STEP-UP PISTON

NOTE: Perform Vacuum Step-Up Piston Gap Qualification adjustment first.

1) With vacuum piston installed, back off curb idle speed screw until throttle valves are seated. Count number of turns required to seat throttle valves.

2) Loosen lifter lock screw. Fully depress piston in bore. At same time, hold pressure against rod lifter tab. Tighten lifter lock screw.

3) Release lifter and piston. Adjust accelerator pump. Readjust curb idle speed screw to its original position.

Fig. 5: Vacuum Step-Up Piston Adjusment

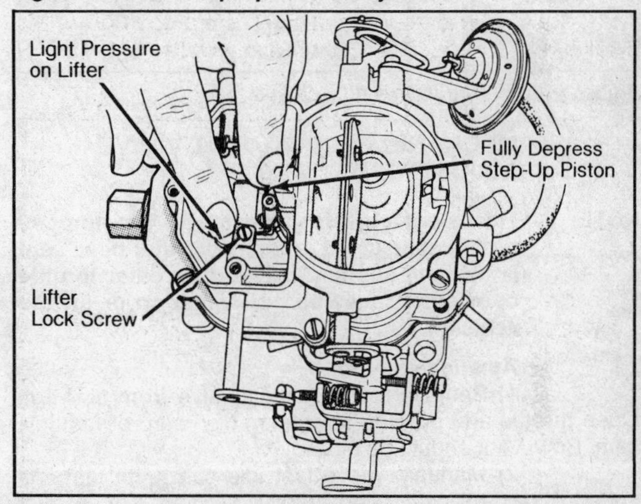

Make adjustment with throttle valves completely closed.

ACCELERATOR PUMP STROKE

1) Remove step-up piston cover plate and gasket. Back off curb idle speed screw until throttle valves are seated. Count number of turns required to seat throttle valves. Fast idle cam must be in open choke position. *See Fig. 6.*

2) Turn curb idle screw clockwise until it just touches stop. Continue 2 more complete turns.

3) Some Chrysler Corp. models may have 2 holes in accelerator pump arm. If so, make sure accelerator pump "S" link is in outer hole.

4) Measure distance between surface of air horn and top of accelerator pump shaft. If adjustment is needed, loosen pump arm adjusting lock screw and turn sleeve to adjust pump travel. When correct measurement is obtained, tighten lock screw.

5) Install step-up piston cover plate and gasket. Readjust curb idle speed screw to its original position.

NOTE: On Chrysler Corp. models, if the accelerator pump adjustment is changed, the Bowl Vent Adjustment must be reset.

CARTER BBD 2-BARREL (Cont.)

Fig. 6: Accelerator Pump Stroke Adjustment

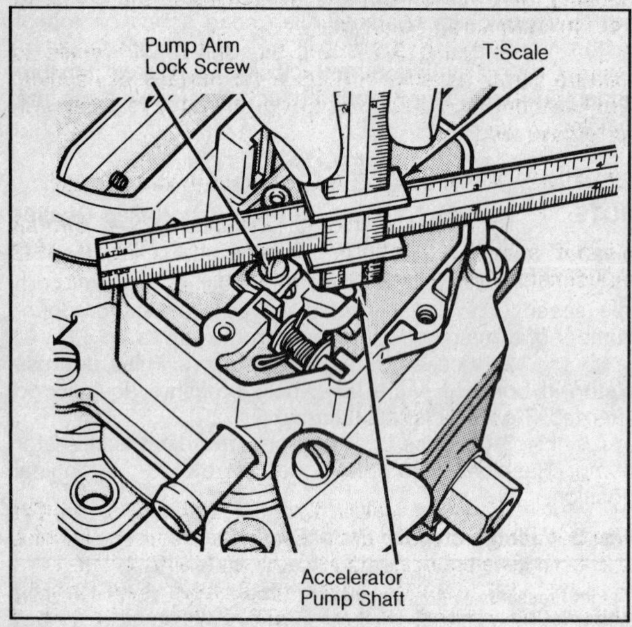

Adjust with throttle valves fully closed.

MECHANICAL BOWL VENT VALVE ADJUSTMENT

NOTE: This is not a precise adjustment. The purpose of this adjustment is to ensure that bowl vent is open at idle and closed at greater throttle openings. It may be performed on or off the vehicle.

American Motors

1) Remove rollover check valve from air horn. Open throttle and position throttle on high step of fast idle cam. Bowl vent should be closed.

2) Manually move fast idle cam until fast idle speed screw drops to 2nd step. Bowl vent should just start to open.

3) If bowl vent valve is not closed on high, 4th or 3rd steps of fast idle cam, bend tab of valve until is it closed.

4) If valve is not starting to open on 2nd step of cam, bend tab of valve until it just lifts off seat.

NOTE: Chrysler Corp. models are equipped with a bowl vent solenoid which allows float vapors to flow to carbon canister only when engine is stopped. There is no vent adjustment necessary on these models.

FAST IDLE CAM POSITION

NOTE: American Motors models use tamper-proof screws to retain choke coil cover. Grind screw heads until cover retaining ring can be removed and then remove remaining portion of cover screws from choke housing.

1) On American Motors models, remove choke coil cover retaining screws. Rotate choke coil cover 90° in the "Rich" direction. Install and tighten 1 slot-type retaining screw. On all models, place fast idle speed screw on 2nd step of fast idle cam. *See Fig. 7.*

Fig. 7: Fast Idle Cam Position Adjustment

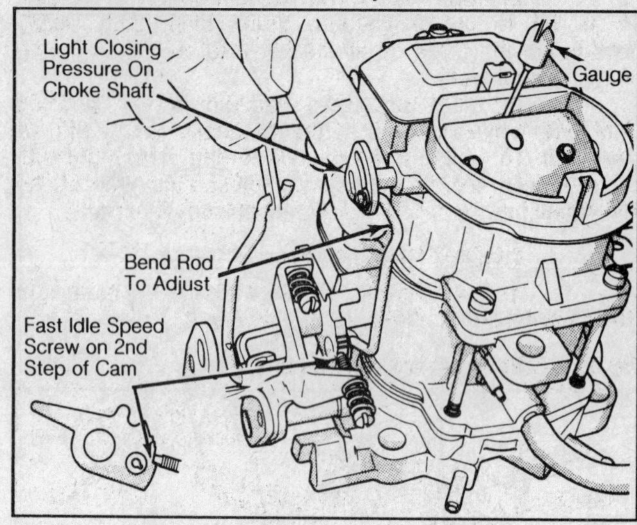

Adjust by bending fast idle cam rod.

2) Hold choke valve toward closed position. Measure fast idle cam specified clearance between upper edge of choke valve and air horn wall.

3) If clearance is not to specification, adjust by bending fast idle cam rod. Bend rod down to increase clearance and up to decrease clearance. On American Motors models, readjust automatic choke and install new tamper-proof choke coil cover screws.

CHOKE VACCUM BREAK (INITIAL CHOKE VALVE CLEARANCE)

1) On American Motors models, remove choke coil cover retaining screw. Rotate choke coil cover 90° in "Rich" direction. Install and tighten 1 slot-type retaining screw. On all models, place fast idle speed screw on highest step of fast idle cam. *See Fig. 8.*

Fig. 8: Choke Vacuum Break Adjustment

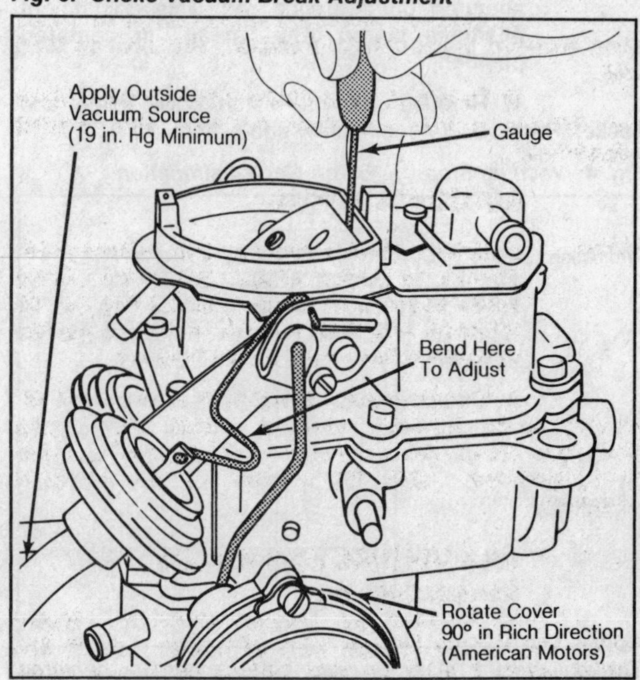

Bend vacuum break diaphragm rod to adjust.

CARTER BBD 2-BARREL (Cont.)

2) Apply an outside vacuum source of at least 19 in. hg to choke vacuum break diaphragm. Apply enough closing force on choke valve to compress spring on diaphragm stem.

3) Measure choke vacuum break specified clearance between upper edge of choke valve and air horn wall. To adjust, bend vacuum break diaphragm rod. On American Motors models, readjust automatic choke and install new tamper-proof choke coil cover screws.

CHOKE UNLOADER

1) Open throttle valves wide open. Apply light closing pressure to choke valve. *See Fig. 9.*

Fig. 9: Choke Unloader Adjustment

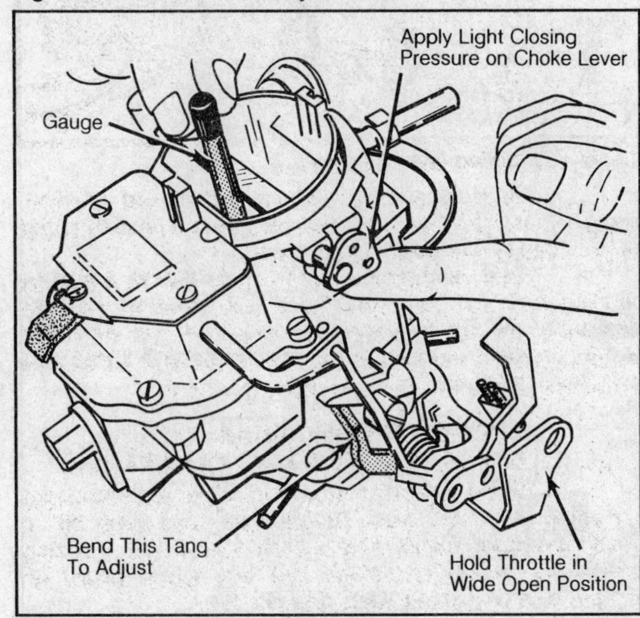

Bend choke unloader tang to adjust.

2) Measure specified choke unloader clearance between upper edge of choke valve and air horn wall.

3) To adjust, bend choke unloader tang. Make sure linkage is free and does not bind after making adjustment.

AUTOMATIC CHOKE

NOTE: **American Motors models use tamper-proof screws to retain choke coil cover. Grind screw heads until cover retaining ring can be removed and then remove remaining portion of cover screws from choke housing.**

Automatic choke adjustment is made by removing choke housing retaining screws and turning housing to correct index or notch on choke housing. Refer to Specification Table for correct position for each carburetor.

IDLE MIXTURE SCREW PLUG

Chrysler Corp. Only

1) Remove air cleaner assembly, vacuum hoses and throttle linkage from carburetor. Locate and center punch a mark on side surface of mixture screw housing, 5/16" from front end of housing in the center of both mixture screw housings.

2) Using 3/16" drill bit, drill at 90° angle to mixture screw housing through outer surface of housing. Concealment plug should drop out. If not, use small drift to remove plug.

CAUTION: **Do not allow drift to contact mixture screw.**

3) Reinstall linkage, vacuum hoses and air cleaner assembly. Perform propane idle mixture RPM adjustment. Reinstall concealment plug.

OVERHAUL

DISASSEMBLY

1) Place carburetor on stand and remove stepper motor or duty cycle solenoid. Remove retaining clip from accelerator pump arm link and remove link.

2) Remove cover plate from over step-up piston and remove gasket. Remove locks and screws from accelerator pump arm and vacuum piston rod lifter. Slide pump lever out of air horn.

3) Lift vacuum piston and step-up rods up and out of air horn as an assembly. Remove the vacuum piston spring. Remove choke vacuum diaphragm hose. Disconnect clips and remove link from choke housing lever and choke lever.

4) On American Motors models, rotate bowl vent assembly up out of bowl as far as possible and remove rubber valve seal.

5) On all models, remove screw and lever from end of choke shaft. Remove choke vacuum break diaphragm. On American Motors models, remove automatic choke assembly. On all models, remove fast idle cam retaining screw and remove fast idle cam, linkage and clip.

6) Remove screws securing air horn and lift air horn up and away from main body. Discard gasket. Turn air horn upside down and compress accelerator pump drive spring. Remove "S" link from pump shaft. Remove pump assembly.

7) Remove fuel inlet needle valve, seat and gasket from main body. Carefully lift out float fulcrum pin retainer and baffle. Lift out floats and fulcrum pin. Remove main metering jets.

8) Remove venturi cluster screws. Lift cluster and gaskets away from main body. Discard gaskets. DO NOT remove idle orifice tubes or main vent tubes from cluster. They may be cleaned with solvent and dried with compressed air while assembled.

9) Turn carburetor upside down and catch accelerator pump discharge and intake check balls as they fall out.

10) Turn idle limiter caps to stop. Remove plastic caps from idle mixture screws. Be sure to count number of turns it takes to set screws for reassembly reference. Remove screws and springs.

11) Remove screws and separate throttle body from main body. Discard gasket. Check choke plate in air horn for freedom of movement. If any sticking or binding is evident, clean thoroughly.

CARTER BBD 2-BARREL (Cont.)

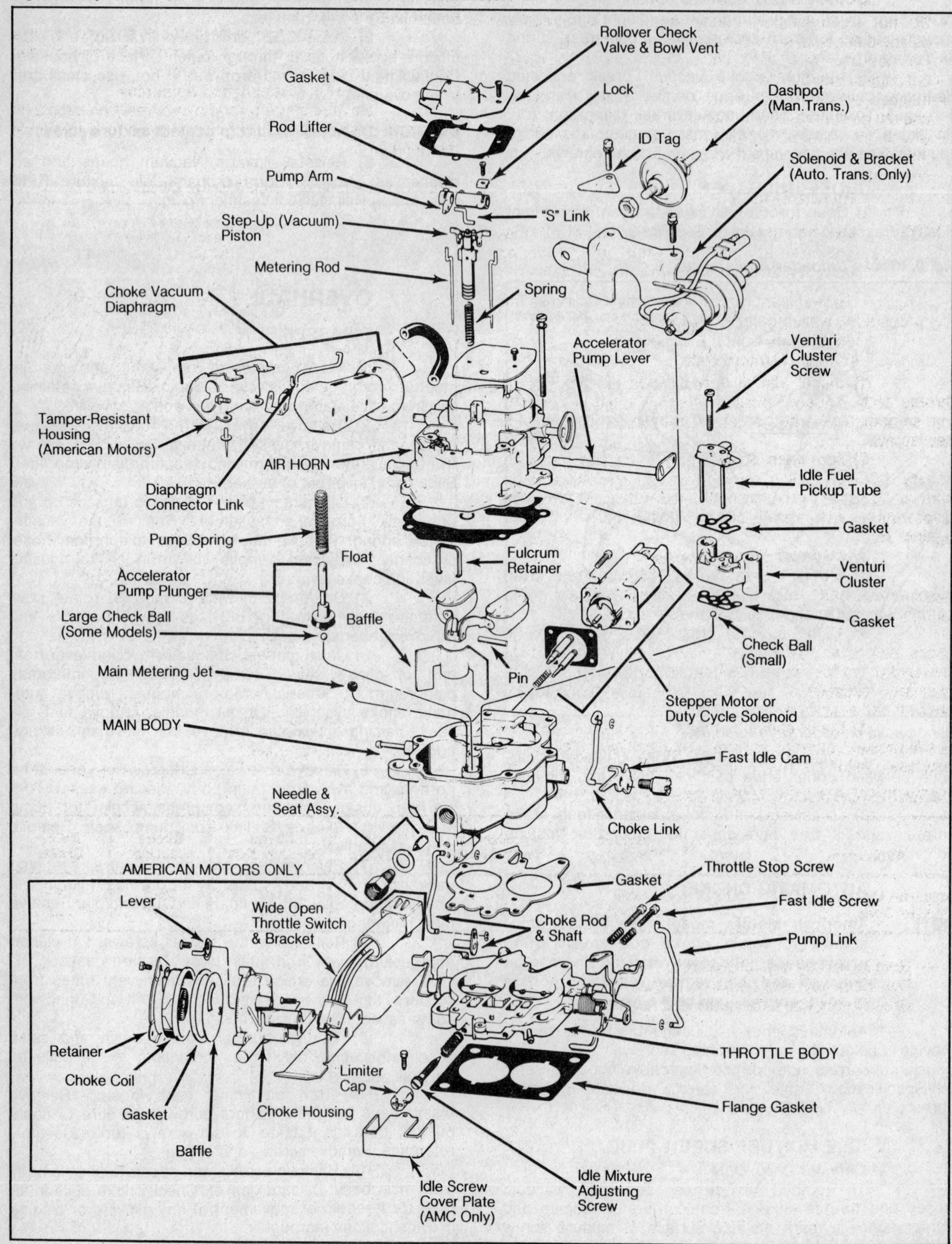

Fig. 10: Exploded View of Carter Model BBD 2-Barrel Carburetor

CARTER BBD 2-BARREL (Cont.)

CLEANING & INSPECTON

- Do not clean rubber, plastic parts or diaphragms, solenoid assemblies or pump plunger in solvent.
- Do not use wire, drill bit or hard parts to clean passages in carburetors.
- Inspect all parts for wear, cracks, nicks or burrs, uneven gasket sealing surfaces or warpage.
- Check for stripped threads, and excessive wear on throttle shafts. Replace throttle body assembly if shafts are worn.

REASSEMBLY

NOTE: Use new gaskets and seals. Make sure new gaskets fit correctly and all holes are punched through and correctly located.

To reassemble carburetor, reverse disassembly procedures while noting the following:

Idle Mixture Screw & Limiter Cap
American Motors Only

1) Install idle mixture screws and springs in throttle body. Tapered portion of screw must be straight and smooth. If tapered portion is grooved or ridged, use a new screw.

2) Turn each screw lightly against its seat with fingers. DO NOT use a screwdriver for installation. Back screws off seated position number of turns noted during disassembly and install plastic limiter caps with tab against stop.

Accelerator Pump Assembly

1) Check operation as follows. Pour clean gasoline into carburetor bowl (1/2" deep). Operate pump plunger several times to fill cylinder and expel all air.

2) Using a small brass rod, hold discharge check ball down on its seat. Raise plunger and press downward. No fuel should be emitted from either intake or discharge passage. If fuel does escape from passages, check if ball seat is damaged or dirty.

3) Clean check ball seat and retest. If leakage is still present, attempt to form a new ball seat. To form a new seat, install discharge check ball and place a piece of drill rod on top of check ball. Lightly tap drill rod with a mallet to form a new seat.

4) Remove and discard check ball and install a new one. Retest as previously described. If service does not correct problems, replace carburetor.

Step-Up Piston & Rod Assembly

Be sure step-up rods move freely on each side of vertical position. Carefully guide step-up rods into main metering jets.

Fig. 11: Locations of Large & Small Check Balls

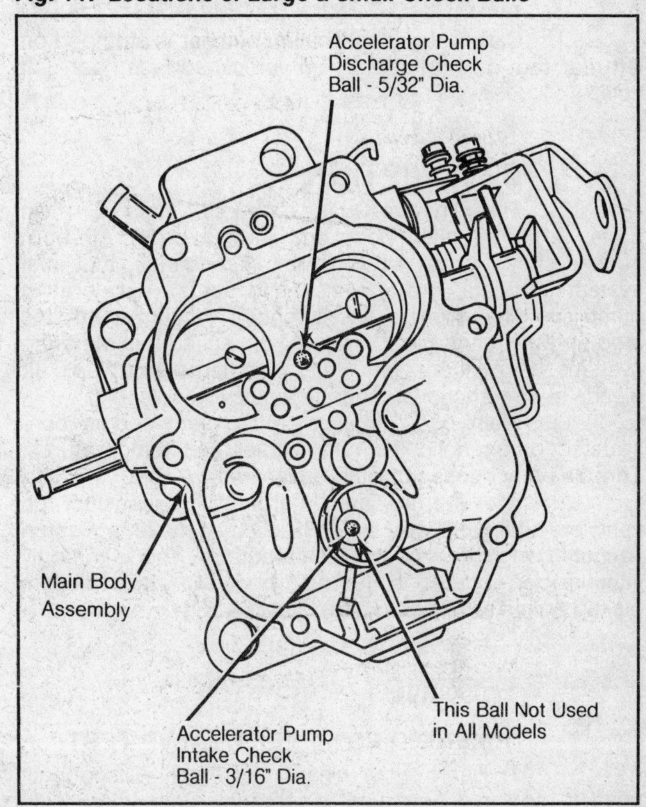

CARBURETOR ADJUSTMENT SPECIFICATIONS

Application	Float Level	Vacuum Piston Gap	Accelerator Pump Stroke	Fast Idle Cam	Choke Vacuum Kick	Choke Unloader	Auto. Choke
American Motors	.250"	.035"	.520"	.095"	.140"	.280"	1
Chrysler Corp.	.250"	.035"	.470"	.070"	.130"	.280"	.....

1 — Gold index key sets choke at 0.
Red index key sets choke at 1 notch rich.
Green index key sets choke at 2 notches rich.

CARTER THERMO-QUAD 4-BARREL

CARBURETOR APPLICATION

CARTER THERMO-QUAD 4-BARREL

Application	Carb. No.
Chrysler Corp. 5.2L Engine	
Calif. & Federal	TQ-9385
High Altitude	TQ-9374

CARBURETOR IDENTIFICATION

Carburetor identification number is stamped on left rear foot of throttle body on vertical surface near bolt hole.

DESCRIPTION

The Thermo-Quad carburetor has 3 main parts: air horn, main body and throttle body. Air horn houses choke valve, air valve for secondaries, fuel inlet system (2 floats, inlet needles and seats), accelerating pump systems, primary boost venturi, vacuum controlled step-up piston and rods, low and high speed fuel metering systems (secondary jets, fuel discharge nozzles, air bleeds and restrictions), and the duty cycle solenoid.

Main body houses primary jets and is constructed of phenolic resin for cooler fuel temperatures. Throttle body houses throttle valves and linkage.

All Thermo-Quad carburetors installed on vehicles equipped with an EGR system have a venturi vacuum port on the side of the carburetor. This is the only vacuum port located in the main body. All other vacuum pickup points are located in the throttle body.

TESTING

SOLENOID BOWL VENT VALVE TEST

1) Remove air cleaner assembly. Disconnect hose to solenoid bowl vent diaphragm. Connect outside vacuum source and apply at least 15 in. Hg vacuum to diaphragm.

2) Look down through air horn vent tube and observe valve movement. Turn ignition on. Remove outside vacuum source. Valve should move to down position until ignition is turned off.

3) If valve does not move with vacuum applied, diaphragm is leaking and must be replaced. If valve does not remain in down position with ignition on (vacuum removed), solenoid or related wiring is faulty.

Fig. 1: Vent Valve Operation Test

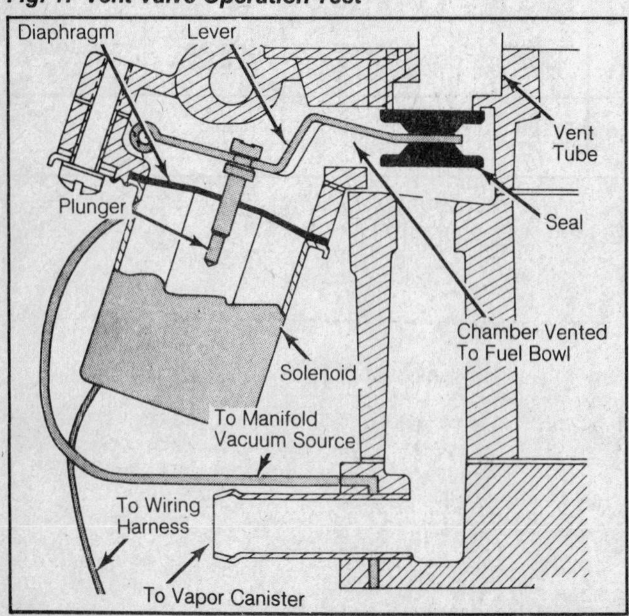

ADJUSTMENT

Thermo-Quad carburetors have unique features which require extra caution during adjustments. Many carburetor components have at least 2 functions. Because of the separate nature of each function, separate but interrelated adjustments must be performed in proper sequence. Some of these adjustments will be necessary only if the carburetor is overhauled or disassembled. These adjustments must be made on a bench.

NOTE: For on-vehicle adjustments, see TUNE-UP PROCEDURES article.

FLOAT LEVEL

1) Turn air horn upside down. Place air horn gasket in position on air horn. Make sure floats are against seated needle valve. *See Fig. 2.*

2) Measure float level specified clearance from bottom side of float to gasket surface. To adjust, bend float lever.

CAUTION: DO NOT allow lip of float lever to press against needle when adjusting. This will damage the needle and cause carburetor flooding and incorrect float level.

Fig. 2: Float Level Adjustment

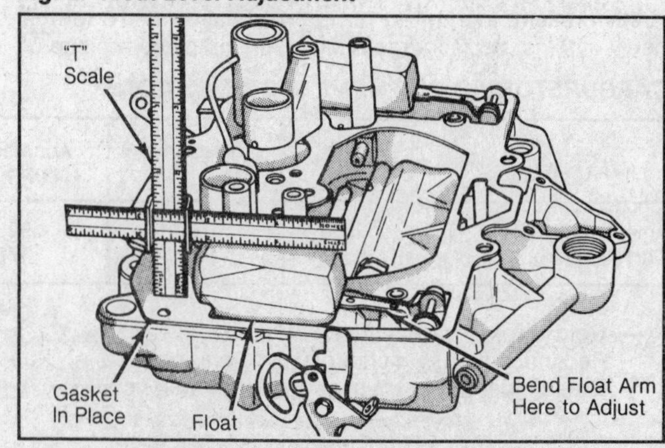

SECONDARY THROTTLE LINKAGE

1) Hold fast idle lever in curb idle position. Turn carburetor upside down. Open throttle valves wide open. *See Fig. 3.*

2) Primary and secondary levers should both contact stops at the same time. To adjust, bend secondary throttle operating rod at point shown in *Fig. 3.*

NOTE: Check linkage for interference and smooth movement after bending linkage rod.

CARTER THERMO-QUAD 4-BARREL (Cont.)

Fig. 3: Secondary Throttle Linkage Adjustment

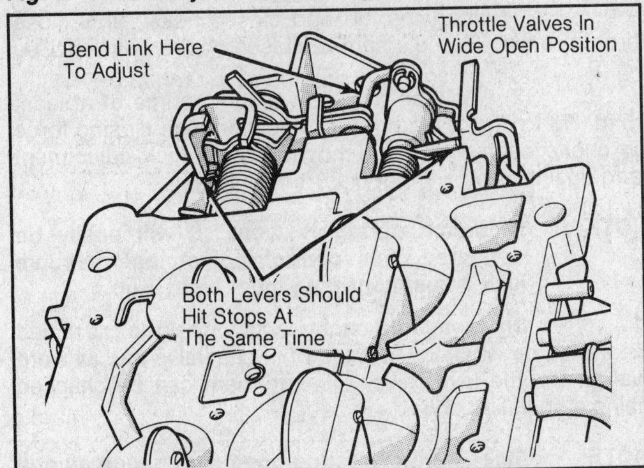

Adjust with throttle valves in wide open position.

SECONDARY AIR VALVE ALIGNMENT

1) Observe carburetor from directly above to locate air valve alignment gap. *See Fig. 4.*

2) With air valve in closed position, gap between air valve and air horn wall must be at its maximum and parallel with air horn gasket.

Fig. 4: Secondary Air Valve Alignment Check

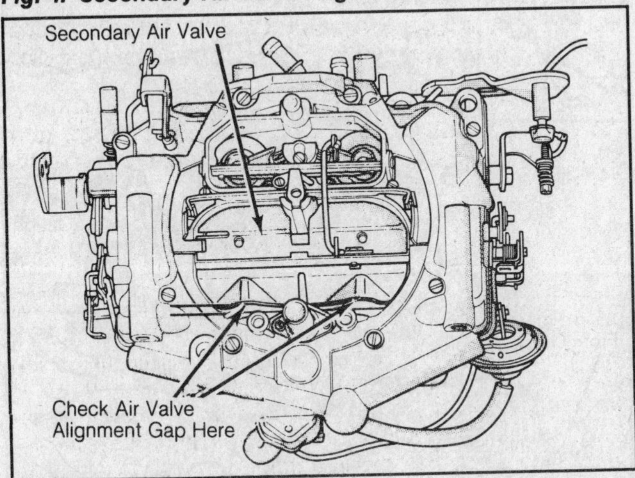

SECONDARY AIR VALVE SPRING TENSION

CAUTION: When performing this adjustment, hold air valve adjustment plug with screwdriver when loosening lock plug. If not, spring may snap out of position. This would require taking the carburetor apart to get the spring out.

1) Loosen air valve lock plug. Turn air valve adjustment plug clockwise. This allows air valve to move to wide open position. *See Fig. 5.*

2) Insert a long slender screwdriver through center of air valve spring adjustment tool (C-4152-B).

3) With special tool positioned on air valve lock plug, turn adjustment plug counterclockwise until air valve lightly touches stop.

4) Lightly press air valve against stop with finger. Now turn adjustment plug additional amount of specified turn(s), counterclockwise. Hold adjustment plug with screwdriver and tighten lock plug with special tool.

Fig. 5: Secondary Air Valve Spring Tension Adjustment

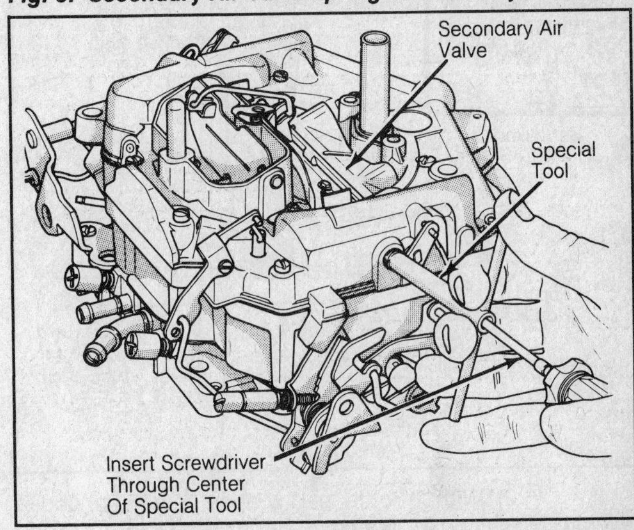

SECONDARY AIR VALVE OPENING

1) Hold secondary air valve wide open. Measure specified gap between raised edge (short side) of air valve and air horn wall. *See Fig. 6.*

2) To adjust, bend short side of air valve with pliers until specified gap is obtained. Corner of air valve is notched to aid in adjustment.

Fig. 6: Air Valve Gap Adjustment

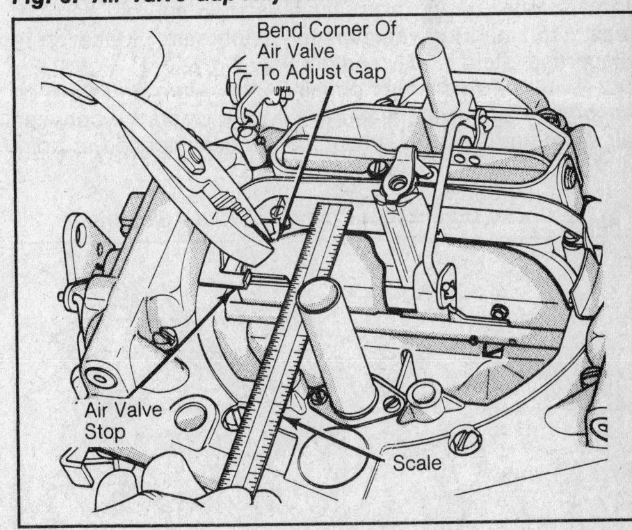

CHOKE CONTROL LEVER

NOTE: If choke control lever adjustment is changed, vacuum kick, fast idle cam position and choke unloader adjustments must also be reset.

1) Place carburetor on a flat surface. Make sure bottom of throttle body is flush with flat surface and

CARTER THERMO-QUAD 4-BARREL (Cont.)

that flat surface extends out under choke control lever. *See. Fig. 7.*

Fig. 7: Choke Control Lever Adjustment

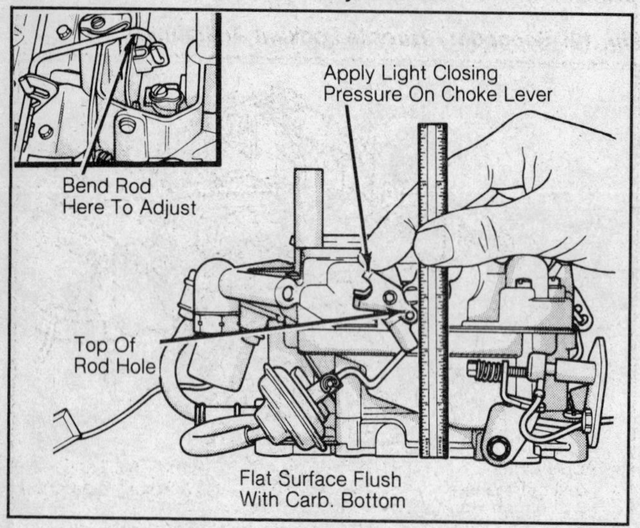

2) With throttle partly open, push on choke lever to close choke. Measure vertical distance from top of rod hole in control lever to flat surface. To adjust, bend rod connecting both choke shafts.

CHOKE DIAPHRAGM CONNECTOR ROD

NOTE: If choke diaphragm connector rod adjustment is changed, vacuum kick adjustment must also be reset.

1) Make sure diaphragm is securely mounted to carburetor. Using an outside vacuum source, apply at least 15 in. Hg vacuum to diaphragm. Make sure diaphragm stem is fully seated. *See. Fig. 8.*

2) Apply light opening (downward pressure) on secondary air valve. Measure specified clearance between air valve and stop. To adjust, bend connector rod at point shown.

Fig. 8: Choke Diaphragm Connector Rod Adjustment

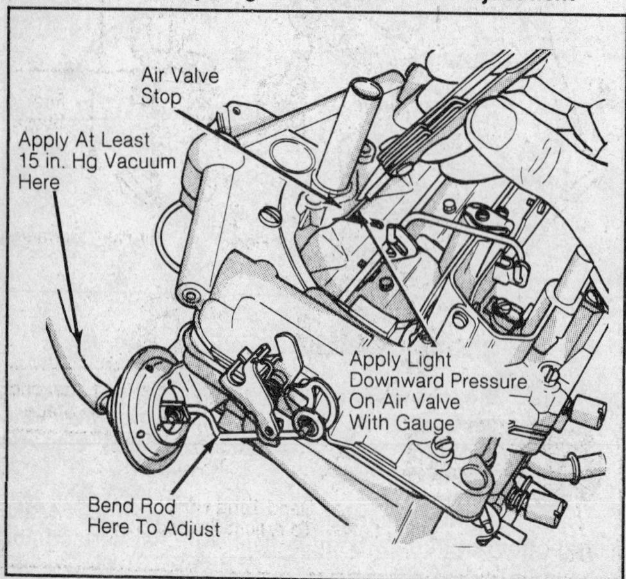

CHOKE VACUUM KICK

1) Open throttle and close choke. Now close throttle to trap fast idle cam at closed choke position. *See Fig. 9.*

2) Apply an outside vacuum source of at least 15 in. Hg to choke diaphragm. Apply enough closing force on choke control lever to move vacuum kick adjustment tang against stop without distorting linkage.

NOTE: If torsion spring is weak, it will easily be deflected. For correct adjustment, vacuum kick adjustment tang must be at stop.

3) Measure choke vacuum kick specified clearance between lower edge of choke valve and air horn wall at throttle lever side. Measurement can be checked using a specified drill or pin gauge.

NOTE: Make sure clearance does not change as drill or pin gauge is inserted or removed.

4) To adjust, insert screwdriver in slot in vacuum kick tang and twist. Do not adjust diaphragm rod. Check all linkage for freedom of movement. Reconnect vacuum hose to diaphragm.

Fig. 9: Choke Vacuum Kick Adjustment

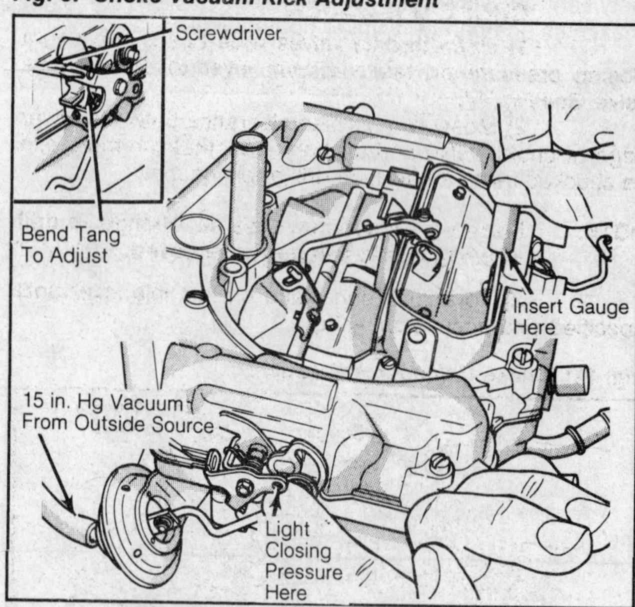

FAST IDLE CAM POSITION

NOTE: If fast idle cam position adjustment is changed, choke unloader and secondary throttle lockout adjustments must also be reset.

1) Position fast idle speed screw on second step of fast idle cam. Close choke valve by applying light closing pressure on fast idle lever. *See Fig. 10.*

2) Measure fast idle cam specified clearance between lower edge of choke valve and air horn wall. Measurement can be checked using a specified drill or pin gauge.

NOTE: Make sure clearance does not change as drill or pin gauge is inserted or removed.

1983 Carter Carburetors

CARTER THERMO-QUAD 4-BARREL (Cont.)

3) To adjust, bend fast idle cam connector rod at point shown until specified clearance is obtained.

Fig. 10: Fast Idle Cam Position Adjustment

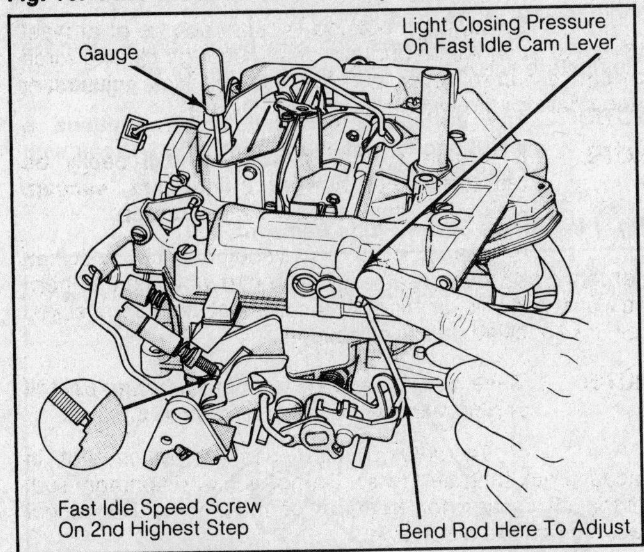

CHOKE UNLOADER

1) Open throttle valves wide open. Apply light closing pressure on fast idle cam lever to close choke valve. *See Fig. 11.*

2) Measure specified clearance between lower edge of choke valve and air horn wall. Measurement can be checked using a specified drill or pin gauge.

NOTE: **Make sure clearance does not change as drill or pin gauge is inserted or removed.**

3) To adjust, bend tang on fast idle lever until specified clearance is obtained.

Fig. 11: Choke Unloader Adjustment

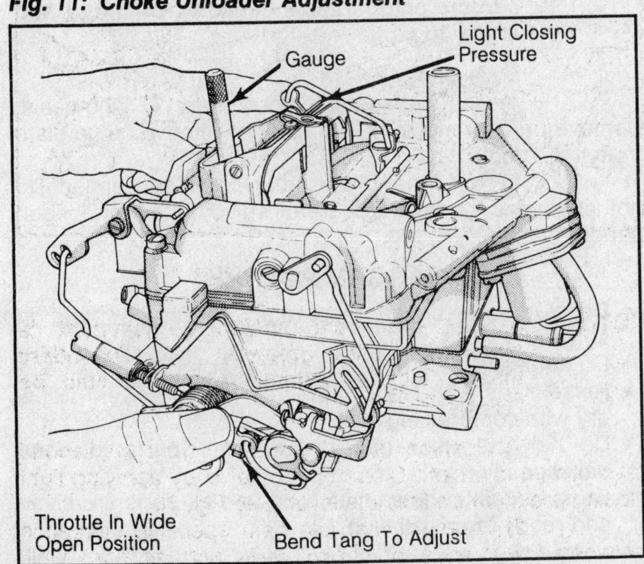

SECONDARY THROTTLE LOCKOUT

1) Move fast idle control lever to wide open choke position. Measure specified clearance between lockout lever and stop. Clearance can be checked using a specified drill or pin gauge. *See Fig. 12.*

2) To adjust, bend tang on lower end of fast idle control lever until specified clearance is obtained.

Fig. 12: Secondary Throttle Lockout Adjustment

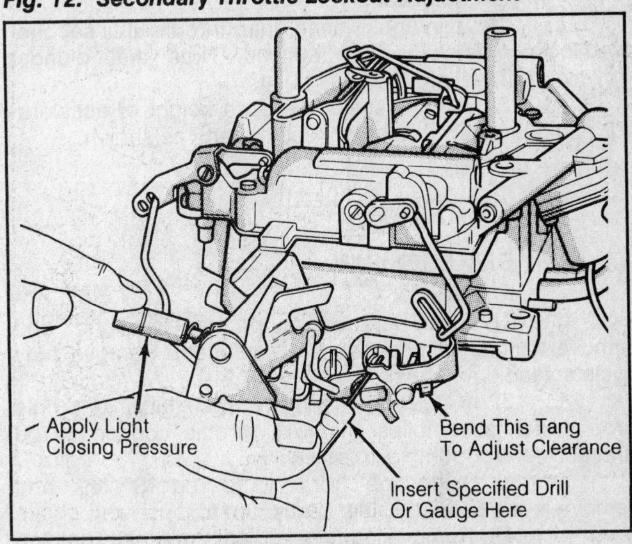

ACCELERATOR PUMP STROKE

NOTE: **Accelerator pump stroke is determined by measurement of accelerator pump plunger height above air horn surface at curb idle. Carburetors with staged pump systems require a second height measurement at a throttle position related to a secondary throttle lockout.**

First Stage

1) Place throttle connector rod in specified hole of pump arm. Using a scale, measure height of

Fig. 13: Accelerator Pump Stroke Adjustment

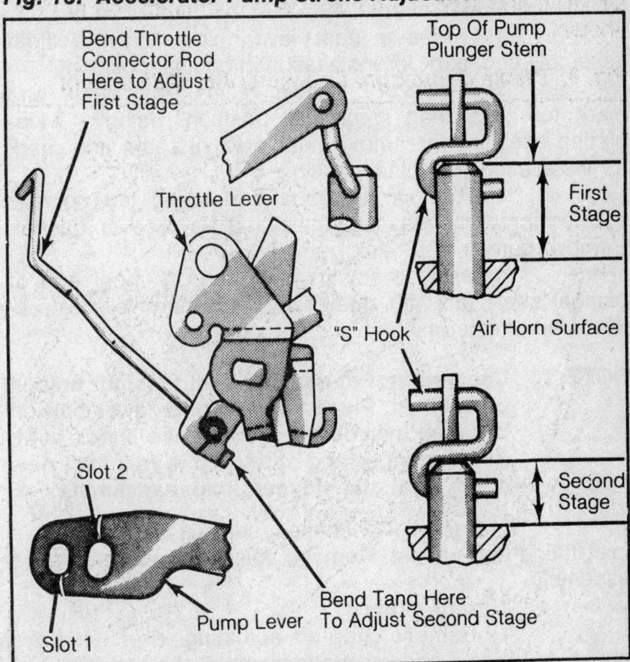

CARTER THERMO-QUAD 4-BARREL (Cont.)

accelerator pump plunger stem at curb idle (from stem top to air horn surface).

2) If measurement is not to specification, adjust plunger height by bending throttle connector rod. *See Fig. 13.*

Second Stage

1) Open choke, then open throttle until secondary lockout latch is just applied. Note that plunger downward travel stops at this point.

2) Using a scale, measure height of accelerator pump plunger. Adjust by bending tang as shown.

OVERHAUL

DISASSEMBLY

Air Horn

1) Place carburetor on repair stand and remove altitude compensator (if equipped). Remove duty cycle solenoid and gasket.

2) If equipped, remove transducer and idle stop switch assemblies. Remove throttle connector rod and accelerator pump arm screw.

3) Disengage from pump rod "S" link and remove lever. Leave "S" link connected to pump rod.

4) Remove retainers and washer holding choke diaphragm connector rod to vacuum diaphragm and air valve lever. Remove retainer holding rod to choke countershaft.

5) Remove step-up piston cover plate and metering rod cover plates. Remove step-up piston and link assembly with step-up rods and piston spring.

6) Remove discharge pump nozzle housing and gasket. Turn carburetor upside down and remove discharge check needle. Remove 10 bowl cover screws.

NOTE: **2 screws are located between choke valve and air horn wall.**

7) Remove bowl cover with floats. Do not set down on float side. Remove float bowl from throttle body.

Bowl Cover

1) Remove float lever pins. Lift out float assembly and mark for installation in original position.

2) Remove 2 needle valves from seats and mark for installation in original position. Using a wide-bladed scewdriver, remove needle valve seats and mark for installation in original position.

3) Remove secondary metering jets, plastic accelerator pump passage tube and bowl cover gasket. Remove pump rod "S" link.

4) Using a small rod placed on upper end of plunger shaft, tap with small hammer to remove accelerator pump plunger assembly.

NOTE: **Use care not to damage plunger shaft hole in bowl cover. Place fingers under lower portion of pump cylinder to catch intake check seat, pump plunger and spring. Always install new check seat and plunger upon reassembly.**

5) Remove "L" shaped fuel inlet hose. Rremove inlet fitting and gasket. Remove solenoid bowl vent valve assembly.

Throttle Body

1) Remove step-up actuating lever. Remove choke diaphragm and bracket assembly with hose. Do not place choke diaphragm assembly in carburetor cleaning solvent.

2) Carefully remove idle limiter caps. To remove idle mixture plugs, drill a 5/64" pilot hole at a 45° angle toward plugs. Redrill hole to 1/8".

3) Drive plugs out with blunt punch. Remove idle mixture screws and springs. *See. Fig. 14.*

NOTE: **The carburetor vacuum fitting contains a small vacuum passage restriction. Clean with compressed air only.**

Fig. 14: Mixture Screw Plugs Removal

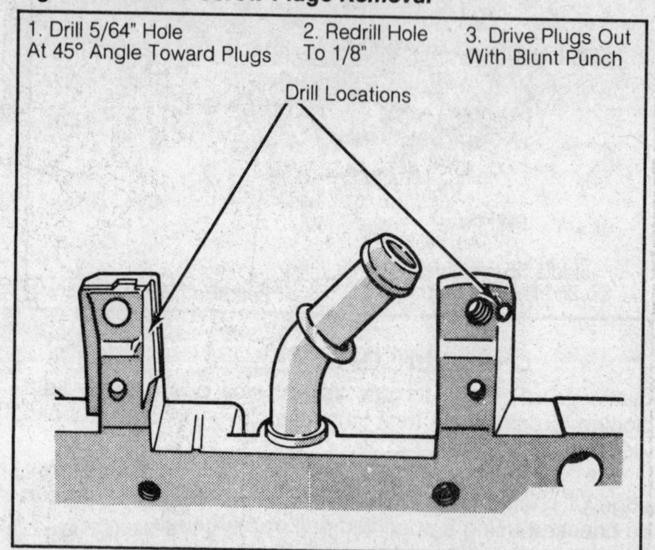

CAUTION: **Manufacturer does not recommend removal of throttle shafts or valves unless absolutely necessary. These parts are precisely adjusted at factory. The slightest misalignment upon reassembly would adversely affect carburetor operation between curb idle and about 30 mph.**

Main Body

1) Remove and discard primary "O" ring seals. Remove primary metering jets. Do not remove baffle plate from main body.

2) No further disassembly is recommended. Do not leave main body in carburetor solvent for a prolonged period of time.

CLEANING & INSPECTION

- Do not soak choke diaphragm or plastic parts in solvent.
- Do not leave main body in solvent for too long a time.
- Rinse parts with HOT water after using solvent. Blow dry with compressed air.
- Do not use wire, drill or any hard parts to clean passages.
- Be sure gasket holes match up and all parts are clean and ready for installation.

REASSEMBLY

To reassemble carburetor, reverse disassembly procedures, using new gaskets and seals. Make sure gaskets fit correcty and that all holes are punched through and correctly located. Also, note the following:

CARTER THERMO-QUAD 4-BARREL (Cont.)

Fig. 15: Exploded View of Carter Thermo-Quad Carburetor

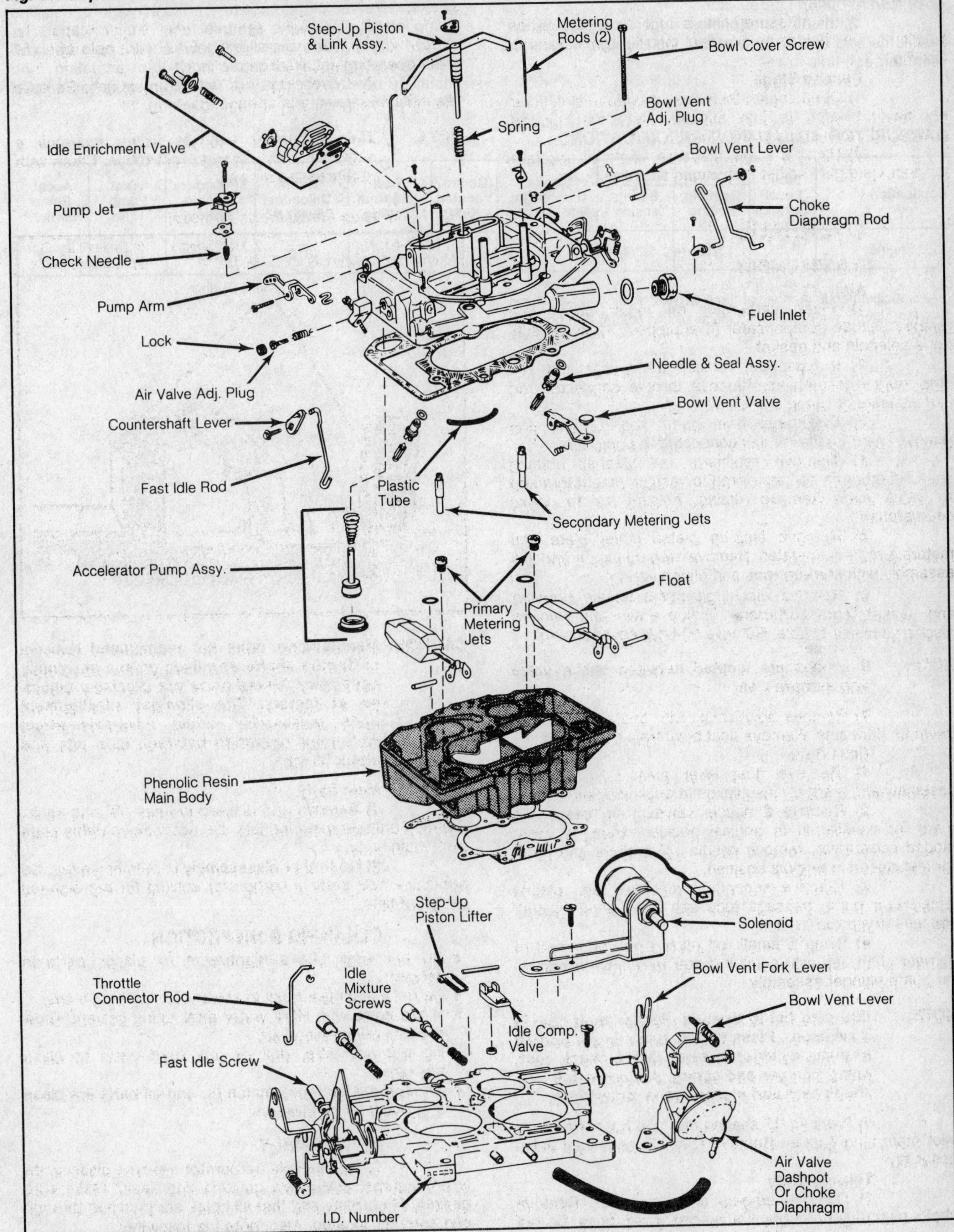

CARTER THERMO-QUAD 4-BARREL (Cont.)

1) Install pump discharge check needle with point toward base of carburetor.

2) Install upper pump plunger spring in cylinder with large end first. Lubricate and install plunger, pushing stem through hole in casting.

3) Install "S" link with lower open end toward choke valve. Install pump arm and screw before installing pump intake check valve assembly.

4) When installing bowl cover, be sure bowl vent operating lever engages bowl vent actuating fork. Install 10 bowl cover screws. Tighten in steps to 36 INCH lbs. (4 N.m).

CARBURETOR ADJUSTMENT SPECIFICATIONS

Application	Float Level Setting	Secondary Air Valve		Choke Diaphragm Rod Setting	Choke Vacuum Kick	Fast Idle Cam Setting	Choke Unloader Setting	Secondary Throttle Lockout	Accel. Pump Hole	Accel. Pump Stroke [2]
		Opening Setting	Spring Tension [1]							
5.2L Engine	29/32"	13/32"	1-3/4	.040"	.130"	.100"	.310"	.060-.090"	2	33/64"

[1] — Specification is number of turns CCW after air valve contacts stop.
[2] — First stage setting. Second stage setting is 25/64", if equipped.

1983 Chrysler Carburetors

CHRYSLER (MIKUNI) 2-BARREL

CARBURETOR APPLICATION

CHRYSLER CORP. (MIKUNI) CARBURETOR NO.

Application	Carb. No.
2.6L Engine	
Federal	MD01 7306
Calif.	MD01 7066
High Altitude	MD01 7307

CARBURETOR IDENTIFICATION

Carburetor identification is located on a metal tag attached to carburetor.

DESCRIPTION

Carburetor is a 2-stage, 2-venturi type. The main curburetor body is made of plastic resin to reduce heat transfer to the float bowl. The automatic choke is a thermo-wax pellet type controlled by engine coolant.

The carburetor meters fuel through primary and secondary jets. A vacuum actuated enrichment system provides additional enrichment during heavy load conditions. A conventional diaphragm-type accelerator pump is used.

ADJUSTMENT

NOTE: **For on-vehicle adjustments, see TUNE-UP PROCEDURES article.**

FLOAT LEVEL

1) Turn air horn assembly upside down (without gasket). Allow weight of float assembly to seat inlet valve. *See Fig. 1.*

2) Measure distance between bottom edge of float to surface of air horn. If distance is not .78" (19.8 mm), adjust by adding or subtracting shims under inlet needle seat.

Fig. 1: Float Level Adjustment

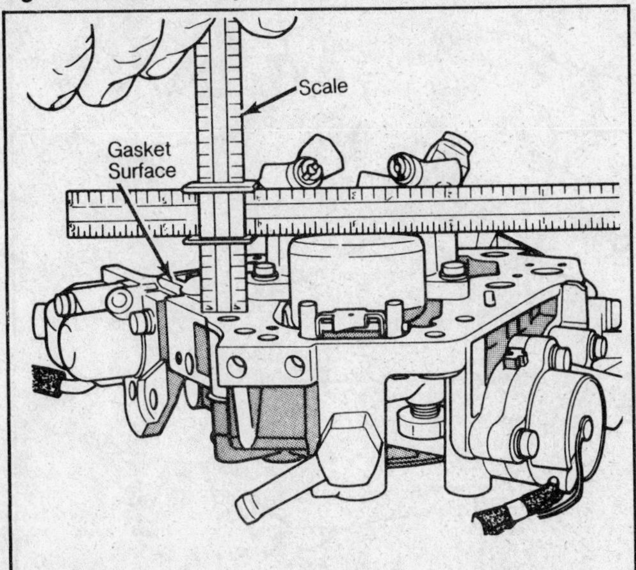

NOTE: **All other adjustments are factory made and should not be changed in service.**

OVERHAUL

DISASSEMBLY

1) Remove water hoses from choke and throttle valve assemblies. Grind off heads of choke cover lock screws (4) and remove cover.

2) Remove clip from throttle opener link, then remove 2 screws and throttle opener. Disconnect fuel solenoid ground wire and remove solenoid. Disconnect throttle return and damper springs and remove choke unloader link.

3) Disconnect vacuum hose and vacuum chamber link. Remove 2 screws and vacuum chamber. Disconnect throttle operating rod link. Remove 2 screws and vacuum hose bracket. Remove 6 air horn screws and lift air horn off carburetor body.

4) Slide pin out and remove float and inlet needle. Remove screw and retainer, then remove needle seat and screen assembly. Be sure not to lose shim from under needle seat.

5) Remove venturi retainers and both primary and secondary venturis. Note position for installation, then remove primary and secondary main jets from pedestals. Remove screws and pedestals.

6) Remove 3 screws from bowl vent solenoid, then remove solenoid and spring. Remove remaining screw and bowl vent assembly. Remove 3 screws on coasting air valve and remove valve. Remove 3 screws on enrichment valve and remove valve cover, gasket and jet.

7) Remove screws and air switching valve. Take out spring retainer sleeve, spring, retainer, and diaphragm seal. Remove screw and lock plate, then pull out primary pilot jet set. Repeat procedure for secondary pilot jet set.

8) From top of air horn, remove primary and secondary air bleed jets. Note locations so jets can be reinstalled properly.

9) Invert body and remove pump wieght, check ball and hex nut. Remove 4 screws from accelerator pump cover and remove cover, diaphragm, spring, pump body with check ball and gasket.

10) Remove 3 screws from jet air control valve on throttle body. Remove cover, spring, spring retainer and diaphragm/seal. Remove circlip from sub-ERG valve lever. Carefully slide pin from sub-ERG valve, catching ball and spring which are inside valve and retained by pin. Remove valve and boot seal.

11) Drill small hole in mixture screw concealment plug and insert screw extractaor to remove plug. Use a narrow pin punch to drive out roll pin from bottom of throttle body. Remove mixture needle and spring.

CLEANING & INSPECTION

- Do not immerse plastic or rubber parts in solvent. Do not soak solenoids or choke assembly in any liquid.
- Blow out all passages with compressed air. Do not use wire or drill bit to clean calibrated orifices or jets.
- Do not use compressed air to blow out any diaphragm fittings if diaphragm is installed.
- Inspect all parts for cracks, burrs, or pitting. Replace any damaged parts and all "O" rings, seals and gaskets.

CHRYSLER (MIKUNI) 2-BARREL (Cont.)

Fig. 2: Exploded View of Chrysler Corp. (Mikuni) 2-Barrel Carburetor

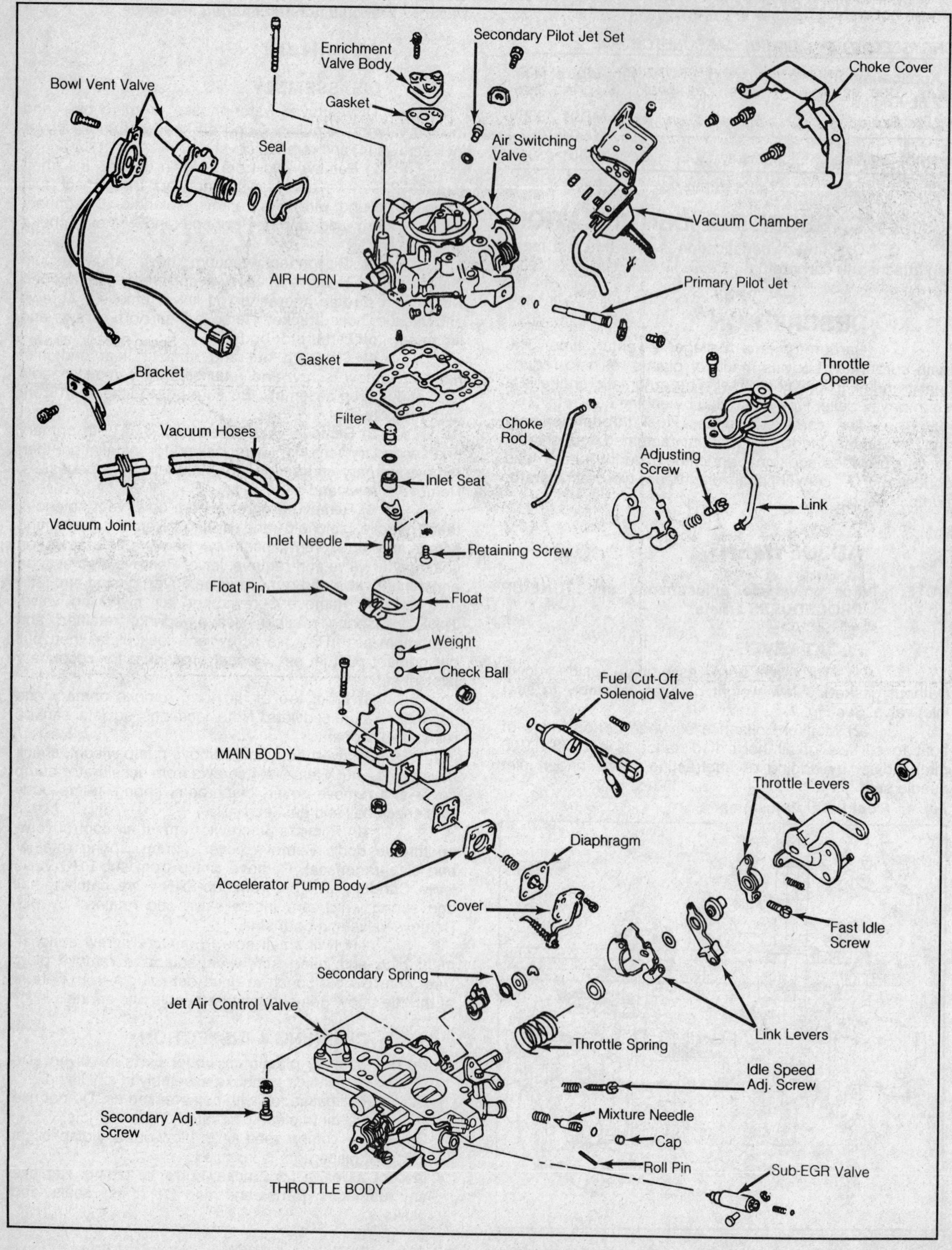

CHRYSLER (MIKUNI) 2-BARREL (Cont.)

- After cleaning parts in solvent, be sure to rinse well with hot water and blow dry with compressed air.

REASSEMBLY

To reassemble, reverse disassembly procedures. Use all new gaskets and seals, ensuring that gaskets are properly positioned and all holes are punched. Note the following:

Fig. 3: Exploded View of Valve & Pump Assemblies for Chrysler (Mikuni) Carburetor

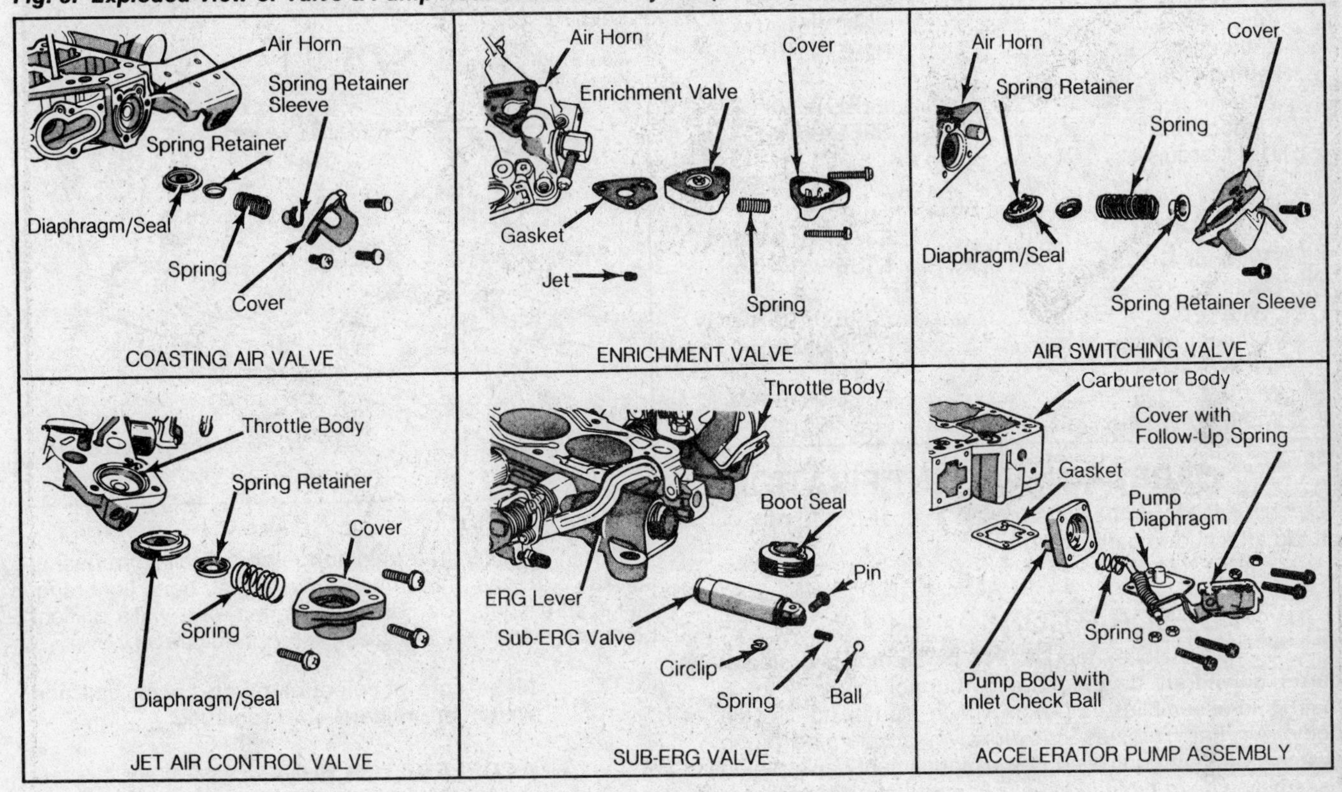

1983 Holley Carburetors

HOLLEY MODEL 1946 SINGLE BARREL

CARBURETOR APPLICATION

FORD MOTOR CO. CARBURETOR NO.

Application	Part. No.
3.3L Engine	
Fairmont & Zephyr	
Nationwide	
With A/C	E2BE-9510-CA
Without A/C	E2BE-9510-BA
High Altitude	
With A/C	E2BE-9510-TA
Without A/C	E2BE-9510-SA
LTD & Marquis	
Sedan	
Federal	
With A/C	E3SE-9510-CA
Without A/C	E3SE-9510-DA
Calif.	
With A/C	E3SE-9510-AA
Without A/C	E3SE-9510-BA
Station Wagon	
With A/C	E3SE-9510-AA
Without A/C	E3SE-9510-BA

CARBURETOR IDENTIFICATION

Part number is stamped in float bowl body or on tag attached to carburetor.

DESCRIPTION

The Holley model 1946 carburetor is a single-barrel downdraft design. The carburetor consists of 3 main sub-assemblies: air horn, main body and throttle body. Air horn houses choke valve, accelerator pump system, vacuum controlled power enrichment valve piston assembly, choke bimetal assembly and fuel bowl and vent assembly.

Main body houses fuel inlet system (float assembly and needle valve), main metering jet, power enrichment valve assembly, accelerator pump check ball and weight. Throttle body houses throttle valve, linkage and tamper-proof idle mixture adjusting needle.

TESTING

ELECTRONIC BOWL VENT SOLENOID

1) Remove air cleaner assembly and turn ignition switch on. Attach hand vacuum pump to carburetor canister vent hose connector and apply 5-10 in. Hg.

2) If no vacuum is held, remove air horn and service or repair bowl vent assembly. If vacuum is held, apply same amount of vacuum to internal vent tube. If vacuum is not held, remove air horn and service or repair bowl vent assembly.

3) If vacuum is held at both points, the bowl vent is operating properly. Install air cleaner assembly and turn ignition off.

ADJUSTMENT

NOTE: **For on-vehicle adjustments, see TUNE-UP PROCEDURES article.**

FLOAT LEVEL

1) With air horn removed, invert main body. Catch accelerator pump check ball and weight if not previously removed. Hold float hinge pin retainer in place with finger. *See Fig. 1.*

Fig. 1: Float Level Adjustment

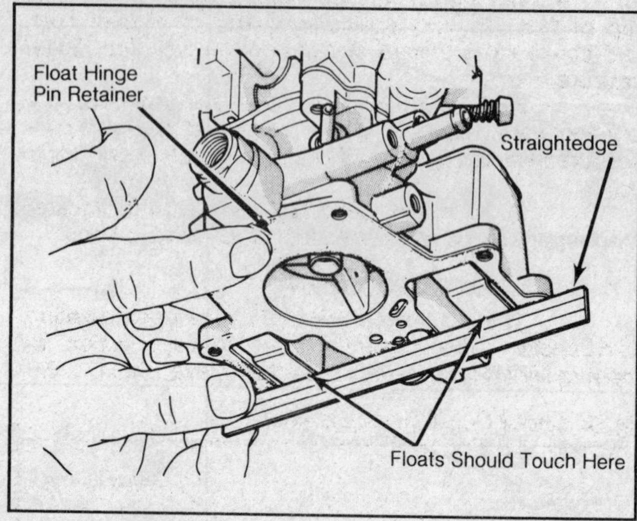

Bend tang to adjust.

2) Place a straightedge across air horn gasket surface and toes of both floats. To adjust, bend float tang. Make sure floats are correctly aligned with walls of float bowl and that they move freely through full travel.

NOTE: **Make sure accelerator pump check ball and weight are reinstalled if removed.**

ACCELERATOR PUMP

1) Make sure accelerator pump rod is in correct slot. *See Fig. 2.*

NOTE: **Inner slot is designated number 1 and outer slot is designated number 2.**

Fig. 2: Accelerator Pump Adjustment

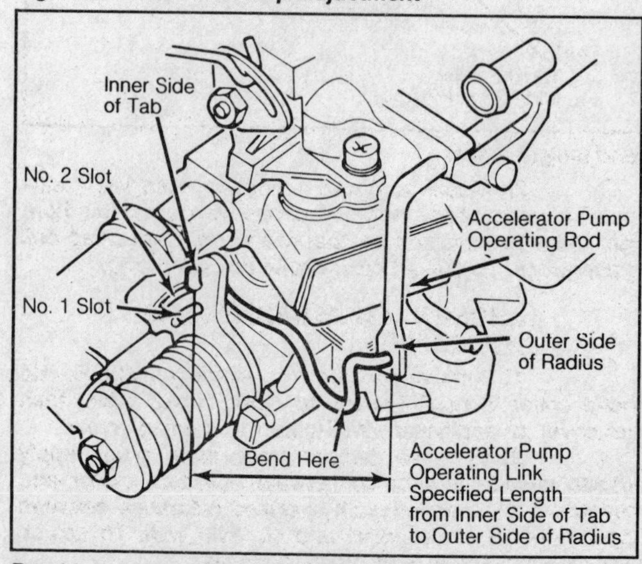

Bend loop in operating link to adjust.

HOLLEY MODEL 1946 SINGLE BARREL (Cont.)

2) Place throttle lever in curb idle position. Measure accelerator pump distance between inner side of tab to outer side of radius. *See Fig. 2.* To adjust, bend existing loop in accelerator pump operating link.

FAST IDLE CAM POSITION

1) Position fast idle speed screw on second step of fast idle cam against shoulder of highest step. Hold choke valve toward closed position with light finger pressure.

2) Measure fast idle cam specified clearance between upper edge of choke valve and air horn wall. Measurement can be checked using a specified drill or pin gauge.

3) To adjust, bend fast idle cam rod (located between automatic choke housing) at "U" shaped bend.

CHOKE UNLOADER

1) Hold throttle valves in wide open position. Hold choke valve toward closed choke position by applying light closing pressure to choke lever. *See Fig. 3.*

Fig. 3: Choke Unloader Adjustment

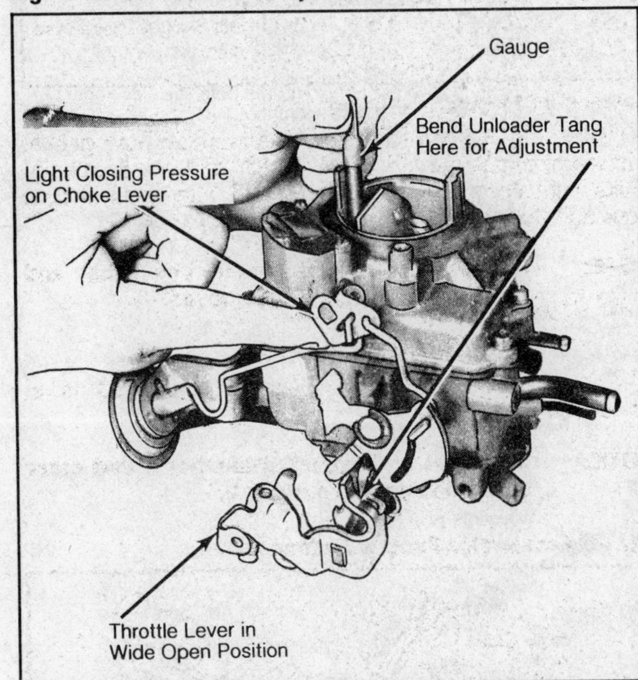

Bend tang to adjust.

2) Measure choke unloader specified clearance between upper edge of choke valve and air horn wall. Measurement can be checked using a specified drill or pin gauge. To adjust, bend choke unloader tang.

CHOKE VACUUM KICK (CHOKE PULLDOWN)

1) Remove choke cover retaining rivets. Rotate choke cover in rich direction to close choke valve, then turn cover an additional 90°. Tighten 1 retaining screw.

2) Remove tamper-proof steel plug. Apply outside vacuum source to activate pulldown motor and measure choke vacuum kick specified clearance between upper edge of choke valve and air horn wall. To adjust, turn adjusting screw in or out as required.

Fig. 4: Choke Vacuum Kick Adjustment

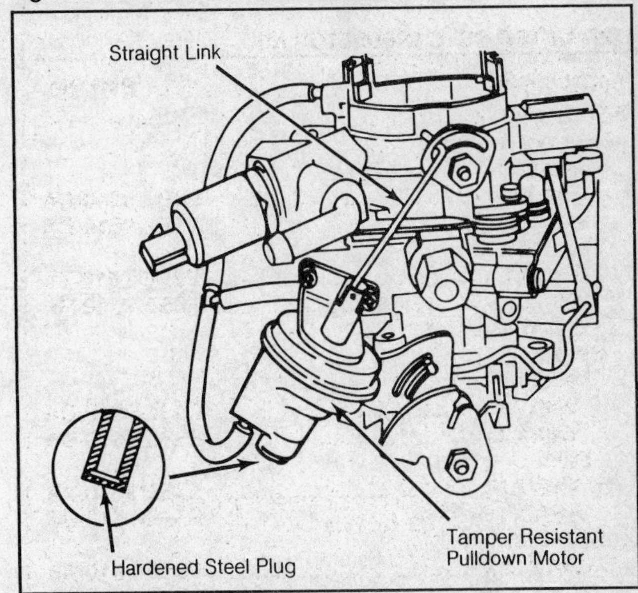

Turn adjusting screw in or out to adjust.

OVERHAUL

NOTE: Holley 1946 carburetors are equipped with tamper-proof choke cap assembly. To remove choke cap assembly, ensure rivet mandrels of bi-metal assembly are well below rivet head and drive mandrel down or out with a 1/16" diameter punch. Using a 1/8" (No. 30) drill, drill out rivet head and drive out rivet with a 1/8" punch. Remove standard screws and choke cap.

DISASSEMBLY

Air Horn

1) Place carburetor on suitable repair stand. Remove 2 pulldown diaphragm bracket screws, disconnect vacuum hose from main body and remove pulldown diaphragm and linkage assembly. Remove bowl vent assembly.

NOTE: Do not clean pulldown diaphragm or bowl vent assemblies in carburetor solvent.

2) Remove fast idle cam retaining clip, fast idle cam and link. Remove choke control lever retaining screw. Remove throttle return spring bracket attaching nut and lock washer.

3) Disengage return spring and carefully remove spring and bracket, noting specific accelerator pump link slot for reassembly reference.

4) Remove bowl cover and screws and remove air horn from main body by tapping loose with plastic hammer. Lift cover straight up until vacuum piston stem, accelerator pump and main well tube are clear of main body.

5) Place air horn upside down on bench and remove gasket. Do not scrape with metal scraper. Use suitable cleaner or nylon scraper to prevent damage to casting gasket surface.

HOLLEY MODEL 1946 SINGLE BARREL (Cont.)

Fig. 5: Exploded View of Holley Model 1946 Single Barrel Carburetor

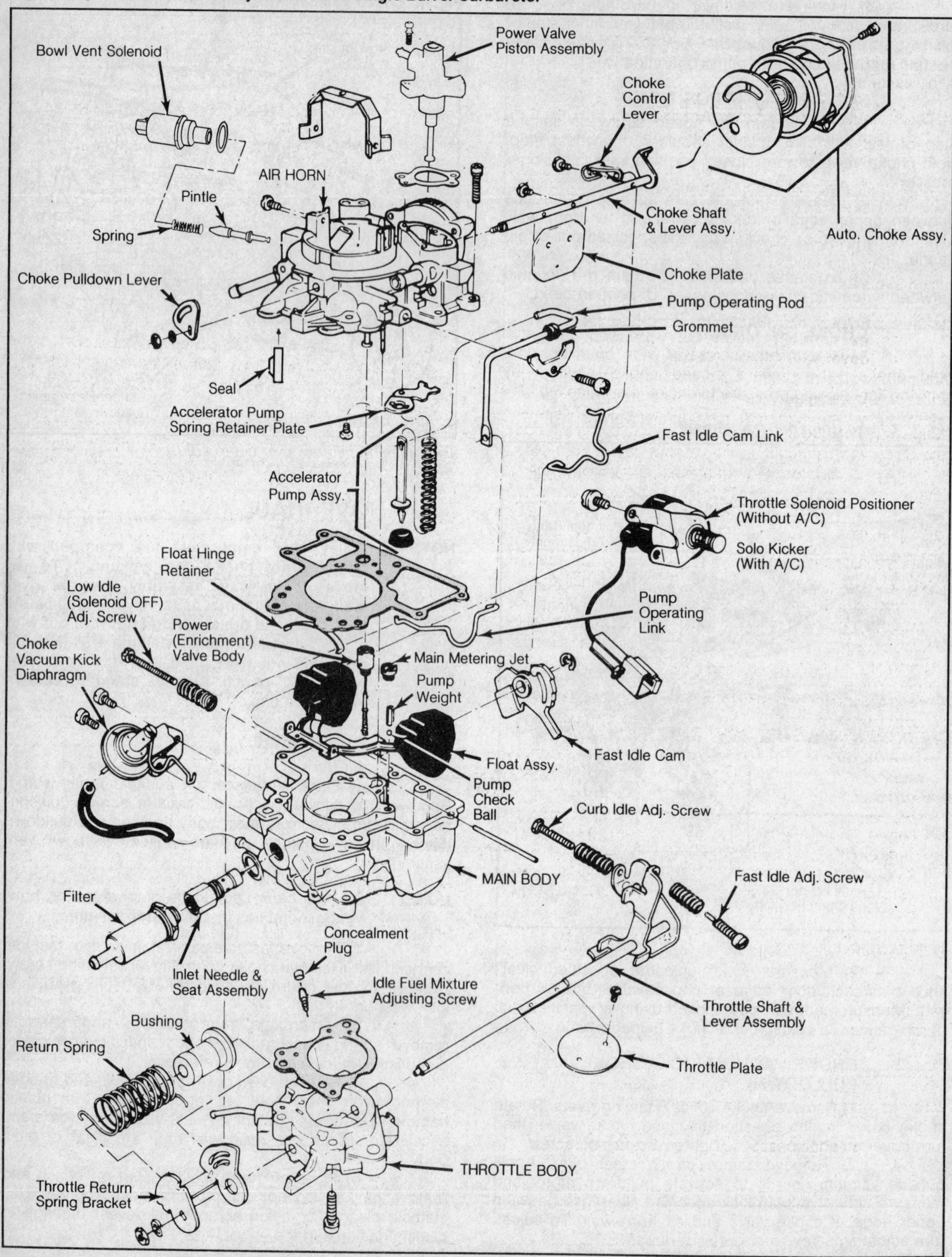

1983 Holley Carburetors

HOLLEY MODEL 1946 SINGLE BARREL (Cont.)

6) Remove accelerator pump operating rod screw and retainer, and accelerator pump assembly retaining screw and pump assembly. Rotate pump operating rod and remove pump drive spring and accelerator pump assembly.

NOTE: **Manufacturer does not recommend removal of choke valve and shaft unless replacement is required.**

7) Remove pump operating rod and grommet. Remove 3 screws retaining power enrichment valve and remove power valve diaphragm assembly.

8) Remove bowl vent valve seat by holding seat against internal vent tube with thin screwdriver and pulling actuating pintle loose from seat.

NOTE: **Main well tube cannot be removed and must be carefully blown out from both sides of cover with compressed air.**

Main Body

1) Remove fuel inlet fitting valve assembly. Remove and discard old gaskets. Remove float shaft retainer, shaft and float assembly. Turn main body upside down and catch pump discharge weight and ball as they fall out.

2) Remove main metering jet with jet wrench or 3/8" wide flat screwdriver. Remove power enrichment valve needle with 3/8" wide screwdriver.

NOTE: **Screwdriver should be modified by cutting a 1/16" wide and 3/8" deep slot in center of blade. This provides clearance for valve stem.**

3) Remove 3 main body-to-throttle body screws and separate assemblies. Remove and discard gasket. Remove low idle speed (TSP Off) adjusting screw and spring, and remove solenoid.

Throttle Body

1) Remove curb idle adjusting screw. Remove fast idle speed adjusting screw and spring.

NOTE: **Manufacturers do not recommend removal of throttle plate or shaft. If damage or wear is evident, replace throttle body assembly.**

2) Drill a 3/32" hole in plug. Install screw extractor and remove plug. Turn mixture screw clockwise until it lightly seats, recording number of turns for reassembly reference. Remove mixture screw and spring.

CLEANING & INSPECTION

- Inspect all gasket mating surfaces for nicks, burrs or any damage that would prevent gasket sealing.
- Do not place choke cover, pulldown diaphragm, bowl vent assembly or pump plunger in cleaning solvent.
- Inspect idle mixture screw tip. If grooved or worn, replace with new needle.
- Ensure all new gaskets match gaskets removed in placement of holes and slots. Use new gaskets only.
- Ensure all parts are clean and free of solvent before assembly. Wash parts in hot water and blow dry with compressed air.

REASSEMBLY

Reassemble carburetor in reverse order of disassembly. Use new gaskets and seals. Make sure gaskets fit correctly and all holes are punched through and correctly located. Install mixture screw concealment plug after final adjustments are made on vehicle.

NOTE: **Choke cap must be installed with rivets to maintain tamper-proof requirement.**

CARBURETOR ADJUSTMENT SPECIFICATIONS

Application	Float Level	Accelerator Pump		Fast Idle Cam	Choke Unloader	Choke Vacuum Kick
		Hole	Stroke			
3.3L Engine	.69"	#2	2.395"	.078"	.150"	.110"

HOLLEY MODEL 6145 SINGLE BARREL

CARBURETOR APPLICATION

CHRYSLER CORP. (HOLLEY) CARBURETOR NO.

Application	Part No.
Chrysler Corp. 3.7L Engine	R-40042A

CARBURETOR IDENTIFICATION

Part number is stamped on main body or on tag attached to carburetor.

DESCRIPTION

The Holley model 6145 is an "Electronic Feedback" type carburetor. The carburetor is designed to maintain an air/fuel ratio within specified limits to allow the catalytic converter to operate effectively. The carburetor is controlled by the Spark Control Computer. The carburetor includes 4 basic fuel metering systems: idle system, main metering system, accelerator system and power enrichment system. In addition to these 4 basic systems, there is a fuel inlet system and choke system.

ADJUSTMENTS

NOTE: For on-vehicle adjustments, see TUNE-UP PROCEDURES article.

FLOAT LEVEL

1) With air horn removed, install float shaft and position assembly in float shaft cradle. Install retaining spring and place air horn gasket on top of the fuel bowl.

2) Turn carburetor upside down and hold air horn gasket in place. Place a straightedge across air horn gasket surface and toes of both floats. *See Fig. 1.*

Fig. 1: Float Level Adjustment

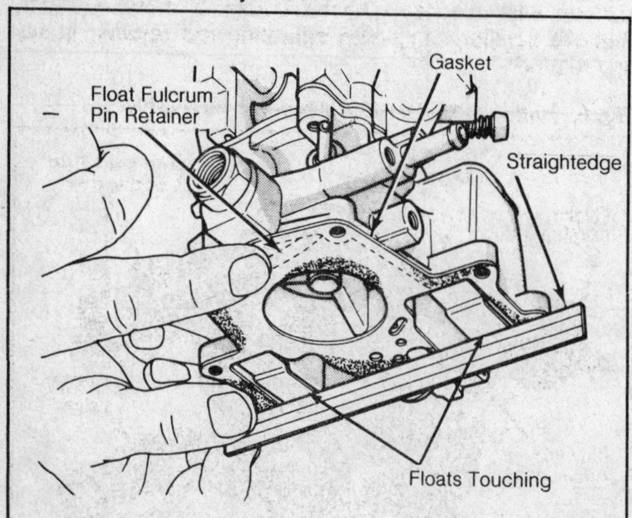

Bend float tang to adjust.

3) To adjust, bend float tang. Make sure floats are correctly aligned with walls of float bowl and that they move freely through full travel.

ACCELERATOR PUMP

1) Place throttle lever in curb idle position. Make sure accelerator pump rod is in correct hole.

2) Measure accelerator pump distance between inner side of tab to outer side of radius. *See Fig. 2.* To adjust, bend accelerator pump operating link.

Fig. 2: Accelerator Pump Adjustment

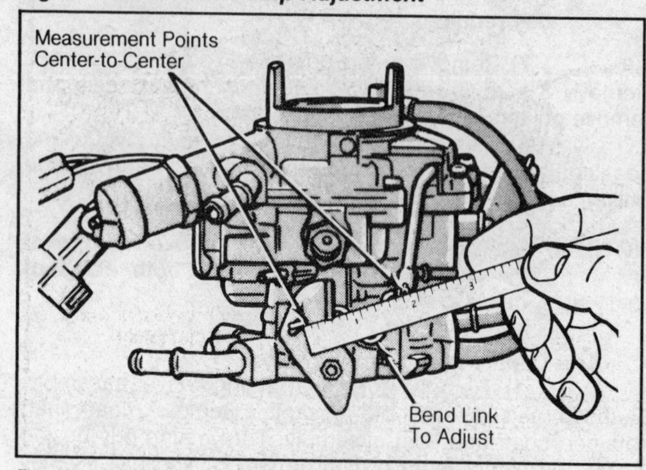

Bend accelerator pump operating link to adjust.

FAST IDLE CAM POSITION

1) Position the fast idle speed screw on second step of the fast idle cam. Hold choke valve toward closed position with light pressure on choke shaft lever. *See Fig. 3.*

Fig. 3: Fast Idle Cam Position Adjustment

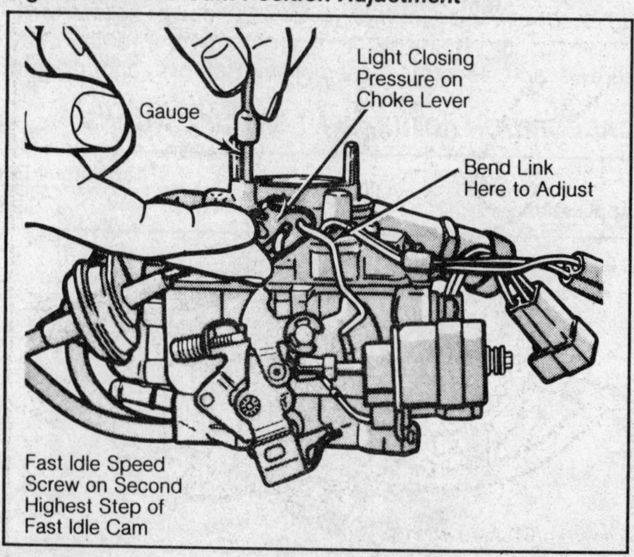

Bend fast idle cam connector rod to adjust.

2) Using specified drill or pin gauge, measure fast idle cam specified clearance between upper edge of choke valve and air horn wall. To adjust, bend fast idle connector rod at angle.

CHOKE UNLOADER

1) Hold throttle valves in wide open position. Hold choke valve toward closed choke position by applying light closing pressure to choke lever. *See Fig. 4.*

HOLLEY MODEL 6145 SINGLE BARREL (Cont.)

Fig. 4: Choke Unloader Adjustment

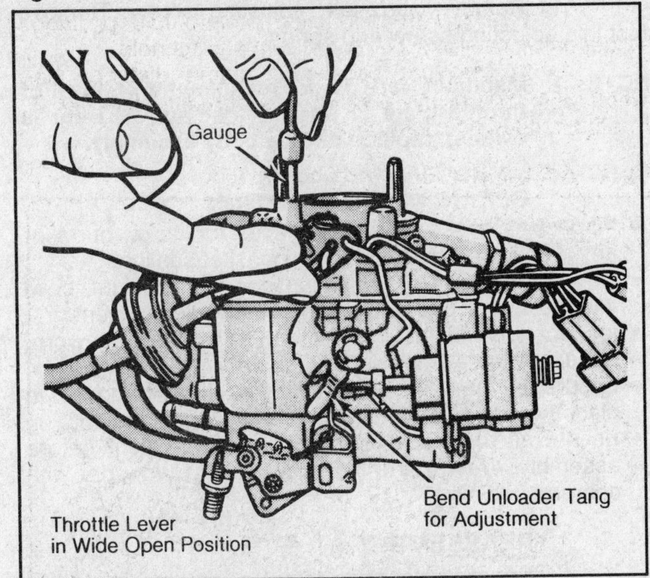

Bend tang on throttle lever to adjust.

2) Using specified drill or pin gauge, measure clearance between top of choke valve and air horn wall at throttle lever side. To adjust, bend tang on throttle lever.

CHOKE VACUUM KICK (CHOKE PULLDOWN)

1) Open throttle then close choke. Now close throttle to trap fast idle cam at closed choke position. *See Fig. 5.*

Fig. 5: Choke Vacuum Kick (Choke Pulldown) Adjustment

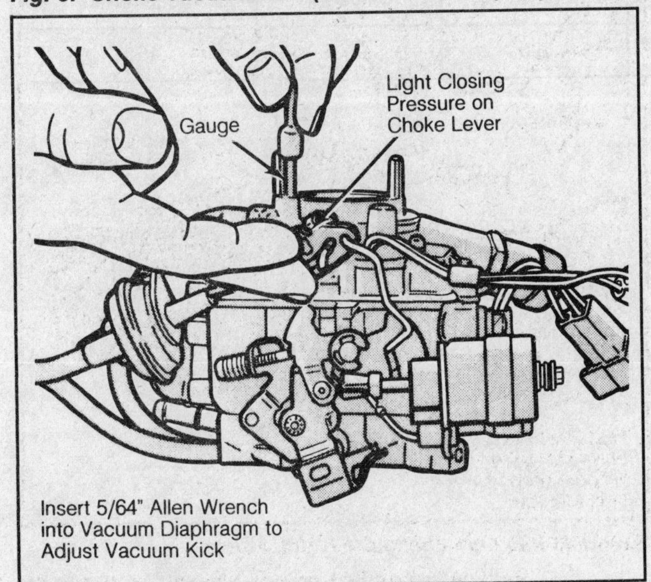

Bend link to adjust.

2) Disconnect vacuum hose from carburetor. Connect an outside vacuum source of at least 15 in. Hg to choke vacuum diaphragm. Apply enough closing pressure on choke valve to compress spring in diaphragm without distorting linkage.

3) Insert a 5/64" Allen wrench into diaphragm and turn to adjust choke vacuum kick. Check for free movement between open and adjusted positions. Correct binding by rebending link and readjusting.

IDLE MIXTURE SCREW PLUG

1) Remove air cleaner assembly, canister purge and air pump diverter valve vacuum hose from carburetor, if equipped. Locate and center punch a mark 1/4" from end of mixture screw housing. Punch mark should be indexed at 2:00 o'clock position.

2) Drill through outer section of housing using 3/16" drill bit. Concealment plug should drop out. If not, use small drift to remove plug.

CAUTION: Do not allow drift to contact mixture screw.

3) Reinstall vacuum hoses and air cleaner assembly. Perform propane idle mixture RPM adjustment. Reinstall concealment plug.

OVERHAUL

DISASSEMBLY

Air Horn

1) Place carburetor on repair stand. Remove wire retainer and bowl vent assembly. Remove Solenoid Idle Stop (SIS). Remove fast idle cam retaining clip, fast idle cam and link. Disconnect link.

2) Remove choke vacuum diaphragm, link and bracket assembly. Disengage link from slot in choke lever. Place diaphragm to one side and clean as special items.

3) Remove nut and washer from throttle shaft. Remove throttle lever and link. Note hole position of lever. Remove screws and duty cycle solenoid. Remove air horn screws.

4) Separate air horn from carburetor body by tapping with a plastic hammer or screwdriver handle. DO NOT pry off. Lift air horn straight up until vacuum piston stem, accelerator pump and main well tube are clear of main body.

5) Remove air horn gasket and clean gasket surface with cleaner. DO NOT use a metal scraper. Remove accelerating pump operating rod retainer screw and retainer.

Fig. 6: Holley Model 6145 Carburetor Assembly

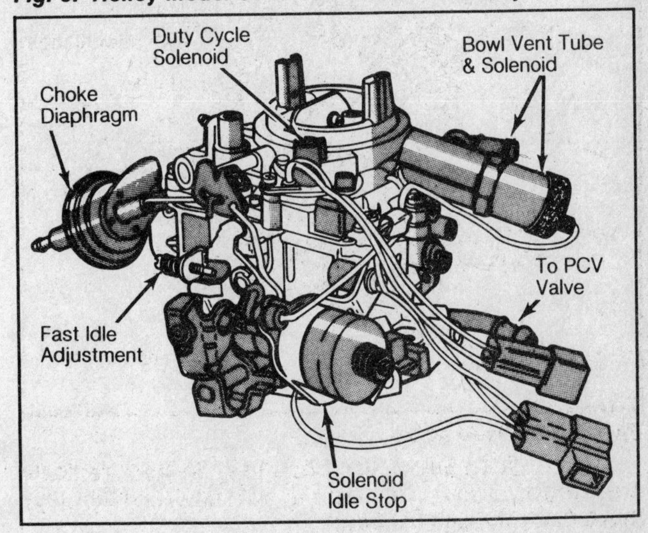

1983 Holley Carburetors

HOLLEY MODEL 6145 SINGLE BARREL (Cont.)

6) Remove accelerator pump assembly retaining screw and pump assembly. Rotate pump operating rod and remove from air horn. Remove pump operating rod grommet.

7) Carefully remove power piston assembly retaining ring staking with a sharp tool. Remove vacuum piston from air horn by depressing piston and allowing it to snap up against retaining ring.

NOTE: Main well tube cannot be removed and must be carefully blown out from both sides of cover with compressed air.

Main Body

1) Remove fuel inlet fitting valve assembly. Remove and discard old gaskets. Remove float shaft retainer, shaft and float assembly. Turn main body upside down and catch pump discharge weight and ball as they fall out.

2) Remove main metering jet with jet wrench or 3/8" wide flat screwdriver. Remove power enrichment valve needle with 3/8" wide screwdriver.

NOTE: Screwdriver should be modified by cutting a 1/16" wide and 3/8" deep slot in center of blade. This provides clearance for valve stem.

3) Remove 3 main body-to-throttle body screws and separate assemblies. Remove and discard gasket. Remove low idle speed (TSP Off) adjusting screw and spring, and remove solenoid.

Throttle Body

Remove curb idle adjusting screw. Remove fast idle adjusting screw and spring.

NOTE: Manufacturers do not recommend removal of throttle plate or shaft. If damage or wear is evident, replace throttle body assembly.

CLEANING & INSPECTION

- Inspect all gasket mating surfaces for nicks, burrs or any damage that would prevent gasket sealing.
- Do not place choke cover, pulldown diaphragm, bowl vent assembly or pump plunger in cleaning solvent.
- Inspect idle mixture screw tip. If grooved or worn, replace with new needle.
- Ensure all new gaskets match gaskets removed in placement of holes and slots. Use new gaskets only.
- Ensure all parts are clean and free of solvent before assembly. Wash parts in hot water and blow dry with compressed air.

REASSEMBLY

Reassemble carburetor in reverse order of disassembly. Use new gaskets and seals. Make sure gaskets fit correctly and all holes are punched through and correctly located. Install mixture screw concealment plug after final adjustments are made on vehicle.

NOTE: Choke cap must be installed with rivets to maintain tamper-proof requirement.

CARBURETOR ADJUSTMENT SPECIFICATIONS

Application	Float Level	Accelerator Pump		Fast Idle Cam	Choke Unloader	Choke Vacuum Kick
		Hole	Stroke			
R-40042A	Flush	#2	1.72"	.090"	.250"	.150"

1983 Holley Carburetors

HOLLEY MODEL 6149 SINGLE BARREL

CARBURETOR APPLICATION

FORD MOTOR CO. CARBURETOR NO.

Application	Part No.
1984 Tempo/Topaz	
2.3L Engine	
Automatic Transmission	E43Z 9510-Z
Manual Transmission	
All Exc. California	E43Z 9510-V
California	[1]

[1] — Part number not available.

CARBURETOR IDENTIFICATION

Part number is stamped on main body or on tag attached to carburetor.

DESCRIPTION

The Holley model 6149 is a single barrel, downdraft design carburetor with "Electronic Feedback" control. The carburetor is designed to maintain an air/fuel ratio within specified limits to allow the catalytic converter to operate effectively. Main, idle and off-idle air/fuel ratios are regulated by the EEC-IV computer. The carburetor consists of 3 main sub-assemblies, the air horn, main body and throttle body.

ADJUSTMENTS

NOTE: **For on-vehicle adjustments, see TUNE-UP PROCEDURES article.**

FLOAT LEVEL

1) With the carburetor air horn assembly removed, hold the float hinge pin retainer in place with finger and invert main body. Catch the check ball and weight as they fall out of the assembly.

2) With gasket removed, place a straight edge across the float bowl cavity and check float position. The outer edge of the floats should be flush with the edge of the casting. Adjust float position as needed by bending float arm.

3) With main body right side up, ensure that floats do not contact fuel bowl walls at any point throughout travel. Be sure to install check ball, then weight, during reassembly.

FEEDBACK CONTROL DIAPHRAGM

1) Drill a 3/32" hole in the concealment plug over the main system feedback diaphragm adjustment screw (located in the air horn screw boss). Use a punch to pry out plug. Turn adjustment screw as needed until top of screw is specified distance below top of air horn adjustment screw boss.

2) After adjustment is made, install new concealment plug and stake in place. Apply 10 in. Hg vacuum at main system feedback vacuum supply tube with hand vacuum pump. Diaphragm should hold vacuum.

Fig. 1: Feedback Control Diaphragm Adjustment

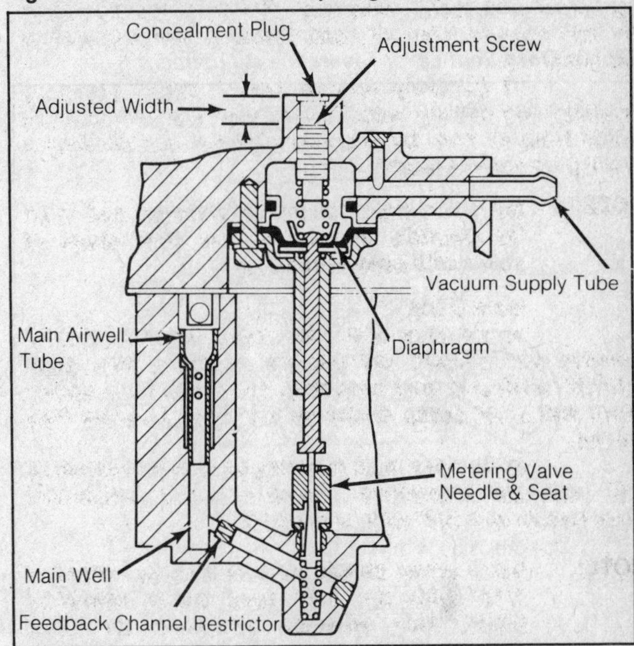

Top of screw must be correct distance below top of boss.

AUXILIARY MAIN JET/PULLOVER VALVE

Measure total distance that adjustment screw protrudes through back side of throttle pick-up lever. If distance is not within acceptable range, turn screw to obtain correct setting. *See Fig. 2.*

Fig. 2: Auxiliary Main Jet/Pullover Valve Adjustment

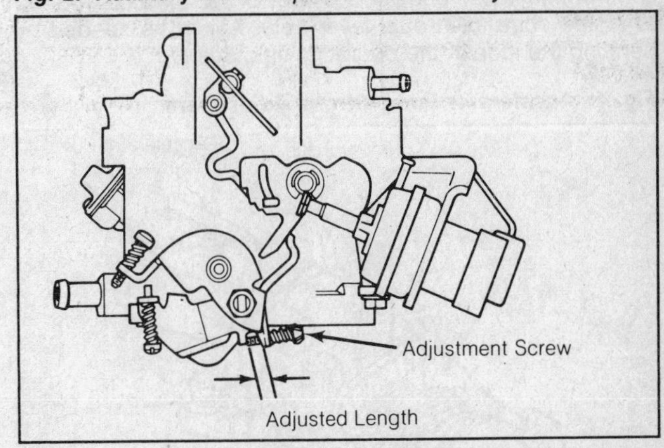

Measure length of screw extending through back of lever.

MECHANICAL FUEL BOWL VENT LEVER

1) With choke plate held wide open and throttle at "TPS Off" position, turn TPS Off idle adjustment screw counterclockwise to close throttle plate completely.

2) Measure clearance between fuel bowl vent actuating lever and fuel bowl vent arm. *See Fig. 3.* If clearance is not correct, bend bowl vent actuator lever at adjustment point until specified clearance is obtained. DO NOT bend the vent arm itself or the part of the actuator lever adjacent to the arm.

HOLLEY MODEL 6149 SINGLE BARREL (Cont.)

3) After reassembly, TPS Off idle speed will have to be readjusted.

Fig. 3: Bowl Vent Lever Clearance Adjustment

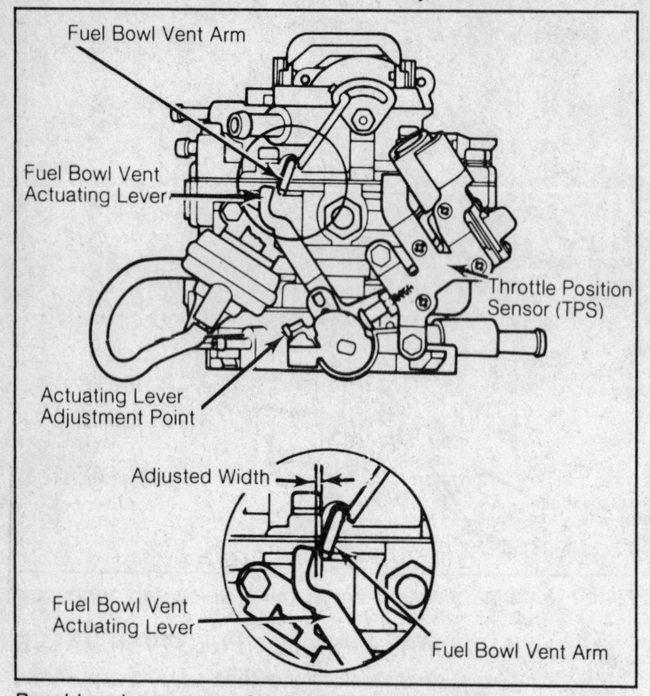

Bend bowl vent actuating lever to adjust clearance.

ACCELERATOR PUMP STROKE

Measure length of accelerator pump operating link from its inside edge at accelerator pump operating rod to inside edge at throttle lever hole. Adjust as needed by bending the loop in the operating link. *See Fig. 4.*

Fig. 4: Accelerator Pump Stroke Adjustment

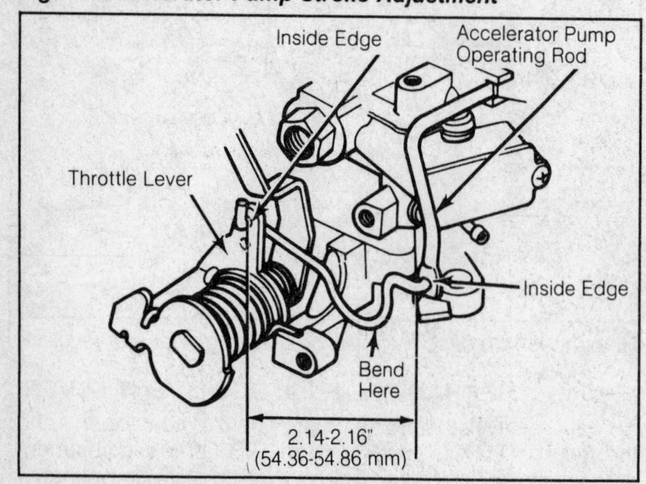

Bend operating link where indicated to adjust link length.

OVERHAUL

DISASSEMBLY

Carburetor

1) With carburetor on repair stand (EGR spacer may be used), remove throttle body-to-main body attaching screws (4) and the lower TPS mounting screw. Tap gently to separate throttle body from main body.

2) Carefully rotate throttle body and disconnect accelerator pump operating link from throttle return spring lever, noting position of link for reassembly reference. Remove throttle body from main body.

3) Remove TPS actuating pin and set aside for reassembly. Remove throttle body gasket and clean throttle body and main body gasket surfaces as needed. DO NOT use a metal gasket scraper on these parts. If any material remains after gasket is removed, use a nylon or hard plastic scraper to clean surfaces.

4) Remove solekicker retaining screws (3) and remove solekicker. While holding choke plate in closed position, remove chokeshaft nut and lockwasher and remove choke pulldown lever. Remove choke control lever retaining screw and fast idle cam retainer.

5) Note position of fast idle cam anti-entrapment spring, relative to fast idle cam and fast idle cam link. Carefully remove fast idle cam, anti-entrapment spring and bushing, fast idle cam link, and retaining bushing and choke control lever as an assembly.

6) Remove air horn-to-main body attaching screws (8). Note location of choke wire clip and part number tag for reassembly reference. Remove the air horn from the main body by lifting straight up. If necessary, tap the air horn straight up with a plastic hammer to separate from main body.

CAUTION: DO NOT tap air horn side-to-side or attempt to pry off of main body. DO NOT rotate air horn when lifting off. This will bend auxiliary main jet/pullover valve operating rod.

7) Remove air horn gasket and clean air horn and main body gasket surfaces as needed. DO NOT use a metal gasket scraper on these parts. If any material remains after gasket is removed, use a nylon or hard plastic scraper to clean surfaces.

Air Horn

1) Remove choke cap assembly. To do so, ensure rivet mandrels of bi-metal assembly are well below rivet head. Drive mandrel down or out with a 1/16" diameter punch. Use a 1/8" (No. 30) drill to drill out rivet head. Drive out rivet with 1/8" punch. Remove standard screws and choke cap.

2) Remove accelerator pump piston bracket retaining screw and remove pump piston/bracket assembly. Remove auxiliary main jet/pullover valve operating rod and spring.

3) Remove accelerator pump operating rod attaching screw and retainer clamp. Rotate accelerator pump operating rod and remove rod and grommet from air horn.

4) Remove main system feedback diaphragm and actuator assembly retaining screws and remove feedback diaphragm actuator assembly, diaphragm seat, "O" ring and spring.

5) Drill a 3/32" hole through sealing disc over the main system feedback diaphragm adjustment screw. Pry out disc with small punch. Main system feedback adjustment screw position must not be altered from the original setting.

HOLLEY MODEL 6149 SINGLE BARREL (Cont.)

Fig. 5: Exploded View of Holley Model 6149 Single Barrel Carburetor

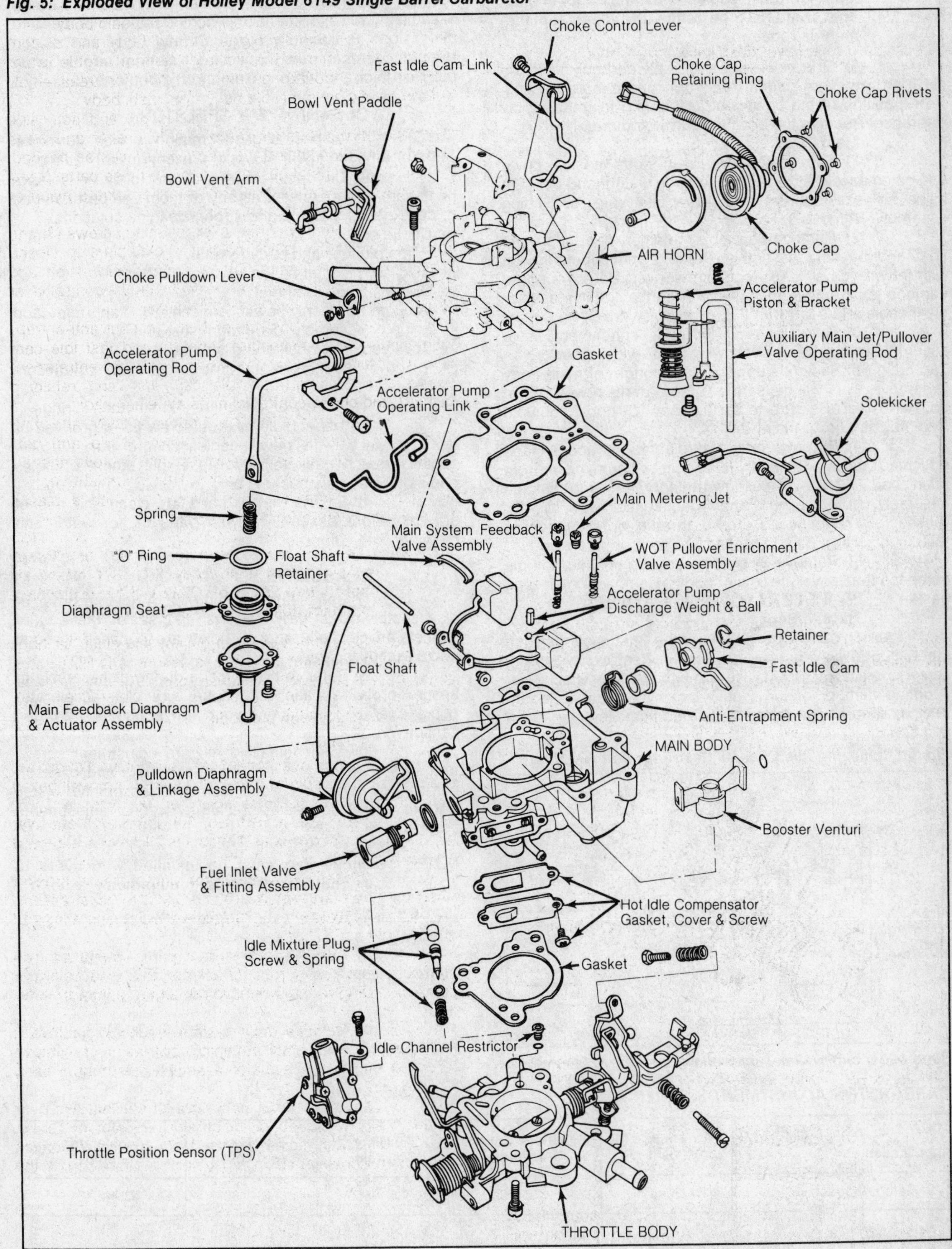

1983 Holley Carburetors

HOLLEY MODEL 6149 SINGLE BARREL (Cont.)

NOTE: **Manufacturer recommends that choke plate and shaft NOT be removed unless replacement is required.**

6) Grip bowl vent arm firmly and pull mechanical fuel bowl vent paddle out from the air horn casting. Note position of the bowl vent arm spring for reassembly reference. Remove the bowl vent arm grommet.

Main Body

1) Turn carburetor main body upside down and catch accelerator pump discharge weight and ball. Set aside for reassembly. Remove fuel inlet valve and fitting assembly. Remove gasket.

2) Remove float shaft retainer, float shaft and float and bushing assembly. Remove main metering jet with jet wrench or 5/16" wide screwdriver. Use care not to damage jet. Remove main system feedback valve assembly (needle and seat) with 3/8" wide screwdriver.

3) Remove WOT pullover enrichment valve assembly (needle and seat) with 5/16" wide screwdriver. Tap main nozzle lightly upward from bottom of main body to remove. This will cause the "O" ring at main well end of nozzle to tear. Be sure to remove any "O" ring fragments from nozzle and/or main well.

4) Remove pulldown diaphragm and linkage attaching screws (2) and disconnect vacuum hose from main body. Remove pulldown diaphragm and linkage assembly. Note location of oxygen sensor wire clip for reassembly reference. Remove throttle position sensor attaching screws (2) and remove sensor from main body.

5) Remove 2 retaining screws holding hot idle compensator cover to main body. Remove cover and gasket.

Throttle Body

1) Center punch and drill a 3/32" hole through steel plug over idle mixture screw. Remove plug with screw extractor. Carefully turn mixture screw clockwise, counting number of turns until screw just seats. Record number of turns for reassembly reference. Remove screw and spring.

Fig. 6: Removing Idle Channel Restrictor and "O" Ring

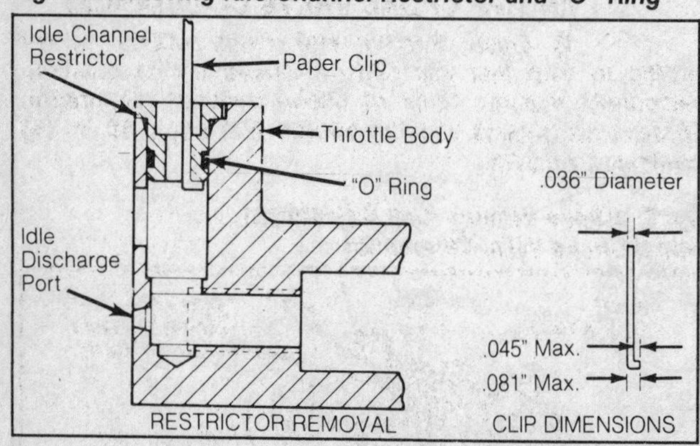

Bend paper clip to dimensions shown to remove restrictor.

2) Remove idle channel restrictor and "O" ring assembly from throttle body with a paper clip bent to dimensions as shown in *Fig. 6.* Carefully insert paper clip through restrictor and hook under bottom edge. Gently pull restrictor and "O" ring from throttle body.

CLEANING & INSPECTION

1) Inspect all gasket mating surfaces for nicks, burrs or any damage that would prevent gasket sealing.

2) Do not place any of the following components in cleaning solvent as any of them can be damaged or destroyed if subjected to strong cleaning solutions:

- Choke cover.
- Pump plunger and cup assembly.
- Auxiliary main jet seal puck.
- Operating rod grommet.
- Vacuum gradient power enrichment diaphragm and actuator assembly, diaphragm seat and "O" ring.
- Bowl vent seal puck and grommet.
- Pulldown diaphragm and linkage assembly or vacuum hose.
- Idle mixture screw or idle channel restrictor "O" rings.

3) Inspect idle mixture screw tip. If grooved or worn, replace with new needle. Ensure that all new gaskets match gaskets removed in placement of holes and slots. Use new gaskets only.

4) Ensure that all parts are clean and free of solvent before assembly. Wash parts in hot water and blow dry with compressed air.

REASSEMBLY

1) Reassemble carburetor in reverse order of disassembly. Use new gaskets and seals. Make sure gaskets fit correctly and all holes are punched through and correctly located.

2) Refer to notes made during disassembly to ensure proper location of choke wire clip, accelerator pump operating link, bowl vent arm spring and oxygen sensor wire clip.

3) When installing mixture adjustment screw, turn screw all the way in until it just seats and back off number of turns recorded during disassembly. Install mixture screw concealment plug after final adjustments are made.

NOTE: **Choke cap must be installed with rivets to maintain tamper-proof requirement.**

CARBURETOR ADJUSTMENT SPECIFICATIONS

Appplication	Float Level	Feedback Control Diaphragm	Auxiliary Main Jet	Fuel Bowl Vent Lever	Accelerator Pump
1984 Tempo/Topaz	Flush	[1] .170-.190"	.335-.355"	.110-.130"	2.14-2.16"

[1] — With "S" stamped in top of boss: .240-.260"

1983 Holley Carburetors

HOLLEY MODEL 5220 2-BARREL

CARBURETOR APPLICATION

CHRYSLER CORP. (HOLLEY) CARBURETOR NO.

Application	Part. No.
2.2L Engine	
Man. Trans.	R-40020A
Auto Trans.	R-40022A

CARBURETOR IDENTIFICATION

Carburetor identification number may be found stamped on side of float bowl or on a metal tag attached to carburetor.

DESCRIPTION

Carburetor is a 2-stage, 2-venturi type. Primary venturi is smaller than secondary. Secondary stage is mechanically operated by linkage to primary and secondary throttle levers. Primary stage includes curb idle, accelerator pump idle transfer, main metering and power enrichment systems. Secondary stage includes main metering and power enrichment systems. A single fuel bowl supplies fuel for both stages. Carburetor is equipped with an electric automatic choke which has a 2-stage bimetal heating element. Manual transmission carburetors have 1 choke valve. Automatic transmission carburetors have 2 choke valves (secondary smaller than primary).

TESTING

CHOKE HEATER

With ignition off, connect a jumper wire between battery positive terminal and choke heater connection. Remove air cleaner and observe choke plate. Choke plate should fully open within 5 minutes when vehicle is parked inside.

NOTE: The choke housing is attached to carburetor with tamper-proof screws. Thermostat setting is not adjustable.

ADJUSTMENT

NOTE: For on-vehicle adjustments, see TUNE-UP PROCEDURES article.

FLOAT LEVEL

1) Remove air horn and gasket. Turn air horn upside down. Allow weight of float to press down against float needle valve. *See Fig. 1.*

2) Measure float level specified clearance between top of float and air horn gasket surface. Clearance can be checked using a specified drill or pin gauge.

3) Make sure float tang still rests on float needle when clearance is checked. To adjust, bend tang that contacts float needle.

NOTE: Do not apply pressure to float needle while checking or changing adjustment.

Fig. 1: Float Level Adjustment

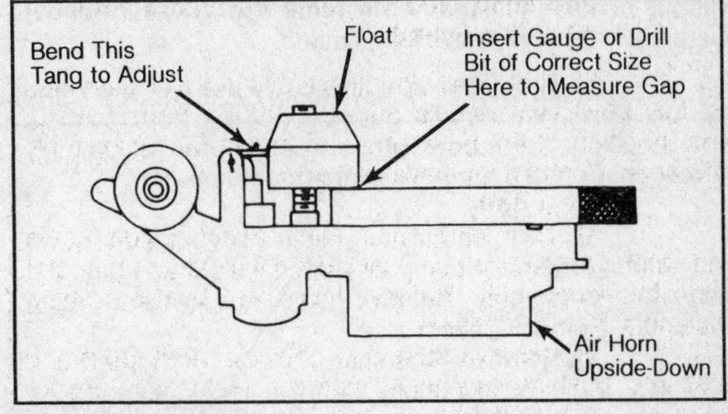

Bend tang to adjust.

FLOAT DROP

1) With air horn and gasket removed, turn right side up. Using a "T" scale, measure specified float drop from air horn gasket surface to bottom of float. *See Fig. 2.*

2) To adjust, bend float tang on float arm that contacts fuel inlet needle seat boss.

Fig. 2: Float Drop Adjustment

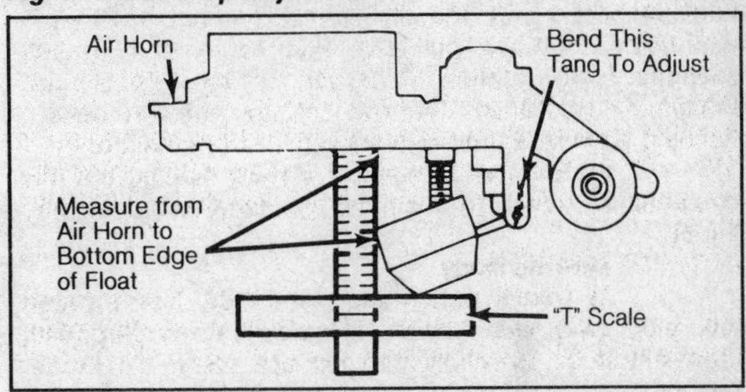

Bend tang to adjust.

CHOKE VACUUM KICK (INITIAL CHOKE VALVE CLEARANCE)

1) Open throttle and close choke. Close throttle to trap fast idle cam in closed choke position. Disconnect vacuum hose at choke vacuum diaphragm. Connect an outside vacuum source and apply 15 in. Hg (minimum) vacuum.

Fig. 3: Choke Vacuum Kick Adjustment (Initial Choke Valve Clearance)

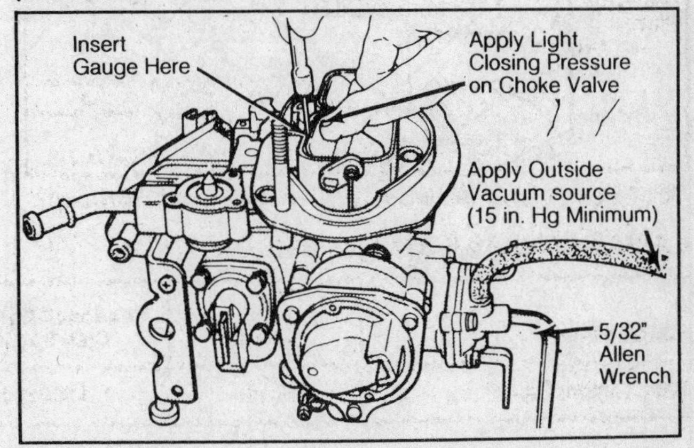

Apply 15 in. Hg (minimum) to adjust.

HOLLEY MODEL 5220 2-BARREL (Cont.)

2) Apply slight closing pressure to choke valve without bending linkage. An internal spring within choke system will compress to stop position.

3) Using specified drill or pin gauge, measure clearance between upper edge of choke valve and air horn wall at primary throttle end of carburetor. *See Fig. 3.*

Fig. 4: Exploded View of Holley Model 5220 2-Barrel Carburetor

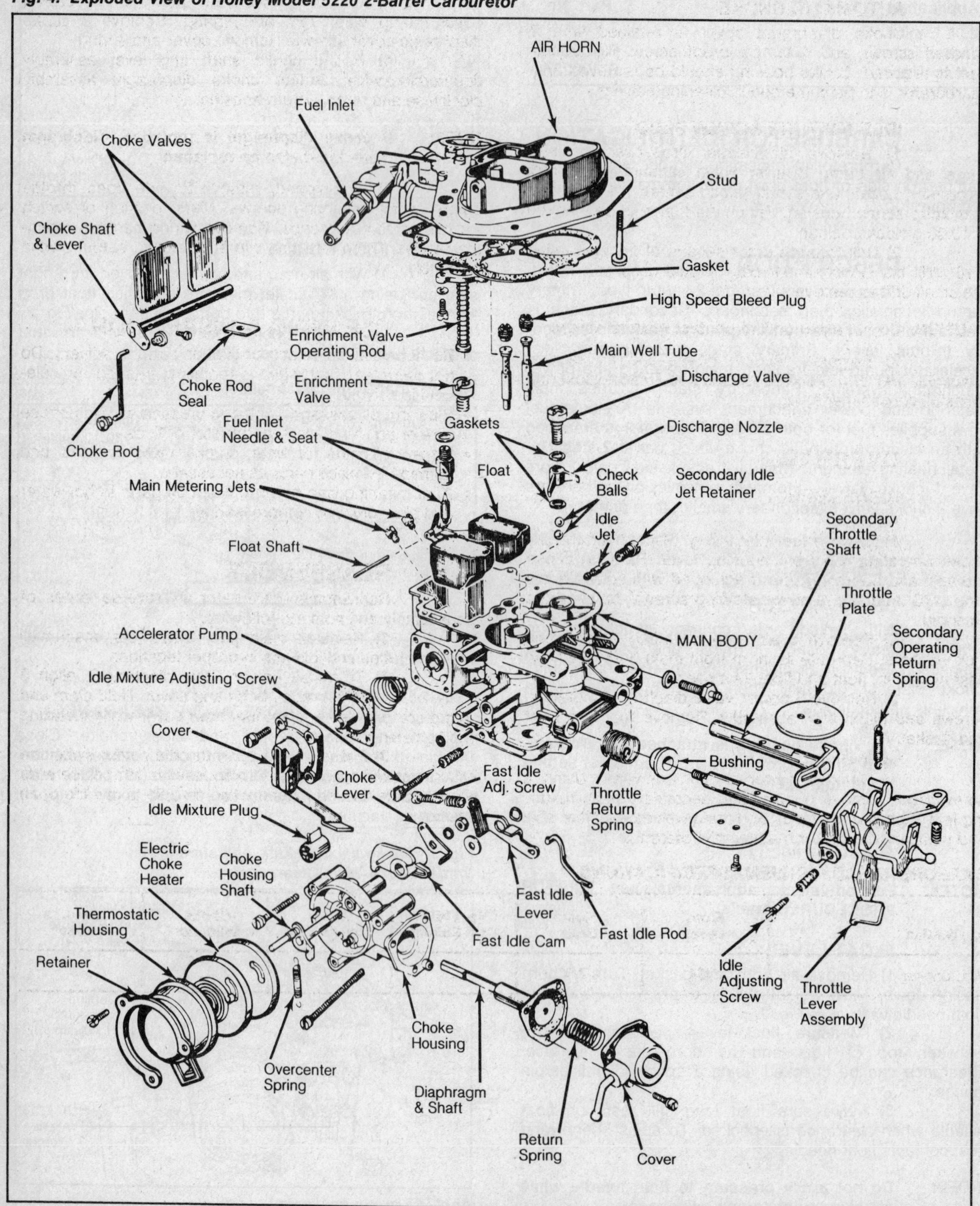

HOLLEY MODEL 5220 2-BARREL (Cont.)

CHOKE UNLOADER

Choke unloader is positioned by fast idle cam. No adjustment is required.

AUTOMATIC CHOKE

Choke diaphragm cover is retained with 2 standard screws and 1 tamper-proof screw. No adjustment is required. Choke housing should be removed only if carburetor is to be immersed in cleaning solvent.

IDLE MIXTURE SCREW PLUG

1) Remove air cleaner crossover, canister purge and air pump diverter valve vacuum hose from carburetor. Locate and center punch a mark 1/4" from end of mixture screw housing. Punch mark should be indexed at 10:00 o'clock position.

2) Drill through outer section of housing using 3/16" drill bit. Concealment plug should drop out. If not, use small drift to remove plug.

CAUTION: Do not allow drift to contact mixture screw.

3) Reinstall vacuum hoses and air cleaner crossover. Perform propane idle mixture RPM adjustment. Reinstall concealment plug.

OVERHAUL

DISASSEMBLY

Air Horn

1) Remove fuel inlet fitting. Disconnect and pry choke operating rod from housing lever. Remove choke rod seal and operating rod. If equipped with solenoid idle stop (A/C models), remove retaining screws, bracket and solenoid.

2) Remove 5 air horn mounting screws and lock washers. Separate air horn from main body. Remove float hinge pin, float and float inlet needle.

3) Remove 3 power valve diaphragm mounting screws and diaphragm assembly. Remove fuel inlet seat and gasket.

Main Body

1) Remove power enrichment valve. Using a screwdriver, remove primary and secondary main metering jets, high speed bleeds and main well tubes. Note size and position of each for reassembly reference.

2) Remove discharge nozzle screw, discharge nozzle and gasket. Turn carburetor upside down and catch accelerator pump discharge weight ball and check ball. (Both balls are same size).

3) Remove 4 accelerator pump cover screws, cover, pump diaphragm and spring. Remove 3 choke diaphragm cover screws. Remove cover and spring.

4) Rotate choke shaft and lever assembly counterclockwise. Rotate choke diaphragm assembly clockwise and remove from housing.

NOTE: If choke diaphragm is replaced, diaphragm cover must also be replaced.

5) If equipped, remove 2 wide open throttle cutout switch mounting screws. Mark location of switch for reassembly reference. Remove wiring harness retaining screws. Open retaining clip and remove cutout switch assembly.

CLEANING & INSPECTION

- Do not immerse plastic or rubber parts in solvent. Do not immerse diaphragm assemblies, dashpot or solenoid in solvent.
- Blow out all passages with compressed air. Do not use wire or drill bit to clean carburetor orifices.
- Inspect all parts for wear, cracks, nicks or burrs, and damage. Replace parts as necessary.
- After cleaning with solvent, wash all parts in hot water and blow dry with compressed air.

REASSEMBLY

Reassemble carburetor in reverse order of disassembly and note the following:

1) Reinstall main jets, bleed jets, main well emulsion tubes and idle jets in proper locations.

2) To install power valve diaphragm, align 3 screw holes in diaphragm, body and cover. Hold stem and spring compressed against fuel bowl cover while installing and tightening screws.

3) Position wide open throttle cutout switch so A/C circuit will open when throttle lever is 10° before wide open throttle and stay open when throttle is in wide open position.

CARBURETOR ADJUSTMENT SPECIFICATIONS

Application	Float Level	Float Drop	Fast Idle Cam Setting	Choke Vacuum Kick	Choke Unloader	Auto. Choke
2.2L Engine	31/64"	1-7/8"	.....	.055"	.....	.....

1983 Holley Carburetors

HOLLEY MODEL 6510-C & 6520 2-BARREL

CARBURETOR APPLICATION

CHRYSLER CORP. (HOLLEY 6520) CARBURETOR NO.

Application	Part No.
1.6L Engine	
With High Altitude	R-40053A
Without High Altitude	R-40015A
1.7L Engine	
With A/C	R-40081A
Without A/C	R-40080A
2.2L Engine	
Man. Trans.	
Federal	R-40003A
California	R-40007A
High Altitude	R-40005A
Auto. Trans.	
Federal	
With A/C	R-40004A
Without A/C	R-40010A
California	
With A/C	R-40008A
Without A/C	R-40012A
High Altitude	
With A/C	R-40006A
Without A/C	R-40014A

GENERAL MOTORS (HOLLEY 6510-C) CARBURETOR NO.

Application	Part No.
1.6L Engine	
Man. Trans.	14048828
Auto. Trans.	
With A/C	14048828
Without A/C	14048829

CARBURETOR IDENTIFICATION

Carburetor part number or identification number may be found stamped on the fuel bowl assembly or on a metal tag attached to carburetor.

DESCRIPTION

The Holley 6510-C and 6520 carburetors are "staged" dual venturi electronic feedback carburetors. The primary bore is smaller than the secondary bore. The primary side of both carburetors contains float systems, idle system, main metering system, pump system and choke system. The secondary side contains main metering system and power system. Fuel for both primary and secondaries is provided by a common fuel supply. The main metering system is incorporated within carburetor primary and secondary.

The primary main metering system provides air/fuel mixture for normal engine operation. The air/fuel mixture is controlled by a mixture control solenoid (General Motors) or duty cycle solenoid (Chrysler Corp.). The control solenoids are electronically actuated by the Spark Control Computer (Chrysler Corp.) or Electronic Control Module (General Motors) to maintain the air/fuel ratio close to 14.7:1 during normal engine operation.

The secondary main metering circuit provides more fuel for full power operation. Both carburetors are equipped with diaphragm-type accelerator pumps to provide additional fuel for sudden acceleration. Both carburetors are equipped with electric chokes to assist cold engine starts.

On General Motors models, a Throttle Position Sensor (TSP) informs the ECM of throttle position and an Idle Speed Control (ISC) actuator increases idle speed when energized by the ECM. On Chrysler Corp. models a Solenoid Idle Stop (SIS) and carburetor switch informs the computer of throttle postion. A wide open throttle/air conditioner cutout switch is also used on Chrysler Corp. models to cancel A/C operation during wide open throttle conditions.

TESTING

ELECTRIC CHOKE

Chrysler Corp.

1) Remove air cleaner and disconnect Dark Blue wire at choke. Using a jumper wire, connect choke to battery positive terminal (ignition off).

2) Choke valve should fully open within 5 minutes when vehicle is parked inside. Remove wire and install air cleaner.

General Motors

1) Remove air cleaner. With engine off, hold throttle valve half open and open and close choke several times. If linkage binds, sticks or operates slowly, clean and service linkages. Ensure vacuum lines are properly connected and perform vacuum break adjustmemt.

2) If electric choke does not open, check voltage at choke heater connection with engine running. If voltage is 12-15 volts, replace electric choke unit.

3) If voltage is low or 0, check all wires and connections. If connection at oil pressure switch is bad, temperature pressure warning light will be off with ignition on and engine not running. Repair wires and connections as required.

4) If steps **2)** and **3)** are okay, replace oil pressure switch.

ADJUSTMENTS

NOTE: **For on-vehicle adjustments, see TUNE-UP PROCEDURES article.**

Fig. 1: Float Level Adjustment

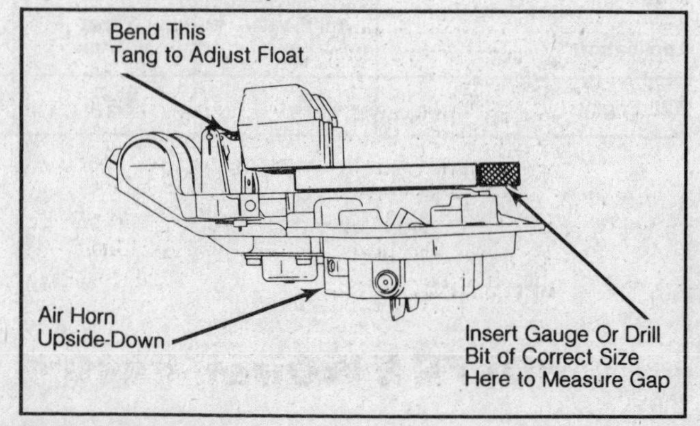

Bend tang to adjust.

HOLLEY MODEL 6510-C & 6520 2-BARREL (Cont.)

FLOAT LEVEL

1) With air horn removed, turn carburetor upside down. Allow weight of float to press down against float needle valve. *See Fig. 1.*

2) Measure float level specified clearance between top of float and air horn gasket surface. Clearance can be checked using a specified drill or pin gauge.

3) Make sure float tang still rests on float needle when clearance is checked. To adjust, bend float tang.

NOTE: Do not apply pressure to float needle while checking or changing adjustment.

FLOAT DROP

Chrysler Corp. Only

1) Hold air horn right side up. Using a "T" scale, measure float drop distance from air horn gasket surface to lower toe of float.

2) To adjust, bend float tang with small screwdriver. Support float while applying pressure to tang.

CHOKE VACUUM BREAK (INITIAL CHOKE VALVE CLEARANCE)

NOTE: All models are equipped with tamper-proof screws to retain choke coil cover. File screw heads until cover retaining ring can be removed and then remove remaining portion of screws from choke housing. New screws are provided in service kit.

1) On Chrysler Corp. models, open throttle, close choke valves, then close throttle. On all models, connect a vacuum source to vacuum break diaphragm and apply enough vacuum (at least 15 in. Hg) to seat diaphragm.

2) On General Motors models, push fast idle cam lever down (clockwise) to close choke valves.

Fig. 2: Choke Vacuum Break (Initial Choke Valve Clearance) Adjustment

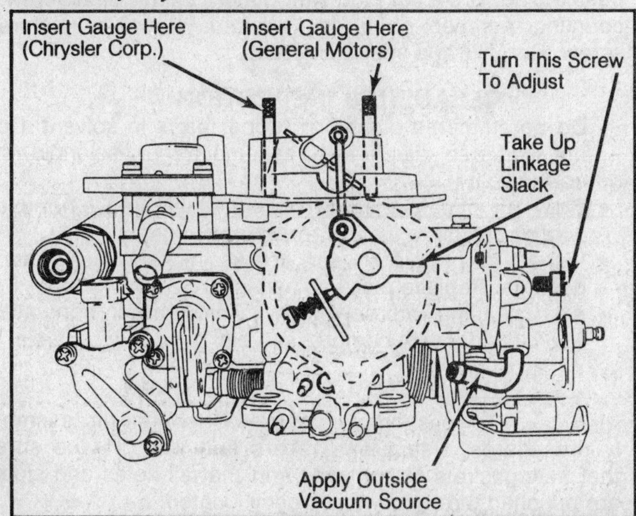

Rotate hex-head screw in center of diaphragm housing to adjust.

3) On Chrysler Corp. models, apply force on top of choke valves to close blades as far as possible and take slack out of linkage (an internal spring will compress). Insert drill or gauge between top of choke valve and bore wall.

4) On General Motors models, take slack out of linkage in the direction of opening the choke. Position drill or gauge between lower edge of choke valve and bore wall.

5) On all models, adjust by rotating hex-head screw in center of diaphragm housing. After adjustment, replace vacuum hose and insert blocking rivet in hex-head screw.

FAST IDLE CAM POSITION

General Motors Only

1) Place fast idle speed screw on 2nd step of fast idle cam. Insert gauge between lower edge of choke valve and inside of air horn wall. *See Fig. 3.*

Fig. 3: Fast Idle Cam Position Adjustment

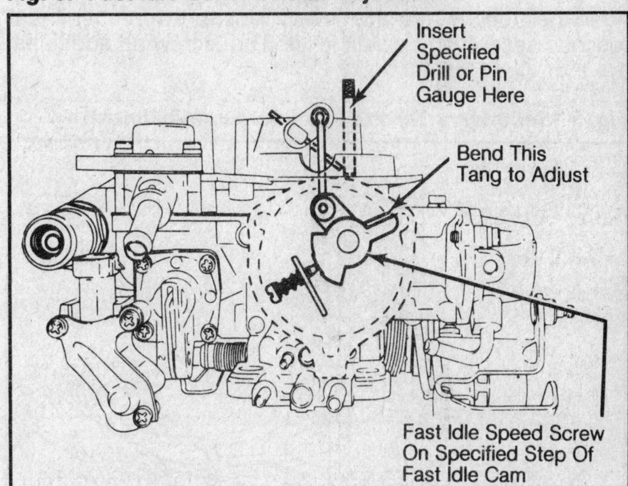

Bend tang to adjust.

2) With clearance correct, choke lever tang should just contact lever on fast idle cam. To adjust, bend tang.

Fig. 4: Choke Unloader Adjustment

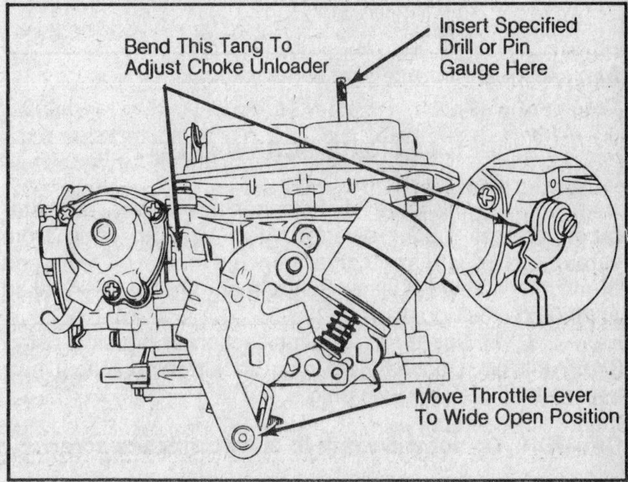

Bend choke unloader tang on fast idle cam to adjust.

HOLLEY MODEL 6510-C & 6520 2-BARREL (Cont.)

CHOKE UNLOADER

General Motors Only

1) Hold throttle valves wide open. Measure choke unloader specified clearance between lower edge of choke valve and air horn wall. *See. Fig. 4.*

2) Clearance can be measured using a specified drill or pin gauge. To adjust, bend choke unloader tang on fast idle cam.

AUTOMATIC CHOKE

NOTE: The choke assembly is installed with a locating tang and cannot be adjusted. Choke assembly removal is not required unless throttle body is to be immersed in carburetor cleaner.

SECONDARY THROTTLE STOP SCREW

General Motors Only

Back off secondary throttle stop screw until it no longer touches throttle lever. Turn screw in until it just touches secondary throttle lever. Turn screw an additional 1/4 turn. *See Fig. 5.*

Fig, 5: Secondary Throttle Stop Screw Adjustment

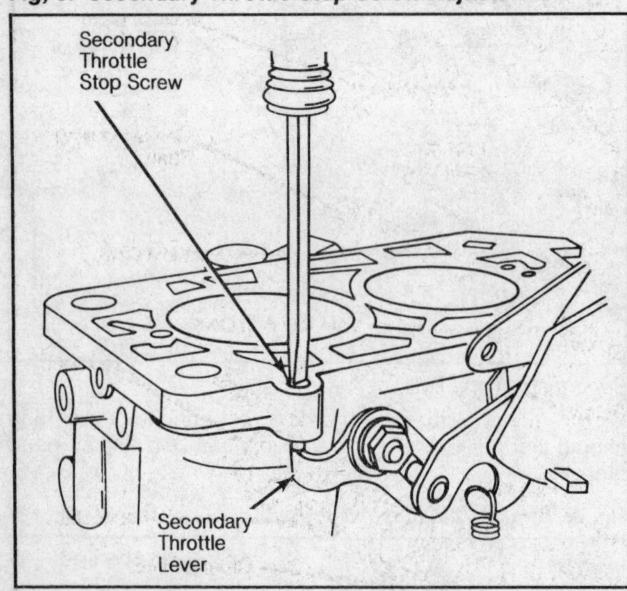

Turn secondary throttle stop screw to adjust.

IDLE MIXTURE SCREW PLUG

Chrysler Corp. Only

1) Remove air cleaner crossover, canister purge and air pump diverter valve vacuum hose from carburetor. Locate and center punch a mark 1/4" from end of mixture screw housing. Punch mark should be indexed at 10:00 o'clock position.

2) Drill through outer section of housing using 3/16" drill bit. Concealment plug should drop out. If not, use small drift to remove plug.

CAUTION: Do not allow drift to contact mixture screw.

3) Reinstall vacuum hoses and air cleaner crossover. Perform propane idle mixture RPM adjustment. Reinstall concealment plug.

OVERHAUL

DISASSEMBLY

Air Horn

1) Remove fuel inlet fitting and filter (General Motors models). Disconnect and remove choke operating rod and discard seal. Remove mixture control solenoid by removing 2 mounting screws.

2) On Chrysler Corp. models, remove anti-rattle spring and idle stop solenoid. Scribe location mark on wide-open throttle switch and remove switch. On all models, remove 5 air horn screws and remove air horn.

3) Remove float pin, float and inlet needle. Remove needle seat and gasket from air horn. On General Motors models, remove bowl vent solenoid. Remove and discard bowl vent seal retainer, diaphragm, seal and spring.

Main Body

1) Remove primary and secondary main metering jets, noting size for correct installation. Also remove primary and secondary high speed bleeds and main well tubes, noting location for reassembly.

2) Remove pump discharge nozzle and gasket. Invert body and catch check ball and spring (General Motors models) or 2 check balls (Chrysler Corp. models).

3) Remove 4 screws and accelerator pump cover. Remove spring and pump diaphragm. On General Motors models, remove Throttle Position Sensor (TSP) before immersing cover in carburetor cleaner.

4) On all models, use a file or grinder to remove heads on choke cover retaining screws. Remove retaining ring and screws, then remove coil ground ring, and coil housing.

5) Remove choke housing shaft nut, lock washer, lever, spring retainer and cam from choke housing shaft. Remove screw and lockwasher, then remove bushing, spring washer, fast idle lever, and washer from housing.

6) Remove choke diaphragm cover retaining screws. Remove cover and spring.

7) On General Motors models, invert carburetor body and place punch in locator point beneath mixture needle plug. Drive out plug with punch. Lightly seat screw, counting number of turns required. Remove mixture screw. Remove idle speed solenoid.

CLEANING & INSPECTION

- Do not immerse plastic or rubber parts in solvent. Do not immerse diaphragm assemblies or solenoid in solvent.
- Blow out all passages with compressed air. Do not use wire or drill bit to clean carburetor orifices.
- Inspect all parts for wear, cracks, nicks or burrs, and damage. Replace parts as necessary.
- After cleaning with solvent, wash all parts in hot water and blow dry with compressed air.

REASSEMBLY

To reassemble carburetor, reverse disassembly procedures. Use new gaskets and seals. Make sure that new gaskets fit correctly and that all holes and slots are punched through and correctly located.

HOLLEY MODEL 6510-C & 6520 2-BARREL (Cont.)

Fig. 6: Exploded View of Holley Model 6510-C 2-Barrel Carburetor

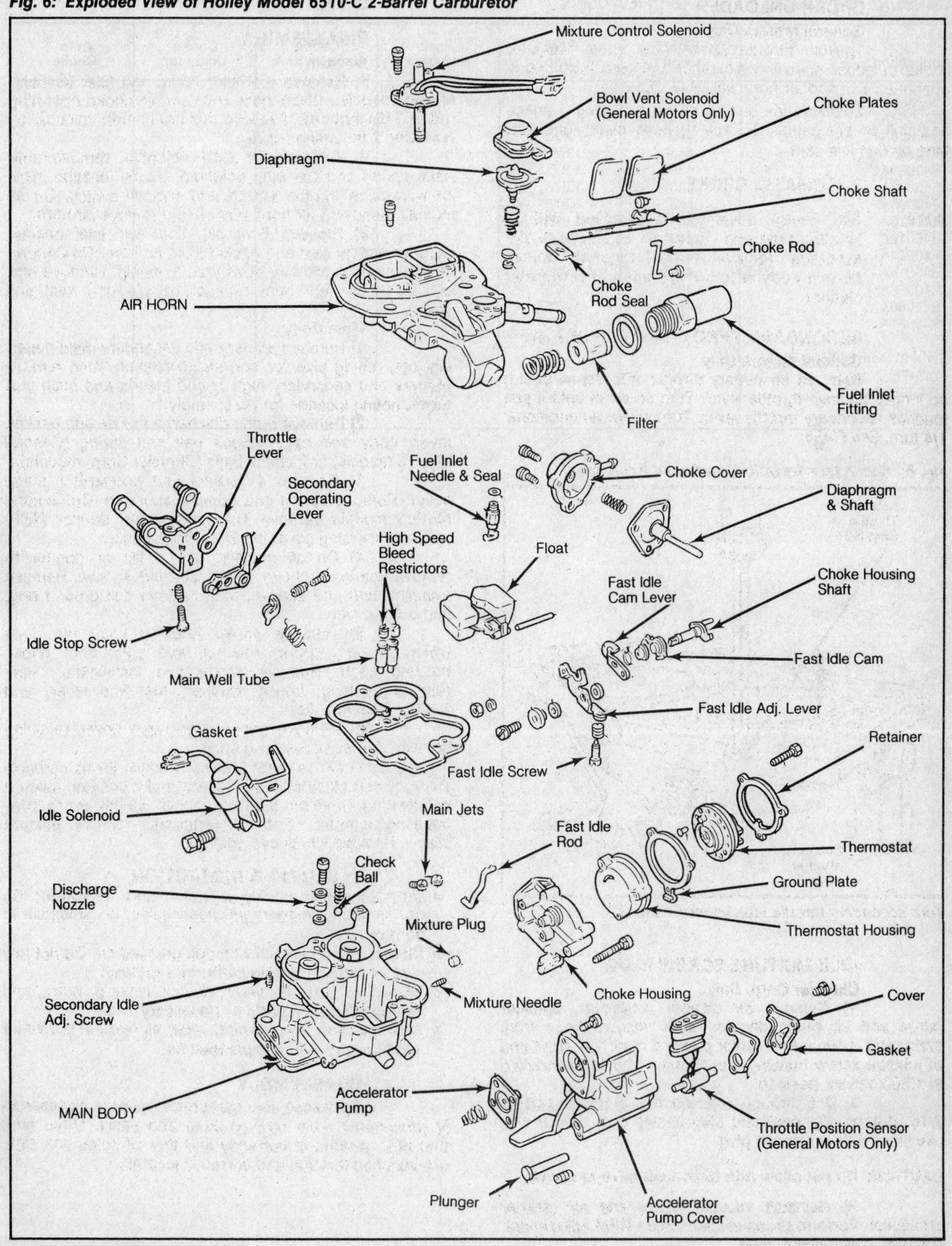

Holley Model 6520 similar.

1983 Holley Carburetors

HOLLEY MODEL 6510-C & 6520 2-BARREL (Cont.)

CARBURETOR ADJUSTMENT SPECIFICATIONS

Application	Float Level	Float Drop	Fast Idle Cam	Choke Vacuum Kick	Choke Unloader	Auto. Choke
Chrysler Corp. (6520)						
R40003A	.480"	1.875"	.....	.070"	.....	[1]
R40004A	.480"	1.875"	.....	.080"	.....	[1]
R40005A	.480"	1.875"	.....	.080"	.....	[1]
R40006A	.480"	1.875"	.....	.080"	.....	[1]
R40007A	.480"	1.875"	.....	.070"	.....	[1]
R40008A	.480"	1.875"	.....	.070"	.....	[1]
R40010A	.480"	1.875"	.....	.080"	.....	[1]
R40012A	.480"	1.875	.....	.070"	.....	[1]
R40014A	.480"	1.875"	.....	.080"	.....	[1]
R40015A	.480"	1.875"	.....	.070"	.....	[1]
R40053A	.480"	1.875"	.....	.070"	.....	[1]
R40080A	.480"	1.875"	.....	.045"	.....	[1]
R40081A	.480"	1.875"	.....	.045"	.....	[1]
General Motors (6510-C)						
14048827	.500"	.....	.080"	.270"	.350"	[1]
14048828	.500"	.....	.080"	.300"	.350"	[1]
14048829	.500"	.....	.080"	.270"	.350"	[1]

[1] — No adjustment required.

HOLLEY 4180-C 4-BARREL

CARBURETOR APPLICATION

FORD MOTOR CO. CARBURETOR NO.

Application	Part No.
Capri & Mustang 5.0L Engine	E3ZE-9510-AUA

CARBURETOR IDENTIFICATION

A carburetor identification tag is attached to the carburetor. The tag contains part number prefix and suffix. Basic part number for all carburetors is 9510. A design change code (if any) is also stamped on the tag. An assembly date code (year, month and day) is also stamped on the tag. *See Fig. 1.*

Fig. 1: Ford Motor Co. Carburetor Identification Tag

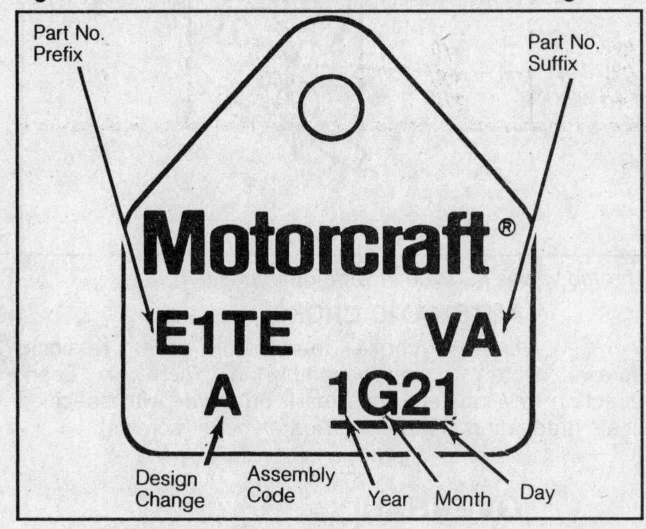

DESCRIPTION

The Holley 4180-C 4-Barrel is a downdraft 2 stage carburetor. It can be considered as 2 separate carburetors: one supplying air/fuel mixture throughout entire range of engine operation (primary stage); the other functioning only when a greater supply of air/fuel is needed (secondary stage).

The primary stage (front section) of carburetor contains a fuel bowl, metering block, and accelerator pump assembly. The secondary (rear) section of carburetor contains a fuel bowl, metering body, and secondary throttle operating diaphragm assembly.

This model carburetor has 5 main systems: idle, main meter, secondary throttle, power enrichemnt and accelerating pump. In addition to these basic systems it also is equipped with a fuel inlet system and automatic choke system.

ADJUSTMENTS

NOTE: For on-vehicle adjustments, see TUNE-UP PROCEDURES article.

FLOAT LEVEL (DRY SETTING)

1) Remove float bowl. Hold upside-down. Float is adjusted correctly if top of float is parallel with float bowl. *See Fig. 2.*

Fig. 2: Float Level Adjustment (Dry Setting)

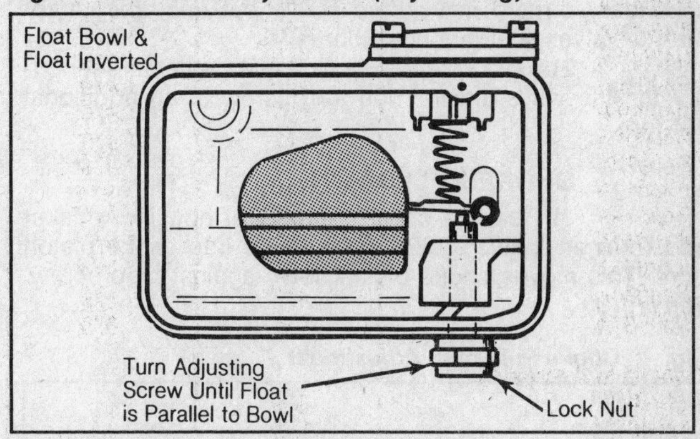

Turn adjusting screw to adjust.

2) To adjust, loosen lock nut and turn adjusting screw until float is parallel to float bowls.

ACCELERATOR PUMP LEVER

1) Place throttle valves in wide open position. Using a feeler gauge, measure specified clearance between the lever adjustment screw head and pump arm with the pump arm manually open. *See Fig. 3.*

Fig. 3: Accelerator Pump Lever Adjustment

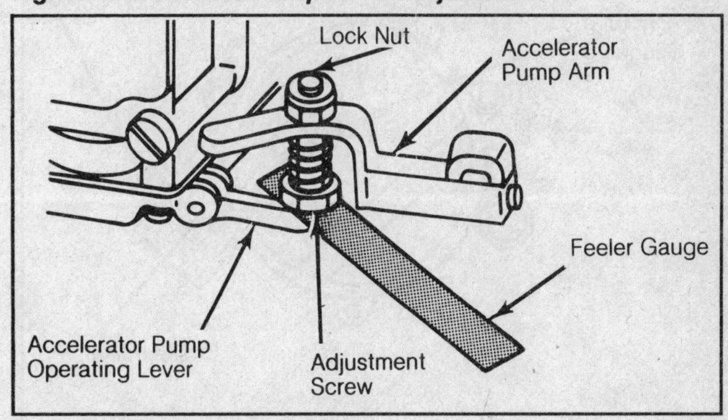

Turn adjusting screw to adjust.

2) To adjust, loosen adjustment screw lock nut. Turn adjusting screw in to increase clearance and out to decrease clearance. Each 1/2 turn of adjustment screw equals .015". Tighten lock nut.

ACCELERATOR PUMP STROKE

NOTE: Accelerator pump stroke has been preset at factory. Setting should not be changed. If original setting has been changed, adjust as follows:

1) Check that plastic accelerator pump cam is aligned with correct hole (top or bottom) in throttle lever. Plastic accelerator pump cam is located behind throttle lever.

HOLLEY 4180-C 4-BARREL (Cont.)

2) If not aligned with correct hole, remove screw. Reposition in correct hole. Install and tighten screw.

SECONDARY THROTTLE VALVES

1) Hold secondary throttle valves closed. Turn secondary throttle valve stop screw out until secondary throttle valves seat in throttle bores.

2) Turn screw in until it just contacts secondary throttle valve lever. Then turn screw in an additional 1/4 turn.

CHOKE PULLDOWN

1) Remove choke thermostat housing, gasket and retainer. Insert a .026" wire gauge into choke piston bore. This moves choke piston down against stop screw. *See Fig. 4.*

Fig. 4: Choke Pulldown Adjustment

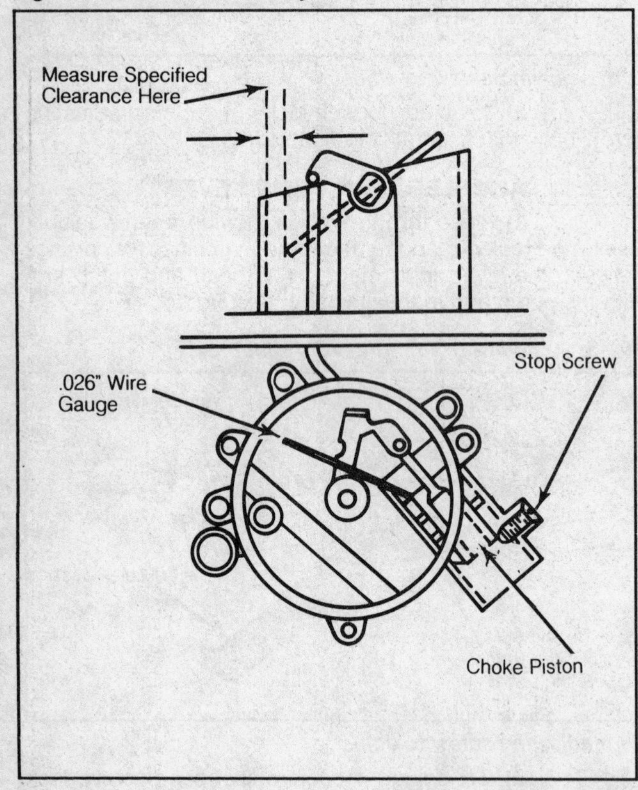

Use .026" wire gauge to hold choke piston down against stop screw.

2) Hold choke valve toward closed position. Measure specified choke pulldown clearance between lower edge of choke valve and air horn wall.

3) If adjustment is required, remove putty covering stop screw. Turn screw clockwise to decrease clearance and counterclockwise to increase clearance.

CHOKE UNLOADER

1) Hold throttle valves wide open. Apply light closing pressure on choke valve. *See Fig. 5.*

2) Measure specified choke unloader clearance between lower edge of choke valve and air horn wall. To adjust, bend pawl on fast idle cam lever.

Fig. 5: Choke Unloader Adjustment

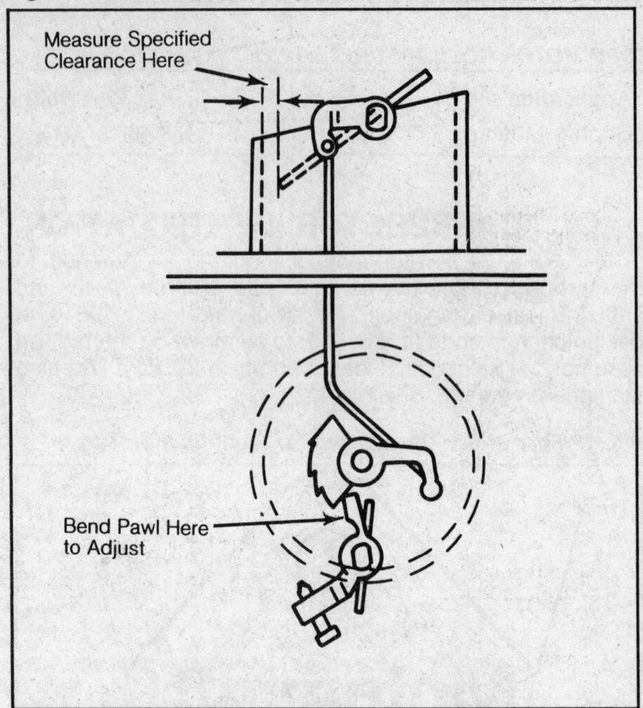

Throttle valves must be in wide open position.

AUTOMATIC CHOKE

Loosen choke thermostat cover retaining screws. Rotate cover assembly in "Rich" or "Lean" direction to align reference mark on cover with specified scale graduation in housing. Tighten cover screws.

OVERHAUL

DISASSEMBLY

Primary Fuel Bowl & Metering Block

1) Remove primary fuel bowl and gasket. Remove metering block and gasket. Discard gaskets.

2) Remove pump transfer tube and "O" rings from main body if it was not removed with metering block. Remove fuel line tube and "O" rings. Discard "O" rings.

3) Using a jet wrench, remove main jets from metering block. Using a socket wrench, remove power valve and gasket.

4) Remove fuel level adjustment screw and gasket. Turn lock nut counterclockwise and remove nut and gasket. Remove fuel inlet needle and seat assembly. Do not disassemble needle and seat, they are replaced as an assembly.

5) Using needle nose pliers, remove float shaft retainer clip. Slide float off shaft and remove spring from float. Remove baffle plate from fuel bowl. Remove fuel level sight plug and gasket.

6) Remove fuel inlet fitting, gasket and filter. Invert fuel bowl and remove accelerator pump cover, diaphragm and spring. Do not remove accelerator pump inlet check ball. Check ball is not serviced separately.

Secondary Fuel Bowl & Metering Block

Remove fuel bowl. Using a clutch type screwdriver, remove metering block screws. Remove

HOLLEY 4180-C 4-BARREL (Cont.)

Fig. 6: Exploded View of Holley Model 4180-C 4-Barrel Carburetor

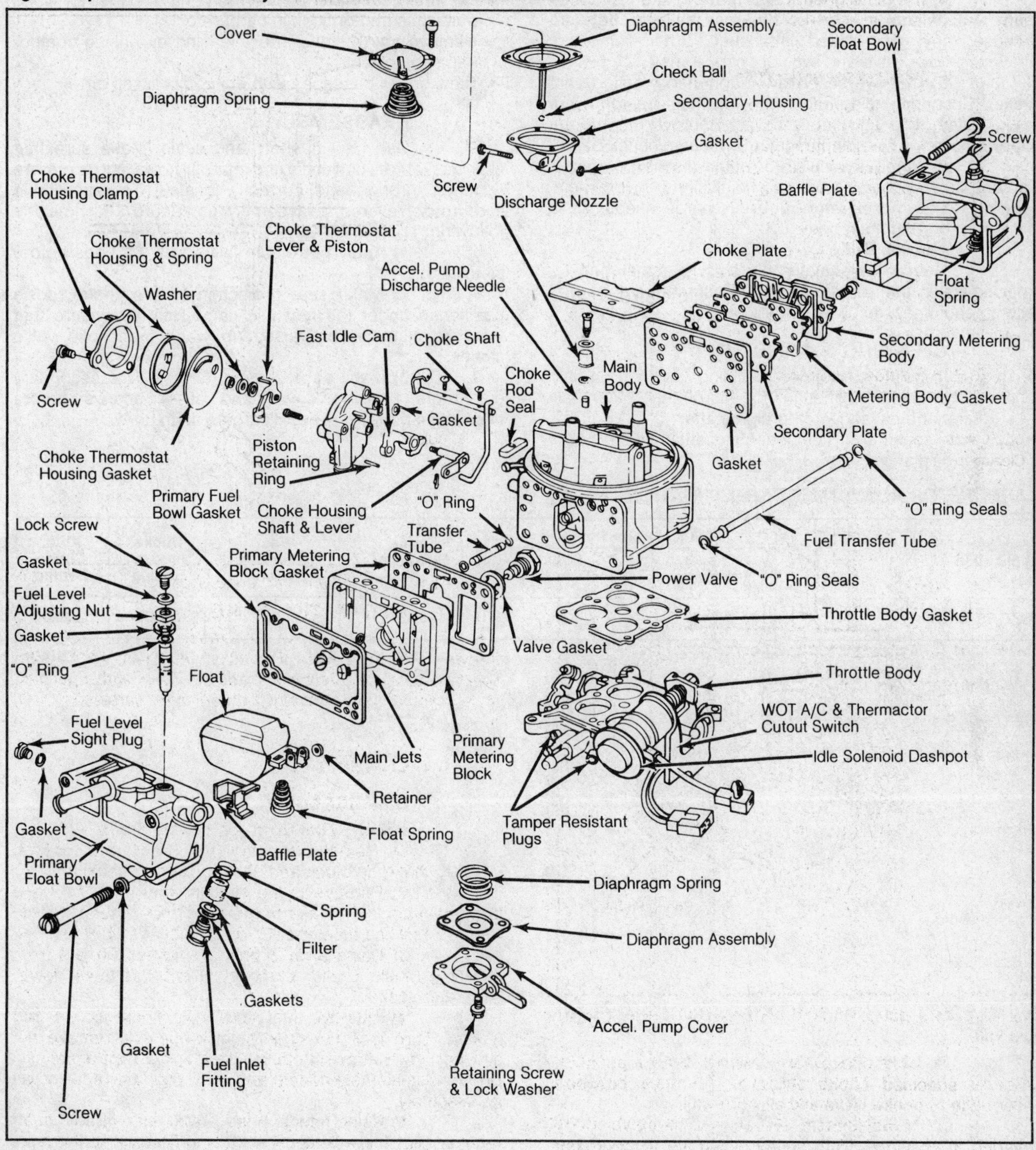

metering block, plate and gaskets. Discard gaskets. Disassemble fuel bowl by following steps **4)** and **5)** in Primary Fuel Bowl and Metering Block.

Main Body

1) Remove air cleaner stud. Remove secondary diaphragm link retainer. Invert carburetor and remove throttle body retaining screws and lock washers. Lift off throttle body and discard throttle body gasket.

2) Remove choke rod cotter pin from choke housing shaft and lever assembly. Remove choke cover, thermostatic spring and gasket. Remove choke main housing and gaskets from main body.

3) Remove choke housing shaft nut, lock washer and spacer. Remove shaft and fast idle cam. Remove choke piston and lever assembly.

1983 Holley Carburetors

HOLLEY 4180-C 4-BARREL (Cont.)

4) If it is necessary to remove choke valve and shaft, tips of choke valve screws may have to be filed because they are staked into shaft. After removing screws, remove valve and slide out choke shaft.

5) Remove secondary diaphragm housing and gasket. Secondary diaphragm housing must be removed before attempting to remove cover. Remove diaphragm housing cover, spring diaphragm and vacuum check ball.

6) Remove accelerator pump discharge nozzle screw. Lift off discharge nozzle and gaskets. Invert main body and catch accelerator pump discharge needle as it falls out of bore in main body.

Throttle Body

Components of throttle body are matched to meet emission control standards. Manufacturer does not recommend disassembly of throttle body.

CLEANING & INSPECTION

- Use a regular carburetor cleaning solution. Soak components long enough to thoroughly clean all surfaces and passages of foreign matter.
- Do not soak any components containing rubber, leather or plastic.
- Do not use wire, drill or any hard parts to clean passages and orifices in carburetor.
- Remove any residue after cleaning by rinsing components in solvent.
- Blow out all passages with dry compressed air.

REASSEMBLY

Use new gaskets and seals. Make sure that new gaskets fit correctly and that all holes and slots are punched through and correctly located. To reassemble carburetor, reverse disassembly procedure and note the following:

1) Apply petroleum jelly to all "O" rings before installation.

2) Make sure projection on the choke rod is positioned under the fast idle cam. This will ensure that fast idle cam will be raised up when the choke valve closes.

3) It will be necessary to install the secondary diaphragm housing cover and all 4 screws before diaphragm housing is installed onto main body.

CARBURETOR ADJUSTMENT SPECIFICATIONS

Application	Accelerator Pump		Choke Pulldown Setting	Fast Idle Cam Setting	Choke Unloader Setting	Auto. Choke Setting
	Lever (Clearance)	Stroke (Hole No.)				
E3ZE-9510-AUA	.015"	#1	.195-.215"	.....	.300"	3 Rich

MOTORCRAFT MODEL 740 2-BARREL

CARBURETOR APPLICATION

FORD MOTOR CO. CARBURETOR NO. [1]

Application	Man. Trans.	Auto. Trans.
1.6L Engine		
(Exc. High Output)		
With FEO [2]	E3EE-DA	.....
Without FEO [2]		
With A/C	E3EE-CA	E3EE-AA,BA
Without A/C	E3EE-EA	E3EE-JA,KA
1.6L Engine		
(High Output)		
4-Speed		
High Alt.		
With A/C	E3GE-SA	.....
Without A/C	E3GE-RA	.....
5-Speed	E3GE-PA	.....
Calif.		
With A/C	.....	E3GE-DA
Without A/C	.....	E3GE-HA
High Alt.		
With A/C	.....	E3GE-FA
Without A/C	.....	E3GE-JA

[1] — Ford basic part number is 9510.
[2] — FEO is Fuel Economy Option.

CARBURETOR IDENTIFICATION

Carburetor part number identification is stamped on a metal tag attached by a bowl cover screw.

DESCRIPTION

Motorcraft Model 740 is a 2-stage dual venturi downdraft type carburetor. It features 5 basic metering systems: choke, idle, main metering, acceleration and power enrichment. Carburetor also includes an altitude compensation system that operates between 3500-4000 feet, depending on engine calibration.

All carburetors are equipped with an idle fuel shut off solenoid. Some models incorporate a decel idle fuel shutoff circuit within the solenoid to shutoff fuel flow to idle system when directed by the computer. Some models are also equipped with a wide open throttle (WOT) A/C cutout switch to disengage air conditioning compressor clutch at wide open throttle operation.

TESTING

NOTE: **Before removing air cleaner, be sure to remove No. 3 and 4 spark plug wires from clip attached to air cleaner. Disconnect vacuum, evaporative and air pump hoses and electrical connections.**

AUTOMATIC ELECTRIC CHOKE

1) Start engine and warm to normal operating temperature. Turn off engine. Remove air cleaner and plug vacuum hoses to air cleaner. Check all vacuum hoses, solenoids and choke wires for proper connections. Be sure all linkage operates freely.

2) Be sure choke cap is properly aligned with index mark. Choke plates should be fully open. If not, disconnect electric choke lead from cap terminal and connect to test light.

3) Ground second test light lead. With engine running, if light does not light, suspect faulty alternator or open circuit in choke lead. If light glows, replace choke cap.

4) Hold throttle 1/4-1/2 open and move choke plates to closed position. Release plates. They should return to fully open position. If not, clean or repair choke system.

5) Use a Rotunda Choke Tester (14-0206) or similar tool to cool the choke bi-metal coil. Hold throttle open and insert tester into choke housing opening for fast idle screw.

6) Apply cool air for 8 minutes, removing tester for 10 seconds every 2 minutes. Choke plates should seat lightly. If not seated by 8 minutes, clean and repair system.

7) Hold choke plates 1/4 open and remove tester. Allow throttle to close. Choke plates should remain partially open and throttle will be in kickdown position. Without touching throttle, start and run engine.

8) Open throttle momentarily and then release it. Choke plates should be vertical and engine speed should drop to normal idle. If not, check for binding parts, broken torsion spring, or replace electric choke cap unit. Turn off engine, remove test equipment and reinstall all components.

FUEL BOWL VENT

1) Apply parking brakes and block wheels. Remove air cleaner. Remove bowl vent hose from canister. Check fuel bowl vent solenoid for external damage and electrical connections. Attach a Rotunda T75L-9487-A tool or equivalent to end of canister hose.

2) Turn ignition switch off and hold choke plates open. Force air into fuel bowl vent system by squeezing tool's rubber bulb. If no fuel is displaced through metering system, start engine and run for 2 minutes. Turn off engine, and repeat test.

3) If fuel is still not displaced, remove test lamp and reconnect solenoid electrical lead. Remove carburetor air horn. Switch ignition on and off.

4) Solenoid plunger should retract when switch is on and extend when off. If so, replace bowl vent plunger seal. If not, replace solenoid, plunger, seal and plunger spring. Reassemble carburetor.

5) With ignition switch on and tool still connected, again force air into fuel bowl vent system. If rubber bulb resists rapid squeezing (pressure build up), bowl vent is working properly. If not, disconnect electrical lead to bowl vent solenoid and connect it to test light. Ground second test light lead.

6) Turn ignition switch on. If test light does not glow and battery is okay, solenoid lead has an open circuit. Repair or replace. If light glows, remove test light and reconnect lead to solenoid.

7) Remove all test equipment and reaasemble all components. Install air cleaner and check all hose

MOTORCRAFT MODEL 740 2-BARREL (Cont.)

connections. Start and run engine at 2500 RPM for 15 seconds and turn off engine.

ADJUSTMENTS

NOTE: For on-vehicle adjustments, see TUNE-UP PROCEDURES article.

FLOAT LEVEL

1) Hold air horn upside down at 45° angle with air horn gasket in place. Float tang should rest lightly on inlet needle. Using suitable drill bit or pin gauge, measure clearance between float toe and air horn casting. *See Fig. 1.*

Fig. 1: Float Level Adjustment

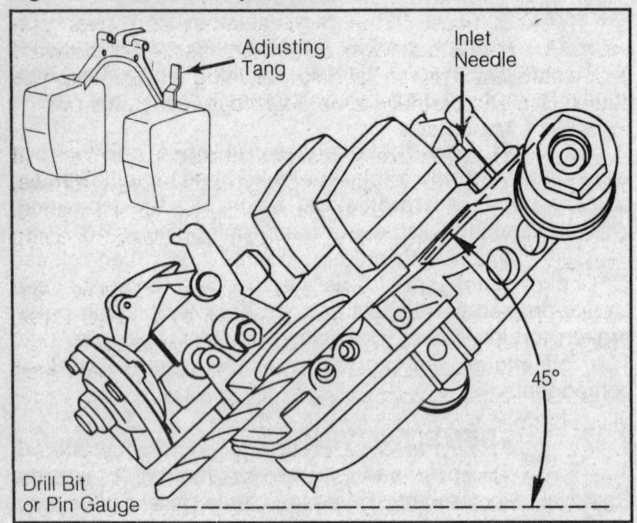

2) To adjust, remove float assembly and bend float level adjusting tang. Do not damage or scratch float tang during adjustment.

FLOAT DROP

1) Suspend air horn assembly in normal position with air horn gasket in place. Measure clearance from air horn gasket to bottom of float.

2) To adjust, remove float assembly and bend float drop tang. *See Fig. 2.*

Fig. 2: Float Drop Adjustment

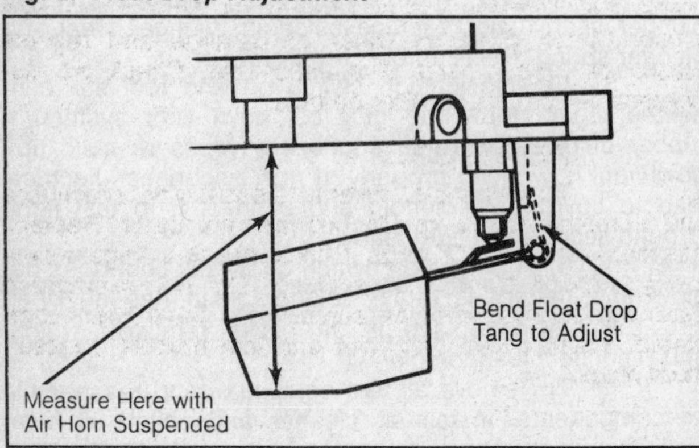

FAST IDLE CAM POSITION

NOTE: Rivets are used to hold choke cap in position. Ensure mandrel is well below rivet head. Then, drive mandrel down or out with a 1/16" punch. Using a 1/8" (No. 30) drill bit, drill out rivets. Drive rivets out with a 1/8" punch. Remove standard screw, retainer and choke cap.

1) Set fast idle screw on kickdown step of cam against shoulder of high step. Manually close choke plate, and measure distance between air horn wall and lower edge of choke plate.

2) To adjust, bend right fork of choke bi-metal shaft (engages fast idle cam) up or down.

NOTE: After adjustment, choke cap and retainer must be installed with rivets (supplied in service kit) and standard screw.

CHOKE VACUUM KICK (CHOKE PULLDOWN)

1) Remove choke cap and retainer as previously described. Place fast idle adjusting screw on high step of fast idle cam by opening throttle lever and rotating choke bi-metal shaft lever counterclockwise until choke plates are fully closed.

2) Using an outside vacuum source, apply 17 in. Hg to vacuum channel next to primary bore on carburetor base. With vacuum applied, spring should not be compressed. Measure clearance between air horn wall and lower edge of choke plate with a drill bit or pin gauge.

3) To adjust, remove choke diaphragm cover and adjusting screw plug. Install cover, and turn adjusting screw in or out until specification is obtained. Remove cover and reinstall plug. Install choke cap and retainer as previously described.

SECONDARY THROTTLE STOP SCREW

The secondary throttle stop screw is preset at the factory and staked in position. No adjustment is required.

AUTOMATIC CHOKE

Adjustment is made by removing choke cap and retainer as previously described and rotating cover until specification is correct. Install choke cap, retainer and rivets.

DASHPOT

NOTE: Dashpot adjustment is to be made after the curb idle has been set or checked. See appropriate TUNE-UP article.

1) With engine off and throttle at the curb idle position, depress dashpot plunger into dashpot assembly. Plunger may be depressed below the dashpot assembly.

2) Measure distance between accelerator lever pad and dashpot. If adjustment is necessary, loosen dashpot adjusting nut and rotate the dashpot to achieve correct specification. On models E3EE-CA, DA, EA, adjust to .08" (2 mm). On all other models, adjust to .16" (4 mm). *See Fig. 3.*

MOTORCRAFT MODEL 740 2-BARREL (Cont.)

Fig. 3: Dashpot Adjustment

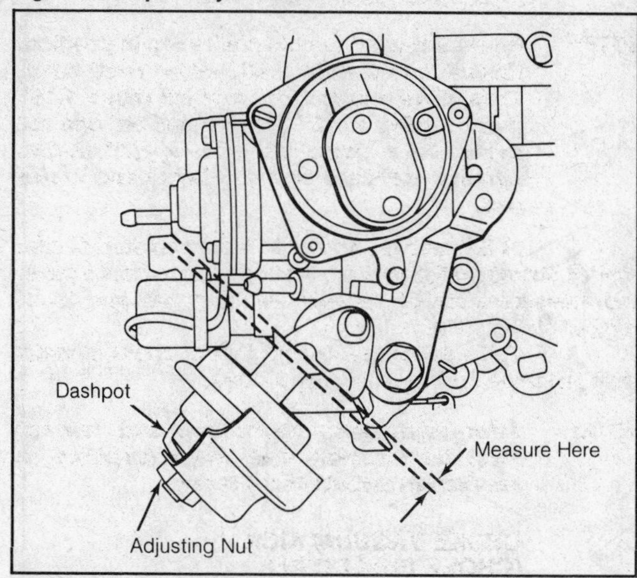

Rotate dashpot to adjust.

WIDE OPEN THROTTLE A/C CUTOUT SWITCH

1) Position fast idle lever in wide open throttle position. Using a feeler gauge, measure distance between fast idle lever actuating pin and switch actuating arm. Also measure distance between fast idle lever and cutout switch. *See. Fig. 4.*

Fig. 4: Wide Open Throttle A/C Cutout Switch Adjustment

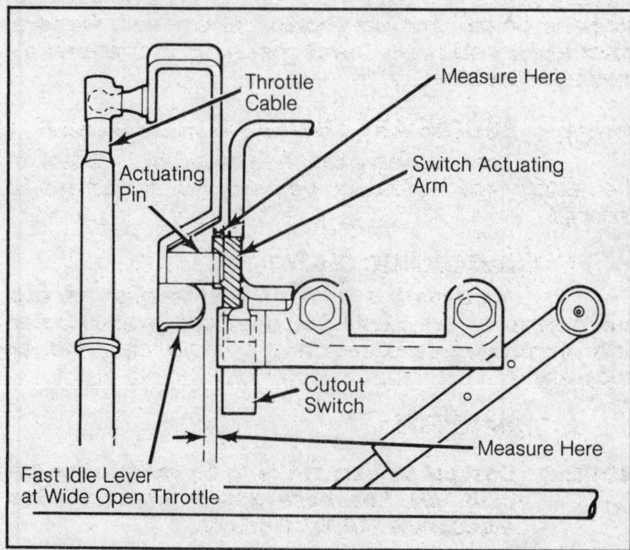

2) If either measurement is less than .120" (3 mm), bend cutout switch support bracket until distance is correct.

OVERHAUL

DISASSEMBLY

NOTE: To prevent damage to throttle plates, install carburetor legs or four 2 1/4" bolts into base, using eight nuts. Use separate container for parts removed from various assemblies.

Air Horn

1) Remove fuel filter. Remove 6 air horn screws and washers. Open throttle enough to clear fast idle screw and carefully lift air horn with gasket off main body. Turn air horn upside down.

2) Remove float hinge pin, float and inlet needle. Remove inlet needle seat and gasket, bowl cover gasket. Remove air horn gasket.

3) Remove 3 choke housing screws. Slide housing away from air horn and disengage primary choke link. Remove "O" ring from vacuum passage.

4) Remove choke pulldown cover retaining screws, pulldown cover and spring. Disengage choke assist spring from choke housing. Remove choke bi-metal shaft nut and lock washer. Remove choke lever.

5) Slide choke bi-metal shaft and lever outward. Pull choke pulldown diaphragm assembly outward until shaft bottoms on plastic retaining collar. Depress plastic clip, and carefully slide diaphragm assembly out.

Main Body

1) Remove vacuum throttle kicker (if equipped). Remove 4 accelerator pump cover screws, pump cover, pump diaphragm and pump return spring. Using needle nose pliers, remove accelerator pump nozzle.

2) Remove idle fuel shutoff solenoid and washer. Remove 3 power valve cover screws, valve cover, spring and diaphragm. Remove dashpot (if equipped).

3) Using a 3/32" drill bit, drill through hardened steel idle mixture concealment plugs and plastic inner plug. Remove plugs with screw extractor.

4) Turn mixture screws in until lightly seated. Count number of turns required to seat screw (to nearest 1/16 turn). Remove mixture screws, springs and "O" rings.

5) Remove primary and secondary fuel discharge nozzles. Carefully mark for reassembly reference. Be sure to note top and bottom ends. Remove primary and secondary jet holder and high speed air bleeds.

NOTE: Idle jets are located in bottom of holders. The air bleeds, main well tubes and main jets are a press fit assembly, but may be removed and assembled by hand.

INSPECTION

Thoroughly clean all parts and use compressed air to clean jets and fuel ports. Do not use wire brush. Check parts for wear or damage and replace plastic or rubber parts if questionable. Check all diaphragms for cracks or other defects.

REASSEMBLY

To assemble, reverse disassembly procedure and note the following: Do not intermix parts. Replace gaskets, seals and "O" rings. Check that all linkage moves freely without binding or sticking. Do not overtighten attaching screws. After all adjustments have been completed, install choke cap rivet and idle mixture concealment plugs.

MOTORCRAFT MODEL 740 2-BARREL (Cont.)

Fig. 5: Exploded View of Motorcraft Model 740 2-Bbl. Carburetor

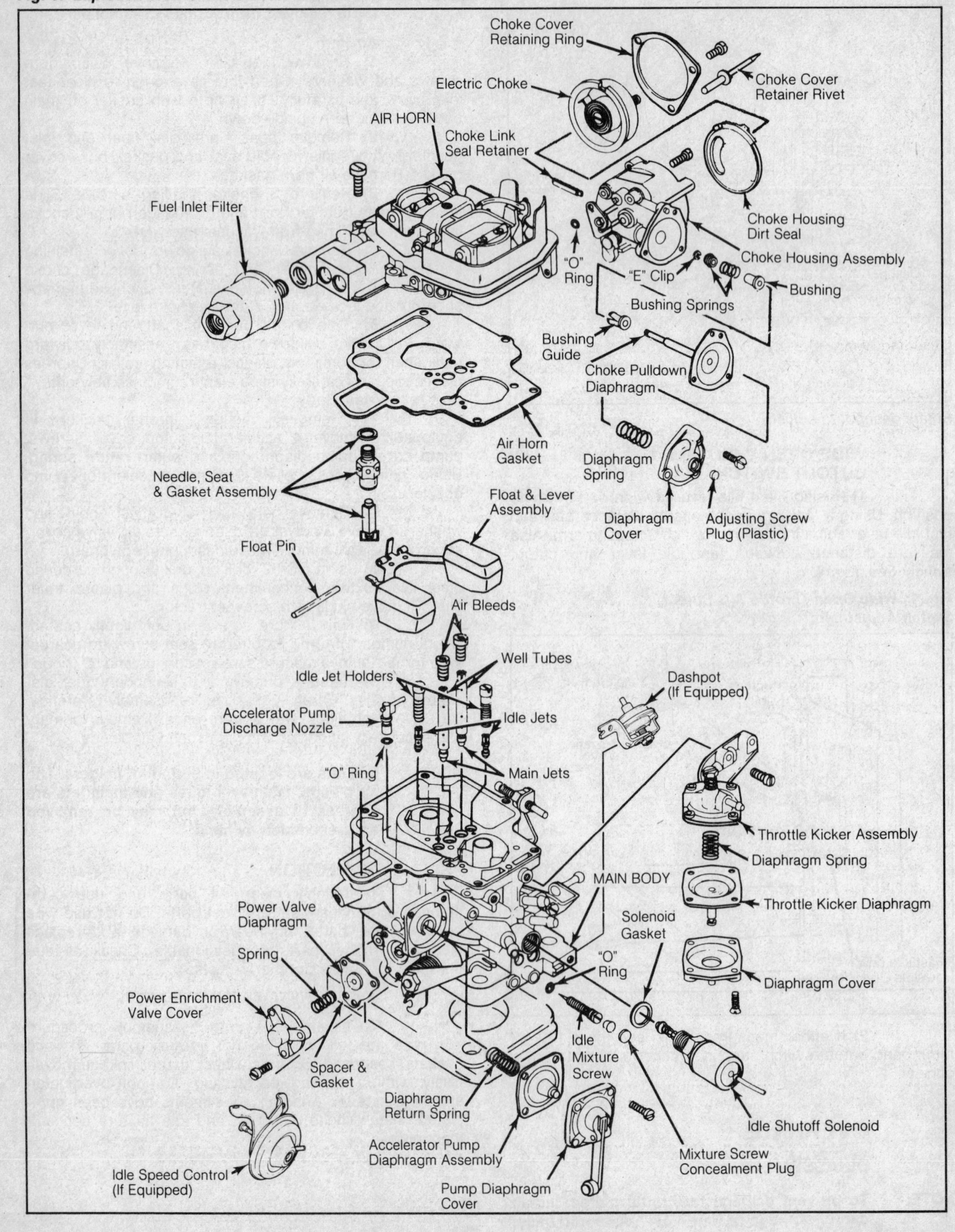

MOTORCRAFT MODEL 740 2-BARREL (Cont.)

CARBURETOR ADJUSTMENT SPECIFICATIONS

Application	Float Level	Float Drop	Fast Idle Cam	Choke Vacuum Kick	Choke Unloader	Auto. Choke
E3EE-AA	.295"	1.69"	.079"	.138"	.138"	.....
E3EE-BA	.295"	1.69"	.079"	.138"	.138"	.....
E3EE-CA	.295"	1.69"	.079"	.315"	.138"	.....
E3EE-DA	.295"	1.69"	.079"	.335"	.138"	.....
E3EE-EA	.295"	1.69"	.079"	.315"	.138"	.....
E3EE-JA	.295"	1.69"	.079"	.138"	.138"	.....
E3EE-KA	.295"	1.69"	.079"	.138"	.138"	.....
E3GE-DA	.295"	1.69"	.079"	.167"	.138"	.....
E3GE-FA	.295"	1.69"	.079"	.167"	.138"	.....
E3GE-HA	.295"	1.69"	.079"	.167"	.138"	.....
E3GE-JA	.295"	1.69"	.079"	.167"	.138"	.....
E3GE-PA	.295"	1.69"	.079"	.256"	.138"	.....
E3GE-RA	.295"	1.69"	.079"	.256"	.138"	.....
E3GE-SA	.295"	1.69"	.079"	.256"	.138"	.....

MOTORCRAFT MODEL 2150 2-BARREL

CARBURETOR APPLICATION

FORD MOTOR CO. CARBURETOR NO.

Application	Carb. No.
3.8L Engine	
Capri & Mustang	
Federal	
With A/C	E3CE-9510-AA
Without A/C	E3CE-9510-BA
California	
With A/C	E3CE-9510-GA
Without A/C	E3CE-9510-HA
High Altitude	
With A/C	E3CE-9510-EA
Without A/C	E3CE-9510-FA
Cougar & Thunderbird	
A.O.T. Trans.	
Federal	
With A/C	E3SE-9510-EA
Without A/C	E3SE-9510-FA
California	
With A/C	E3SE-9510-JA
Without A/C	E3SE-9510-KA
High Altitude	
With A/C	E3SE-9510-GA
Without A/C	E3SE-9510-HA
C5 Trans.	
Federal	
With A/C	E3SE-9510-LA
Without A/C	E3SE-9510-MA
California	
With A/C	E3SE-9510-NA
Without A/C	E3SE-9510-PA
LTD & Marquis	
Federal	
With A/C	E3SE-9510-EA
Without A/C	E3SE-9510-FA
California	
With A/C	E3SE-9510-JA
Without A/C	E3SE-9510-KA
High Altitude	
With A/C	E3SE-9510-GA
Without A/C	E3SE-9510-HA

CARBURETOR IDENTIFICATION

Carburetor can be identified by a tab attached to the air horn. This tag contains number and design change codes in addition to the build date. Always refer to the tag number when ordering or replacing parts.

DESCRIPTION

Motorcraft 2150 carburetors consist of a float system and 4 fuel metering systems: choke system, acceleration system, main metering system and power enrichment system. In addition to these systems, some carburetors may be equipped with some or all of the following systems: altitude compensation, high speed pullover system throttle positioners and/or variable high speed bleed system. The float system maintains a preset level of fuel in the fuel bowl. The fuel bowl is internally vented to the air cleaner on all models. Some models are also internally vented to the canister. Some carburetors have a filler block in the fuel bowl on the left side.

Fig. 1: Ford Motor Co. Carburetor Identification Tag

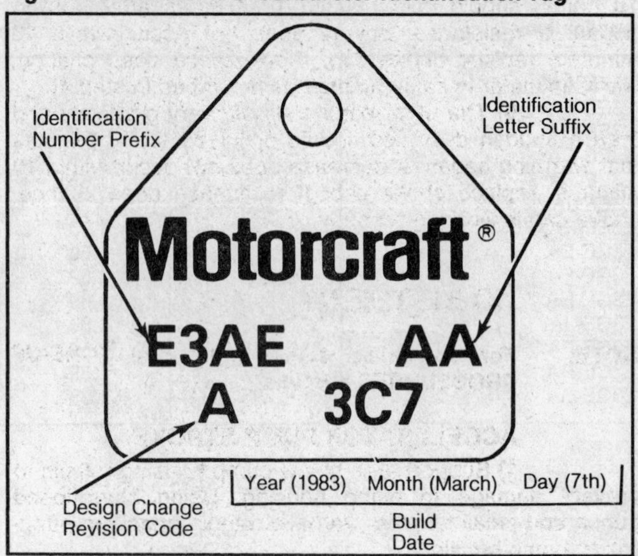

TESTING

ELECTRIC CHOKE

Choke Cap Continuity

1) With ignition off, connect test lamp between battery positive terminal and choke cap terminal. Using a jumper wire, connect one end to choke clamp shroud and other end to battery negative terminal.

2) Test lamp should glow. If not, connect jumper wire directly to choke cap ground pin. If lamp glows, correct poor connection between choke clamp shroud and choke cap ground pin. If lamp does not glow, replace choke cap.

3) Leave test lamp connected and remove jumper wire. Test lamp should glow. If not, locate and repair open in ground circuit. Reconnect electrical lead to choke cap.

4) Connect test lamp between choke cap shroud and battery negative terminal. Start engine. Test lamp should glow. If not, locate and repair open circuit between choke cap and alternator stator terminal. If no open circuit is found, check alternator output and service as required. Stop engine and remove test equipment.

Choke Cap Resistance

1) Using a heat source (100 watt bulb), hold close to face of choke cap for 3-5 minutes to heat cap to temperature above internal switching point.

2) Using an ohmmeter set on 30 ohm (maximum) scale, connect ohmmeter between choke cap terminal and choke cap shroud. Ensure metal-to-metal contact is obtained.

3) Ohm reading should be under 30 ohms, but not 0. If not to specifications, repeat test. If reading is still not to specifications, replace choke cap.

4) Using a choke tester, cool choke cap by directing cold air towards oval-shaped insulator (not case) around cap terminal. Ohm reading should slowly increase

MOTORCRAFT MODEL 2150 2-BARREL (Cont.)

and then a sudden increase (under 10 ohms) should occur.

5) Stop cooling. The sudden increase (of under 10 ohms) should occur within 10 minutes after cooling began. If resistance change does not occur within 10 minutes, replace choke cap. If resistance does change, warm insulator in same manner as described in step **4)**.

6) The ohm reading should vary gradually and then a sudden decrease should occur within 10 minutes that warming began. If decrease does not occur within 10 minutes, replace choke cap. If resistance does change, choke cap is working properly.

ADJUSTMENT

NOTE: **For on-vehicle adjustments, see TUNE-UP PROCEDURES article.**

ACCELERATOR PUMP STROKE

1) Support area below pump housing roll pin to prevent damage to pump housing. Using blunt-tipped punch and small hammer, remove roll pin attaching pump link to pump housing.

2) Lift pump link and rod up and over carburetor until keyed end of rod is aligned with keyed hole in pump overtravel lever. Remove and reposition rod in specified hole and reassemble pump link and rod assembly. *See Fig. 2.*

Fig. 2: Accelerator Pump Stroke Adjustment

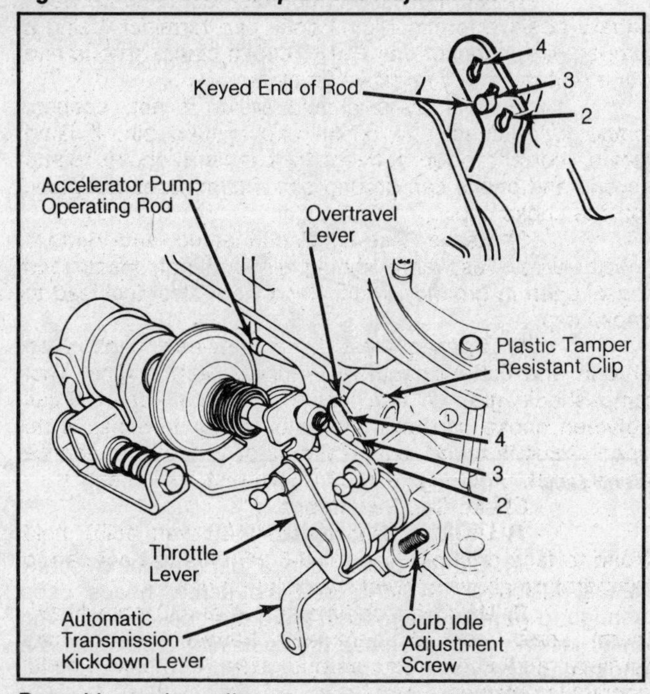

Reposition rod to adjust.

FLOAT LEVER (DRY SETTING)

NOTE: **Dry float setting is preliminary adjustment only. Final adjustment (wet setting) must be made after carburetor is installed on vehicle.**

1) With air horn removed, depress float tab to seat fuel inlet needle. Measure distance from top of main body (gasket removed) to float, at point 1/8" from free end of toe. *See Fig. 3.*

Fig. 3: Float Level Adjustment (Dry Setting)

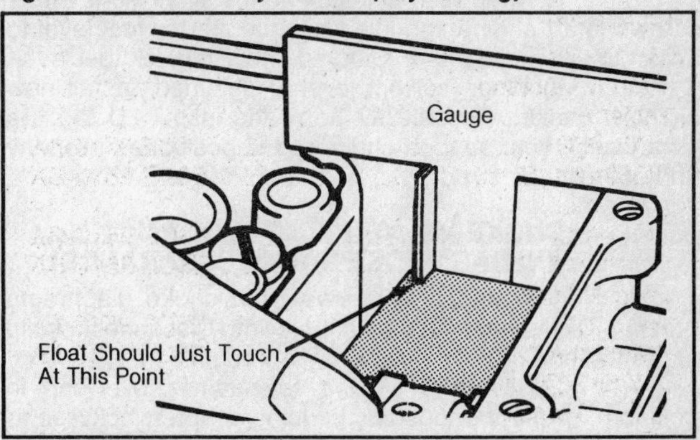

Bend float tab to adjust.

2) If adjustment is necessary, bend float tab. Do not allow float tab to contact needle as Viton needle tip may be damaged.

FLOAT LEVEL (WET SETTING)

1) Warm engine to normal operating temperature. Ensure vehicle is on flat, level surface. Stop engine. Remove air cleaner.

2) Insert gauge (Rotunda Tool T83L-9550-A) or equivalent, pointed end into the fuel bowl vent stack and rest level across other vent. Syphon fuel into sight tube and allow fuel to reach level.

3) Read fuel level on sight tube. If level is in specified band, adjustment is not required. If level is not correct, note on sight tube the amount of deviation and proceed to adjust.

4) Stop engine. Remove choke link, air horn attaching screws, vent hose and air horn assembly. Measure distance from top of machined surface of main body to level of fuel in fuel bowl. Make measurement at least 1/4" away from sides of bowl for accurate readings. *See Fig. 4.*

Fig. 4: Float Level Adjustment (Wet Setting)

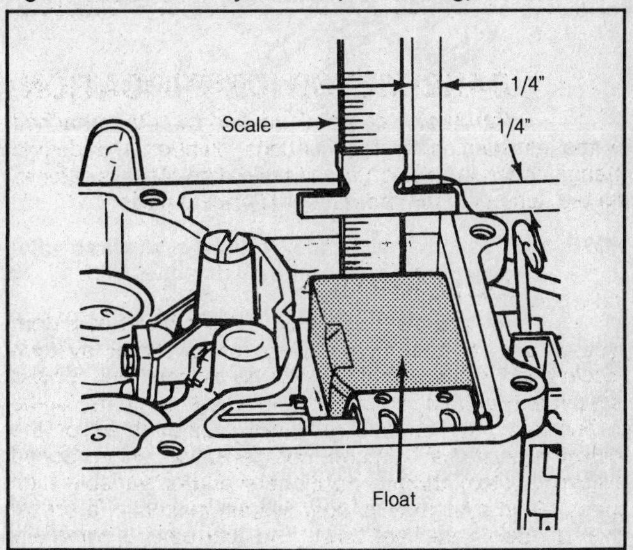

Bend float tab to adjust.

MOTORCRAFT MODEL 2150 2-BARREL (Cont.)

5) Stop engine before adjusting to avoid fire danger from fuel spray. Bend float tab (contacting inlet valve) up to raise fuel level and down to lower level.

6) After each adjustment, install air horn with 2 screws, start engine and idle long enough for fuel level to adjust to new adjustment. Stop engine. Recheck fuel level.

7) When correct level is obtained, install new air horn gasket. Replace air horn and install I.D tag. Be sure plastic dust seal on choke rod is positioned properly and does not bind rod.

CHOKE VALVE PULLDOWN (INITIAL CHOKE VALVE CLEARANCE)

1) Remove 2 screws from choke diaphragm bracket. Disconnect vacuum supply line. Disconnect circlip at the rod and remove pulldown diaphragm.

2) Install 3 screws to retain choke cap in position. Rotate thermostatic housing counterclockwise to lightly close choke plate and turn additional 90°.

3) Apply external vacuum source to activate pulldown motor or manually force diaphragm to retracted position. Using a drill bit or pin gauge, measure clearance between lower edge of choke plate and air horn wall.

4) To adjust, rotate adjusting screw until correct clearance is obtained. *See Fig. 5.* Perform Fast Idle Cam Index adjustment.

Fig. 5: Choke Pulldown Adjustment (Initial Choke Valve Clearance)

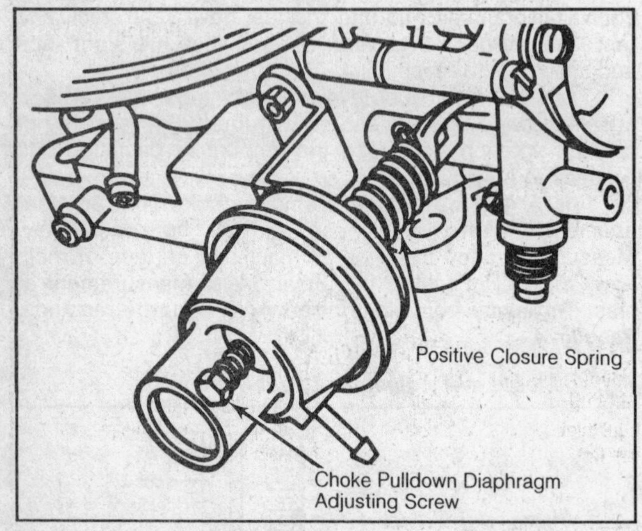

Rotate adjusting screw to adjust.

FAST IDLE CAM INDEX

NOTE: Fast idle cam index must be checked after any choke pulldown adjustment.

1) With thermostatic housing in rich position (step 2) in Choke Valve Pulldown adjustment procedure) open throttle to set fast idle cam. Apply external vacuum source to pulldown diaphragm.

2) Open throttle and watch fast idle cam. Fast idle cam should drop to kickdown step and fast idle screw should be opposite cam "V" notch.

3) To adjust, turn idle cam lever adjustment screw. *See Fig. 6.* Reconnect vacuum hose and perform Automatic Choke adjustment to reset thermostatic housing to specification.

Fig. 6: Fast Idle Cam Index Adjustment

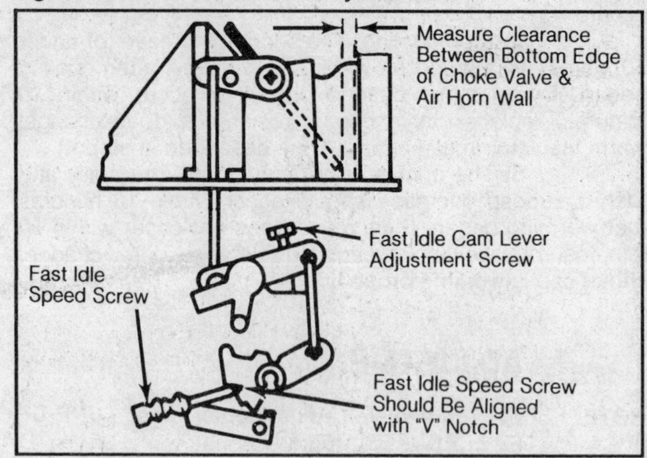

Turn fast idle cam lever adjustment screw to adjust.

CHOKE UNLOADER

1) Hold throttle wide open. Using specified drill bit or pin gauge, measure clearance between lower edge of choke plate and air horn wall.

2) To adjust, bend metal tang on fast idle speed lever attached to throttle shaft. *See Fig. 7.* Make sure tang does not touch edge of cam to avoid wide open throttle sticking condition. Rotate throttle lever several times to check for any binding during unloader operation.

Fig. 7: Choke Unloader Adjustment

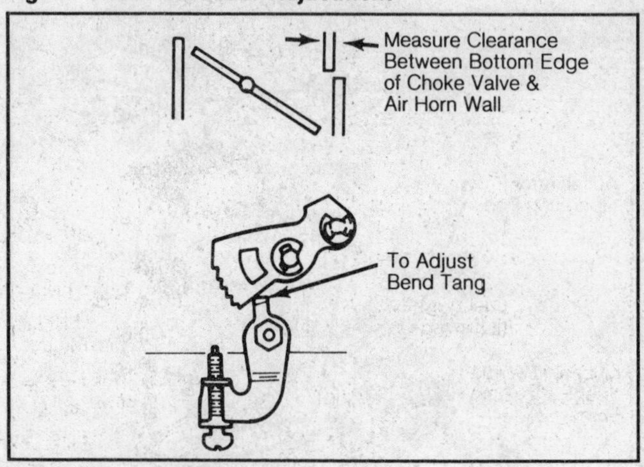

Bend tang to adjust.

AUTOMATIC CHOKE

1) Center punch choke cap retaining screw heads. Using a 1/4" drill, drill the screw heads deep enough to remove the retainer from the choke cap. Using small locking pliers, remove the remaining portion of the choke cap screws.

2) Apply 1/2" bead of epoxy sealer to each side of choke cover gasket, next to the 3 screw bosses. Install gasket and choke cap with new break-away screws.

3) Rotate cover assembly in "Rich" or "Lean" direction to align reference mark on choke cover with specified mark on housing. Tighten break-away screws until head of screw breaks off.

MOTORCRAFT MODEL 2150 2-BARREL (Cont.)

Fig. 8: Exploded View of Motorcraft Model 2150 Carburetor Assembly

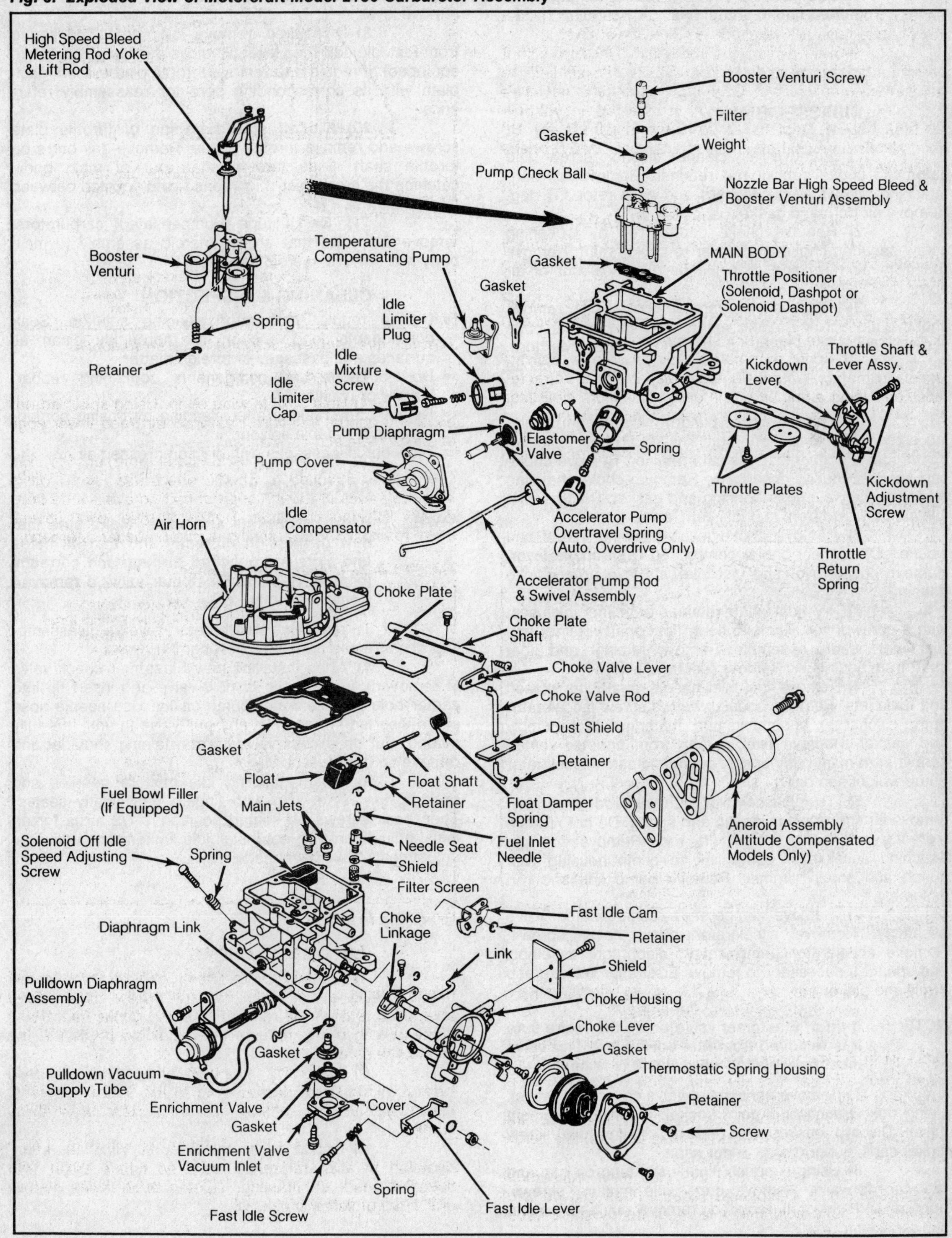

MOTORCRAFT MODEL 2150 2-BARREL (Cont.)

NOTE: Ensure bi-metal spring tab is engaged in slotted choke shaft lever.

OVERHAUL

DISASSEMBLY

Air Horn

1) Remove air cleaner anchor screw and automatic choke control rod retainer. Remove air horn attaching screws, lock washers and carburetor I.D. tag. Remove air horn and gasket.

2) Remove choke control rod by loosening screw securing choke shaft lever to choke shaft. Remove rod from air horn and slide plastic dust seal out of air horn.

3) If necessary to remove choke plate, remove choke plate screw staking marks. Remove choke plate screws. Slide choke plate out of shaft from top of air horn. Remove burrs from choke plate screw holes on choke shaft. Slide choke shaft out of air horn.

Main Body

1) Remove choke pulldown diaphragm retaining screws. Remove diaphragm link circlip and pulldown diaphragm. Remove fast idle cam retainer. Remove choke cap as previously described. Remove choke housing retaining screws, choke housing and gasket. Remove fast idle cam and rod from fast idle cam lever.

2) Remove choke lever retaining screw and washer. Disconnect choke control rod from choke lever. Remove choke lever and fast idle cam lever from choke housing.

3) Pry float shaft retainer from fuel inlet seat with a screwdriver. Remove float, float shaft retainer and fuel inlet needle assembly. Remove retainer and float shaft from float lever. Remove fuel bowl filler.

4) Remove fuel inlet needle, seat, filter screen and main jets. Remove booster venturi screw (accelerator pump discharge), booster venturi, metering rod assembly and gasket. Remove filter screen from booster venturi screw. Turn main body upside down and catch accelerator pump weight and ball.

5) To disassemble metering rod assembly, remove lift spring retaining clip and spring. Do not remove metering rod hanger from lift rod. Remove roll pin attaching accelerator pump link to pump housing with punch and small hammer. Remove pump link and rod assembly.

6) Remove temperature compensated valve assembly. Remove accelerator pump cover screws. Remove accelerator pump cover, diaphragm assembly and spring. If necessary to remove Elastomer valve, grasp firmly and pull out.

NOTE: If tip of Elastomer valve broke off, make sure it is removed from fuel bowl. Elastomer valve must be replaced whenever it is removed.

7) Remove enrichment valve cover and gasket. Using box wrench or 8-point socket, remove enrichment valve. Discard gasket. To remove idle mixture screw limiter caps, support area under cap.

8) Using a punch, lightly tap tang on cap and tap cap forward. Remove caps, idle mixture screws, springs and plugs. If required, remove nut and washer securing fast idle adjusting lever to throttle shaft and remove lever.

9) If required, remove idle screw and spring from fast idle adjusting lever. Remove throttle positioner (if equipped). If required to remove throttle plates, mark each plate with its corresponding bore for reassembly reference.

10) File off staked portion of throttle plate screws and remove throttle plates. Remove any burrs on throttle shaft. Slide throttle shaft out of main body, catching the mechanical high speed cam (located between throttle plates).

11) On altitude compensated carburetors, remove 3 screws that attach aneroid assembly to main body and remove aneroid assembly.

CLEANING & INSPECTION

- Use a regular carburetor cleaning solution. Soak components long enough to thoroughly clean all surfaces and passages of foreign matter.
- Do not soak any components containing rubber, leather or plastic.
- Remove any residue after cleaning by rinsing components in a suitable solvent.
- Blow out all passages with dry compressed air.

REASSEMBLY

NOTE: Use new gaskets and seals. Make sure that new gaskets fit correctly and that all holes and slots are punched through and correctly located. Replace Elastomer valve if removed from main body.

To reassemble carburetor, reverse disassembly procedure and note the following:

1) When installing new Elastomer check valve (if removed), lubricate tip of new valve and insert tip into center hole of accelerator pump cavity. Use needle nose pliers inserted in fuel bowl and pull valve in until it is fully seated. Cut off excess valve tip at retaining shoulder and remove tip from fuel bowl.

2) When installing idle mixture needles and springs, turn screws in with fingers until lightly seated. Then back screws off seated position 1 1/2 turns for an initial adjustment. Do not install idle limiter caps until final adjustments have been made.

1983 Motorcraft Carburetors

MOTORCRAFT MODEL 2150 2-BARREL (Cont.)

CARBURETOR ADJUSTMENT SPECIFICATIONS

Application	Float Level		Accel. Pump	Choke Pulldown	Fast Idle Cam	Choke Unloader	Auto. Choke
	Dry	Wet					
Ford Motor Co. (2150)							
E3CE-9510-AA	7/16"	13/16"	#3	.103"	"V" Notch	.250"	"V" Notch
E3CE-9510-BA	7/16"	13/16"	#3	.103"	"V" Notch	.250"	"V" Notch
E3CE-9510-EA	7/16"	13/16"	#3	.113"	"V" Notch	.250"	"V" Notch
E3CE-9510-FA	7/16"	13/16"	#3	.113"	"V" Notch	.250"	"V" Notch
E3CE-9510-GA	7/16"	13/16"	#3	.103"	"V" Notch	.250"	"V" Notch
E3CE-9510-HA	7/16"	13/16"	#3	.103"	"V" Notch	.250"	"V" Notch
E3SE-9510-EA	7/16"	13/16"	#3	.113"	"V" Notch	.250"	"V" Notch
E3SE-9510-FA	7/16"	13/16"	#3	.113"	"V" Notch	.250"	"V" Notch
E3SE-9510-GA	7/16"	13/16"	#3	.120"	"V" Notch	.250"	"V" Notch
E3SE-9510-HA	7/16"	13/16"	#3	.120"	"V" Notch	.250"	"V" Notch
E3SE-9510-JA	7/16"	13/16"	#3	.101"	"V" Notch	.250"	"V" Notch
E3SE-9510-KA	7/16"	13/16"	#3	.101"	"V" Notch	.250"	"V" Notch
E3SE-9510-LA	7/16"	13/16"	#3	.107"	"V" Notch	.250"	"V" Notch
E3SE-9510-MA	7/16"	13/16"	#3	.107"	"V" Notch	.250"	"V" Notch
E3SE-9510-NA	7/16"	13/16"	#3	.107"	"V" Notch	.250"	"V" Notch
E3SE-9510-PA	7/16"	13/16"	#3	.107"	"V" Notch	.250"	"V" Notch

1983 Motorcraft Carburetors

MOTORCRAFT MODEL 7200 VV 2-BARREL

CARBURETOR APPLICATION

FORD MOTOR CO.

Application	[1] Ford Motor Co. Part No.
5.8L (351") V8	E2AE-NA or E2AE-AJA

[1] — Ford basic part number is 9510.

CARBURETOR IDENTIFICATION

Carburetor part number identification is stamped on left side of the upper throttle body. Stamped number also contains part number prefix and suffix. Basic part number for all carburetors is 9510. A design change code (if any) is included on the stamped number. An assembly date code (year, month and day) is also included on the stamped number. *See Fig. 1.*

Fig. 1: Ford Motor Co. Carburetor Identification Stamp

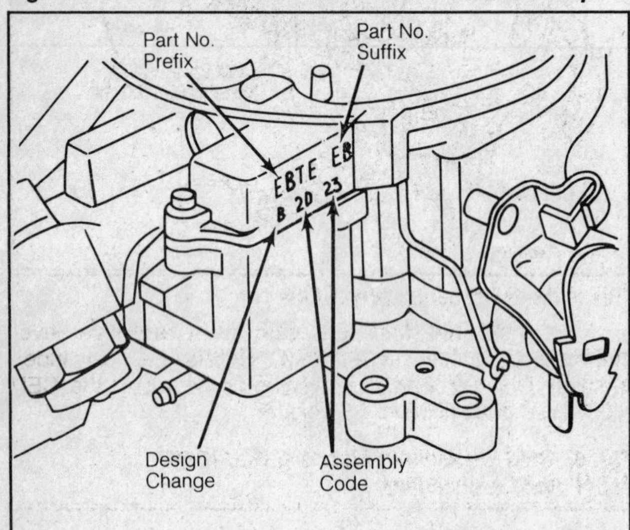

Identification is stamped on left side of the upper throttle body.

DESCRIPTION

Motorcraft model 7200 variable venturi carburetor differs from other standard type carburetors. It has the ability to change the area of the venturi for varying engine speed and load conditions.

This is accomplished by dual venturi valves, controlled by engine vacuum and throttle position. Depending upon engine speed and load conditions, the position of the venturi valves change (move in and out of the air stream) to determine the air flow to the 2 carburetor throats.

The venturi valves are connected to 2 tapered main metering rods, which ride in the main metering jets. When the venturi valve position changes, the metering rods vary the amount of fuel flow through the carburetor.

Systems on the 7200 carburetor include: fuel inlet, main metering, control vacuum, cold enrichment, accelerator pump system and an all-electric dual-stage choke.

The 7200 carburetor is equipped with a feedback control system. This system works in conjunction with an on-board electronic control module. The air bleed feedback system uses a stepper motor to regulate bleed air admitted into main metering system. This provides a more precise metering of the air/fuel ratio, as dictated by the module through a series of sensors.

ADJUSTMENT

NOTE: For on-vehicle adjustments, see TUNE-UP PROCEDURES article.

FLOAT LEVEL

1) Remove upper body assembly. Remove and discard upper body gasket. Construct a gauge to specified float level setting.

2) Turn upper body assembly upside-down. Using gauge, measure distance from cast surface of upper body to bottom of float. *See Fig. 2.*

Fig. 2: Float Level Adjustment

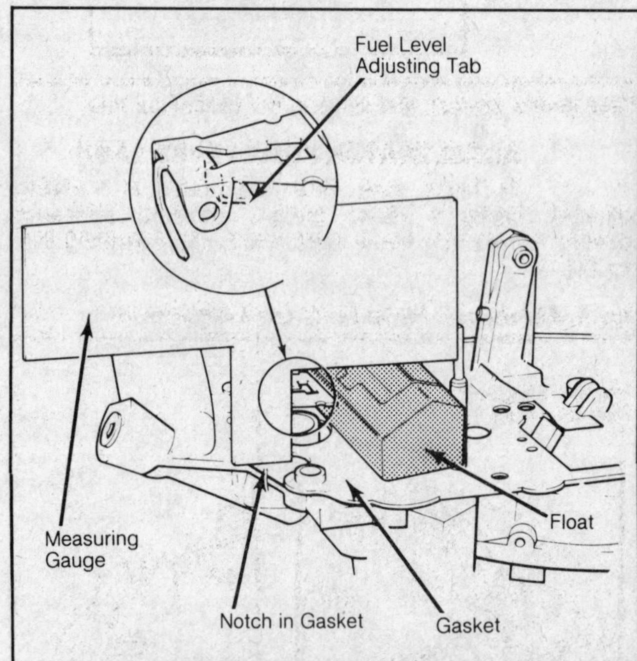

Construct a gauge to specified float level setting.

3) To adjust, bend adjusting tab on float arm. Bend away from inlet needle to decrease setting and toward inlet needle to increase setting.

FLOAT DROP

1) With upper body and gasket removed, hold upper body in upright position and allow float to hang. *See Fig. 3.*

2) Construct a gauge to specified float drop setting. Using gauge, measure distance from cast surface of upper body to bottom of float. *See Fig. 3.*

3) To adjust, bend float lever stop tab on float arm. Bend away from hinge pin to increase setting and toward hinge pin to decrease setting.

MOTORCRAFT MODEL 7200 VV 2-BARREL (Cont.)

Fig. 3: Float Drop Adjustment

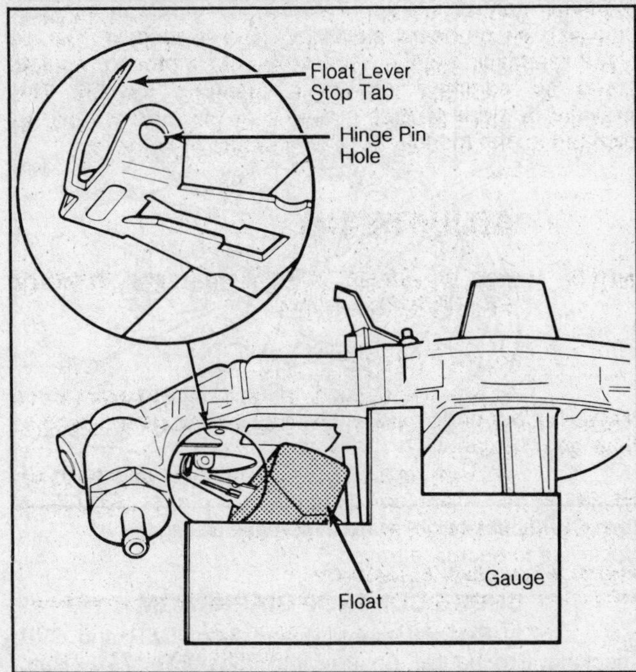

Place gauge against cast surface, not gasket surface.

ACCELERATOR PUMP LEVER LASH

1) Make sure curb idle speed is correctly adjusted. Using a feeler gauge, measure clearance between accelerator pump stem and pump operating link. *See Fig. 4.*

Fig. 4: Accelerator Pump Lever Lash Adjustment

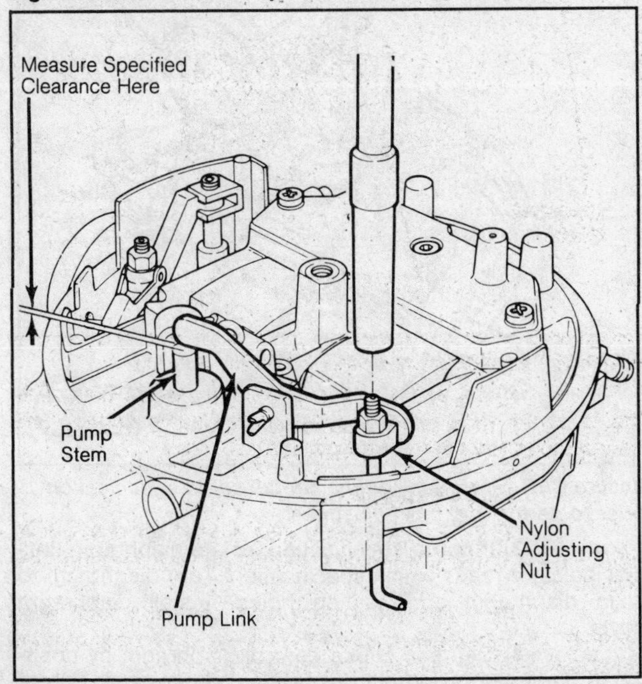

This adjustment must be checked whenever curb idle speed is adjusted.

2) If clearance is not to specification, tighten or loosen nut on end of link to obtain specified clearance.

COLD ENRICHMENT METERING ROD (CER) & CONTROL VACUUM REGULATOR (CVR)

Checking Procedure

1) Perform steps **1)** and **2)** of Automatic Choke adjustment procedure. Position dial indicator on carburetor, with indicator stem on top surface of enrichment rod.

2) Install choke weight (T77L-9848-A7 or equivalent) on choke bimetal lever. With cold enrichment metering rod (CER) seated, install dial indicator with tip on CER top surface. Zero dial indicator. *See Fig. 5.*

Fig. 5: Cold Enrichment Metering Rod (CER) Adjustment

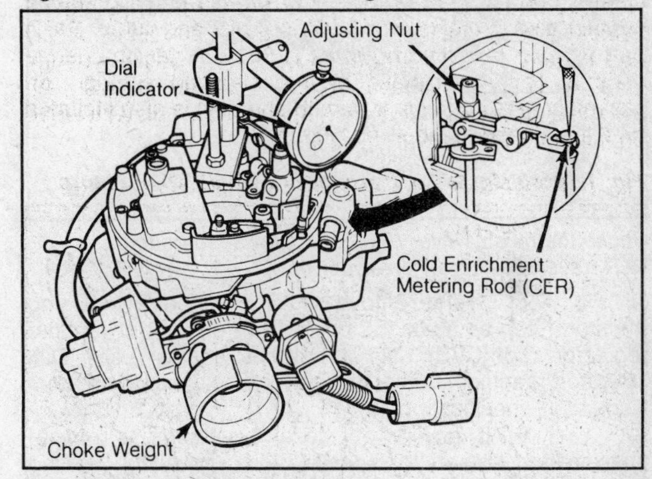

This is the initial set-up procedure.

3) Free fast idle cam from fast idle lever interference. Install stator cap. Rotate cap to index position. Dial indicator reading should be within the CER "75°F Run" specification. *See Fig. 6.*

Fig. 6: Cold Enrichment Metering Rod (CER) "75°F Run" Adjustment

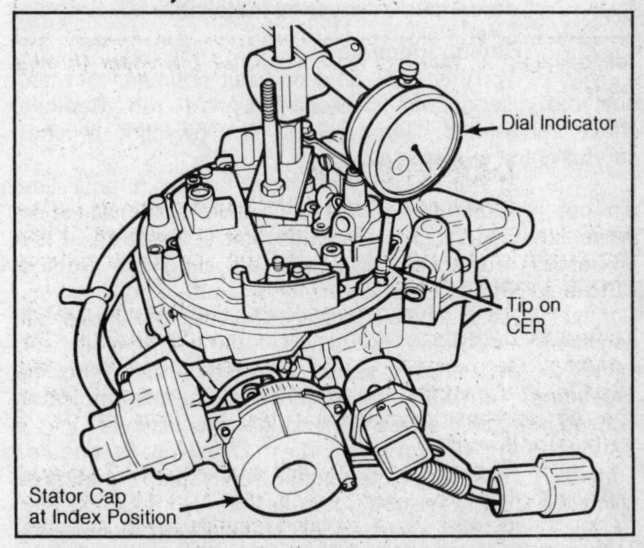

Stator cap mounted and rotated to index position.

4) Do not remove or zero dial indicator. Remove stator cap. Rotate thermostat lever clockwise, until CER travel stop screw is bottomed on upper body. Dial indicator reading should be within the CER "0°F Start" specification. *See Fig. 7.*

MOTORCRAFT MODEL 7200 VV 2-BARREL (Cont.)

Fig. 7: Cold Enrichment Metering Rod (CER) "0°F Start" Adjustment

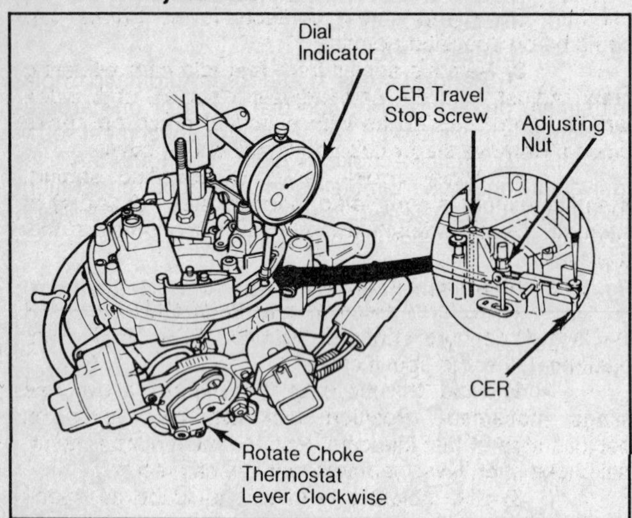

Choke thermostat lever rotated clockwise to bottom CER travel stop screw on upper body.

5) Do not remove or zero dial indicator. Using the stator cap as a weight, push down on control vacuum regulator rod (CVR) until it bottoms against seat. Dial indicator reading should be within the "Control Vacuum Regulator" specification.

6) If any 1 of these 3 settings is out of specification, reset to specifications following Setting Procedure.

NOTE: **Adjusting nuts are filled with epoxy sealer after final adjustment is made by manufacturer. To adjust, new parts must be installed. Also, choke control rod has undercut groove designed to break at 10 INCH. lbs. (1 N.m) torque. If rod breaks during setting procedure, new rod must be installed.**

Setting Procedure

1) Turn CER adjusting nut counterclockwise, until nut disengages from choke control rod. Remove choke control rod. Remove dust seal by lifting retainer carefully, and sliding seal out.

2) Remove clip on choke hinge pin, and slide pin out of casting. Remove CER lever, CVR adjusting swivel, and adjusting nut as an assembly. Install new CER lever, CVR adjusting swivel, and adjusting nut. Tighten CER adjusting nut to lower, and locate into position. Connect lever to CVR adjusting swivel. Install hinge pin and clip.

3) Perform steps **2)** and **3)** of Checking Procedure. Turn CER adjustment nut until dial indicator reading is within the CER "75°F Run" specification.

4) Perform step **4)** of Checking Procedure. Turn CER travel stop screw, until dial indicator reading is within the CER "0°F Start" specification.

5) Perform step **5)** of Checking Procedure. Hold CVR nut with a 3/8" wrench. Using a 3/32" Allen wrench, turn CVR counterclockwise to increase travel and clockwise to decrease travel. *See Fig. 8.*

6) Apply epoxy to nuts and stop screw. Replace choke cap following steps **3)** and **4)** of Automatic Choke adjustment procedure.

Fig. 8: Control Vacuum Regulator (CVR) Adjustment

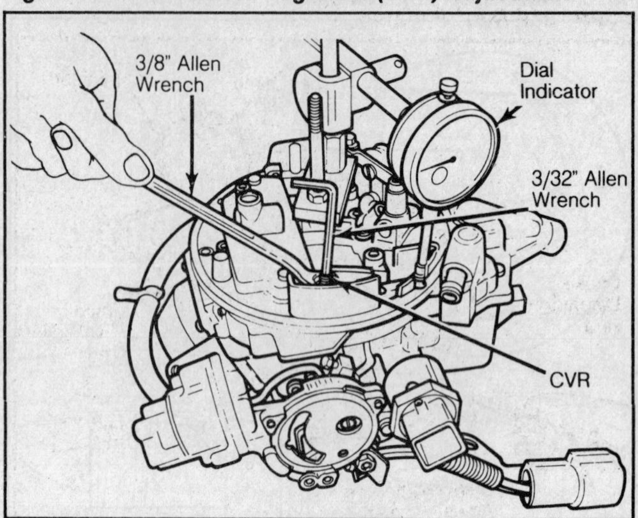

Turn CVR counterclockwise to increase travel and clockwise to decrease travel.

CHOKE CONTROL DIAPHRAGM

1) Perform steps **1)** and **2)** of CER and CVR Checking Procedure. Ensure that the CER "75°F Run" adjustment is set to specification.

2) Remove diaphragm cover. Using finger pressure, seat diaphragm. Dial indicator reading should be within the CER "75°F Run" specification. *See Fig. 9.*

Fig. 9: Choke Control Diaphragm Adjustment at CER "75°F Start" Position

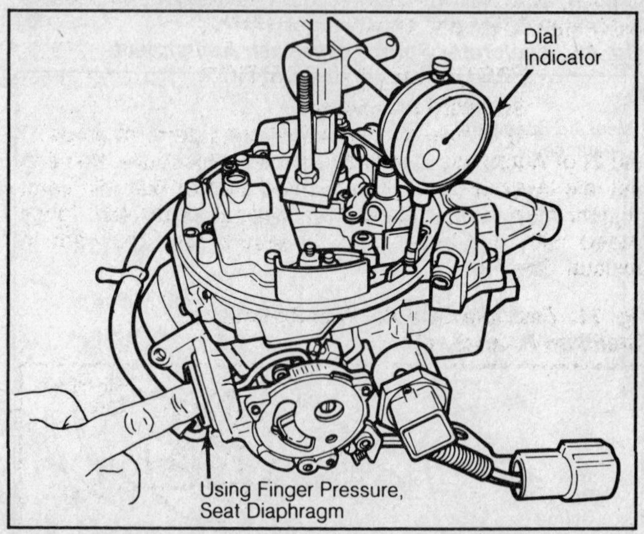

Ensure CER "75°F Run" adjustment is set to specification prior to performing this adjustment.

3) If not to specification, rotate diaphragm until dial indicator reads within specification. Turn diaphragm to align diaphragm and casting holes. Install diaphragm cover.

4) Depress choke control diaphragm by pushing in diaphragm rod until diaphragm bottoms out. Rotate thermostat lever clockwise, until choke shaft lever pin touches fast idle intermediate lever. Dial indicator reading should be within the CER "0°F Run" specification. *See Fig. 10.*

MOTORCRAFT MODEL 7200 VV 2-BARREL (Cont.)

Fig. 10: Choke Control Diaphragm Adjustment at CER "0°F Run" Position

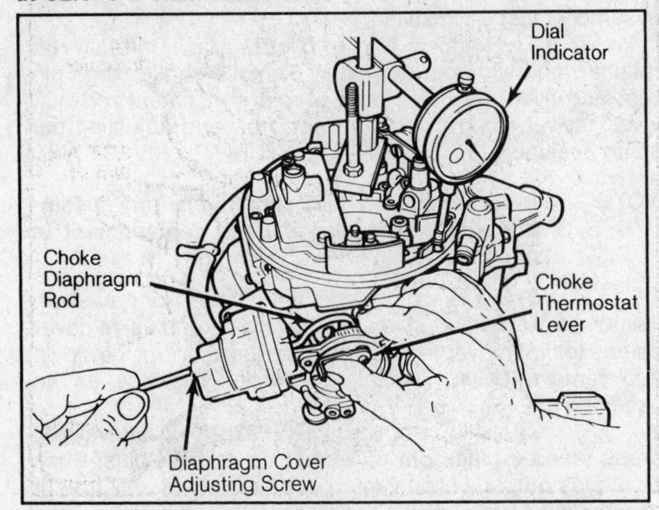

Hold thermostat lever in position so choke shaft lever pin is touching fast idle intermediate lever.

5) If dial indicator reading is not to specification, remove lead ball covering choke control diaphragm cover adjusting screw. Turn adjusting screw clockwise to increase height and counterclockwise to decrease height. Install a new lead ball over adjusting screw.

NOTE: If lead ball is not removable, install a new, unplugged cover.

6) After adjustment, install lead ball. Using steps **3)** and **4)** of Automatic Choke adjustment, install diaphragm cover and choke cap assembly.

FAST IDLE CAM POSITION

Standard Procedure

1) Before making adjustment, perform steps **1)** and **2)** of Automatic Choke adjustment procedure. Position fast idle lever in corner of specified step of fast idle cam. Highest step is considered 1st step. Hold throttle lightly closed with a rubber band to secure fast idle cam in position. *See Fig. 11.*

Fig. 11: Fast Idle Cam Position Adjustment (Standard Procedure)

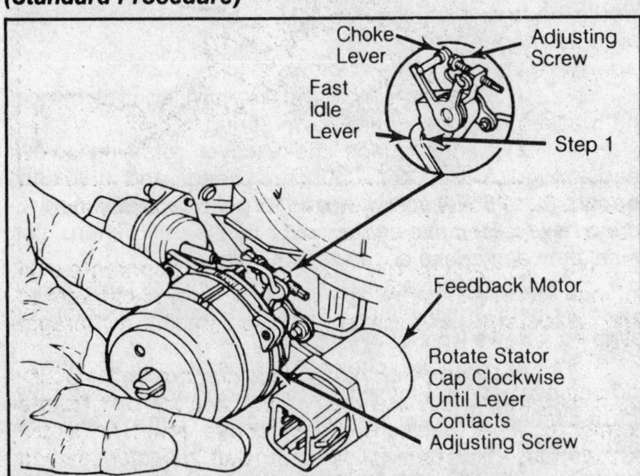

Highest step is considered 1st step.

2) Install stator cap T77L-9848-A (or equivalent) in place of choke cover. Rotate stator cap clockwise, until fast idle speed screw contacts lever. Choke cap should be on specified notch.

3) Remove sealer from fast idle cam adjusting screw. Adjust fast idle cam adjusting screw, until index mark on stator cap aligns with specified notch on choke housing. Remove stator cap and install choke cover.

4) Adjust choke cover to specified setting. When adjustment is completed, perform steps **3)** and **4)** of Automatic Choke adjustment procedure to complete this adjustment.

Alternate Procedure

1) Perform steps **1)** and **2)** of CER and CVR Checking Procedure. Ensure that the CER "75°F Run" adjustment is set to specification.

2) Hold throttle slightly open to allow free linkage movement. Position fast idle cam lever on specified step of fast idle cam. Rotate choke bimetal lever, until choke shaft lever contacts fast idle cam screw.

3) Dial indicator reading should be as specified. To adjust, turn adjusting screw clockwise to increase reading and counterclockwise to decrease reading.

NOTE: Turning adjusting screw in clockwise direction turns cam in counterclockwise direction.

4) When adjustment is completed, perform steps **3)** and **4)** of Automatic Choke adjustment procedure to complete this adjustment.

AUTOMATIC CHOKE

1) Center punch choke cover retaining screw heads. Align a 1/4" drill on screw head, and drill only enough to remove screw head. Repeat for remaining 2 screw heads. Remove choke cover by inserting sharp, flat chisel between choke cover gasket layers.

2) Using small pliers, remove remaining portion of retaining screws from choke housing. Carefully clean epoxy and gasket from choke cover and housing using gasket scraper. Remove choke cover carefully. Choke cover and gasket are sealed to housing with epoxy sealer.

3) Apply 1/2" bead of epoxy sealer to each side of choke cover gasket, adjacent to the 3 screw bosses. Install gasket and choke cover using new break-away screws.

4) Rotate cover assembly in "Rich" or "Lean" direction to align reference mark on choke cover with specified scale graduation on housing. Tighten each break-away screw until head of screw breaks off. Ensure that bimetal spring tab is engaged in slotted choke shaft lever.

VENTURI VALVE WIDE OPEN THROTTLE (WOT) OPENING

1) Center punch expansion plug covering venturi valve (WOT) stop adjustment screw. Center punch until loose. Plug is located at rear of main body on throttle side of carburetor.

2) Using a 5/32" Allen wrench, remove adjustment screw. Hold throttle valves wide open. Apply light closing pressure on venturi valve.

3) Measure venturi valve closing gap clearance between venturi valve and air horn wall. Using a 5/64" Allen wrench, turn venturi valve limiter adjustment screw on venturi valve arm to set closing gap clearance.

MOTORCRAFT MODEL 7200 VV 2-BARREL (Cont.)

4) Using a 5/32" Allen wrench, install adjustment screw and spring. Recheck specified clearance.

5) Hold throttle plates wide open. Apply light closing pressure on venturi valve. Measure maximum opening clearance, between venturi valve and venturi opening wall.

6) Using a 3/32" Allen wrench, turn throttle (WOT) stop adjustment screw until maximum opening clearance is within specification.

7) Install a new expansion plug in access hole.

Fig. 12: Venturi Valve Wide Open Throttle (WOT) Opening Adjustment

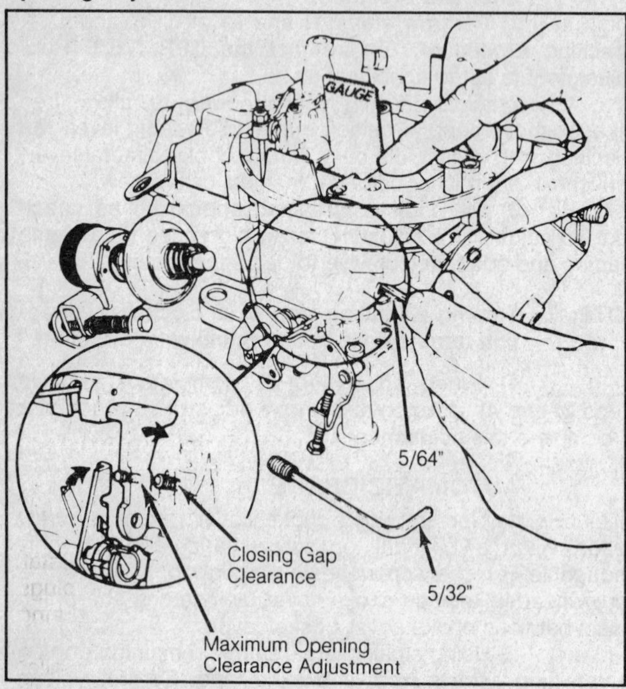

Use a 5/64" Allen wrench to adjust closing gap clearance and a 3/32" Allen wrench to adjust maximum opening clearance.

OVERHAUL

DISASSEMBLY

Upper Body

1) Mount carburetor in a holding fixture. Remove fuel inlet fitting, filter, gasket and spring. Remove clips from accelerator pump and choke control rods. Disconnect rods.

2) Remove air cleaner stud. Remove 7 screws and upper body. Note position of long screw for reassembly reference. Place upper body upside-down on a clean surface. Remove float hinge pin and float assembly. Remove upper body gasket.

3) Remove fuel inlet valve, seat and gasket. Remove accelerator pump link and nut, accelerator pump adjusting nut, and pump link. Remove accelerator pump overtravel spring, clip, and washer. Remove pump rod and dust seal.

4) Remove cold enrichment rod (CER) adjusting nut by turning counterclockwise. Adjusting nuts are filled with epoxy sealer after final adjustment is made by manufacturer. Sealer may cause breakage of choke control rod. Undercut design of choke control rod allows it to break at 10 INCH lbs. (1 N.m). If breakage occurs, new assembly must be installed.

5) Remove choke control rod. Carefully lift retainer, and slide out dust seal. Remove choke hinge pin clip, and slide pin out. Remove cold enrichment rod nut, lever, swivel, control vacuum regulator, and adjusting nut as an assembly.

NOTE: Disassembly of cold enrichment rod assembly is only required if parts replacement is necessary.

6) Slide cold enrichment rod from casting. Remove 2 Torx-head screws, securing venturi valve cover plate. Holding cover in place, turn carburetor upside-down and remove cover, gasket, and roller bearings as an assembly.

7) Using remover (T77L-9928-A or equivalent), press tapered plugs out of venturi valve pivot pins. Push pivot pins out, and slide venturi valve rearward until free of casting. Remove pivot pin bushings.

8) Remove metering rod pivot pins (on outer side of venturi valve), metering rods, and springs. Mark rods "throttle" or "choke" for reassembly reference.

9) Block venturi valve wide open. Using jet plug removal tool (T77L-9533-B or equivalent), remove main jet cup plugs, recessed in upper body casting. Using a jet wrench (T77L-9533-A or equivalent), turn each metering jet clockwise, counting number of turns required to seat them in bottom of casting. Record number of turns to nearest 1/4 turn.

10) Turn jet assemblies counterclockwise to remove. Remove "O" rings. Mark or identify main metering jets as to choke or throttle side for reassembly reference. Remove accelerator pump plunger assembly.

11) Remove venturi valve limiter adjusting screw from throttle side of venturi valve. If necessary for cleaning, remove 1/8" pipe plug in fuel inlet casting boss.

Main Body

1) Remove venturi valve diaphragm cover, spring guide and spring. Carefully loosen diaphragm and slide out of main body. Place hand under carburetor to catch accelerator pump check ball and weight as it is turned upside-down. Place carburetor upside-down on a clean surface.

2) Remove 5 throttle body screws. Remove throttle body and gasket. Using a 1 5/8" socket, remove feedback stepper motor.

Throttle Body

1) Remove any throttle return control device and bracket. Disconnect kickdown spring.

2) Center punch choke cover retaining screw heads. Align a 1/4" drill on screw head, and drill only enough to remove screw head. Repeat for remaining 2 screw heads. Remove choke cover by inserting sharp, flat chisel between choke cover gasket layers.

3) Remove retaining ring, choke cover, and gasket. Using small pliers, remove remaining portion of retaining screws from choke housing.

4) Remove choke thermostatic lever screw, and remove lever. Slide choke shaft and lever assembly out of casting, and remove fast idle cam. Remove fast idle cam adjusting screw.

5) Remove choke diaphragm rod clip, and remove the fast idle intermediate lever. Center punch

MOTORCRAFT MODEL 7200 VV 2-BARREL (Cont.)

choke control diaphragm cover retaining screw heads. Align a 1/4" drill on screw head, and drill only enough to remove screw head.

6) Repeat for remaining screw head. Remove choke control diaphragm cover and spring. Remove choke control diaphragm and rod. Disconnect rod from diaphragm.

7) If necessary to remove choke housing bushing, file off staking from around bushing. Carefully press bushing out, while supporting casting.

8) Remove choke heat tube fitting. Remove off idle (TSP) adjusting screw. Remove throttle shaft retaining nut. Remove fast idle adjusting lever, fast idle lever and adjusting screw.

9) Remove large throttle position sensor retaining clip. Scribe a mark across throttle position sensor and throttle body for reassembly reference. Remove 2 retaining screws, throttle position sensor and roll pin.

10) If necessary to remove throttle valves, scribe alignment mark along shaft. Identify throttle valves as to choke side or throttle side. Throttle valve screws are staked in place. Staking must be removed before removing screws. Remove screws and throttle valves.

11) To remove throttle shaft, drive limiter lever stop pin down until it is flush with shaft. Remove clip next to venturi valve limiter screw. Slide throttle shaft out of casting. Remove transmission kickdown adjustment screw. Remove venturi valve limiter lever and bushing assembly.

REASSEMBLY

Throttle Body

1) Support throttle shaft assembly, and drive out venturi valve limiter stop pin. Discard pin. Position venturi valve limiter assembly in throttle body and slide throttle shaft into place. Install clip.

2) Place throttle valves in correct position (noted during disassembly). Install new screws, and tighten until just snug. Close throttle, and lightly tap plates to center. Tighten throttle plate screws, and stake into position.

3) Drive venturi valve limiter stop pin into shaft. Leave 1/8" (3 mm) of pin exposed. Install throttle position sensor roll pin. Slide throttle position sensor over shaft. Engage roll pin with socket. Hold firmly, and rotate throttle position sensor clockwise to align marks made during disassembly. Install screws and large clip.

4) Install fast idle lever, adjusting lever, and fast idle adjusting screw. Install and tighten throttle shaft nut. Install off idle (TSP) adjusting screw. Install choke heat tube fitting. Install choke shaft bushing in housing. Support housing when installing bushing. Stake into position.

5) Install fast idle intermediate lever, large clip, fast idle cam, and adjusting screw. Install choke control diaphragm and rod. Connect rod to lever.

6) Install choke shaft and lever assembly. Install choke thermostatic lever in position. Install and tighten lever screw.

7) Install choke control diaphragm spring, cover, and new break-away cover screws. Apply 1/2" bead of epoxy sealer to each side of choke cover gasket, adjacent to the 3 screw bosses. Install gasket, choke cover, and retaining ring using new break-away screws. Install throttle control device and bracket

Main Body

1) Position throttle body gasket on main body. Assemble main body to throttle body. Install screws and tighten securely. Drop accelerator pump check ball and weight into position in main body.

NOTE: **Do not install venturi valve limiter stop screw and plug at this time. They are installed after carburetor is assembled and venturi valve limiter is adjusted.**

2) Slide venturi valve diaphragm into position. Install diaphragm spring, spring guide, cover and cover screws. Install venturi valve diaphragm adjustment screw. Install pintle spring, gasket pintle valve, and feedback stepper motor.

Upper Body

1) Install 1/8" pipe plug in fuel inlet boss. Install venturi valve limiter adjustment screw in venturi valve. Lubricate "O" rings with mild soapy solution. Install "O" rings on main metering jets.

2) Using jet wrench used during disassembly, install main metering jets in correct holes. Turn jets clockwise until they are lightly seated in casting. Turn each jet counterclockwise number of turns recorded during disassembly.

3) Using plug driver (T77L-9533-C or equivalent), drive main jet plugs into casting recesses. Tap lightly on tool until plugs bottom in casting. Install metering rods and springs on venturi valve, in position noted during disassembly. Install metering rod pivot pins.

4) Install venturi valve, carefully guiding metering rods into jets. If springs are correctly installed, metering rods will spring back up when depressed. Install venturi valve bushings and pivot pins. Install tapered plugs in pivot pins using tool used to remove plugs during disassembly.

5) Install venturi valve cover plate roller bearings, gasket, and cover plate. Install and tighten screws. Install accelerator pump operating rod and dust seal. Attach clip and washer. Slide accelerator pump overtravel spring on to rod.

6) Install accelerator pump lever and swivel assembly into pump link. Install accelerator pump link screw and nut. Install accelerator pump adjusting nut.

7) Install fuel inlet valve seat gasket, seat and valve. Install float bowl gasket. Place float in position and install hinge pin. Install accelerator pump return spring, cup, plunger, internal vent valve and retainer. Place pump piston assembly in position in hole in upper body.

8) If choke control rod broke during disassembly, install new rod. Install upper body on main body. Guide accelerator pump piston assembly into cavity in main body. Make sure venturi valve diaphragm stem engages venturi valve.

9) Install fuel filter spring, filter, inlet fitting gasket, and inlet fitting. Install air cleaner stud. Install choke control rod dust seal. Tap seal gently to straighten retainer.

10) Slide cold enrichment rod into upper body. Assemble cold enrichment rod adjusting nut, lever, swivel, control vacuum regulator, and adjusting nut. Install assembly on carburetor, and tighten nut enough to seat assembly.

11) Install choke hinge pin and retaining clip. Install choke control rod. Perform Cold Enrichment Rod adjustment. Adjust fast idle cam.

MOTORCRAFT MODEL 7200 VV 2-BARREL (Cont.)

Fig. 13: Exploded View of Motorcraft Model 7200 VV 2-Barrel Carburetor

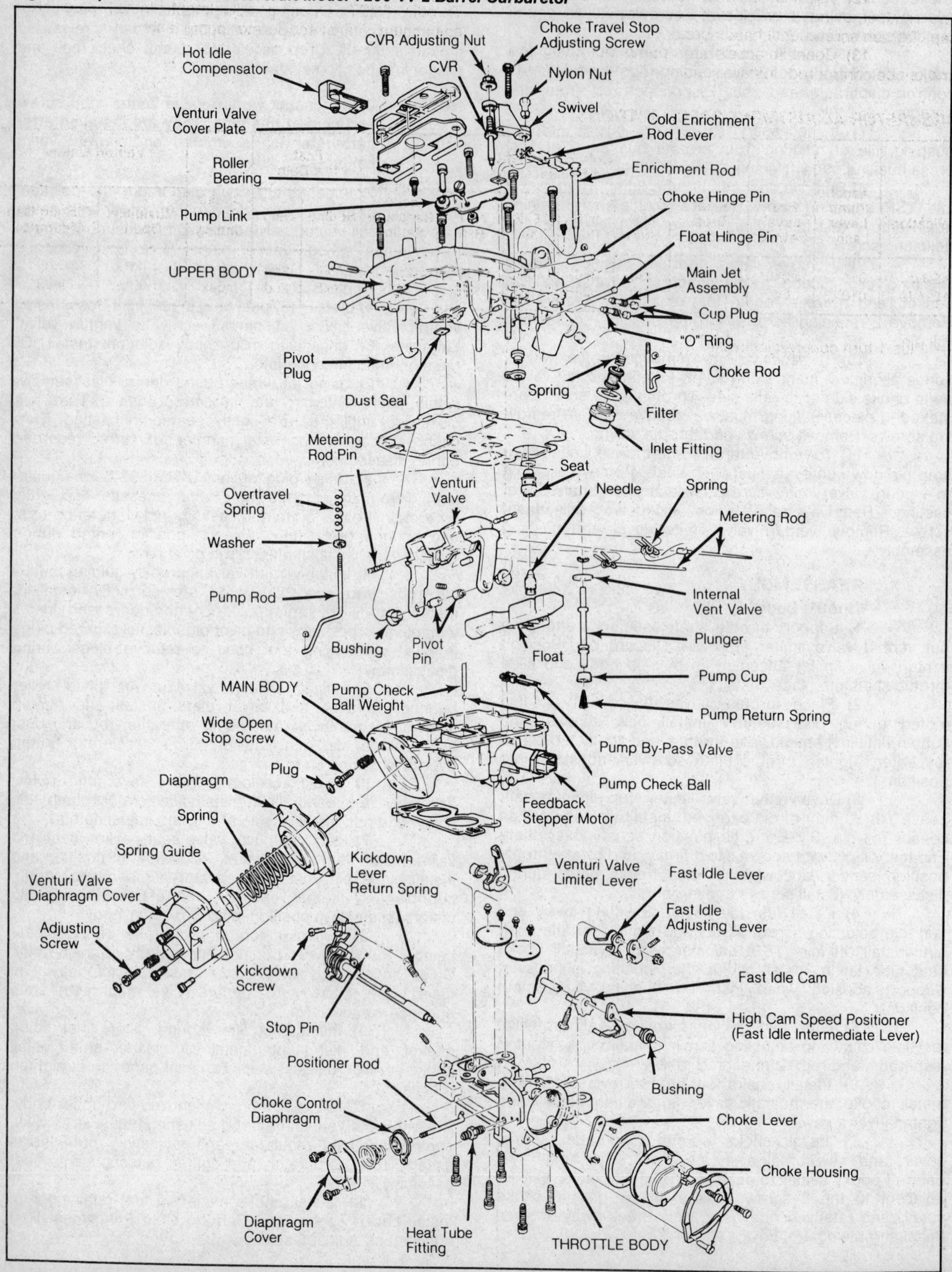

1983 Motorcraft Carburetors

MOTORCRAFT MODEL 7200 VV 2-BARREL (Cont.)

12) Install choke thermostat gasket, housing, and retainer using 3 break-away screws. Adjust choke cap. Tighten screws until heads break off.

13) Connect accelerator pump operating rod and choke control rod. Install retaining clips. Install venturi valve limiter stop screw. Perform Venturi Valve Wide Open Throttle (WOT) Opening adjustment. Install plug after adjustment. Adjust accelerator pump lash.

CARBURETOR ADJUSTMENT SPECIFICATIONS

Application	Accel. Pump Lever Lash [1]	Fuel Level Setting	Float Drop Setting	Cold Enrichment Rod Specifications				Control Vacuum Regulator Setting	Fast Idle Cam		Choke Cover Setting	Venturi Limiter	
				0°F Start	0°F Run	75°F Start	75°F Run		Setting	Stop		Maximum Open	Closing Gap Clearance
E2AE-NA	.010" [1]	1.040"	1.460"	.490"	.350"	.460"	.125"	.250"	.350"	2nd	Index	1.00"	.400"
E2AE-AJA	.010" [1]	1.040"	1.460"	.490"	.350"	.460"	.125"	.250"	.350"	2nd	Index	1.00"	.400"

[1] — Plus 1 turn counterclockwise.

1983 Rochester Carburetors

ROCHESTER MODELS 2SE & E2SE 2-BARREL

CARBURETOR APPLICATION

AMERICAN MOTORS (ROCHESTER) CARBURETOR NO.

Application	Man. Trans.	Auto Trans.
Eagle		
2.5L Engine		
Federal (2SE)	17082380	17082380
Calif. (E2SE)	17083385	17083384

GENERAL MOTORS (ROCHESTER) CARBURETOR NO.

Application	Man. Trans.	Auto. Trans.
2.8L Engine		
Without A/C	17083451	17083450
With A/C	17083453	17083452
2.8L Engine		
High Output		
Without A/C	17083455	17083454
With A/C	17083455	17083456
Camaro & Firebird		
Without A/C	17083631	17083630
With A/C	17083633	17083632

CARBURETOR IDENTIFICATION

The Rochester 2SE and E2SE carburetor numbers are stamped vertically on the float bowl next to vacuum tube "B" location. If float bowl is replaced, follow manufacturer's instructions contained in service package to transfer part number to new float bowl.

Fig. 1: Carburetor Identification Label

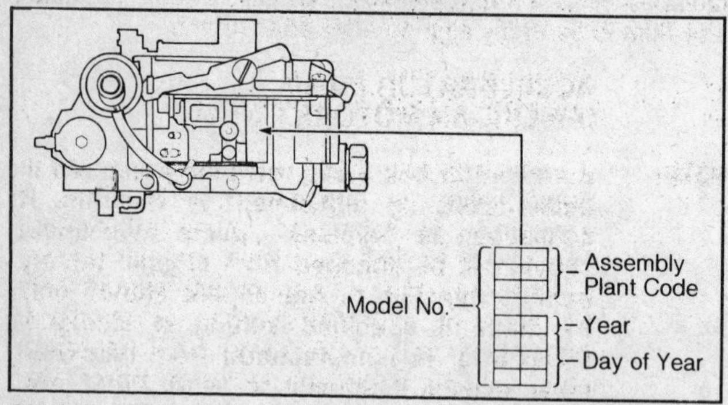

Original part number must be transfered from old float bowl if new float bowl is installed.

DESCRIPTION

The Rochester Varajet Carburetor models 2SE and E2SE are 2-stage, 2-barrel downdraft carburetors. The primary stage consists of a triple venturi with a 35 mm bore. The secondary stage has a 46 mm bore and is equipped with an air valve with a single tapered metering rod. Both are equipped with integral, electronically-activated chokes, a choke vacuum break diaphragm and an idle speed solenoid.

All E2SE models are equipped with an electrically operated mixture control solenoid. The mixture control solenoid is mounted on the air horn and extends into fuel bowl. Fuel metering is controlled by the mixture control solenoid plunger opening and closing the fuel passage to the main metering jet.

All General Motors models are equipped with a Throttle Position Sensor (TPS) to electrically signal the ECM of throttle position. On American Motors models with A/C, an Idle Speed Solenoid (ISS) is used to maintain idle speed during A/C operation.

NOTE: **No attempt should be made to set curb idle speed with the Idle Speed Solenoid.**

All General Motors carburetors are equipped with a temperature regulated pump system with a thermostatically controlled by-pass valve. The by-pass valve is permanently pressed into the air horn. All carburetors are equipped with tamper-resistant features: Factory-adjusted rich mixture screws, factory-adjusted lean mixture screws, riveted choke coil housing and hardened steel pump lever (E2SE models only). All models are also equipped with idle mixture screw plugs.

CAUTION: **NO ATTEMPT should be made to adjust screws except when required by a Computer Command Control System performance check, a major overhaul, or replacement of the air horn, float bowl or throttle body.**

ADJUSTMENT

NOTE: **For on-vehicle adjustments, see TUNE-UP PROCEDURES article.**

ANGLE GAUGE ADJUSTMENT TOOL

Manufacturer recommends that some carburetor adjustments be performed using a choke valve angle gauge (Kent-Moore Tool No. J-26701). While preparations and actual adjustments may vary with each individual adjustment, the procedure for using the angle gauge to check the choke valve angle remains the same. Use the following procedure to perform adjustments requiring the use of the choke angle gauge. *See Fig. 2.*

Fig. 2: Choke Valve Angle Gauge

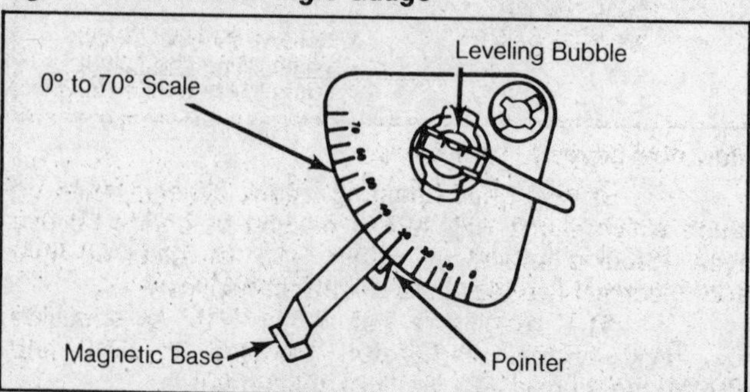

This gauge must be used to perform some adjustments.

1) Rotate degree scale on angle gauge so that 0° mark is opposite pointer.

2) With choke valve closed, place angle gauge magnet squarely on choke valve.

3) Rotate leveling bubble on angle gauge until it is centered.

4) Rotate degree scale until specified degree mark is opposite pointer.

1983 Rochester Carburetors

ROCHESTER MODELS 2SE & E2SE 2-BARREL (Cont.)

5) Now perform individual adjustment preparation as outlined in the following carburetor adjustments requiring an angle gauge.

6) If bubble is centered, adjustment is correct. If not, adjust carburetor as outlined in adjustment procedure.

FLOAT LEVEL (WET SETTING)

NOTE: This is an on-vehicle adjustment.

1) Remove air horn vent stack and screen. If using float gauge J-9789-135, remove air horn screw next to open vent. If using float gauge BT-8104, removal of screw is not necessary. *See Fig. 3.*

2) With engine running at idle, choke wide-open, insert gauge in bridge or guide hole. Gauge J-9789-135 has a tang which fits into screw hole to hold gauge upright. Gauge BT-8104 requires use of the bridge to hold gauge upright. Allow float gauge to float freely. *See Fig. 3.*

NOTE: Pressing down on float gauge could result in float damage or carburetor flooding.

Fig. 3: Wet Float Level Adjustment

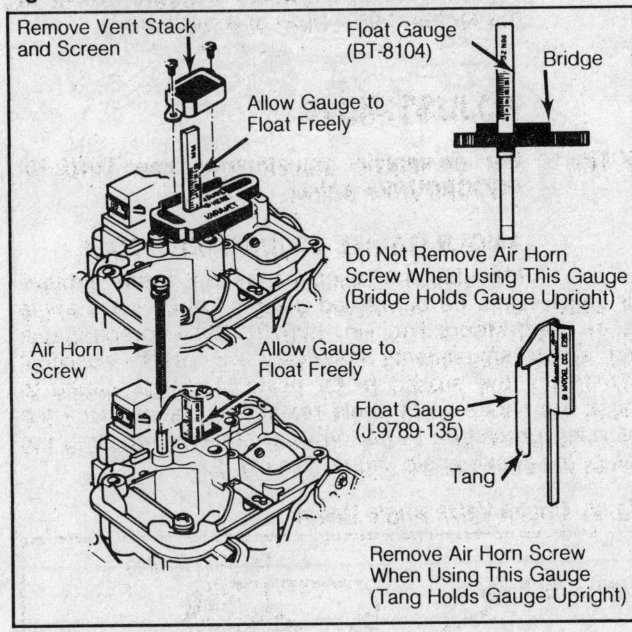

Allow float gauge to float freely.

3) With gauge floating freely, observe mark on gauge which aligns with top of casting or bridge (at eye level). Reading should be within 1/16" of specified float level. Incorrect fuel pressure will affect fuel level.

4) If reading is not within 1/16" of specified float level, remove carburetor. Remove air horn and perform Float Level (Dry Setting) adjustment.

FLOAT LEVEL (DRY SETTING)

1) Remove air horn and gasket from float bowl. Hold float retainer firmly down while lightly pushing float down against needle. *See Fig. 4.*

2) Position a "T" scale over large toe of float at point furthest away from float hinge pin. Measure distance from float bowl casting to float.

Fig. 4: Dry Float Level Adjustment

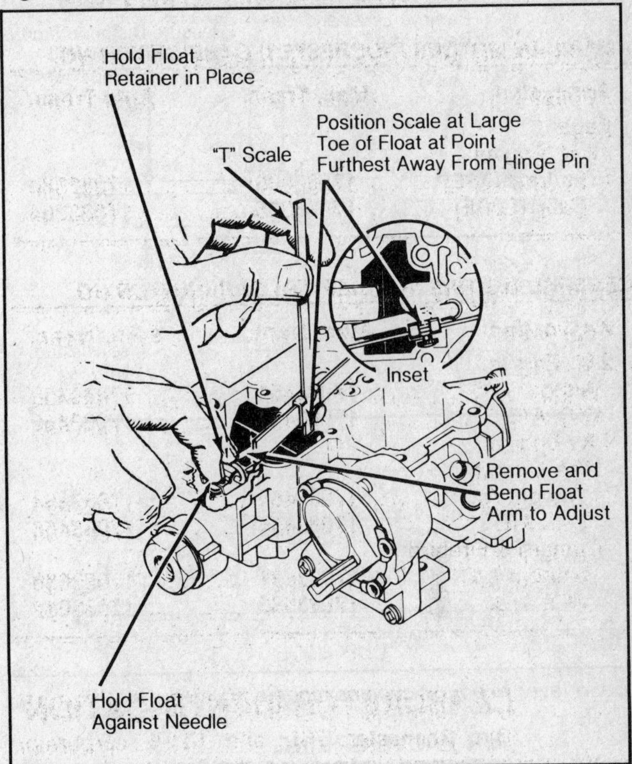

Bend float arm to adjust.

3) To adjust, remove float and bend float arm. Use care in removing float as some models may be equipped with a float stabilizer spring. Check to make sure float is correctly aligned after adjustment.

ACCELERATOR PUMP (AMERICAN MOTORS ONLY)

NOTE: If carburetor has a clip retaining pump rod in pump lever, no adjustment is required. If connection is "clipless", pump adjustment should not be changed from original factory setting. See Fig. 5. Adjustment should only be made if specified setting is changed. Pump lever is manufactured from hardened steel, making it difficult to bend. Pump arm should not be removed to make adjustment unless absolutely necessary.

1) Close throttle valves completely. Make sure fast idle speed screw is off fast idle cam. *See Fig. 5.*

2) Using a "T" scale, measure accelerator pump specified distance from cast surface of air horn to top of pump stem.

3) To adjust, remove pump lever screw and washer. Remove pump lever by rotating lever and removing from pump rod. Secure lever in a vise and bend end of lever at small segment.

4) Install pump lever washer and retaining screw. Recheck pump adjustment and, when correct, tighten retaining screw. Open and close throttle and check for free linkage movement and pump lever alignment.

ROCHESTER MODELS 2SE & E2SE 2-BARREL (Cont.)

Fig. 5: Accelerator Pump Adjustment

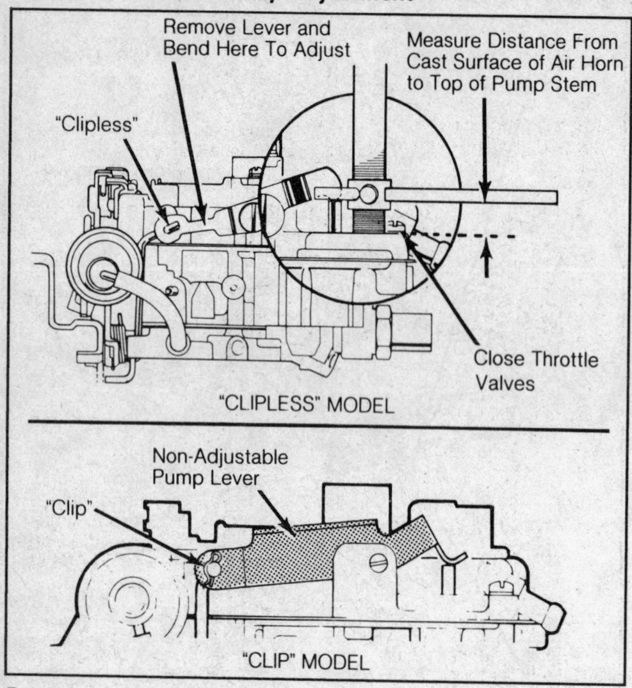

Bend lever to adjust clipless models.

AIR VALVE SPRING (GENERAL MOTORS ONLY)

1) Remove intermediate choke rod to gain access to lock screw, if required. Using an Allen wrench, loosen air valve lock screw. Using a screwdriver, turn tension adjusting screw clockwise until air valve opens slightly. *See Fig. 6.*

Fig. 6: Air Valve Spring Adjustment (General Motors Only)

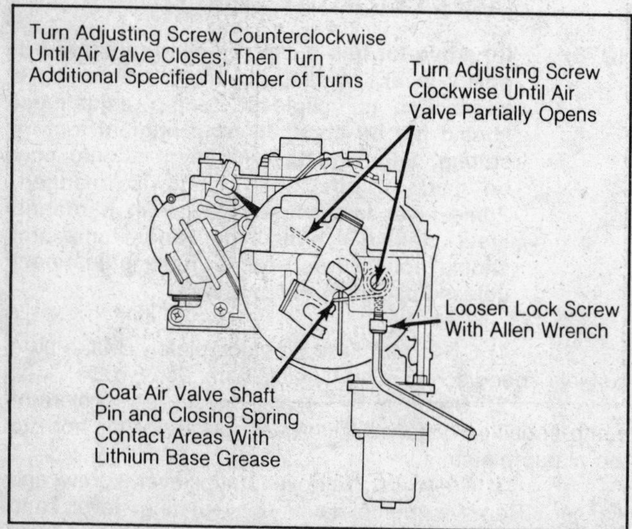

Remove intermediate choke rod to gain access to lock screw, if required.

2) Turn tension adjusting screw counterclockwise until air valve just closes. Turn adjusting screw additional specified turns (counterclockwise).

3) Tighten air valve lock screw. Coat air valve shaft pin and closing spring contact areas with lithium base grease.

CHOKE COIL LEVER

NOTE: **Do not remove rivets and retainers holding choke cover and coil assembly in place unless necessary to check choke coil lever adjustment. If rivets and cover are removed, a new rivet service kit must be installed.**

Fig. 7: Choke Coil Lever Adjustment

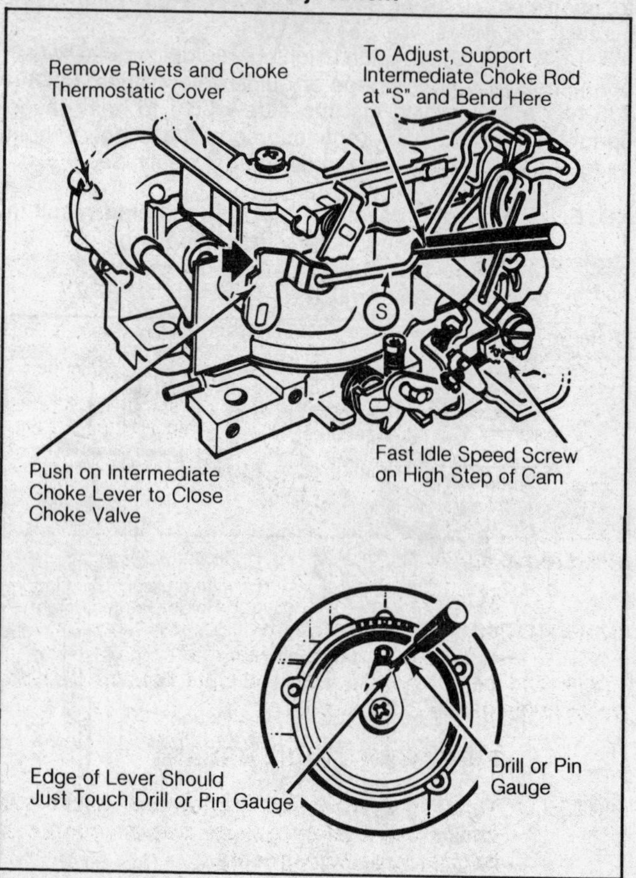

Bend rod to adjust.

1) Remove rivets and choke thermostatic cover from choke housing. Place fast idle screw on high step of fast idle cam. *See Fig. 7.*

2) Push on intermediate choke lever until choke valve is fully closed.

3) Insert a specified drill or pin gauge in hole provided in choke housing. Edge of choke lever inside housing should just touch drill or pin gauge.

4) To adjust, support intermediate choke rod at "S" in *Fig. 7* and bend intermediate choke rod. Reinstall choke cover and adjust.

CHOKE ROD (FAST IDLE CAM)

NOTE: **Choke coil lever adjustment must be correct before proceeding. This adjustment makes use of choke angle gauge. See procedure at beginning of Adjustments.**

ROCHESTER MODELS 2SE & E2SE 2-BARREL (Cont.)

1) Attach rubber band to intermediate choke lever. Open throttle to allow choke valve to close. Set up angle gauge.

2) Place fast idle speed screw on second step of fast idle cam against shoulder of highest step. *See Fig. 8.* Close choke valve by pushing on choke shaft lever to open choke valve and to make contact with closing tang.

Fig. 8: Choke Rod (Fast Idle Cam) Adjustment

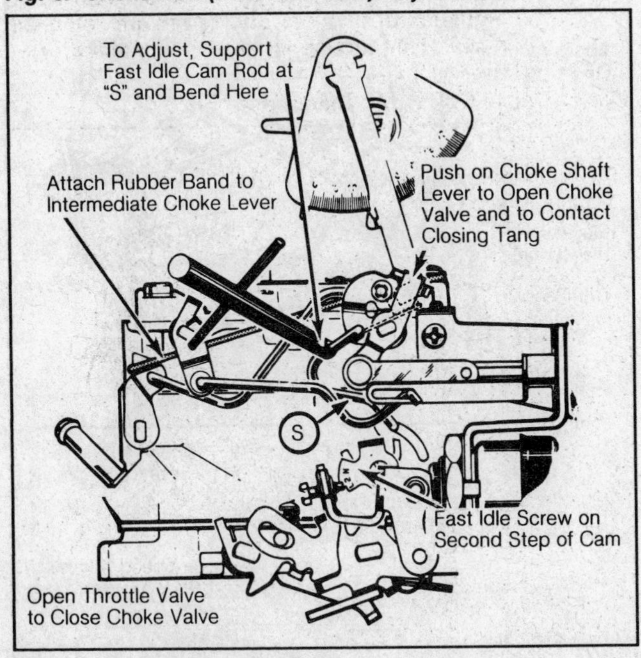

Bend rod to adjust.

3) Bubble on choke angle gauge should be centered with specified degree mark opposite pointer.

4) To adjust, support fast idle cam rod at "S" in *Fig. 8* and bend fast idle cam rod until bubble of choke valve angle gauge is centered.

PRIMARY VACUUM BREAK

NOTE: This adjustment is performed using the choke valve angle gauge. See procedure at beginning of Adjustments.

1) Attach rubber band to intermediate choke lever. Open throttle to allow choke valve to close.

2) Set up angle gauge and set angle to specification. Using an outside vacuum source of at least 18 in. Hg, retract vacuum break plunger. Plug air bleed hole with tape or pump plunger cup, if equipped. *See Fig. 9.* Air valve rod should not prevent seating of vacuum break diaphragm.

NOTE: Be sure plunger bucking spring is compressed and seated (plunger fully extended), if equipped.

3) To adjust on models with hex-head adjustment, use a 1/8" hex wrench to turn screw in rear cover until bubble is centered. Apply RTV silicone sealant over screw head to seal setting. To adjust on models without hex-head adjustment, support vacuum break rod and bend rod with vacuum still applied. *See Fig. 9.*

Fig. 9: Primary Vacuum Break Adjustment

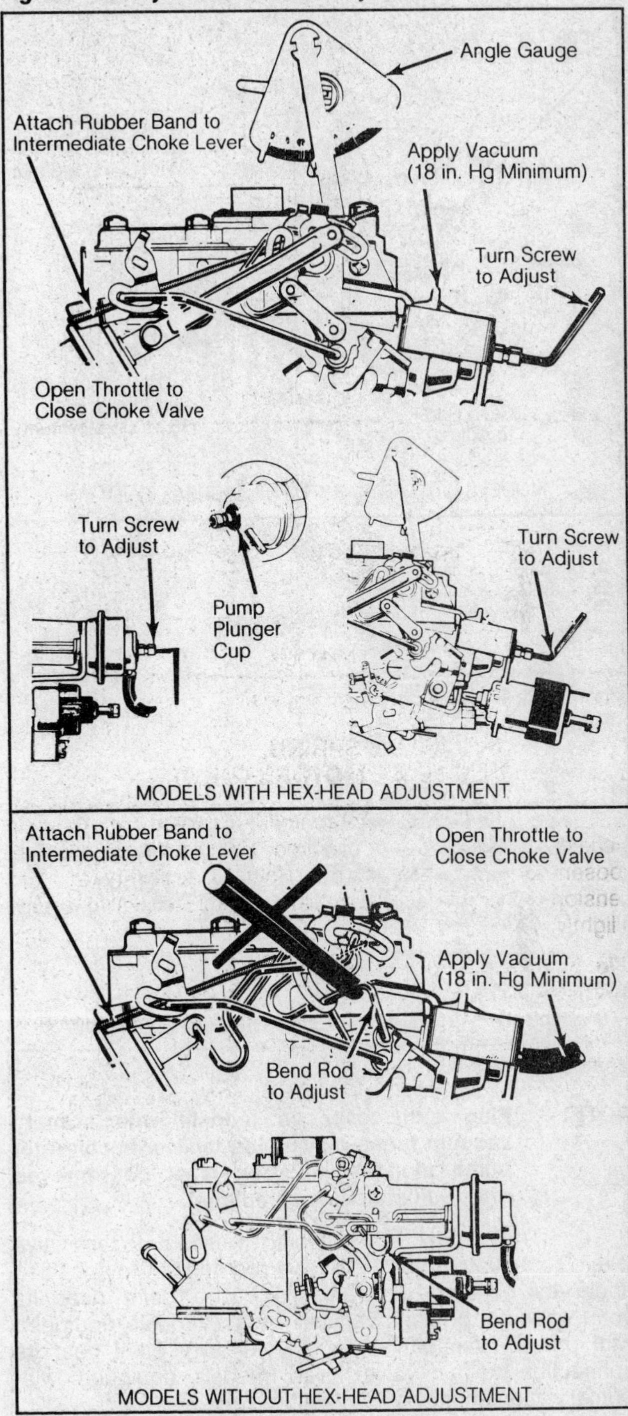

Turn screw or bend rod with vacuum still applied.

AIR VALVE ROD

NOTE: This adjustment is made by using the choke valve angle gauge. See procedure at beginning of Adjustments.

1) Set up angle gauge on air valve. Using an outside vacuum source of at least 18 in. Hg, seat primary choke vacuum break diaphragm plunger. *See Fig. 10.*

ROCHESTER MODELS 2SE & E2SE 2-BARREL (Cont.)

Fig. 10: Air Valve Rod Adjustment

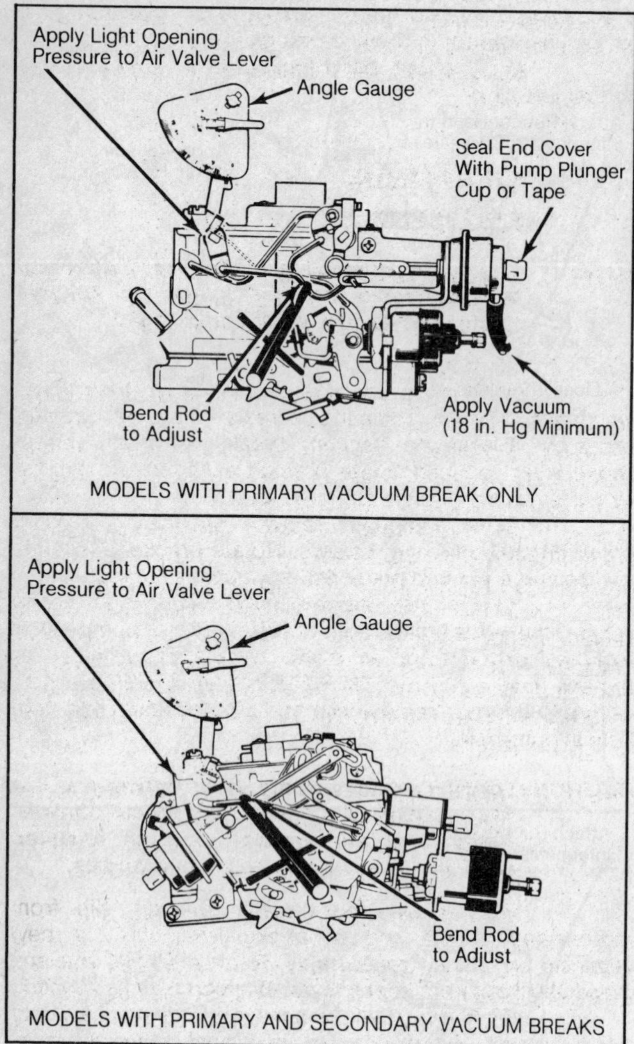

Bend rod to adjust.

NOTE: Plug end cover on models with primary vacuum break only, using tape or accelerator pump plunger cup. Cup must be removed after adjustment is completed.

2) Apply light opening pressure to air valve lever. To adjust, support air valve rod and set to specified angle by bending air valve rod at a point near its connection to primary vacuum break (models equipped with primary vacuum break only) or at a point near its connection to air valve lever (models equipped with primary and secondary vacuum breaks).

AUTOMATIC CHOKE

Choke coil cover is retained on housing with rivets to prevent tampering with factory adjustment. If necessary to remove cover, refer to Disassembly and Reassembly procedures in this Section.

SECONDARY VACUUM BREAK

NOTE: This adjustment is performed using the choke valve angle gauge. See procedure at beginning of Adjustments.

Fig. 11: Secondary Vacuum Break Adjustment

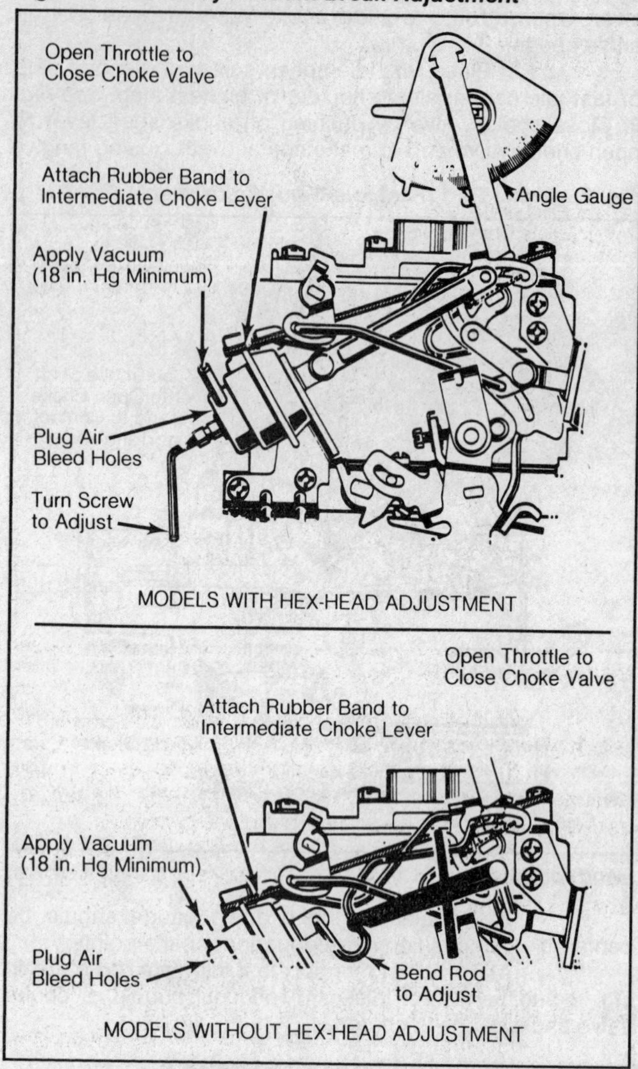

Turn screw or bend rod with vacuum still applied.

1) Attach rubber band to intermediate choke lever. Open throttle to allow choke valve to close.

2) Set up angle gauge and set angle to specification. Using an outside vacuum source of at least 18 in. Hg, retract vacuum break plunger. *See Fig. 11.*

3) Where applicable, plug air bleed holes and ensure plunger stem is fully extended to compress plunger bucking spring.

4) To adjust on models with hex-head adjustment, use a 1/8" hex wrench to turn screw in rear cover until bubble is centered. Apply RTV silicone sealant over screw head to seal setting. To adjust on models without hex-head adjustment, support vacuum break rod and bend rod with vacuum still applied. *See Fig. 11.*

CHOKE UNLOADER

NOTE: This adjustment is performed using the choke valve angle gauge. See procedure at beginning of Adjustments.

1) Attach rubber band to intermediate choke lever. Open throttle to allow choke valve to close. *See Fig. 12.*

ROCHESTER MODELS 2SE & E2SE 2-BARREL (Cont.)

Fig. 12: Choke Unloader Adjustment

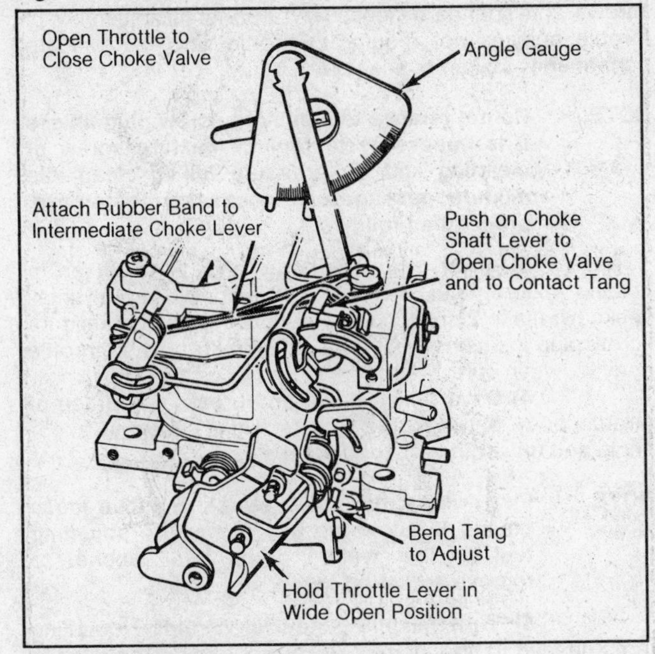

Bend choke unloader tang to adjust.

2) Set up angle gauge and set angle to specifications. Hold throttle lever in wide open position.

3) Push on choke shaft lever to open choke valve and to make contact with closing tang. To adjust, bend tang on throttle lever until bubble is centered.

4) Remove gauge and reinstall choke cover and coil assembly if previously removed. Install service rivet and retainer kit.

SECONDARY LOCKOUT

1) Hold choke valve wide open by pushing down on intermediate choke lever. *See Fig. 13.*

2) Open throttle lever until end of secondary actuating lever is opposite toe of lockout lever.

Fig. 13: Secondary Throttle Lockout Adjustment

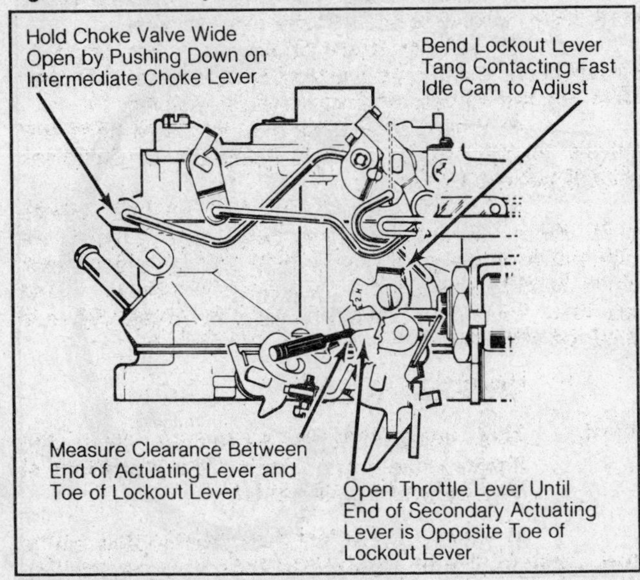

Bend lockout lever to adjust.

3) Measure specified clearance between end of actuating lever and toe of lockout lever. Measurement can be checked using a drill or pin gauge of specified size.

4) To adjust, bend lockout lever tang contacting fast idle cam.

OVERHAUL

DISASSEMBLY

NOTE: **Before disassembling carburetor, mount unit in a suitable holding fixture to prevent damage to throttle valves or linkage.**

Air Horn

1) Remove idle speed solenoid/primary vacuum break bracket retaining screws. Remove bracket assembly. Disengage vacuum break link from slot in choke lever. Lift and rotate bracket assembly to remove air valve rod from slot in air valve lever.

2) If equipped, remove secondary vacuum break bracket attaching screws. Rotate bracket assembly to disengage vacuum break link from choke lever slot.

3) On 2SE models (NOT USING a clip to secure the accelerator pump rod), remove pump lever retaining screw from air horn. Rotate pump lever to remove from pump rod. On E2SE models (using a clip to secure pump rod), remove clip and remove pump rod from hole in pump lever.

CAUTION: **DO NOT remove pump lever retaining screw from models using clip as pump rod retainer. Pump lever and washer must be removed from air horn assembly on these models.**

4) Remove and discard retaining clip from intermediate choke rod at choke lever. Use a new retaining clip during reassembly. Remove choke rod and plastic bushing from choke lever. Bushing may be reused.

5) If equipped, remove hot idle compensator valve screws. Remove valve and seal from air horn. Discard seal. Valve removal is necessary to gain access to short air horn-to-bowl attaching screw.

6) On E2SE models, remove 3 mixture control solenoid screws and remove mixture control solenoid using a light twisting motion. Remove and discard solenoid gasket, plunger seal and plunger seal retainer.

7) Remove all air horn-to-float bowl screws and lock washers. Remove vent stack and screen assembly. Rotate fast idle cam up as far as possible. Rotate air horn and tilt to disengage fast idle cam rod from slot in fast idle cam and pump rod from pump lever hole.

NOTE: **If pump plunger comes out of float bowl with air horn removal, remove pump plunger from air horn. Air horn gasket should remain on float bowl. Do not remove fast idle cam screw and cam from float bowl. These parts must remain permanently in place as installed by manufacturer. Service replacement float bowl will include fast idle cam screw and cam.**

8) Disconnect fast idle cam rod from choke lever by aligning tang on rod with slot in lever. Lift off air horn assembly.

9) If equipped, remove TPS plunger by pushing downward through seal in air horn. Remove seal retainer

ROCHESTER MODELS 2SE & E2SE 2-BARREL (Cont.)

and seal. Remove accelerator pump plunger seal from air horn after using a small screwdriver to remove staking around each seal retainer.

NOTE: **Use fingers only (no tools) when removing plunger to prevent damage to sealing surface. Use care in removing plunger seal retainer and plunger stem seal retainer to prevent damage to air horn. Discard seals and retainers.**

10) No further disassembly of air horn is required. Air valve and choke valve attaching screws are staked in place and not removable. New service replacement air horn assembly includes secondary metering rod and air valve assemblies with preset factory adjustments. No attempt should be made to change air valve settings.

Float Bowl

1) Remove air horn gasket. Remove pump plunger and pump spring from pump well. Remove plastic filler block from float valve.

2) Remove float assembly and float valve, pulling up on retaining pin. If equipped, remove float stabilizing spring with float assembly. Remove float needle seat, gasket and extended metering jet from float bowl. Use jet tool or screwdriver that fully fits slot in top of jet.

NOTE: **Do not remove or adjust small calibration screw located deep inside metering jet. Adjustment should be made only if required by a Computer Command Control System performance check.**

3) On E2SE models, push up from bottom on electrical connector and remove TPS and connector from float bowl. Remove spring from bottom of TPS well in bowl. On 2SE models, press down on power piston stem and allow it to snap up. Repeat this until plastic retainer is dislodged and remove power piston and metering rod assembly.

4) Remove spring from power piston bore. If necessary to remove metering rod from hanger, compress spring on metering rod and align groove on rod with slot in holder. Care must be taken not to damage tip of metering rod.

5) Remove main metering jet using a screwdriver that fits tight in groove. Using a small slide hammer, remove plastic retainer holding pump discharge spring and check ball in place in float bowl. Discard retainer.

6) To remove choke cover and coil assembly, align a .159" (No. 21) drill on choke cover retaining rivet. Drill only enough to remove rivet heads. Remove rivets, choke cover and coil assembly. Remove screw from end of intermediate choke shaft in choke housing. Remove choke coil lever from shaft.

7) Slide intermediate choke shaft out of float bowl. Remove choke housing screws and remove choke housing. Remove fuel inlet nut, gasket, check valve/filter and spring.

8) Remove 4 screws securing throttle body to float bowl. Remove throttle body. Remove throttle body insulator gasket.

Throttle Body

1) Hold throttle valves wide open. Disengage pump rod from throttle lever by rotating rod until tang on rod aligns with slot in lever.

2) Remove curb idle and fast idle speed screws and springs if necessary. Further disassembly of throttle body is not required. Throttle valve screws are permanently staked in position.

NOTE: **Do not remove idle mixture screw plug unless it is necessary to replace mixture screw or cleaning and air pressure fail to clean idle mixture passages. If necessary to remove, proceed as follows:**

3) Invert throttle body and position on a holding fixture with manifold side up. Using a small hacksaw, make 2 small cuts, one on either side of mixture screw plug location. Position a small flat punch on throttle body between cuts.

4) Drive punch down and break out portion of throttle body between the 2 cuts. Hold punch at a 45° angle and drive out hardened steel plug.

NOTE: **Plug will shatter when struck. Remove loose pieces to allow the use of mixture adjusting tool or thin walled deep 3/16" socket to remove adjusting screw and spring.**

5) Turn mixture screw in carefully, counting turns needed to seat screw. Record number to be used in reassembly, then remove mixture screw.

CLEANING & INSPECTION

- Do not soak any components containing rubber, leather or plastic. Definitely do not soak idle speed solenoid, mixture control solenoid, throttle position sensor, electric choke, diaphragms, pump plunger and

Fig. 14: Testing Mixture Control Solenoid (Disassembled From Carburetor)

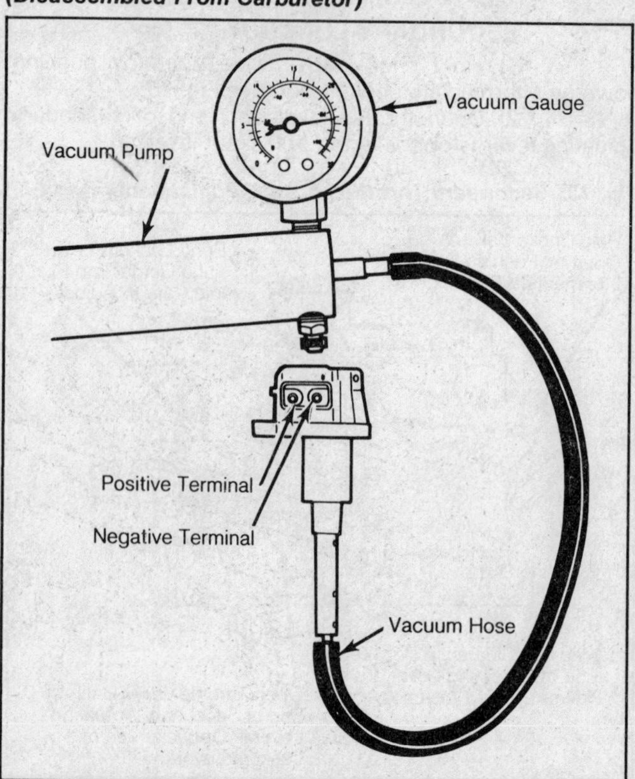

Connect to battery voltage for testing.

ROCHESTER MODELS 2SE & E2SE 2-BARREL (Cont.)

Fig. 15: Exploded View of Rochester 2SE 2-Barrel Carburetor

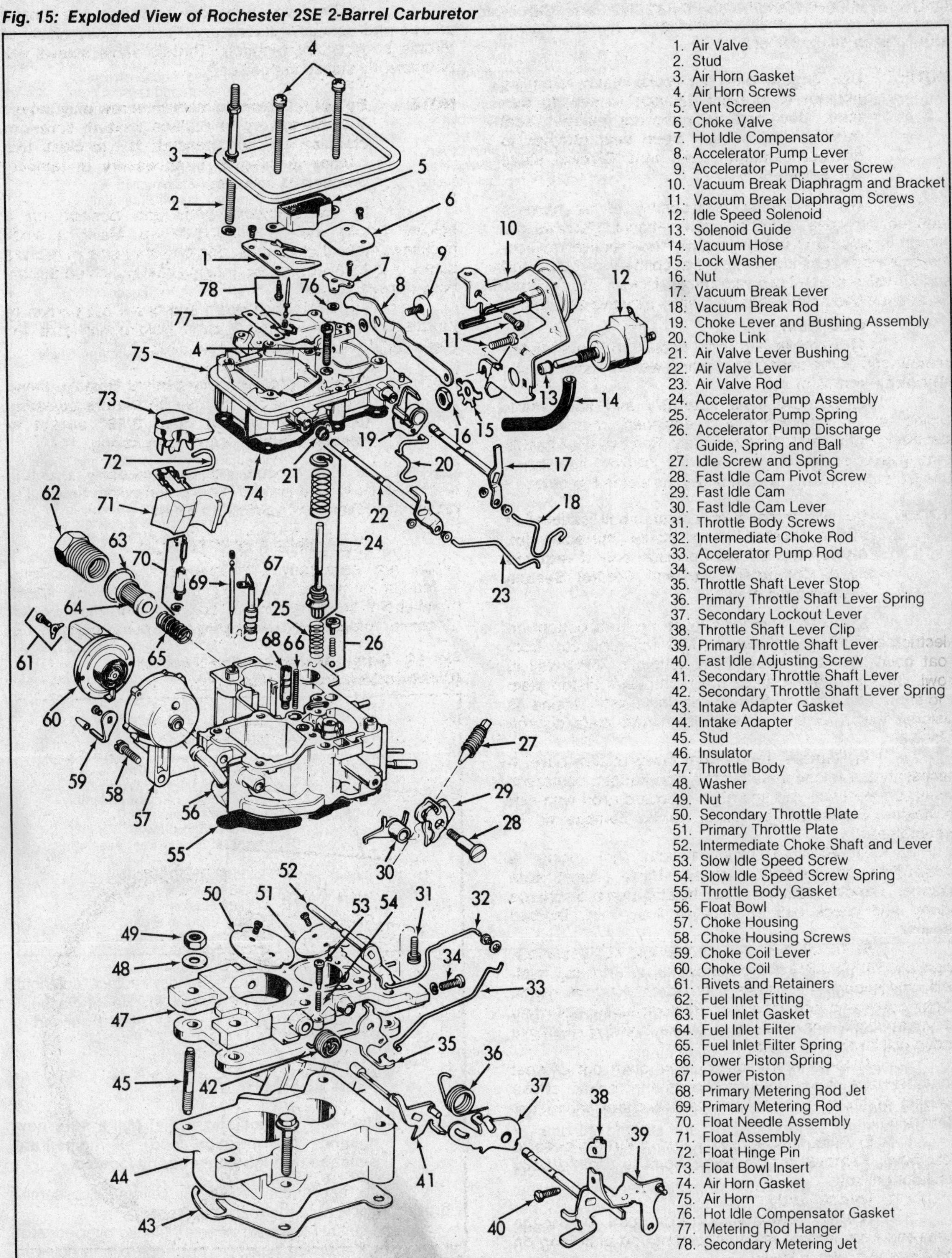

ROCHESTER MODELS 2SE & E2SE 2-BARREL (Cont.)

Fig. 16: Exploded View of Rochester E2SE 2-Barrel Carburetor

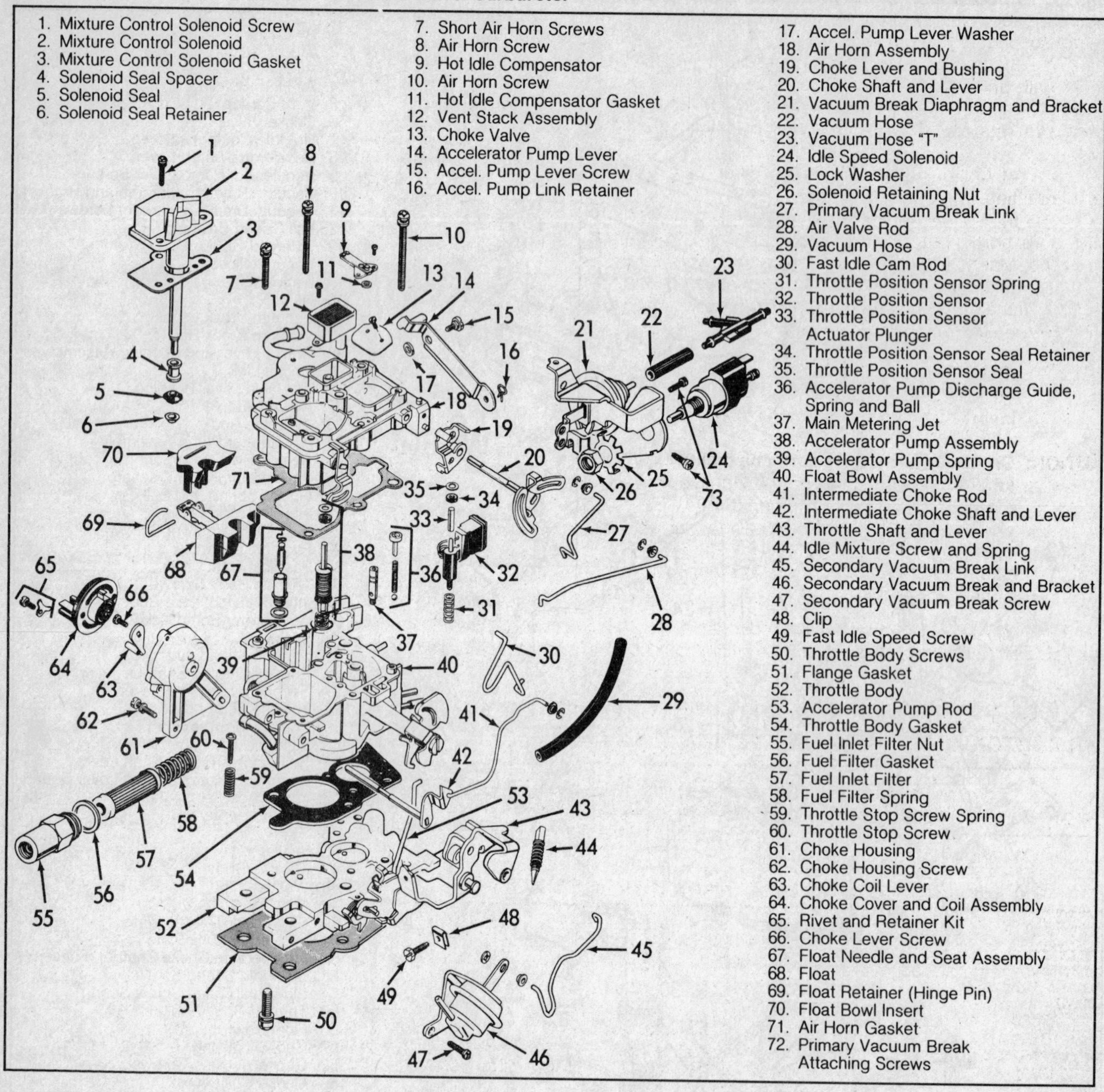

plastic filler block. Plastic bushings will withstand normal cleaning.

- Use a regular carburetor cleaning solution. Soak components long enough to thoroughly clean all surfaces and passages of foreign matter.
- Remove any residue after cleaning by rinsing components in a suitable solvent.
- Blow out all passages with dry compressed air.
- Test mixture control solenoid for sticking, binding or leaking. Connect jumper wire between battery positive terminal and right (positive) solenoid terminal. Connect another jumper wire between battery negative terminal and left (negative) solenoid terminal. Remove rubber seal and retainer from solenoid stem and attach hand vacuum pump and gauge. *See Fig. 14.* Apply 25 in. Hg of vacuum. Time leak-down rate from 20 in. Hg to 15 in. Hg. If time exceeds 5 seconds, replace solenoid. Remove jumper wires. Apply 15 in. Hg of vacuum. Vacuum should drop to zero in less than 1 second. If not, replace solenoid.

REASSEMBLY

NOTE: **Use new gasket and seals. Make sure new gaskets fit correctly and all holes are punched through and properly located.**

To reassemble carburetor, reverse disassembly procedure and note the following:

1) Install fuel inlet needle pull clip over edge of flat on float arm facing float. Do not hook clip in holes in float arm.

1983 Rochester Carburetors

ROCHESTER MODELS 2SE & E2SE 2-BARREL (Cont.)

2) After throttle body is installed on float bowl, make sure secondary lockout tang is in correct position to engage secondary lockout lever.

3) Install new accelerator pump discharge check ball and spring plastic retainer. Insert end of retainer in spring and place in position in float bowl. Lightly tap retainer into position until it is flush in float bowl.

4) Make sure holes in fuel filter face toward fuel intlet fitting when filter is installed.

5) Some linkage retaining clips are dished. Make sure portion of clip that bends outward is toward end of rod. Make sure clip makes full contact with rod.

6) Place fast idle screw on high step of fast idle cam. Install choke coil cover, aligning notch in cover with raised boss on housing cover flange.

NOTE: If choke cover and coil assembly was removed from housing, a service rivet kit must be installed to restore tamper-resistant feature.

CAUTION: On E2SE models, be sure coil pick-up lever is located inside choke coil tang. Also, on electric chokes, the ground contact is provided by a metal plate at rear of choke cover assembly. Do not install a choke cover gasket between electric choke assembly and choke housing.

7) Mixture control solenoid connector must be installed with Pink wire on right hand terminal of connector, as viewed from harness end. On some models, the connector latch may require minor filing to allow proper latching.

8) Install air horn screws, noting location and type of screw for correct installation. Tighten screws evenly, securely and in proper sequence. *See Fig. 17.*

Fig. 17: Air Horn Screw Location & Tightening Sequence

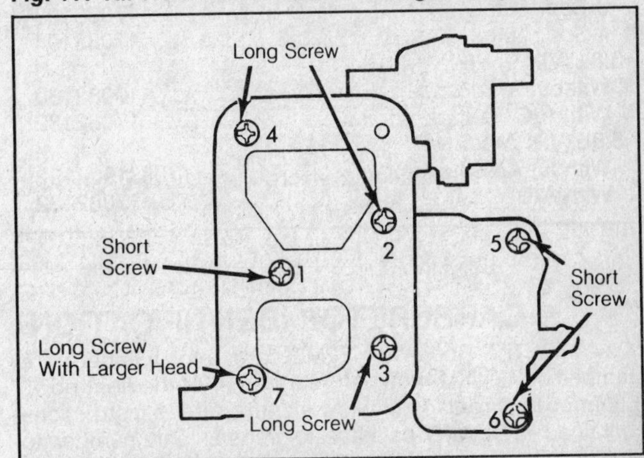

9) On E2SE models, install mixture control solenoid seal on solenoid stem. Using a 3/16" socket and hammer, lightly tap retainer in place, on stem, leaving a slight clearance between retainer and seal. Apply silicone grease to seal before installation of solenoid.

CARBURETOR ADJUSTMENT SPECIFICATIONS

Application	Float Level	Accel. Pump	Choke Coil Lever	Choke Rod	Air Valve Rod	Air Valve Spring[1]	Vacuum Break Primary	Vacuum Break Secondary	Auto. Choke	Choke Unloader	Secondary Lockout
American Motors											
2SE											
17082380	7/32" [2]	1/8"	.085"	18°	2° [3]	.....	21°	.....	TR	34°	.065"
E2SE											
17083384	9/64"	1/8"	.085"	18°	2° [3]	.....	19°	.....	TR	34°	.085"
17083385	9/64"	1/8"	.085"	18°	2° [3]	.....	19°	.....	TR	34°	.085"
General Motors											
E2SE											
17083450	1/4"	TR	.085"	28°	1°	1	27°	35°	TR	45°	.025"
17083451	1/4"	TR	.085"	28°	1°	1	27°	35°	TR	45°	.025"
17083452	1/4"	TR	.085"	28°	1°	1	27°	35°	TR	45°	.025"
17083453	1/4"	TR	.085"	28°	1°	1	27°	35°	TR	45°	.025"
17083454	1/4"	TR	.085"	28°	1°	1	27°	35°	TR	45°	.025"
17083455	1/4"	TR	.085"	28°	1°	1	27°	35°	TR	45°	.025"
17083456	1/4"	TR	.085"	28°	1°	1	27°	35°	TR	45°	.025"
17083630	1/4"	TR	.085"	28°	1°	1	27°	35°	TR	45°	.025"
17083631	1/4"	TR	.085"	28°	1°	1	27°	35°	TR	45°	.025"
17083632	1/4"	TR	.085"	28°	1°	1	27°	35°	TR	45°	.025"
17083633	1/4"	TR	.085"	28°	1°	1	27°	35°	TR	45°	.025"

TR — Tamper-Resistant. [1] — Number of Turns. [2] — Auto. Trans. = 9/64". [3] — Maximum Degree Setting.

1983 Rochester Carburetors

ROCHESTER E2ME 2-BARREL

CARBURETOR APPLICATION

GENERAL MOTORS (ROCHESTER) CARBURETOR NO.

Application	Man. Trans.	Auto. Trans.
3.0L (VIN E) V6		
3-Spd. Auto.	.....	17083193
4-Spd. Auto.	.....	17083194
3.8L (VIN 9) V6		
Without A/C	.....	17082130
With A/C	.....	17082132
3.8L (VIN A) V6		
Without A/C	.....	17083190, 192
With A/C	.....	17082182

CARBURETOR IDENTIFICATION

The Rochester E2ME carburetor numbers are stamped vertically on the left rear corner of the float bowl. If float bowl is replaced, follow manufacturer's instructions contained in service package to transfer part number to new float bowl. Some models have machined pump wells to reduce the pump well taper. Models with machined pump wells will have the letters "MW" stamped on the float bowl near vacuum tube location "T" and the accelerator pump.

Fig. 1: Carburetor Identification Label

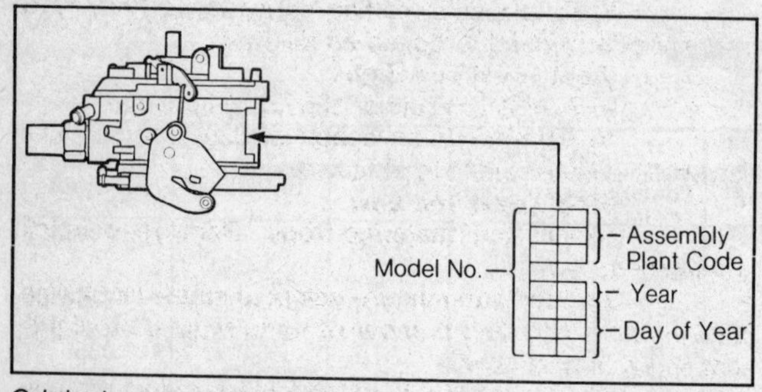

Original part number must be transfered from old float bowl if new float bowl is installed.

DESCRIPTION

The Rochester Dualjet carburetor model E2ME is a single-stage, 2-barrel downdraft carburetor. Each bore is 1-3/8" in diameter and each bore has a separate and independent idle circuit.

All E2ME models are equipped with an electrically operated mixture control solenoid. The mixture control solenoid, mounted in the fuel bowl, controls air and fuel metered to the idle and main metering systems. Fuel metering is controlled by 2 special stepped metering rods, operating in removable jets, positioned by a plunger in the mixture control solenoid.

All models are equipped with a Throttle Position Sensor (TPS), mounted in the float bowl; an Idle Speed Control (ISC) device; and models without ISC but with A/C, are equipped with an Idle Speed Solenoid (ISS). The TPS signals the Electronic Control Module (ECM) of the Computer Command Control (CCC) system on throttle position. The ISC, mounted on the fuel bowl, controls normal curb idle speed and acts as a dashpot on deceleration and throttle closing. The ISS maintains a specific idle speed during A/C operation.

NOTE: **No attempt should be made to set curb idle speed with the Idle Speed Solenoid or the Idle Speed Control device.**

All carburetors are equipped with tamper-resistant features: Factory-adjusted rich mixture stop screws, factory-adjusted lean mixture screws, riveted choke coil housings, idle air bleed valves, TPS and idle mixture needles.

CAUTION: **NO ATTEMPT should be made to adjust screws except when required by a Computer Command Control System performance check, a major overhaul, or replacement of the air horn, float bowl or throttle body.**

All carburetors are equipped with a front vacuum break with a leaf-type bucking spring. Some models may use both a front and rear vacuum break to control choke valve openings during initial engine starting and cold driveaway.

TESTING

ELECTRIC CHOKE

NOTE: **This test should be performed when air temperature is 60-80°F (15-27°C).**

1) Allow choke to cool to permit full closing of choke blade when throttle is opened slightly. Start engine and time the interval required for choke blade to reach full open position. (Start timing when engine starts). If choke blade does not fully open within 3 1/2 minutes, proceed with test.

2) With engine running, check voltage at choke heater connection. If voltage is about 12-15 volts, replace electric choke unit. If voltage is low or zero, check all wires and connections and repair as required. Power for choke unit is through the oil pressure switch. Ensure switch circuitry is good.

3) If procedure in step **2)** does not correct the problem, replace oil pressure switch.

ADJUSTMENT

NOTE: **For on-vehicle adjustments, see TUNE-UP PROCEDURES article.**

ANGLE GAUGE ADJUSTMENT TOOL

Manufacturer recommends that some carburetor adjustments be performed using a choke valve angle gauge (Kent-Moore tool No. J-26701). While preparations and actual adjustment may vary with each individual adjustment, the procedure for using the angle gauge to check the choke valve angle remains the same. Use the following procedure to perform adjustments requiring the use of the choke valve angle gauge.

ROCHESTER E2ME 2-BARREL (Cont.)

Fig. 2: Choke Valve Angle Gauge

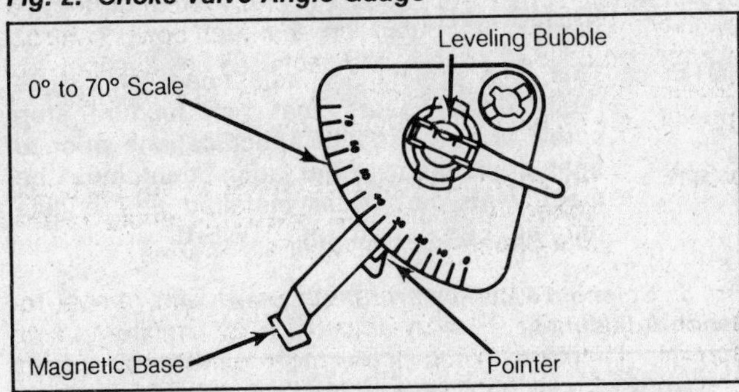

This gauge must be used to perform some adjustments.

1) Rotate degree scale on angle gauge so that 0° mark is opposite pointer.

2) With choke valve closed, place angle gauge magnet squarely on choke valve.

3) Rotate leveling bubble on angle gauge until it is centered.

4) Rotate degree scale until specified degree mark is opposite pointer.

5) Now perform individual adjustment preparation as outlined in the following carburetor adjustments requiring an angle gauge.

6) If bubble is centered, adjustment is correct. If not, adjust carburetor as outlined in adjustment procedure.

FLOAT LEVEL (WET SETTING)

NOTE: This is an on-vehicle adjustment.

1) With engine running at idle and choke wide open, carefully insert float gauge into vent slot or vent hole (next to air cleaner mounting stud) in air horn. Allow gauge to float freely. *See Fig. 3.*

NOTE: Pressing down on float gauge could result in float damage or carburetor flooding.

Fig. 3: Wet Float Level Adjustment

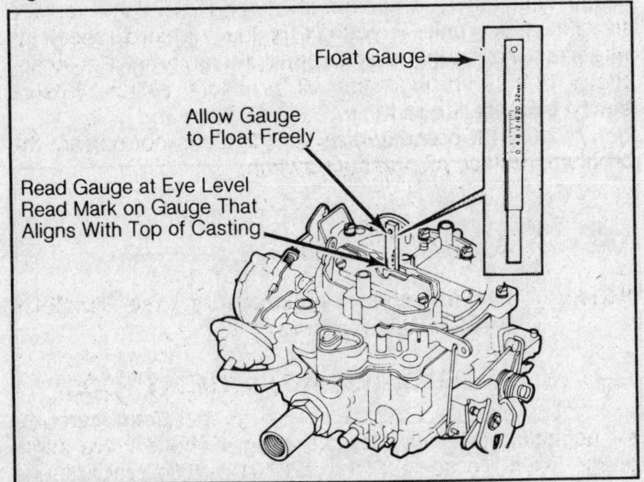

Allow float gauge to float freely.

2) With gauge floating freely, observe mark on gauge which aligns with top of casting (at eye level). Reading should be within 1/16" of specified float level. Incorrect fuel pressure will affect fuel level.

3) If reading is not within 1/16" of specified float level, remove carburetor. Remove air horn and perform Float Level (Dry Setting) adjustment.

Fig. 4: Dry Float Level Adjustment

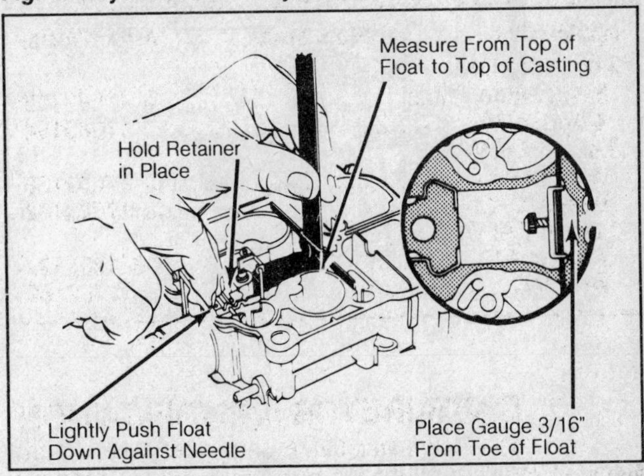

Follow procedures to properly adjust float level.

FLOAT LEVEL (DRY SETTING)

1) Remove air horn and gasket from float bowl. Hold float retainer down firmly. Lightly push float down against needle. *See Fig. 4.*

2) Position a "T" scale over toe of float at a point 3/16" from end of float toe. Measure distance from top of float bowl casting to top of float.

3) If float level setting varies more than 1/16" from specified setting, proceed as follows:

Float Level Too High

a) Hold float retainer clip firmly in place.

b) Push down on center of float pontoon until correct float level setting is obtained.

Float Level Too Low

a) Lift out metering rods. Remove solenoid connector screws.

b) Turn lean mixture solenoid screw clockwise, counting and recording number of turns required to lightly seat screw in float bowl.

c) Turn screw counterclockwise and remove. Lift solenoid and connector from float bowl.

d) Remove float and bend arm up to adjust. Make sure float is correctly aligned after adjustment.

e) Reinstall components in reverse order that they were removed. Back out solenoid mixture screw number of turns noted in step **b)**.

SOLENOID LEAN MIXTURE SCREW (BENCH ADJUSTMENT)

NOTE: This is a preliminary adjustment only. It is required to ensure that lean mixture screw is set close to specifications prior to final adjustment. Final adjustment must be made with carburetor installed and engine running. See appropriate TUNE-UP article.

1) Install plastic aneroid cavity insert beneath mixture control solenoid connector in float bowl, if used. Ensure insert is installed with inset aligned with recess of bowl cavity and seated flush with bowl casting surface.

1983 Rochester Carburetors

ROCHESTER E2ME 2-BARREL (Cont.)

Fig. 5: Solenoid Lean Mixture Screw Bench Adjustment

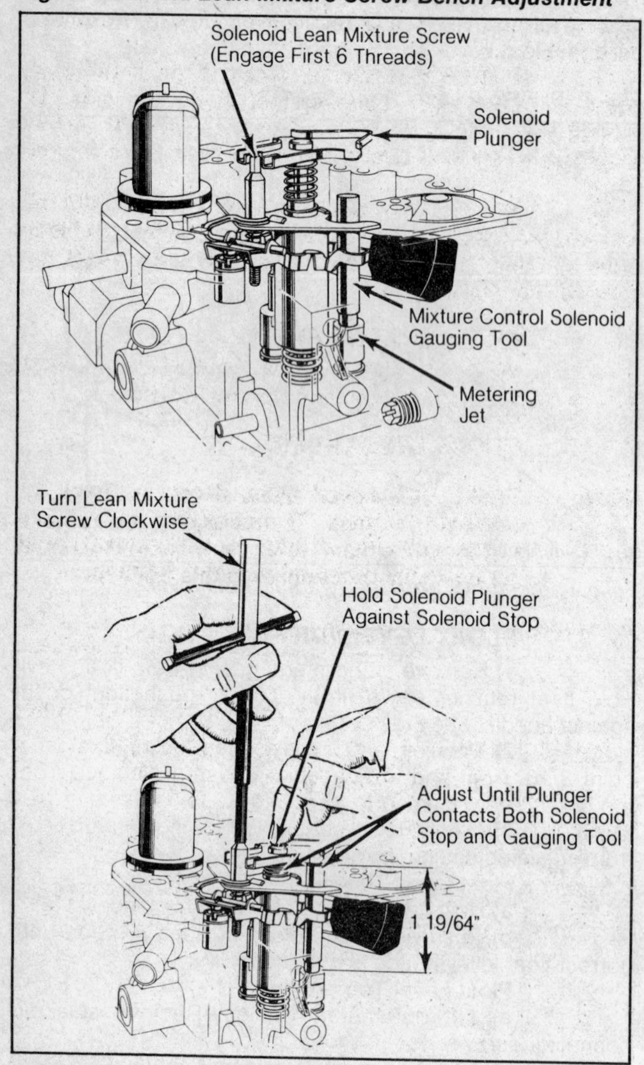

Lean mixture screw should be installed with first 6 threads engaged in float bowl.

Tang on upper lip of insert goes in deep slot in bowl closest to fuel inlet nut.

2) Install mixture control solenoid screw tension spring between raised bosses next to float hanger pin. Carefully install mixture control solenoid in float chamber. Align pin on end of solenoid with hole in raised boss at bottom of bowl. Align connector wires to fit in slot in bowl or plastic insert, if used.

3) Install solenoid lean mixture screw through hole in solenoid bracket and tension spring in float bowl. The first 6 threads of the mixture screw should be engaged to assure proper installation.

4) Install mixture control solenoid gauging tool over throttle side metering jet rod guide. Temporarily install solenoid plunger. *See Fig. 5.*

5) Hold solenoid plunger against solenoid stop. Using a "double D" wrench, slowly turn lean mixture screw clockwise until solenoid plunger just contacts gauging tool. *See Fig. 5.*

6) Adjustment is correct when solenoid plunger is contacting BOTH the solenoid stop and gauging tool. Remove solenoid plunger and gauging tool.

SOLENOID RICH MIXTURE STOP SCREW (BENCH ADJUSTMENT)

NOTE: This is a preliminary adjustment only. It is required to ensure that rich mixture stop screw is set close to specifications prior to final adjustment. Final adjustment must be made with carburetor installed and engine running. See appropriate TUNE-UP article.

Fig. 6: Solenoid Rich Mixture Stop Screw Bench Adjustment

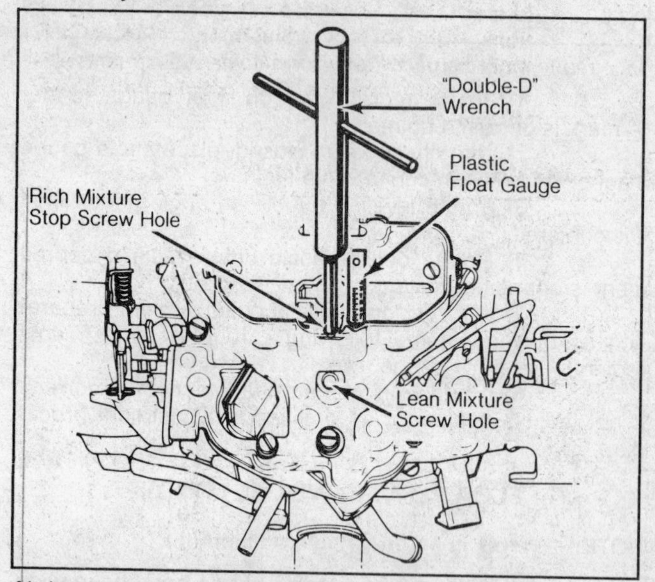

Air horn must be properly installed prior to adjustment.

1) With solenoid lean mixture screw properly set and air horn installed, insert plastic float gauge in vertical "D" shaped vent hole in air horn casting.

2) With float gauge installed, read mark (in inches) on gauge that lines up with top of air horn casting at eye level. Record reading. Lightly depress float gauge and again read mark on gauge that lines up with top of casting. Record reading.

3) Subtract the 2 readings taken in step **2)**. This difference is the total solenoid travel. Using a "double

Fig. 7: Installing Lean Mixture Screw Plug and Rich Mixture Stop Screw Plug

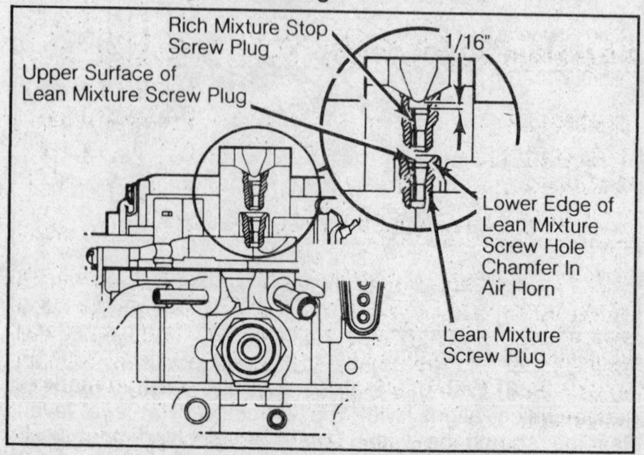

Plugs seal settings and prevent loss of fuel vapor.

ROCHESTER E2ME 2-BARREL (Cont.)

D" wrench, turn rich mixture stop screw until total solenoid travel (difference between readings) is 4/32". *See Fig. 6.*

4) After adjustment, install lean mixture screw plug and rich mixture stop screw plug. Plugs must be installed to seal settings and to prevent fuel vapor loss. *See Fig. 7.*

IDLE MIXTURE (BENCH ADJUSTMENT)

NOTE: This is a preliminary adjustment only. It is required to ensure that mixture screws and idle air bleed valve are set close to specifications prior to final adjustment. Final adjustment must be made with carburetor installed and engine running. See appropriate TUNE-UP article.

Fig. 8: Idle Mixture Bench Adjustment

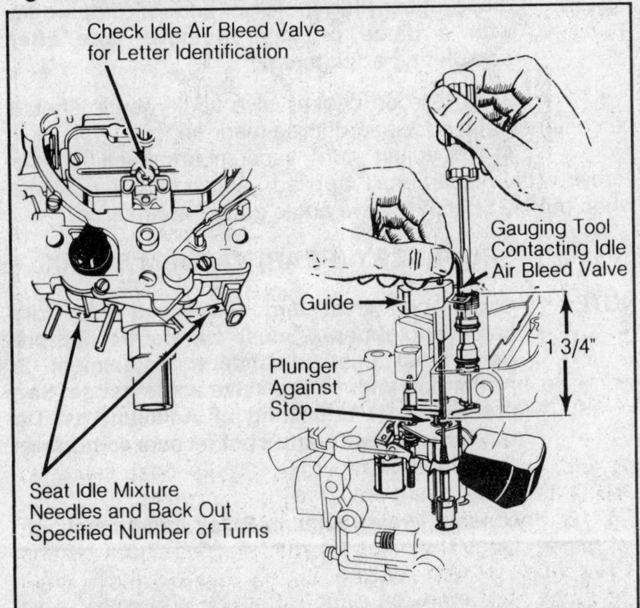

Final adjustments must be performed with carburetor installed and engine running.

1) With air horn properly installed, lightly seat mixture screws. Back out specified number of turns. *See Idle Mixture Screw Chart.*

IDLE MIXTURE SCREW CHART

Application	Mixture Screw Preset (Turns)
17082130, 132	1 1/4
All Others	3 [1]

[1] — Final adjustment performed on-vehicle.

2) The idle air bleed valve is sealed with a riveted cover. This cover should not be removed unless required for cleaning, part replacement, improper dwell readings, or if Computer Command Control System Performance Check indicates that carburetor requires adjustment.

3) If idle air bleed cover was previously removed, or if conditions described in step **2)** are met, check idle air bleed valve for a letter inscribed on top of valve. This will determine the correct on-vehicle adjustment procedure.

4) To adjust idle air bleed valve, if required, insert air bleed valve gauging tool in throttle side "D" shaped vent hole in air horn casting. Upper end of tool should be positioned over open cavity next to valve. *See Fig. 8.*

5) Hold the gauging tool down lightly so solenoid plunger is against solenoid stop. Adjust air bleed valve so gauging tool will pivot over and just contact top of valve. *See Fig. 8.*

ACCELERATOR PUMP

No pump adjustment is required on carburetors for the Computer Command Control system.

CHOKE COIL LEVER

NOTE: Choke coil cover uses rivets in place of retaining screws. If necessary to remove choke coil cover, refer to Disassembly and Reassembly procedures in this Section.

Fig. 9: Choke Coil Lever Adjustment

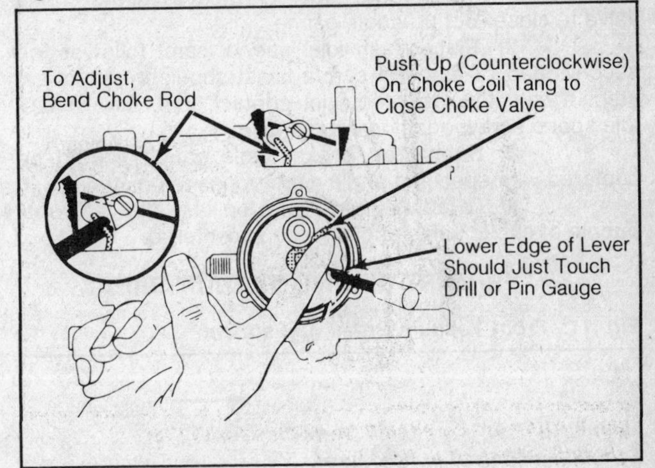

Bend choke rod to adjust.

1) Remove retaining rivets. Remove choke cover and coil assembly from choke housing. *See Fig. 9.*

2) Position fast idle speed cam follower on high step of fast idle cam.

3) Push up (counterclockwise) on choke coil tang to close choke valve.

4) Insert specified drill or pin gauge in hole provided in choke housing. Lower edge of choke lever inside housing should just touch drill or pin gauge.

5) To adjust, bend choke rod. *See Fig. 9.*

CHOKE ROD (FAST IDLE CAM)

NOTE: Choke coil lever adjustment must be correct before performing this adjustment. Fast idle speed adjustment must be performed using the Emission Control Tune-Up Decal with carburetor installed and vehicle running. Adjustment is performed with choke valve angle gauge. See procedure at beginning of Adjustments. Do not remove rivets and choke cover to perform this adjustment.

ROCHESTER E2ME 2-BARREL (Cont.)

Fig. 10: Choke Rod (Fast Idle Cam) Adjustment

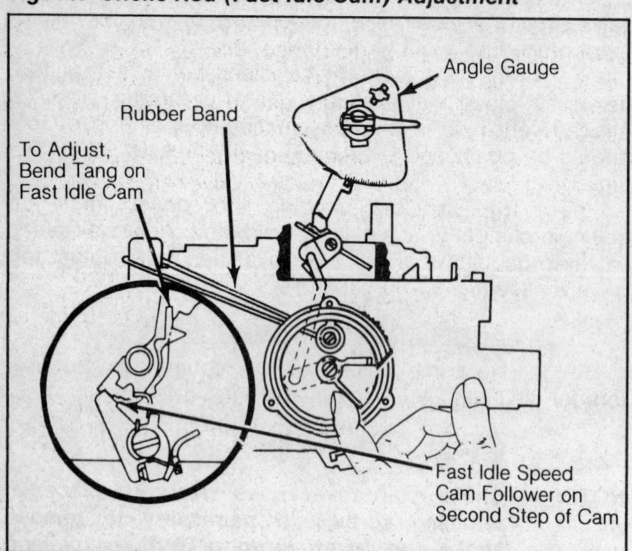

Bend tang on fast idle cam to adjust.

1) Attach rubber band to Green tang of intermediate choke shaft. Open throttle to allow choke valve to close. Set up angle gauge.

2) Place fast idle speed cam follower on second step of fast idle cam against shoulder of highest step. If cam follower does not contact cam, turn in fast idle speed screw additional turns. *See Fig. 10.*

3) Bubble on choke angle gauge should be centered with specified angle mark opposite pointer.

4) To adjust, bend tang on fast idle cam until bubble of choke valve angle gauge is centered.

PRIMARY (FRONT) VACUUM BREAK

Fig. 11: Front Vacuum Break Adjustment

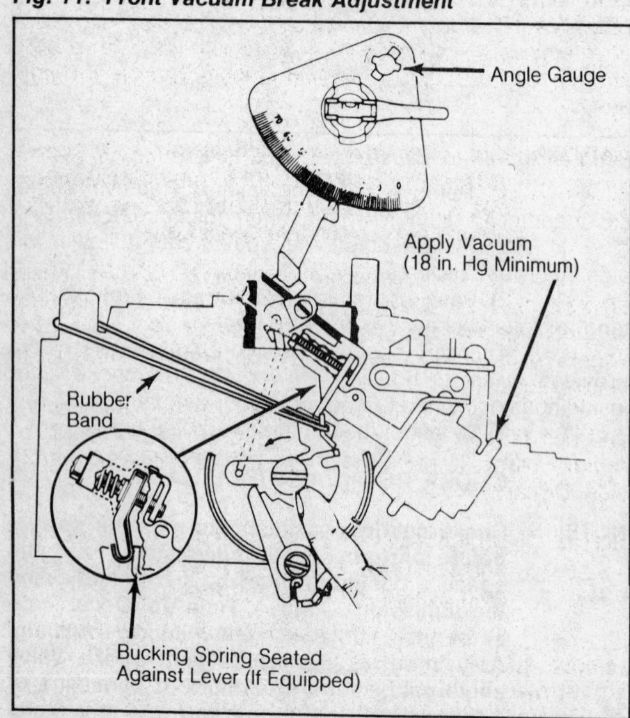

Turn vacuum break adjustment screw to adjust.

NOTE: **Choke coil lever and choke rod (fast idle cam) adjustments must be correct before performing this adjustment. Adjustment is performed with choke valve angle gauge. See procedure at beginning of Adjustments. Do not remove rivets and choke cover to perform this adjustment.**

1) Attach rubber band to Green tang of intermediate choke shaft. Open throttle to allow choke valve to close. Set up angle gauge.

2) Using an outside vacuum source of at least 18 in. Hg, seat primary (front) vacuum break diaphragm. Be sure leaf bucking spring is seated against lever, if equipped. *See Fig. 11.*

NOTE: **On models equipped with air bleed, remove rubber cover from filter and plug vacuum tube with a piece of tape. If bleed hole is in end of diaphragm, plug hole in end of diaphragm with a piece of tape. Remove tape after completing adjustment.**

3) Bubble on choke valve angle gauge should be centered with specified degree mark opposite pointer.

4) To adjust, turn vacuum break adjustment screw with vacuum still applied. Adjustment is correct when bubble of choke valve angle gauge is centered.

SECONDARY (REAR) VACUUM BREAK

NOTE: **Choke coil lever and choke rod (fast idle cam) adjustments must be correct before performing this adjustment. Adjustment is performed with choke valve angle gauge. See procedure at beginning of Adjustments. Do not remove rivets and choke cover to perform this adjustment.**

Fig. 12: Secondary (Rear) Vacuum Break Adjustment

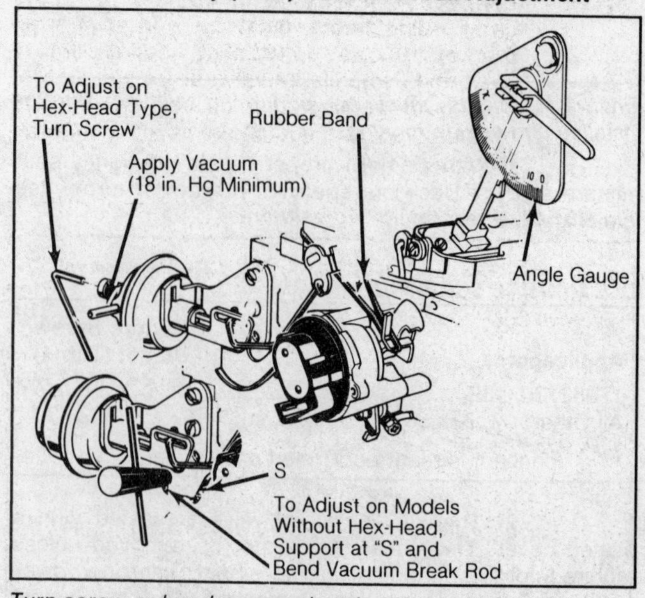

Turn screw or bend vacuum break rod to adjust.

1) Attach rubber band to Green tang of intermediate choke shaft. Open throttle to allow choke valve to close. Set up angle gauge.

ROCHESTER E2ME 2-BARREL (Cont.)

2) Using an outside vacuum source of at least 18 in. Hg, seat secondary (rear) vacuum break diaphragm. Be sure leaf bucking spring is compressed, if equipped. *See Fig. 12.*

NOTE: On models equipped with air bleed, remove rubber cover from filter and plug vacuum tube with a piece of tape. If bleed hole is in end of diaphragm, plug hole in end of diaphragm with tape. On delay models with air bleed, plug end cover with an accelerator pump plunger cup. Remove tape or cup after completion of adjustment.

3) Close choke by pushing up on choke coil lever or vacuum break lever tang. Hold choke closed with a rubber band.

4) Bubble on choke valve angle gauge should be centered with specified degree mark opposite pointer.

5) To adjust on models equipped with hex adjustment, use a 1/8" hex wrench to turn adjustment screw in rear cover of vacuum break with vacuum still applied. To adjust on models without hex adjustment, support rod at "S" and bend vacuum break rod with vacuum still applied. Adjustment is correct when bubble of choke valve angle gauge is centered.

AUTOMATIC CHOKE

NOTE: Choke coil cover is retained in place with rivets. No adjustment is required. If necessary to remove choke coil cover, refer to Disassembly and Reassembly procedures. Remove choke cover only if a major overhaul is required or if the choke cover requires replacement.

CHOKE UNLOADER

NOTE: Choke coil lever and choke rod (fast idle cam) adjustments must be correct before performing this adjustment. Adjustment is performed with choke valve angle gauge. See procedure at beginning of Adjustments. Do not remove rivets and choke cover to perform this adjustment.

Fig. 13: Choke Unloader Adjustment

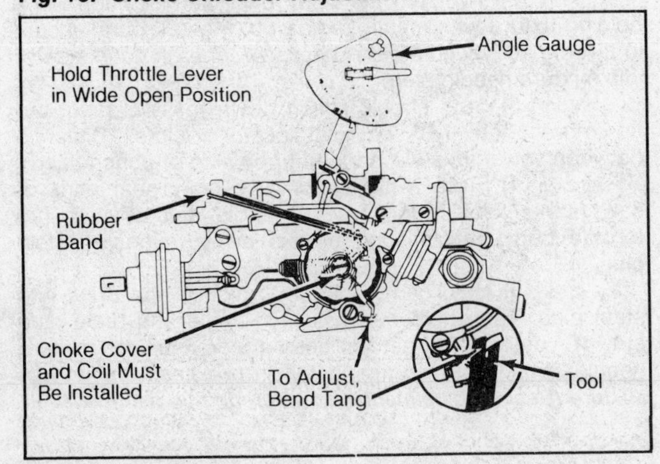

Bend tang to adjust.

1) Attach rubber band to Green tang of intermediate choke shaft. Open throttle to allow choke valve to close. Set up angle gauge. *See Fig. 13.*

2) Hold throttle lever in wide open position. Bubble on choke valve angle gauge should be centered with specified degree mark opposite pointer.

3) To adjust, bend choke unloader tang on fast idle lever until bubble of choke valve angle gauge is centered. Remove gauge.

OVERHAUL

DISASSEMBLY

NOTE: Place carburetor on a suitable working stand to avoid damaging throttle valves during overhaul.

Air Horn

1) Remove ILC, ISC or ISS and bracket assembly. Remove upper choke lever from choke shaft end by removing screw. Rotate lever to remove choke rod from slot in lever. Remove choke rod from lower (inner) choke lever inside float bowl casting.

NOTE: Hold lever outward and twist rod counterclockwise to remove.

2) Using a drift punch, drive pump lever pivot pin inward until end of pin is against air cleaner locating boss on air horn casting. Remove pump lever and disconnect lever from pump link.

CAUTION: Be careful when removing roll pin to avoid damage to pump lever bosses.

3) Remove front (primary) vacuum break hose from tube on float bowl and mark for reassembly reference. Remove 7 air horn screws. Then remove 2 countersunk screws located next to venturi. Lift air horn straight up to remove. Gasket should remain on float bowl.

CAUTION: Use care not to damage mixture control solenoid connector, TPS adjustment lever, and small tubes protruding from air horn. Do not attempt to remove small tubes.

4) Remove front (primary) vacuum break diaphragm and bracket assembly. Remove TPS plunger by pushing plunger up through seal in air horn. Use fingers only to remove plunger to prevent damage to sealing surface.

5) After removing air horn, lean mixture screw and rich mixture stop screw plugs must be removed. To remove plugs, invert air horn and drive out from bottom side. Discard plugs.

NOTE: Do not turn rich mixture stop screw in air horn unless screw requires replacement or solenoid plunger travel is incorect.

6) Remove TPS seal by inverting air horn and remove staking from around seal retainer with a small screwdriver. Remove and discard retainer and seal. Use care removing retainer and seal to prevent damage to air horn casting.

ROCHESTER E2ME 2-BARREL (Cont.)

7) Further disassembly of air horn assembly is not required for cleaning purposes. Choke valve and choke valve screws should not be removed. The air horn has an idle air bleed valve which is preset at the factory and sealed. The idle air bleed valve should not be removed from air horn unless System Performance Check of Computer Command Control system indicates need for adjustment or repair.

NOTE: **Air horn assembly, with idle air bleed valve installed, should be cleaned only in low volatile cleaning solvent. Do not place air horn (with idle air bleed valve) in carburetor cleaner. No tamper-resistant plug should be removed during normal carburetor cleaning and servicing unless carburetor or mixture control solenoid has been diagnosed as cause of poor engine performance.**

8) If necessary to replace idle air bleed valve or disassemble air horn for immersion in carburetor cleaner, cover internal bowl vents and air inlets to bleed valve with tape. Drill off rivet heads of bleed valve cover with a .110" (No. 35) drill. Drive remainder of rivet out of tower with drift and small hammer. Lift out cover over valve and remove remaining rivet pieces from inside tower.

9) After removing cover, check for letter identification on top of idle air bleed valve. This will determine the necessary adjustment procedure after reassembly. Turn valve counterclockwise and remove from air horn. Remove and discard "O" ring seals from air bleed valve. Air bleed valve is serviced as a complete assembly only.

Float Bowl

1) Hold pump plunger stem down and raise corner of air horn gasket to remove pump plunger from pump well. Remove solenoid metering rod plunger by lifting straight up. Remove rubber seal from around mixture control solenoid connector. Remove air horn gasket by lifting off dowel locating pins. Discard gasket.

2) Remove pump return spring from pump well. Remove staking holding Throttle Position Sensor in bowl. To do so, protect gasket sealing surface by laying a flat piece of metal across casting.

3) Using a small screwdriver, lightly depress and hold TPS sensor down against spring tension. Carefully remove staking from around TPS sensor by prying upward with a small chisel against the metal piece (not bowl casting).

4) Push up from bottom on electrical connector and remove TPS and connector assembly from bowl. Use care not to damage sensor during removal. Remove spring from bottom of TPS well in float bowl. Remove plastic filler block over float chamber.

5) Carefully remove each metering rod from metering jet. Make sure return spring is removed with each rod. Remove the spring by sliding off metering rod.

6) Remove mixture control solenoid-to-float bowl screws. Do not remove solenoid connector from float bowl at this time.

7) Using adjustment tool (J-28696-10) on upper end of lean mixture screw, turn screw counterclockwise and remove. Carefully lift solenoid and connector assembly from bowl.

NOTE: **Do not remove plunger return spring or connector and wires from solenoid body. Solenoid and connector are serviced as an assembly.**

8) If equipped, remove plastic insert from cavity in float bowl beneath solenoid connector. Remove solenoid screw tension spring (next to float hanger clip).

9) Remove float assembly and needle valve by lifting straight up on retaining clip. Remove needle valve seat and gasket.

10) Remove large mixture control solenoid tension spring from boss on bottom of float bowl located between metering jets. Remove metering jets (if necessary).

11) Remove accelerator pump discharge check ball retainer and check ball. Remove accelerator pump well baffle (if necessary).

12) If equipped, remove secondary (rear) vacuum break diaphragm and bracket. Rotate unit to remove vacuum break rod from slot in diaphragm plunger. Vacuum break link is not removed until choke assembly is removed from float bowl.

13) Align a .159" (No. 21) drill on choke cover retaining rivets and drill only enough to remove each rivet head. Drive out remainder of rivets with drift and hammer.

14) Remove 3 retainers and choke cover assembly. Remove screw and washer from inside housing. Slide housing out. Remove lower choke lever from inside float bowl cavity by inverting bowl.

15) If equipped, remove secondary (rear) vacuum break rod from intermediate choke lever. Remove choke coil lever screw from end of intermediate choke shaft in choke housing.

16) Remove choke coil lever from intermediate choke shaft. Remove intermediate choke shaft from housing by sliding outward. Remove fast idle cam from intermediate choke shaft. Turn float bowl over and remove lower choke lever.

17) Remove fuel inlet fitting, gasket, check valve/filter assembly and spring. Remove throttle body screws. Separate throttle body from float bowl and remove insulator gasket.

Throttle Body

1) Remove accelerator pump rod from throttle lever by rotating rod until tang on rod aligns with slot in lever.

2) Turn throttle body over and position on a holding fixture with manifold side up. Make 2 parallel cuts in throttle body with a small hacksaw, one on each side of idle mixture needle plug.

3) Cuts should reach down to steel plug, but no more than 1/8" beyond locator points. Distance between saw marks will depend upon size of punch used.

4) Place a flat punch at a point near ends of saw marks. Hold punch at 45° angle and drive it into throttle body until casting breaks away, exposing steel plug.

5) Hold center punch vertically and drive into steel plug. Then hold punch at 45° angle and drive plug out of casting. Repeat process for remaining mixture needle. When removing or installing needles, *refer to Idle Mixture (Bench Adjustment) procedure in this Section.*

ROCHESTER E2ME 2-BARREL (Cont.)

Fig. 14: Exploded View of Rochester E2ME 2-Barrel Carburetor

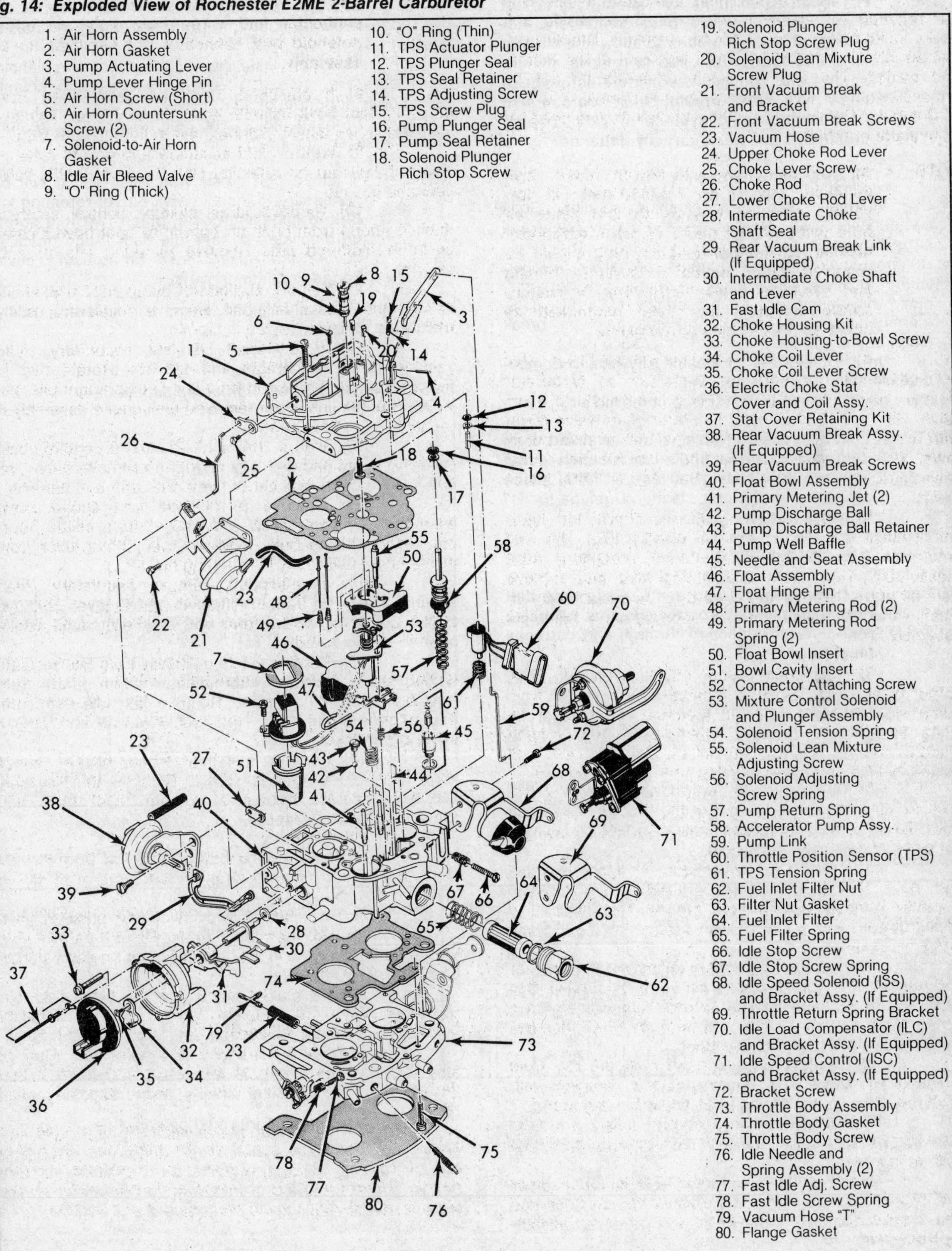

ROCHESTER E2ME 2-BARREL (Cont.)

NOTE: **Hardened steel plug will shatter. It is not necessary to remove plug completely. Remove just enough pieces to allow idle mixture adjusting tool to be used to remove mixture screws and springs. Idle mixture screw head has a "double-D" configuration and can also be removed using a piece of 7/32" copper tubing that has been partially flattened.**

CLEANING & INSPECTION

- Use a regular carburetor cleaning solution. Soak components long enough to thoroughly clean all surfaces and passages of foreign matter.
- Do not soak any components containing rubber, leather or plastic. Particularly do not soak air horn with bleed valve installed, electric choke, ISS, ISC, TPS, thermostatic choke cover and coil, vacuum break diaphragms, pump plunger and other such parts.
- Remove any residue after cleaning by rinsing components in a suitable solvent.
- Blow out all passages with dry compressed air.

NOTE: **If idle air bleed valve is not removed from carburetor, air horn should be cleaned with a low volatile cleaning solvent. DO NOT place air horn in carburetor cleaner. Damage to "O" rings may occur.**

REASSEMBLY

NOTE: **Use new gaskets and seals. Make sure that new gaskets fit correctly and that all holes and slots are punched through and correctly located.**

Reassemble carburetor in reverse order of disassembly, noting the following:

1) The intermediate choke shaft lever and fast idle cam are assembled correctly when tang on lever is beneath fast idle cam.

2) When installing float and retaining pin, make sure open end of float retaining pin faces accelerator pump well.

3) When installing fuel inlet valve, hook pull clip over edge of flat on float arm. Do not hook clip in holes in float arm.

4) When installing mixture control solenoid, make sure pin on end of solenoid aligns with hole in raised boss at bottom of float bowl.

5) Install, adjust and plug all screws to restore tamper-resistant design.

NOTE: **If choke coil cover was removed, it will be necessary to install service rivet retaining kit. Before installing cover, place fast idle screw on high step of fast idle cam. Align notch in cover with raised boss on housing cover flange and install rivets.**

6) Install air horn screws and tighten securely, evenly and in order shown in *Fig. 15*.

Fig. 15: Air Horn Screw Tightening Sequence

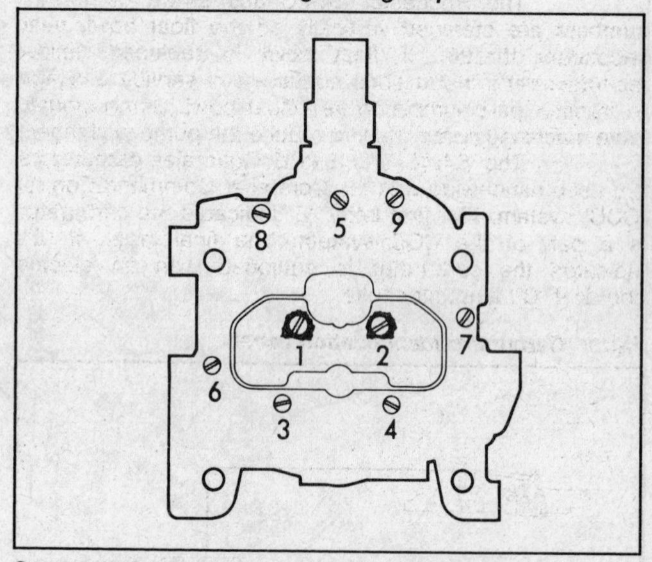

Screws 1 and 2 are countersunk next to venturi.

CARBURETOR ADJUSTMENT SPECIFICATIONS

Application	Float Level	Accel. Pump	Choke Coil Lever	Choke Rod	Idle Air Bleed	Vacuum Break Primary	Vacuum Break Secondary	Auto. Choke	Choke Unloader
17082130	3/8"	TR	.120"	20°	1 3/4" [1]	27°	.....	TR	38°
17082132	3/8"	TR	.120"	20°	1 3/4" [1]	27°	.....	TR	38°
17082182	5/16"	TR	.120"	18°	1 3/4"	28°	24°	TR	32°
17083190	5/16"	TR	.120"	18°	1 3/4"	28°	24°	TR	32°
17083192	5/16"	TR	.120"	18°	1 3/4"	28°	24°	TR	32°
17083193	5/16"	TR	.120"	17°	1 3/4"	23°	28°	TR	27°
17083194	5/16"	TR	.120"	17°	1 3/4"	27°	25°	TR	35°

TR — Tamper-Resistant

[1] — Final adjustment performed on-vehicle.

1983 Rochester Carburetors

ROCHESTER E4MC & E4ME 4-BARREL

CARBURETOR APPLICATION

GENERAL MOTORS (ROCHESTER) CARBURETOR NO.

Application	Man. Trans.	Auto. Trans.
3.8L (Turbo) V6	......	17083242, 244
4.1L (VIN 4) V6	......	17082265, 266 17082267, 268 17083248
5.0L (VIN H) V8	......	17083204
5.0L (VIN S) V8	17083207	17083204
5.0L (VIN Y) V8 [1]	......	17083250, 253, 17083553

[1] — Only E4MC application.

CARBURETOR IDENTIFICATION

The Rochester E4MC and E4ME carburetor numbers are stamped vertically on the float bowl, near secondary throttle. If float bowl is replaced, follow manufacturer's instructions contained in service package to transfer part number to new float bowl. Some models have machined pump wells to reduce the pump well taper.

The E4MC and E4ME Quadrajet carburetors are used nationwide with the Computer Command Control (CCC) system. The first letter "E" indicates the carburetor is a part of the CCC system. The final letter, if "E", indicates the carburetor is equipped with an electric choke; if "C", a hot air choke.

Fig. 1: Carburetor Identification Label

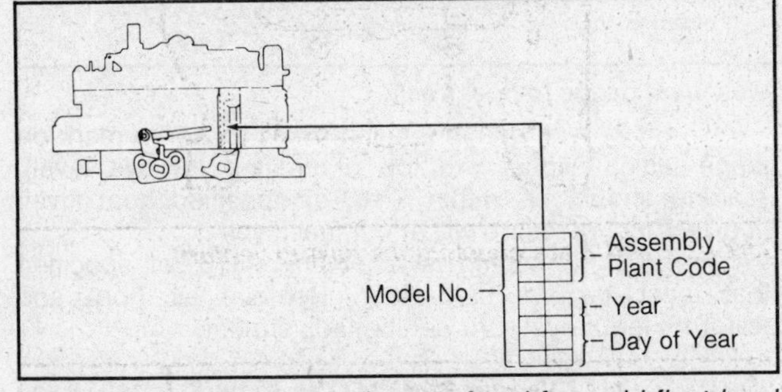

Original part number must be transfered from old float bowl if new float bowl is installed.

DESCRIPTION

The E4MC and E4ME carburetors are of a 2-stage, downdraft design. Each bore has a triple venturi system. The secondary side is composed of 2 large throttle bores, using the air valve principle, in which fuel is metered in direct proportion to the amount of air passing through the secondary throttle bores. A baffle is attached to the secondary side of the air horn, above the main well bleed tubes. This deflects incoming air to improve secondary nozzle operation on heavy acceleration.

The E4MC carburetor uses a float bowl-mounted heated air choke assembly; the E4ME, an electrically-actuated choke assembly. All E4MC and most E4ME models have 2 vacuum break diaphragm assemblies, the front and rear, while some E4ME models have only the front vacuum break assembly.

Both the E4MC and E4ME models are used in conjunction with the Computer Command Control (CCC) System. The carburetors are equipped with an electrically-actuated mixture control solenoid mounted in the float bowl. Fuel metering is controlled by stepped metering rods that operate in removable jets.

Both models include tamper-resistant factory settings of the mixture control solenoid rich mixture stop screw and lean mixture screw, idle air bleed valve, TPS, ILC, ISC, ISS and idle mixture screws. No attempt should be made to adjust these except during major overhaul or replacement of air horn, float bowl or throttle body. Both electric and hot air chokes have riveted covers which must not be removed except for major overhaul.

The 5.0L (VIN Y) engine is equipped with an Idle Load Compensator (ILC) attached to the fuel bowl. The ILC adjusts curb idle speed by sensing changes in manifold vacuum (engine load). To prevent the ILC from reacting too quickly to vacuum changes, a Differential Vacuum Delay Valve (DVDV) is installed between the ILC and vacuum source. The DVDV delays operation of the ILC until vacuum change is constant. All other engines may be equipped with an Idle Speed Control (ISC) on the fuel bowl. Controlled by the ECM, the ISC controls the normal curb idle speed and acts as a dashpot on deceleration and throttle closing. On vehicles without ILC or ISC, but with air conditioning, an Idle Speed Solenoid (ISS) maintains a specific idle speed during A/C operation.

TESTING

ELECTRIC CHOKE

NOTE: **This test should be performed when air temperature is 60-80°F (15-27°C).**

1) Allow choke to cool to permit full closing of choke blade when throttle is opened slightly. Start engine and time the interval required for choke blade to reach full open position. (Start timing when engine starts). If choke blade does not fully open within 3-1/2 minutes, proceed with test.

2) With engine running, check voltage at choke heater connection. If voltage is about 12-15 volts, replace electric choke unit. If voltage is low or zero, check all wires and connections and repair as required. Power for choke unit is through the oil pressure switch. Ensure switch circuitry is good.

3) If procedure in step **2)** does not correct the problem, replace oil pressure switch.

HOT AIR CHOKE

1) Start and warm engine to normal operating temperature. Ensure choke valve fully opens. If valve does not fully open, check choke housing and hot air inlet to determine if sufficient heat is reaching choke coil.

2) If choke housing and/or hot air inlet are cool, check for loss of vacuum to choke housing, restricted heat inlet in choke housing, restricted hot air inlet pipe or hose and restricted manifold choke heat stove passages. Repair or replace as required.

DIFFERENTIAL VACUUM DELAY VALVE

1) Using a "T" fitting, connect a vacuum gauge in vacuum line from valve to ILC. Connect a vacuum pump to port 1 of valve. Apply 17.8 in. Hg vacuum to port 1 and

ROCHESTER E4MC & E4ME 4-BARREL (Cont.)

observe gauge. Gauge should read 16.9 in. Hg vacuum within 6-9 seconds. *See Fig. 2.*

Fig. 2: Location and Identification of Differential Vacuum Delay Valve Ports

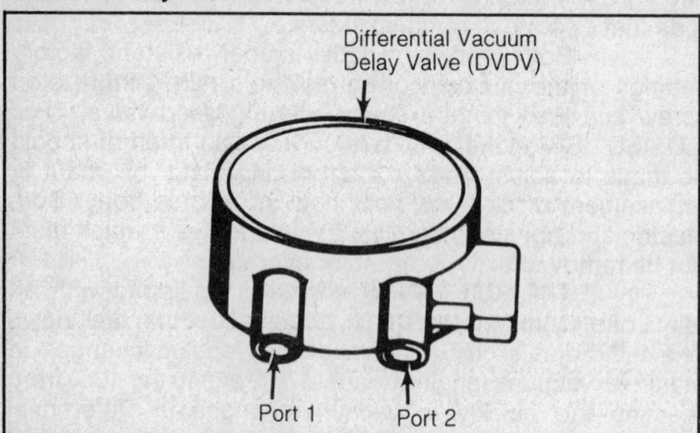

Identify ports for testing procedure.

2) Remove vacuum gauge and "T" fitting. Connect vacuum pump to port 2 and leave port 1 open. Air should flow through valve when .5 in. Hg vacuum is applied.

ADJUSTMENTS

NOTE: **For on-vehicle adjustments, see TUNE-UP PROCEDURES article.**

ANGLE GAUGE ADJUSTMENT TOOL

Manufacturer recommends that some carburetor adjustments be performed using a choke valve angle gauge (Kent-Moore tool No. J-26701). While preparations and actual adjustment may vary with each individual adjustment, the procedure for using the angle gauge to check the choke valve angle remains the same. Use the following procedure to perform adjustments requiring the use of the choke valve angle gauge.

Fig. 3: Choke Valve Angle Gauge

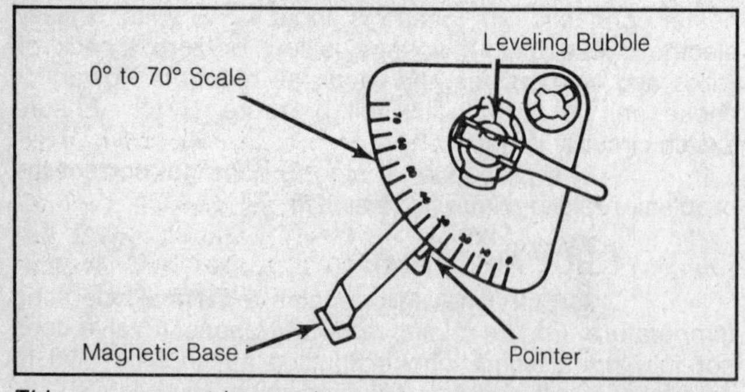

This gauge must be used to perform some adjustments.

1) Rotate degree scale on angle gauge so that 0° mark is opposite pointer.

2) With choke valve closed, place angle gauge magnet squarely on choke valve.

3) Rotate leveling bubble on angle gauge until it is centered.

4) Rotate degree scale until specified degree mark is opposite pointer.

5) Now perform individual adjustment preparation as outlined in the following carburetor adjustments requiring an angle gauge.

6) If bubble is centered, adjustment is correct. If not, adjust carburetor as outlined in adjustment procedure.

FLOAT LEVEL (WET SETTING)

NOTE: **This is an on-vehicle adjustment.**

1) With engine running at idle and choke wide open, carefully insert float gauge into vent slot or vent hole (next to air cleaner mounting stud) in air horn. Allow gauge to float freely. *See Fig. 4.*

NOTE: **Pressing down on float gauge could result in float damage or carburetor flooding.**

Fig. 4: Wet Float Level Adjustment

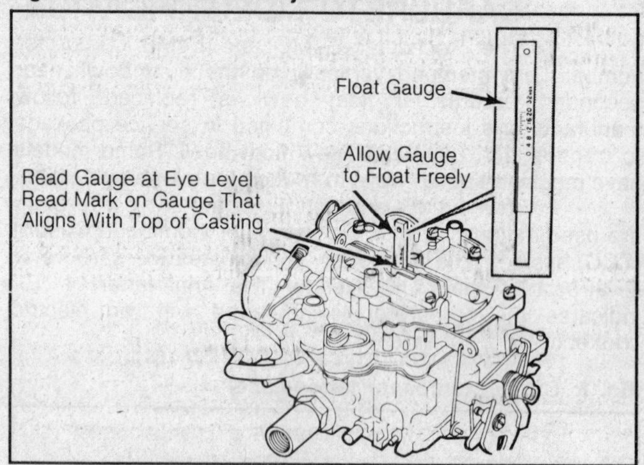

Allow float gauge to float freely.

2) With gauge floating freely, observe mark on gauge which aligns with top of casting (at eye level). Reading should be within 1/16" of specified float level. Incorrect fuel pressure will affect fuel level.

3) If reading is not within 1/16" of specified float level, remove carburetor. Remove air horn and perform Float Level (Dry Setting) adjustment.

FLOAT LEVEL (DRY SETTING)

1) Remove air horn and gasket from float bowl. Hold float retainer down firmly. Lightly push float down against needle. *See Fig. 5.*

2) Position a "T" scale over toe of float at a point 3/16" from end of float toe. Measure distance from top of float bowl casting to top of float.

3) If float level setting varies more than 1/16" from specified setting, proceed as follows:

Float Level Too High

a) Hold float retainer clip firmly in place.

b) Push down on center of float pontoon until correct float level setting is obtained.

Float Level Too Low

a) Lift out metering rods. Remove solenoid connector screws.

b) Turn lean mixture solenoid screw clockwise, counting and recording number of turns required to lightly seat screw in float bowl.

ROCHESTER E4MC & E4ME 4-BARREL (Cont.)

c) Turn screw counterclockwise and remove. Lift solenoid and connector from float bowl.

d) Remove float and bend arm up to adjust. Make sure float is correctly aligned after adjustment.

e) Reinstall components in reverse order that they were removed. Back out solenoid mixture screw number of turns noted in step **b)**.

Fig. 5: Dry Float Level Adjustment

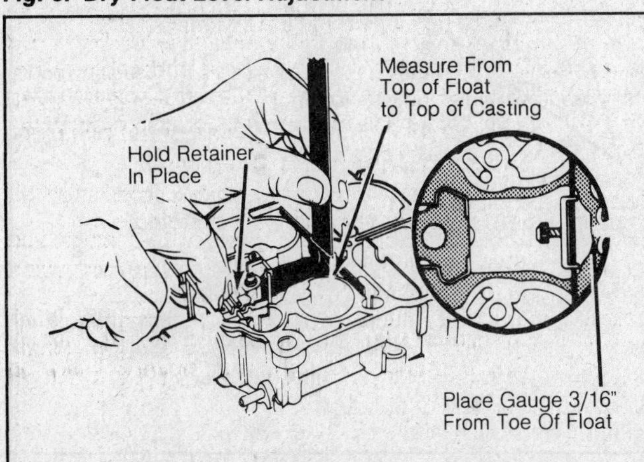

Follow procedures to properly adjust float level.

SOLENOID LEAN MIXTURE SCREW (BENCH ADJUSTMENT)

NOTE: **This is a preliminary adjustment only. It is required to ensure that lean mixture screw is set close to specifications prior to final adjustment. Final adjustment must be made with carburetor installed and engine running. See appropriate TUNE-UP article.**

1) Install plastic aneroid cavity insert beneath mixture control solenoid connector in float bowl, if used. Ensure insert is installed with inset aligned with recess of bowl cavity and seated flush with bowl casting surface. Tang on upper lip of insert goes in deep slot in bowl closest to fuel inlet nut.

2) Install mixture control solenoid screw tension spring between raised bosses next to float hanger pin. Carefully install mixture control solenoid in float chamber. Align pin on end of solenoid with hole in raised boss at bottom of bowl. Align connector wires to fit in slot in bowl or plastic insert, if used.

3) Install solenoid lean mixture screw through hole in solenoid bracket and tension spring in float bowl. The first 6 threads of the mixture screw should be engaged to assure proper installation.

4) Install mixture control solenoid gauging tool over throttle side metering jet rod guide. Temporarily install solenoid plunger. *See Fig. 6.*

5) Hold solenoid plunger against solenoid stop. Using a "double D" wrench, slowly turn lean mixture screw clockwise until solenoid plunger just contacts gauging tool. *See Fig. 6.*

6) Adjustment is correct when solenoid plunger is contacting BOTH the solenoid stop and gauging tool. Remove solenoid plunger and gauging tool.

Fig. 6: Solenoid Lean Mixture Screw Bench Adjustment

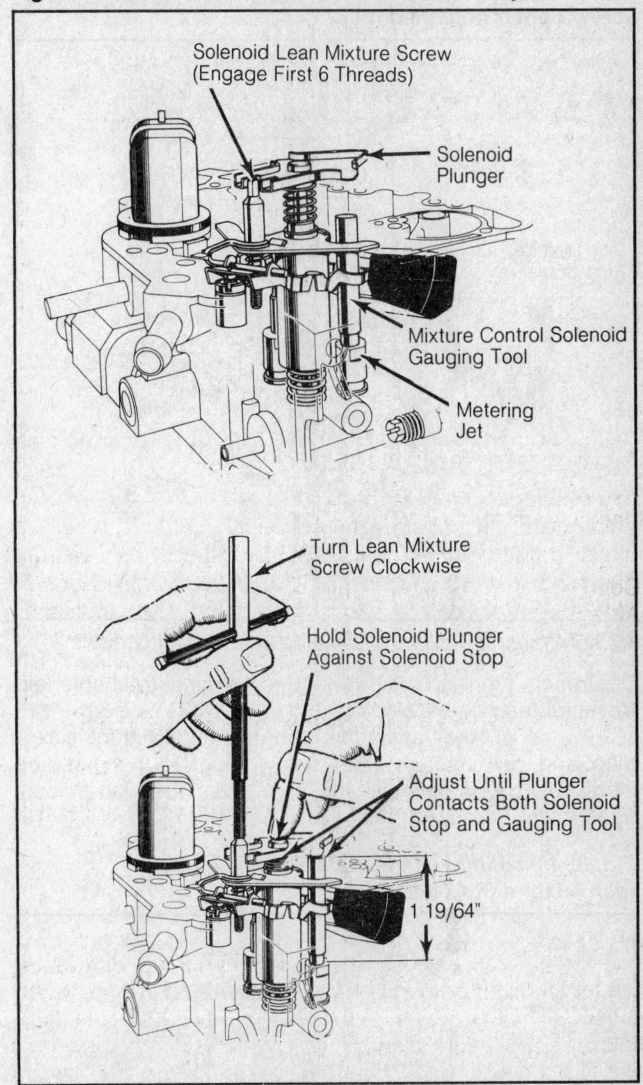

Lean mixture screw should be installed with first 6 threads engaged in float bowl.

SOLENOID RICH MIXTURE STOP SCREW (BENCH ADJUSTMENT)

NOTE: **This is a preliminary adjustment only. It is required to ensure that rich mixture stop screw is set close to specifications prior to final adjustment. Final adjustment must be made with carburetor installed and engine running. See appropriate TUNE-UP article.**

1) With solenoid lean mixture screw properly set and air horn installed, insert plastic float gauge in vertical "D" shaped vent hole in air horn casting.

2) With float gauge installed, read mark (in inches) on gauge that lines up with top of air horn casting at eye level. Record reading. Lightly depress float gauge and again read mark on gauge that lines up with top of casting. Record reading.

3) Subtract the 2 readings taken in step **2)**. This difference is the total solenoid travel. Using a "double

ROCHESTER E4MC & E4ME 4-BARREL (Cont.)

Fig. 7: Solenoid Rich Mixture Stop Screw Bench Adjustment

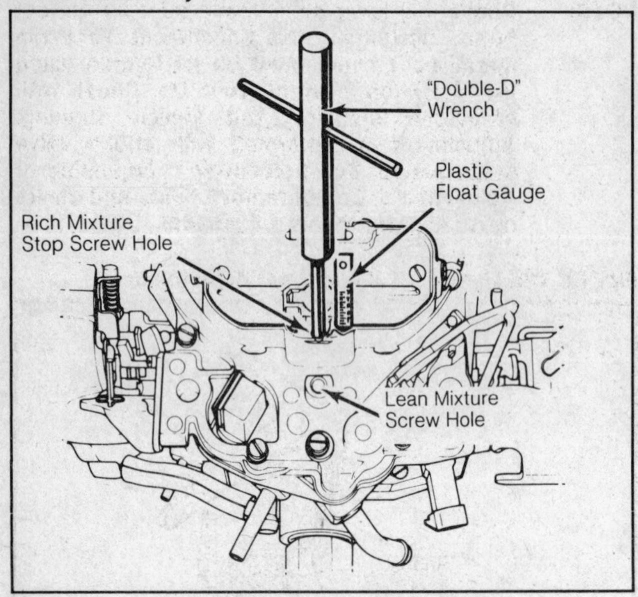

Air horn must be properly installed prior to adjustment.

D" wrench, turn rich mixture stop screw until total solenoid travel (difference between readings) is 4/32". *See Fig. 7.*

4) After adjustment, install lean mixture screw plug and rich mixture stop screw plug. Plugs must be installed to seal settings and to prevent fuel vapor loss. *See Fig. 8.*

Fig. 8: Installing Lean Mixture Screw Plug and Rich Mixture Stop Screw Plug

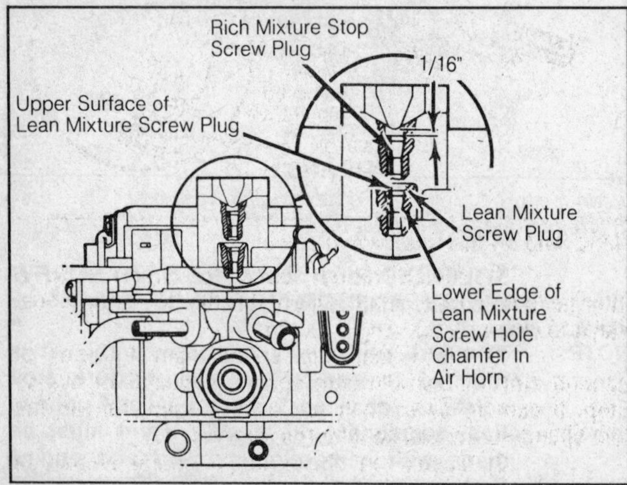

Plugs seal settings and prevent loss of fuel vapor.

IDLE MIXTURE (BENCH ADJUSTMENT)

NOTE: This is a preliminary adjustment only. It is required to ensure that mixture screws and idle air bleed valve are set close to specifications prior to final adjustment. Final adjustment must be made with carburetor installed and engine running. See appropriate TUNE-UP article.

Fig. 9: Idle Mixture Bench Adjustment

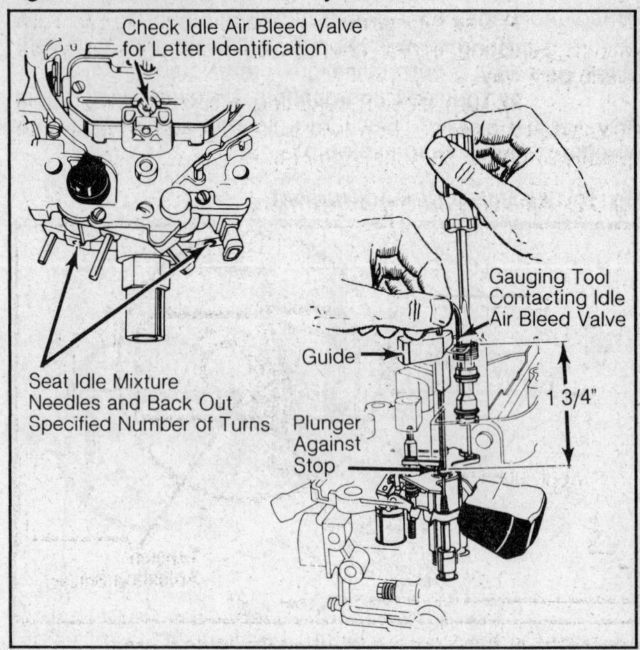

Final adjustments must be performed with carburetor installed and engine running.

1) With air horn properly installed, lightly seat mixture screws. Back out specified number of turns. *See Idle Mixture Screw Chart.*

IDLE MIXTURE SCREW CHART

Application	Mixture Screw Preset (Turns)
17083204, 207	3 3/8
All Others	3 [1]

[1] — Final adjustment performed on-vehicle.

2) The idle air bleed valve is sealed with a riveted cover. This cover should not be removed unless required for cleaning, part replacement, improper dwell readings, or if Computer Command Control System Performance Check indicates that carburetor requires adjustment.

3) If idle air bleed cover was previously removed, or if conditions described in step **2)** are met, check idle air bleed valve for a letter inscribed on top of valve. This will determine the correct on-vehicle adjustment procedure.

4) To adjust idle air bleed valve, if required, insert air bleed valve gauging tool in throttle side "D" shaped vent hole in air horn casting. Upper end of tool should be positioned over open cavity next to valve. *See Fig. 9.*

5) Hold the gauging tool down lightly so solenoid plunger is against solenoid stop. Adjust air bleed valve so gauging tool will pivot over and just contact top of valve. *See Fig. 9.*.

ACCELERATOR PUMP ROD

No pump adjustment is required on carburetors for the Computer Command Control system.

ROCHESTER E4MC & E4ME 4-BARREL (Cont.)

AIR VALVE SPRING

1) Use hex wrench to loosen lock screw. Turn tension adjusting screw counterclockwise until air valve opens part way.

2) Turn tension adjusting screw clockwise until air valve just closes. Then turn adjusting screw clockwise specified number of turns. *See Fig. 10.*

Fig. 10: Air Valve Spring Adjustment

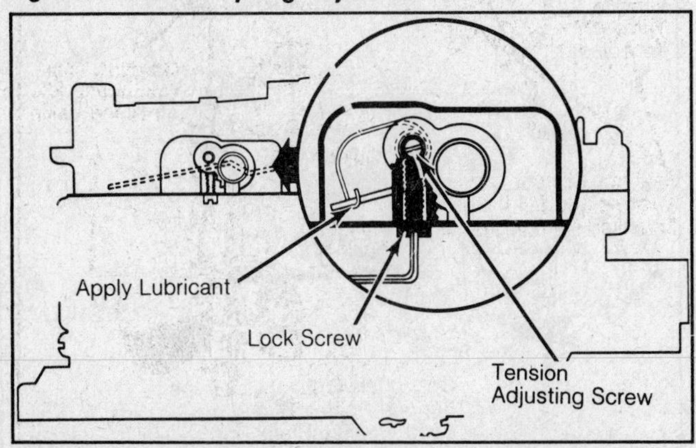

Apply lithium base grease to lubricate contact area.

3) Hold adjusting screw and tighten lock screw. Apply lithium base grease to lubricate contact area.

CHOKE COIL LEVER

NOTE: **Choke coil cover uses rivets in place of retaining screws. If necessary to remove choke coil cover, refer to Disassembly and Reassembly procedures in this Section.**

Fig. 11: Choke Coil Lever Adjustment

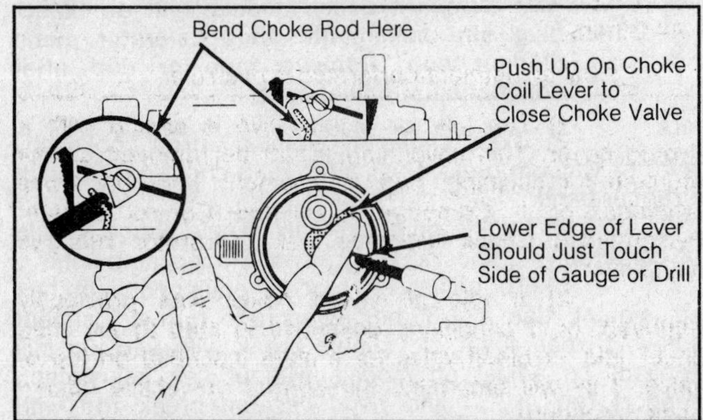

Bend choke rod to adjust.

1) Remove retaining rivets. Remove choke cover and coil assembly from choke housing. *See Fig. 11.*

2) Position fast idle speed cam follower on high step of fast idle cam.

3) Push up (counterclockwise) on choke coil tang to close choke valve.

4) Insert specified drill or pin gauge in hole provided in choke housing. Lower edge of choke lever inside housing should just touch drill or pin gauge.

5) To adjust, bend choke rod. *See Fig. 11.*

NOTE: **Electric choke units do not use a gasket between choke cover and choke housing.**

CHOKE ROD (FAST IDLE CAM)

NOTE: **Choke coil lever adjustment must be correct before performing this adjustment. Fast idle speed adjustment must be performed using the Emission Control Tune-Up Decal with carburetor installed and vehicle running. Adjustment is performed with choke valve angle gauge. See procedure at beginning of Adjustments. Do not remove rivets and choke cover to perform this adjustment.**

Fig. 12: Choke Rod (Fast Idle Cam) Adjustment

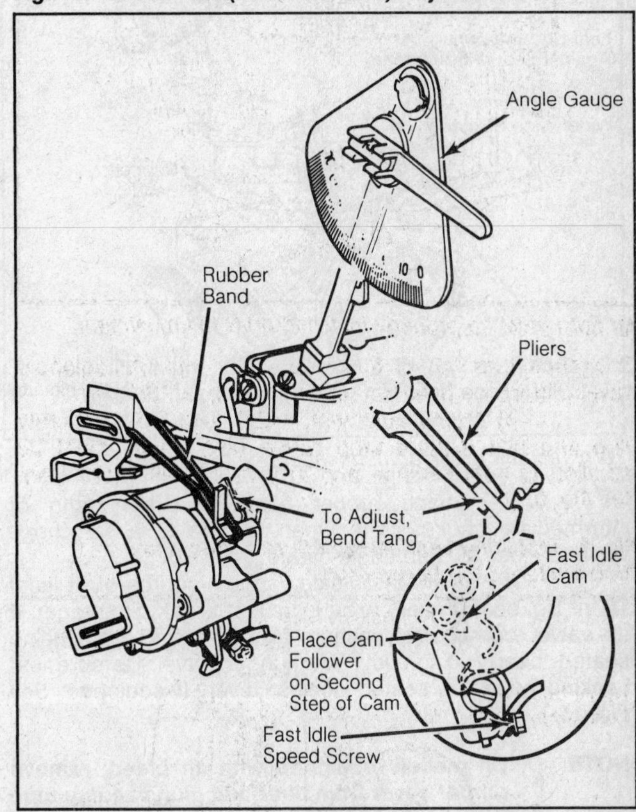

Bend tang on fast idle cam to adjust.

1) Attach rubber band to Green tang of intermediate choke shaft. Open throttle to allow choke valve to close. Set up angle gauge.

2) Place fast idle speed cam follower on second step of fast idle cam against shoulder of highest step. If cam follower does not contact cam, turn in fast idle speed screw additional turns. *See Fig. 12.*

3) Bubble on choke angle gauge should be centered with specified angle mark opposite pointer.

4) To adjust, bend tang on fast idle cam until bubble of choke valve angle gauge is centered.

PRIMARY (FRONT) VACUUM BREAK

NOTE: **Choke coil lever and choke rod (fast idle cam) adjustments must be correct before performing this adjustment. Adjustment is performed with choke valve angle gauge. See procedure at beginning of Adjustments. Do not remove rivets and choke cover to perform this adjustment.**

ROCHESTER E4MC & E4ME 4-BARREL (Cont.)

Fig. 13: Front Vacuum Break Adjustment

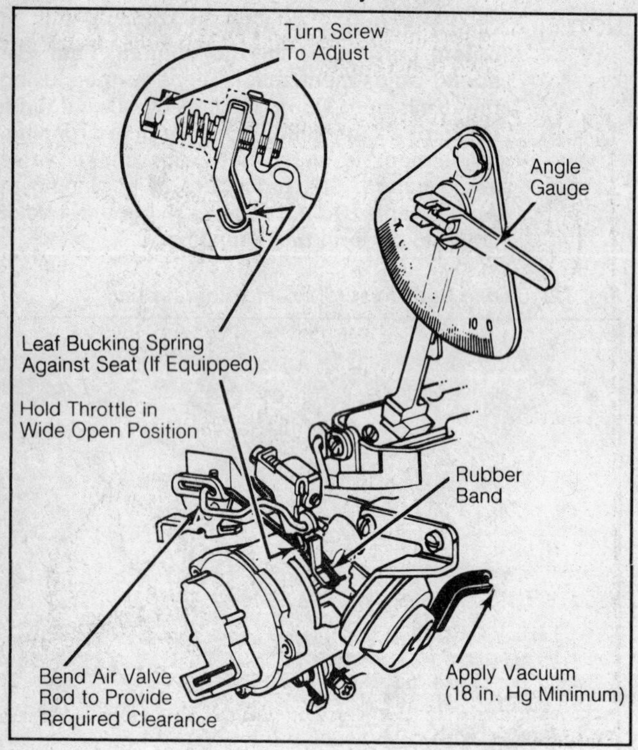

Turn vacuum break adjustment screw to adjust.

1) Attach rubber band to Green tang of intermediate choke shaft. Open throttle to allow choke valve to close. Set up angle gauge.

2) Using an outside vacuum source of at least 18 in. Hg, seat primary (front) vacuum break diaphragm. If air valve rod restricts vacuum break plunger from being seated, bend rod to allow full plunger travel. Be sure leaf bucking spring is seated against lever, if equipped. *See Fig. 13.*

NOTE: On models equipped with air bleed, remove rubber cover from filter and plug vacuum tube with a piece of tape. If bleed hole is in end of diaphragm, plug hole in end of diaphragm with a piece of tape. Remove tape after completing adjustment.

3) Bubble on choke valve angle gauge should be centered with specified degree mark opposite pointer.

4) To adjust, turn vacuum break adjustment screw with vacuum still applied. Adjustment is correct when bubble of choke valve angle gauge is centered.

SECONDARY (REAR) VACUUM BREAK

NOTE: Choke coil lever and choke rod (fast idle cam) adjustments must be correct before performing this adjustment. Adjustment is performed with choke valve angle gauge. See procedure at beginning of Adjustments. Do not remove rivets and choke cover to perform this adjustment.

1) Attach rubber band to Green tang of intermediate choke shaft. Open throttle to allow choke valve to close. Set up angle gauge.

Fig. 14: Secondary (Rear) Vacuum Break Adjustment

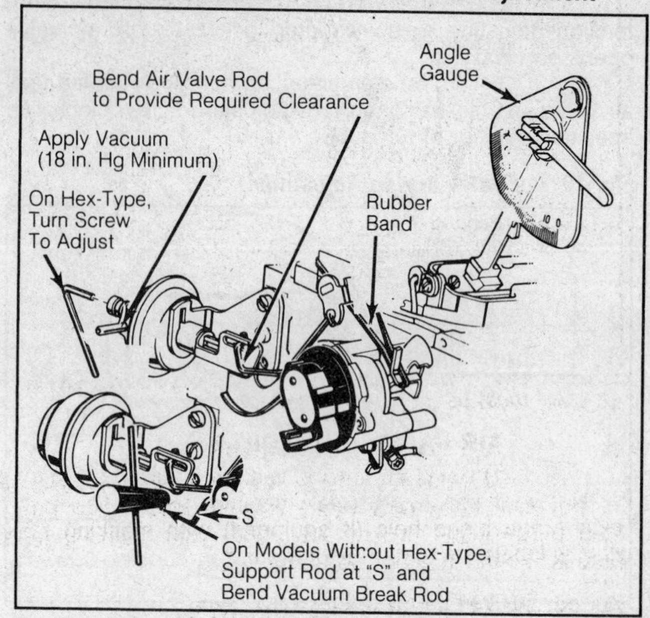

Turn screw or bend vacuum break rod to adjust.

2) Using an outside vacuum source of at least 18 in. Hg, seat secondary (rear) vacuum break diaphragm. If air valve rod restricts vacuum break plunger from being seated, bend rod to allow full plunger travel. Be sure leaf bucking spring is compressed, if equipped. *See Fig. 14.*

NOTE: On models equipped with air bleed, remove rubber cover from filter and plug vacuum tube with a piece of tape. If bleed hole is in end of diaphragm, plug hole in end of diaphragm with tape. On delay models with air bleed, plug end cover with an accelerator pump plunger cup. Remove tape or cup after completion of adjustment.

3) Close choke by pushing up on choke coil lever or vacuum break lever tang. Hold choke closed with a rubber band.

4) Bubble on choke valve angle gauge should be centered with specified degree mark opposite pointer.

5) To adjust on models equipped with hex adjustment, use a 1/8" hex wrench to turn adjustment screw in rear cover of vacuum break with vacuum still applied. To adjust on models without hex adjustment, support rod at "S" and bend vacuum break rod with vacuum still applied. Adjustment is correct when bubble of choke valve angle gauge is centered.

AIR VALVE ROD - FRONT

1) Using an outside vacuum source, at least 18 in. Hg, seat primary (front) vacuum break diaphragm. Plug purge bleed hole (if equipped) with masking tape. Hole is located in end of diaphragm. *See Fig. 15.*

2) Make sure air valve is completely closed. Measure clearance between rod and end of slot in lever. Clearance can be checked using a specified drill or pin gauge. *See Fig. 15.*

3) Bend rod at point shown to adjust clearance in slot to .025" with vacuum still applied. Remove tape and reconnect vacuum hose to diaphragm.

ROCHESTER E4MC & E4ME 4-BARREL (Cont.)

Fig. 15: Air Valve Rod Adjustment - Front

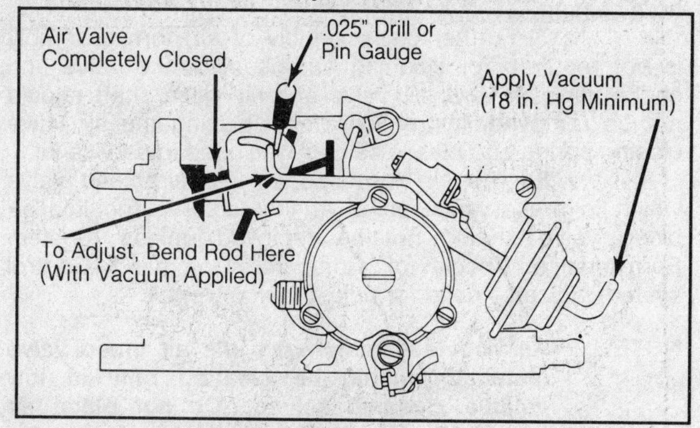

Air valve must be completely closed.

AIR VALVE ROD - REAR

1) Using an outside vacuum source, at least 18 in. Hg, seat secondary (rear) vacuum break diaphragm. Plug purge bleed hole (if equipped) with masking tape. Hole is located in end of diaphragm.

Fig. 16: Air Valve Rod Adjustment - Rear

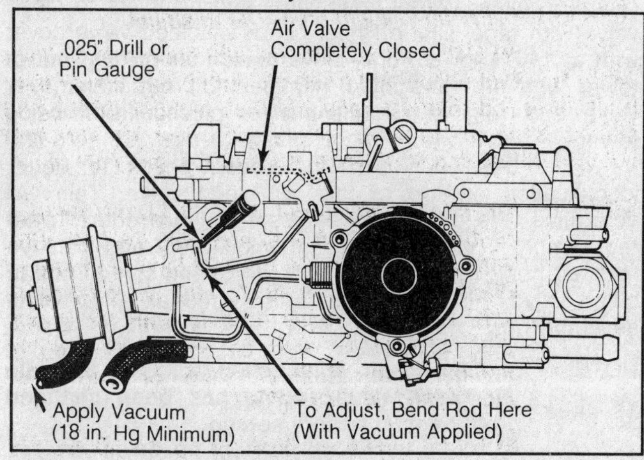

Air valve must be completely closed.

2) Make sure air valve is completely closed. Measure clearance between rod and end of slot in lever. Clearance can be checked using a specified drill or pin gauge. *See Fig. 16.*

3) Bend rod at point shown to adjust clearance in slot to .025" with vacuum still applied. Remove tape and reconnect vacuum hose to diaphragm.

AUTOMATIC CHOKE

NOTE: **Choke coil cover is retained in place with rivets. No adjustment is required. If necessary to remove choke coil cover, refer to Disassembly and Reassembly procedures in this Section. Only remove choke cover if major overhaul is required or if choke cover requires replacement.**

CHOKE UNLOADER

NOTE: **Choke coil lever and choke rod (fast idle cam) adjustments must be correct before performing this adjustment. Adjustment is performed with choke valve angle gauge. See procedure at beginning of Adjustments. Do not remove rivets and choke cover to perform this adjustment.**

Fig. 17: Choke Unloader Adjustment

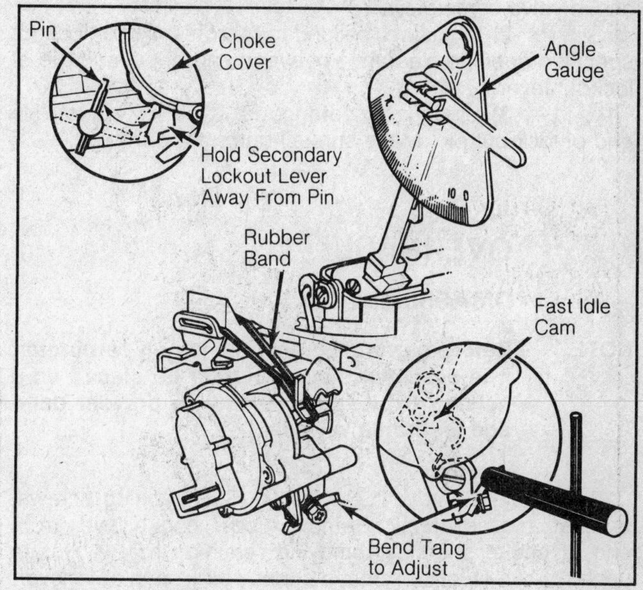

Bend tang to adjust.

1) Attach rubber band to Green tang of intermediate choke shaft. Open throttle to allow choke valve to close. Set up angle gauge. Hold secondary lockout lever away from pin. *See Fig. 17.*

2) Hold throttle lever in wide open position. Bubble on choke valve angle gauge should be centered with specified degree mark opposite pointer.

3) To adjust, bend choke unloader tang on fast idle lever until bubble of choke valve angle gauge is centered. Remove gauge.

SECONDARY THROTTLE VALVE LOCKOUT

Lockout Lever Side Clearance

1) Hold choke valve and throttle valves completely closed. *See Fig. 18.*

Fig. 18: Secondary Throttle Valve Lockout Adjustment

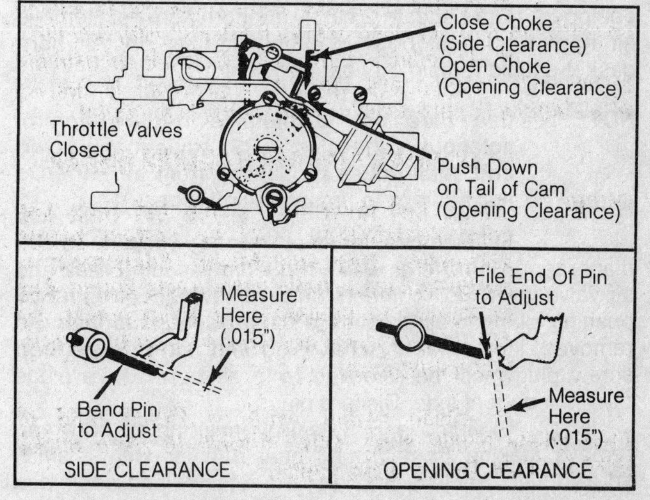

ROCHESTER E4MC & E4ME 4-BARREL (Cont.)

2) Measure secondary throttle valve lockout specified side clearance between pin and lockout lever.

3) Specified lockout lever side clearance is .015". To adjust, bend pin.

Lockout Lever Opening Clearance

1) Push down on tail of fast idle cam and open choke valve completely.

2) Measure secondary throttle valve lockout specified opening clearance between end of pin and toe of lockout lever.

3) Specified clearance is .015", To adjust, file end of lock out pin. Make sure all burrs are removed.

OVERHAUL

DISASSEMBLY

NOTE: **Before performing any service on carburetor, it is essential that carburetor be placed on a holding fixture (J-9789-118) to prevent damage to throttle valves.**

Air Horn

1) Remove ILC, ISC or ISS attaching screws, bracket and assembly. Remove upper choke lever from end of choke shaft by removing retaining screw. Rotate upper choke lever to remove choke rod from slot in lever. Remove choke rod from lower lever inside float bowl casting. Remove rod by holding lower lever outward with small screwdriver and twisting rod counterclockwise.

2) Remove secondary metering rods by removing small screw in top of metering rod hanger. Lift up on metering rod hanger until secondary metering rods clear air horn. Metering rods may be disassembled from hanger by rotating ends out of holes in end of hanger.

3) Using a small drift punch, drive pump lever pivot pin (roll pin) inward until pin is against air cleaner locating boss on air horn casting. Disconnect pump rod from pump lever. Remove vacuum hose from front vacuum break unit and note location for reassembly reference. Remove 11 air horn-to-float bowl screws. Remove 2 countersunk screws located near venturi.

CAUTION: **Be careful when removing roll pin to avoid damage to pump lever bosses.**

4) Remove secondary air baffle deflector (if equipped) from beneath 2 center air horn screws. Remove air horn from float bowl by lifting straight up. Air horn gasket should remain on float bowl.

NOTE: **Use care not to damage mixture control solenoid connector, TPS adjustment lever, and small tubes protruding from air horn. Do not attempt to remove small tubes.**

5) Remove primary (front) vacuum break diaphragm. Remove air valve rod from vacuum break and air valve lever. Using fingers only, remove TPS plunger by pushing plunger up through air horn seal. If air horn is removed, lean mixture screw plug and rich mixture stop screw plug must be removed from air horn. Drive plugs out from bottom side. Discard plugs.

6) Remove TPS seal by inverting air horn and remove staking from around seal retainer with a small screwdriver. Remove and discard retainer and seal. Use care removing retainer and seal to prevent damage to air horn casting.

7) Further disasssembly of air horn assembly is not required for cleaning purposes. Choke valve and choke valve screws, air valve and air valve shaft should not be removed. Instructions for replacing the air valve closing spring and plastic cam are included in service kit.

8) The air horn has an idle air bleed valve which is preset and sealed at the factory. The idle air bleed valve should not be removed unless "System Performance Check" of Computer Command Control system indicates need for adjustment or repair.

NOTE: **Air horn assembly, with idle air bleed valve installed, should be cleaned only in low volatile cleaning solvent. Do not place air horn (with idle air bleed valve) in carburetor cleaner. No tamper-resistant plug should be removed during normal carburetor cleaning and servicing unless carburetor or mixture control solenoid has been diagnosed as cause of poor engine performance.**

9) If necessary to replace idle air bleed valve or disassemble air horn for immersion in carburetor cleaner, cover internal bowl vents and air inlets to bleed valve with tape. Drill off rivet heads of bleed valve cover with a .110" (No. 35) drill. Drive remainder of rivet out of tower with drift and small hammer. Lift out cover over valve and remove remaining rivet pieces from inside tower.

10) After removing cover, check for letter identification on top of idle air bleed valve. This will determine the necessary adjustment procedure after reassembly. Turn valve counterclockwise and remove from air horn. Remove and discard "O" ring seals from air bleed valve. Air bleed valve is serviced as a complete assembly only.

NOTE: **A missing air valve cover indicates that idle air bleed valve setting has been changed from original factory setting.**

Float Bowl

1) Remove solenoid metering rod plunger by lifting straight upward. Remove rubber seal from around mixture control solenoid connector. Remove air horn gasket by lifting off of dowel locating pins. Discard gasket.

2) Remove pump plunger and return spring from pump well. Remove staking holding TPS in bowl. To do so, protect gasket surface by laying a flat piece of metal across casting.

3) Using a small screwdriver, lightly depress and hold TPS down against spring tension. Carefully remove staking from around TPS by prying upward with a small chisel against the metal piece (not bowl casting).

4) Push up from bottom on electrical connector and remove TPS and connector assembly from bowl. Use care not to damage sensor during removal. Remove spring from bottom of TPS well. Remove plastic filler block from float valve.

5) Carefully remove each metering rod from metering jet. Make sure return spring is removed with each rod. Remove return spring by sliding it off metering rod.

6) Remove screws connecting mixture control solenoid connector to float bowl. Do not remove connector from float bowl at this time. Using adjusting tool (J-

ROCHESTER E4MC & E4ME 4-BARREL (Cont.)

28696), remove lean mixture screw. Carefully lift solenoid and connector assembly from bowl.

NOTE: **Do not remove plunger return spring or connector from solenoid body. Solenoid and connector are serviced as an assembly.**

7) Remove plastic insert from solenoid connector cavity in float bowl (if used). Remove solenoid screw tension spring (next to float hanger clip). Remove float assembly and needle valve by lifting straight up. Remove needle valve seat and gasket.

8) Remove large mixture control solenoid tension spring from boss on bottom of float bowl located between metering jets. Remove primary main metering jets (if necessary).

NOTE: **Do not attempt to remove secondary metering jets (metering orifice plates). Secondary jets are permanent and if damaged, float bowl must be replaced.**

9) Remove accelerator pump discharge check ball retainer and check ball. Remove secondary air baffle, if replacement is required. Remove accelerator pump well baffle (if necessary).

10) If equipped, remove rear vacuum break hose and retaining screws. Rotate vacuum break to remove vacuum break link from slot in plunger head. Do not remove non-adjustable vacuum break link until after removal of choke assembly from float bowl.

11) Align a .159" (No. 21) drill on choke cover retaining rivets and drill only enough to remove rivet head. Using a drift and hammer, drive remainder of rivets out of choke housing. Remove 3 retainers, choke cover gasket (hot air type chokes) and choke cover from choke housing.

NOTE: **Do not remove baffle plate from beneath thermostatic coil on choke cover of hot air type chokes.**

12) Remove retaining screw and washer from inside choke housing. Slide choke housing from float bowl. On hot air type chokes, remove plastic type seal from vacuum inlet boss of choke housing. If equipped, remove rear vacuum break link from intermediate choke lever.

13) Remove secondary throttle valve lockout lever from float bowl. Remove lower choke lever from inside float bowl cavity by turning float bowl upside down. Remove coil lever retaining screw from end of intermediate choke shaft and remove lever.

14) Slide intermediate choke shaft from choke housing. Remove fast idle cam from intermediate choke shaft. On hot air type chokes, remove and discard cup seal inside choke housing shaft hole.

15) Remove intermediate choke shaft cup seal from float bowl insert. Do not remove insert. Invert float bowl to remove lower choke lever from bowl cavity. Remove fuel inlet nut, gasket and filter. Remove 3 throttle body-to-float bowl screws and throttle body.

Throttle Body

1) Remove accelerator pump rod from throttle lever by rotating rod until tang aligns with slot in lever.

NOTE: **Further disassembly of throttle body is not required for normal cleaning. Throttle valve screws are permanently staked in position. Throttle body is serviced as complete assembly. Do not remove mixture screw plugs unless diagnosis indicates the carburetor is cause of poor engine performance or idle mixture needles or throttle body must be replaced. If necessary to remove plugs, continue as follows:**

2) Turn throttle body over, and position on a holding fixture with manifold side up. Make 2 parallel cuts in throttle body using small hacksaw, cutting on each side of idle mixture needle plug. Cuts should reach down to steel plug, but no more than 1/8" beyond locator points. Distance between saw marks will depend upon size of punch used.

3) Place a flat punch at a point near ends of saw marks. Hold punch at 45° angle and drive it into throttle body until casting breaks away, exposing steel plug.

4) Hold punch vertically and drive it into steel plug. Then hold punch at 45° angle and drive plug out of casting. Repeat process for remaining mixture needle. When removing or installing needles, *refer to Idle Mixture (Bench Adjustment) procedure*.

NOTE: **Hardened steel plug will shatter. It is not necessary to remove plug completely. Remove just enough pieces to allow idle mixture adjusting tool to be used to remove mixture screws and springs. Idle mixture screw head has a "double-D" configuration and can also be removed using a piece of 7/32" copper tubing that has been partially flattened.**

CLEANING & INSPECTION

- Use a regular carburetor cleaning solution. Soak components long enough to thoroughly clean all surfaces and passages of foreign matter.
- Do not soak any components containing rubber, leather or plastic. Particularly do not soak air horn with idle air bleed valve installed, electric choke, ISS, ILC, ISC, TPS, thermostatic choke cover and coil, vacuum break diaphragms, pump plunger and other such parts.
- Remove any residue after cleaning by rinsing components in a suitable solvent.
- Blow out all passages with dry compressed air.

REASSEMBLY

NOTE: **Use new gaskets and seals. Make sure that new gaskets fit correctly and that all holes and slots are punched through and correctly located.**

Reassemble carburetor in reverse order of disassembly, noting the following:

1) The intermediate choke shaft lever and fast idle cam are assembled correctly when tang on lever is beneath fast idle cam.

2) When installing float and retaining pin, make sure open end of float retaining pin faces accelerator pump well.

ROCHESTER E4MC & E4ME 4-BARREL (Cont.)

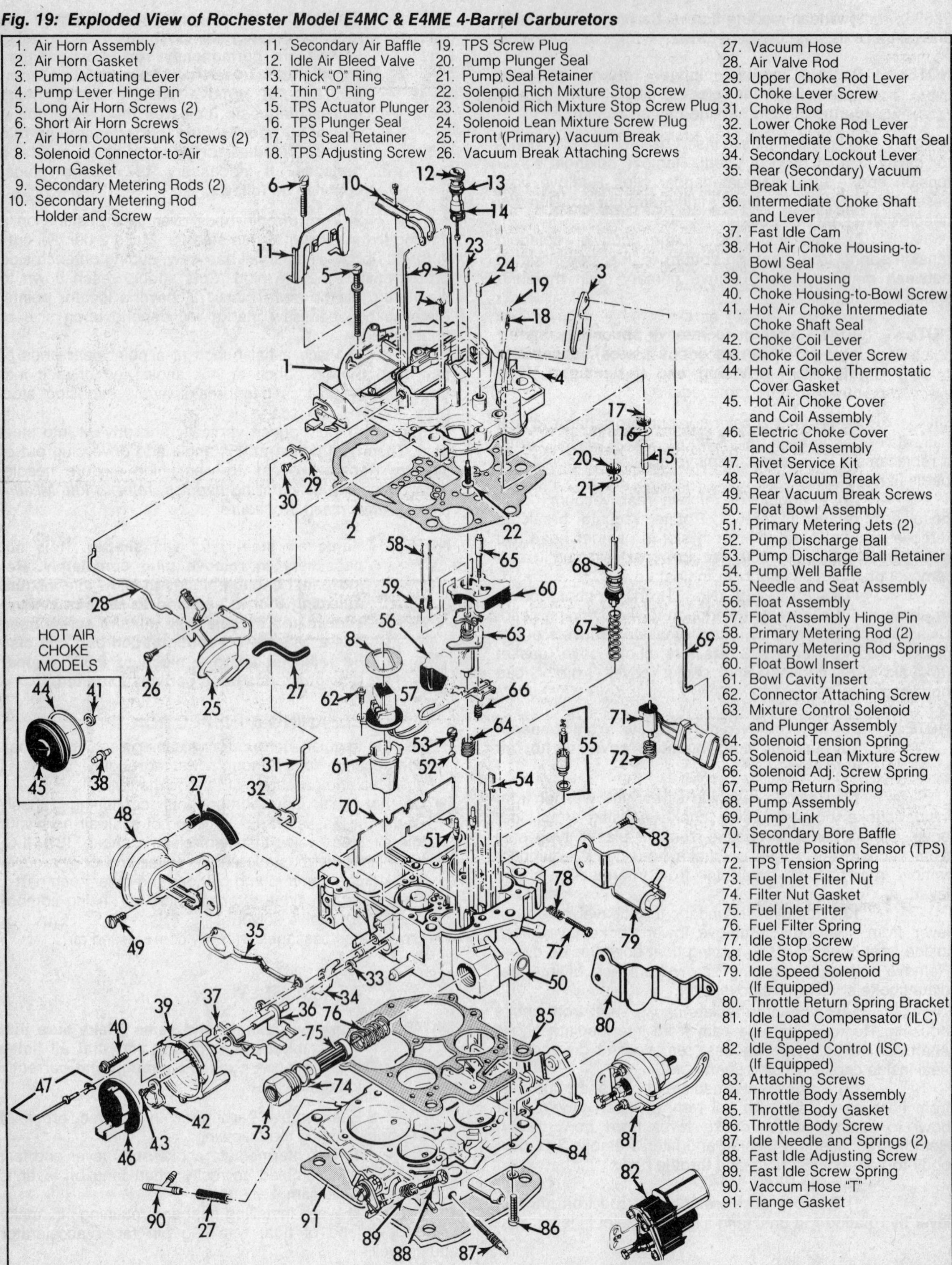

Fig. 19: Exploded View of Rochester Model E4MC & E4ME 4-Barrel Carburetors

ROCHESTER E4MC & E4ME 4-BARREL (Cont.)

3) When installing fuel inlet valve, hook pull clip over edge of flat on float arm. Do not hook clip in holes in float arm.

4) When installing mixture control solenoid, make sure pin on end of solenoid aligns with hole in raised boss at bottom of float bowl.

5) Install, adjust and plug all screws to restore tamper-resistant design.

NOTE: If choke coil cover was removed, it will be necessary to install service rivet retaining kit. Before installing cover, place fast idle screw on high step of fast idle cam. Align notch in cover with raised boss on housing cover flange and install rivets.

6) Place fast idle screw on high step of fast idle cam. Install choke coil cover if removed, aligning notch in cover with tab on cover retainer (supplied in service kit). Be sure coil tang engages pick-up lever. Install blind rivets.

NOTE: On E4ME models, ground contact for electric choke is provided by metal plate located at rear of choke cover assembly. Do not install choke cover gasket between electric choke and housing.

7) Install air horn screws and tighten evenly, securely and in sequence shown in *Fig. 20*.

Fig. 20: Air Horn Screw Tightening Sequence

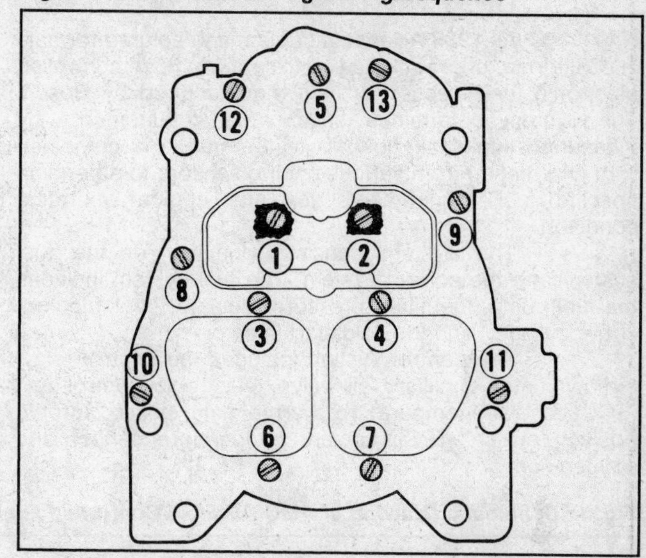

Screws 1 and 2 are countersunk next to venturi.

CARBURETOR ADJUSTMENT SPECIFICATIONS

Application	Float Level	Accel. Pump	Idle Air Bleed	Air Valve Spring [1]	Choke Coil Lever	Choke Rod	Vacuum Break		Air Valve Rod	Auto. Choke	Choke Unloader	Secondary Lockout
							Primary	Secondary				
E4MC												
17083250	7/16"	TR	1 3/4"	1/2	.120"	14°	27°	42°	.025"	TR	35°	.015"
17083253	7/16"	TR	1 3/4"	1/2	.120"	14°	27°	41°	.025"	TR	35°	.015"
17083553	7/16"	TR	1 3/4"	1/2	.120"	14°	27°	41°	.025"	TR	35°	.015"
E4ME												
17082265	3/8"	TR	1 3/4"	5/8	.120"	24.5°	26°	26°	.025"	TR	32°	.015"
17082268	3/8"	TR	1 3/4"	5/8	.120"	18°	26°	26°	.025"	TR	32°	.015"
17083204	11/32"	TR	1 3/4"	7/8	.120"	20°	27°	.....	.025"	TR	38°	.015"
17083207	11/32"	TR	1 3/4"	7/8	.120"	38°	27°	.....	.025"	TR	38°	.015"
17083242	9/32"	TR	1 3/4"	9/16	.120"	24.5°	20°	.....	.025"	TR	38°	.015"
17083244	1/4"	TR	1 3/4"	9/16	.120"	24.5°	21°	16°	.025"	TR	32°	.015"
17083248	3/8"	TR	1 3/4"	5/8	.120"	24.5°	26°	26°	.025"	TR	32°	.015"

TR — Tamper Resistant

[1] — Specification is number of turns.

1983 Fuel Injection

AMC AIR FLOW CONTROLLED FUEL INJECTION

Alliance (California)

DESCRIPTION

All 1983 Alliance models manufactured for sale in California are equipped with an air flow controlled electronic fuel injection system manufactured by Bosch. The system determines engine fuel requirements by measuring intake air flow. This information is combined with information from various engine sensors to determine specific fuel requirements for any engine operating condition.

The system consists primarily of the fuel system and the control system. The fuel system includes the fuel pump, fuel filter, pressure regulator, fuel injectors (1 per cylinder) and the cold start injector.

The control system includes the control relay, airflow meter, auxiliary air valve, electronic control unit (ECU), coolant temperature thermo time switch, throttle position switch (TPS), coolant temperature sensor and oxygen sensor.

OPERATION

FUEL DELIVERY

Fuel is supplied to the fuel rail assembly, mounted on the intake manifold, by an in-tank electric fuel pump. A constant system pressure of about 36 psi (2.5 kg/cm²) is maintained by the pressure regulator. The regulator is mounted on the intake manifold chamber in line with the fuel return line. It contains a spring controlled diaphragm which is exposed to fuel pressure on 1 side and intake manifold pressure on the other. Fuel delivered in excess of that required to maintain system pressure is bypassed by the regulator and returned to the fuel tank via the fuel return line.

Fuel is supplied to the intake manifold from the fuel rail assembly, through the fuel injectors. The injectors are electro-magnetic solenoid valves. A needle valve in the injector is held against a seat by a coiled spring. An electrical armature at the back of the valve reacts to electrical signals from the ECU by pulling the injector needle off its seat. This allows fuel to be injected into the

Fig. 1: Schematic Drawing of AMC Air Flow Controlled Fuel Injection System

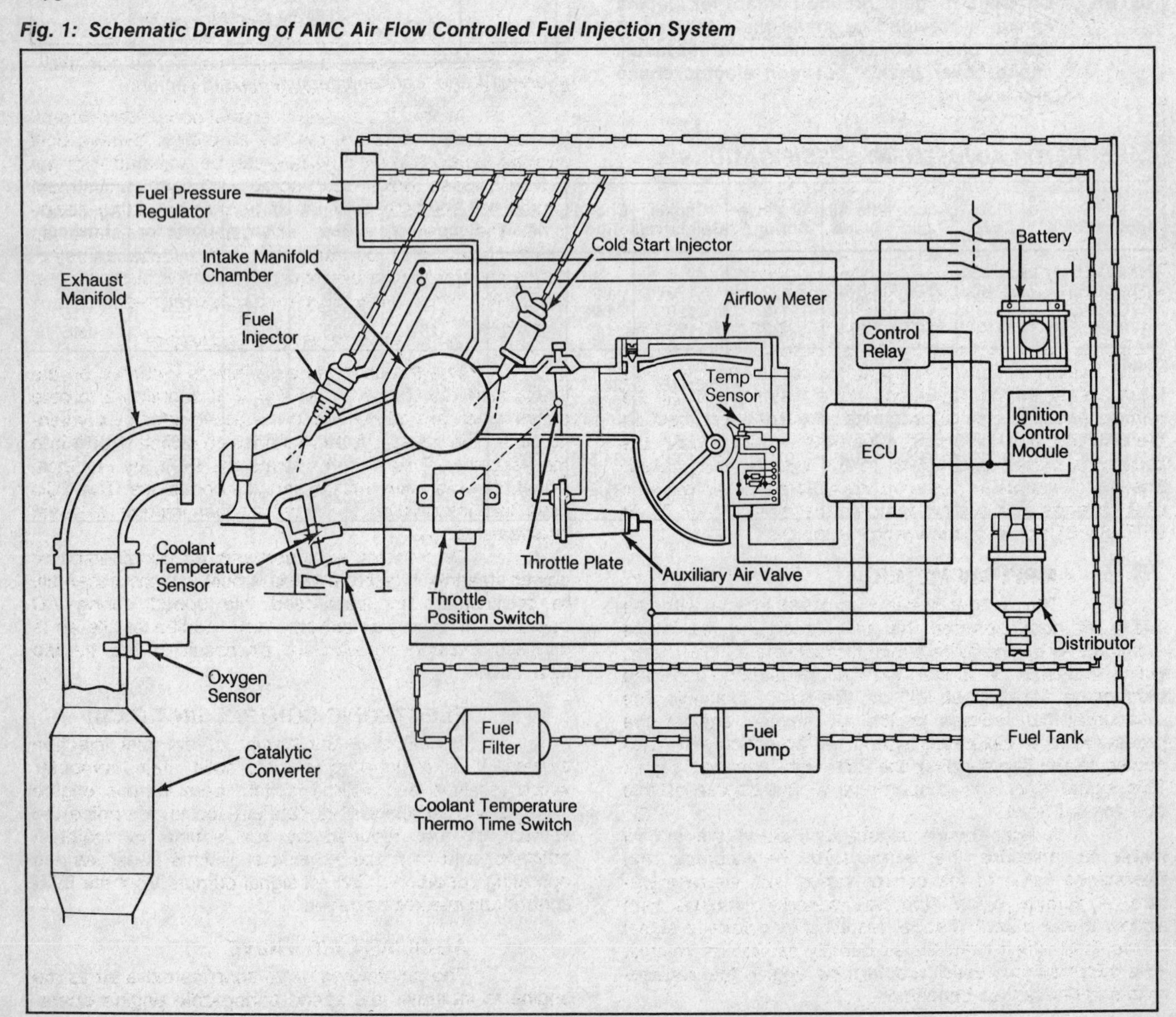

AMC AIR FLOW CONTROLLED FUEL INJECTION (Cont.)

intake manifold. Since fuel pressure is maintained at a constant level, the amount of fuel injected is dependent only upon the length of time that the injector is held open (injector "on" time). All injectors are fired simultaneously, twice per engine revolution.

Fig. 2: Fuel Delivery System

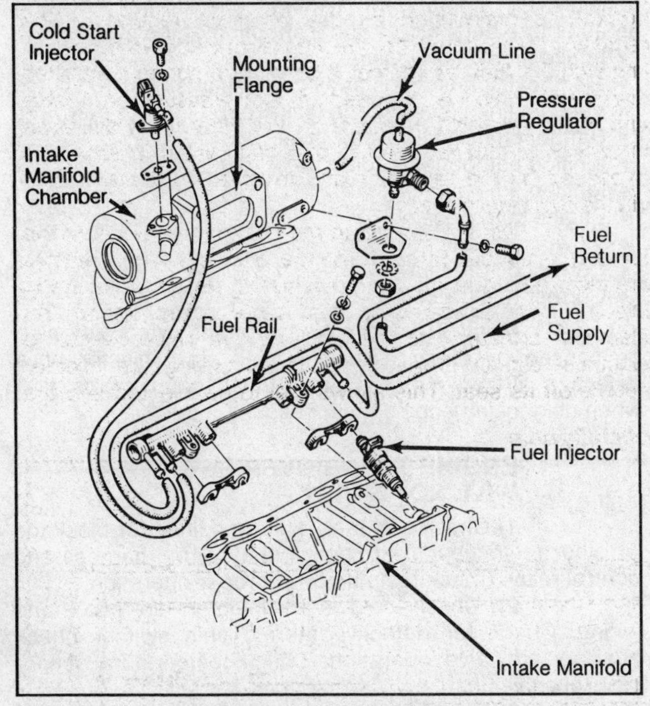

Throttle body assembly (not shown) mounts to flange on intake manifold chamber.

During starter engagement, with cold engine, additional fuel is supplied by the cold start injector. Power to the injector is routed through the coolant temperature thermo time switch, mounted in the water jacket of the cylinder head. The switch contains an electrical contact on the end of a bimetallic strip. When the engine is cold, the contact is closed and power to the injector is supplied. The switch maintains power to the injector for a maximum of 8 seconds at a coolant temperature of -4°F (-20°C). At 95°F (35°C), power to the injector is cut off.

AIRFLOW METER

The airflow meter is located in line with the intake air duct, between the air cleaner and the intake manifold. All engine air is drawn through the airflow meter, which contains a tunnel with a measuring flap and dampening flap (offset 90° on the same casting). The measuring flap swings in the air stream against the pressure of a calibrated spring. A potentiometer connected to the flap supplies the ECU with a voltage signal. This signal is directly proportional to the degree of flap opening (air flow).

A temperature sensor is fitted in the airflow meter to measure the temperature of incoming air. Resistance value of the sensor varies with air temperature. A voltage signal from the sensor combines with airflow meter output voltage, resulting in a voltage signal to the ECU which indicates air density as well as volume. This information is used to determine engine fuel requirements under various conditions.

Fig. 3: Cutaway of Airflow Meter Assembly

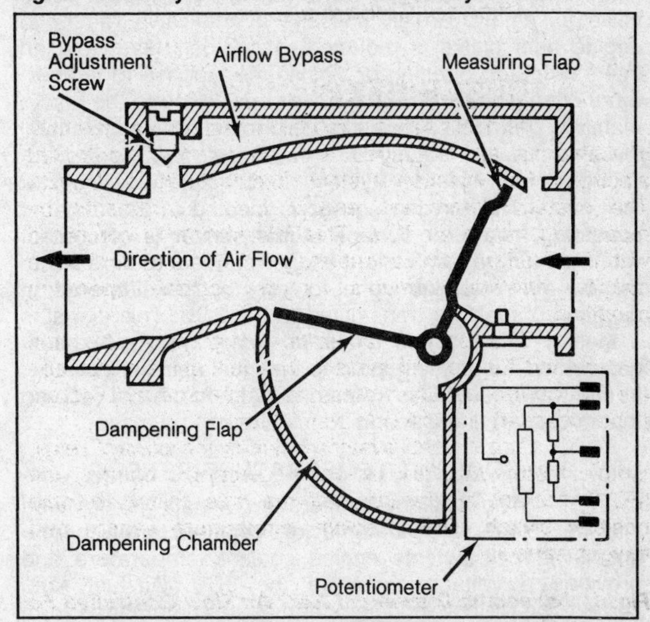

Bypass adjustment screw is sealed. No adjustment should be required under normal driving conditions.

At idle, the air flap is almost completely closed. Idle air requirements are met by an airflow bypass built into the meter. Idle air flow rate can be adjusted with the airflow bypass adjustment screw, although adjustment should not be necessary under normal operating conditions. The screw is sealed with a tamper resistant cap which should only be removed, and bypass adjusted, during a major engine overhaul, when a new airflow meter is installed, or if CO readings are excessively high.

THROTTLE PLATE ASSEMBLY

The throttle plate assembly is mounted on the intake manifold chamber. *See Fig. 2.* It contains 2 throttle plates which are connected to the accelerator by conventional throttle linkage. A throttle position switch is built into the assembly. This switch informs the ECU, by electrical signal, of wide open throttle and idle conditions. The ECU uses this information to adjust air/fuel mixture to meet engine demands.

On vehicles equipped with air conditioning or power steering, a fast idle valve is built into the assembly to compensate for decreased idle speed during AC operation or during an extreme turn. Additional idle air is supplied through an auxiliary air circuit in the throttle assembly.

ELECTRONIC CONTROL UNIT (ECU)

The ECU is the "brain" of the fuel injection system. It is a pre-programmed, solid state computer which receives and interprets data from various engine sensors and switches. This data is used to determine the amount of fuel required by the engine to maintain efficiency and minimize exhaust emissions under varying operating conditions. Control signal outputs from the ECU control fuel injector operation.

AUXILIARY AIR VALVE

The auxiliary air valve supplies extra air to the engine to increase idle speed during cold engine opera-

AMC AIR FLOW CONTROLLED FUEL INJECTION (Cont.)

tion. Air is supplied to the valve from in front of the throttle valve assembly. An air passage in the valve reacts to engine heat (valve is mounted to cylinder head) and an integral heater, opening or closing in response to temperature changes. Air from the valve is delivered to the intake manifold chamber, bypassing the throttle valve assembly.

OXYGEN SENSOR

The oxygen sensor is located in the exhaust manifold. The outer surface of the sensor is in contact with exhaust gases, while the inner surface is exposed to outside air. A voltage signal, created by the difference in oxygen contents, is transmitted to the ECU. This signal is a measurement of the unburned oxygen in the exhaust gas, which is directly related to the intake air/fuel mixture. In this way, the ECU is kept up to date on air/fuel ratio so that necessary adjustments to mixture can be made.

COOLANT TEMPERATURE SENSOR

The coolant temperature sensor is screwed into the cylinder head water jacket, adjacent to the thermo time switch. It detects engine coolant temperature and provides a voltage signal to the ECU. Air/fuel ratio corrections for cold engine operation are determined from this signal.

CONTROL RELAY

The control relay is mounted on the front of the right shock tower. It controls power input to the fuel pump, injectors, ECU, auxiliary air valve and the throttle position switch.

ADJUSTMENTS

NOTE: For on-vehicle adjustments, see appropriate TUNE-UP article.

THROTTLE POSITION SWITCH

With the throttle plate assembly removed, loosen the 2 throttle position switch (TPS) attaching screws. Hold the throttle plates against the idle stop and slowly rotate the TPS in the direction of the throttle plate opening until the inner stop is felt. Tighten the attaching screws. If properly adjusted, the clicking of the micro-switch in the TPS should be heard just before the stop is reached.

Fig. 4: Throttle Position Switch Adjustment

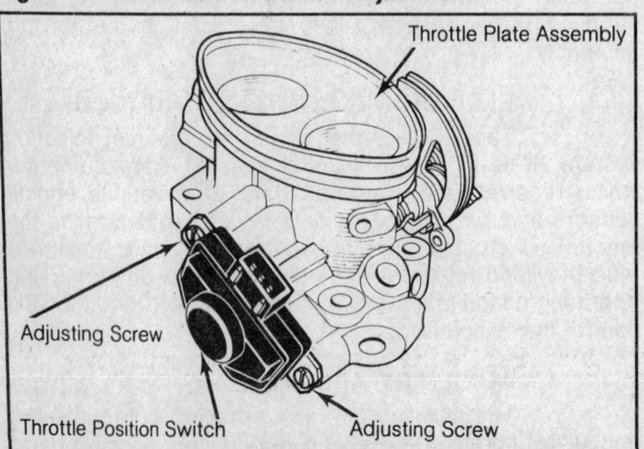

Turn switch until stop is felt and tighten adjusting screws.

TROUBLE SHOOTING

PRELIMINARY CHECKS

Several driveability problems may result from faulty or poor wiring, loose and/or leaking hose connections, or basic engine systems malfunctions. To avoid unnecessary component testing, check the following areas before beginning trouble shooting of the system.

- Intake air system leaks.
- Electrical connections at all components.
- Vacuum lines (secure and leak-free).
- Battery charge and water level.
- Ignition components (distributor, plugs, coil).
- Ignition timing.
- Engine compression.
- Valves properly adjusted.
- Correct oil pressure.
- Correct fuel pressure.

Most of the engine symptoms listed may also be caused by either a leaking cold start injector or a defective airflow meter. Check these components first when diagnosing engine malfunctions.

ENGINE TURNS OVER BUT WILL NOT START

1) Check fuel tank, filter and lines for blockage or other restriction. Test control relay wiring harness and control relay. Check fuel pump for proper operation.

2) Check cold start injector operation and wiring. Check for defective thermo time switch. Check auxiliary air valve operation. Check temperature sensor resistance values.

3) If malfunction remains after checking and/or repairing noted systems, replace ECU with a known good unit. If malfunction ceases, original ECU is defective and must be replaced.

ENGINE STARTS, THEN DIES

1) Check fuel tank, filter and lines for blockage or other restriction. Check auxiliary air valve operation. Check temperature sensor resistance values.

2) Check and adjust idle speed as needed. Check for proper adjustment of air bypass screw on airflow meter.

3) If malfunction remains after checking and/or repairing noted systems, replace ECU with a known good unit. If malfunction ceases, original ECU is defective and must be replaced.

ROUGH IDLE

1) Check fuel tank, filter and lines for blockage or other restriction. Check auxiliary air valve operation. Check temperature sensor resistance values.

2) Check throttle position switch. Adjust or replace as needed. Check and adjust idle speed. Check individual injector operation. Ensure that air bypass screw on airflow meter is properly adjusted.

3) If malfunction remains after checking and/or repairing noted systems, replace ECU with a known good unit. If malfunction ceases, original ECU is defective and must be replaced.

IDLE SPEED INCORRECT

Check basic idle speed adjustment, air bypass adjustment and auxiliary air valve operation.

1983 Fuel Injection

AMC AIR FLOW CONTROLLED FUEL INJECTION (Cont.)

INCORRECT CO VALUE

1) Check temperature sensor resistance values. Check and adjust idle speed as needed.

2) Check individual fuel injectors for correct operation. Check and adjust air bypass in airflow meter as needed.

ERRATIC ENGINE RPM

Check individual fuel injector operation. Check and adjust air bypass in airflow meter as needed.

ENGINE MISS WHILE DRIVING

Check injector operation. Replace ECU with a known good unit and test drive vehicle. If miss is gone, original ECU is defective and should be replaced.

POOR FUEL ECONOMY

Check temperature sensor resistance values. Check and adjust air bypass screw on airflow meter as needed.

LACK OF POWER

1) Check fuel tank, filter and lines for blockage or other restriction. Check and adjust or replace throttle position switch as needed. Check individual fuel injectors for correct operation.

2) If malfunction remains after checking and/or repairing noted systems, replace ECU with a known good unit. If malfunction ceases, original ECU is defective and must be replaced.

TESTING

NOTE: When testing resistance or voltage values, a high impedence (digital) volt-ohm meter must be used.

INTAKE AIR SYSTEM

1) Air leaks in the intake system can cause various engine difficulties. To check for leaks, disconnect the air line from the auxiliary air valve at the intake manifold chamber. Apply a soapy water solution to any connections or joints where leaks are likely to occur.

2) Plug the exhaust pipe with a shop towel or rag. Apply compressed air (15 psi maximum) at the hose connection on the intake manifold chamber and open the throttle plate. The presence of bubbles or foam at any point in the system indicates the presence of air leaks. Repair as needed.

FUEL SYSTEM

Fuel Pump Pressure & Regulator

1) Install a "T" fitting in the fuel line between the pressure regulator and the fuel rail assembly and connect a pressure gauge. Disconnect the vacuum line from the pressure regulator and attach a vacuum pump in its place.

2) Locate the system diagnostic connectors on the inner fender well, just in front of the right side shock tower. The connectors are covered by plastic caps. Flip off the caps and install a jumper wire between terminals 5 and 6 of the small connector (D1). *See Fig. 5.* Fuel pressure should be about 70 psi (5.0 kg/cm²). If not, check fuel pump, fuel filter and electrical circuits.

3) Apply about 16 in. Hg vacuum to the regulator. Fuel pressure should drop to 17-23 psi (1.2-1.6 kg/cm²). If not, replace the pressure regulator.

Fig. 5: Diagnostic Connector Identification

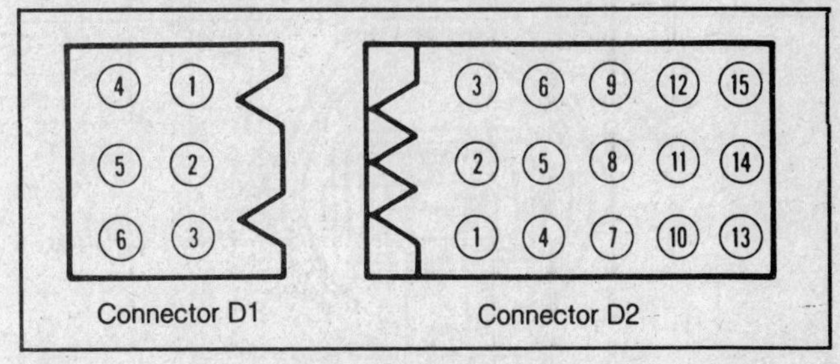

Connectors are mounted on right side inner fender well.

Fuel Pump Output

1) Disconnect the fuel return line from the pressure regulator. Attach a length of fuel hose to the regulator with the other end in a graduated container.

2) Attach a jumper wire between terminals 5 and 6 of diagnostic connector D1 to activate pump. The system should pump at least 1 pint of fuel in 30 seconds. If not, ensure that the fuel filter is not clogged. Check pump and regulator operation and electrical circuits.

Fuel Injector Leakage

1) Disconnect all injector wire connectors. Remove the fuel rail assembly, with injectors and cold start injector, from intake manifold.

2) Attach a jumper wire between terminals 5 and 6 of diagnostic connector D1 and observe injectors. No fuel should leak from any injector.

Injector Operation

1) Remove fuel rail assembly, with injectors, from intake manifold. Attach jumper wire between terminals 5 and 6 of diagnostic connector D1.

2) Briefly apply 12V power and ground to 1 injector at a time. Injector should spray fuel and cut off cleanly when power is removed. If not, replace faulty injector.

AUXILIARY AIR VALVE

Air Valve

1) With air valve assembly at about 70°F (20°C) and electrical connector and air hoses disconnected, air passage in valve should be slightly open. This may be verified by looking into the valve from the inlet and outlet sides.

2) Use jumper wires to connect valve terminals directly to battery voltage. Observe the air passage. Passage should be completely closed in about 10 minutes. If not, replace the valve.

Wiring Harness

Disconnect wiring connector from valve. With the engine cold, connect a test light to the connector terminals and start engine. The light should come on. If not, replace or repair wiring harness.

COOLANT TEMPERATURE THERMO TIME SWITCH

1) Check resistance values between switch terminals and from each terminal to ground. *See Fig. 6.* Checks should be made with coolant temperature below 85°F (30°C) and again with coolant temperature above 105°F (40°C).

2) Compare results to values given in *Thermo Time Switch Resistance Values* table. If resistance is incorrect, replace switch.

AMC AIR FLOW CONTROLLED FUEL INJECTION (Cont.)

Fig. 6: Thermo Time Switch Terminal Identification

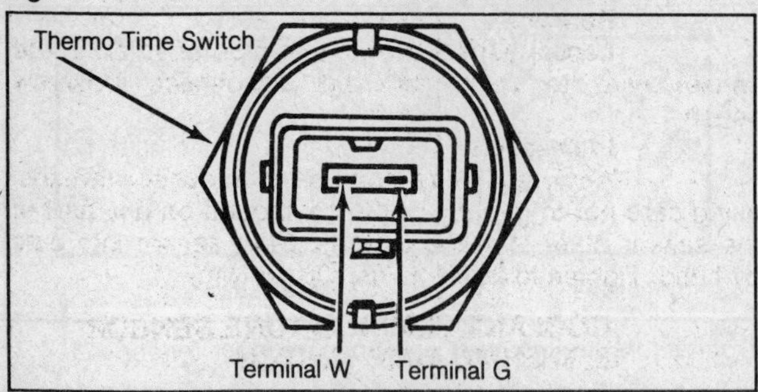

Check resistance values between terminals and from each terminal to ground.

CONTROL RELAY & ECU GROUND

With the ignition switch in the "ON" position, engine coolant temperature below 77°F (25°C) and engine off, check resistance value between terminal 3 of diagnostic connector D1 and terminal 7 of connector D2. If value is anything other than zero, check control relay and ECU ground circuits.

THERMO TIME SWITCH RESISTANCE VALUES

Measured Between Terminals	Resistance (Ohms) Below 85°F (30°C)	Above 105°F (40°C)
G and W	25-40	50-80
G and Ground	25-40	50-80
W and Ground	0	100-160

COOLANT TEMPERATURE SENSOR

1) With the ignition switch in the "ON" position, engine coolant temperature below 77°F (25°C) and engine off, check resistance between terminals 12 and 7 of diagnostic connector D2. Readings should vary from 25,-000 ohms at a coolant temperature of 68°F (20°C), to about 320 ohms at 175°F (80°C).

2) If readings are incorrect, check wiring circuit and repair as needed. If circuit is good, replace temperature sensor.

THROTTLE POSITION SWITCH

1) With the ignition switch in the "ON" position, engine coolant temperature below 77°F (25°C) and engine off, test resistance between terminals 13 and 6 of diagnostic connector D2. Reading should be infinite. Check between terminals 4 and 13 of connector D2 with throttle closed. Resistance should be zero.

2) With meter between terminals 4 and 6 of D2 and throttle at wide open position, resistance should be zero. If any of the readings are incorrect, check wiring circuit and repair as needed. If circuit is good, replace TPS.

REMOVAL & INSTALLATION

ELECTRONIC CONTROL UNIT

Removal & Installation

Locate the electronic control unit (ECU) under the right side of the dash. Remove retaining screws and remove ECU from mounting bracket. Disconnect electrical connector. Reverse removal procedure to install.

Fig. 7: Electronic Control Unit Location & Removal

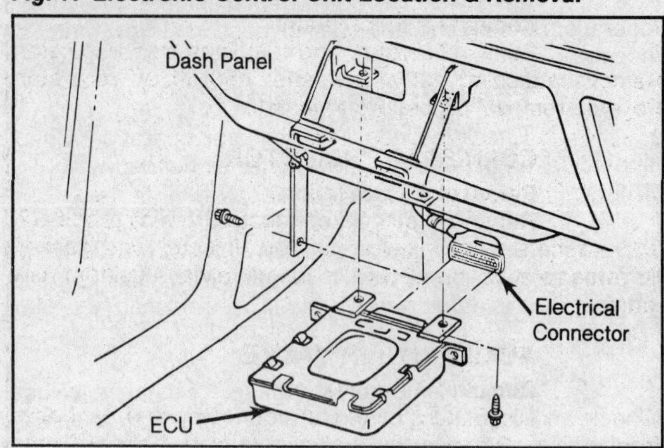

ECU is located in pasenger compartment, below right side of dash panel.

AIRFLOW METER

Removal

1) Disconnect electrical connector and loosen intake and output air duct clamps. Separate air ducts from airflow meter.

2) Remove mounting screws holding meter to mounting bracket and remove meter.

Fig. 8: Airflow Meter Removal

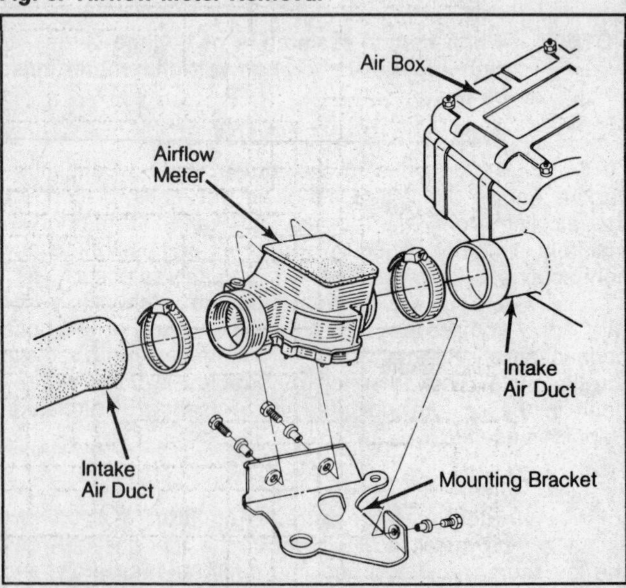

Airflow meter is mounted in the intake air duct, between the air box and the throttle valve assembly

Installation

Reverse removal procedure to install. Ensure that electrical connecter is securely attached.

FUEL INJECTORS

Removal & Installation

Remove intake manifold chamber. Disconnect fuel and electrical lines from injectors. Remove fuel rail retaining bolts (2) and pull fuel rail from injectors. Pull the

AMC AIR FLOW CONTROLLED FUEL INJECTION (Cont.)

injectors out of the intake manifold. Reverse removal procedure to install injectors.

FUEL PRESSURE REGULATOR

Removal & Installation

Remove vacuum and fuel lines from regulator. Remove attaching nut and washer and lift off regulator. Reverse removal procedure to install.

COLD START INJECTOR

Removal & Installation

Remove electrical connector, retaining bolts (2) and washers from injector. Lift out injector and gasket. Reverse removal procedure to install, always using a new gasket.

AUXILIARY AIR VALVE

Removal & Installation

Disconnect electrical connector and air hoses from valve. Remove air valve retaining bolts (2) and remove valve. Reverse removal procedure to install.

OXYGEN SENSOR

Removal

Locate sensor in exhaust pipe adapter. Trace sensor wire to connector and disconnect. Unscrew sensor.

Installation

Apply anti-seize compound to sensor threads, using care not to get any of the compound on any part of the sensor other than the threads. Start sensor into pipe by hand. Tighten to 28-34 ft. lbs. (38-46 N.m).

COOLANT TEMPERATURE SENSOR & THERMO TIME SWITCH

Removal & Installation

1) The sensor and switch are located on the end of the cylinder head, screwed into the water jacket. Removal procedures are the same for both components.

2) Disconnect electrical connector. Remove sensor/switch from cylinder head and install new sensor/switch quickly to prevent coolant loss. The temperature sensor is White in color, the switch is Brown.

Fig. 9: AMC Air Flow Controlled Fuel Injection System Wiring Diagram

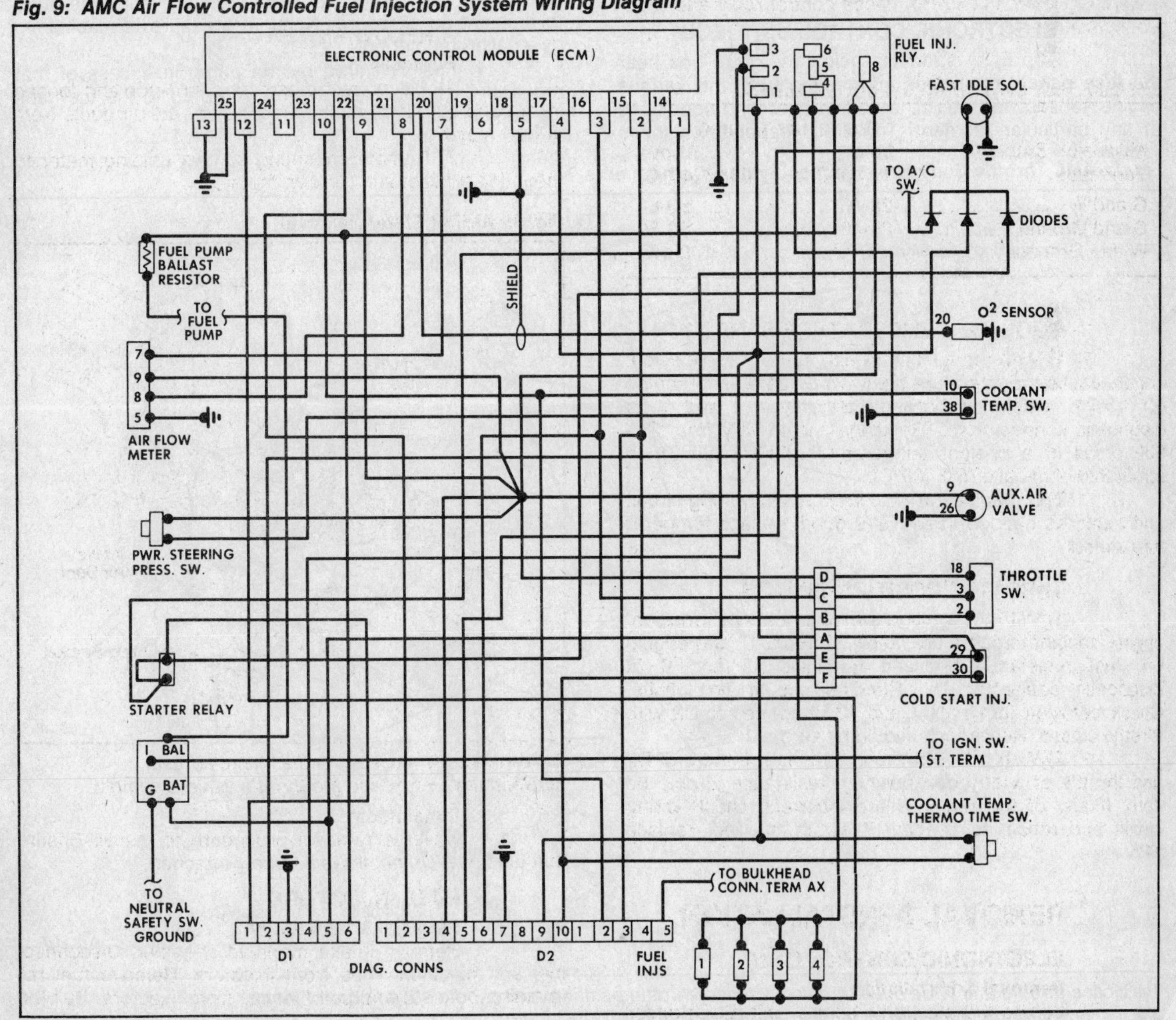

1983 Fuel Injection

AMC THROTTLE BODY FUEL INJECTION

Alliance (Federal)

DESCRIPTION

The AMC throttle body fuel injection system (TBI) uses an electronically controlled fuel injector to inject a metered spray of fuel above the throttle blade in the throttle body.

The TBI system is comprised of 2 sub-systems: the Fuel System and the Control System. Major components of the fuel system include an in-tank electric fuel pump, fuel filter, pressure regulator and a fuel injector.

Major components of the control system include the manifold air/fuel mixture temperature sensor, coolant temperature sensor, manifold absolute pressure sensor, wide open throttle switch, closed throttle switch, oxygen sensor, electronic control unit, throttle position sensor and an idle speed control motor.

OPERATION

ELECTRONIC CONTROL UNIT (ECU)

The ECU is located below the glove box near the fuse panel. It receives information from the various engine sensors to determine engine operating conditions at any particular moment. The ECU responds to these signals by sending a control signal to the fuel injector to determine the amount of time that the injector will be left open (injector "on" time). *See Fig. 2.*

FUEL INJECTOR

The fuel injector is mounted in the throttle body such that fuel is injected into the incoming air flow. When electric current is supplied to the injector, the armature and pintle assembly move a short distance against a spring, opening a small orifice at the end of the injector. Fuel supplied to the injector is forced around the pintle valve and through this opening, resulting in a fine spray of fuel. Since fuel pressure at the injector is kept constant, the volume of fuel injected is dependent only on the length of time that the injector is energized.

During engine start-up, the injector delivers an extra amount of fuel to aid in starting.

FUEL PRESSURE REGULATOR

The fuel pressure regulator is an integral part of the throttle body. It consists of a diaphragm operated relief valve with 1 side exposed to fuel pressure, the other to ambient air pressure. Nominal pressure is maintained by a calibrated spring.

Fuel delivered by the pump in excess of that required for engine operation is returned to the fuel tank via the fuel return line.

Fig. 1: AMC Throttle Body Fuel Injection System Components

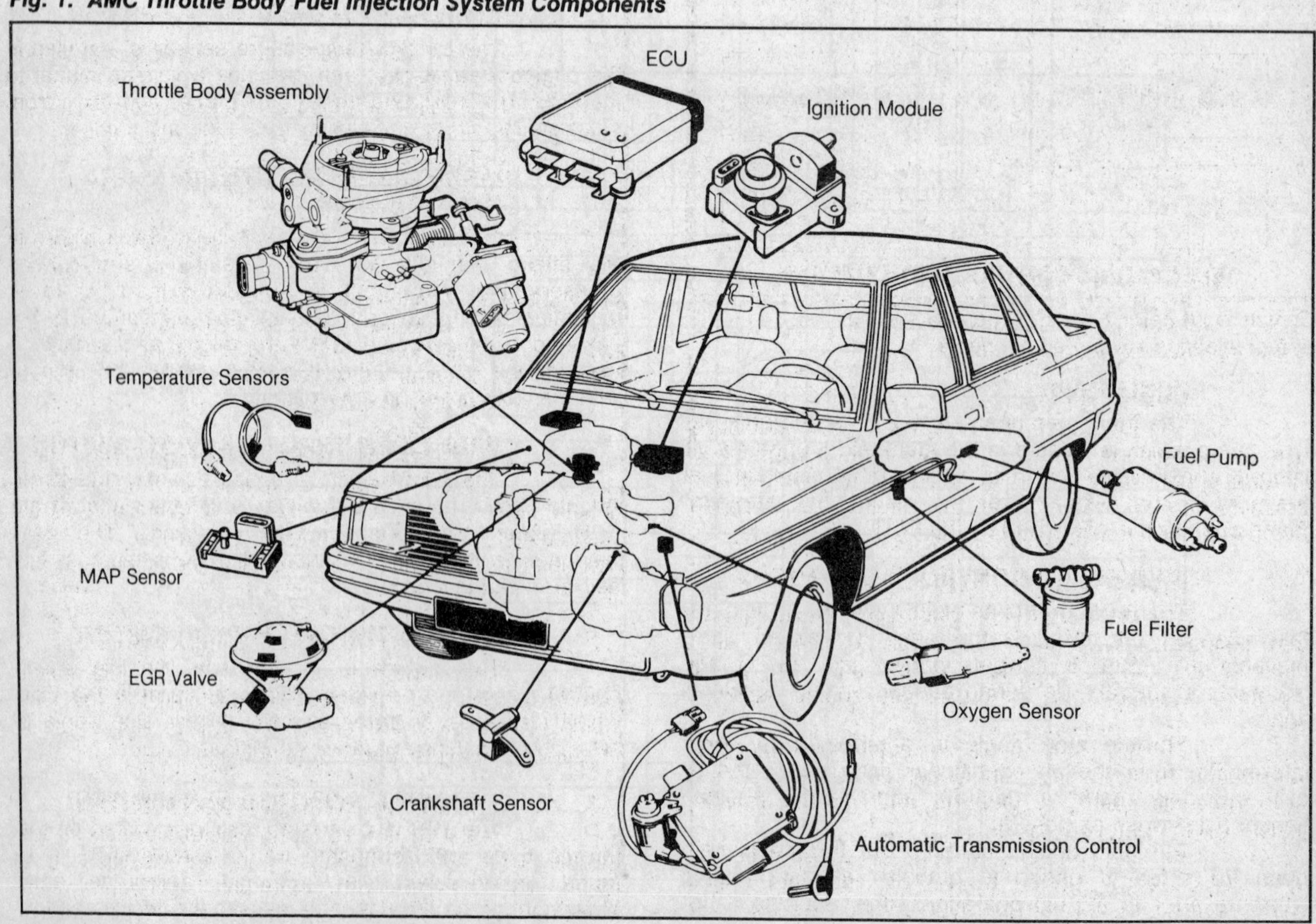

The closed throttle and wide open throttle switches, throttle position sensor, idle speed control motor and fuel pressure regulator are all located on the throttle body assembly.

AMC THROTTLE BODY FUEL INJECTION (Cont.)

Fig. 2: ECU Input Signals and Output Controls

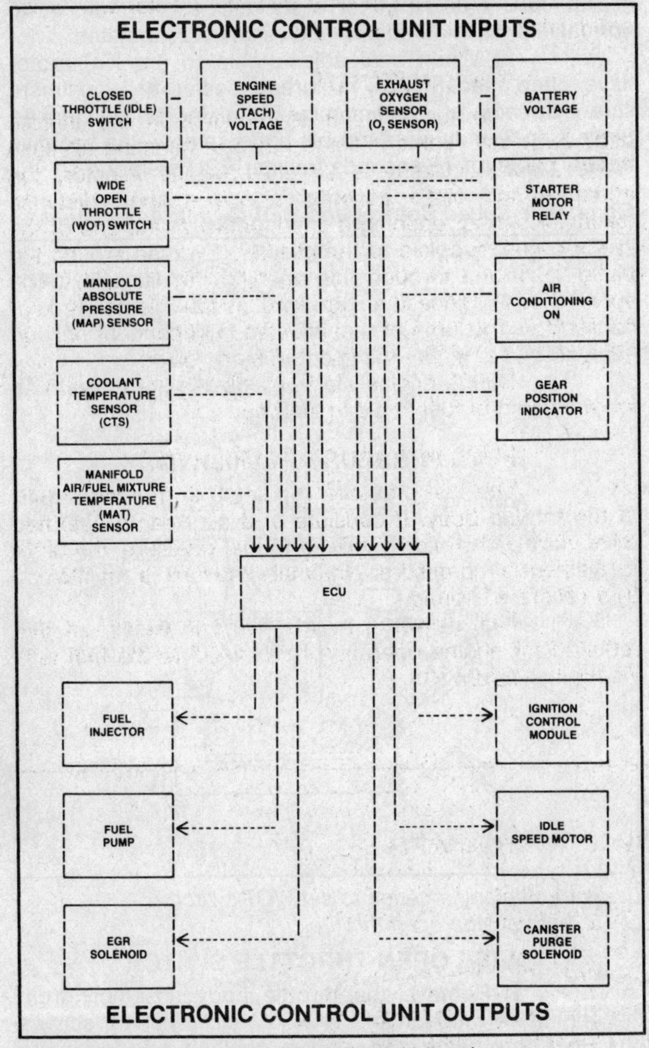

Sensor input determines ECU control signals to fuel injection system components.

FUEL PUMP

The fuel pump is an electrically operated roller type pump which is located in the fuel tank. It contains an integral check valve which is designed to maintain fuel pressure in the system after the engine has stopped. Pump operation is controlled by the ECU.

IDLE SPEED CONTROL (ISC) MOTOR

The ISC motor is an electrically driven actuator that changes the throttle stop angle by acting as a movable idle stop. It controls engine idle speed and maintains a smooth idle during sudden engine decelera-tion.

Throttle stop angle is determined by input information from the air conditioner compressor (on or off), transaxle (park or neutral), and throttle position sensor (wide open or closed).

For cold engine starting, the throttle is held open for a longer period to provide adequate engine warm-up prior to normal operation. When starting a hot engine, throttle open time is shorter.

Under normal engine operating conditions, engine idle is maintained at a pre-programmed RPM which may vary slightly due to engine operating conditions. Under certain engine deceleration conditions, the throttle is held slightly open.

OXYGEN (O_2) SENSOR

The amount of oxygen in exhaust gases varies according to the air/fuel ratio of the intake charge. The oxygen sensor detects this content and transmits a low voltage signal to the ECU.

The oxygen sensor is located in the exhaust pipe adaptor. The outer surface of the sensor is exposed to exhaust gases, the inner surface to outside air. The difference in the amount of oxygen contacting the inner and outer surfaces of the sensor creates a pressure, which results in a small voltage signal. This signal, which is a measure of the unburned oxygen in the exhaust gas, is transmitted to the ECU.

If the amount of oxygen in the exhaust system is low (rich mixture), the sensor voltage signal will be high. If the mixture is lean, the oxygen sensor will generate a low voltage signal.

MANIFOLD AIR/FUEL TEMPERATURE (MAT) SENSOR

The MAT sensor is installed in the intake manifold in front of an intake port. This sensor provides a voltage signal to the ECU representing the temperature of the air/fuel mixture in the intake manifold.

COOLANT TEMPERATURE SENSOR

The coolant temperature sensor is installed in the engine water jacket and provides a voltage signal to the ECU. The ECU determines cold engine operation from this signal and responds by enriching the fuel mixture.

MANIFOLD ABSOLUTE PRESSURE (MAP) SENSOR

The MAP sensor detects absolute pressure in the intake manifold as well as ambient atmospheric pressure. This information is supplied to the ECU as an indication of engine load. The sensor is mounted in the passenger compartment under the middle of the dash. A vacuum line from the throttle body supplies the sensor with manifold pressure information.

WIDE OPEN THROTTLE (WOT) SWITCH

The WOT switch is mounted on the side of the throttle body. The switch provides a voltage signal to the ECU under wide open throttle conditions. The ECU responds to this signal by increasing the amount of fuel delivered by the injector.

CLOSED THROTTLE (IDLE) SWITCH

This switch is integral with the idle speed control motor and provides a voltage signal to the ECU which increases or decreases the throttle stop angle in response to engine operating conditions.

THROTTLE POSITION SENSOR (TPS)

The TPS is a variable resistor mounted on the throttle body and connected to the throttle shaft. It is found on vehicles with automatic transaxles only. Movement of the throttle cable causes the throttle shaft to rotate (opening or closing the throttle). The sensor detects this movement and provides the ECU with an appropriate voltage signal. The ECU uses this signal to determine

AMC THROTTLE BODY FUEL INJECTION (Cont.)

engine operating conditions for the automatic transmission control system.

ADJUSTMENTS

NOTE: **The following adjustment procedures should not be necessary during normal vehicle operation or maintenance. Adjustment of the listed components should only be required when a faulty component is replaced with a new one.**

IDLE SPEED CONTROL MOTOR

1) With air cleaner removed, air conditioner off (if equipped) and engine at normal operating temperature, connect a tachometer to terminals 1 (+) and 3 (-) of the small diagnostic connecter (D1). *See Fig. 3.* Turn ignition off and observe ISC motor plunger. The plunger should move to fully extended position.

Fig. 3: TBI System Diagnostic Connector Location With Terminal Identification

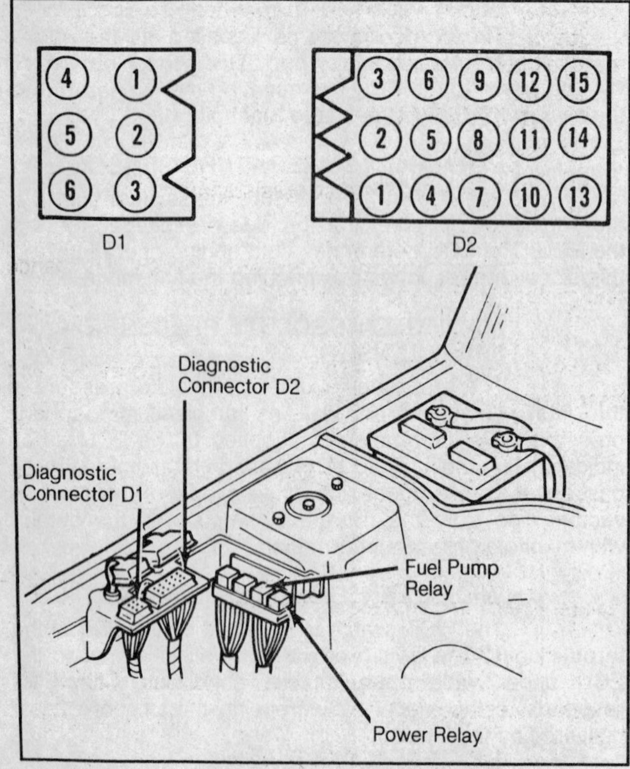

Diagnostic connectors and relays are mounted on a common bracket, just in front of the shock tower.

2) Disconnect the ISC motor wire connector and start the engine. Idle speed should be 3300-3700 RPM. If not, turn adjusting nut on plunger until correct idle is obtained. *See Fig. 4.*

3) Hold the closed throttle switch plunger all the way in while opening the throttle. Release the throttle. The throttle lever should not make contact with the plunger. If contact is made, inspect throttle linkage and/or cable for binding or damage. Repair as needed.

4) Reconnect the ISC motor wire connector and turn ignition off for 10 seconds. Motor should move to fully extended position. Start the engine. Engine should idle at 3300-3700 RPM for a short time and then fall to normal idle. Turn off engine and remove tachometer.

5) When final adjustments to the ISC motor have been made, apply a thread sealer to adjustment screw threads to prevent movement. Install air cleaner. Since step **3)** may set a trouble code, remove the negative battery cable for 10 seconds to clear ECU memory.

Fig. 4: Idle Speed Control and WOT Switch Adjustment

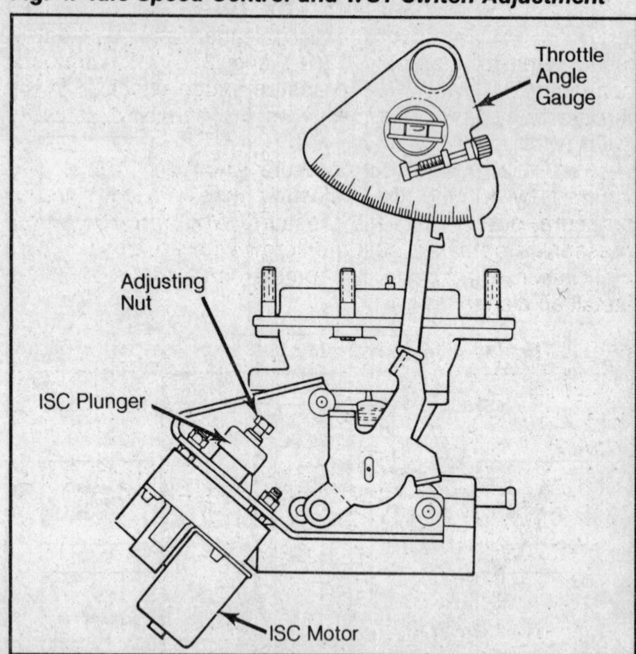

Use a throttle angle gauge to set WOT switch at 15° before wide open throttle.

WIDE OPEN THROTTLE SWITCH

1) Remove the throttle body assembly from the engine and loosen the WOT switch retaining screws (2). Hold throttle in wide open position and attach a throttle angle gauge to the flat surface of the lever. *See Fig. 4.*

Fig. 5: Wide Open Throttle Switch

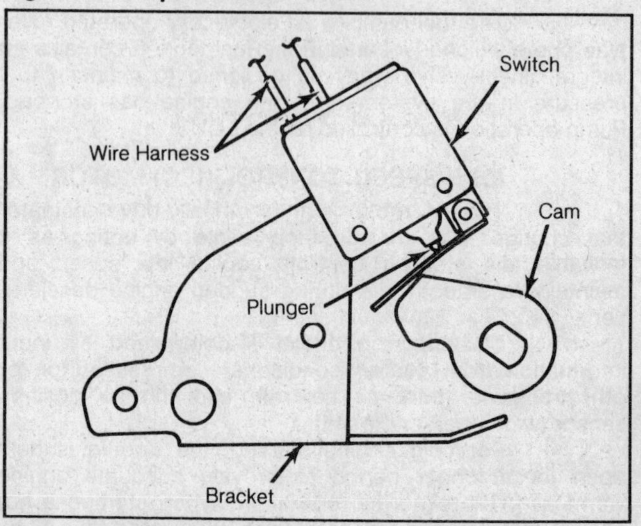

Plunger should be just closed with throttle at 15° before wide open position.

AMC THROTTLE BODY FUEL INJECTION (Cont.)

2) Rotate scale to align the 15 degree mark with the pointer. Level the gauge. Rotate scale to align zero with the pointer and close the throttle enough to center the bubble. This positions the throttle at 15° before wide open.

3) Adjust the WOT switch lever on the throttle cam so that the plunger is just closed. Tighten the retaining screws and remove the gauge.

FUEL PRESSURE REGULATOR

1) Remove the air cleaner and connect a tachometer to terminals 1 (+) and 3 (-) of diagnostic connector D1. With a fuel pressure gauge attached to the throttle body test fitting, start engine and hold at about 2000 RPM.

2) Adjust fuel pressure to obtain 14.5 psi (1.0 kg/cm²) by turning the adjusting screw in to increase pressure, out to decrease pressure. When proper system pressure is obtained, seal the screw with a lead plug. Turn off ignition, disconnect tachometer and cap test fitting. Install air cleaner.

Fig. 6: Throttle Body Assembly

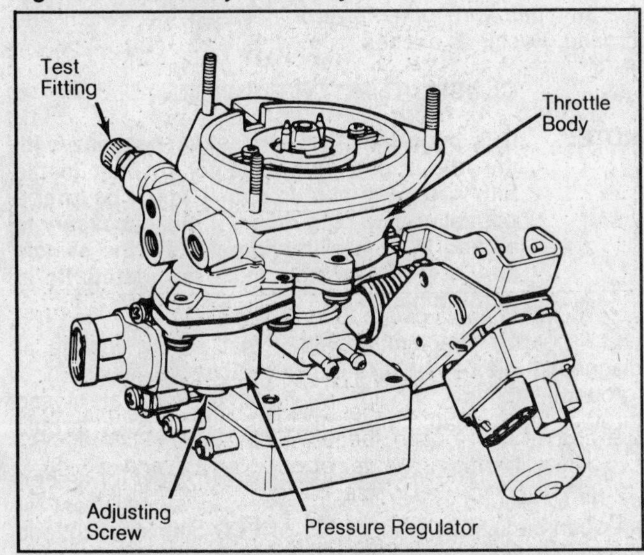

Attach pressure gauge at test fitting and turn allen head adjusting screw to obtain correct system pressure.

TROUBLE SHOOTING

PRELIMINARY CHECKS

The following systems and components must be in good condition and operating properly before assuming a fuel injection system malfunction.

- Air filter.
- All support systems and wiring.
- Battery connections and specific gravity.
- Compression pressure.
- Electrical connections on components and sensors.
- Emission control devices.
- Fuel system pressure and flow.
- Ignition system.
- Vacuum hose to MAP sensor.
- Vacuum line, fuel hose and pipe connections.

SYSTEM DIAGNOSIS

The AMC TBI fuel injection system is equipped with a self-diagnostic capacity. When a failure occurs within the system, a trouble code is stored in the ECU.

To recall trouble codes, install a test light between pins 2 and 4 of diagnostic connector D2. Push the WOT switch lever on the throttle body to wide open position and close the ISC motor plunger (activates closed throttle switch). Turn the ignition switch on and observe the test bulb.

The ECU test bulb will light for a moment, then go out. This should always occur, regardless of whether or not any trouble codes are stored, to indicate that the ECU is functional.

The bulb will then indicate all stored trouble codes as a series of brief flashes (flash, flash for code 2, flash, flash, flash, for code 3, etc.). If multiple trouble codes are stored in the ECU, the first code stored is indicated first, followed by a short pause, and any remaining codes. After a longer pause, the cycle repeats. Each trouble code indicates the malfunction of a specific sensor or sensors. Note codes.

Some injection system difficulties or abnormalities may occur without setting a trouble code. If this happens, refer to specific problem descriptions listed after trouble code references.

TROUBLE SHOOTING

CODE 1

Check MAT sensor resistance.

CODE 2

Check coolant temperature sensor resistance and replace if needed. Check MAT sensor.

CODE 3

Check WOT switch, closed throttle switch and associated wiring harness.

CODE 4

Simultaneous closed throttle switch and MAP sensor failure. Check and replace as needed.

CODE 5

Simultaneous WOT switch and MAP sensor failure. Check and replace as needed.

CODE 6

Check oxygen sensor operation. Check for correct fuel pressure.

NO TEST BULB FLASH

Check battery voltage to ECU with key on. Check ECU ground. Simultaneous WOT and coolant temperature switch contact, check both switches. No battery voltage to test bulb. Defective test bulb. Battery voltage less than 11.5 Volts.

CONTINUOUS FUEL PUMP OPERATION

Check fuel pump relay for short to ground.

NO FUEL PUMP OPERATION WITH STARTER MOTOR ENGAGED

Fuel pump defective. Check for open circuit.

AMC THROTTLE BODY FUEL INJECTION (Cont.)

POOR IDLE WHEN STARTED COLD

ISC motor not extending when engine stopped. Check ISC motor, ECU or wiring harness.

ERRATIC IDLE SPEED

ISC motor inoperative. No ECU output.

BATTERY LOSES CHARGE WITH KEY OFF

ECU does not turn off after engine is shut down. Check for fully closed throttle with engine off. Check MAP sensor voltage supply. Voltage should go from 5V to zero within 30 seconds after key off.

POOR IDLE, OXYGEN SENSOR INACTIVE

Check for defective EGR solenoid valve.

CANISTER PURGE ERRATIC

Defective solenoid. Check cannister purge.

LOW FUEL PRESSURE

Fuel pressure below 14 psi (1.0 kg/cm²). Check fuel pump operation.

EXCESSIVE FUEL PRESSURE

Fuel pressure above 15 psi (1.1 kg/cm²). Check for restricted fuel return line or fittings. Check pressure regulator.

ENGINE WILL NOT START

Defective WOT switch. Insufficient fuel supply or pressure. Fuel pump inoperative. Primary ignition input to ECU defective. No battery voltage at injector. Injector resistance too high. Leaking injector. No start signal voltage. ISC motor plunger is not extended. Coolant temperature sensor inoperative. ECU faulty.

ENGINE STARTS BUT WILL NOT IDLE

Check fuel pump operation. Check for ignition system malfunction.

POOR FUEL ECONOMY/DRIVEABILITY

High fuel pressure. Injector defective. WOT switch malfunction.

TESTING

NOTE: **When test calls for volt-ohmmeter, use of a high impedence (digital) type is required.**

MANIFOLD AIR/FUEL TEMP. SENSOR

1) Disconnect the wiring harness connector from the MAT sensor. Test resistance of the sensor with an ohmmeter. Resistance ranges from 300 ohms to 300,000 ohms (10,000 ohms at room temperature). Replace sensor if outside of specified range.

2) Test resistance of the wiring harness between pin 13 of ECU harness connector J2 and the sensor connector, and between pin 11 of connector J2 and sensor connector. See *Fig. 9* for connector identification. Repair harness if resistance is greater than 1 ohm.

COOLANT TEMPERATURE SENSOR

1) Disconnect wiring harness from sensor. Disconnect the wiring harness connector. Test resistance of sensor. If resistance is not 300-300,000 ohms (10,000 ohms at room temperature), replace the sensor.

2) Test resistance of the wiring harness between pin 14 of ECU connector J2 and the sensor connector. Test resistance between pin 11 of connector J2 and sensor connector. Repair wiring harness if any open circuit is found.

WIDE OPEN THROTTLE (WOT) SWITCH

1) Disconnect the wiring harness from the WOT switch and test resistance while opening and closing switch manually. When switch is closed, resistance should be infinite. A low resistance should be indicated at the wide open position. Test switch operation several times. Replace switch if defective. Reconnect wiring harness.

2) With ignition switch ON, test for WOT switch voltage between pin 6 and pin 7 (ground) of diagnostic connector D2. Voltage should be 0 with switch in wide open position and greater than 2 volts in any other position.

3) If voltage is always zero, test for short circuit to ground in the wiring harness or switch. Check for open circuit between pin 19 of ECU connector J2 and the switch connector. Repair or replace as needed.

4) If voltage is always greater than 2 volts, test for an open wire or connector between the switch and ground. Repair as needed.

CLOSED THROTTLE SWITCH

NOTE: **It is important that all testing be done with the idle speed control motor plunger in the fully extended position, as it would be after a normal engine shut down. If it is necessary to extend the motor plunger to test the switch, an ISC motor failure can be suspected. Refer to ISC motor test.**

1) With ignition "ON", test switch voltage at diagnostic connector D2 between pin 13 and pin 7 (ground). Voltage should be close to zero at closed throttle and greater than 2 volts off closed throttle position.

2) If the voltage is always zero, test for a short circuit to ground in the wiring harness or switch. Test for an open circuit between pin 20 of ECU connector J2 and throttle switch.

3) If voltage is always more than 2 volts, test for an open circuit in the wiring harness between the ECU and switch connector. Check for open circuit between the switch connector and ground. Repair or replace wiring harness as needed.

MANIFOLD ABSOLUTE PRESSURE SENSOR

1) Test MAP sensor output voltage at MAP sensor connector pin B (as marked on sensor body) with the ignition switch ON and the engine OFF. Output voltage should be 4.0-5.0 volts.

NOTE: **Voltage should drop 0.5-1.5 volts with hot engine, at idle.**

2) Test pin 12 of ECU connector J2 for 4.0-5.0 volts to verify wiring harness condition.

3) Check for MAP sensor supply voltage of 4.5-5.5 volts at sensor connector, pin C, with ignition ON. Similar voltage should be present at pin 2 of ECU connector J2. Repair or replace wiring harness if required.

1983 Fuel Injection

AMC THROTTLE BODY FUEL INJECTION (Cont.)

Test for sensor ground between pin 13 of ECU connector J2 and pin A of sensor connector.

4) Check for ground from pin 13 of ECU connector J2 to pin F of connector J1. If an open circuit is indicated, check for a good sensor ground on the flywheel housing near the starter motor.

5) If ground is good, the ECU must be replaced. Before replacing ECU, check to see if pin 13 of ECU connector J2 is shorted to 12 volts. If so, correct the condition before replacing ECU.

OXYGEN SENSOR

1) Test continuity of harness between O_2 sensor connector and pin 9 of ECU harness connector J2. Ensure that the wiring harness is not shorted to ground. Repair or replace as necessary.

2) Test continuity between sensor ground (exhaust manifold) and pin 13 of ECU connector J2. Repair harness if needed.

3) Check sensor operation by driving vehicle with a test lamp (no. 158 bulb) connected between pins 2 and 4 of diagnostic connector D2.

4) Bulb lighted at start is normal operation for test circuit. If the bulb does not light after warm up, the O_2 sensor is functioning normally. If the bulb stays lit or lights after the engine warms up, replace the O_2 sensor.

5) Before installing new sensor, check for system failures which may have caused O_2 sensor malfunction. System failures which can affect O_2 sensor are: EGR solenoid control, canister purge control, PCV system, secondary ignition circuit and fuel delivery system.

ELECTRONIC CONTROL UNIT

1) If all components have been checked and/or repaired, but a system failure or problem still exists, the ECU may be at fault. However, it is extremely important to note that the ECU is a very reliable unit and must always be the final component replaced if a doubt exists concerning the cause of an injection system failure.

2) The only way to confirm an ECU malfunction is to take the unit to an AMC/Renault dealer and have it tested. This is the only sure way to avoid replacing a good ECU.

REMOVAL & INSTALLATION

THROTTLE BODY ASSEMBLY

Removal

1) Disconnect throttle cable and return spring. Disconnect wire harness connectors from fuel injector, WOT switch and ISC motor. Disconnect fuel supply and return lines from throttle body.

2) Disconnect vacuum lines and identify for reassembly reference. Remove the throttle body-to-intake manifold retaining nuts (4) and lift throttle body assembly from manifold.

Installation

Reverse removal procedure to install. Always use a new gasket between the throttle body and intake manifold.

Fig. 7: Removing Throttle Body Assembly

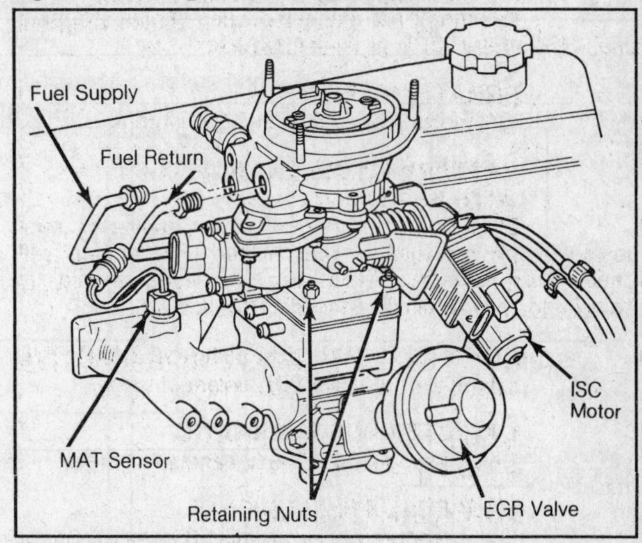

If throttle body is replaced, ISC motor/WOT switch and bracket assembly may be transferred to new unit.

FUEL INJECTOR

Removal

1) Remove air cleaner and injector wire connector. Remove the injector retainer clip attaching screws (2) and the retainer clip.

Fig. 8: Fuel Injector Assembly

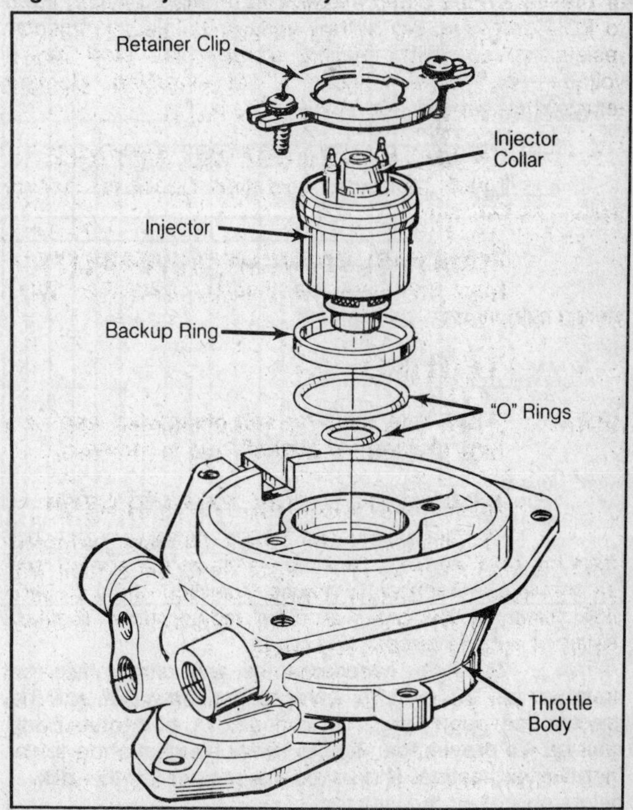

New "O" rings must be used any time that the injector is removed and replaced.

1983 Fuel Injection

AMC THROTTLE BODY FUEL INJECTION (Cont.)

Fig. 9: AMC Throttle Body Fuel Injection System Wiring Diagram

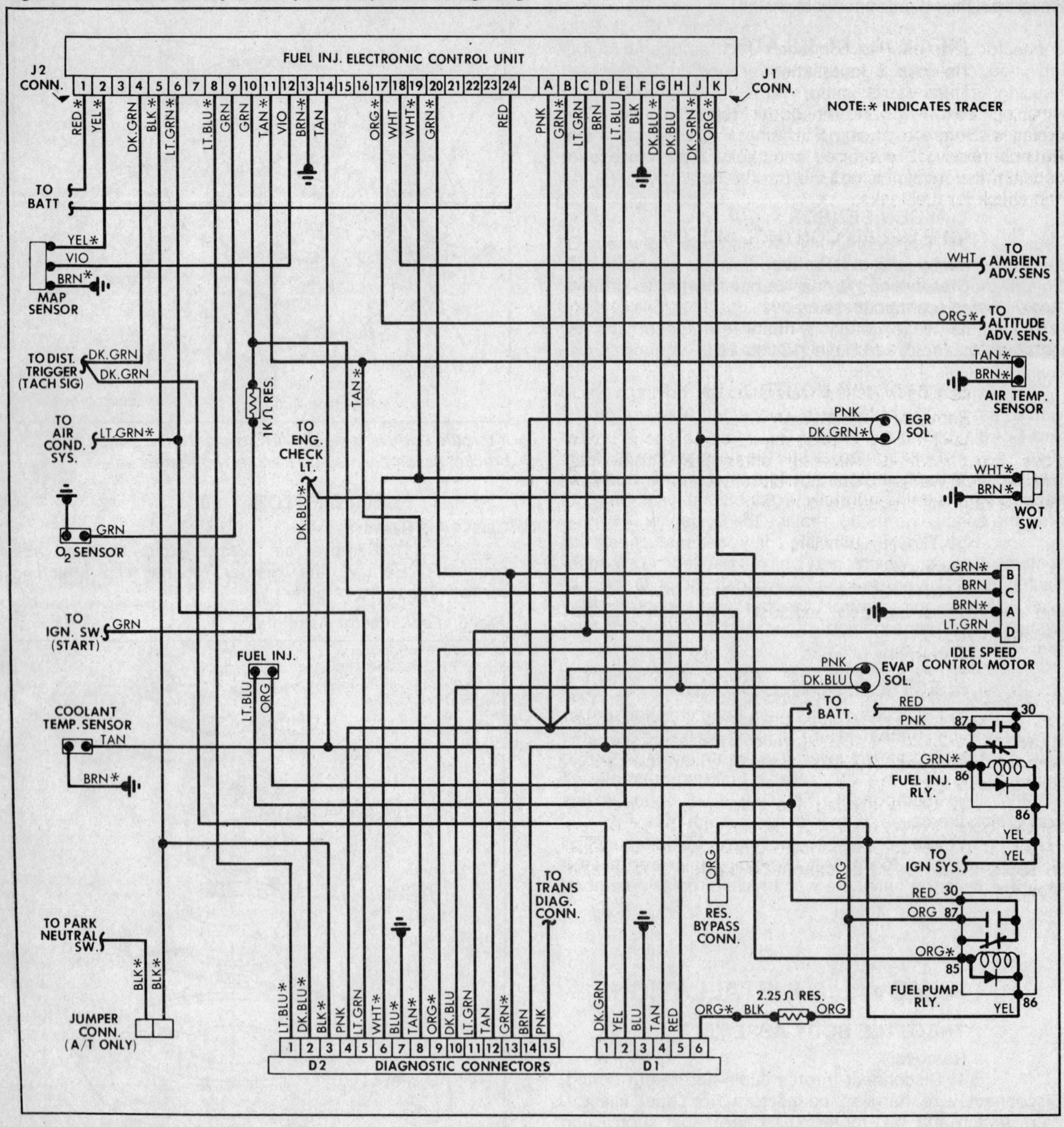

2) Using a wooden dowel as a pivot, place the tip of a flat blade screwdriver under the collar of the injector and gently pry injector out of the throttle body housing. To prevent damage to the housing, a shop towel or other protection should be placed under the dowel before prying out the injector.

3) Discard the injector "O" rings. Do not discard the backup ring that fits over the upper "O" ring.

Installation

1) Lubricate new "O" rings with light oil and tall in the injector housing. Install the backup ring over the upper "O" ring. Set the injector in place and push and twist into position until seated.

2) Turn injector so that wiring terminals are properly aligned. Install the retainer clip and retaining screws. Reattach injector wiring connector.

THROTTLE POSITION SENSOR

Removal & Installation

Disconnect wire connector from sensor and remove the 2 Torx head retaining screws. Remove the

AMC THROTTLE BODY FUEL INJECTION (Cont.)

throttle position sensor from the throttle shaft lever. Reverse removal procedures to install.

PRESSURE REGULATOR

Removal & Installation

Remove pressure regulator-to-throttle body retaining screws (3). Remove the regulator assembly, noting the location of all parts for reassembly reference. Reverse removal procedures to install, using a new gasket between the regulator and the throttle body. Start engine and check for fuel leaks.

IDLE SPEED CONTROL MOTOR

Removal & Installation

Disconnect the throttle return spring and ISC motor wiring connector. Remove the motor-to-bracket retaining nuts (3). Separate the motor from the bracket. To install motor, reverse removal procedures.

ELECTRONIC CONTROL UNIT

Removal & Installation

Locate ECU in passenger compartment, below glove box. Remove retaining screws and mounting bracket. Remove the ECU and disconnect wire harness. Reverse removal procedure to install.

OXYGEN SENSOR

Removal

Disconnect the wire connector from sensor and unscrew sensor from exhaust pipe adaptor. Clean threads in adaptor.

Installation

1) Apply antiseize compound to sensor threads. DO NOT allow compound to adhere to any other part of the sensor. Hand start the sensor into place and tighten to 20-25 ft. lbs. (27-34 N.m). Check that the wire terminal ends are properly seated in the connector. Connect wire.

2) Do not push the rubber boot over the sensor body lower than 1/2" above the base of the sensor. If the sensor wire should break, the sensor must be replaced. These wires cannot be spliced or otherwise repaired.

1983 Fuel Injection

CHRYSLER ELECTRONIC FUEL INJECTION

Imperial

DESCRIPTION

The Chrysler Electronic Fuel Injection System is used on the 5.2L (318") engine in Imperial models only. The system includes several main sub-systems: air induction, fuel delivery, fuel control, emission control, and computer control.

The air induction system includes a heated air system, an air flow meter, air cleaner, throttle body, throttle position potentiometer, throttle switch, and Automatic Idle Speed (AIS) motor.

The fuel delivery system provides fuel from the pump to (and from) the fuel control system. It is composed of an in-tank fuel pump, 2 fuel filters, check valve, pressure regulator, by-pass orifice, return line, and return check valve.

Fuel control does the actual delivery of fuel into the engine. This job is done using a variable flow pump mounted on a support plate under the air cleaner and above the throttle body. In addition to the pump, the system includes a fuel flowmeter and temperature sensor, fuel pressure switch, and fuel injector assembly. A power module provides the power to operate the control pump.

Emission controls are directly controlled by the fuel injection computer, but are not unique to the injection engine. These controls include EGR, air injection management and switching, evaporative emission control, and crankcase ventilation.

A computer controls the fuel injection system and regulates the air/fuel ratio. In addition, the computer controls ignition and emission systems. Various engine sensors are used to provide input to the computer. Two other modules assist the computer in controlling the fuel injection system: the Automatic Shut-Down Module and the Power Module.

OPERATION

GENERAL

The Electronic Fuel Injection system is unique in that it actually measures the volume of both fuel and air entering the engine. The air flow meter measures the volume of air entering the air cleaner, and the computer signals the control motor to add enough fuel to achieve the desired 14.7:1 air/fuel ratio. Finally, the oxygen sensor and other engine sensors help the computer to fine-tune the mixture to accomodate various driving conditions that require a richer or leaner mixture.

AIR INDUCTION

The air induction system conditions and measures the amount of air entering the engine. A standard air temperature system heats incoming air and maintains it at a chosen temperature. A temperature sensing valve, check valve, and vacuum motor control the heating functions.

A special duct on the air cleaner is used to swirl the incoming air. A special sensor then determines the quantity of air entering, and feeds a control signal to the computer. When the engine is cranking, not enough air flows for the sensor to work so air flow is estimated by the computer.

Fig. 1: Electronic Fuel Injection System Schematic

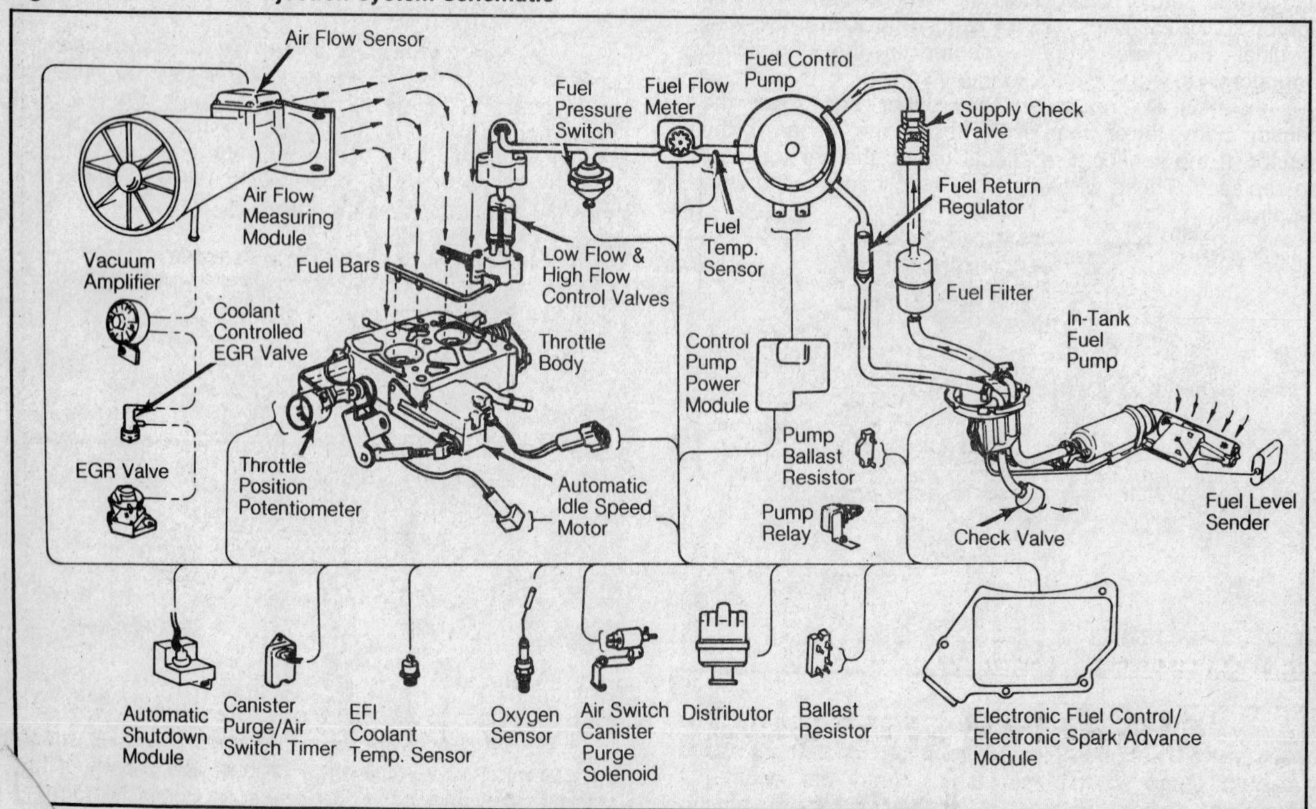

1983 Fuel Injection

CHRYSLER ELECTRONIC FUEL INJECTION (Cont.)

Fig. 2: EFI Air Induction System Components

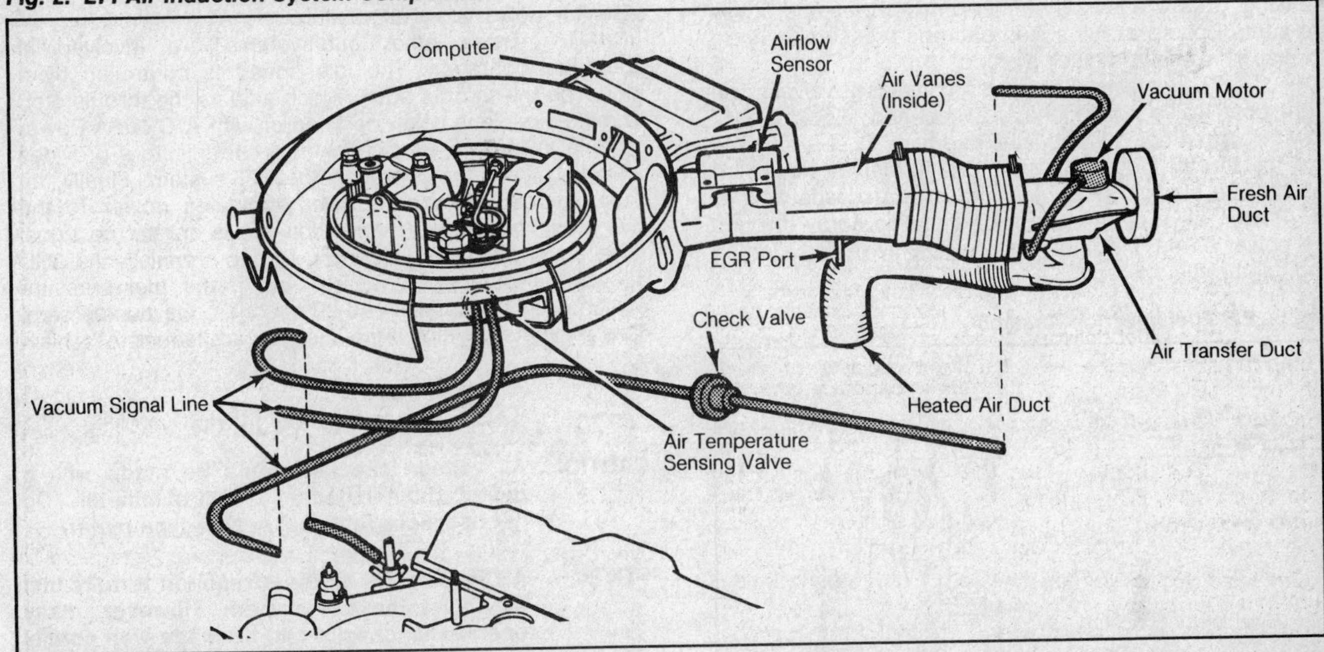

The final component in the air induction system is the throttle body. It is located on top of the intake manifold and contains the throttle blades, several vacuum ports, and the Automatic Idle Speed (AIS) motor. In addition, a throttle switch and throttle position sensor are used to inform the computer of throttle position and engine load. When the throttle is closed, the AIS controls idle speed by moving the throttle linkage stop. When the throttle is open, the position sensor enables the computer to vary enrichment. If the throttle is floored and the engine is not running, no fuel will flow (to help prevent flooding).

Fig. 3: EFI Throttle Body Assembly

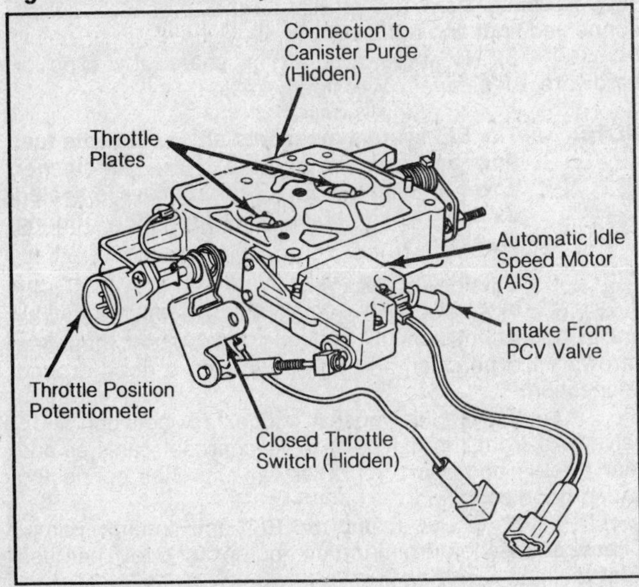

FUEL DELIVERY

The fuel delivery system begins with a 2-speed electric pump in the fuel tank. When the engine is cranking, battery voltage is applied to the pump to produce high pressure and volume, to minimize cranking times. When the engine starts, current flows through a ballast resistor, lowering pump pressure and volume and extending pump life.

Fuel flows through a pair of filters located near the tank, then on to the control pump reservoir (like a float bowl). Fuel not used returns to the tank through a regulator and check valve. A small orifice allows vapors to return to the tank when the engine is not running.

FUEL CONTROL

The fuel control system uses a small electric pump to provide fuel at varying pressure to the injectors. Unlike other EFI systems (GM and Ford), the injectors spray constantly. The Chrysler system controls the amount of fuel flowing, rather than the time the injectors are open. The entire fuel control system is mounted on the fuel support plate, above the throttle body.

Fig. 4: Fuel Control Support Plate Assembly

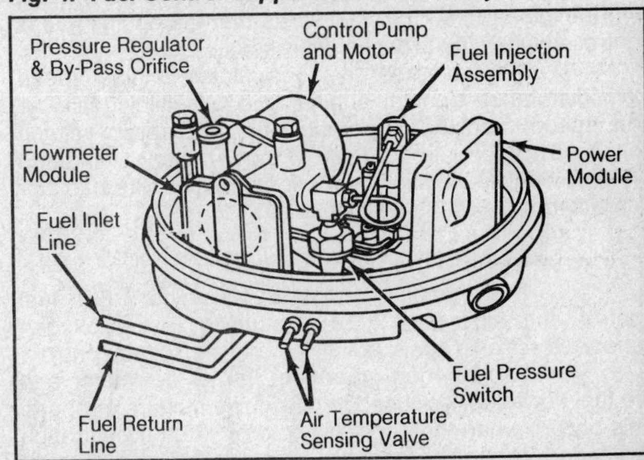

A flowmeter and temperature sender enable the computer to calculate the amount and density of fuel going to the injectors. The pressure switch is normally open when the engine is running. However, during cranking, pressure is low, so the switch closes and drives the control pump at full speed until the pressure is up to normal. This ensures quick starting.

The injection assembly contains 2 valves. The Light Load valve opens above 21 psi and allows fuel to flow through 4 holes in the light load bars. Fuel is sprayed into the throttle body and atomized further by ridges on the throttle blades. When fuel pressure exceeds 34 psi, the Power valve opens and allows fuel to spray through the power bars. This normally occurs only during starting and full-throttle operation.

Fig. 5: EFI Fuel Injection Assembly

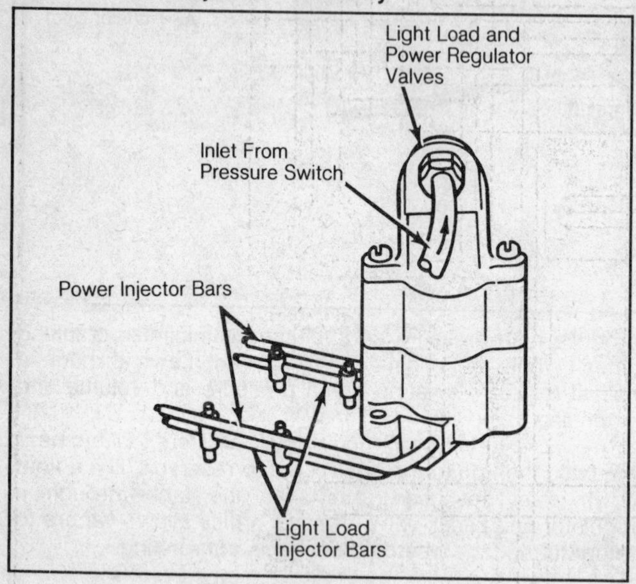

ENGINE SENSORS

The computer needs information to determine engine operating conditions and requirements. The air flowmeter, fuel flowmeter, fuel pressure switch, fuel temperature switch and throttle sensors are described in air and fuel sections. Other sensors include oxygen sensor, engine coolant temperature (used to compute warm-up enrichment), and a back-up closed throttle switch. This switch is actually a brake switch in parallel with the idle stop switch. It ensures that the engine idle is controlled when the brake is depressed.

The computer also calculates engine speed from distributor signals, engine load by dividing airflow and speed, and A/C operation by compressor clutch voltage. These inputs are used to modify spark timing and fuel injection. In addition, emission systems like canister purge and air injection are controlled.

COMPUTER OPERATION

The computer controls 4 circuits: EFI fuel control, the air/fuel mixture fine-tuning (using oxygen sensor), electronic spark advance, and idle speed control.

In open-loop operation, the air flowmeter and the fuel flowmeter are used to determine mixture strength. This occurs when the engine is cold or when acceleration is needed. When the oxygen sensor is hot and cruising operation occurs, the system enters closed-loop operation.

In closed-loop, the oxygen sensor reports the amount of unburned oxygen in the exhaust to the computer. The computer then drives the control pump faster or slower to adjust mixture.

Three other sub-systems are involved in computer operation. The idle speed is controlled by a motor on the throttle body, which adjusts the throttle stop to maintain idle in cold operation or with A/C on. A Power Module inside the air cleaner near the injectors provides 23-volt current for operating the EFI system. Finally, an Automatic Shut-Down Module terminates power to the fuel pumps whenever the ignition key is on, but no signal is received from the distributor. During cranking, the ASD allows the pumps to operate, but if the fuel pressure switch does not close in 10-20 seconds, the pumps stop. This prevents flooding if the injectors are leaking.

TROUBLE SHOOTING

CAUTION: All voltage checks should be made with a digital, high-impedance volt-ohmmeter. Do not use a conventional needle-type meter.

NOTE: A Chrysler EFI tester is required to fully test or adjust the EFI system. However, many operational checks can be made with normal shop equipment. These trouble shooting procedures cover the fuel injection system only. For information on the ignition or emission functions, see appropriate articles in ELECTRICAL or COMPUTERIZED ENGINE CONTROLS Sections.

SYSTEM VISUAL CHECK

Inside Air Cleaner

1) Proper wires connected to control pump, fuel pressure switch, and fuel flowmeter. *See Fig. 6 (wiring diagram) for identification.*

2) Power module ground wire connected to support plate screw. Fuel lines and pressure switch connected tight and not leaking.

3) No wires are cut or chafed by clips or hardware. Air cleaner cover tightly sealed.

NOTE: The EFI system measures air to calculate fuel flow and will not operate if the air cleaner cover is removed. Ensure that cover is sealed except when observing fuel flow during cranking.

Outside Air Cleaner

1) All electrical connections are tight and wires are in good condition. All electrical component mounting screws must be clean and tight to ensure a good ground connection.

2) Vacuum hoses connected between PCV valve and front throttle body port, charcoal canister and rear throttle body port. All other vacuum lines connected and in good condition.

3) Check fuses for EFI and in-tank pump. Check connection from in-tank pump to body harness near tank.

NO-START CHECKS

1) Remove air cleaner. Disconnect coil secondary wire and connect it to ground. Crank engine and check for fuel flow at injectors. If flow is okay, check ignition system.

1983 Fuel Injection

CHRYSLER ELECTRONIC FUEL INJECTION (Cont.)

Fig. 6: EFI Wiring Diagram

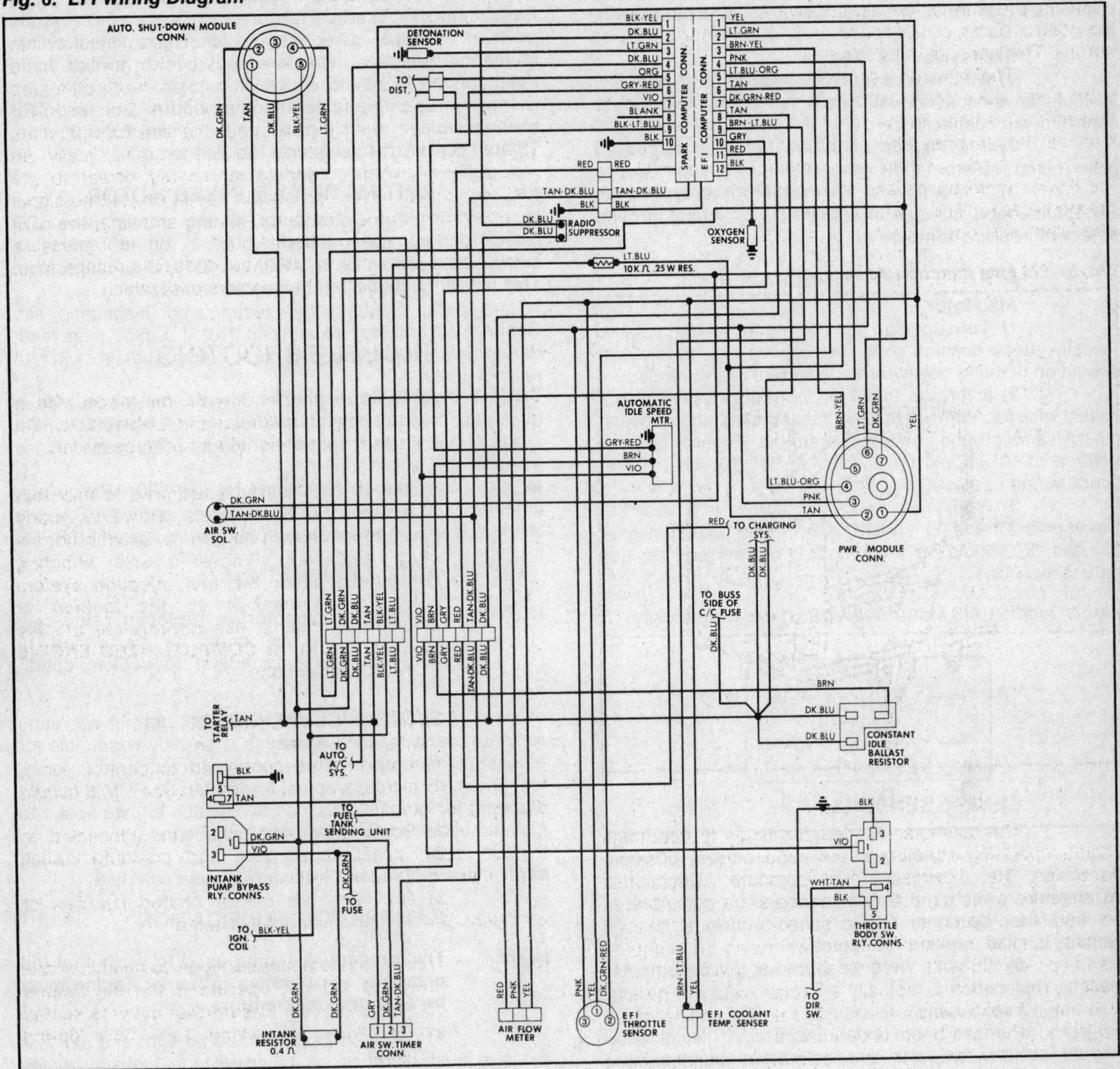

CAUTION: Coil secondary wire must be grounded if not connected to cap while engine is being cranked. Otherwise, damage to computer may occur.

2) If no fuel is seen, perform "In-Tank Pump Test". If fuel flow is minimal, perform "Fuel Pressure Test". If fuel flow is excessive or evidence of flooding is seen, perform "Excessive Fuel Flow" test.

In-Tank Pump Test

1) Check continuity and resistance of in-tank pump ballast resistor. Resistor is at right top of cowl and should have 0.4 ohms resistance.

2) Continuity should be present between one side of ballast resistor and pin 3 of pump relay connector (right fender well). Continutiy should exist between other side of resistor and pin 1 in connector. Pin 5 should be grounded.

3) Insert positive voltmeter probe into rear of relay connector at pin 3 while connector is hooked up. Connect other probe to ground and crank engine. Voltmeter should indicate 8-10 volts. Insert probe at pin 4 and crank engine. Voltmeter should indicate 9 volts. If not, check battery and supply to pump relay.

4) If voltage is present, check continuity between pin 3 of relay connector and Dark Green wire at pump (fuel tank).

Fuel Pressure Test

1) Check battery for at least 12 volts. Connect pressure gauge to "T" at fuel supply fitting on fuel plate. Crank engine.

CHRYSLER ELECTRONIC FUEL INJECTION (Cont.)

2) Fuel pressure should be at least 8 psi. If not, check fuel pick-up, fuel filters, fuel lines or blocked vent lines.

Excessive Fuel Flow

1) With air cleaner cover removed, turn key on. If fuel flows continuously from injectors, disconnect control pump connector.

2) If fuel continues to flow, replace fuel control plate (pump, injectors, flowmeter).

3) If fuel flow stops, problem is in computer. Substitute good computer and retest. If original proves defective, replace computer.

STARTS, THEN STALLS CHECKS

AIS Motor

1) Turn ignition on but do not start engine. Visually check position of throttle arm at AIS motor. Arm should be pointing downward and toward rear of engine.

2) If throttle arm is in correct position, check ballast resistor. With ignition on, measure voltage between pin "A" and ground, then between pin "B" and ground. Voltage at "A" should be 6 volts, at "B", 10 volts. If not, check wiring harness.

3) Resistance (with connectors removed) between pins "C" and "D" should be 9-11 ohms, and between "D" and "E" should be 4-6 ohms. If not correct, replace ballast resistor.

Fig. 7: Ignition/AIS Motor Ballast Resistor Connections

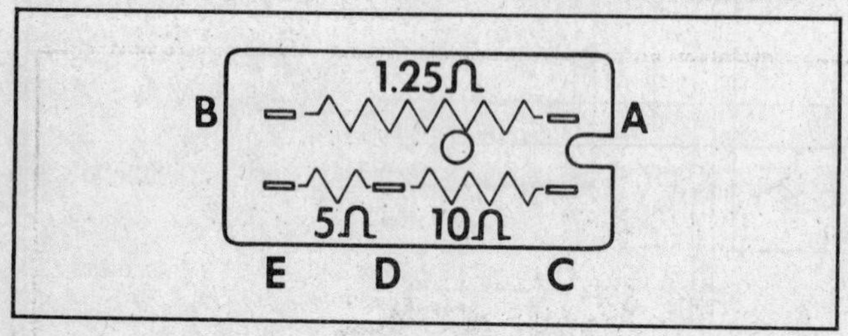

4) If arm at motor was in correct position, disconnect 10-pin connector at computer. Connect a voltmeter between pin 6 of connector and ground. At least 8 volts should be present. If not, check wiring harness. If harness is okay, replace AIS motor.

5) If 8 volts were measured at pin 6, computer must be replaced.

Fuel Supply

Perform test under "No-Start Checks" and inspect fuel flow, fuel pressure, and voltage to pump.

Computer Supply

1) Disconnect 12-pin EFI connector from module inside computer on air cleaner housing. Connect a voltmeter between pin 8 of connector and ground, then crank engine.

2) Voltmeter should indicate at least 9 volts. If not reconnect connector and check wiring harness to starter relay. If voltage is correct, replace computer.

ADJUSTMENTS

THROTTLE POSITION POTENTIOMETER

NOTE: **Throttle position potentiometer is mounted with break-off screws. Screws must be drilled and removed, then replaced before adjustment is possible.**

1) Connect EFI tester to vehicle. Place toggle switch to EFI position and rotary switch to throttle position, then turn ignition on. Move diagnostic aid switch to manual position, then move AIS control switch down and hold until AIS motor stops.

2) Depress AIS by-pass button and read TPP voltage. Adjust switch position to obtain 4.0-5.0 volts. Tighten break-off screws until heads snap off.

AUTOMATIC IDLE SPEED MOTOR

1) Turn ignition on. Motor should move arm rearward and open throttle blades. When vehicle is started, idle should be 580 RPM in "D" and should remain constant. If not, adjustment may be necessary.

2) Connect EFI tester with diagnostic aid. Connect tachometer pick-up to No. 1 spark plug lead, battery leads to battery, and place diagnostic aid switch to normal position.

3) Start engine and run until warm. Move diagnostic aid switch to manual and depress control switch until engine speed no longer decreases. Place transmission selector in "D".

4) Idle speed should be 530-630 RPM. If not, adjust to 580 RPM by turning screw on end of AIS motor linkage. One turn of screw will change idle speed 50 RPM.

AUTO-CALIBRATION

NOTE: **Whenever computer is replaced, auto-calibration procedure must be performed to allow computer to adjust to vehicle conditions.**

1) Start and run engine until normal operating temperature is reached. If engine is already warm, idle for at least 90 seconds to allow timer to run out.

2) Increase speed to 2000-2500 RPM and hold constant for at least 90 seconds. Reduce engine speed to idle and allow to idle for at least 150 seconds.

3) Repeat step **2)** once more so computer can verify initial calibration. Procedure is now complete.

CALIBRATION VERIFICATION

NOTE: **This procedure can be used to verify that the computer is operating properly. Engine must be at normal temperature.**

1) Air cleaner cover must be tight and exhaust system must be checked to ensure no leaks or holes exist. Connect EFI tester to system and connect a CO meter to tailpipe.

2) Remove air pump hose from downstream air injection tube and plug tube. Connect diagnostic aid to AIS motor. Start engine, leave transmission selector in "P", and place speed control switch in manual position. Idle for at least 90 seconds.

3) Disconnect oxygen sensor wire and ground wiring harness side of connector. Increase engine speed to 2000-2500 RPM and hold it constant with diagnostic aid control.

4) CO reading must be between 0.5-3.5%. If higher than 3.5%, replace computer. Remove test equipment and reconnect air injection tube.

1983 Fuel Injection

CHRYSLER CORP. THROTTLE BODY

E-Class, New Yorker, 600

DESCRIPTION

Chrysler Throttle Body Fuel Injection system is a computer controlled system which uses a throttle-body assembly with a single fuel injector to control air/fuel ratio under varying engine operating conditions.

Fuel is supplied to engine through an electronically controlled (pulsed) injector valve located in the throttle body assembly on top of intake manifold. Power to injector is supplied by power module while length of time that injector is left open is the responsibility of logic module.

Logic module determines amount of fuel to be metered through injector valve based on engine operating condition information supplied to it by various engine sensors and switches. Input signals from these sensors/switches are converted, by logic module, into control signals.

These control signals are then sent to the power module which responds by issuing electrical signals to specific components to alter air/fuel ratio and/or ignition timing to meet indicated conditions. Logic module is a digital, pre-programmed computer which controls ignition timing, emission control devices and idle speed in addition to air/fuel ratio.

OPERATION

FUEL SUPPLY

An electric fuel pump is located in the fuel tank as an integral part of fuel gauge sending unit. This pump supplies fuel at 36 psi (2.5 kg/cm²) to throttle body assembly. Power to fuel pump is supplied by power module via Automatic Shutdown (ASD) relay. Power module is supplied with an operating signal from distributor. If this signal is not received, ASD relay is not activated and power to fuel pump is cut off.

THROTTLE BODY ASSEMBLY

Throttle Body

Throttle body is mounted on intake manifold, in same position as a conventional carburetor. It houses fuel injector, pressure regulator, throttle position sensor, and automatic idle speed motor. Air flow control is via a throttle blade in base of throttle body. Throttle body chamber provides for metering, atomization and distribution of fuel into incoming air stream.

Fuel Injector

Fuel injector is mounted in throttle body so that fuel from injector is directed into incoming air stream. While power to injector is supplied by power module, it is controlled by indirect signal from logic module. When electric current is supplied to injector, an integral armature and pintle valve

Fig. 1: Schematic Diagram of Power/Logic Module Input Signals & Output Controls

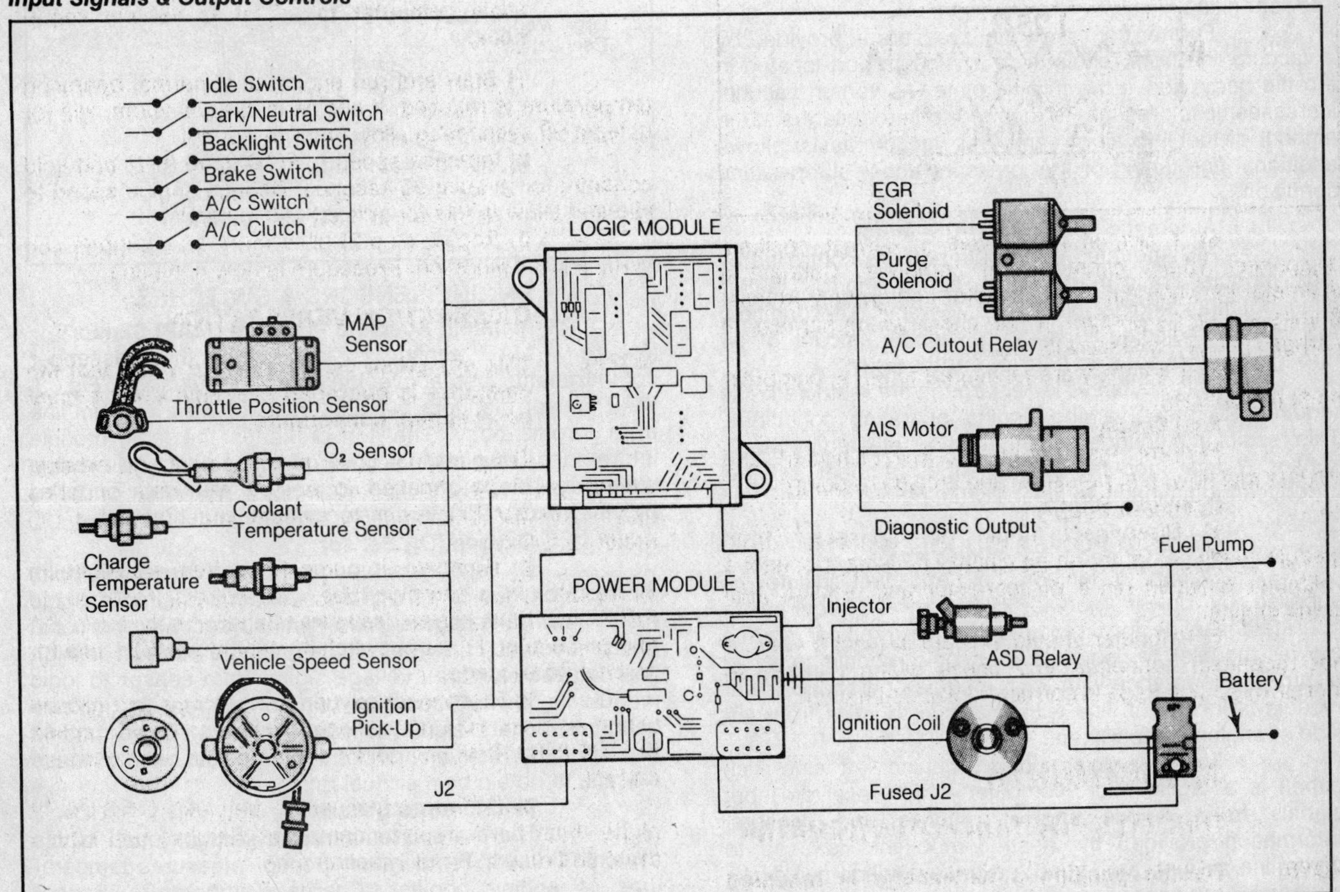

move a short distance against a spring, opening a small orifice.

Fuel supplied to injector is forced around pintle valve and through this opening, resulting in a fine spray of fuel in the shape of a hollow cone. A constant pressure is maintained across injector (by pressure regulator), so the length of time that this opening is maintained (injector "on" time) determines the amount of fuel entering engine.

Fig. 2: Cross-Sectional View of Fuel Injector

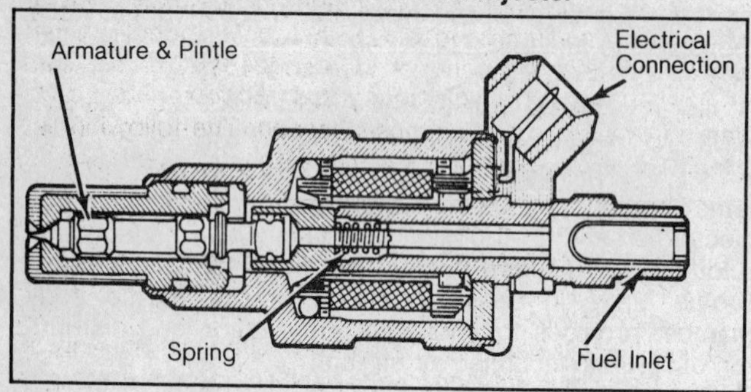

Pressure Regulator

Pressure regulator is located downstream from fuel injector, on the throttle body. Regulator is equipped with a spring loaded rubber diaphragm which covers a fuel return port. Fuel flow past the injector enters regulator, and is restricted from flowing back to tank by blocked return port. When fuel pressure reaches 36 psi (2.5 kg/cm²), spring is compressed enough to allow fuel into return line.

Further control of fuel pressure is provided by a vacuum line from regulator to a vacuum port located in throttle body, above the throttle plate. As venturi vacuum increases, less pressure is required to introduce the same amount of fuel into air stream. This vacuum assist allows additional fine tuning of fuel pressure under all operating conditions.

Automatic Idle Speed (AIS) Motor

AIS (mounted on throttle body) is controlled by logic module. Logic module uses sensor input to determine optimum engine idle speed for any idle condition. AIS is then adjusted to allow a specific amount of air through an air bypass on back of throttle body.

This bypass is enlarged or restricted, as required, to meet varying engine operating conditions. This results in a change in air/fuel ratio, detected by the O_2 sensor. Logic module then changes amount of fuel introduced to maintain an ideal air/fuel ratio.

LOGIC & POWER MODULES

Power to ignition coil and fuel injector is supplied by power module. High current required to operate these devices requires that their power source (power module) be isolated from logic module to avoid electrical interference with logic module operation. Power module is located in line with intake air duct at front left side of engine compartment.

Logic module (located behind left side kick panel) is a digital micro-computer which receives input signals from various engine switches and sensors. Information provided by these components is used to determine air/fuel ratio, spark advance, ignition coil dwell, automatic idle speed actuation and purge, and EGR control solenoid cycles.

Logic module constantly monitors its own input and output circuits. If a fault is found in any major system, a numbered code is stored in the logic module. *See Fault Codes.* The stored codes indicate specific problem areas within the system.

Power module provides power to ignition coil and fuel injector. It also energizes Automatic Shutdown (ASD) relay, which activates fuel pump, ignition coil, and power module itself. The module receives a signal from the distributor and sends this signal to logic module.

If this signal is absent, ASD relay is not activated and power to fuel pump and ignition coil is shut off. Power module reduces battery voltage to a regulated 8.0 volt output the distributor and logic module.

Fig. 3: Location of Logic Module, MAP Sensor & ASD Relay

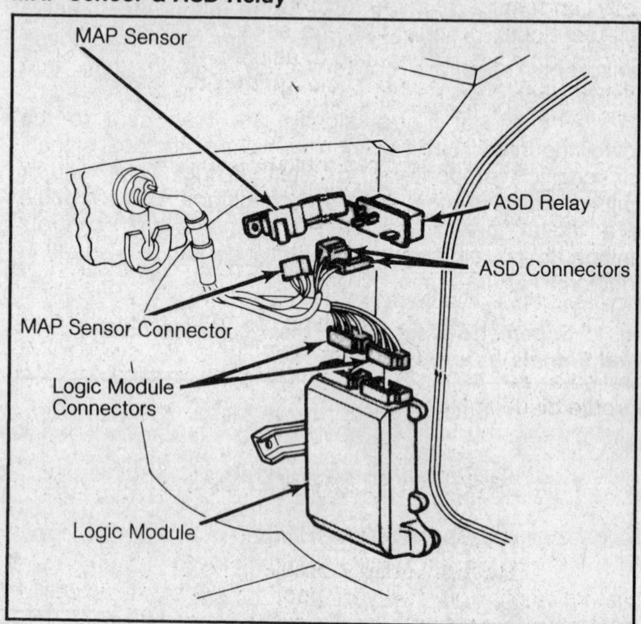

ENGINE SENSORS & SWITCHES

Manifold Absolute Pressure (MAP) Sensor

MAP sensor is located in the passenger compartment, just above the logic module. *See Fig. 3.* MAP sensor monitors manifold vacuum via a vacuum line from throttle body. The sensor keeps the logic module informed of manifold vacuum conditions and barometric pressure. This information, combined with data supplied by other sensors, determines correct air/fuel ratio.

Oxygen (O_2) Sensor

O_2 sensor (located in top of exhaust manifold) monitors oxygen content of the exhaust and supplies logic module with a voltage signal which is directly proportional to this content. If oxygen content of the exhaust is high (lean air/fuel mixture), voltage signal from sensor to logic module is low. As oxygen content decreases (mixture becomes richer), signal voltage increases. Logic module can then alter fuel injector "on" time, in response to these signals, to obtain best air/fuel ratio.

Temperature Sensors

There are 2 temperature sensors used in this system. Coolant Temperature Sensor measures temperature of engine coolant. Charge Temperature Sensor measures temperature of the incoming air/fuel mixture.

1983 Fuel Injection

CHRYSLER CORP. THROTTLE BODY (Cont.)

Coolant temperature sensor is mounted in thermostat housing to monitor engine coolant temperature. It supplies logic module with a voltage signal which varies with coolant temperature. Charge temperature sensor (mounted in intake manifold) supplies logic module with temperature of incoming air/fuel mixture.

Information provided by these 2 sensors allows logic module to demand slightly richer air/fuel mixtures and higher idle speeds during cold engine operation. If coolant temperature switch malfunctions, information supplied by charge temperature sensor is sufficient until temperature sensor can be repaired or replaced.

Throttle Position Sensor (TPS)

TPS is a variable resistor activated by movement of throttle shaft. It is mounted on the throttle body and senses angle of throttle blade opening. A voltage signal, produced by the sensor, is transmitted to logic module where it is used to adjust air/fuel ratio during acceleration, deceleration, idle, and wide open throttle conditions.

Engine Switches

Several switches provide operating information to logic module. These include idle, neutral safety, electric backlight, air conditioning, air conditioning clutch, and brake light switches. If one or more of these switches is sensed in the "on" position, logic module signals AIS to increase idle speed to a specific RPM.

With air conditioning on and throttle blade above a specific angle, wide open throttle cut-out relay prevents air conditioning clutch from engaging until throttle blade angle is reduced.

TROUBLE SHOOTING

PRELIMINARY CHECKS

Most driveability problems in the Chrysler EFI system result from faulty or poor wiring, or loose and/or leaking hose connections. To avoid unnecessary component testing, a visual check should be performed before beginning trouble shooting procedures to help spot these common faults. A preliminary visual check should include:

- Air ducts to air cleaner and from air cleaner to throttle body.
- Electrical connections at all components. Clean, tight and unbroken. Check vacuum lines for secure, leak-free connections in these areas:
- Throttle body (2 front, 2 rear).
- EGR and purge solenoids (located on a common bracket at right rear corner of engine compartment).
- Vapor canister.
- PCV valve to intake manifold vacuum port.
- Back pressure transducer.
- MAP sensor.

Ensure that the following electrical connectors are securely attached:

- 21-way connectors (2) at logic module (Black connector to Black socket, Tan connector to Tan socket).
- 3-way connector at MAP sensor.
- 3-way and 1-way connectors at ASD Relay.
- 12-way and 10-way connectors at power module.
- 3-way connector at EGR and purge solenoids.
- 2-way connector at speed sensor (located in line with speedometer cable).
- 2-way connector at charge temperature sensor.
- 6-way connector at AIS motor and TPS (and ground wire to manifold).
- 2-way connector at fuel injector.
- O_2 connector.
- 2-way connector at coolant temperature sensor.
- 3-way connector at distributor.

FAULT CODES

The Chrysler Throttle Body Fuel Injection system is equipped with a self-diagnostic capability which stores certain "fault codes" in the logic module when system malfunctions occur. These codes may be recalled to aid in system diagnosis. *See Entering On-Board Diagnosis in Testing & Diagnosis section.* The following list presents these codes and the system malfunctions which they represent.

Code 11

Problem with distributor circuit. No distributor signal to logic module since restoration of battery voltage.

Code 13

Problem with MAP sensor pneumatic system. Appears if sensor vacuum level does not change between start and start/run transfer speed (500-600 RPM).

Code 14

Problem with MAP sensor electrical system. MAP sensor signal outside of .02-4.9 volt range.

Code 15

Problem with Speed Sensor circuit. Engine speed above 1470 RPM, sensor indicates less than 2 MPH. Code valid only if sensed while vehicle is moving.

Code 21

Problem with O_2 Sensor feedback circuit. Occurs if engine temperature is above 170°F (77°C), engine speed is above 1500 RPM, but O_2 sensor stays rich or lean for more than 60 seconds.

Code 22

Problem with Coolant Temperature Sensor circuit. Appears if the temperature sensor indicates an incorrect temperature or a temperature that changes too fast to be real.

Code 23

Problem with Charge Temperature Sensor circuit. Appears if the charge temperature sensor indicates an incorrect temperature or a temperature that changes too fast to be real.

Code 24

Problem with TPS circuit. Appears if the sensor signal is either below .16 volts or above 4.7 volts.

Code 25

Problem with AIS control circuit. Appears if proper voltage from AIS system is not present. An open harness or motor will not activate this code.

Code 31

Problem with Canister Purge Solenoid circuit. Appears when the proper voltage at the purge solenoid is not present (open or shorted system).

Code 32

Problem with Power Loss Lamp circuit. Appears when proper voltage to the circuit is not present (open or shorted system).

Code 33

Open or shorted circuit at air conditioning WOT cut-out relay circuit.

Code 34

Open or shorted circuit at EGR solenoid.

CHRYSLER CORP. THROTTLE BODY (Cont.)

Code 41
Problem with charging system. Appears if battery voltage from the ASD relay is below 11.75 volts.

Code 42
Problem in the ASD relay circuit. Appears if, during cranking, battery voltage from ASD relay is not present for at least 1/3 of a second after first distributor pulse, or if battery voltage is present for more than 3 seconds after engine stalls (last distributor pulse).

Code 43
Problem in the interface circuit. Appears if the anti-dwell or injector control signal is not present between the logic module and power module.

Code 44
Problem in the Logic Module. Appears if an internal failure exists in the logic module.

Code 51
Problem in Standby Memory. Appears if direct battery feed is interrupted to the logic module. This code will disappear after about 30 ignition key on/off cycles once the logic module receives a distributor signal.

Codes 52, 53, 54
Problem in the Logic Module. Appears if an internal failure exists in the Logic Module.

Code 55
This is the "end of message" code. This code will always appear as the final code after all other fault codes have been displayed.

Code 88
This will be the first code displayed. It implies the start of the message, and only appears on the Diagnostic Readout tool.

TESTING & DIAGNOSIS

SYSTEM DIAGNOSIS

The self-diagnostic capabilities of this system, if properly utilized, can greatly simplify testing.

If, at any time, the logic module receives an incorrect signal or no signal from either the Coolant Temperature Sensor, MAP sensor or TPS, a Power Loss Lamp on the instrument panel is illuminated. This lamp acts as a warning device to inform the operator that a malfunction in the system has occurred and immediate service is required.

When certain malfunctions occur, the logic module enters the "Limp-In Mode". In this mode, the logic module compensates for failure of components by substituting information from other sources. This allows vehicle to be operated until proper repairs can be made.

If Power Loss Lamp comes on, or if certain driveability or engine performance difficulties exist, the probable source of these difficulties may be determined by entering "On Board Diagnosis" and recording the fault codes as they are displayed.

Once these codes are known, refer to the *Trouble Shooting* section to determine the questionable circuit. Then use *Fig. 5* and *Component Connector Identification Charts* to locate testing points for each circuit. Test circuits and repair or replace as needed.

ENTERING ON-BOARD DIAGNOSIS

1) Attach the Chrysler Diagnostic Readout Tool (C-4805) to self-test connector. The connector is located in engine compartment near right side strut tower. If this test box is not available, codes may be read off of the flashing light emitting diode (LED) on the logic module.

Fig. 4: View of Logic Module Showing Location of Light Emitting Diode (LED)

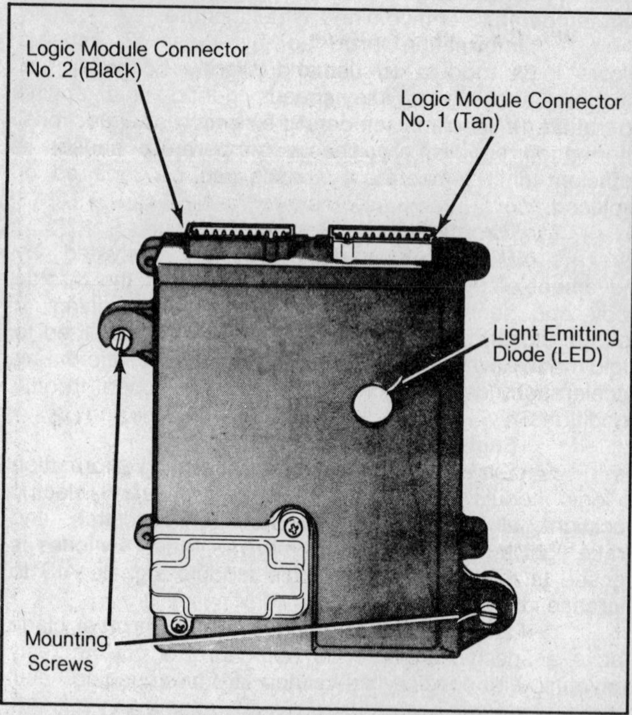

2) Start engine (if possible). Move transmission shift lever through all positions, ending in Park. Turn A/C switch on, then off (if present).

3) Stop the engine and, without starting it again, turn the key on, off, on, off and on. Record fault codes as displayed on Diagnostic Readout, or by counting flashes of the LED.

4) Codes displayed by the LED are indicated by a series of flashes. For example, code 23 is displayed as flash, flash, pause, flash, flash, flash. After a slightly longer pause, any other codes stored are displayed in numerical order.

5) The setting of a specific fault code is the result of a particular system failure, NOT a specific component. Therefore, the existance of a particular code denotes the probable area of the malfunction, not necessarily the failed component itself.

COMPONENT CONNECTOR IDENTIFICATION CHARTS

NOTE: **Information on this system is also covered in the COMPUTERIZED ENGINE CONTROLS Section. Additional diagnostic information that relates strictly to the engine control portion of this system can be found in the CHRYSLER CORP. ELECTRONIC FUEL CONTROL article.**

CHRYSLER CORP. THROTTLE BODY (Cont.)

COMPONENT CONNECTOR IDENTIFICATION CHARTS

LOGIC MODULE PINS — CONNECTOR 1

Pin No.	Wire Color	Wire Function
1	Blk	Input ground to prevent "noise" on sensor signals.
2	Blk/Lt. Bl	Common ground for engine sensors.
3	Org	8 volt power supply from power module. Provides for 5 volt sensor supply.
4	Vio	5 volt power supply for MAP sensor.
5	Vio/Yel	Injector pulse width info. input.
6	Vio	NONE
7	Yel	Supplies ignition timing info. to power module.
8	Dk. Gry	NONE
9	Yel/Red	NONE
10	NONE	NONE
11	Gry	Distributor input signal. Provides timing and RPM info.
12	Wht/Org	Vehicle speed input. Provides vehicle stopped or moving info. to determine AIS control and fuel delivery.
13	Bl/Blk	Fuel gauge display information.
14	Lt. Grn	Provides for "HOLD" function on test box.
15	Pnk	Supplies fault codes and O_2 switching information to test box.
16 & 17	Dk. Bl	Fused power input (J2) from power module. Provides AIS voltage and signals processor not to accept sensor info. with ignition off.
18	NONE	NONE
19	NONE	NONE
20	Org/Wht	5 volt power supply for TPS.
21	Brn/Red	Battery voltage supply to retain memory with engine off.

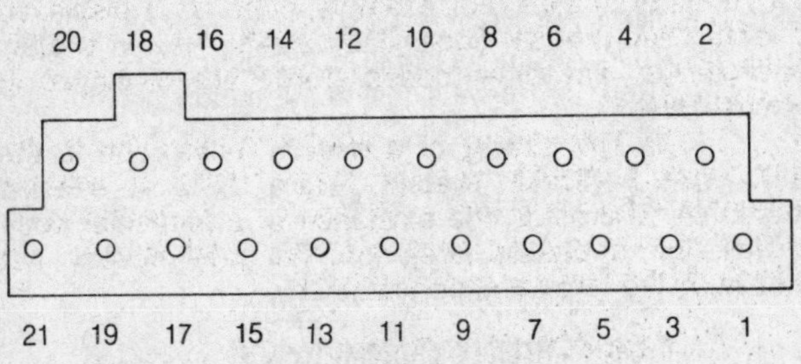

20 18 16 14 12 10 8 6 4 2

21 19 17 15 13 11 9 7 5 3 1

SPEED SENSOR CONNECTOR TERMINALS

Pin No.	Wire Color	Wire Function
1	Wht/Org	Output signal to logic module: indicates vehicle moving or stopped.
2	Blk/Lt. Bl	Ground for sensor through logic module.

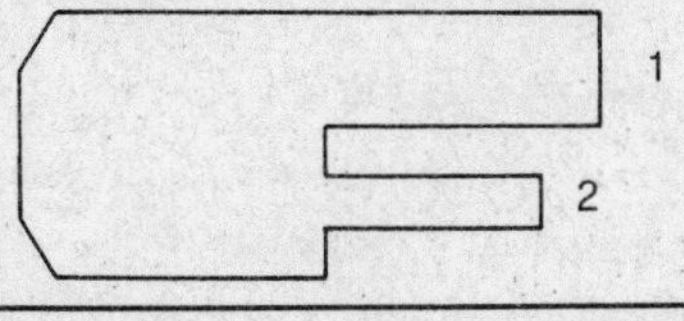

1
2

LOGIC MODULE PINS — CONNECTOR 2

Pin No.	Wire Color	Wire Function
1	Brn/Yel	Neutral/Park switch input. Information modifies AIS control and timing at idle.
2	Lt Bl/Yel	Rear defrost input. AIS increases idle speed when extra engine load is sensed.
3	Dk Grn/Red	NONE
4	Dk Grn/Red	MAP sensor input. Provides engine load info., throttle limp-in as needed.
5	Org/Dk. Bl	TPS input. Informs logic module of wide open throttle. Provides signal to unload flooded engine and idle signal to adjust AIS position, timing, and fuel delivery rate. Informs logic module when MAP limp-in required.
6	Dk Grn	Battery voltage from ASD relay. Modifies pulse width in response to voltage variation.
7	Brn	A/C clutch input. Increases idle speed during A/C operation.
8	Tan	Coolant temp. sensor input. Modifies spark advance, injector pulse width, AIS control.
9	Dk. Bl/Yel	A/C switch input. Sets AIS at higher RPM in response to high engine loads.
10	Blk/Red	Charge temp. sensor input. Used for coolant temp. limp-in when needed.
11	Dk. Bl/Org	WOT relay output. Provides ground to shut off A/C clutch under wide open throttle conditions.
12	Gry/Red	AIS control output. Drive signal to AIS motor.
13	Wht/Tan	Brake switch input. Influences TPS position.
14	Brn	AIS control output. Drive signal to AIS motor.
15	Lt. Bl/Red	Power ground for logic module.
16	Lt. Bl/Red	Back-up power ground for logic module.
17	Blk/Org	Provides ground for POWER LOSS lamp on instrument panel when in limp-in mode.
18	Gry/Yel	Provides ground to activate EGR, or to turn EGR off when engine is cold.
19	Pnk	Provides ground to activate purge solenoid; removes canister purge when engine is cold.
20	NONE	NONE
21	Blk	O_2 sensor input. Provides logic module with O_2 sensor info. to modify fuel pulse width.

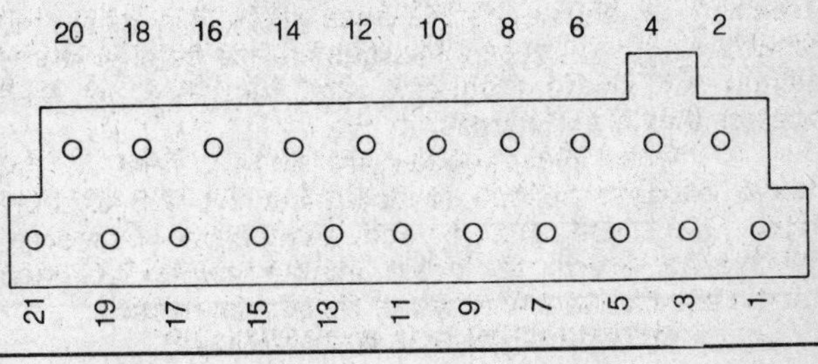

20 18 16 14 12 10 8 6 4 2

21 19 17 15 13 11 9 7 5 3 1

1983 Fuel Injection

CHRYSLER CORP. THROTTLE BODY (Cont.)

ASD RELAY CONNECTOR TERMINALS

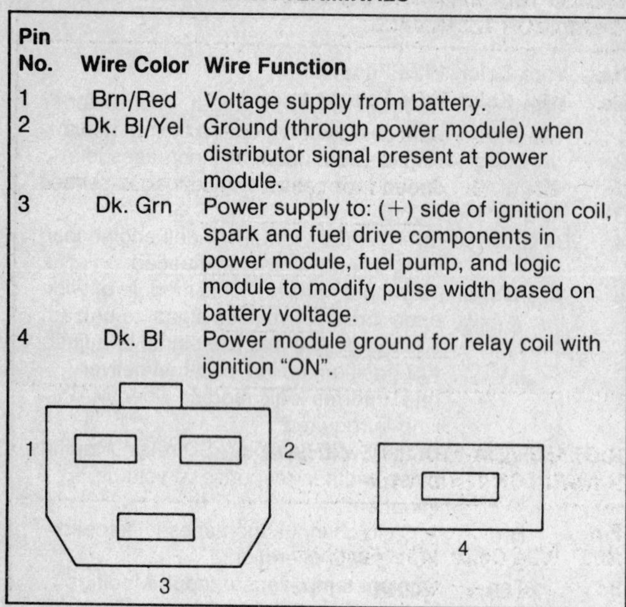

Pin No.	Wire Color	Wire Function
1	Brn/Red	Voltage supply from battery.
2	Dk. Bl/Yel	Ground (through power module) when distributor signal present at power module.
3	Dk. Grn	Power supply to: (+) side of ignition coil, spark and fuel drive components in power module, fuel pump, and logic module to modify pulse width based on battery voltage.
4	Dk. Bl	Power module ground for relay coil with ignition "ON".

POWER MODULE PINS — 12-PIN CONNECTOR

Pin No.	Wire Color	Wire Function
1	Vio/Yel	Injector control input. Provides injector pulse width instructions from logic module.
2	Blk/Lt. Bl	Noise ground. Prevents "noise" on sensor signals.
3	NONE	NONE
4	NONE	NONE
5	NONE	NONE
6	NONE	NONE
7	Gray	Distributor signal input. Activates power module to supply ground for ASD relay.
8	NONE	NONE
9	Yel/Red	NONE
10	Yel	Anit-Dwell input. Receives spark advance info. from logic module.
11	Vio	NONE
12	Org	8 volt output. Supply voltage for Hall pick-up and logic module.

POWER MODULE PINS — 10-PIN CONNECTOR

Pin No.	Wire Color	Wire Function
1	Blk/Yel	Triggers ignition coil (-).
2	Dk. Bl	J2 feed from ignition switch.
3	Dk. Bl	Fused J2 power to: Logic module to drive AIS motor; ASD relay to activate relay coil.
4	Tan	Provides pulse width signal to injector.
5	Wht	Injector feedback signal used to control injector response.
6	NONE	NONE
7	Dk. Bl/Yel	Provides ground to ASD relay when distributor signal present.
8	Dk. Grn	Power supply for spark and fuel drive components in power module.
9	Blk	Ground for power module.
10	Blk	Back-up ground for power module.

THROTTLE POSITION/AIS MOTOR CONNECTOR TERMINALS

Pin No.	Wire Color	Wire Function
1	Blk/Lt. Bl	Sensor ground through logic module.
2	Org/Wht	5 volt power supply from logic module.
3	Org/Dk. Bl	Sensor output signal to logic module connector 2, pin 5.
4	NONE	NONE
5	Brn	#2 drive signal to AIS motor.
6	Gry/Red	#1 drive signal to AIS motor.

1983 Fuel Injection

CHRYSLER CORP. THROTTLE BODY (Cont.)

DISTRIBUTOR CONNECTOR TERMINALS

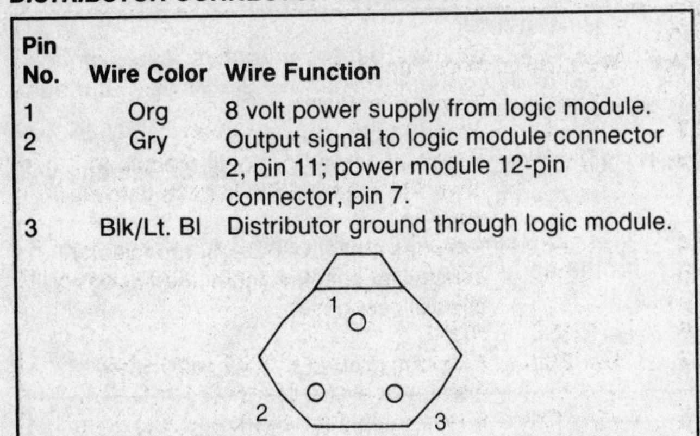

Pin No.	Wire Color	Wire Function
1	Org	8 volt power supply from logic module.
2	Gry	Output signal to logic module connector 2, pin 11; power module 12-pin connector, pin 7.
3	Blk/Lt. Bl	Distributor ground through logic module.

EGR/PURGE SOLENOID CONNECTOR TERMINALS

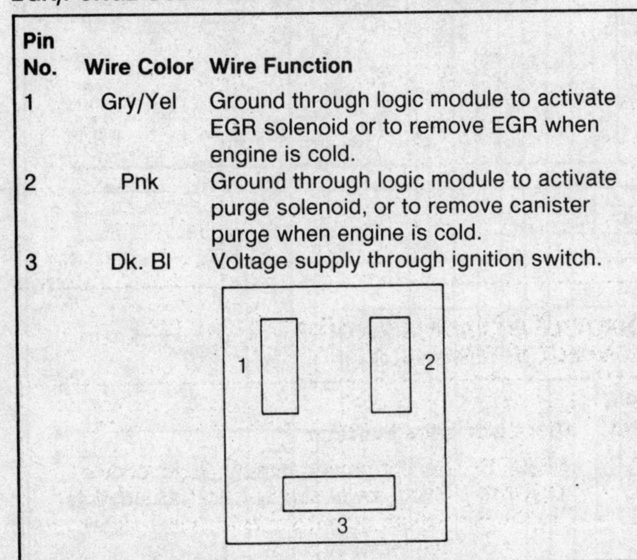

Pin No.	Wire Color	Wire Function
1	Gry/Yel	Ground through logic module to activate EGR solenoid or to remove EGR when engine is cold.
2	Pnk	Ground through logic module to activate purge solenoid, or to remove canister purge when engine is cold.
3	Dk. Bl	Voltage supply through ignition switch.

WIDE OPEN THROTTLE A/C RELAY CONNECTOR TERMINALS

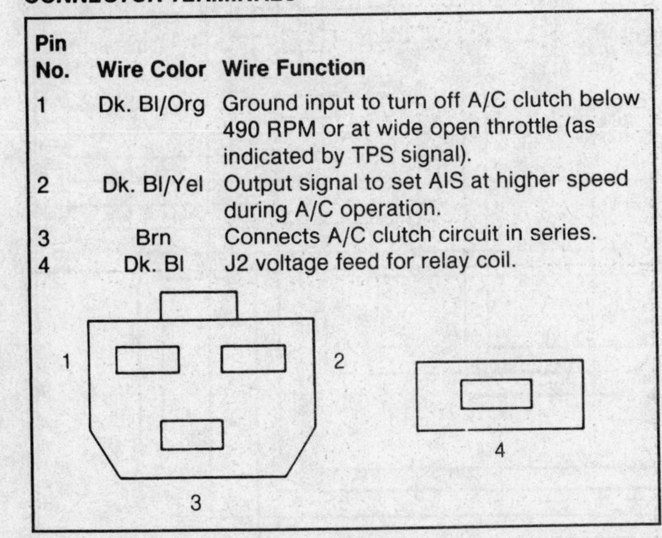

Pin No.	Wire Color	Wire Function
1	Dk. Bl/Org	Ground input to turn off A/C clutch below 490 RPM or at wide open throttle (as indicated by TPS signal).
2	Dk. Bl/Yel	Output signal to set AIS at higher speed during A/C operation.
3	Brn	Connects A/C clutch circuit in series.
4	Dk. Bl	J2 voltage feed for relay coil.

CHARGE TEMPERATURE SENSOR CONNECTOR TERMINALS

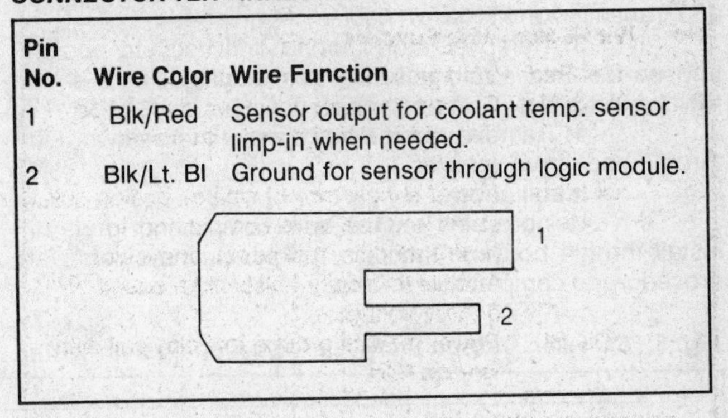

Pin No.	Wire Color	Wire Function
1	Blk/Red	Sensor output for coolant temp. sensor limp-in when needed.
2	Blk/Lt. Bl	Ground for sensor through logic module.

COOLANT TEMPERATURE SENSOR CONNECTOR TERMINALS

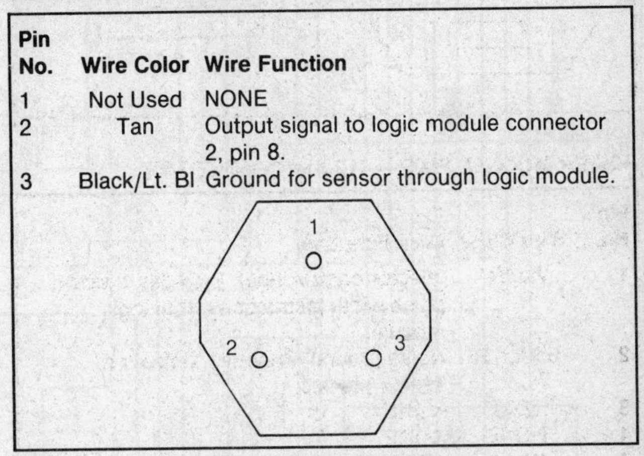

Pin No.	Wire Color	Wire Function
1	Not Used	NONE
2	Tan	Output signal to logic module connector 2, pin 8.
3	Black/Lt. Bl	Ground for sensor through logic module.

MAP SENSOR CONNECTOR TERMINALS

Pin No.	Wire Color	Wire Function
1	Vio	5 volt power supply from logic module.
2	Dk. Grn/Red	Sensor output to logic module connector 2, pin 4.
3	Blk/Lt. Bl	Ground for sensor through logic module.

1 2 3

REMOVAL & INSTALLATION

THROTTLE BODY

Removal

1) Release fuel system pressure. Disconnect battery negative cable. Disconnect fuel injector wiring connector and 6-way throttle body connector.

1983 Fuel Injection

CHRYSLER CORP. THROTTLE BODY (Cont.)

2) Remove ground wire from 6-way connector. Remove air cleaner hose, throttle cable and speed control and transmission kickdown cables (if equipped).

3) Remove return spring and vacuum hoses. Loosen fuel intake and return hose clamps. Using a shop towel, twist and pull off each hose.

4) Remove throttle body mounting screws. Lift throttle body from vehicle.

Installation

Using a new gasket, with tabs facing forward, install throttle body on intake manifold. Reverse removal procedure to complete installation.

AUTOMATIC IDLE SPEED (AIS) MOTOR

Removal

1) Disconnect battery negative cable and 6-way throttle body connector. Remove 2 screws that mount AIS to adaptor.

CAUTION: DO NOT remove clamp on AIS or damage will result.

2) Remove wiring clips and 2 AIS wires from 6-way throttle body connector. Using a small screwdriver, lift

Fig. 5: Chrysler Throttle Body Fuel Injection System Wiring Diagram

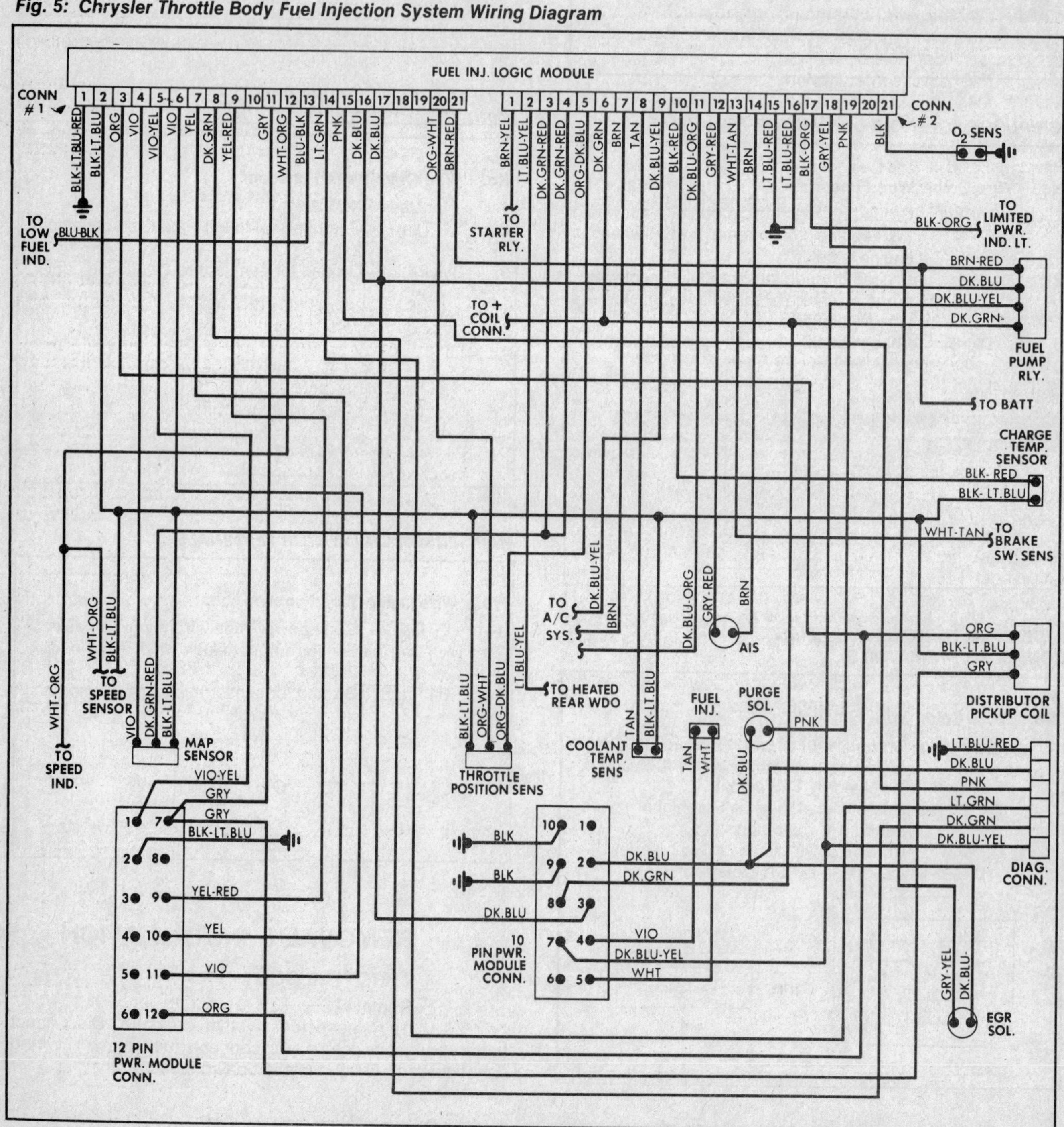

locking tab from inside 6-way throttle body connector for each TPS wire blade terminal.

3) Remove each blade from connector. Make note of wiring position for reassembly. Lift AIS from adaptor. Carefully remove 2 "O" rings from AIS.

Installation

To install, reverse removal procedure. Ensure wires are inserted into correct locations.

LOGIC MODULE

Removal & Installation

Remove right side kick panel. Remove 2 module mounting screws and wiring connectors. Remove module. To install, reverse removal procedure.

POWER MODULE

Removal & Installation

Remove air cleaner duct from power module. Remove battery. Remove 3 module mounting screws. Remove wiring connectors from module. Remove module. To install, reverse removal procedure.

MANIFOLD ABSOLUTE PRESSURE (MAP) SENSOR

Removal

Remove glove box assembly. Remove vacuum hose and wiring harness from sensor. Remove sensor mounting screws. Remove sensor.

Installation

To install, reverse removal procedure and check that vacuum hose is attached to bulkhead nipple.

THROTTLE POSITION SENSOR (TPS)

Removal

1) Disconnect battery negative cable and 6-way throttle body connector. Remove 2 screws mounting TPS to throttle body.

2) Unclip wiring clip from convoluted tube and remove mounting bracket. Lift TPS off throttle shaft. Remove "O" ring.

3) Pull 3 TPS wires off convoluted tubing. Using a small screwdriver, lift locking tab from inside 6-way throttle body connector for each TPS wire blade terminal.

4) Remove each blade from connector. Make note of wiring position for reassembly.

Installation

To install, reverse removal procedure. Ensure wires are inserted into correct locations.

FORD MOTOR CO. ELECTRONIC FUEL INJECTION

Ford
 Crown Victoria, Thunderbird
Lincoln
 Continental, Mark VI, Town Car
Mercury
 Cougar, Grand Marquis

DESCRIPTION

The Ford electronic fuel injection system (EFI) basically consists of 4 sub-assemblies: fuel delivery, air induction, engine sensors and the Electronic Control Assembly (ECA) of the Electronic Engine Control (EEC-III) system. The fuel delivery system includes an in-tank high pressure fuel pump, a primary fuel filter, a secondary fuel filter, fuel supply and return lines, fuel injectors and fuel pressure regulator.

The air induction system includes the throttle body, intake manifold and the cold engine speed control. Engine sensors are as follows: Throttle Position Sensor (TPS), Barometric and Manifold Absolute Pressure (B/MAP) sensors, Engine Coolant Temperature (ECT) sensor, Air Charge Temperature (ACT) sensor, EGR Valve Position (EVP) sensor, Crankshaft Position (CP) sensor and Exhaust Gas Oxygen (EGO) sensor.

OPERATION

FUEL DELIVERY

A high pressure electric fuel pump, located inside fuel tank, supplies fuel to the injectors. The pump receives power through starter relay, fuel pump relay, and EEC power relay. When ignition switch is turned to "ON" position, EEC power relay is activated, closing EEC power relay contacts. Power is provided to fuel pump relay and to a timer within the EEC module. If the ignition switch is not turned to the "START" position within 1 second, the EEC module timing device will deactivate the fuel pump relay. When the fuel pump relay is activated, fuel pump operates on low voltage. The fuel pump is deactivated when fuel pump relay is deactivated. This circuitry provides pre-pressurization of the fuel system.

When the ignition switch is turned to the "START" position, starter relay is energized. This relay provides power to starter motor and fuel pump, by-passing the fuel pump relay. This circuit provides full system voltage to fuel pump during cranking modes.

After the engine starts and the ignition switch is returned to "ON" position, power to fuel pump is again supplied through fuel pump relay. The EEC module senses engine RPM and deactivates the fuel pump when engine stops or engine speed falls below 120 RPM.

Fig. 1: Ford EEC-III/EFI System Components

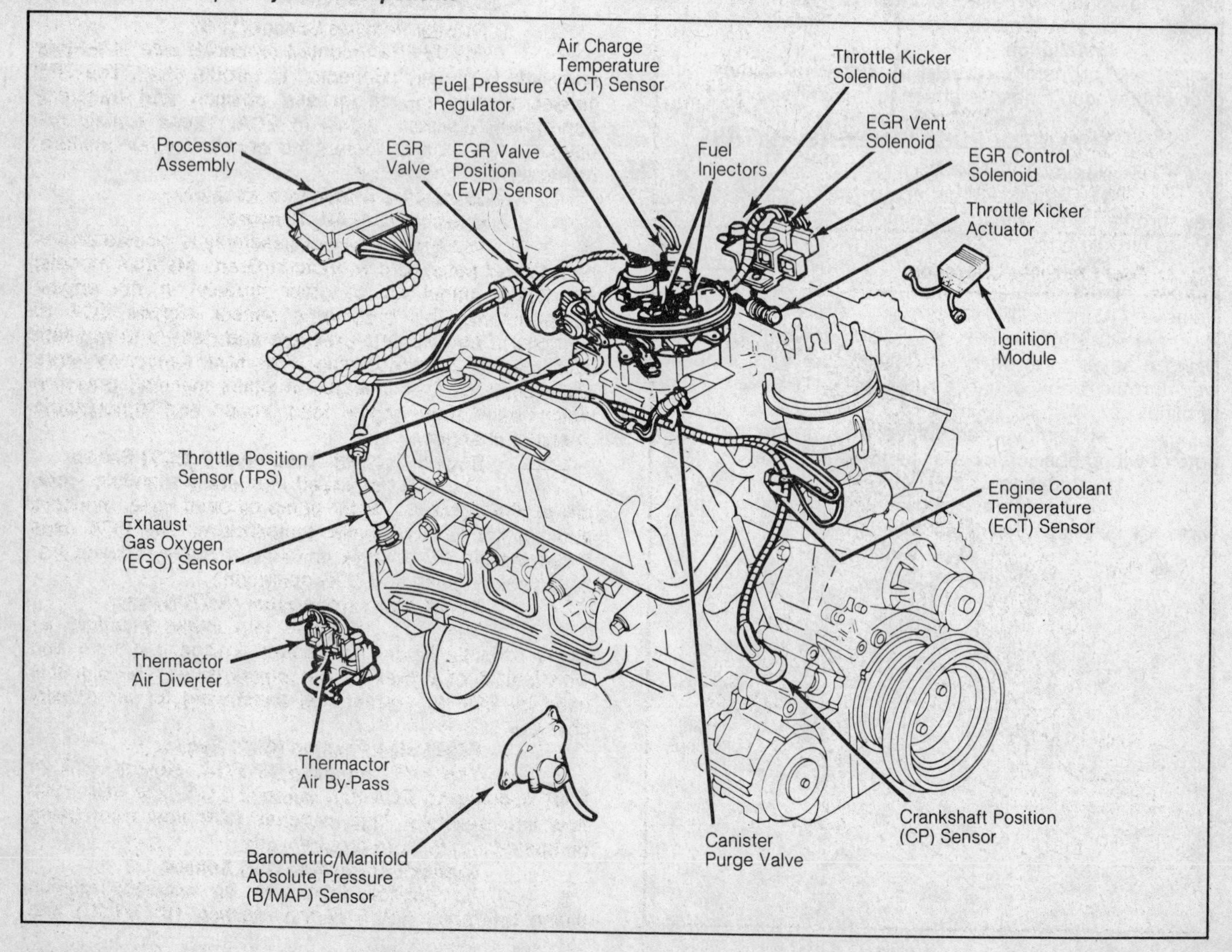

1983 Fuel Injection

FORD MOTOR CO. ELECTRONIC FUEL INJECTION (Cont.)

The inertia switch, located in the trunk, is designed to open the fuel pump power circuit in the event of a collision. This switch is reset by pushing both buttons on switch simultaneously. The switch should not be reset until fuel system has been inspected for damage or leaks.

Fuel is pumped through fuel filters to the fuel injectors and pressure regulator mounted on throttle body. The fuel pressure regulator controls fuel pressure to 39 psi (2.74 kg/cm²) across the fuel injectors. Fuel in excess of that used to maintain constant pressure is returned to fuel tank through the fuel return line.

Injectors are actuated, spraying calculated amount of fuel into engine, at twice the crankshaft speed. Only open time varies to satisfy fuel requirements.

Fig. 2: Inertia Switch Location

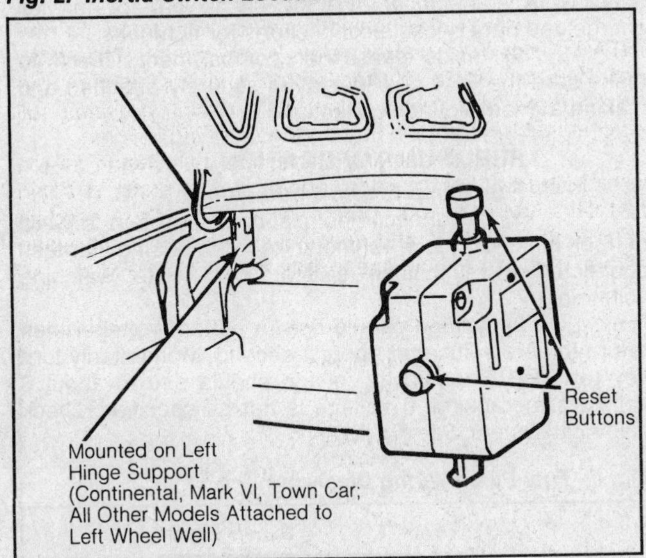

Fig. 3: Fuel Charging Operation

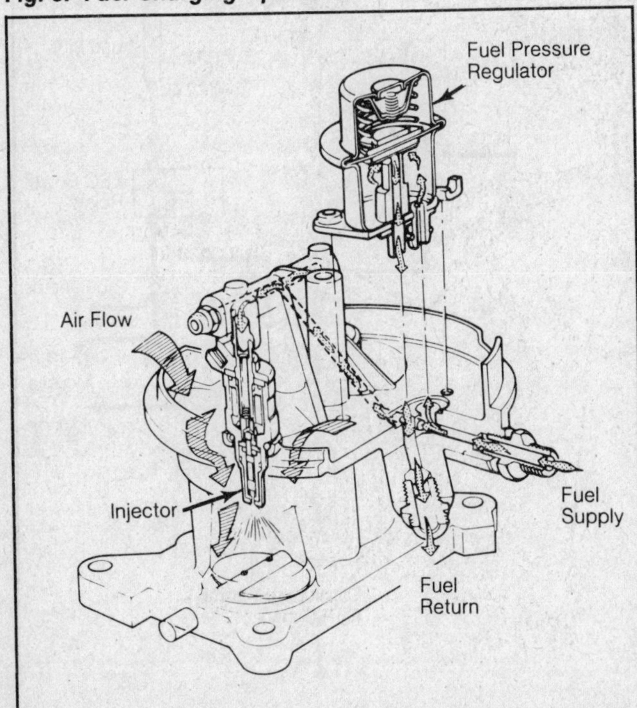

Fig. 4 Cutaway View of Injector Valve

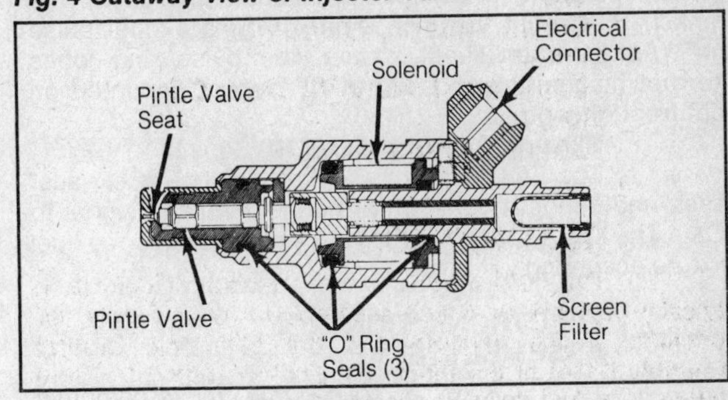

AIR INDUCTION

Air enters the engine through the throttle body at a rate controlled by the throttle valves, which are connected to the accelerator linkage. Fast idle speed position (cold engine speed control) of the throttle valves is controlled by a fast idle cam connected to and positioned by a bimetal spring (similar to a conventional automatic choke bimetal). The fast idle cam drops, reducing fast idle, as bimetal is heated by an electric heating element and is assisted by a vacuum controlled kickdown mechanism.

ENGINE SENSORS

Throttle Position Sensor (TPS)

The TPS is mounted on choke side of throttle body and is directly connected to throttle shaft. The TPS senses throttle movement and position and transmits appropriate electrical signal to ECA. These signals are used by the ECA to determine proper fuel/air mixture, spark and EGR operation.

Barometric & Manifold Absolute Pressure (B/MAP) Sensors

The B/MAP sensor assembly is located on the right fender panel (Crown Victoria/Grand Marquis models; left fender panel on all other models) in the engine compartment. The barometric sensor signals ECA of changes in atmospheric pressure and density to regulate calculated air flow into engine. The MAP sensor monitors and signals ECA of changes in intake manifold pressure which result from engine load, speed and atmospheric pressure changes.

Engine Coolant Temperature (ECT) Sensor

The ECT, threaded into intake manifold water jacket directly above water pump by-pass hose, monitors and signals ECA of water temperature. The ECA uses these signals for mixture enrichment during cold operation, ignition timing and EGR operation.

Air Charge Temperature (ACT) Sensor

The ACT, threaded into intake manifold air runner directly below accelerator linkage, monitors and signals ECA of air/fuel charge temperatures. This signal is used by ECA to correct fuel enrichment for air density changes.

EGR Valve Position (EVP) Sensor

The EVP, mounted to EGR, signals ECA of EGR opening so ECA can subtract EGR flow from total flow into manifold. This excludes EGR flow from being computed into mixture requirements.

Crankshaft Position (CP) Sensor

To provide ECA with an accurate ignition timing reference (when piston reaches 10° BTDC) and

FORD MOTOR CO. ELECTRONIC FUEL INJECTION (Cont.)

injector operation (twice each crankshaft revolution), the crankshaft vibration damper is fitted with a 4-lobe "pulse ring". As the crankshaft rotates, the pulse ring lobes interrupt magnetic field at tip of CP sensor (mounted on right front of engine).

Exhaust Gas Oxygen (EGO) Sensor

The EGO monitors oxygen content of exhaust gases and sends a constantly changing voltage signal to ECA. The ECA analyzes signal and changes air/fuel mixture accordingly.

ELECTRONIC CONTROL ASSEMBLY (ECA)

The ECA is a solid state micro-computer consisting of a processor assembly and a calibration assembly. This unit is located in the passenger compartment under the instruent panel. The ECA is the "brain" of the EEC-III/EFI system.

Processor Assembly

The processor assembly is housed in an aluminum case and contains circuits designed to continuously sample input signals from sensors, calculate and send out proper control signals to adjust air/fuel ratio, spark timing and emission system operation. The processor also provides a continuous reference voltage of 8-10 volts to some of the sensors (B/MAP, EVP and TPS).

Calibration Assembly

The calibration assembly is contained in a black plastic housing which plugs into the top of the processor assembly. It contains the "memory" and programming used to provide the processor assembly with operating information for that particular vehicle and recalls information from its memory when required.

NOTE: **Different calibration information is used in different vehicle applications, such as Federal and California.**

TESTING & DIAGNOSIS

NOTE: **Due to the complexity of the EEC-III system, full testing cannot be done unless a special tester is used. Instructions for testing come with the tester, which is available from Owatonna Tool Co. However, some checks can be made using regular shop equipment. These checks are outlined in the following procedures:**

1) No repairs or adjustments can be made to the ECA components. If diagnosis shows Processor or Calibration units are not functioning properly, they must be replaced.

2) Shorting the wiring harness across a solenoid valve can burn out circuitry in the ECA that controls the solenoid valve actuator.

3) The EEC system contains transistors which CANNOT tolerate excessive voltage surges or transient voltage. Never try to jump-start the vehicle with 24 volts.

4) Fuel supply lines will remain pressurized for long periods of time after key is turned off. This pressure must be relieved before servicing fuel system by removing air cleaner and cautiously depressing pin in Schrader valve on fuel charging main body. This will expel fuel into throttle body.

BASIC EEC-III/EFI TROUBLE SHOOTING

1) Perform basic ignition system and fuel system checks to ensure there is fuel and spark.

2) Remove air cleaner assembly and inspect all vacuum and pressure hoses for proper connection to fittings, or any broken, cracked or pinched conditions.

3) Inspect EFI sub-system wiring harnesses for proper connections to the EGR solenoid valves. Red wire to both, Yellow wire to vacuum solenoid and Dark Green wire to vent solenoid.

4) Check for any loose or detached connectors, broken or detached wires. Ensure all terminals are seated firmly and are not corroded. Check for partially broken or frayed wires or any shorting between wires.

5) Inspect sensors for physical damage. Inspect vehicle electrical system. Check battery for full charge and battery cable connections for tightness.

6) Inside passenger compartment, check to make sure the ECA power relay is securely attached and making a good ground connection.

FUEL PUMP OPERATION

Fuel Pump Electrical Continuity

1) Disconnect electrical connector just forward of fuel tank. Connect voltmeter to body wiring harness connector. Turn ignition switch "ON" while watching voltmeter.

2) Voltage should rise to battery voltage, then return to zero volts after about 1 second. Momentarily turn key to "START" position. Voltage should rise to about 8 volts while cranking. If voltage is not as specified, check electrical system. *See Fig. 5.*

Fig. 5: Fuel Pump Wiring Diagram

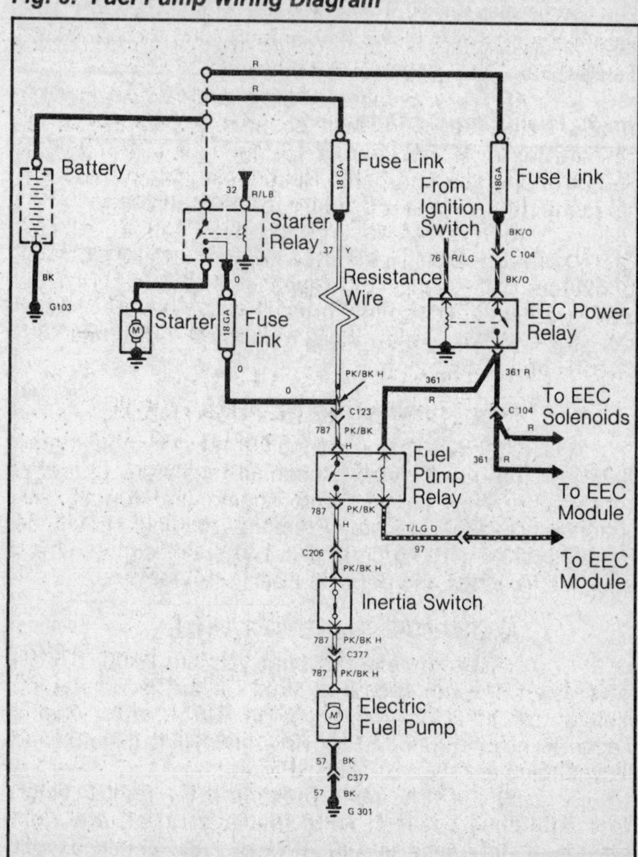

1983 Fuel Injection

FORD MOTOR CO. ELECTRONIC FUEL INJECTION (Cont.)

Fuel Pump Operation

1) Disconnect fuel return line at fuel charging main body and connect hose to a calibrated container (at least 1 quart capacity). Connect pressure gauge to fuel pressure test fitting.

2) Disconnect electrical connector to fuel pump located ahead of fuel tank. Connect an auxiliary wiring harness to connector of fuel pump. Energize pump for 10 seconds by connecting wiring harness to fully charged 12 volt battery. Observe fuel pressure while pump is energized. Allow fuel to drain into container and observe volume of fuel discharged. De-energize pump and note pressure.

3) The fuel pump is operating properly if fuel pressure reaches 35-45 psi (2.46-3.16 kg/cm²), fuel flow is 10 ozs. in 10 seconds (minimum) and fuel pressure maintains minimum 30 psi (.2 kg/cm²) immediately after de-energization. If all 3 conditions are met, check for engine and electrical problems.

4) If pressure condition is met, but fuel flow is not met, check for blocked filter(s) and fuel supply lines. After correcting problem, repeat test procedure. If fuel flow still does not meet specifications, replace fuel pump.

5) If flow specification is met, but pressure is not met, check for worn or damaged pressure regulator valve on throttle body. If both pressure and fuel flow specifications are met, but pressure will not maintain after de-energization, check for leaking injector valve(s) and/or pressure regulator valve. If injector valve(s) and pressure regulator valve are okay, replace fuel pump.

INJECTOR PRESSURE TEST

1) Connect pressure gauge to fuel pressure test fitting. Disconnect coil connector from coil. Disconnect electrical lead from one injector and pressurize fuel system. Disable fuel pump by disconnecting inertia switch or fuel pump relay. Observe pressure gauge reading.

2) Crank engine for 2 seconds. Turn ignition off and wait 5 seconds, then observe pressure drop. If pressure drop is between 2-16 psi (.14-1.12 kg/cm²), injector is operating properly. Reconnect injector, activate fuel pump, then repeat procedure for other injector.

3) If pressure drop is less than 2 psi (.14 kg/cm²) or more than 16 psi (1.12 kg/cm²), switch electrical connectors on injectors and repeat test. If pressure drop does not meet specification, replace disconnected injector with same color code, then reconnect both injectors properly and repeat test.

FUEL PRESSURE REGULATOR TEST

Reconnect coil connector at coil and inertia switch or fuel pump relay. Reconnect injectors properly. Connect pressure gauge. Start engine and run at idle. Observe pressure reading. Pressure reading should be 35-45 psi (2.46-3.16 kg/cm²). If not to specification, check fuel lines for kinks and perform Fuel Pump tests.

MARGINAL INJECTOR TEST

1) Disconnect and plug vacuum hose to EGR valve. Start and run engine at 1800 RPM. Disconnect left injector electrical connector. Note RPM after engine stabilizes around 1200 RPM. Reconnect left injector and allow engine to return to 1800 RPM.

2) Perform same procedure for right injector. Note difference between RPM readings of left and right injector. If difference is 100 RPM or less, check oxygen sensor. If difference is more than 100 RPM, replace both injectors.

NOTE: **Refer to "FORD MOTOR CO. EEC-III ENGINE CONTROL SYSTEM" in Computerized Engine controls section for test of oxygen sensor.**

REMOVAL & INSTALLATION

CAUTION: **Fuel system is pressurized to 39 psi (2.74 kg/cm²). For safety, cover valve at end of fuel rail with rag when relieving pressure in fuel lines.**

THROTTLE BODY ASSEMBLY

Removal

Remove air cleaner assembly. Relieve fuel pressure at Schrader valve on end of injector rail. Remove all throttle control linkage, vacuum lines, fuel lines and electrical connections. Remove throttle body retaining nuts and throttle body.

Installation

Install throttle body assembly in reverse order of removal, using new gasket between throttle body and intake manifold. Check TV cable adjustment after replacement of throttle body assembly.

FUEL INJECTORS & FUEL PRESSURE REGULATOR

NOTE: **Metric fasteners are painted blue.**

Removal

1) Remove throttle body assembly. Place on suitable stand, in inverted position. Remove 4 screws from base of throttle body. Remove throttle body from upper fuel charging body.

2) Remove 3 fuel pressure regulator retaining screws and remove regulator. Remove nut holding injector retaining bracket to upper body and remove retaining bracket. Disconnect wiring harness from injectors and remove injectors from upper body, noting location of each.

Installation

1) Replace injector "O" rings and lubricate with light oil. Push injectors into their original location, install retainer bracket and nut.

2) Replace pressure regulator "O" ring and gasket and lubricate "O" ring with light oil. Install pressure regulator and 3 screws. Install connectors to injectors and install throttle body to manifold.

FAST IDLE BIMETAL & PULLDOWN ASSEMBLY

Removal

1) Note position of index mark on choke cap housing. Drill rivet heads from bimetal cover retaining ring with a .128" (No. 30) drill. Drive remaining portion of rivet body from housing. Remove bimetal cover retaining ring and cover.

2) Remove thermostat lever screw and lever. Remove fast idle cam assembly. Remove fast idle control rod positioner. Hold pulldown diaphragm cover tightly in position. Remove 2 screws and fast idle pulldown cover. Remove spring, spring retainer and pulldown diaphragm.

FORD MOTOR CO. ELECTRONIC FUEL INJECTION (Cont.)

Fig. 6: Exploded View of Throttle Body & Fuel Charging Assembly

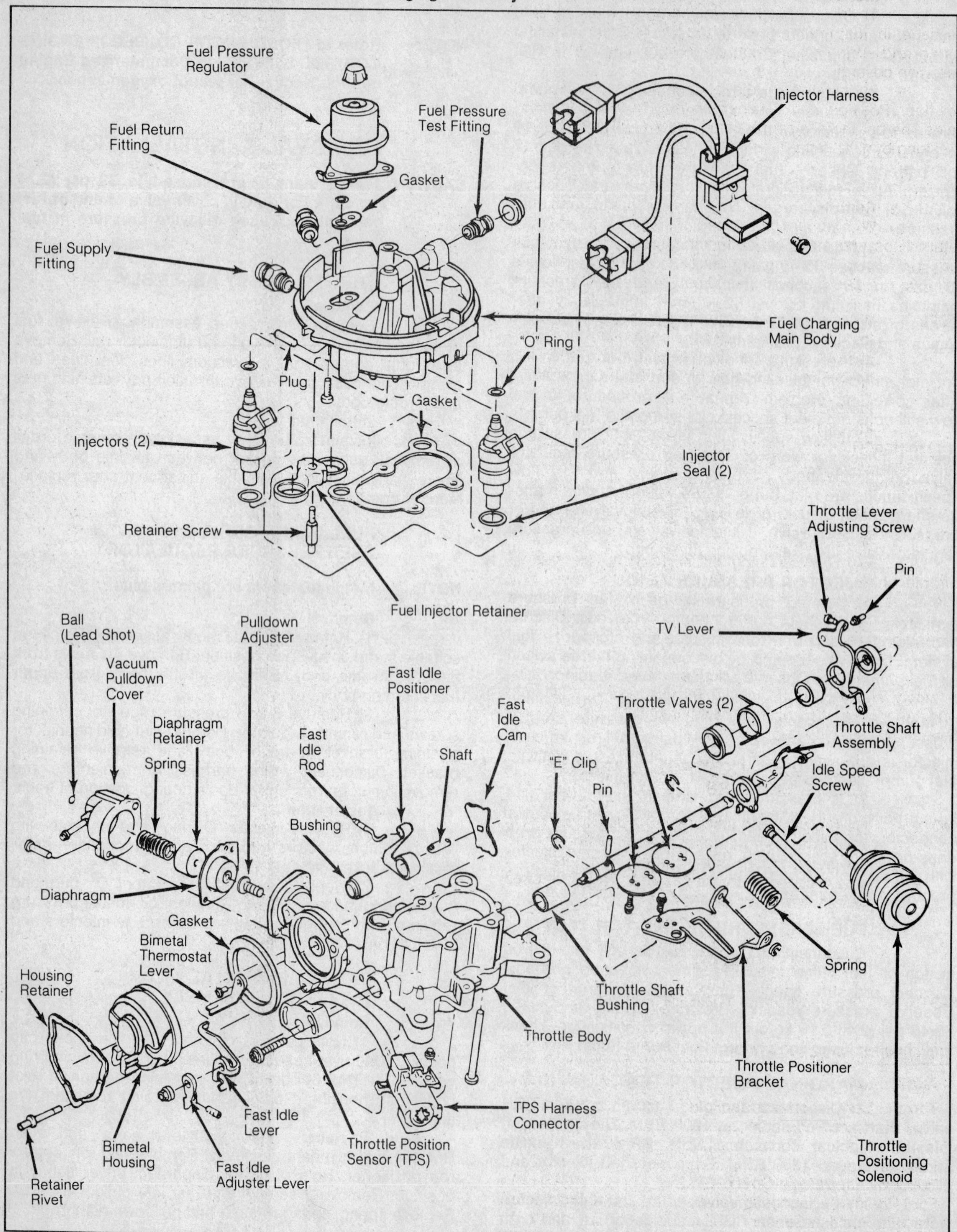

FORD MOTOR CO. ELECTRONIC FUEL INJECTION (Cont.)

Installation

1) Install pulldown diaphragm with vacuum passage in diaphragm toward top of housing. Holding spring and spring retainer on diaphragm, carefully install pulldown cover and screws.

2) Install fast idle control bimetal to original position. Position cap retainer on cap, making sure all holes line up. Install new retaining rivets (1/8" diameter by 1/2" long by 1/4" head).

FUEL PUMP

Removal

With fuel tank removed, disconnect supply and return lines and electrical connector. Using suitable tool, turn fuel pump lock ring counterclockwise and remove. Remove fuel pump assembly and seal. Discard seal.

NOTE: **Whenever the fuel pump is removed from the tank, the rubber hoses, clamps and mounting gasket must be replaced. If not replaced, hoses could become brittle and deteriorate.**

Installation

Install new seal and hold in place with heavy grease. Install gasket, pump unit and locking ring, making sure seal does not move. Reconnect fuel lines and electrical connector. Install fuel tank.

THROTTLE POSITION SENSOR (TPS)

Removal

Remove retaining nut from fast idle side of throttle shaft. Remove fast idle cam adjuster lever, fast idle actuating lever and "E" clip from throttle shaft. Scribe a locating mark on TPS and throttle body, remove TPS retaining screws and TPS.

Installation

Install TPS with scribe mark at 12 o'clock position. Holding firmly against throttle body, rotate into original position and install screws. Install "E" clip, fast idle levers and retaining nut.

ELECTRONIC CONTROL ASSEMBLY (ECA) & SENSORS

NOTE: **No removal and installation procedures available from manufacturer. If engine sensors are removed, install using sealing compound on threads. Refer to Description and Operation in this article for locations.**

ADJUSTMENTS

NOTE: **See appropriate TUNE-UP article.**

TIGHTENING SPECIFICATIONS

Application	INCH Lbs. (N.m)
Throttle Body-to-Intake Manifold	120 (13.5)
Fuel Pressure Regulator	27-40 (3.0-4.5)
Injector Bracket	30-60 (3.4-6.8)
Fast Idle Lever Nut	18 (2.0)
Pulldown Diaphragm Cover	16 (1.8)
Fuel Pressure Diagnostic Valve	48-84 (5.4-9.5)
Throttle Position Sensor	12 (1.4)

1983 Fuel Injection

FORD MOTOR CO. MULTI-POINT FUEL INJECTION

Ford
Escort, EXP (1.6L)
Thunderbird Turbo Coupe (2.3L Turbo)
Mustang (2.3L Turbo)
Mercury
Lynx, LN7 (1.6L)
Capri (2.3L Turbo)

NOTE: **Information for the 2.3L Turbo engine is limited to description and operation. Information was not available from manufacturer at time of publication.**

DESCRIPTION

The Ford multi-point fuel injection system consists of 4 basic sub-systems: fuel delivery, air induction, engine sensors and the Electronic Control Assembly (ECA) of the EEC-IV computer. The fuel delivery system includes a high pressure fuel pump and the fuel charging manifold assembly (including the fuel injectors and fuel pressure regulator). The 2.3L Turbo engine is equipped with a low pressure, in-tank fuel pump which delivers fuel to chassis-mounted high pressure pump.

The air induction system consists of the air cleaner, air vane meter assembly, throttle body and intake manifold. Engine sensors supply the ECA with engine operating information. These sensors are the throttle position sensor, engine coolant sensor, vane air flow sensor, vane air temperature sensor and oxygen sensor.

The Electronic Control Assembly (ECA) is the "brain" of the system. Information supplied to the ECA by the engine sensors is interpreted as specific engine operating conditions. The ECA then controls engine functions to produce ideal air/fuel mixture and ignition timing in response to these conditions.

Fig. 2: 2.3L Turbo Engine Multi-Point Injection System

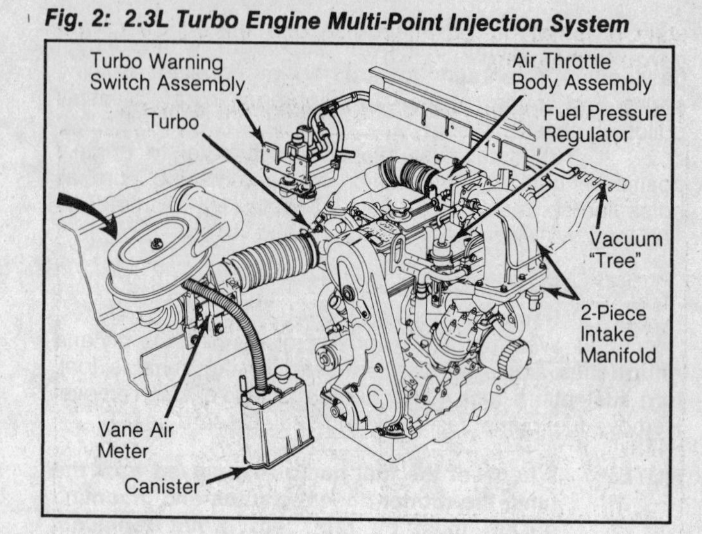

OPERATION

FUEL DELIVERY

On the 1.6L engine, a high pressure fuel pump draws fuel from tank and delivers it to fuel charging manifold assembly. Power to pump is supplied through the fuel pump relay (located on a bracket above the ECA) and inertia switch. Operation of the fuel pump relay is controlled by the ECA module which regulates power to the pump, based on changing engine operating conditions.

The fuel pump relay is activated by the ECA with ignition switch in "START" or "RUN" positions. When ignition switch is turned to either position, the relay is activated to supply initial line pressure to system. If engine

Fig. 1: 1.6L Engine Multi-Point Injection System

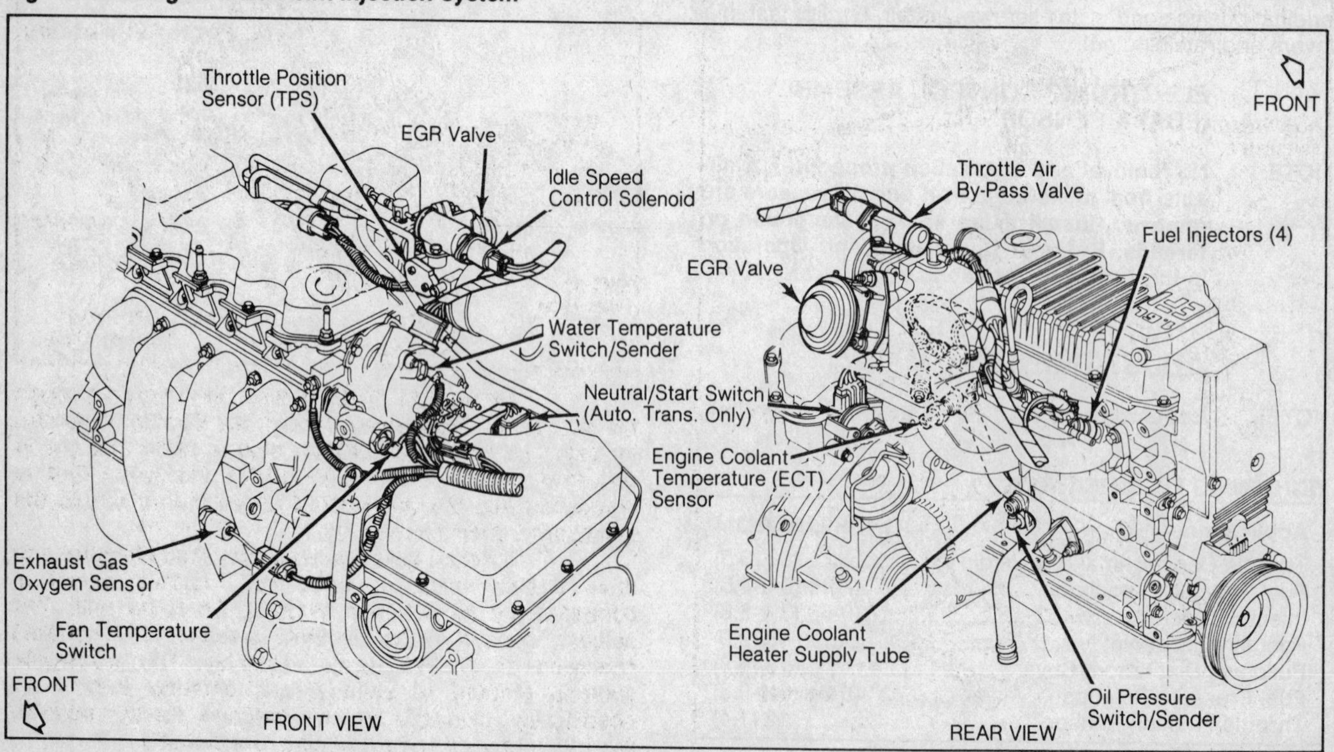

FORD MOTOR CO. MULTI-POINT FUEL INJECTION (Cont.)

stalls or is not started within 1 second, the ECA shuts off power to the pump.

Fig. 3: 1.6L Engine Fuel Charging Manifold Assembly

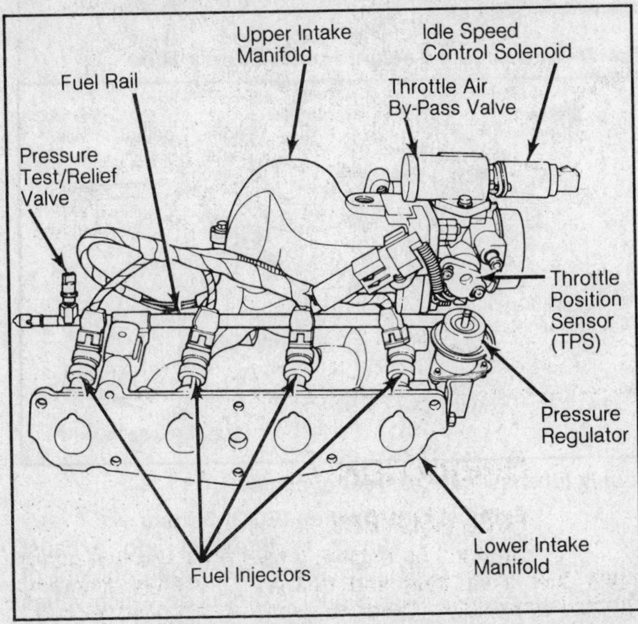

The inertia switch is located behind left rear kick panel. It is designed to open the fuel pump power circuit in the event of a collision. This switch must be manually reset by pushing the button on top of the switch. The inertia switch should not be reset until fuel system has been inspected for damage or leaks.

Fig. 4: 2.3L Turbo Fuel Charging Manifold Assembly

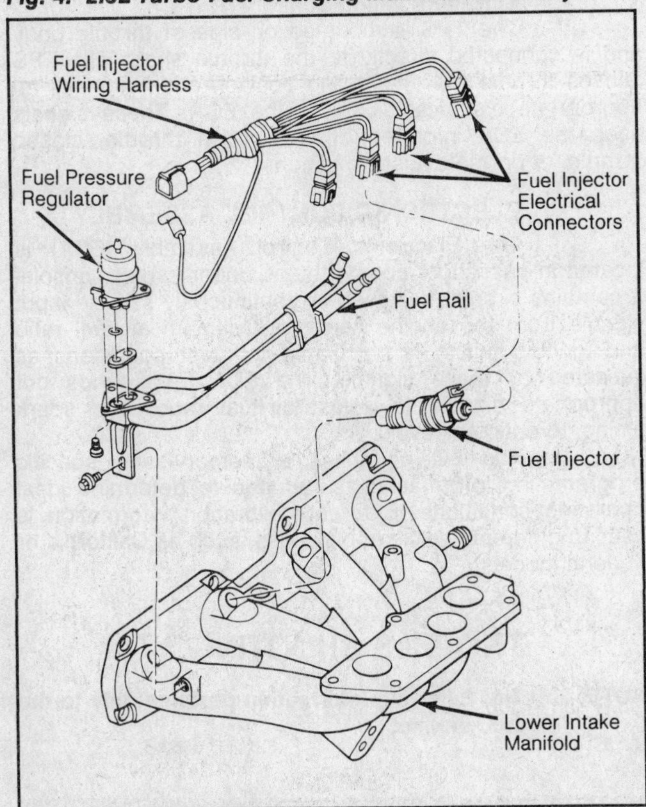

Fuel is pumped through fuel lines to fuel injectors and pressure regulator, mounted on fuel rail. The injectors are fitted into the air intake manifold just above intake valves. Fuel pressure at injectors is maintained at a constant value by pressure regulator. Fuel supplied by fuel pump in excess of that required for engine operation is by-passed by the regulator and returned to fuel tank via fuel return line.

All injectors are energized, simultaneously, once every crankshaft revolution. Engine fuel requirements are satisfied by varying amount of time that injectors are left open (injector "on" time). This injector "on" time is determined and controlled by the ECA.

The 2.3L Turbo engine fuel delivery system uses an in-tank, low pressure fuel pump to deliver fuel to chassis-mounted high pressure fuel pump. Control and operation of fuel delivery system is performed by the ECA of the EEC-IV computer, similar to the 1.6L engine. Specific detailed information was not available from manufacturer at time of publication.

AIR INDUCTION

On the 1.6L engine, air enters the engine through the throttle assembly at a rate controlled by the throttle valve, which is connected to conventional throttle linkage.

An air by-pass channel is incorporated into assembly to satisfy both cold and warm idle air flow requirements when throttle valve is in a fully closed position. Air flow through by-pass channel is controlled by air by-pass valve which is mounted directly to throttle body. Air by-pass valve function is in turn controlled by signals from the ECA.

Fig. 5: 1.6L Engine Air Induction System

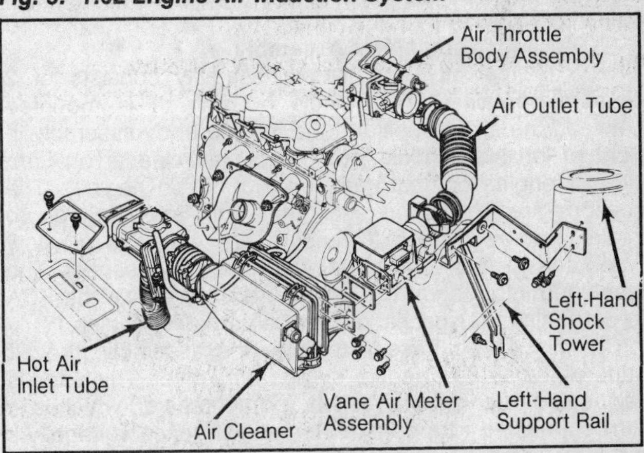

On the 2.3L Turbo engine, air is drawn through the air cleaner and passes through the throttle assembly. Incoming air enters compressor side of turbo unit and is delivered under pressure to intake manifold. Fuel is introduced into the pressurized air as the air enters the combustion chamber. *See Fig. 6.*

Exhaust gases leave combustion chamber and drive turbine wheel of turbo unit. Turbine speed is controlled by an actuator mounted on turbo unit. The actuator senses intake manifold pressure and controls operation of the wastegate assembly. The wastegate controls amount of exhaust gas entering turbine by opening and closing a by-pass passage, thereby controlling turbine speed and preventing "overboost".

FORD MOTOR CO. MULTI-POINT FUEL INJECTION (Cont.)

Fig. 6: 2.3L Turbo Engine Air Induction System

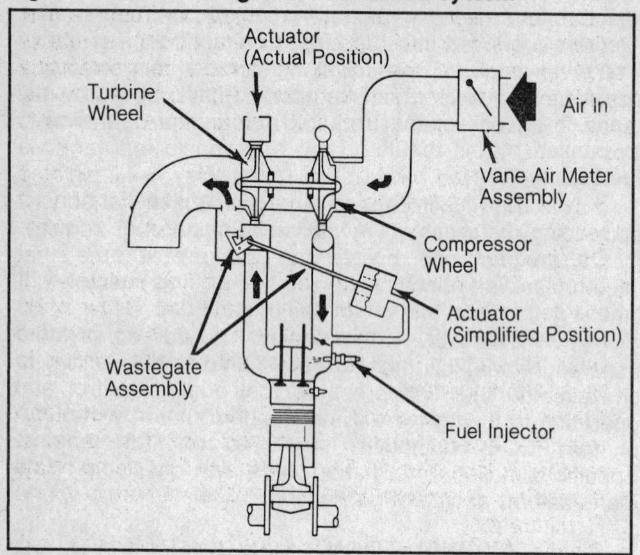

This is a simplified drawing to graphically show air induction system. Components are not positioned as they may appear on engine.

ENGINE SENSORS

In order for the ECA to properly perform its function, it must be kept constantly informed of engine operating conditions. It is the function of the engine sensors to supply the ECA, via electrical signal, with specific information as required to determine engine operating conditions. The ECA can then send out electrical signals of its own to control fuel flow (determining air/fuel ratio) and ignition timing. Individual sensor operation is as follows:

Air Vane Meter Assembly

The air vane meter assembly consists of 2 sensors contained in a single housing. It is mounted between the air cleaner and the throttle body assembly in front of left side shock tower (under air cleaner on right side of engine compartment on 2.3L turbo engine). The sensors are positioned such that both are exposed to intake air flow. These 2 sensors are the vane air flow (VAF) sensor and vane air temperature (VAT) sensor. The combined information from these sensors allows the ECA to determine the specific mass of air entering engine.

As air passes through the assembly, the air vane of the air flow sensor swings on a pivot. This vane is connected to a variable resistor (potentiometer) which is in turn connected to a constant 5 volt reference voltage. As air vane angle changes, so does voltage signal from potentiometer to the ECA. This voltage signal, therefore, represents a specific rate of air flow. When this information is combined with incoming air temperature information, as supplied by air temperature sensor, the actual mass of air entering the engine can be determined.

NOTE: **The following information pertains only to the 1.6L engine. No information was available from manufacturer for the 2.3L Turbo engine at time of publication.**

Engine Coolant Temperature (ECT) Sensor

The ECT sensor, located in engine coolant heater supply tube at rear of engine, monitors and signals the ECA of engine coolant temperature. This information is interpreted by the ECA as either cold or normal operating temperature. This information particularly influences ECA control of fuel mixture enrichment and EGR operation. *See Fig. 7.*

Fig. 7: 1.6L Engine Coolant Heater Supply Tube

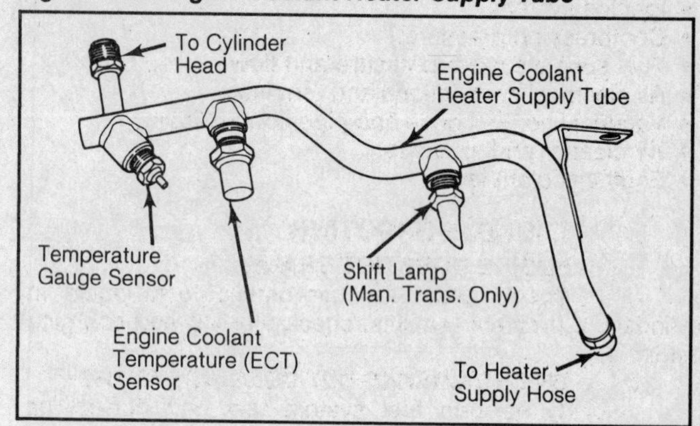

Supply tube is located at rear of engine.

Exhaust Gas Oxygen (EGO) Sensor

The EGO sensor is threaded into exhaust manifold where it constantly monitors oxygen content of exhaust gases. A voltage signal is produced which varies according to difference in oxygen content between exhaust gases and surrounding atmosphere. This signal is sent to the ECA.

Since oxygen content of exhaust gases is directly related to air/fuel ratio of the fuel mixture, the ECA can translate exhaust gas oxygen content to air/fuel ratio. It can then alter fuel delivery rate as needed to deliver the ideal ratio for current engine operating conditions.

Throttle Position Sensor (TPS)

The TPS is mounted on side of throttle body and is connected directly to the throttle shaft. The TPS senses throttle movement and position and transmits an appropriate electrical signal to the ECA. These signals keep the ECA informed of wide open throttle, closed throttle, or normal cruise conditions.

ELECTRONIC CONTROL ASSEMBLY

The Electronic Control Assembly (ECA) is located in passenger compartment, under center console. It contains circuits designed to continuously sample input signals from the engine sensors. Optimum air/fuel ratio and ignition timing is calculated to meet conditions as indicated by these signals. The ECA then sends out appropriate signals to adjust air/fuel ratio, and spark timing, to optimum levels.

The ECA contains a memory and specific programming information as required to determine ideal operating conditions. Different calibration information is used in different vehicle applications, such as California or Federal models.

TROUBLE SHOOTING

NOTE: **The following information pertains only to the 1.6L engine.**

FORD MOTOR CO. MULTI-POINT FUEL INJECTION (Cont.)

PRELIMINARY CHECKS

The following systems and components must be in good condition and operating properly before beginning diagnosis of the fuel injection system:

- All support systems and wiring.
- Battery connections and specific gravity.
- Ignition system.
- Compression pressure.
- Fuel supply system pressure and flow.
- All electrical connections and terminals.
- Vacuum line, fuel hose and pipe connections.
- Air cleaner and air ducts.
- Engine coolant level.

TROUBLE SHOOTING

ENGINE DOES NOT CRANK

Check and clear hydrostatic lock (liquid in cylinder). If problem remains, check starting and charging systems.

ENGINE CRANKS BUT DOES NOT START

1) Perform fuel system test and correct as required. Repair any known fuel leaks before proceeding with test. If problem remains, continue trouble shooting procedure.

2) Check ignition system. Ensure spark plugs, ignition coil, distributor and wiring are operating properly. If problem remains, continue trouble shooting procedure.

3) Perform fuel pump test and correct as required. If vehicle still does not start, test fuel pump circuit, injectors and injector circuit. If problem remains, continue trouble shooting procedure.

4) Perform sensor tests and repair as required. If vehicle still does not start, problem is not located within the fuel injection system. Check for other engine malfunctions which may prevent engine from starting (basic timing, ignition system, charging system, etc.).

TESTING & DIAGNOSIS

FUEL SYSTEM

1) Connect fuel pressure gauge to pressure relief valve on fuel rail assembly. *See Fig. 3.* Pressurize fuel system by starting and running engine or turning ignition off and to "RUN" position several times. Fuel pressure should be 35-45 psi (2.5-3.0 kg/cm²).

2) If pressure is not correct, check to ensure ignition coil is connected. Ensure that injectors, fuel pressure regulator or fuel delivery lines and connections are not leaking.

3) If no pressure reading can be obtained, check fuel pump circuit. When fuel pressure is obtained, turn key off. Pressure must not drop more than 4 psi (.3 kg/cm²) within 2 minutes after ignition is turned off.

4) If pressure drops more than specified, check for hydrostatic lock, leaking injector and/or faulty pressure regulator.

FUEL PUMP CIRCUIT

1) Fuel pump operation is satisfactory if the following conditions are met: Operating pressure is 35-45 psi (2.5-3.0 kg/cm²), fuel flow is at least 7.5 ounces in 10 seconds and fuel pressure remains at a minimum of 30 psi (2.1 kg/cm²) immediately after deactivation. If all conditions are met, check for engine or electrical problems.

2) Turn ignition to "RUN" position with engine off. Connect negative lead of a digital volt/ohm meter (DVOM) to good chassis ground. Connect positive lead of DVOM to each of the following circuits to completely check fuel pump circuit. If an open fusible link is located, repair short or ground in circuit before replacing fusible link.

- Circuit 361 (Red wire) at fuel pump relay — If reading is less than 10.5 volts, recharge or replace battery. If reading is greater than 10.5 volts, circuit is okay. Continue test.
- Circuit 37 (Yellow wire) at fuel pump relay — If reading is less than 10.5 volts, locate and repair open between fuel pump relay and vehicle battery positive post. If reading is greater than 10.5 volts, circuit is okay. Continue test.
- Circuit 97 (Tan wire with Light Green dot) at fuel pump relay — Insert positive lead and crank engine. If reading is less than 10.5 volts, replace fuel pump relay. If reading is greater than 10.5 volts, circuit is okay. Continue test.
- Circuit 787 (Pink wire with Black hash mark) at fuel pump relay — Insert positive lead and crank engine. If reading is less than 10.5 volts, replace fuel pump relay. If reading is greater than 10.5 volts, circuit is okay. Continue test.
- Locate inertia switch. Perform test at both terminals during engine cranking. If reading is less than 10.5 volts at 1 terminal, replace inertia switch. If reading is less than 10.5 volts at both terminals, locate and repair open between inertia switch and fuel pump relay. If reading is greater than 10.5 volts, inertia switch is okay. Continue test.
- Circuit 787 (Pink wire with Black hash mark) at fuel pump — Insert lead and crank engine. If reading is less than 10.5 volts, locate and repair open between inertia switch and fuel pump. If reading is greater than 10.5 volts, circuit is okay. Continue test.
- Circuit 57 (Black wire) at fuel pump — Insert lead and crank engine. If reading is greater than 1 volt, locate and repair fuel pump ground circuit. If reading is less than 1 volt, service or repair fuel pump.

INJECTORS

1) Pressurize fuel system and disconnect wiring connectors from all 4 injectors. Connect a fuel pressure gauge to pressure relief valve on fuel rail. Connect 1 injector at a time and crank engine for 5 seconds. Record pressure immediately after cranking.

2) Repeat procedure for all 4 injectors. Pressure readings of all injectors should be within 4 psi (.3 kg/cm²) of each other. If any injector is outside this range it must be replaced.

INJECTOR CIRCUIT

1) Connect a non-powered 12 volt test lamp between pins 11 and 3 of ECA plug J2. Crank engine and note results. Then connect test lamp between pins 11 and 4 of ECA plug J2.

2) If test lamp does not glow on 1 or both tests, verify that battery voltage is recorded at pin 11 of plug J2. If voltage is not present, repair wire or replace battery. If voltage is present, replace ECA. If test lamp glows brightly on 1 or both tests, check circuits 95 (Tan wire with Purple dot) and 96 (Tan wire with Orange dot) to

FORD MOTOR CO. MULTI-POINT FUEL INJECTION (Cont.)

injectors. If test lamp glows dimly on both tests, circuits are okay. Continue test.

3) Remove test lamp and fuel pump relay. Using a DVOM, measure voltage between same pins tested in step **1)** while cranking engine. If difference between voltage readings is more than 1 volt, disconnect ECA plugs and inspect for corroded or damaged pins. Reconnect plugs and retest. If voltage readings still vary more than 1 volt, replace ECA. If voltage difference is less than 1 volt, circuits are okay. Continue test.

4) Reconnect fuel pump relay. Turn ignition off. Disconnect electrical connectors at injectors 2, 3, and 4. Set DVOM on 20 ohm range and measure resistance between pins 3 and 11 of ECA plug J2 (injector 1). Record reading. Disconnect electrical connector at injector 1 and reconnect connector at injector 2. Measure resistance between same pins again. Record reading.

5) Disconnect electrical connector at injector 2 and reconnect connector at injector 3. Measure resistance between pins 4 and 11 of plug J2. Record reading. Disconnect electrical connector at injector 3 and reconnect connector at injector 4. Measure resistance between same pins again. Record reading.

6) If all 4 readings in steps **4)** and **5)** are not 2.0-3.5 ohms, check wiring harness on injector(s) and repair as required. If wiring harness(es) is okay, replace injector(s). If all 4 readings are correct, circuits are okay. Continue test.

7) Disconnect all injector electrical connectors and connect pressure gauge to pressure relief valve. Pressurize fuel system. Connect electrical connector at injector 1. Crank engine for 5 seconds and record pressure reading immediately after end of 5 second crank cycle. Repeat procedure on remaining injectors, testing only 1 injector at a time.

8) If all 4 readings in step **7)** are not within 4 psi (.3 kg/cm²) of each other, replace injector(s) that is incorrect. If all readings are acceptable, check for fuel contamination or other engine malfunctions and test again. If problem remains, disconnect ECA plugs and check for corroded or damaged pins. Retest. If problem still exists, replace ECA.

SENSOR REFERENCE VOLTAGE CIRCUIT

1) Connect a voltmeter between pin 11 of ECA plug J2 and the Black/White wire in the self-test connector. Turn ignition switch on and note voltage. If below 10.5 volts, check and repair battery voltage supply as necessary.

2) If voltage measured is 10.5 volts or above, move voltmeter leads to pins 11 and 12 of ECA plug J1. Voltmeter should now read 4.0-6.0 volts. If voltage reading is too high, check wiring harness for shorts to battery voltage. If voltage reading is too low, check for a shorted sensor.

AIR TEMPERATURE SENSOR

Disconnect plug J1 from the ECA. Connect an ohmmeter between pins 8 and 12 of plug J1. Resistance should be 100-5000 ohms. If resistance is not correct, repair wiring harness or replace air flow meter. Check resistance between pin 8 of plug J1 and ground. If resistance is less than 10,000 ohms, a short to ground is present. Repair as necessary.

AIR FLOW METER

1) Connect voltmeter to pins 10 and 12 of ECA plug J1. Voltmeter should read 0.2-0.5 volts with ignition on/engine off and 1.35-2.7 volts with engine running. If voltage reading is correct, check ECA plugs for damage or corrosion and correct as necessary. If problem still exists, replace ECA.

2) If voltage reading is incorrect, check harness as follows: Turn ignition off and disconnect ECA and air flow meter. Connect an ohmmeter between ground and each of pins 10, 11 and 12 at ECA plug J1. If continuity exists at any pin, a short to ground is indicated and must be repaired.

3) Check continuity of wires leading from pins 10, 11 and 12 to air flow meter. Repair any open circuits as necessary. If no opens or shorts to ground are present, and problem still exists, replace air flow meter.

THROTTLE POSITION SENSOR

1) Disconnect ECA plug J1. Connect an ohmmeter between ground and pins 9, 11, and 12 of plug. No continuity should exist between ground and any pin. Connect ohmmeter to all combinations of the 3 pins. No open circuits should exist.

2) If circuit does not perform as specified, disconnect harness from sensor and repeat test at sensor. If continuity to ground or an open circuit between pins still exists, replace sensor. If sensor performs as specified, check and repair wiring harness as needed.

COOLANT TEMPERATURE SENSOR

Disconnect plug J1 from ECA. Connect an ohmmeter between pin 7 and ground. Resistance should be greater than 10,000 ohms. If resistance is less than 10,000 ohms, check wiring harness for a short to ground. Connect an ohmmeter to pins 7 and 12 of connector. Resistance should be as specified in *Coolant Temperature Sensor Resistance* table. If not, check wiring harness for open circuits or replace sensor.

COOLANT TEMPERATURE SENSOR RESISTANCE

Temperature °F (°C)	Resistance (Ohms)
40 (4)	155,000
60 (16)	95,000
200 (93)	2350
240 (116)	1300

IDLE SPEED CONTROL SOLENOID

1) Check and adjust curb idle if needed. Disconnect the ECA from the vehicle wiring harness. Connect an ohmmeter across terminals 9 and 10 of ECA plug J2. Resistance should be 6-14 ohms.

2) If resistance is incorrect, check resistance at solenoid terminals. If resistance is correct (6-14 ohms), locate and repair short in wiring harness leading to solenoid. If resistance between terminals 9 and 10 is still incorrect, replace ISC solenoid. Reconnect ECA and ISC solenoid.

3) Turn ignition switch on and check voltage at Red wire in ISC solenoid connector. If voltage is not 10.5 volts or greater, find and repair open circuit in Red wire leading to solenoid. Check for 10.5 or more volts at Purple

FORD MOTOR CO. MULTI-POINT FUEL INJECTION (Cont.)

wires in ISC connector. If not present, check for short circuits in Purple wires leading to ISC.

ELECTRONIC CONTROL ASSEMBLY

The only means of testing the ECA itself is to substitute a good ECA for the suspect ECA. Substitution of a new ECA should only be carried out after all other components and systems have been tested and repaired. Installing a new ECA while a problem still exists elsewhere in the system can result in destroying the new ECA.

Fig. 8: 1.6L Engine Multi-Point Fuel Injection System Wiring Diagram

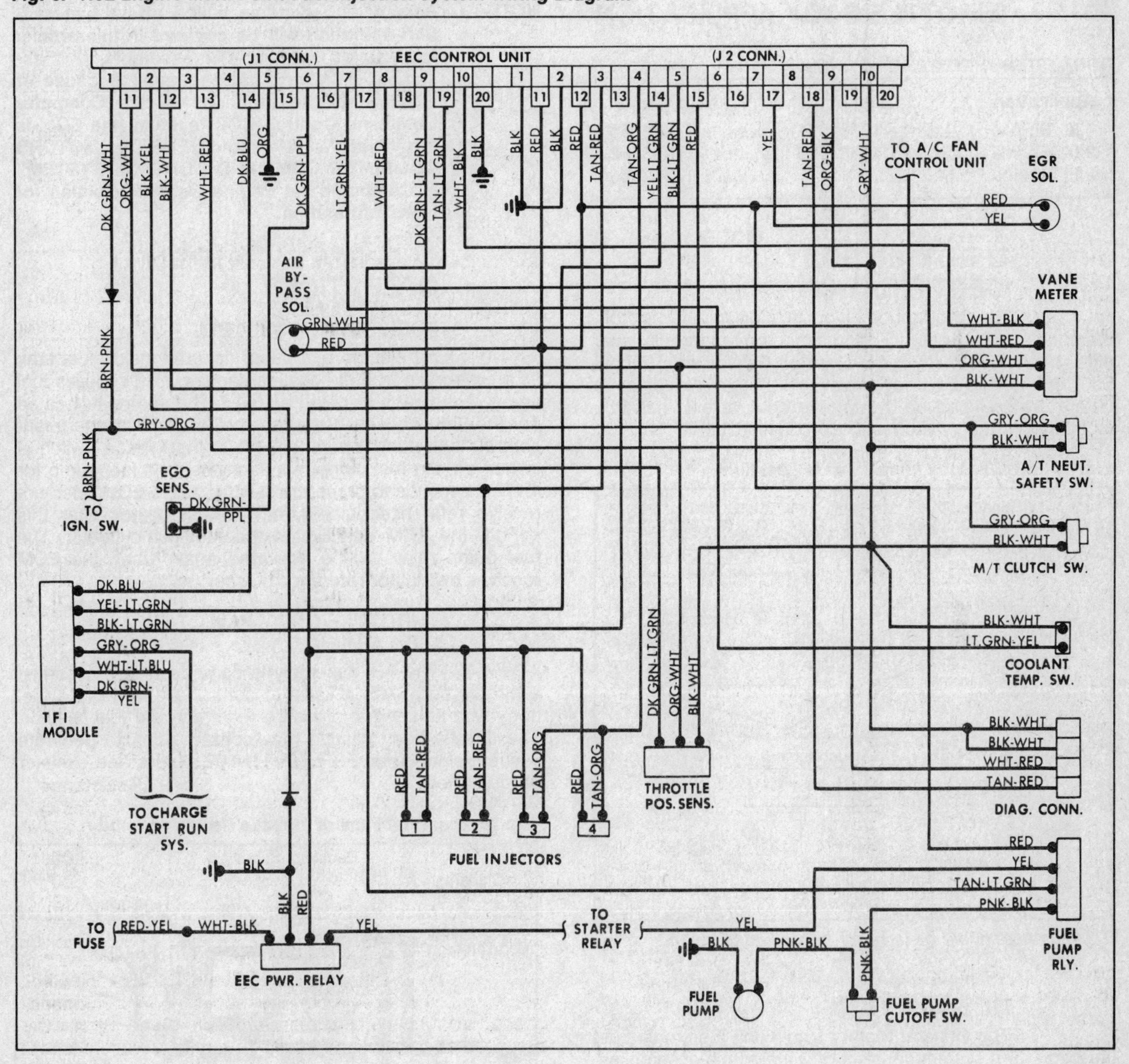

GENERAL MOTORS ELECTRONIC — SINGLE UNIT

Buick Century, Skyhawk, Skylark
Cadillac Cimarron
Chevrolet Camaro, Cavalier, Celebrity, Citation
Oldsmobile Ciera, Firenza, Omega
Pontiac Firebird, Phoenix, 2000, 6000

THROTTLE BODY APPLICATION

ROCHESTER THROTTLE BODY NO.

Application	Man. Trans.	Auto. Trans.
1.8L Engine	17082061	17082066
2.0L Engine	17083083	17083082
2.5L Engine	......	17083060

THROTTLE BODY IDENTIFICATION

The throttle body identification number is "roll-stamped" on the front mounting flange on the throttle lever side (Model 300) or Throttle Position Sensor side (Model 500) of the throttle body. *See Fig. 1.* Alphabetical code letters are stamped on the throttle body at external tube locations to identify vacuum hose connections.

Fig. 1: Throttle Body Identification Location

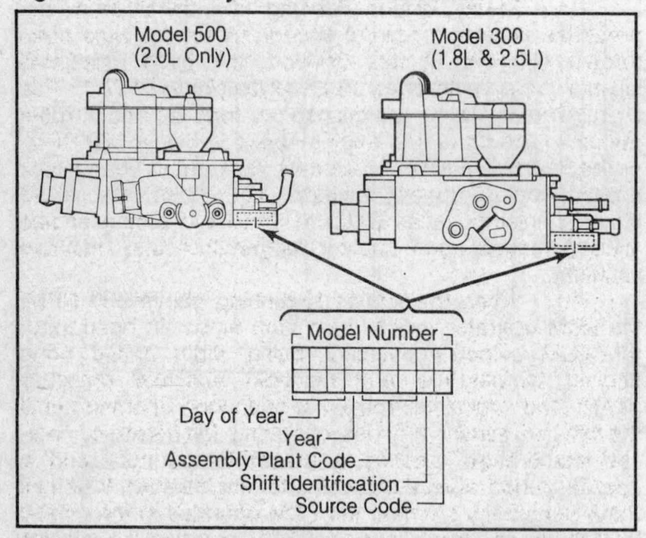

This number should be used for service information.

DESCRIPTION

The General Motors single unit Electronic Fuel Injection (EFI) system consists of 7 major sub-assemblies: fuel supply system, Throttle Body Injector (TBI) assembly, Idle Air Control (IAC) system, Electronic Control Module (ECM), Electronic Spark Timing (EST), data sensors and emission controls.

The Model 300 TBI assembly is used on 1.8L and 2.5L engines. The Model 500 TBI unit is used only on the 2.0L engine. The major difference between the 2 models is that the Model 500 has the Throttle Position Sensor (TPS) and throttle lever located on opposite sides from the Model 300.

Fuel is supplied to engine through an electronically pulsed (timed) injector valve located in throttle body unit on top of intake manifold. The ECM controls amount of fuel metered through injector valve based upon engine demand and efficiency information. The ECM is a digital electronic computer which receives and computes signals from various data sensors.

NOTE: **Primary sub-systems which affect fuel system operation will be covered in this article: fuel supply system, TBI assembly, IAC assembly, ECM and data sensors. Because of the interrelated functions of the Computer Command Control (CCC) system (the ECM is the "brain"), refer to "GENERAL MOTORS COMPUTER COMMAND CONTROL SYSTEM" in Computerized Engine Controls Section for more information.**

OPERATION

FUEL SUPPLY SYSTEM

An electric fuel pump (located inside fuel tank as an integral part of fuel gauge sending unit) supplies fuel under pressure to throttle body. A fuel pump relay located on the left or right side of the engine compartment controls fuel pump operation. When the ignition switch is turned on, the fuel pump relay activates the fuel pump for 1 1/2-2 seconds to prime the injector. If the ECM does not receive reference pulses from the distributor after this period, the ECM deactivates the fuel pump circuit. The fuel pump relay will be activated again when the ECM receives distributor reference pulses.

THROTTLE BODY INJECTOR (TBI) ASSEMBLY

The TBI assembly is composed of 2 castings: a throttle body with a valve to control air flow and a fuel body with an integral pressure regulator and fuel injector. The throttle body casting may contain ports to generate vacuum signals for EGR valve, MAP sensor and canister purge system.

Fig. 2: Sectional View of Throttle Body Assembly

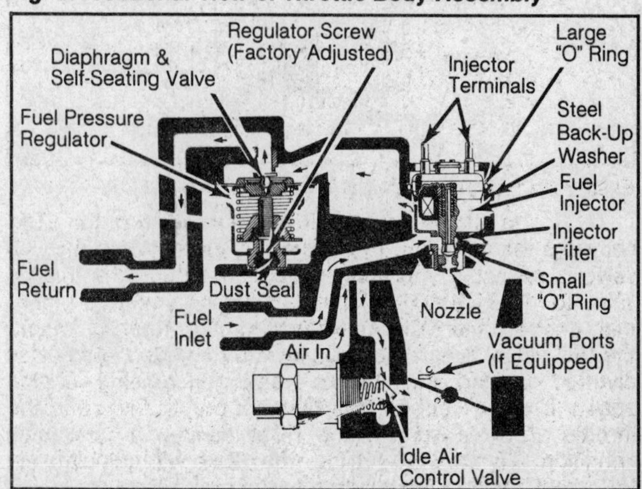

This view applies to both the Model 300 and Model 500 throttle body assemblies.

The pressure regulator is a diaphragm-operated relief valve with injector pressure on one side and air cleaner pressure on the other side. The pressure regulator maintains a constant pressure drop of about 10 psi (.7 kg/cm²) across the injector throughout all engine operating conditions. *See Fig. 2.*

The fuel injector is a solenoid-operated device controlled by the ECM. Fuel is supplied at the lower end of the injector by the fuel supply system. The ECM activates the solenoid which lifts a normally closed ball valve off its seat. Fuel under pressure is injected in a conical spray pattern at the walls of the throttle bore above the throttle valve. Excess fuel passes through the pressure regulator and is returned to fuel tank.

During engine cranking, the fuel injector is pulsed (activated) once for each distributor reference pulse received by the ECM. This is referred to as the synchronized mode. In the non-synchronized mode, the injector is pulsed once every 6.25-12.50 milliseconds depending upon engine calibration and operating conditions. In this mode, the pulse is totally independent of distributor reference pulses.

IDLE AIR CONTROL (IAC) ASSEMBLY

The IAC assembly consists of an electrically controlled motor which positions the IAC valve in the air by-pass channel around the throttle valve. The IAC valve is a part of the throttle body casting. The ECM calculates the desired position of the IAC valve based upon battery voltage, coolant temperature, engine load and engine speed to control idle speed while preventing stalls due to engine load changes.

Fig. 3: Idle Air Control Pintle Valve Design

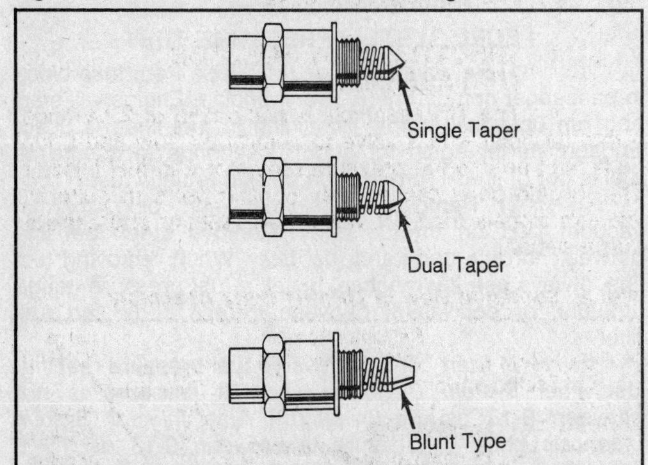

Ensure correct replacement is used during service.

If engine speed is lower than desired, the ECM activates the motor to retract the IAC valve. When the IAC valve is retracted, more air is diverted around the throttle valve to increase engine speed. If engine speed is higher than desired, the ECM activates the IAC motor to extend the IAC valve. When the IAC valve is extended, less air is diverted around the throttle valve, decreasing engine speed. If engine speed falls below a preset level and the throttle valve is closed, the ECM senses a near stall condition. To prevent stalling, the ECM will calculate an IAC valve position based upon barometric pressure.

Three different designs of IAC pintle valves are used. The first design is a single 35° taper, the second is a dual taper and the third is a blunt type. *See Fig. 3.* Care should be used to ensure correct replacement during service.

ELECTRONIC CONTROL MODULE (ECM)

The ECM is located in the passenger compartment and is the "brain" of the EFI system and Computer Command Control system. Locations vary, but the ECM is generally located under the instrument panel behind the glove compartment or behind the passenger footwell kick panel. Information from all data sensors is received and processed by the ECM to produce proper pulse duration ("on" time) for the injector, correct idle speed and proper spark timing. The ECM performs calculations to control the following EFI operating conditions: engine start, engine flooding, engine running, fuel enrichment during acceleration, lean fuel mixture during deceleration, fuel cutoff and battery voltage correction.

During engine starts, the ECM delivers an injector pulse for each distributor reference pulse received (synchronized mode). The injector pulse width is based upon coolant temperature and throttle position. The air/fuel ratio is determined by the ECM when throttle position is less than 80 percent open. Engine starting air/fuel ratio ranges from 1.5:1 at -33°F (-36°C) to 14.7:1 at 220°F (104°C). The lower the coolant temperature, the longer the injector pulse width (richer air/fuel ratio). The higher the coolant temperature, the shorter the injector pulse width (leaner air/fuel ratio).

During engine flooding, the driver must depress the accelerator pedal enough to set the wide open throttle position. At this position, the ECM calculates injector pulse width equal to an air/fuel ratio of 20:1. This air/fuel ratio will be maintained as long as the throttle remains wide open and engine speed is below 600 RPM. If the throttle position becomes less than 80 percent and/or engine speed exceeds 600 RPM, the ECM changes injector pulse width to that used during engine starting (based upon coolant temperature and manifold vacuum).

When the engine is running above 600 RPM, the ECM operates in the open loop mode. In open loop, the ECM calculates injector pulse width based upon coolant temperature and manifold absolute pressure (MAP). The engine will remain in open loop operation until the oxygen sensor reaches operating temperature, coolant temperature reaches a preset temperature and a specific period of time elapses after engine start. When all these conditions are met, the ECM operates in the closed loop mode. In closed loop, the ECM controls the injector pulse width according to oxygen sensor signals to maintain the air/fuel ratio at 14.7:1. In either mode, the injector is pulsed once for each distributor reference.

Fuel enrichment during acceleration is provided by the ECM. Sudden opening of the throttle plate causes a rapid increase in MAP. Pulse width is directly related to MAP, throttle position and coolant temperature. The higher the MAP and wider the throttle angle, the wider the pulse width (richer mixture). During enrichment, the injector pulses are not in proportion to distributor reference signals (non-synchronized). Any reduction in throttle angle cancels fuel enrichment.

During normal deceleration, the air/fuel mixture must be leaner. The ECM calculates the injector pulse width similar to that during fuel enrichment. Fuel output is reduced due to fuel remaining in the intake manifold.

GENERAL MOTORS ELECTRONIC — SINGLE UNIT (Cont.)

During sudden deceleration, when MAP, throttle position and engine speed are reduced to preset levels, fuel flow is cutoff completely to remove fuel from the engine. This deceleration fuel cutoff overrides the normal deceleration mode. During either deceleration mode, the injector pulses are not in proportion to distributor reference signals.

Battery voltage corrections by the ECM are performed during all operating modes of the EFI system. As battery voltage decreases, the ECM increases the injector pulse width with a correction factor stored in the ECM's memory.

DATA SENSORS

Each sensor furnishes an electrical signal to ECM, modifying injector pulse to conform to engine operating conditions. These sensors are as follows:

Coolant Temperature Sensor (CTS)

The CTS is located in the thermostat housing. This sensor is a variable resistant (thermister) type which transmits an electrical signal (proportionate to engine temperature) to the ECM.

Oxygen Sensor

The oxygen sensor is mounted in the exhaust manifold. This sensor is similar to a small battery. The voltage output of the sensor indicates to the ECM the amount of oxygen in the exhaust gases. The ECM corrects the air/fuel ratio according to signals received by the oxygen sensor only when the system is operating in closed loop.

CAUTION: **No attempt should be made to measure oxygen sensor voltage output. Current drain of conventional voltmeter could permanently damage sensor, shift sensor calibration range and/or render sensor unserviceable. Do not connect jumper wire, test leads or other electrical connectors to sensor.**

Manifold Absolute Pressure (MAP) Sensor

The MAP sensor is mounted on the right side of the engine compartment or on the air cleaner. This sensor is a variable resistant type which has a vacuum hose connected to the throttle body. The sensor monitors changes in intake manifold pressure which result from engine load and speed changes. As MAP changes, the electrical resistance of the sensor changes. The ECM uses the resistance value of the sensor to control injector pulse width. The MAP sensor also allows for altitude compensation of the air/fuel ratio.

Vehicle Speed Sensor (VSS)

The VSS is mounted behind the speedometer in the instrument cluster. This sensor provides the ECM with pulses to determine vehicle speed. This information is used by the ECM to control the IAC assembly, canister purge and torque converter clutch.

NOTE: **Vehicle should not be driven without the VSS installed.**

Throttle Position Sensor (TPS)

The TPS is mounted on side of throttle body and is connected to throttle shaft. This sensor converts throttle angle to an electrical signal for use by the ECM to determine engine fuel requirements.

Engine Speed Sensor

The engine speed signal comes from the Hall Effect Unit mounted above the distributor on the 2.5L engine and from terminal "R" of the conventional HEI module in the distributor on all other models. Pulses from the distributor are sent to the ECM where the time between these pulses is used to calculate engine speed. The ECM adds spark advance modifications to the signal and sends the signal back to the distributor.

NOTE: **More sensors are used by the ECM to control engine performance and other systems. Refer to "GENERAL MOTORS COMPUTER COMMAND CONTROL SYSTEM" in Computerized Engine Controls Section for more information.**

TROUBLE SHOOTING

PRELIMINARY CHECKS

The following systems and components must be in good condition and operating properly before beginning diagnosis of the fuel injection system:

- All support systems and wiring.
- Battery connections and specific gravity.
- Ignition system.
- Compression pressure.
- Fuel supply system pressure and flow.
- All electrical connections and terminals.
- Vacuum line, fuel hose and pipe connections.

NOTE: **Trouble shooting and diagnosis of fuel system should begin with determining fuel system pressure. Before performing any test on the fuel system, pressure must be released from the system.**

FUEL SYSTEM PRESSURE TEST

1) Remove "FUEL PUMP" fuse from fuse block in passenger compartment. Crank engine. Engine will start and run until fuel supply remaining in fuel lines is used. Engage starter again for about 3 seconds to assure all fuel is out of lines. Turn ignition off and replace fuse.

2) Remove air cleaner and plug thermal vacuum port on throttle body. Remove steel fuel line between throttle body and fuel filter. When removing fuel line, always use 2 wrenches. Install a fuel pressure gauge (J-29658 or equivalent) between throttle body and fuel filter.

3) Start car and observe fuel pressure reading. Use *Fuel System Diagnosis* chart if pressure is not between 9-13 psi (.6-.9 kg/cm²). Use *Injector System Diagnosis* chart if pressure is between 9-13 psi (.6-.9 kg/cm²).

4) Depressurize fuel system as described in step **1)**. Remove fuel pressure gauge and reinstall steel line between filter and throttle body. Start car and watch for leaks. Remove plug from throttle body thermal vacuum port and reinstall air cleaner.

HESITATES, SLUGGISH, SAGS OR POOR MILEAGE

1) Visually check vacuum hoses for leaks, restrictions and proper routing. Check for air leaks around throttle body mounting and intake manifold. Check spark plugs, ignition wiring, ignition timing and idle speed.

2) Check air cleaner damper door operation. Visually check air cleaner and air filter for dirt and clogging. Check EGR and EST operation. Check MAP sensor output. Check exhaust system for restrictions. With injector connector disconnected, check for fuel leakage from injector while cranking.

3) Ensure fuel pressure is steady 9-13 psi (.6-.9 kg/cm²) at all operating ranges. Visually check TPS for sticking or binding. With injector electrical connector disconnected, check for fuel leakage from injector while cranking.

4) Check for open HEI ground (circuit 453). Check fuel injector fuel filter for blockage. Check fan control circuit (if equipped). Check A/C compressor control and torque converter clutch (TCC) system. *Refer to "GENERAL MOTORS COMPUTER COMMAND CONTROL SYSTEM" in Computerized Engine Controls Section for testing procedures.*

CUTS OUT OR STALLS

1) Check for intermittent open or short to ground in the following circuits: 5 volt reference (416), HEI reference (430), fuel pump circuit (120), injector drive circuits (467 and 468), IAC drive circuits (441, 442, 443 or 444).

2) Check for restricted fuel filter. Ensure fuel pressure is 9-13 psi (.6-.9 kg/cm²) at all operating ranges. Inspect fuel injector "O" rings for damage. Ensure steel back-up washer is located beneath large "O" ring.

SURGE

Check for intermittent open or short to ground in the following circuits: transmission converter clutch (420 and 422), HEI bypass (424), EST (423). *Refer to "GENERAL MOTORS COMPUTER COMMAND CONTROL SYSTEM" in Computerized Engine Controls Section for testing procedures.*

HARD STARTING (HOT OR COLD)

1) Test for high resistance in coolant temperature sensor circuit. Visually check TPS for sticking or binding. Ensure fuel pressure is 9-13 psi (.6-.9 kg/cm²) at all operating ranges.

2) On 2.5L engine, fuel pressure leakdown after ignition is turned off should be gradual. An instant drop in pressure indicates a leaking in-tank fuel pump coupling, hose or check valve.

3) On all engines, check fuel pump relay. Disconnect oil pressure switch. If engine cranks but will not start, perform fuel system diagnosis (at point where fuel pump fuse proves okay).

4) Check injector. With injector harness connector disconnected, check for fuel leakage while cranking. Check cranking circuit. *Refer to "GENERAL MOTORS COMPUTER COMMAND CONTROL SYSTEM" in Computerized Engine Controls Section for testing procedure.*

TESTING & DIAGNOSIS

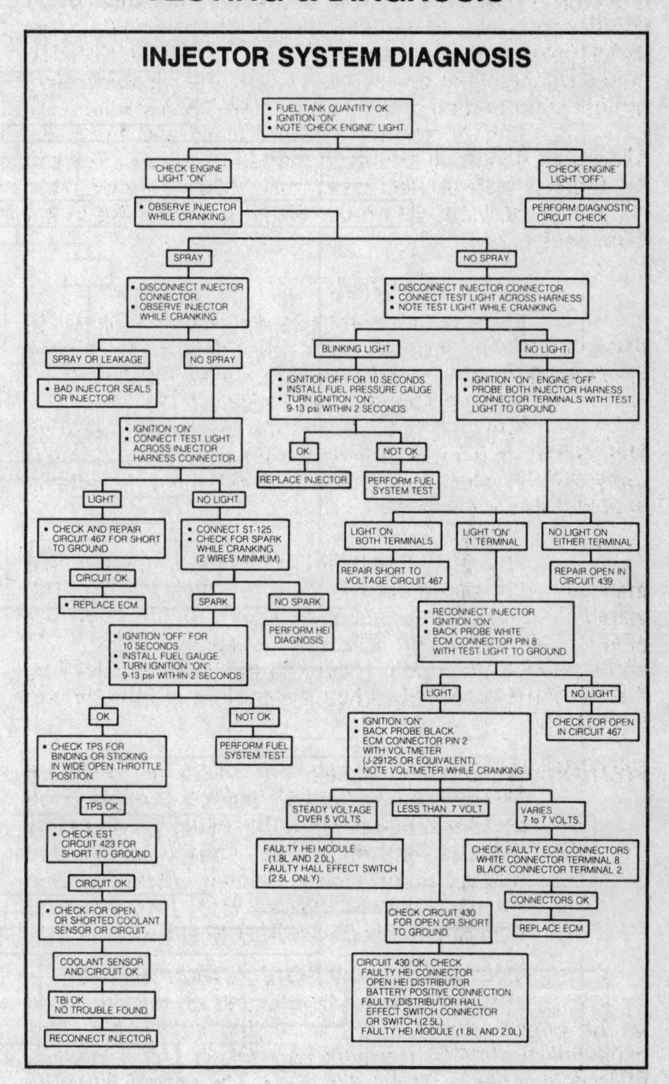

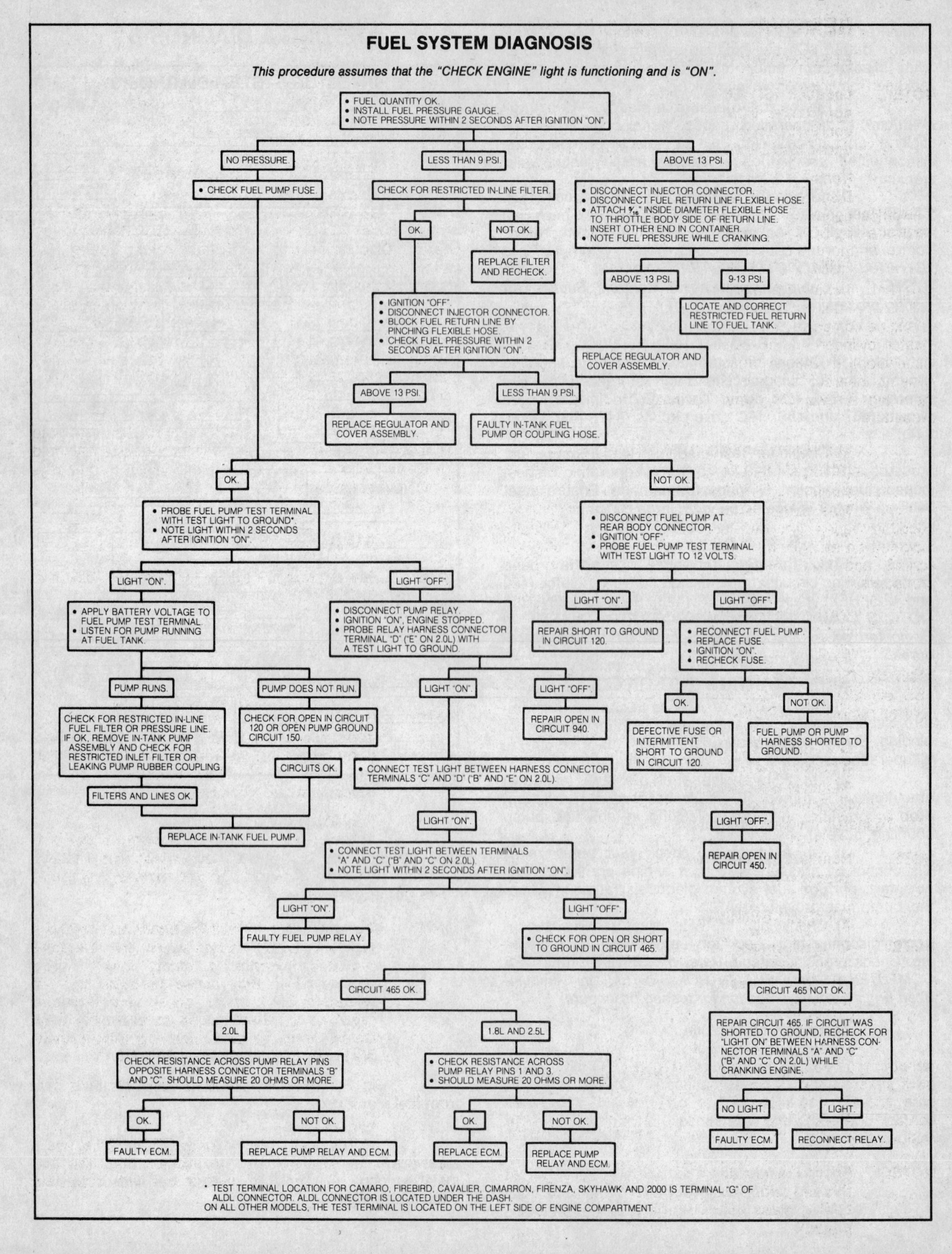
FUEL SYSTEM DIAGNOSIS
This procedure assumes that the "CHECK ENGINE" light is functioning and is "ON".
• FUEL QUANTITY OK. • INSTALL FUEL PRESSURE GAUGE. • NOTE PRESSURE WITHIN 2 SECONDS AFTER IGNITION "ON".
NO PRESSURE.
LESS THAN 9 PSI.
ABOVE 13 PSI.
• CHECK FUEL PUMP FUSE.
CHECK FOR RESTRICTED IN-LINE FILTER.
• DISCONNECT INJECTOR CONNECTOR. • DISCONNECT FUEL RETURN LINE FLEXIBLE HOSE. • ATTACH 5/16" INSIDE DIAMETER FLEXIBLE HOSE TO THROTTLE BODY SIDE OF RETURN LINE. INSERT OTHER END IN CONTAINER. • NOTE FUEL PRESSURE WHILE CRANKING.
OK.
NOT OK.
REPLACE FILTER AND RECHECK.
ABOVE 13 PSI.
9-13 PSI.
LOCATE AND CORRECT RESTRICTED FUEL RETURN LINE TO FUEL TANK.
• IGNITION "OFF". • DISCONNECT INJECTOR CONNECTOR. • BLOCK FUEL RETURN LINE BY PINCHING FLEXIBLE HOSE. • CHECK FUEL PRESSURE WITHIN 2 SECONDS AFTER IGNITION "ON".
REPLACE REGULATOR AND COVER ASSEMBLY.
ABOVE 13 PSI.
LESS THAN 9 PSI.
REPLACE REGULATOR AND COVER ASSEMBLY.
FAULTY IN-TANK FUEL PUMP OR COUPLING HOSE.
OK.
NOT OK.
• PROBE FUEL PUMP TEST TERMINAL WITH TEST LIGHT TO GROUND*. • NOTE LIGHT WITHIN 2 SECONDS AFTER IGNITION "ON".
• DISCONNECT FUEL PUMP AT REAR BODY CONNECTOR. • IGNITION "OFF". • PROBE FUEL PUMP TEST TERMINAL WITH TEST LIGHT TO 12 VOLTS.
LIGHT "ON".
LIGHT "OFF".
LIGHT "ON".
LIGHT "OFF".
• APPLY BATTERY VOLTAGE TO FUEL PUMP TEST TERMINAL. • LISTEN FOR PUMP RUNNING AT FUEL TANK.
• DISCONNECT PUMP RELAY. • IGNITION "ON", ENGINE STOPPED. • PROBE RELAY HARNESS CONNECTOR TERMINAL "D" ("E" ON 2.0L) WITH A TEST LIGHT TO GROUND.
REPAIR SHORT TO GROUND IN CIRCUIT 120.
• RECONNECT FUEL PUMP. • REPLACE FUSE. • IGNITION "ON". • RECHECK FUSE.
PUMP RUNS.
PUMP DOES NOT RUN.
LIGHT "ON".
LIGHT "OFF".
OK.
NOT OK.
CHECK FOR RESTRICTED IN-LINE FUEL FILTER OR PRESSURE LINE. IF OK, REMOVE IN-TANK PUMP ASSEMBLY AND CHECK FOR RESTRICTED INLET FILTER OR LEAKING PUMP RUBBER COUPLING.
CHECK FOR OPEN IN CIRCUIT 120 OR OPEN PUMP GROUND CIRCUIT 150.
REPAIR OPEN IN CIRCUIT 940.
DEFECTIVE FUSE OR INTERMITTENT SHORT TO GROUND IN CIRCUIT 120.
FUEL PUMP OR PUMP HARNESS SHORTED TO GROUND.
CIRCUITS OK.
• CONNECT TEST LIGHT BETWEEN HARNESS CONNECTOR TERMINALS "C" AND "D" ("B" AND "E" ON 2.0L).
FILTERS AND LINES OK.
REPLACE IN-TANK FUEL PUMP.
LIGHT "ON".
LIGHT "OFF".
• CONNECT TEST LIGHT BETWEEN TERMINALS "A" AND "C" ("B" AND "C" ON 2.0L). • NOTE LIGHT WITHIN 2 SECONDS AFTER IGNITION "ON".
REPAIR OPEN IN CIRCUIT 450.
LIGHT "ON".
LIGHT "OFF".
FAULTY FUEL PUMP RELAY.
• CHECK FOR OPEN OR SHORT TO GROUND IN CIRCUIT 465.
CIRCUIT 465 OK.
CIRCUIT 465 NOT OK.
2.0L
1.8L AND 2.5L
REPAIR CIRCUIT 465. IF CIRCUIT WAS SHORTED TO GROUND, RECHECK FOR "LIGHT ON" BETWEEN HARNESS CONNECTOR TERMINALS "A" AND "C" ("B" AND "C" ON 2.0L) WHILE CRANKING ENGINE.
CHECK RESISTANCE ACROSS PUMP RELAY PINS OPPOSITE HARNESS CONNECTOR TERMINALS "B" AND "C". SHOULD MEASURE 20 OHMS OR MORE.
• CHECK RESISTANCE ACROSS PUMP RELAY PINS 1 AND 3. • SHOULD MEASURE 20 OHMS OR MORE.
OK.
NOT OK.
OK.
NOT OK.
NO LIGHT.
LIGHT.
FAULTY ECM.
REPLACE PUMP RELAY AND ECM.
REPLACE ECM.
REPLACE PUMP RELAY AND ECM.
FAULTY ECM.
RECONNECT RELAY.
* TEST TERMINAL LOCATION FOR CAMARO, FIREBIRD, CAVALIER, CIMARRON, FIRENZA, SKYHAWK AND 2000 IS TERMINAL "G" OF ALDL CONNECTOR. ALDL CONNECTOR IS LOCATED UNDER THE DASH.
ON ALL OTHER MODELS, THE TEST TERMINAL IS LOCATED ON THE LEFT SIDE OF ENGINE COMPARTMENT.

GENERAL MOTORS ELECTRONIC — SINGLE UNIT (Cont.)

REMOVAL & INSTALLATION

ELECTRONIC CONTROL MODULE (ECM)

NOTE: **Location of ECM varies between model application. ECM is located within passenger compartment either behind right kick panel or under instrument panel.**

Removal & Installation

Disconnect negative battery cable. Disconnect 2 electrical connectors from ECM. Remove ECM mounting hardware and ECM. To install, reverse removal procedure.

FUEL PUMP RELAY

Removal & Installation

Fuel pump relay is located on left or right side of engine compartment. Relay is mounted in area of brake master cylinder and is closest relay to fender (for left installation). If relay is mounted on right side, fuel pump relay is nearest firewall. Remove electrical connector, mounting screws and relay. To install, reverse removal procedure.

MANIFOLD ABSOLUTE PRESSURE (MAP) SENSOR

Removal and Installation

MAP sensor is located in engine compartment. Location varies between application, but is generally mounted on air cleaner. Remove vacuum hose, mounting screws and MAP sensor. To install, reverse removal procedure.

VEHICLE SPEED SENSOR (VSS)

Removal & Installation

Remove instrument cluster and speedometer assembly. Disconnect VSS from speedometer. Disconnect VSS electrical connector and remove VSS. To install, reverse removal procedure.

COOLANT TEMPERATURE SENSOR (CTS)

Removal & Installation

Disconnect electrical connector and remove CTS. To install, reverse removal procedure.

NOTE: **Handle CTS with care to prevent damage to sensor calibration.**

OXYGEN SENSOR

NOTE: **Oxygen sensor may be difficult to remove when engine temperature is below 120°F (49°C). Excessive force may damage threads.**

Removal & Installation

Disconnect electrical connector. Do not attempt to remove single wire from oxygen sensor. Carefully back sensor out of exhaust manifold. Handle sensor with care and do not allow dirt or other foreign matter to contact louvered end of sensor. To install, reverse removal procedure.

NOTE: **Prior to reinstalling a serviceable sensor, coat threads with liquid graphite compound containing glass beads (special anti-seize compound).**

FUEL PUMP

Removal & Installation

Disconnect negative battery cable. Remove pressure from fuel lines as described under Fuel Pump Pressure Test. Remove fuel lines. Lower fuel tank. Remove attaching screws and fuel pump. To install, reverse removal procedure.

THROTTLE BODY ASSEMBLY

Removal

1) Relieve pressure from fuel lines as explained under Fuel Pump Pressure Test. Remove air cleaner. Disconnect throttle linkage, return spring and cruise control linkage (if equipped). Disconnect and identify all electrical connectors from throttle body.

2) Disconnect and identify all vacuum hoses from throttle body for installation reference. Disconnect fuel lines from throttle body using 2 wrenches. Remove 3 throttle body-to-manifold bolts. Model 500 uses 2 long bolts to secure air cleaner isolator and 1 throttle body-to-manifold bolt. Remove throttle body.

Installation

To install, reverse removal procedure and note the following: Ensure throttle body and intake manifold sealing surfaces are clean. Always use new throttle body-to-manifold gasket.

ADJUSTMENTS

NOTE: **See appropriate article in TUNE-UP SERVICE PROCEDURES.**

OVERHAUL

DISASSEMBLY

NOTE: **Before performing any service on throttle body assembly, it is essential that throttle body be placed on a holding fixture (J-9789-118, BT 30-15 or equivalent) to prevent damage to throttle valve.**

Fuel Meter Cover

1) Remove 5 cover-to-meter body screws and lock washers. Lift off fuel meter cover with fuel pressure regulator assembly attached. Do not remove fuel meter cover gasket. *See Fig. 4.*

NOTE: **Do not remove screws attaching pressure regulator to fuel meter cover. The pressure regulator includes a spring under heavy tension which may cause personal injury if released. Fuel meter cover and pressure regulator are serviced as an assembly only. Do not immerse cover and regulator assembly in any type of cleaning solvent.**

2) Remove fuel pressure regulator dust seal from fuel meter body.

Fuel Injector

1) With fuel meter cover gasket in place, use a screwdriver to carefully pry the injector from the fuel metering body. Carefully lift injector out with a twisting motion. *See Fig. 5.*

Fig. 4: Removing Fuel Meter Cover Assembly

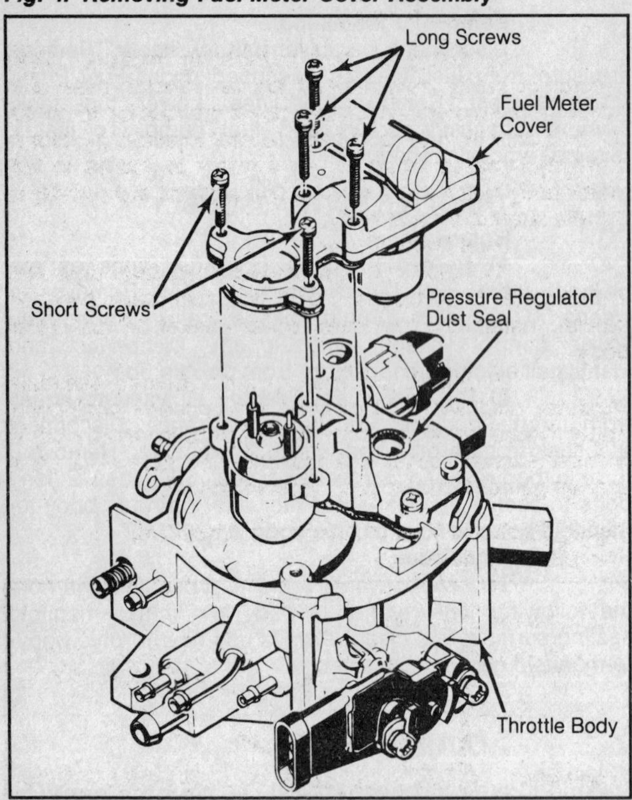

Do not remove fuel meter cover gasket at this time.

NOTE: Use care in removing injector to prevent damage to electrical connectors, fuel filter and nozzle. Injector is serviced as complete assembly only.

Fig. 5: Fuel Injector Assembly Removal

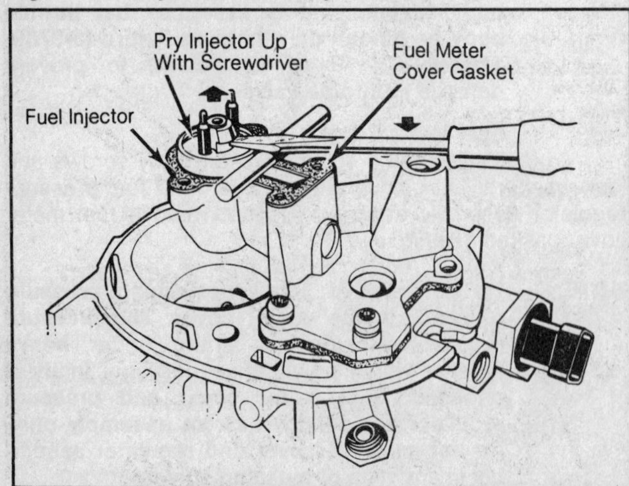

Keep fuel meter cover gasket in place until injector is removed to prevent damage to casting.

2) Carefully rotate injector filter back and forth to remove from base of injector. Remove large "O" ring and steel back-up washer at top of injector cavity in fuel meter body. Remove small "O" ring at bottom of injector cavity.

Fuel Meter Body

Remove fuel inlet and outlet nuts and gaskets from fuel meter body. Remove air cleaner stud. Remove 3 fuel meter body-to-throttle body screws and lock washers. Remove fuel meter body and gasket. Remove insulator gasket.

Throttle Body

1) Disassembly of throttle body unit for immersion in cleaning solvent requires removal of TPS and IAC assembly. Throttle valve screws are staked in position and should not be removed. If necessary to remove TPS, continue as follows:

2) Invert throttle body assembly and place on clean, flat surface. Remove and discard 2 TPS attaching screws, lock washers and retainers. Remove TPS from throttle body. *See Fig. 6.*

3) If necessary, remove TPS actuator lever-to-throttle shaft screw. Remove IAC assembly from throttle body. Remove and discard IAC gasket.

Fig. 6: Removing TPS Assembly

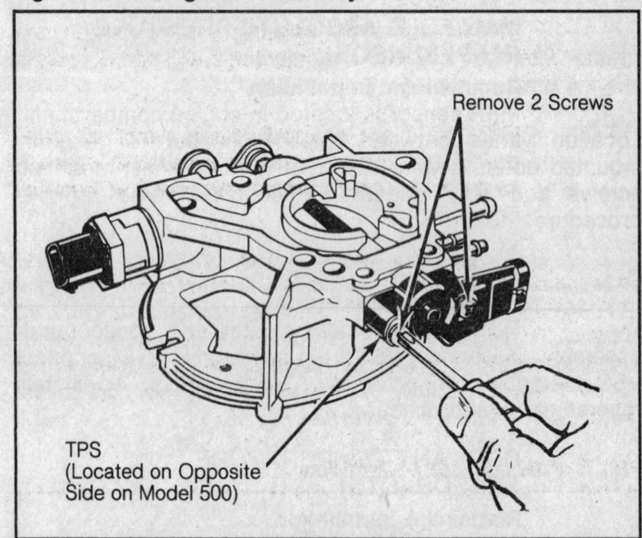

Invert throttle body unit to remove TPS.

CLEANING & INSPECTION

1) Clean all metal parts in a cold immersion-type cleaner and blow dry with compressed air.

2) Do not immerse TPS, IAC, fuel meter cover and pressure regulator assembly, fuel injector, fuel filter, rubber parts and diaphragms in cleaner.

3) Inspect mating surfaces for damage that may prevent gasket sealing. Repair or replace components which may be cause of problems listed under *Trouble Shooting and Diagnosis.*

REASSEMBLY

Throttle Body

Place throttle body on holding fixture. Install IAC assembly with new gasket. Tighten securely. Install TPS actuator lever by aligning flats on lever with flats on end of shaft. Do not install TPS until complete assembly of throttle body assembly.

GENERAL MOTORS ELECTRONIC — SINGLE UNIT (Cont.)

NOTE: Before installing IAC assembly, measure distance that valve extends from motor housing. Measuring from gasket mounting surface of housing to end of pintle, distance should not exceed 1 1/8" (28 mm). If not to specification, push pintle inward (ISC valve with collar on electrical connector) or compress pintle retaining spring toward IAC body while turning pintle inward with a clockwise motion (IAC valve without collar on connector). On IAC valves without collar, return spring to original position with straight portion of spring end aligned with flat surface under pintle head.

Fuel Meter Body

1) Install fuel meter body insulator gasket on throttle body. Cutout portions of gasket must match cutouts on throttle body. Install fuel meter body on gasket.

2) Apply thread locking compound (supplied in service kit) on 3 attaching screws. Install lock washers and screws. Tighten screws. Install fuel inlet and outlet nuts with new gaskets.

Fuel Injector

1) Using a slight twisting motion, install fuel injector filter on nozzle end of injector until seated against injector base.

NOTE: Filter is cone-shaped. Large end of filter points up toward injector electrical connectors. Filter should cover raised rib at base of injector.

2) Lubricate "O" rings with automatic transmission fluid. Push small "O" ring on nozzle end of injector until seated against injector fuel filter. Install steel back-up washer in recess in injector cavity of fuel meter body. Install large "O" ring directly above back-up washer. Press "O" ring down in cavity recess until flush with top of fuel meter body casting surface. *See Fig. 7.*

Fig. 7: Fuel Injector Installation

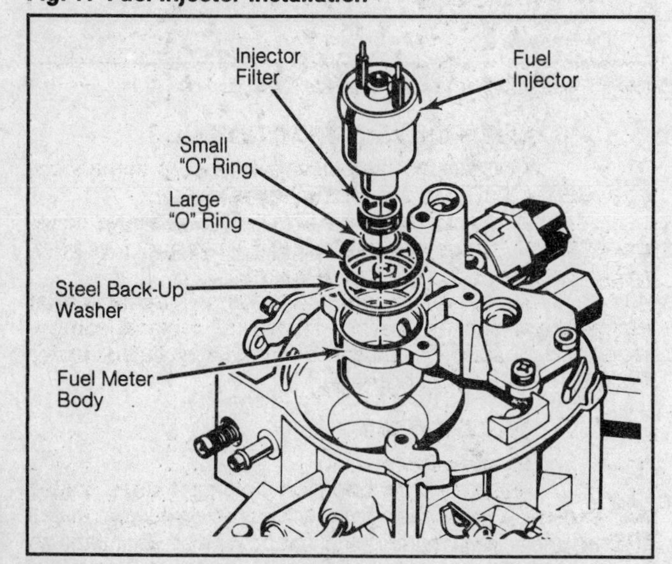

Lubricate "O" rings with automatic transmission fluid.

NOTE: "O" rings and back-up washer must be installed in this manner. Do not attempt to seat "O" rings and washer after injector is placed in cavity.

3) Using a pushing/twisting motion, install injector in cavity. Align raised lug on injector base with notch in fuel meter body. Push down on injector to center "O" ring in bottom of cavity and to seat injector. Injector is correctly installed when lug on injector is seated in fuel meter body notch and electrical connections are parallel to throttle shaft in throttle body.

Fuel Meter Cover

1) Install new fuel pressure regulator dust seal in fuel meter body recess. Install new fuel return passage gasket. Install new fuel meter cover gasket on fuel meter body.

2) Install fuel meter cover. Ensure pressure regulator dust seal and gaskets are properly positioned. Apply thread locking compound (supplied in service kit) to 5 cover screws. Install lock washers and screws (2 short screws go next to injectors). Tighten screws.

Fig. 8: Exploded View of Rochester Single Unit Throttle Body Assembly

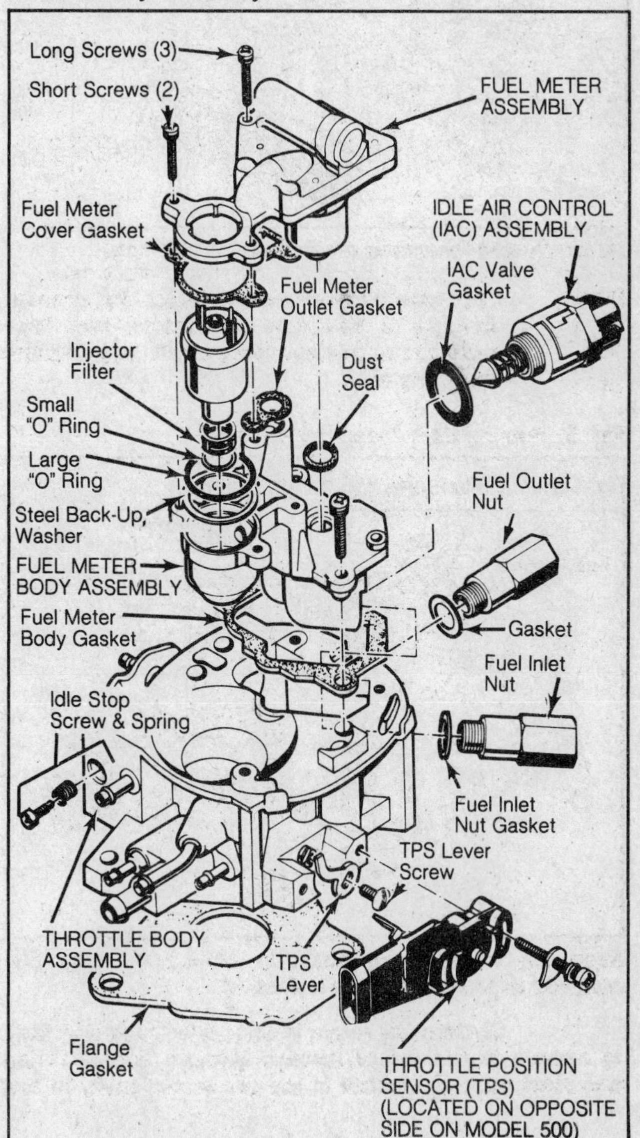

GENERAL MOTORS ELECTRONIC — SINGLE UNIT (Cont.)

Throttle Position Sensor (TPS)

Place throttle valve in normal closed idle position. Install TPS on throttle body with pick-up lever above throttle actuator lever. Install retainer, lock washers and 2 new attaching screws (coated with locking compound).

NOTE: **TPS adjustment must be done with throttle body installed on vehicle. See appropriate article in TUNE-UP SERVICE PROCEDURES.**

TIGHTENING SPECIFICATIONS

Application	Ft. Lbs. (N.m)
Oxygen Sensor	30 (41)
Throttle Body-to-Manifold Bolts	17 (23)
Idle Air Control (IAC) Assembly	13 (18)
Fuel Inlet and Outlet Nuts	22 (30)

Fig. 9: 1.8L and 2.5L Fuel Injection Wiring Diagram

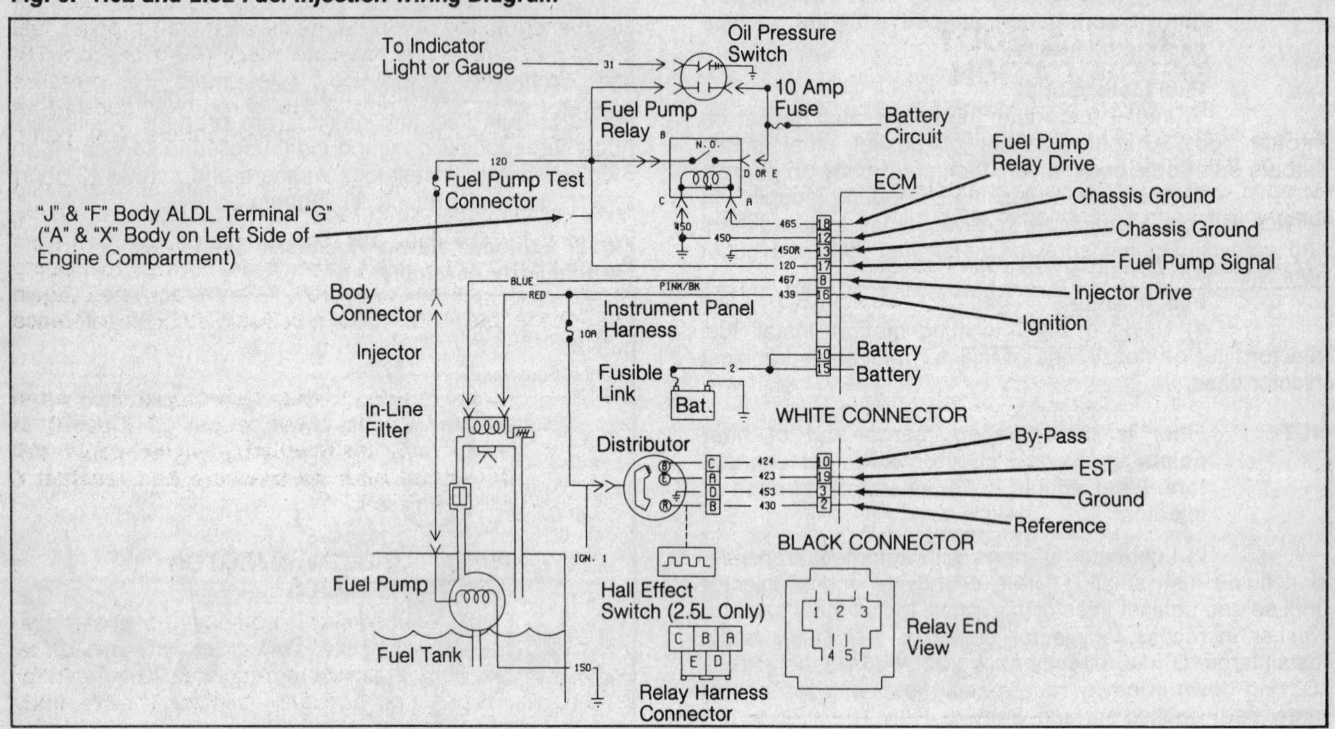

Fig. 10: 2.0L Fuel Injection Wiring Diagram

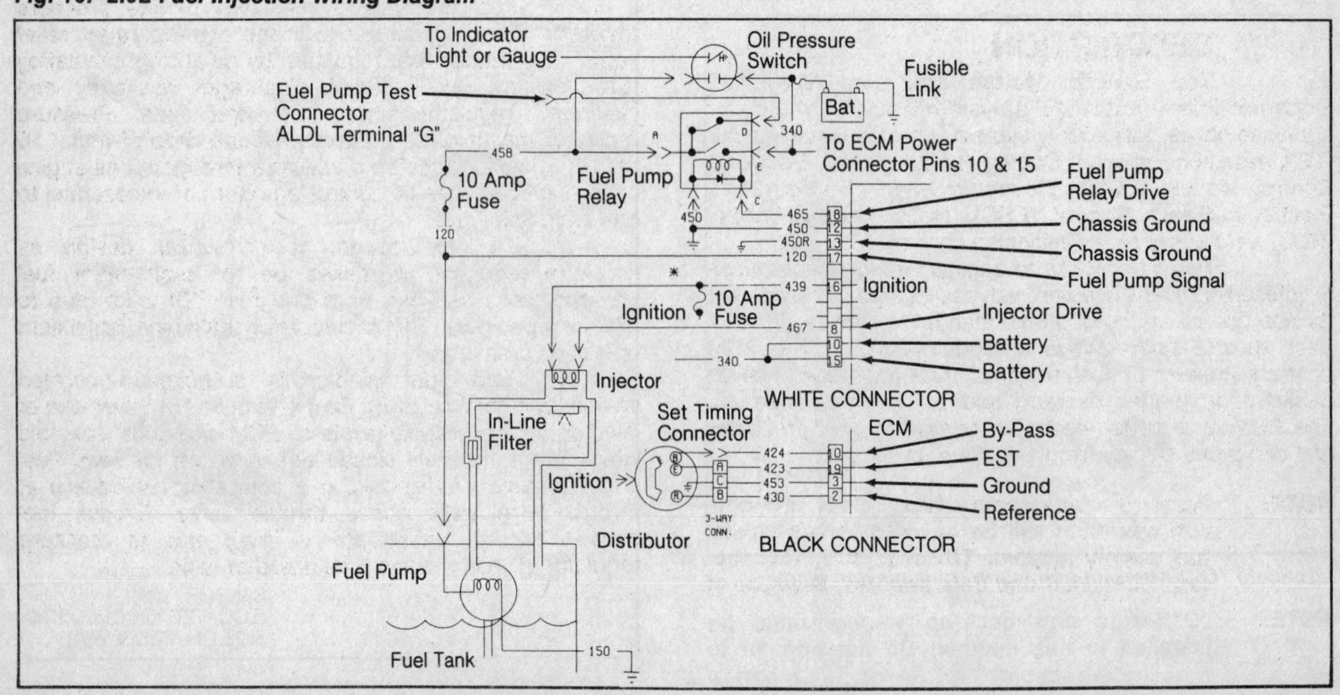

GENERAL MOTORS ELECTRONIC — DUAL UNIT

Camaro, Corvette, Firebird

THROTTLE BODY APPLICATION

ROCHESTER THROTTLE BODY NO.

Application	Man. Trans.	Auto. Trans.
5.0L Engine	17083054	17083054
5.7L Engine	17083053	17083055

THROTTLE BODY IDENTIFICATION

The throttle body identification number is "roll-stamped" on the front mounting flange on the throttle lever side of the throttle body. *See Fig. 1.* Code letters are stamped on the throttle body at external tube locations to identify vacuum hose connections.

Fig. 1: Throttle Body Identification Location

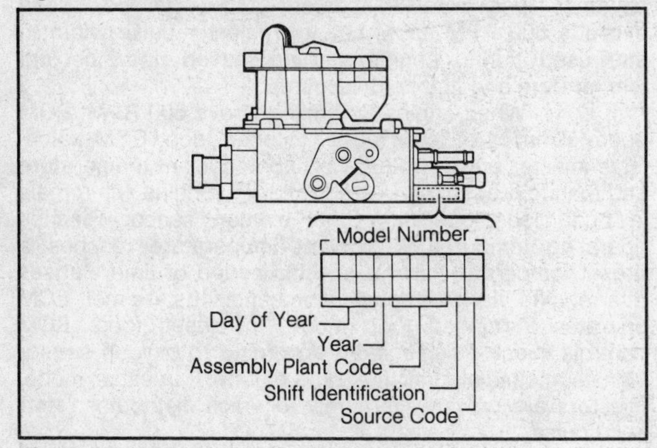

This number should be used for service information.

DESCRIPTION

The General Motors dual unit (cross-fire) Electronic Fuel Injection (EFI) system consists of 9 major sub-assemblies: fuel supply system, Throttle Body Injector (TBI) assembly, Idle Air Control (IAC) system, Electronic Control Module (ECM), Electronic Spark Timing (EST), Electronic Spark Control (ESC), Hood Louver Control (HLC), data sensors and emission controls.

Fuel is supplied to engine through electronically pulsed (timed) injector valves located in separate throttle bodies on top of intake manifold (1 for each bank). Each throttle body unit is a Model 400 unit. The ECM controls amount of fuel metered through injector valves based upon engine demand and efficiency information. The ECM is a digital electronic computer which receives and computes signals from various data sensors.

NOTE: **Primary sub-systems which affect fuel system operation will be covered in this article: fuel supply system, TBI assembly, IAC system, ECM, HLC and data sensors. Because of the interrelated functions of the Computer Command Control (CCC) system (the ECM is the "brain"), refer to "GENERAL MOTORS COMPUTER COMMAND CONTROL SYSTEM" in Computerized Engine Controls Section for more information.**

OPERATION

FUEL SUPPLY SYSTEM

An electric fuel pump (located inside fuel tank as an integral part of fuel gauge sending unit) supplies fuel under pressure to fuel pressure accumulator on front TBI unit. From the accumulator, fuel enters the pressure regulator on rear TBI unit. A fuel pump relay (located on left side of engine compartment) controls fuel pump operation.

When ignition switch is turned on, fuel pump relay activates fuel pump for 1 1/2-2 seconds to prime the injectors. If ECM does not receive reference pulses from the distributor after this period, it deactivates fuel pump circuit. The fuel pump circuit will be activated again through the relay when ECM receives distributor reference pulses.

NOTE: **Power to relay from battery is provided when oil pressure is above 4 psi (.3 kg/cm²). If pump relay malfunctions, engine could still be started after oil pressure has reached 4 psi (.3 kg/cm²).**

THROTTLE BODY INJECTOR (TBI) ASSEMBLIES

Each TBI assembly is composed of 2 castings: a throttle body with a valve to control air flow, and a fuel body with an integral pressure regulator (rear unit) or accumulator (front unit) and fuel injector. Throttle body casting may contain ports to generate vacuum signals for EGR valve, MAP sensor and canister purge system.

Fuel pressure is regulated by the pressure regulator. The regulator is a diaphragm-operated relief valve. Fuel pressure is regulated by balancing circulating fuel flow on one side of diaphragm assembly and calibrated regulator spring on other side. Pressure regulator maintains a constant pressure drop of about 10 psi (.7 kg/cm²) across both injectors throughout all engine operating conditions by controlling return of excess fuel to fuel tank. *See Fig. 2.*

The accumulator is of similar design as pressure regulator. It makes up for momentary fuel pressure drop between front and rear TBI units (due to injector openings). The accumulator maintains consistent operating pressures.

Each fuel injector is a solenoid-operated device controlled by ECM. Fuel is supplied at lower end of injector by fuel supply system. ECM activates solenoid which lifts a normally closed ball valve off its seat. Fuel under pressure is injected in a conical spray pattern at throttle bore walls above throttle valve. Excess fuel passes through accumulator of front unit, to pressure regulator of rear unit and is returned to tank.

GENERAL MOTORS ELECTRONIC — DUAL UNIT (Cont.)

Fig. 2: Sectional View of Throttle Body Assemblies

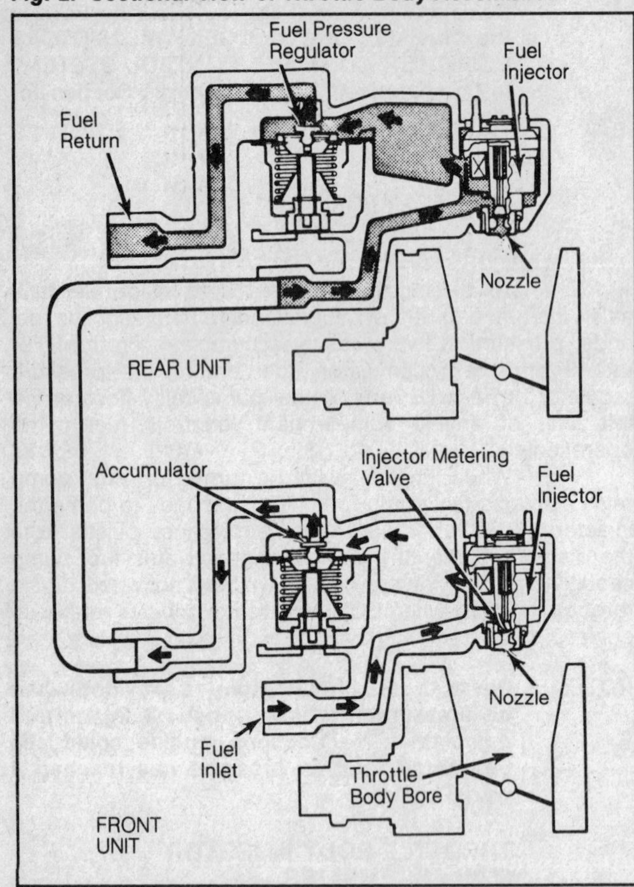

Both units are Model 400 units.

IDLE AIR CONTROL (IAC) SYSTEM

The IAC system consists of an electrically controlled motor which positions IAC valve in air by-pass channel around throttle plate of each TBI unit. The IAC valve is a part of the throttle body casting. The ECM calculates desired position of each IAC valve based upon battery voltage, coolant temperature, engine load and engine speed. It controls idle speed while preventing stalls due to engine load changes.

If engine speed is lower than desired, ECM activates motor to retract IAC valve. When IAC valve is retracted, more air is diverted around throttle plate, increasing engine speed. If engine speed is higher than desired, ECM activates motor to extend IAC valve. When IAC valve is extended, less air is diverted around throttle plate decreasing engine speed. If engine speed falls below a preset speed and the throttle plate is closed, ECM senses a near stall condition. To prevent stalling, ECM will calculate an IAC valve position based upon barometric pressure.

ELECTRONIC CONTROL MODULE (ECM)

The ECM is located behind instrument panel and is the "brain" of EFI and Computer Command Control systems. Information from all data sensors is received and processed by the ECM to produce proper pulse duration for each injector, correct idle speed and proper spark timing. The ECM performs calculations to control the following EFI operating conditions: engine start, engine flooding, engine running, fuel enrichment during acceleration, lean fuel mixture during deceleration, fuel cutoff and battery voltage correction.

During engine starts, the first signal sent to injectors is a "prime" pulse. This pulse charges intake manifold with fuel during or just prior to engine starting. This pulse width (injector "on" time) is not synchronized with HEI distributor reference pulses. Prime pulses will be delivered for a length of time dependent upon coolant temperature.

After delivering prime pulses, ECM will deliver a pulse for each distributor reference pulse received. Air/fuel ratio is determined by ECM based upon throttle position and coolant temperature. The lower the coolant temperature, the longer the injector pulse width (richer air/fuel ratio). The higher the coolant temperature, the shorter the injector pulse width (leaner air/fuel ratio).

During engine flooding, accelerator pedal must be depressed enough to set wide open throttle position. At this position, ECM calculates injector pulse width equal to an air/fuel ratio of 20:1. This air/fuel ratio will be maintained as long as throttle remains wide open and engine speed is below 600 RPM. If throttle position becomes less than 80 percent and/or engine speed exceeds 600 RPM, ECM changes injector pulse width to that used during engine starting (based upon coolant temperature and manifold vacuum).

When engine is running above 600 RPM, ECM operates in open loop mode. In open loop, ECM calculates injector pulse width based upon coolant temperature and manifold absolute pressure (MAP). Engine will remain in open loop operation until oxygen sensor reaches operating temperature, coolant temperature reaches a preset temperature and a specific period of time elapses after engine start. When all these conditions are met, ECM operates in closed loop mode. In closed loop, ECM controls injector pulse width according to oxygen sensor signals, maintaining air/fuel ratio of 14.7:1. In either mode, injectors are pulsed alternately for each distributor reference pulse.

Fuel enrichment during acceleration is provided by ECM. Sudden opening of throttle plates causes a rapid increase in MAP. Pulse width is directly equal to MAP, throttle position and coolant temperature. The higher the MAP and wider the throttle angle, the wider the pulse width (richer mixture). During enrichment, injector pulses are not in proportion with distributor reference signals. Any reduction in throttle angle will cancel fuel enrichment.

During normal deceleration, air/fuel mixture must be leaner. ECM calculates injector pulse width similar to that during fuel enrichment. Fuel output is reduced due to fuel remaining in the intake manifold. During sudden deceleration, when MAP, throttle position and engine speed are at preset levels, fuel flow is cut off completely to remove fuel from the engine. This deceleration fuel cutoff overrides normal deceleration mode. During either deceleration mode, injector pulses are not in proportion to distributor reference signals.

Battery voltage corrections by ECM are performed during all operating modes of EFI system. As battery voltage decreases, ECM increases injector pulse width with a correction factor stored in ECM's memory.

Hood Louver Control (HLC) system is controlled by ECM. When engine coolant temperature and throttle position meet preset specifications, ECM activates HLC relay which opens hood louver to allow additional air into engine.

GENERAL MOTORS ELECTRONIC — DUAL UNIT (Cont.)

DATA SENSORS

Each sensor furnishes an electrical signal to ECM, modifying injector pulse to conform to engine operating conditions. These sensors are as follows:

Coolant Temperature Sensor (CTS)

The CTS is located in thermostat housing. This sensor is a variable resistance type which transmits an electrical signal (proportionate to engine temperature) to the ECM.

Oxygen Sensor

Oxygen sensor is mounted in exhaust manifold, directly behind cross-over pipe. This sensor is similar to a small battery. Voltage output of sensor indicates to ECM the amount of oxygen in exhaust gases. ECM corrects air/fuel ratio (according to signals received by oxygen sensor) only when system is operating in closed loop.

CAUTION: No attempt should be made to measure oxygen sensor voltage output. Current drain of conventional voltmeter could permanently damage sensor. Do not connect jumper wire, test leads or other electrical connectors to sensor.

Manifold Absolute Pressure (MAP) Sensor

The MAP sensor is mounted on left side of engine compartment. This sensor is a variable resistance type which has a vacuum hose connected to throttle body. The sensor monitors changes in intake manifold pressure which result from engine load and speed changes. As MAP changes, electrical resistance of sensor changes. ECM uses resistance value of sensor to control injector pulse width.

Vehicle Speed Sensor (VSS)

The VSS is mounted behind speedometer in instrument cluster. This sensor provides ECM with pulses to determine vehicle speed. This information is used by ECM to control IAC system.

NOTE: Vehicle should not be driven without VSS installed or speedometer cable connected.

Throttle Position Sensor (TPS)

TPS is mounted on side of rear throttle body and is connected to throttle shaft. A throttle rod connects both front and rear throttle body units to ensure throttle valve of each unit is positioned the same. This sensor converts throttle angle to an electrical signal for use by ECM to determine engine fuel requirements.

NOTE: The throttle rod end bearing is permanently attached to throttle lever stud of rear unit. Throttle rod must not be removed from rear unit. If throttle rod bearing needs replacement, rear throttle body unit must be replaced.

Engine RPM Reference

The "R" terminal of the HEI distributor module is used to send engine RPM signals to ECM.

NOTE: More sensors are used by ECM to control engine performance and other systems. Refer to "GENERAL MOTORS COMPUTER COMMAND CONTROL SYSTEM" in Computerized Engine Controls Section for more information.

TROUBLE SHOOTING

PRELIMINARY CHECKS

The following systems and components must be in good condition and operating properly before beginning diagnosis of the fuel injection system:

- All support systems and wiring.
- Battery connections and specific gravity.
- Ignition system.
- Compression pressure.
- Fuel supply system pressure and flow.
- All electrical connections and terminals.
- Vacuum line, fuel hose and pipe connections.

NOTE: Trouble shooting and diagnosis of fuel system should begin with determining fuel system pressure. Before performing any test on the fuel system, pressure must be released from the system.

FUEL SYSTEM PRESSURE TEST

1) Remove "FUEL PUMP" fuse from fuse block in passenger compartment. Crank engine. Engine will start and run until fuel supply remaining in fuel lines is used. Engage starter again for about 3 seconds to ensure all fuel is out of lines. Turn ignition off and replace fuse.

2) Remove air cleaner and plug thermal vacuum port on throttle body. Remove steel fuel line between front and rear throttle body units. When removing fuel line, always use 2 wrenches. Install a fuel pressure gauge (J-29658 or equivalent) between throttle body units.

3) Reinstall "FUEL PUMP" fuse. Start car and observe fuel pressure reading. Use Fuel System Diagnosis chart if pressure is not 9-13 psi (.6-.9 kg/cm²). Use Injector System Diagnosis chart if pressure is 9-13 psi (.6-.9 kg/cm²).

4) Depressurize fuel system as described in step **1)**. Remove fuel pressure gauge and reinstall steel line between throttle bodies. Reinstall "FUEL PUMP" fuse. Start car and watch for leaks. Remove plug from throttle body thermal vacuum port and reinstall air cleaner.

HESITATES, SLUGGISH, SAGS OR POOR MILEAGE

1) Visually check MAP hose for leaks or restriction and TPS for sticking or binding. Check for air leaks around throttle body mounting and intake manifold. Ensure fuel pressure is steady 9-13 psi (.6-.9 kg/cm²) at all operating ranges. Ensure base timing is correct.

2) With injector connectors disconnected, check for fuel leakage from injectors while cranking. Check for open HEI ground (circuit 453). Check fuel injector fuel filters for blockage. Check TBI balance adjustment. *See appropriate article in TUNE-UP SERVICE PROCEDURES.*

3) Check A/C compessor control and torque converter clutch (TCC) system. *Refer to "GENERAL MOTORS COMPUTER COMMAND CONTROL SYSTEM" in Computerized Engine Controls Section for testing procedures.*

CUTS OUT OR STALLS

1) Check for intermittent open or short to ground in the following circuits: 5 volt reference (416), HEI reference (430), fuel pump circuit (120), injector drive

GENERAL MOTORS ELECTRONIC — DUAL UNIT (Cont.)

circuits (467 and 468), IAC drive circuits (441, 442, 443 or 444).

2) Check for restricted fuel filter. Ensure fuel pressure is 9-13 psi (.6-.9 kg/cm²) at all operating ranges. Inspect fuel injecter "O" rings for damage. Ensure steel back-up washer is located beneath large "O" ring of each injector.

SURGE

Check for intermittent open or short to ground in the following circuits: transmission converter clutch (420 and 422), HEI by-pass (424), EST (423). Perform EGR diagnosis. *Refer to "GENERAL MOTORS COMPUTER COMMAND CONTROL SYSTEM" in Computerized Engine Controls Section for testing procedures.*

HARD STARTING (HOT OR COLD)

1) Check for high resistance in coolant sensor circuit. Visually check TPS for sticking or binding. Ensure fuel pressure is 9-13 psi (.6-.9 kg/cm²) at all operating ranges.

2) Check fuel pump relay. Disconnect oil pressure switch. If engine cranks but will not start, perform fuel system diagnosis (at point where fuel pump fuse proves okay).

3) Check injectors. With injector harness connectors disconnected, check for fuel leakage while cranking.

4) Check cranking circuit. *Refer to "GENERAL MOTORS COMPUTER COMMAND CONTROL SYSTEM" in Computerized Engine Controls Section for testing procedure.*

TESTING & DIAGNOSIS

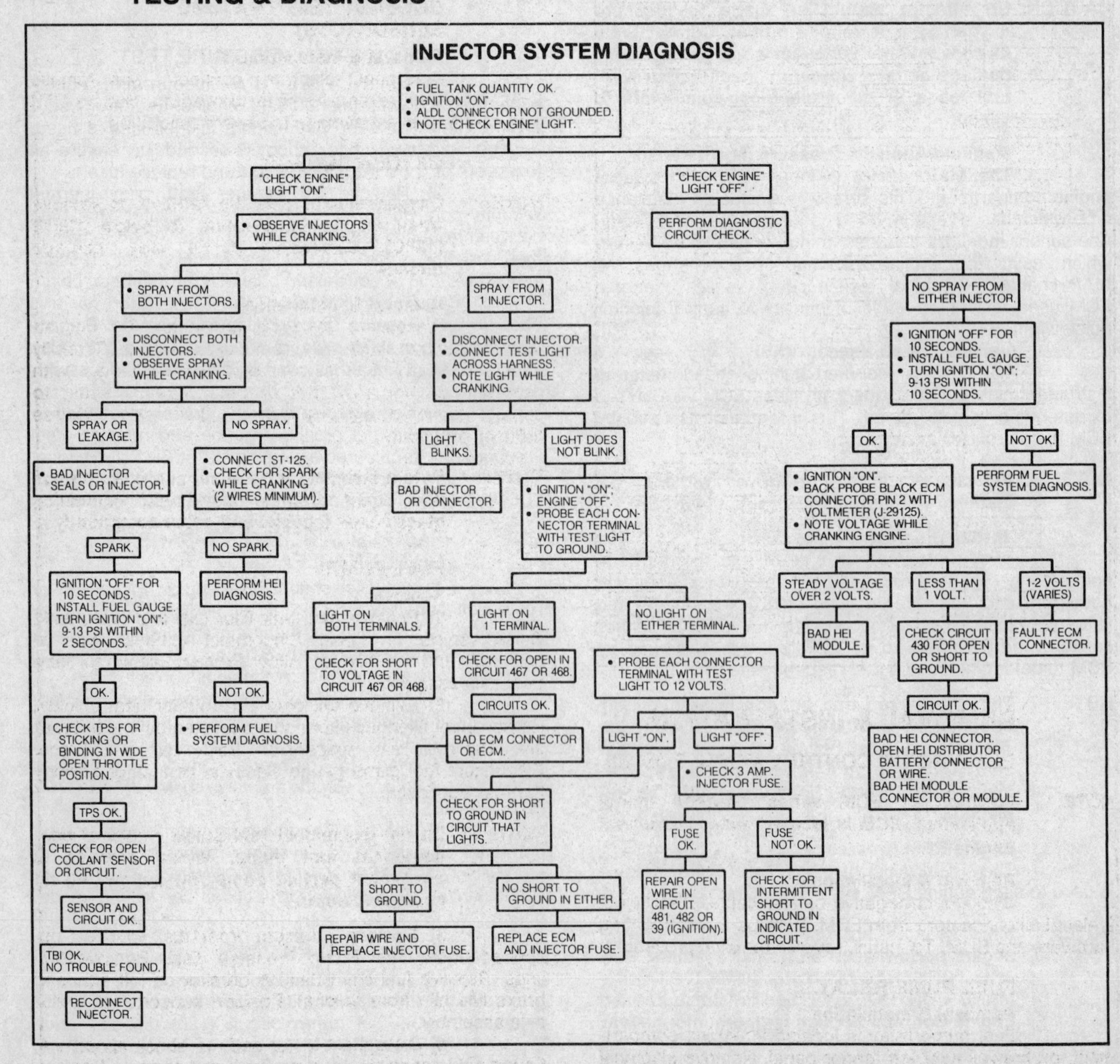

GENERAL MOTORS ELECTRONIC — DUAL UNIT (Cont.)

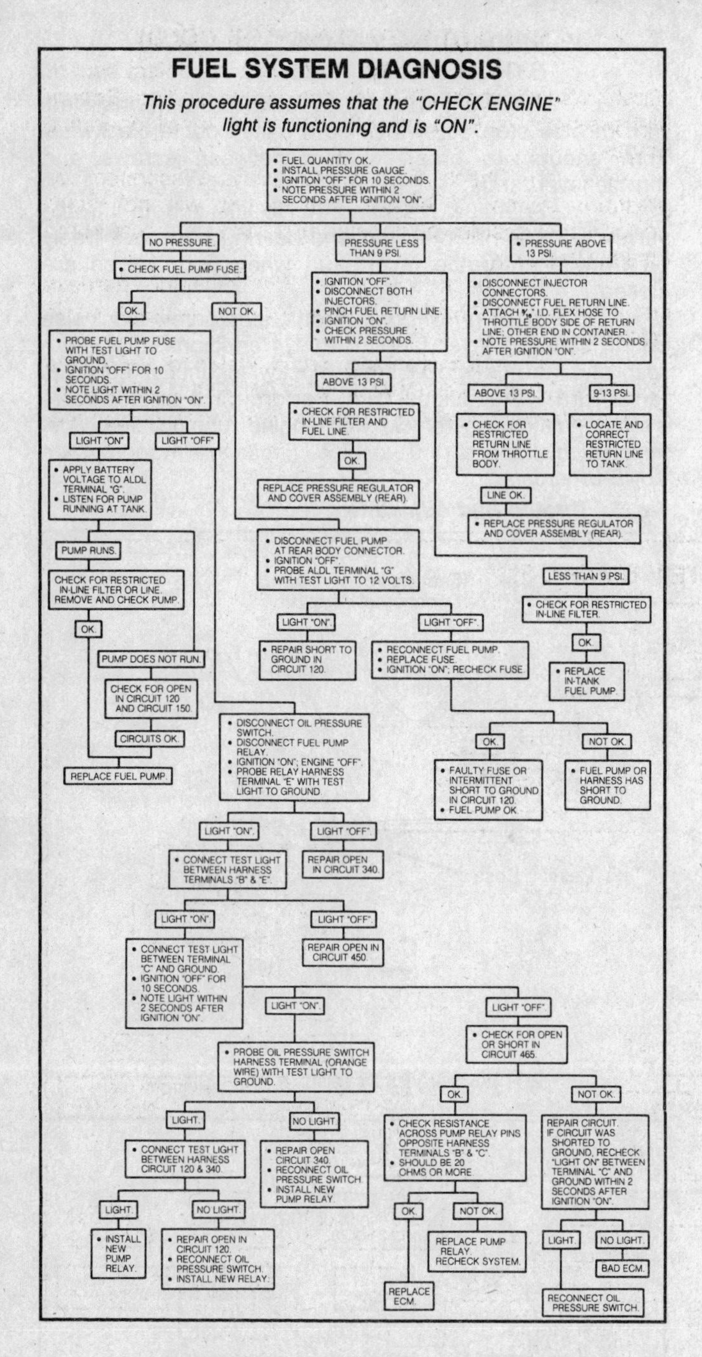

REMOVAL & INSTALLATION

ELECTRONIC CONTROL MODULE (ECM)

NOTE: Location of ECM varies between model application. ECM is located under instrument panel.

Removal & Installation

Disconnect negative battery cable. Disconnect 2 electrical connectors from ECM. Remove ECM mounting hardware and ECM. To install, reverse removal procedure.

FUEL PUMP RELAY

Removal & Installation

Fuel pump relay is located in engine compartment, on firewall near left fender panel. Remove electrical connector, mounting screws and relay. To install, reverse removal procedure.

MANIFOLD ABSOLUTE PRESSURE (MAP) SENSOR

Removal & Installation

MAP sensor is located in engine compartment, on firewall near left fender panel on all models. Remove vacuum hose, mounting screws and MAP sensor. To install, reverse removal procedure.

VEHICLE SPEED SENSOR (VSS)

Removal & Installation

Remove instrument cluster and speedometer assembly. Disconnect VSS from speedometer. Disconnect VSS electrical connector and remove VSS. To install, reverse removal procedure.

COOLANT TEMPERATURE SENSOR (CTS)

Removal & Installation

Disconnect electrical connector and remove CTS. To install, reverse removal procedure. Handle CTS with care to prevent damage to sensor calibration.

OXYGEN SENSOR

NOTE: Oxygen sensor may be difficult to remove when engine temperature is below 120°F (48°C). Excessive force may damage threads.

Removal & Installation

Disconnect electrical connector. Do not attempt to remove single wire from oxygen sensor. Carefully back sensor out of cross-over pipe. Handle sensor with care and do not allow dirt or other foreign matter to contact louvered end of sensor. To install, reverse removal procedure.

NOTE: Before installing a used sensor, coat threads with liquid graphite compound containing glass beads (special anti-seize compound).

FUEL PUMP

Removal

1) Remove fuel tank filler cap and drain tank. Raise vehicle on hoist. Disconnect exhaust pipe at converter and rear hanger. Allow exhaust system to hang over axle assembly.

2) Remove tail pipe and muffler heat shields. Remove fuel filler neck heat shield located behind left rear tire. Remove rear suspension track bar and brace. Disconnect fuel pump gauge electrical connector at body harness connector.

NOTE: Do not disconnect fuel pump electrical connector at fuel pump. Wiring harness is permanent part of pump. Do not pry up on cover connector.

3) Remove pressure from fuel lines as described under Fuel Pump Pressure Test. Remove fuel lines. Remove fuel line retaining bracket on left side and brake line clip from bracket. Position support jack under axle assembly.

4) Disconnect lower ends of shock absorbers. Lower axle assembly. Remove both coil springs. Remove

GENERAL MOTORS ELECTRONIC — DUAL UNIT (Cont.)

fuel tank straps. Lower rear suspension as far as possible without damaging brake lines. Remove tank by rotating front of tank down and sliding to right. Remove fuel pump attaching screws and fuel pump.

Installation

To install, reverse removal procedure.

THROTTLE BODY ASSEMBLIES

Removal

1) Relieve pressure from fuel lines as explained under Fuel Pump Pressure Test. Remove air cleaner. Disconnect electrical connectors from injectors, IAC motors and TPS. Disconnect and identify all vacuum lines.

2) Remove throttle cable and transmission detent cable. Remove throttle rod from between front and rear throttle body units. Do not attempt to remove rod at rear throttle body unit. Throttle rod bearing is permanently attached to rear throttle lever stud. Remove cruise control cable (if equipped).

3) Disconnect fuel lines from each throttle body unit using 2 wrenches. Remove throttle body-to-manifold bolts. Remove each throttle body unit as an assembly.

4) If manifold cover or either throttle body requires replacement, do the following: If equipped, remove throttle stop screw plugs. Using a prick punch, mark location over center line of throttle stop screw to drill a hole.

5) Using a 5/32" drill, drill a hole through throttle body casting to hardened steel plug. Using a 1/16" punch, drive through bottom of drilled hole and knock out plug.

6) If throttle synchronizing screw has a spot-welded retaining collar to seal factory setting, grind off weld. Block throttle lever movement, relieving spring force against throttle synchronizing screw, to prevent damage to screw during removal and installation.

7) Remove screw and collar. Discard collar. Reinstall screw and remove blocking from throttle lever. Collar must be removed to prevent interference with air cleaner and possible personal injury.

Installation

To install, reverse removal procedure and note the following: Install front throttle body first. Ensure throttle body assemblies and intake manifold sealing surfaces are clean. Always use new throttle body-to-manifold gaskets. Perform preliminary throttle valve synchronization adjustment. *See Adjustments.*

NOTE: Throttle body units must be installed in original position. Do not interchange front and rear units. After installation, minimum idle speed, throttle valve synchronization and throttle rod alignment must be checked and adjusted as required.

ADJUSTMENTS

NOTE: For all on-vehicle adjustments not covered in this article, see appropriate TUNE-UP article.

NOTE: The following procedure applies only if the manifold cover, either throttle body unit or throttle body castings have been replaced.

PRELIMINARY THROTTLE VALVE SYNCHRONIZATION

1) With throttle body units properly installed, turn throttle stop screws of both units counterclockwise. Turn enough to break contact between screws and throttle lever tangs.

2) Adjust each screw to allow both throttle valves to close. Throttle rod end bearing will move freely on front unit throttle lever stud when both valves are closed.

3) Turn front unit throttle stop screw clockwise until it contacts lever tang. Turn 1/4 additional turn. Turn rear unit throttle stop screw clockwise until it contacts tang. Turn 1/2 additional turn. Perform final throttle valve synchronization on-vehicle with engine running. *See "Fuel Injected Idle Speed (5.0L or 5.7L Engines)" in appropriate TUNE-UP article.*

Fig. 3: Throttle Rod Adjustment

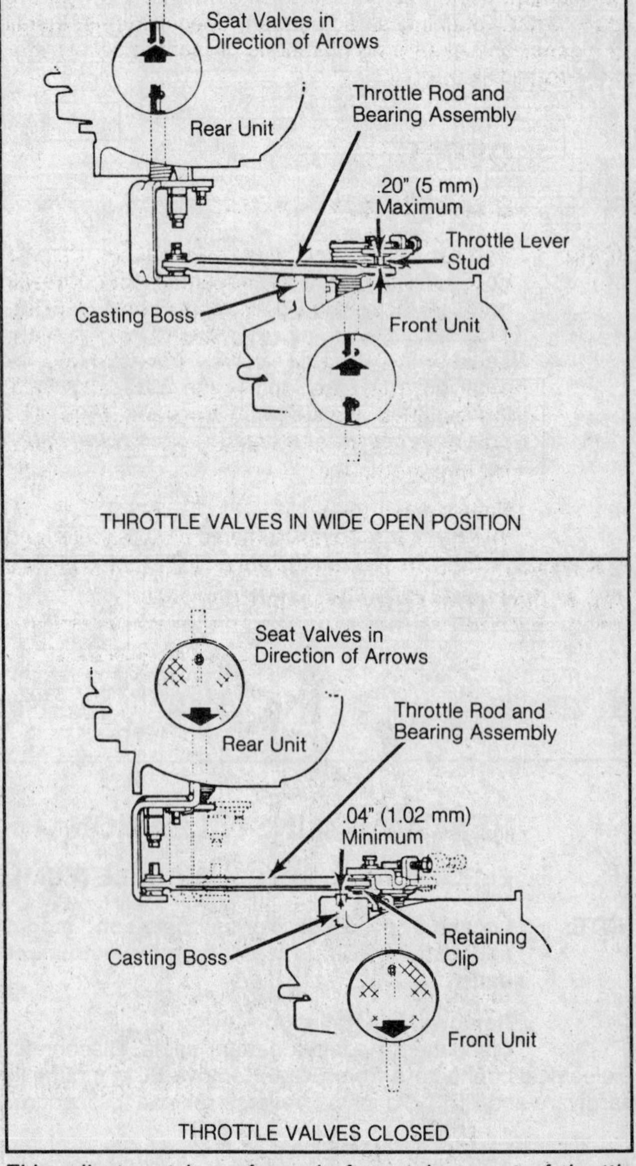

This adjustment is performed after replacement of throttle body or manifold cover.

4) After performing idle speed adjustment, check throttle rod alignment. Push rear unit throttle lever to position both front and rear units in wide open throttle position. Push throttle valves in direction of arrows. Move throttle rod and bearing assembly toward front unit casting boss. *See Fig. 3.*

5) Measure clearance at outside edge of throttle rod and bearing assembly on front unit. Clearance must not exceed .20" (5 mm) maximum. *See Fig. 3.* If greater, replacement item must be exchanged and adjustment procedure repeated. If correct, install new throttle rod and bearing assembly retaining clip.

6) Move both throttle levers through total travel and fully close throttle valves. Push throttle levers in direction of arrows. Measure clearance at inside edge of throttle rod and bearing assembly on front unit. Clearance must be .04" (1.02 mm) minimum. *See Fig. 3.*

7) If clearance is less than specified, remove throttle rod and bearing assembly retaining clip. Exchange replacement assembly and perform adjustment procedure again. After obtaining all adjustment specifications, install air cleaner and ensure no binding is present in accelerator and throttle linkages.

OVERHAUL

DISASSEMBLY

NOTE: **Before performing any service on throttle body assembly, it is essential that throttle body be placed on a holding fixture (J-9789-118, BT 30-15 or equivalent) to prevent damage to throttle valve. Disassembly of each throttle body unit is the same. DO NOT interchange components between front and rear units. Mark and identify each component for identification.**

Fuel Meter Cover

1) Remove 5 cover-to-meter body screws and lock washers. Lift off fuel meter cover with fuel pressure regulator assembly (rear unit) or accumulator assembly (front unit) attached. Do not remove fuel meter cover gasket at this time. *See Fig. 4.*

Fig. 4: Fuel Meter Cover Assembly Removal

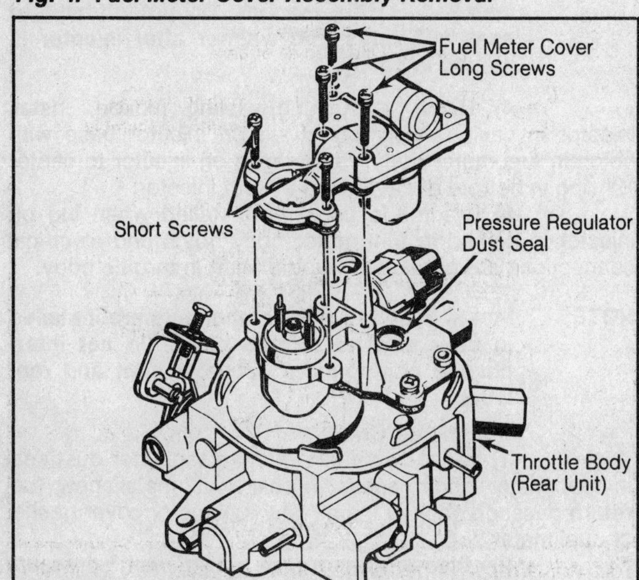

Do not remove fuel meter cover gasket at this time.

CAUTION: **Do not remove 4 screws attaching pressure regulator (accumulator) to fuel meter cover. The regulator (accumulator) includes a spring under heavy tension which may cause personal injury if released. Fuel meter cover and pressure regulator (accumulator) are serviced as an assembly only. Do not immerse assembly in any type of cleaning solvent.**

2) Remove fuel pressure regulator (rear unit) or accumulator (front unit) dust seal from fuel meter body.

Fuel Injector

1) With fuel meter cover gasket in place, use a screwdriver to carefully pry the injector from the fuel metering body. Carefully lift injector out with a twisting motion. Remove fuel meter cover gasket. *See Fig. 5.*

NOTE: **Use care in removing injector to prevent damage to electrical connectors, fuel filter and nozzle. Injector is serviced as complete assembly only. Injectors are not interchangeable between front and rear units.**

2) Carefully rotate injector filter back and forth to remove from base on injector. Remove large "O" ring and steel back-up washer on top of injector cavity in fuel meter body. Remove small "O" ring at bottom of injector cavity.

Fig. 5: Fuel Injector Assembly Removal

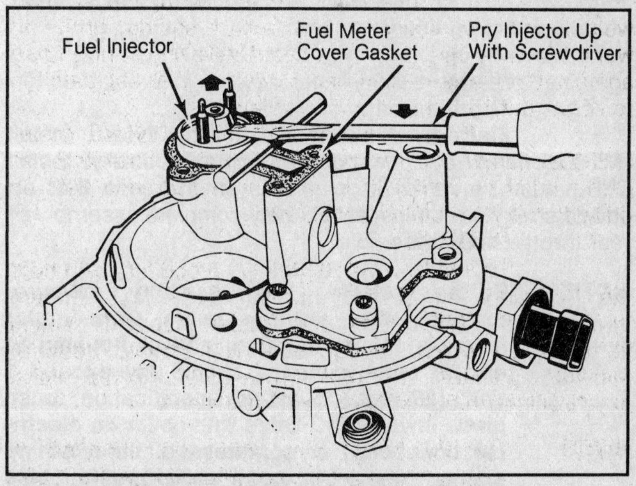

Keep fuel meter cover gasket in place until injector is removed to prevent damage to casting.

Fuel Meter Body

Remove fuel inlet and outlet nuts and gaskets from fuel meter body. Remove air cleaner stud (if equipped). Remove 3 fuel meter body-to-throttle body screws and lock washers. Remove fuel meter body and gasket.

Throttle Body

1) Disassembly of throttle body unit for immersion in cleaning solvent requires removal of TPS (rear unit) and IAC assemblies. Throttle valve screws are staked in position and should not be removed. If necessary to remove TPS, continue as follows:

GENERAL MOTORS ELECTRONIC — DUAL UNIT (Cont.)

Fig. 6: TPS Assembly Removal (Rear Unit Only)

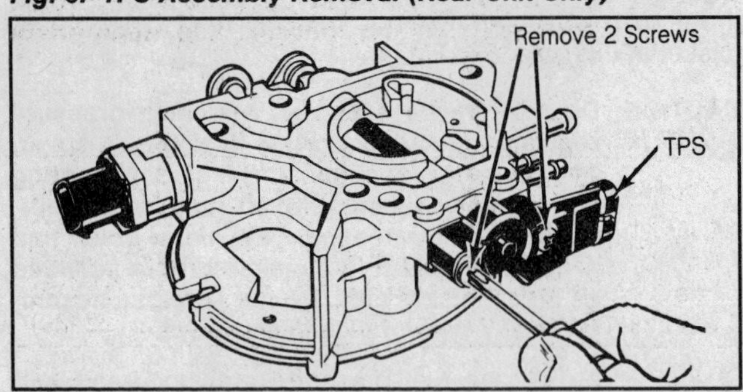

Invert throttle body to remove TPS.

2) Invert throttle body assembly and place on clean, flat surface. Remove and discard TPS attaching screws. Remove lock washers, retainers and TPS from throttle body. *See Fig. 6.*

3) If necessary, remove TPS actuator lever-to-throttle shaft screw. Remove IAC assembly and gasket from each throttle body. Remove and discard IAC gaskets.

CLEANING & INSPECTION

1) Clean all metal parts in a cold immersion-type cleaner and blow dry with compressed air.

2) Do not immerse TPS, IAC, fuel meter cover and pressure regulator (accumulator) assembly, fuel injector, fuel filter, rubber parts and diaphragms in cleaner.

3) Inspect mating surfaces for damage that may prevent gasket sealing. Repair or replace components which may be cause of problems listed under Trouble Shooting and Diagnosis.

REASSEMBLY

Throttle Body

Place throttle body on holding fixture. Install IAC assembly with new gasket. Tighten securely. Install TPS actuator lever by aligning flats on lever with flats on end of shaft. Do not install TPS until complete assembly of rear throttle body assembly.

NOTE: **Before installing IAC assembly, measure distance that valve extends from motor housing. Measuring from end of housing to end of cone, distance should not exceed 1 1/8" (28 mm). If not to specification, push pintle inward (IAC valve with collar on electrical connector) or compress pintle retaining spring toward IAC body while turning pintle inward with a clockwise motion (IAC valve without collar on connector). On IAC valves without collar, return spring to original position with straight portion of spring end aligned with flat surface under pintle head.**

Fuel Meter Body

1) Install fuel meter body gasket on throttle body. Cutout portions of gasket must match cutouts on throttle body. Install fuel meter body on gasket.

2) Apply thread locking compound (supplied in service kit) on 3 attaching screws. Install lock washers and screws. Tighten screws. Install fuel inlet and outlet nuts with new gaskets.

Fuel Injector

1) Using a slight twisting motion, install fuel injector filter on nozzle end of injector until seated against injector base.

NOTE: **Filter is cone-shaped. Large end of filter points up toward injector electrical connectors. Filter should cover raised rib at base of injector.**

2) Lubricate "O" rings with automatic transmission fluid. Push small "O" ring on nozzle end of injector until seated against injector fuel filter. Install steel back-up washer in recess in injector cavity of fuel meter body.

3) Install large "O" ring directly above back-up washer. Press "O" ring down in cavity recess until flush with top of fuel meter body casting surface. *See Fig. 7.*

Fig. 7: Fuel Injector Installation

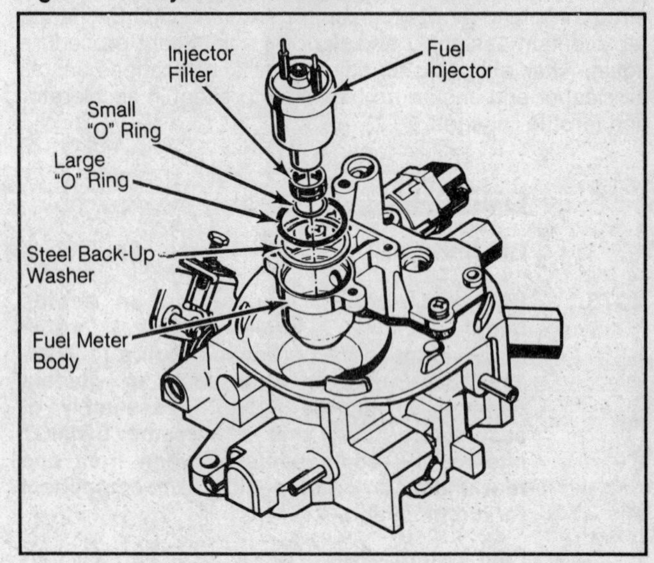

Lubricate "O" rings with automatic transmission fluid.

NOTE: **"O" rings and back-up washer must be installed in this manner. Do not attempt to seat "O" rings and washer after injector is placed in cavity.**

4) Using a pushing/twisting motion, install injector in cavity. Align raised lug on injector base with notch in fuel meter body. Push down on injector to center "O" ring in bottom of cavity and to seat injector.

5) Injector is correctly installed when lug on injector is seated in fuel meter body notch and electrical connections are parallel to throttle shaft in throttle body.

NOTE: **Insure injectors and components are installed in their original throttle body. Do not interchange components between front and rear units.**

Fuel Meter Cover

1) Install new fuel pressure regulator dust seal in fuel meter body recess in rear unit. Install new fuel return passage gasket. Install new fuel meter cover gasket on fuel meter body.

2) Install fuel meter cover with pressure regulator on rear unit. Install fuel meter cover with

GENERAL MOTORS ELECTRONIC — DUAL UNIT (Cont.)

accumulator on front unit. Apply thread locking compound (supplied in service kit) to 5 cover screws. Install lock washers and screws (2 short screws go next to injector). Tighten screws.

NOTE: Pressure regulator has a taller regulator "can" than the accumulator assembly.

Throttle Position Sensor (TPS)

Place throttle valve in normal closed idle position. Install TPS on rear throttle body with pick-up lever above throttle actuator lever tang. Install retainer, lock washers and 2 new attaching screws (coated with locking compound).

NOTE: TPS adjustment must be done with throttle body installed on vehicle. See appropriate TUNE-UP article.

TIGHTENING SPECIFICATIONS

Application	Ft. Lbs. (N.m)
Oxygen Sensor	30 (41)
Throttle Body-to-Manifold Bolts	10-14 (14-19)
Idle Air Control (IAC) Assembly	13 (18)
Fuel Inlet and Outlet Nuts	22 (30)

Fig. 8: Exploded View of Rochester Dual Unit (Crossfire) Throttle Body Assembly (Exploded View of Front Unit is Typical for Rear Unit)

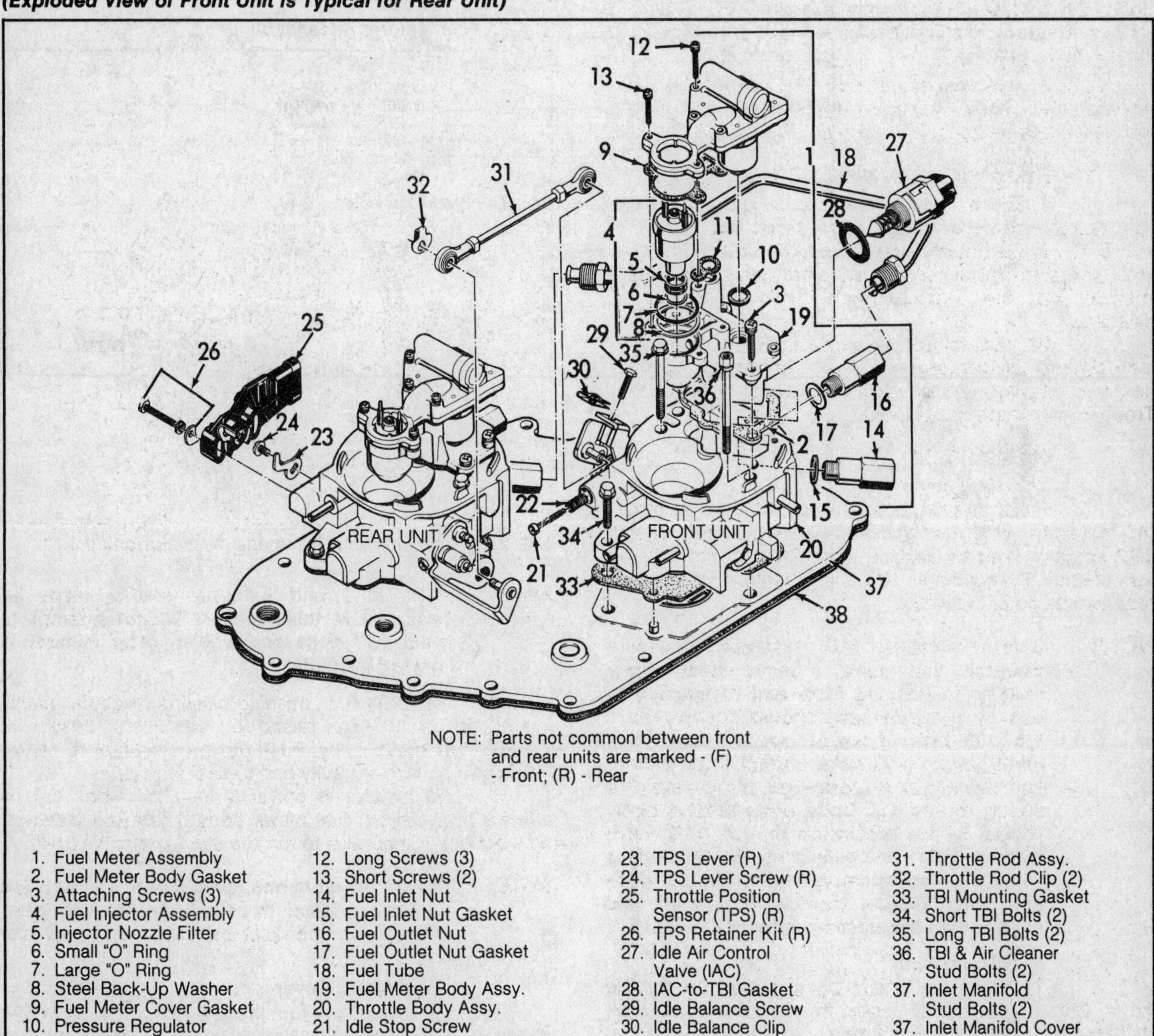

1. Fuel Meter Assembly
2. Fuel Meter Body Gasket
3. Attaching Screws (3)
4. Fuel Injector Assembly
5. Injector Nozzle Filter
6. Small "O" Ring
7. Large "O" Ring
8. Steel Back-Up Washer
9. Fuel Meter Cover Gasket
10. Pressure Regulator Dust Seal (R)
11. Fuel Meter Outlet Gasket
12. Long Screws (3)
13. Short Screws (2)
14. Fuel Inlet Nut
15. Fuel Inlet Nut Gasket
16. Fuel Outlet Nut
17. Fuel Outlet Nut Gasket
18. Fuel Tube
19. Fuel Meter Body Assy.
20. Throttle Body Assy.
21. Idle Stop Screw
22. Idle Stop Screw Spring
23. TPS Lever (R)
24. TPS Lever Screw (R)
25. Throttle Position Sensor (TPS) (R)
26. TPS Retainer Kit (R)
27. Idle Air Control Valve (IAC)
28. IAC-to-TBI Gasket
29. Idle Balance Screw
30. Idle Balance Clip (Service Only)
31. Throttle Rod Assy.
32. Throttle Rod Clip (2)
33. TBI Mounting Gasket
34. Short TBI Bolts (2)
35. Long TBI Bolts (2)
36. TBI & Air Cleaner Stud Bolts (2)
37. Inlet Manifold Stud Bolts (2)
37. Inlet Manifold Cover
38. Manifold Cover Gasket

1983 Fuel Injection

GENERAL MOTORS ELECTRONIC — DUAL UNIT (Cont.)

Fig. 9: Fuel Injection System Wiring Diagram

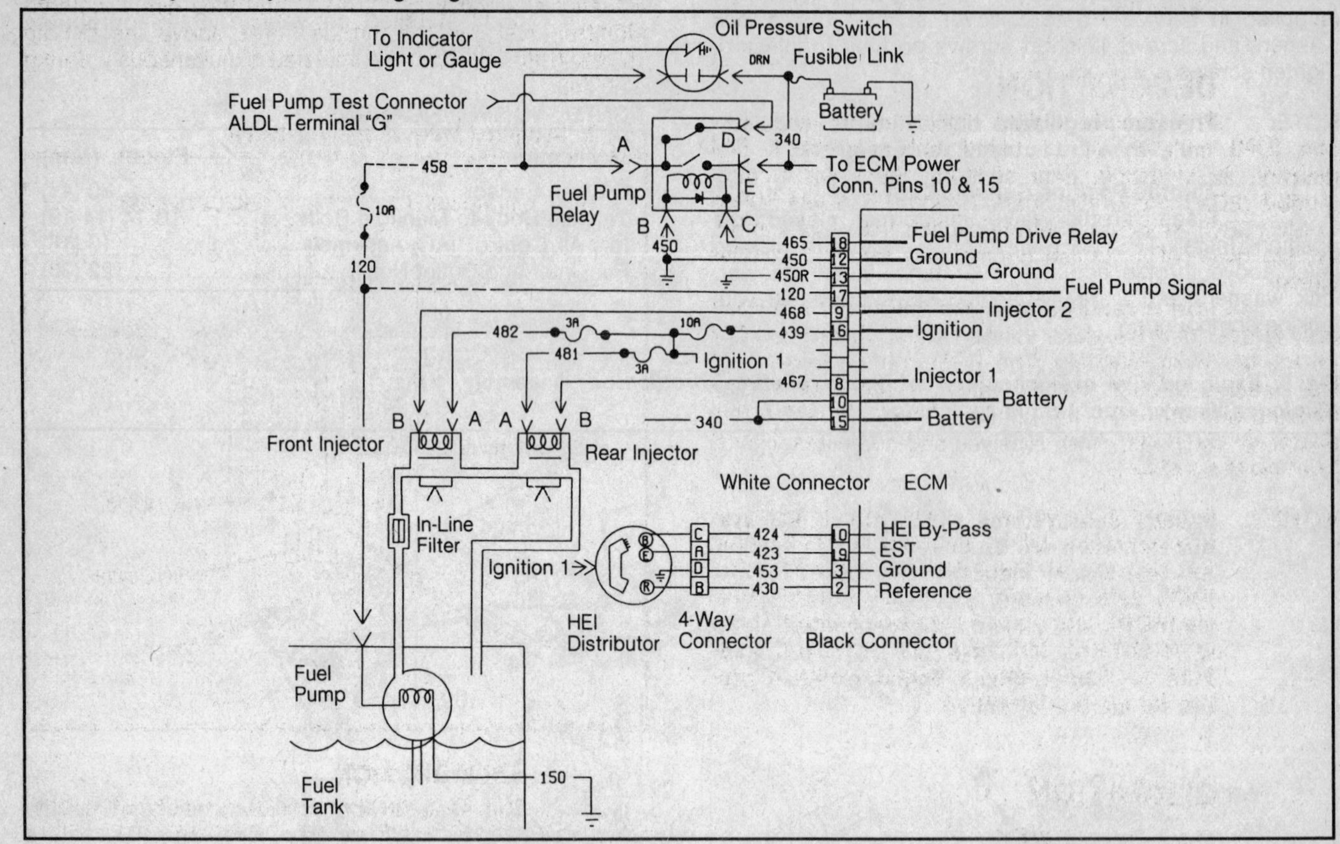

1983 Fuel Injection

GENERAL MOTORS DIGITAL

Cadillac
4.1L V8

DESCRIPTION

The General Motors digital fuel injection system (DFI) consists of 11 major sub-assemblies: fuel delivery, air induction, data sensors, Electronic Control Module (ECM), Electronic Spark Timing (EST), Idle Speed Control (ISC), emission controls, closed loop fuel control, system diagnostics, cruise control and torque converter clutch.

Fuel is supplied to engine through 2 electronically pulsed (timed) injector valves located in throttle body on top of intake manifold. The ECM controls amount of fuel metered through injector valves based upon engine demand and efficiency information. The ECM is a digital electronic computer which receives and computes signals from various sensors.

NOTE: **Primary sub-systems which affect fuel system operation will be covered in this section: fuel delivery, air induction, Idle Speed Control (ISC), data sensors, Electronic Control Module (ECM), and closed loop fuel control. Refer to "GENERAL MOTORS DFI CONTROL SYSTEM" in Computerized Engine Controls section for more information.**

OPERATION

FUEL DELIVERY

An electric fuel pump (located inside fuel tank as an integral part of fuel gauge sending unit) supplies fuel under pressure to throttle body. The ECM actuates fuel pump through fuel pump relay located in relay panel when ignition is turned on or to start position. If engine stalls or is not cranked within 1 second after ignition is turned on, ECM will deactivate fuel pump.

The fuel pressure regulator is an integral part of throttle body. A diaphragm-operated relief valve regulates fuel pressure. Relief valve is exposed to atmospheric pressure on bottom side and top side senses fuel pressure to maintain constant 10.5 psi pressure across fuel injectors. Fuel in excess of that used to maintain pressure is returned to fuel tank through fuel return line.

Fig. 1: Sectional View of Fuel Pressure Regulator

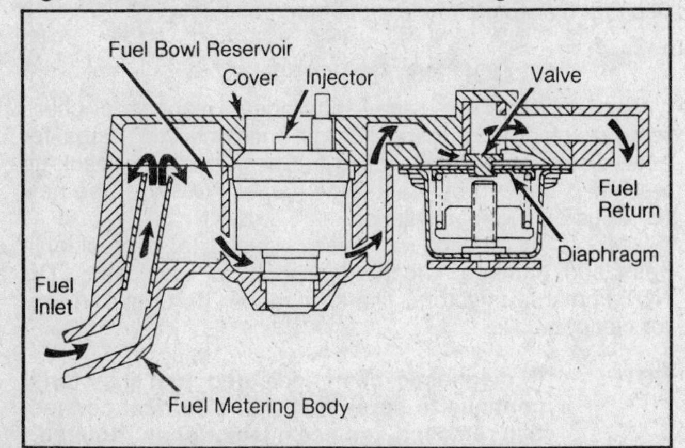

During normal running, 2 fuel injectors are actuated alternately by the ECM and they direct metered atomized fuel into the throttle bores above the throttle valves. Both injectors are actuated simultaneously during cranking.

Fig. 2: Sectional View of Injector Valve

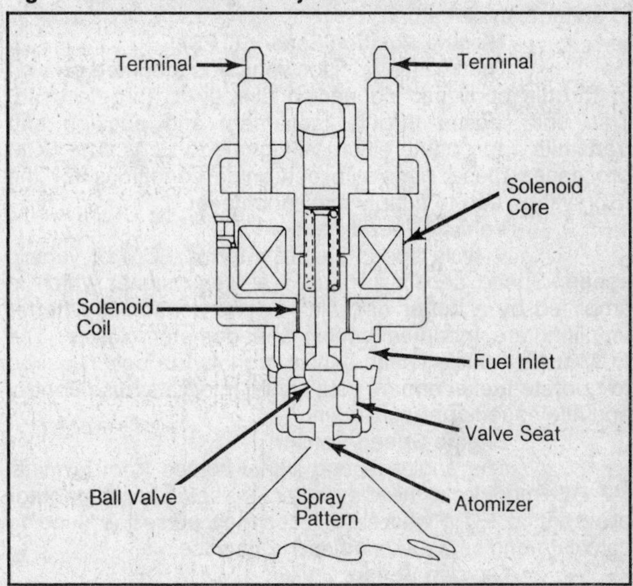

AIR INDUCTION

The air induction system consists of throttle body and intake manifold. Air for combustion enters throttle body and is distributed to each cylinder through intake manifold. Throttle body contains special distribution skirt below each injector valve to improve fuel distribution. Air flow rate is controlled by throttle valves which are connected to accelerator linkage. Idle speed is determined by position of throttle valves and is controlled by ISC.

DATA SENSORS

Each sensor furnishes an electronic signal to ECM, modifying injector pulse to conform to operating conditions of the engine. These sensors are as follows:

Manifold Air Temperature Sensor (MAT)

This sensor is mounted in the intake manifold directly in front of the throttle body. The MAT sensor measures air/fuel mixture temperature in the intake manifold. The sensor resistance changes as air temperature changes. ECM receives this change in signal and adjusts injector pulse accordingly. Low temperature produces high resistance.

Coolant Temperature Sensor (CTS)

The CTS is located in the left front corner of the intake manifold. This sensor provides information to ECM for fuel enrichment, ignition timing, EGR operation, canister purge control, air management, early fuel evaporation control, idle speed control and closed loop fuel control.

Manifold Absolute Pressure Sensor (MAP)

The MAP sensor is mounted under the instrument panel near the right side A/C outlet. A hose from the throttle body to the MAP provides a vacuum signal. The sensor monitors changes in intake manifold pressure which result from engine load and speed variations. As intake manifold pressure increases, additional fuel is

GENERAL MOTORS DIGITAL (Cont.)

required. MAP sends this information to ECM so that the pulse width is increased (time injector is open). As manifold pressure decreases, pulse width is shortened.

Barometric Pressure Sensor (BARO)

The BARO sensor is mounted on the MAP sensor bracket. This unit senses ambient or barometric pressures and signals the ECM on pressure changes due to altitude and weather.

Throttle Position Sensor (TPS)

The throttle position sensor is mounted on side of throttle body and connected directly to throttle shaft. This unit senses throttle movement and position and transmits appropriate electrical signals to ECM. The ECM processes these signals to determine conditions for the ISC system and to supply fuel enrichment.

Vehicle Speed Sensor

Vehicle speed sensor informs ECM of vehicle speed. Speed sensor produces a weak signal which is amplified by a buffer amplifier. Speed sensor and buffer amplifier are mounted behind speedometer cluster. The ECM uses vehicle speed sensor signals for logic required to operate fuel economy data panel, integral cruise control and idle speed control system.

Engine Speed Sensor

The engine speed signal comes from terminal #7 HEI module in the distributor. Pulses from distributor are sent to ECM where time between pulses is used to calculate engine speed and spark advance.

Oxygen Sensor

Oxygen sensor used in DFI system is a closed end Zirconia sensor placed in exhaust gas stream. This sensor generates a very weak voltage which varies with oxygen content of exhaust gases. As oxygen content of exhaust gases increases, a leaner mixture is indicated by low voltage output. As oxygen content decreases, a richer mixture is indicated by higher voltage output. The ECM corrects air/fuel ratio according to signals received from oxygen sensor.

CAUTION: **No attempt should be made to measure oxygen sensor voltage output. Current drain of conventional voltmeter could permanently damage sensor, shift sensor, shift sensor calibration range and/or render sensor unusable. Do not connect jumper wire, test leads or other electrical connectors to sensor.**

ELECTRONIC CONTROL MODULE

The ECM is mounted under the right end of instrument panel and consists of various printed circuit boards mounted in a metal box. All sensor inputs are fed into ECM and are processed to produce proper pulse duration for injectors, correct idle speed and proper spark advance. All sensors send analog inputs, which are converted to digital inputs before processing.

IDLE SPEED CONTROL (ISC)

The ISC is an electrically driven actuator which changes throttle valve angle, in idle position, according to commands from the ECM. This function is by-passed when throttle is opened enough to bring the TPS off its idle circuit. The ISC is located on side of throttle body.

CLOSED LOOP FUEL CONTROL

Closed loop fuel control maintains an air/fuel ratio of 14.7:1. Oxygen sensor monitors oxygen content of exhaust gases, sends information to ECM and ECM corrects air/fuel mixture for deviations from ideal ratio.

TROUBLE SHOOTING & DIAGNOSIS

NOTE: **Diagnosis of fuel system should begin with determining correct fuel pump operation. Connect fuel pressure gauge (J-25400-300) to fuel line servicing fitting and measure fuel pressure while cranking engine. Use Fuel System Diagnosis chart if pressure is not between 9-12 psi. Use Injector System Diagnosis chart if pressure is between 9-12 psi.**

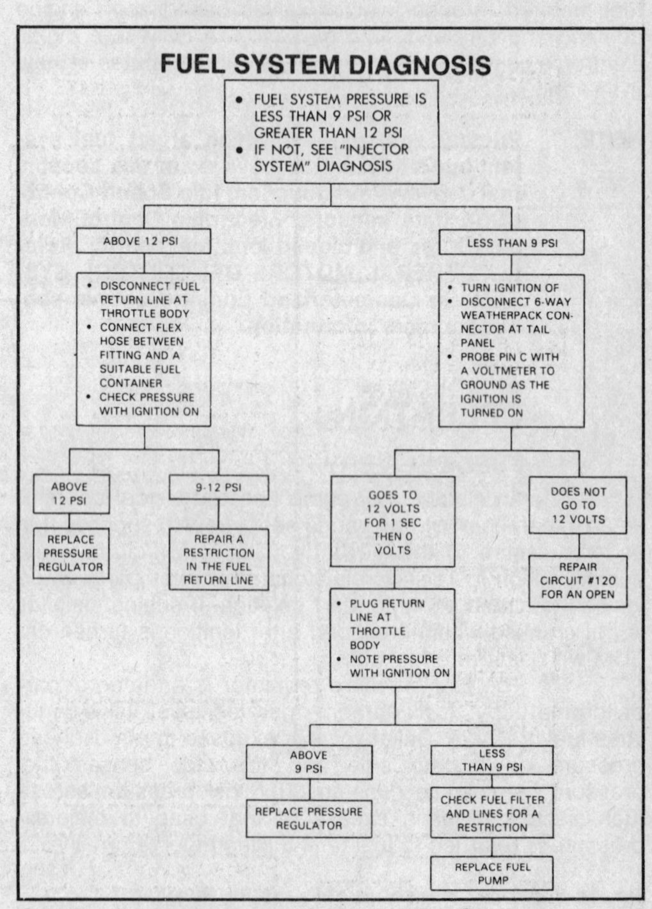

See Fig. 5 for pin and circuit number locations.

FLOODING, ROUGH IDLE

1) After using appropriate diagnostic chart, remove injector(s). Inspect large and small "O" rings for cuts, distortion or other damage. Check that steel back-up washer is located beneath large (upper) "O" ring. Use new "O" rings during reinstallation.

2) Inspect fuel injector fuel filters for cleanliness and damage. Clean or replace as necessary. DO NOT immerse injectors, filters or rubber parts in carburetor cleaner.

NOTE: **If diagnostic chart indicated fuel injector(s) continue to spray fuel with electrical connection removed, replace injector(s) as required.**

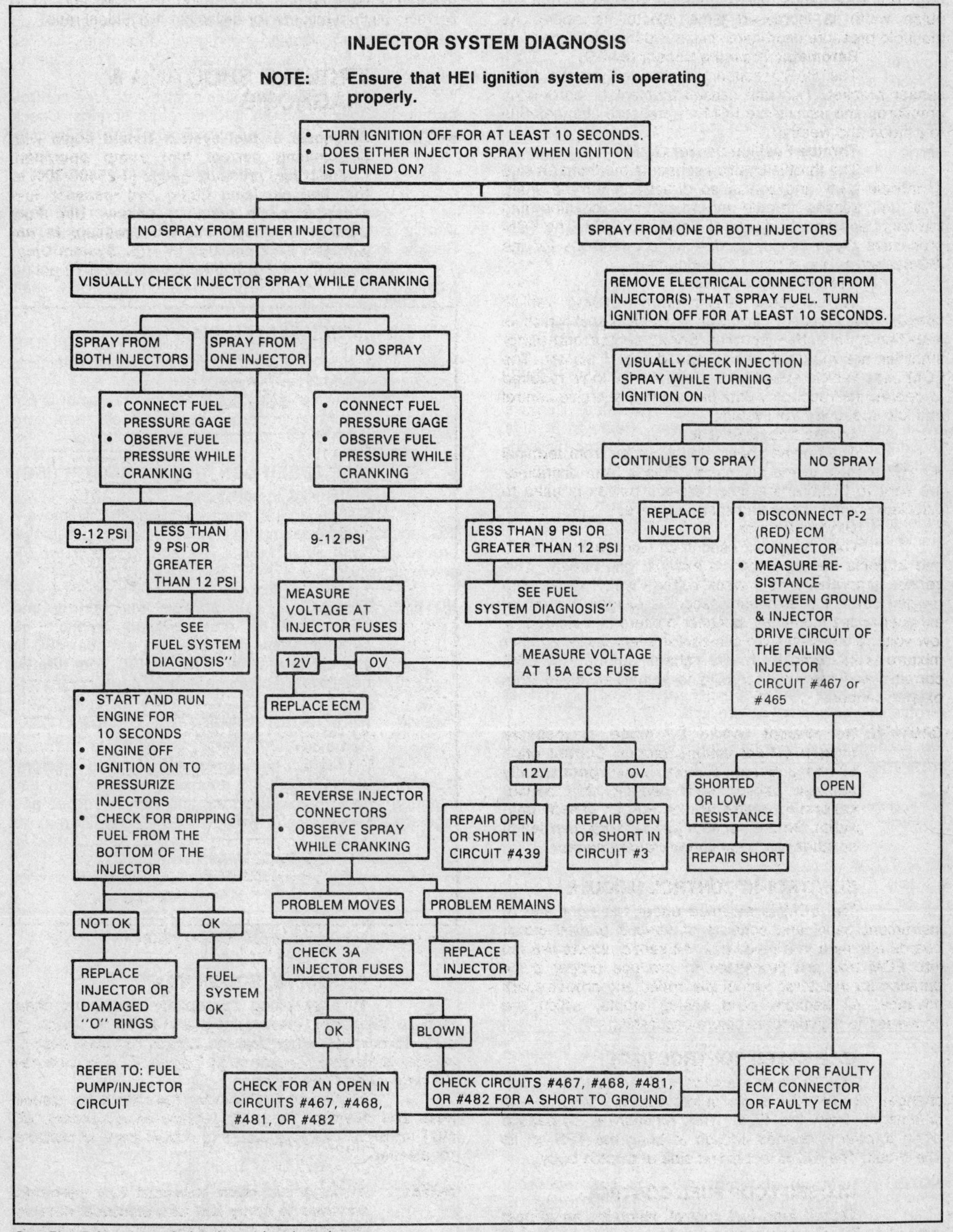

See Fig. 5 for pin and circuit number locations.

GENERAL MOTORS DIGITAL (Cont.)

HARD STARTING, HESITATION POOR COLD OPERATION

Follow appropriate diagnostic chart, then remove injectors and inspect for dirt or plugging. Clean and replace as necessary. Check for restricted inlet and outlet passages or inoperative pressure regulator. Repair or replace defective parts.

NOTE: DO NOT remove 4 fuel pressure regulator screws from fuel metering cover. Fuel pressure regulator and cover are serviced as an assembly only. Do not soak pressure regulator, fuel meter cover, injectors, filters, diaphragms or rubber components in carburetor cleaner.

REMOVAL & INSTALLATION

ELECTRONIC CONTROL MODULE (ECM)

Removal

Disconnect battery negative cable. Remove lower right instrument panel cover. Remove 3 nuts securing ECM and 1 nut securing ground strap. Disconnect harness connectors and remove ECM.

Installation

Position ECM under right end of instrument panel and attach harness connectors. Place ECM onto its bracket and install ground strap and retaining nuts. Install lower instrument panel and connect negative battery cable.

THROTTLE BODY ASSEMBLY

Removal

1) Remove air cleaner. Disconnect and clear ISC actuator, TPS and injector electrical connections. Remove throttle return springs, cruise control linkage, throttle linkage and downshift cable.

Fig. 3: Assembled View of Throttle Body Assembly

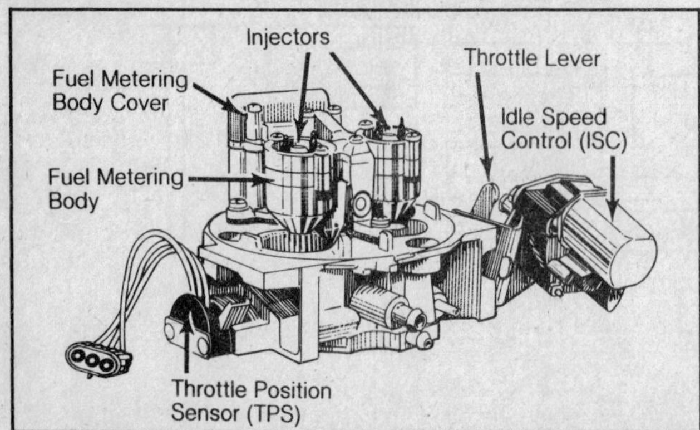

2) From rear of throttle body, remove fuel inlet line, fuel return line, brake booster line, MAP hose and AIR hose, noting positions for installation. Remove PCV, EVAP and EGR hoses from front of throttle body, noting positions. Remove 3 throttle body mounting screws, throttle body and gasket.

NOTE: Removal of throttle body is not necessary unless throttle shafts or throttle body replacement is required.

Installation

1) Position throttle body and new gasket on intake manifold. Install and tighten mounting screws. Connect fuel lines, vacuum hoses and electrical connections.

2) Install downshift cable, cruise control, throttle linkages and both throttle return springs. Check and adjust ISC and TPS. *See appropriate TUNE-UP article.*

THROTTLE POSITION SENSOR (TPS)

Removal

1) Remove TPS electrical connector. Remove throttle body. Remove and discard TPS attaching screws. Remove lock washers and retainers.

2) Remove TPS from throttle body, noting location of TPS pick-up lever in relation to throttle shaft lever tang for installation reference.

Installation

1) Position TPS over throttle shaft with TPS pick-up lever following throttle lever tang. Install retainers, lock washers and 2 new screws.

2) Tighten screws so TPS will move but is not loose. Install throttle body and reconnect electrical connector. Adjust TPS. *See appropriate TUNE-UP article.*

IDLE SPEED CONTROL ACTUATOR (ISC)

Removal & Installation

Disconnect ISC electrical connector. Remove 2 ISC mounting screws and ISC. To install, reverse removal procedure and adjust ISC. *See appropriate TUNE-UP article.*

NOTE: The ISC is calibrated at the factory and should not be disassembled. Replace as complete assembly only. Do not soak ISC in carburetor cleaner. Remove ISC from throttle body before cleaning throttle body.

INJECTORS & PRESSURE REGULATOR

Removal

Disconnect harness connectors from injectors. Remove 8 screws securing pressure regulator and fuel metering cover to throttle body and remove cover and regulator. With a lifting-twisting motion, carefully remove

Fig. 4: Exploded View of Injector Components

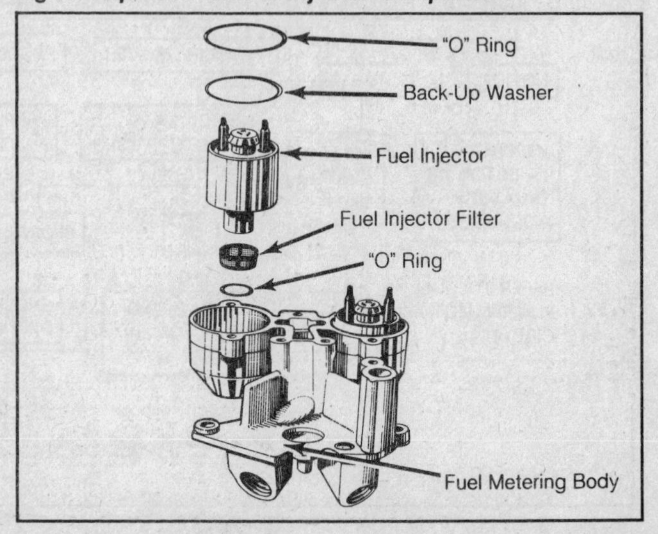

injectors. Discard upper and lower "O" rings being careful not to lose upper "O" ring back-up washer.

NOTE: **DO NOT remove 4 fuel pressure regulator screws from fuel metering cover. Fuel pressure regulator and fuel metering cover are serviced as an assembly only. Do not soak fuel metering cover in carburetor cleaner as fuel pressure regulator diaphragms and gaskets will be damaged.**

Installation

Lubricate and install new "O" rings. Position injectors in fuel metering body with connectors aligned in a "cross-car" orientation. Install fuel metering cover assembly and retaining screws. Tighten screws evenly and install harness connectors.

FUEL METERING BODY

Removal & Installation

Remove throttle body. Remove fuel inlet and outlet line fitting nuts and gaskets from fuel metering body. Remove 3 retaining screws, lock washers, metering body and gasket. To install, reverse removal procedure and use new gasket.

NOTE: **DO NOT remove fuel distribution skirt retaining screw. Skirt is integral part of throttle body and is not serviced separately.**

MAP & BARO SENSORS

Removal

1) Remove right side lower instrument panel and glove box liner. Disconnect harness connectors from both sensors and vacuum hose from MAP sensor.

2) Remove screw holding ground strap to mounting bracket and remove mounting bracket screws. Remove sensors and bracket as an assembly.

Installation

Reverse removal procedure and note MAP sensor has female connector on sensor and BARO sensor has male connector on sensor. Reinstall glove box liner and lower instrument panel.

COOLANT TEMPERATURE SENSOR

Removal

Drain radiator until coolant level is below that of sensor. Disconnect harness connector from sensor and remove sensor from block.

Installation

Apply non-hardening sealer to threads of sensor and install sensor. Reconnect harness connector. Refill radiator.

MAT SENSOR

Removal & Installation

Remove sensor from manifold (directly in front of throttle body). When installing, coat threads with a non-hardening sealer.

ADJUSTMENTS

NOTE: **See appropriate TUNE-UP article.**

TIGHTENING SPECIFICATIONS

Application	Ft. Lb. (N.m)
Throttle Body Mounting Screws	15 (20)
Temperature Sensors	15 (20)
Fuel Filter	15 (20)

Fig. 5: DFI Fuel Pump & Injector Circuit

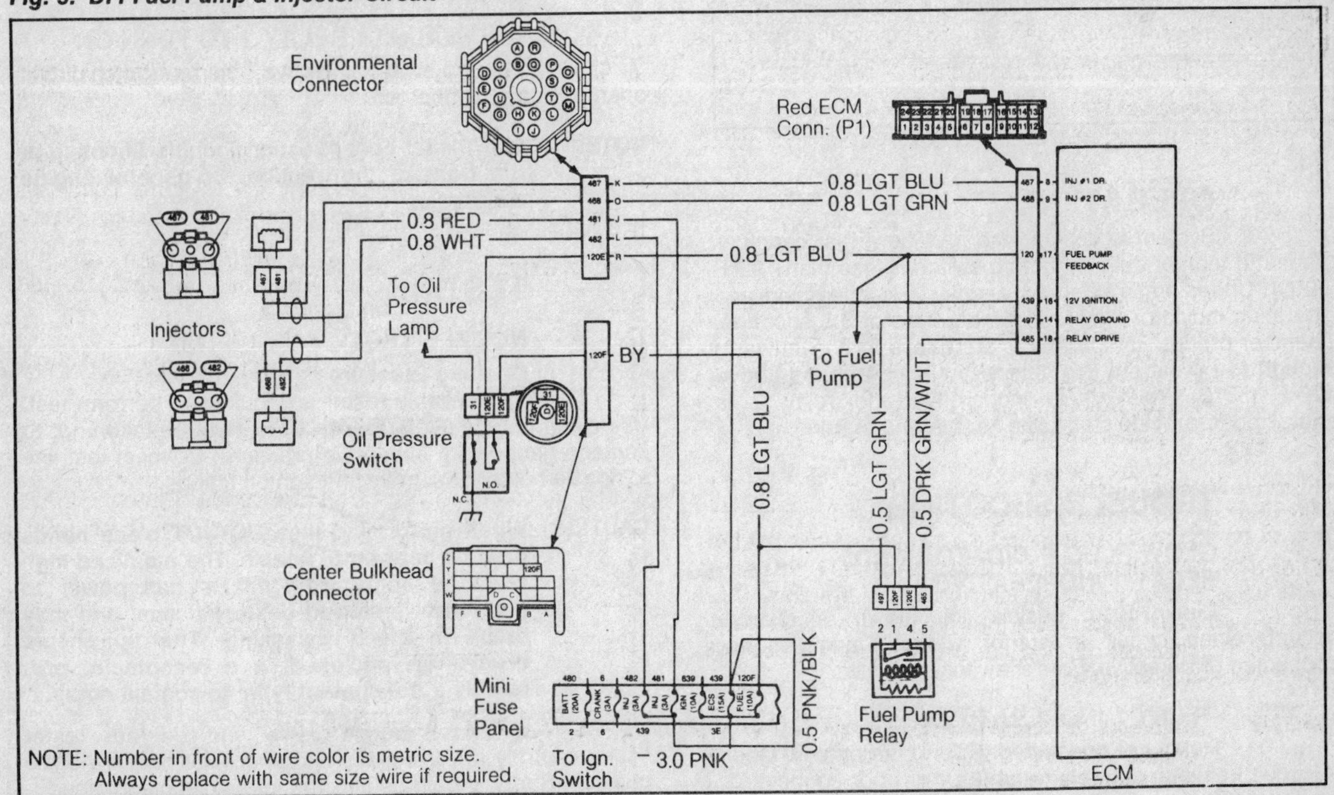

1983 Fuel Injection

GENERAL MOTORS DIESEL — 4 CYL.

Chevette, 1000

DESCRIPTION

Chevette/1000 diesel fuel injection system consists of a mechanical injection pump driven by camshaft through a cogged belt, 4 high pressure fuel pipes, 4 injection nozzles, a fuel filter with an integral water separator, a fuel cut solenoid mounted on injection pump and a glow plug system to warm engine for starting.

Chevette/1000 diesel engines are electronically controlled in the start and warm-up modes to make for easier cold starting and cold driving. An electronic module monitors and corrects combustion chamber temperatures during preheat and afterglow modes. System consists of a controller, glow plug relay, dropping resistor, sensing resistor, glow plugs, thermo switch, 2 glow plug relays and 2 fusible links.

Fig. 1: Chevette Diesel Fuel Injection Fuel System

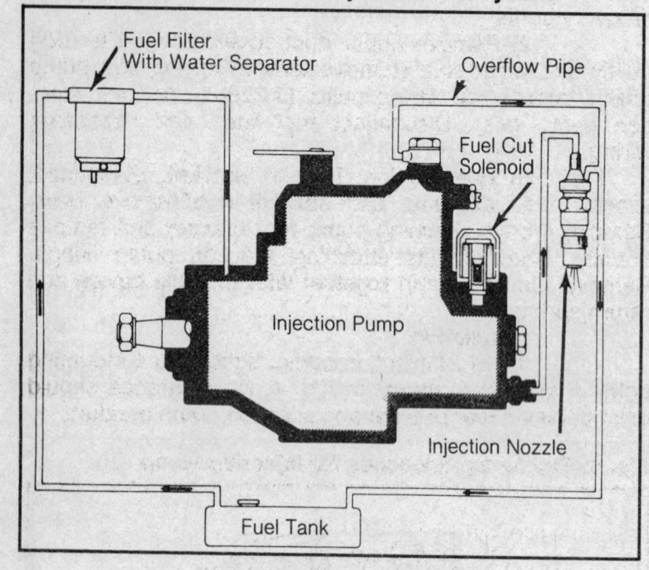

OPERATION

System is designed to provide a fast chamber preheat if temperature at thermo switch is less than 122°F (50°C). Under these conditions, relay 1 is energized and glow plug indicator light is lit for a period of 3.5 seconds. Chamber preheat temperatures are raised to a level warm enough to permit starting vehicle. At temperatures above 122°F (50°C), relay 1 is inoperative and relay 2 is energized to provide stabilizing heat during starting.

TROUBLE SHOOTING

GLOW PLUG INDICATOR AND RELAY 1 INOPERATIVE

Blown fuse. Fusible link blown or disconnected. Open circuit in starter wiring. Controller not connected or defective. Starter switch defective.

RELAY 1 INOPERATIVE

Relay not connected. Open in relay coil. Open in circuit between controller and relay or poor connection. Open in relay grounding circuit. Defective controller. Circuit between signal feed wire of sensing resistor and controller open or poorly connected. Sensing resistor terminals disconnected. Relay main terminal disconnected. Defective relay. Quick preheat terminals disconnected, poorly connected or open in wiring. Grounding terminal of engine harness disconnected.

GLOW PLUG INDICATOR INOPERATIVE

Bulb burned out. Circuit has open or poor connection. Defective controller.

RELAY 1 TURNS OFF WITHIN 2 SECONDS

One or more glow plugs inoperative. Loose connections at controller. Defective controller.

RELAY 1 WILL NOT TURN OFF

Defective controller.

RELAY 1 OPERATES WITH COOLANT TEMPERATURE ABOVE 122°F (50°C)

Coolant temperature above 122°F (50°C). Thermo switch defective (switch remains on and does not turn off). Circuit shorted to ground.

GLOW PLUG INDICATOR AND RELAY 2 INOPERATIVE

Starter switch "R" circuit open or poorly connected.

RELAY 2 INOPERATIVE

Relay terminals not connected. Relay coil open. Circuit between relay 2 and starter "R" terminal open or poorly connected.

GLOW PLUG INDICATOR REMAINS ON AND CAUSES RELAY 1 TO TURN ON

Thermo switch defective. Thermo switch circuit open or poorly connected.

NOTE: See Diesel Fuel Injection Trouble Shooting at the front of the section for general engine diagnosis.

TESTING

NOZZLE TEST

Opening Pressure

1) A reliable tester is required to perform test. Use clean test oil (SAE J9670). Care must be taken not to damage gauge with excessive pressure. Connect test line to nozzle holder assembly and tighten fittings.

CAUTION: When performing test, DO NOT place hands or arms near tip of nozzle. The atomized high pressure spray from nozzle has power to penetrate flesh and destroy tissue, and may result in blood poisoning. The tip should always be enclosed in a receptacle, preferably a transparent type, to contain spray.

2) Close gauge valve and operate tester handle sharply several times and check for proper nozzle position. Spray should be injected into a clean container.

1983 Fuel Injection

GENERAL MOTORS DIESEL — 4 CYL. (Cont.)

3) Open gauge valve and operate tester handle slowly to determine injector opening pressure. Observe gauge reading just before oil is sprayed from tip. A buzzing noise will occur when spray is injected. Minimum opening pressure is 1706 psi (120 kg/cm²).

Spray Pattern

Check spray pattern by operating handle 1 stroke about every 2 seconds and observe spray pattern. The pattern should be uniform and injected at correct angle of nozzle being tested.

Fig. 2: Diesel Fuel Injector Spray Pattern

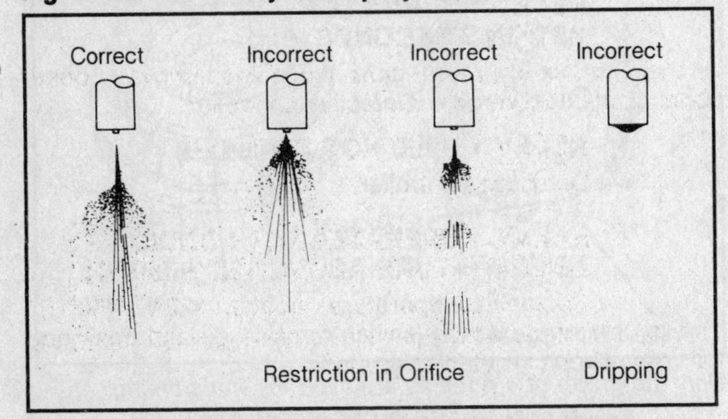

Do not place hands or arms under nozzle during test.

CAUTION: Pressure gauge should be closed for the test or it may be damaged. Test spray is flammable. Keep vapor away from open flames.

Nozzle Leakage

Check for nozzle leakage by applying 142.2 psi (10 kg/cm²) to nozzle. Tip should remain dry without an accumulation of fuel at spray holes. A slight wetting is allowed after 10 seconds if no droplets are formed.

GLOW PLUG SYSTEM

Glow Plug Relay 1 or 2

With a circuit tester, make a continuity test across terminals "C" and "D" with battery voltage applied to terminals "A" and "B". Replace relay if no continuity is indicated.

Fig. 3: Glow Plug Relay Terminal Locations

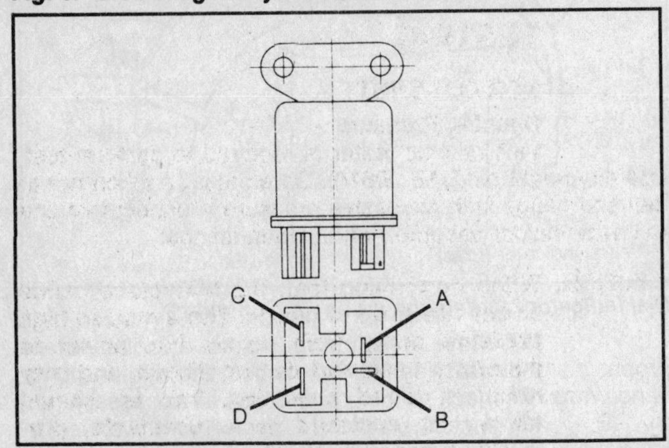

Dropping Resistor

Check for continuity across terminals. If no continuity, replace resistor.

Glow Plug

Check for continuity across plug terminals and plug body. If no continuity, heater wire is broken and should be replaced.

Thermo Switch

Submerge end of thermo switch in water and gradually raise water temperature and make a continuity test across terminal and body. If no continuity, replace switch.

Fusible Link

Check continuity across fusible link terminals. If no continuity, link is fused out and should be replaced.

REMOVAL & INSTALLATION

INJECTION PUMP

Removal

1) Disconnect battery ground cable. Drain cooling system. Remove fan shroud, radiator and coolant recovery bottle.

2) Remove upper dust cover. Loosen tension pulley and plate bolt. Remove tension spring and pump gear attaching nut. Using puller (J-22888), remove injection pump gear. Disconnect fuel lines and necessary wiring.

3) Remove fuel filter at bracket. Disconnect injector lines at pump and nozzles and remove lines. Remove 4 bolts attaching pump rear bracket and remove bracket. Remove nuts attaching injection pump flange. Remove injection pump together with fast idle device and return spring.

Installation

1) Install injection pump, tightening 4 mounting bolts in sequence shown in *Fig. 4.* No clearance should exist between rear bracket and injection pump bracket.

Fig. 4: Tightening Sequence for Injection Pump

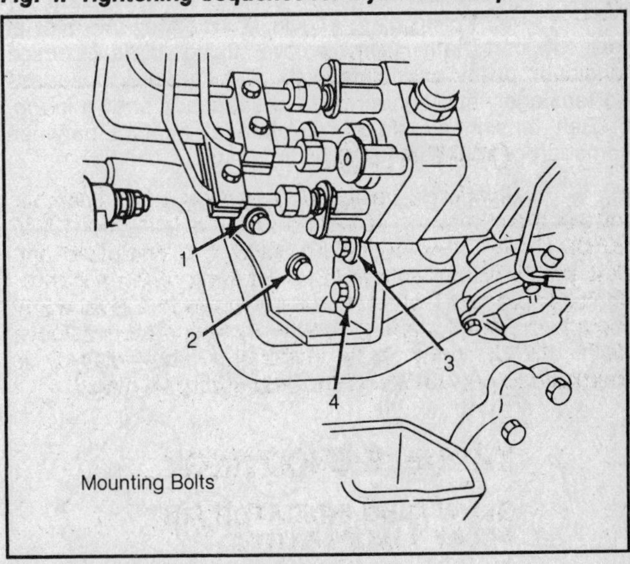

No clearance should exist between rear bracket and pump bracket.

2) Install injection pump pulley by aligning it with key groove. Align mark on gear with mark on front plate. *See Fig. 5.* Tighten nut using a 8 mm by 1.25" lock bolt to prevent turning pulley. Remove cam cover.

1983 Fuel Injection

GENERAL MOTORS DIESEL — 4 CYL. (Cont.)

Fig. 5: Aligning Marks For Injection Pump Gear

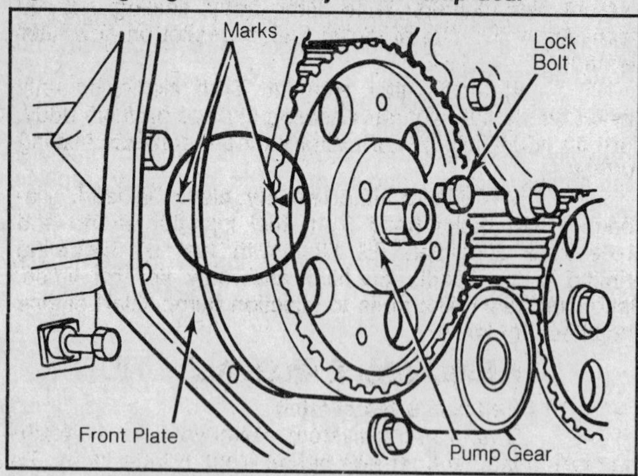

3) With No. 1 piston at TDC, install fixing plate (J-29761) to slot in rear of camshaft to prevent camshaft from rotating. Remove camshaft gear attaching bolt.

4) Using puller (J-22888), remove cam gear. Reinstall cam gear loosely so it can be turned by hand. Install the timing belt noting the following: Belt should be properly tensioned between pulleys, cogs on belt and pulley should be engaged properly, crankshaft should not be turned and timing belt looseness should be concentrated on tension pulley.

5) Depress tension pulley with finger and install tension spring. Loosely tighten tension pulley bolts, tightening top bolt first to prevent movement of pulley. Tighten camshaft pulley bolt. Remove injection pump gear lock bolt.

6) Remove fixing plate on end of camshaft. Check that No. 1 piston is at TDC. DO NOT turn crankshaft in attempt to make adjustment. Check that injection pump pulley mark is in line with mark on plate.

7) Fixing plate should fit smoothly into slot at rear of camshaft, then remove fixing plate. Loosen tensioner pulley and plate bolts. Concentrate looseness on tensioner then tighten bolts in sequence shown in *Fig. 6.* Belt tension should be checked at a point between camshaft gear and injection pump gear.

Fig. 6: Tensioner Bolt Tightening Sequence

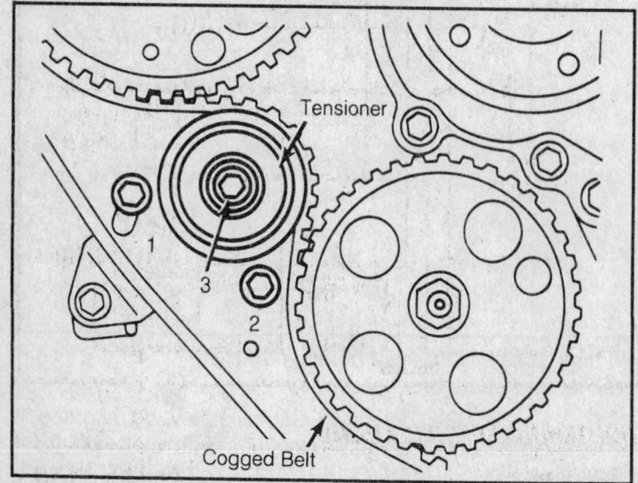

Check belt tension between camshaft gear and injection pump gear.

8) Insure that No. 1 piston is at TDC. Check that timing belt is properly tensioned and that marks are aligned.

9) Remove distributor head screw and washer. Install static timing gauge (J-29763) with lift approximately .04" (1 mm) from plunger. Bring No. 1 piston to a point 45-60° before TDC by turning crankshaft. Turn dial indicator on timing gauge to zero.

Fig. 7: Damper Pulley Alignment Notches

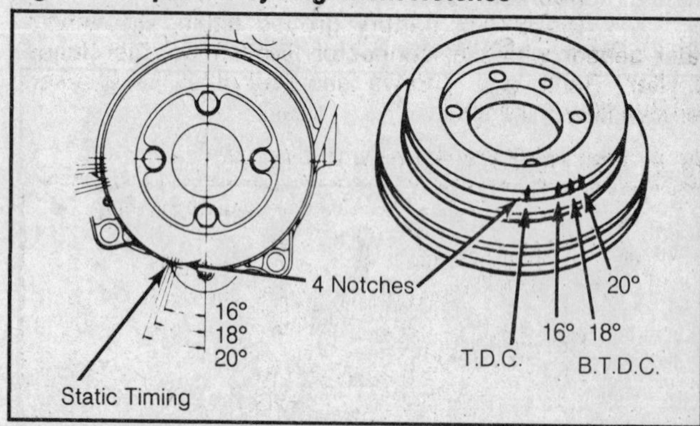

Only the group of 4 notches are used for static timing.

10) The damper pulley has a series of notched lines on it. There are 4 notches on one side and 7 on the other. The 4 lines are used for static timing. Turn crankshaft until the 18° line is in alignment with pointer on dial indicator. Read dial indicator.

11) Standard reading should be .02" (.5 mm). Turn crankshaft in normal direction of rotation. If reading on dial indicator deviates from specified range, hold crankshaft at 18° position and loosen 2 nuts on injection pump flange.

Fig. 8: Static Timing Setting

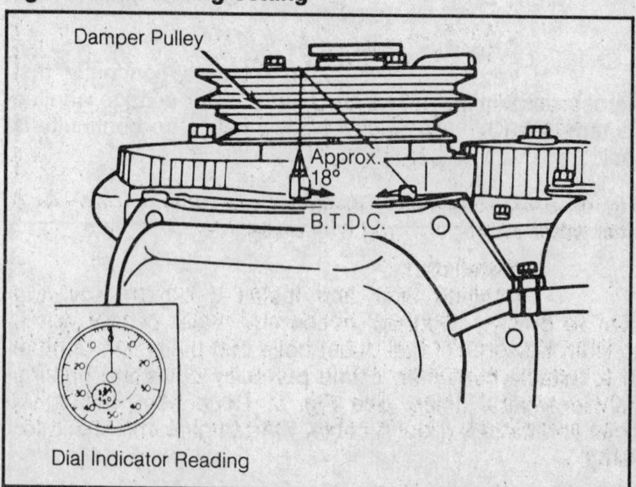

Dial indicator reading should be .02" (.5 mm).

12) Move injection pump to a point where proper dial indicator reading is reached and tighten pump flange nuts. Recheck reading and adjust as necessary.

13) Install distributor screw and washer in injection pump. Install cam cover, fuel injection lines and fuel filter. Connect necessary lines and hoses and install upper dust cover.

14) Install coolant recovery bottle, radiator, fan shroud and fill radiator with coolant. Adjust idle speeds.

GENERAL MOTORS DIESEL — 4 CYL. (Cont.)

INJECTION NOZZLE

Removal & Installation

Disconnect battery ground cable. Remove fresh air duct. Remove PCV hose. Remove injection lines at injection nozzle and loosen lines at pump. Remove return line and injection nozzle. To install, reverse removal procedure.

FUEL FILTER

Removal

Disconnect battery ground cable. Disconnect water sensor wiring at connector. Disconnect fuel hoses at filter. Remove 2 screws securing filter to bracket. Remove filter assembly.

Fig. 9: Fuel Filter and Element Assembly

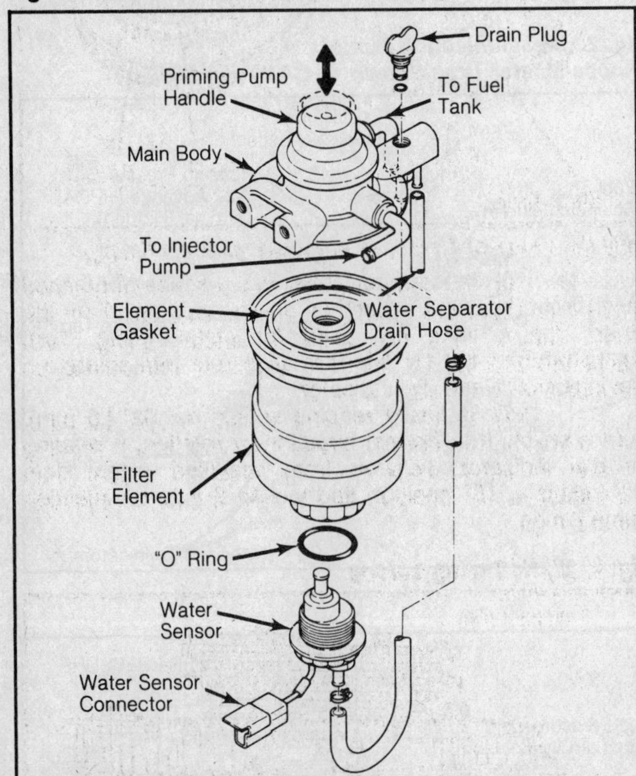

Coat water sensor "O" ring with diesel fuel.

Installation

Position filter and install 2 screws securing filter to bracket. Connect hoses and water sensor wiring to filter. Disconnect fuel outlet hose and place end of hose in a suitable container. Prime pump by operating priming handle several times. *See Fig. 9.* Reconnect fuel outlet hose and battery ground cable. Start engine and check for leaks.

FUEL FILTER ELEMENT

Removal & Installation

1) Disconnect battery ground cable. Disconnect water sensor wiring at connector. Disconnect sensor from drain hose. Using a filter wrench, remove filter element by turning counterclockwise. Do not spill fuel while removing element.

2) Drain fuel from filter element. Remove water sensor from bottom of old element. *See Fig. 9.* Remove and wipe off water sensor "O" ring. Apply thin film of clean diesel fuel to "O" ring. Install "O" ring on water sensor.

3) Install water sensor on bottom of new filter element and tighten. Wipe filter body sealing surface clean. Apply thin film of diesel fuel to gasket on new filter element.

4) Install filter element. Turn clockwise until gasket on element contacts sealing surface on main body. Turn an additional 2/3 turn after element contacts sealing surface.

5) Connect water sensor electrical lead. Disconnect fuel outlet hose from fuel injection pump and place in a container. Fill filter with fuel by operating priming pump handle on filter assembly several times. Reconnect fuel outlet hose to injection pump. Start engine and check for leaks.

ENGINE BLOCK HEATER

Removal & Installation

Drain cooling system. Remove screws retaining block heater and remove heater from cylinder body. To install, reverse removal procedure.

PCV VALVE

Removal & Installation

Disconnect PCV connecting hose. Remove 2 screws securing PCV valve to cam cover, and remove valve and gasket. To install, reverse removal procedure.

BAFFLE PLATE

Removal & Installation

Remove cam cover. Remove 7 screws securing baffle to cam cover. To install, reverse removal procedure.

Fig. 10: Glow Plug System Wiring Diagram

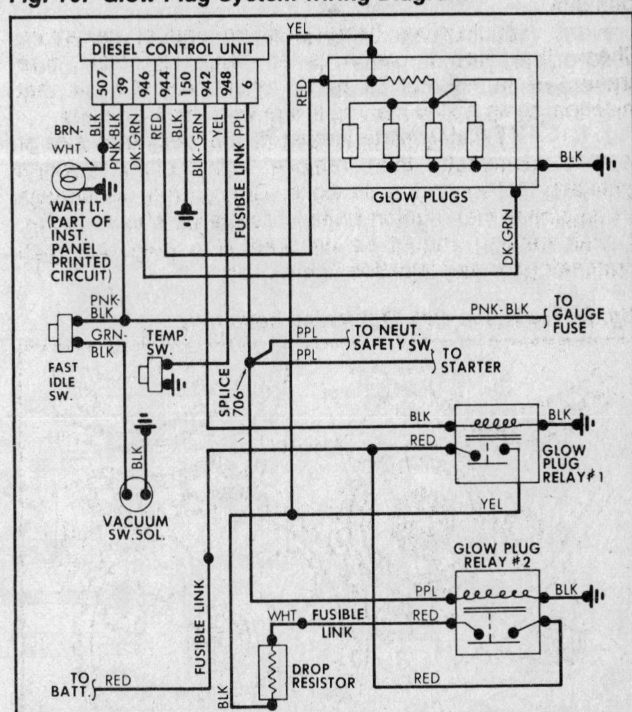

TIGHTENING SPECIFICATIONS

Application	Ft. Lbs. (N.m)
Camshaft Pulley Bolt	45 (61)
Tensioner Pulley Nut	45 (61)

1983 Fuel Injection

GENERAL MOTORS DIESEL — V6 & V8

DESCRIPTION

Diesel mechanical fuel injection systems differ greatly from electronic fuel injection systems. In this diesel system, a mechanical high pressure rotary pump, gear driven by the camshaft at camshaft speed, injects a precisely metered amount of fuel to each cylinder at the proper time. The pump is mounted on top of the engine and provides necessary timing advance under all operating conditions.

High pressure fuel pipes (6 or 8) carry fuel from pump to an injection nozzle in each cylinder. All pipes are exactly the same length to insure that there is no variance in timing. Engine RPM is controlled by a rotary fuel metering valve. As accelerator pedal is pushed down, throttle cable opens metering valve to allow increased fuel delivery. A built-in low pressure transfer pump delivers fuel to main injection pump.

A fuel filter is located between the electric (V6) or mechanical (V8) fuel supply pump (mounted on side of engine block) and the fuel injection pump. Any excess fuel is returned to tank by a fuel return system.

OPERATION

AIR INDUCTION SYSTEM

An air crossover housing is located on top of engine over injection pump. It is bolted to intake manifold with 4 bolts and serves as the only air inlet in the system. No fuel passes through crossover. It is an open-chambered housing with a single inlet drawing air through an air filter assembly mounted above. Crossover unit has 2 branches, one leading to each side of intake manifold. Gaskets are installed between crossover and manifold to prevent vacuum leaks. Starter fluid should NEVER be used or sprayed into crossover. If crossover is removed, air screens must be installed.

FUEL TANK-TO-PUMP SYSTEM

Diesel fuel is drawn from fuel tank by an engine mounted electric (V6) or mechanical (V8) fuel supply pump. Electric pump receives battery current when ignition switch is in "RUN" or "START" positions and puts out about 5 3/4-8 3/4 psi (.40-.62 kg/cm²) to the fuel injection pump. Maximum operating current is 3 amps. Mechanical pump is driven by an eccentric cam mounted on crankshaft and puts out about 5 1/2-6 1/2 psi (.39-.46 kg/cm²) to fuel injection pump.

A small screen type filter is located in fuel tank at the fuel pick-up. A larger sealed 11-12 micron fuel filter is located on rear of engine between fuel supply pump and fuel injection pump. Diesel fuel arrives at center inlet fitting on injection pump after leaving filter. A fuel return line is provided to return any excess fuel to tank.

Fig. 2: Diesel Injection Pump (Roosa-Master Type Shown — CAV Type Similar)

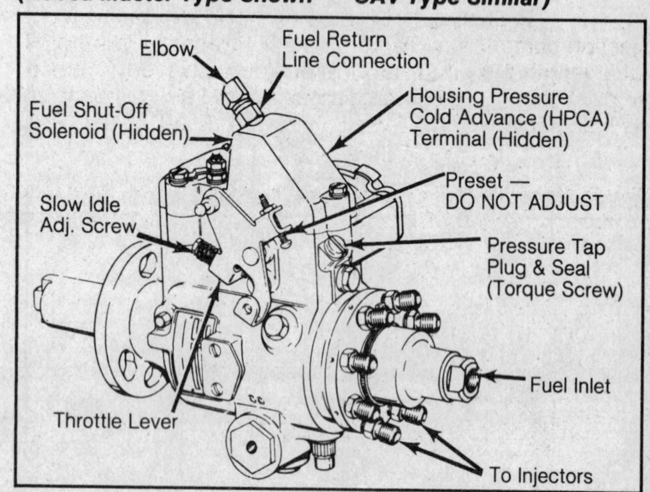

Fig. 1: CAV Type Diesel Injection Pump Fuel Circuit Diagram

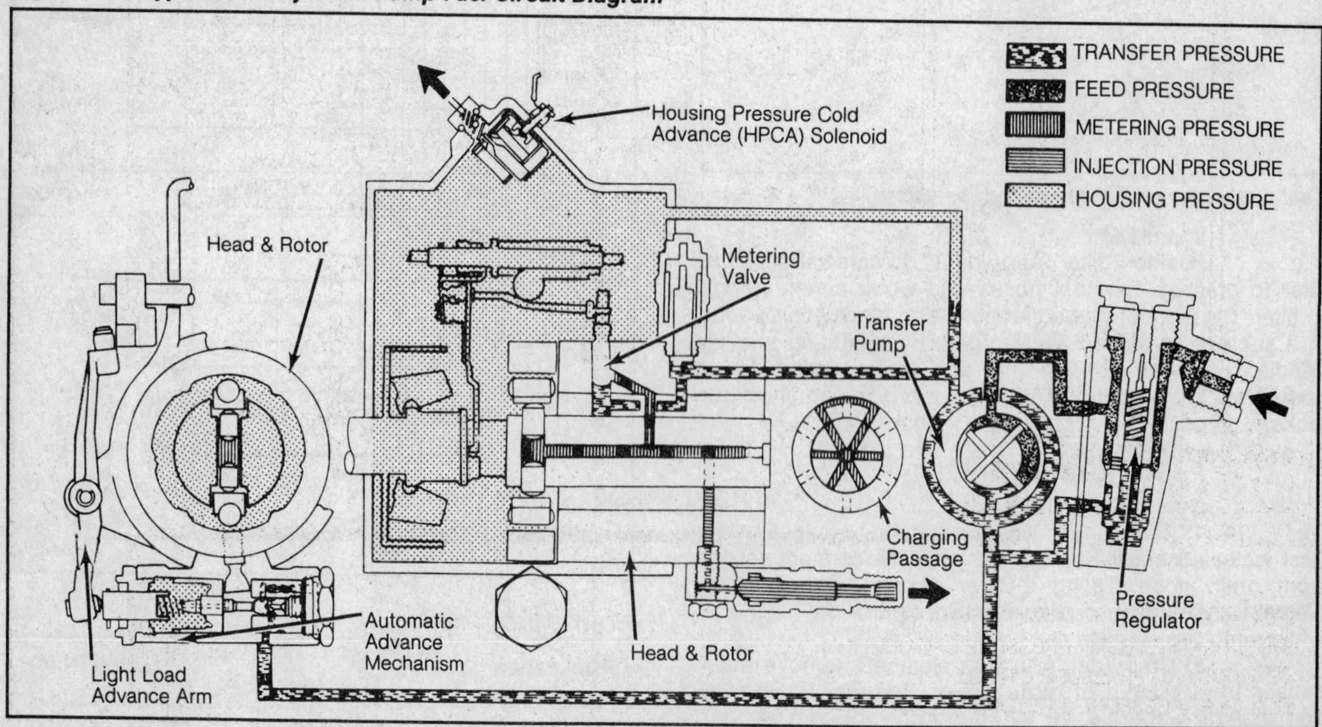

1983 Fuel Injection

GENERAL MOTORS DIESEL — V6 & V8 (Cont.)

DIESEL INJECTION PUMP

High pressure diesel injection pump is mounted to top of engine below air crossover. Pump is cam driven at speed equal to camshaft. Because of this, pump can precisely govern time and amount of fuel injection.

A built-in fuel pressure regulator and transfer pump picks up fuel at pump inlet, and pushes it through a passage to pump head. The pump head distributes fuel, still at transfer pump pressure of 8-12 psi (.56-.84 kg/cm²), to metering valve, governor and automatic advance mechanisms. Fuel then passes to rotary fuel metering valve and into a charging passage. As pump shaft rotates, fuel is fired, under high pressure, through each delivery pipe to an injector. Pump is not serviceable and must be exchanged in case of a malfunction.

FUEL DELIVERY PIPES

High pressure pipes (6 or 8) are routed from injection pump to an injector in each cylinder. Pipes are of equal length but are bent differently to achieve this equal length. Pipes are not interchangeable and are pre-bent by the manufacturer.

GLOW PLUGS

Glow plugs are small heaters provided to assist in cold starting. Glow plug controller and relay cycle 12 volts to these 6 volt heaters, which causes them to heat rapidly. After engine starts, glow plugs remain on for about a minute, then shut off. If ignition is turned on and engine is not started, glow plugs will continue to cycle until the batteries are discharged.

CAUTION: Do not manually by-pass glow plug relay; glow plugs will be ruined instantly.

Fig. 4: Diesel Glow Plug & Injection Nozzle Location

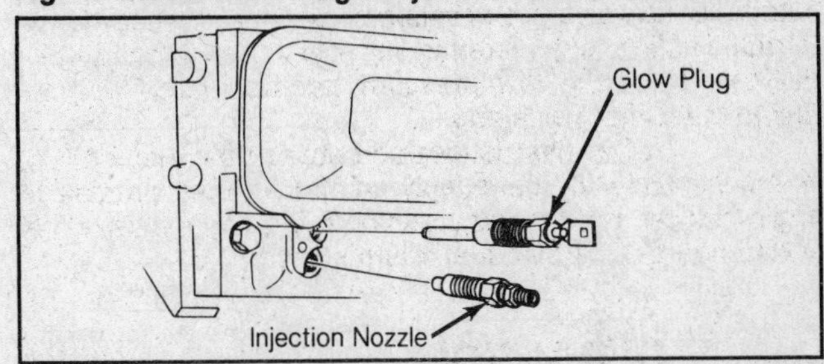

Fig. 3: Roosa-Master Type Diesel Injection Pump Fuel Circuit Diagram

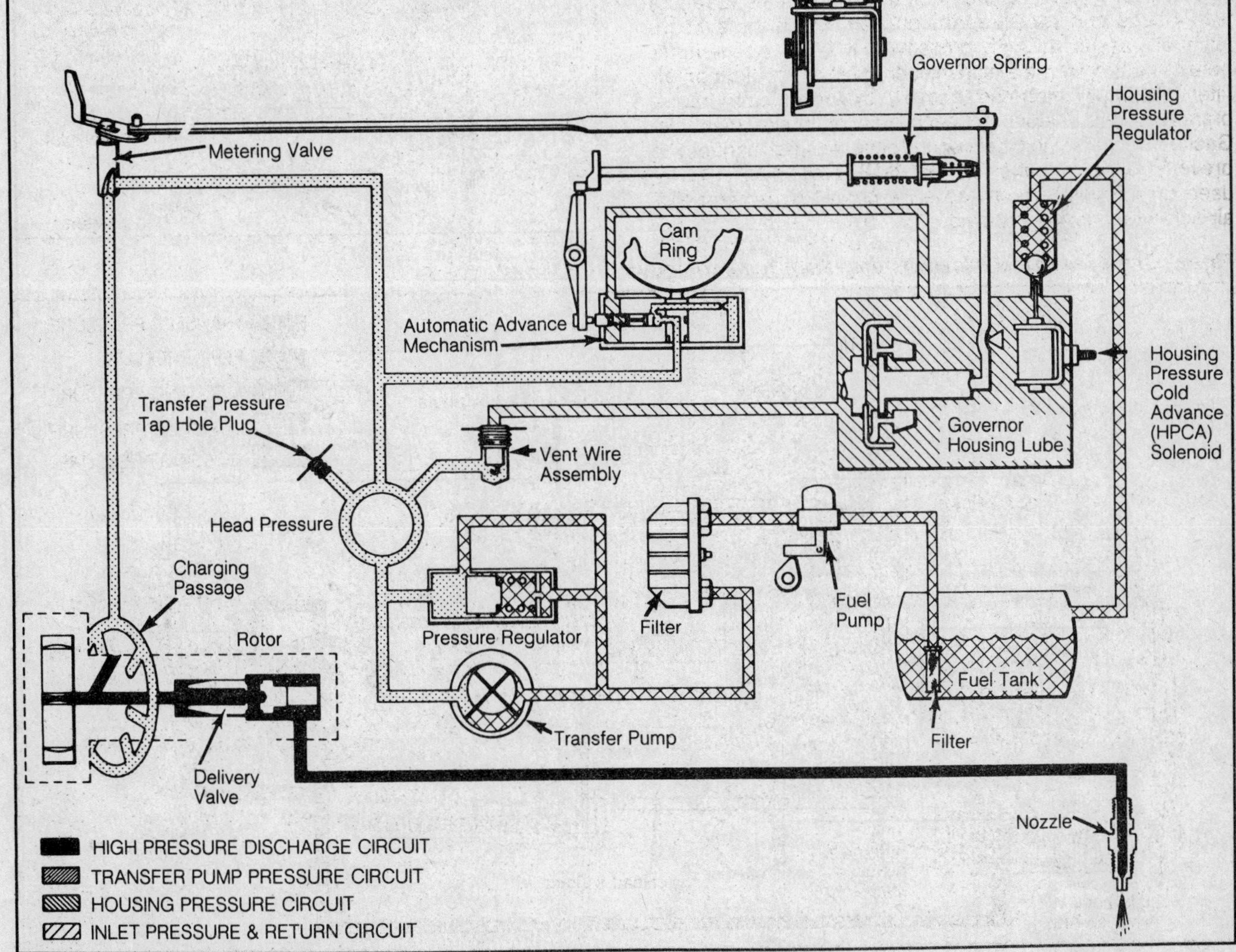

GENERAL MOTORS DIESEL — V6 & V8 (Cont.)

TROUBLE SHOOTING

ELECTRONIC GLOW PLUG SYSTEM DIAGNOSIS

(ALL MODELS)

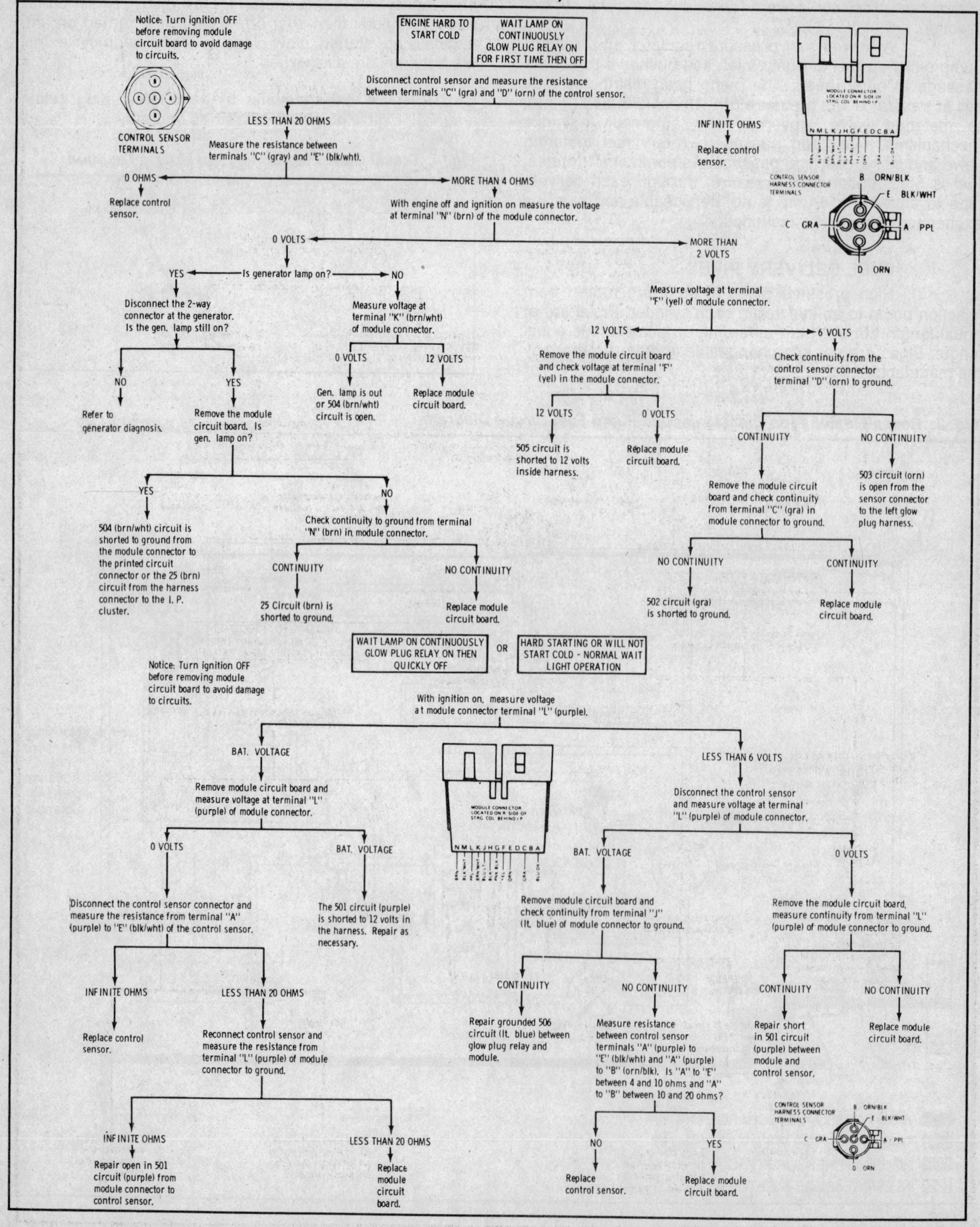

1983 Fuel Injection

GENERAL MOTORS DIESEL — V6 & V8 (Cont.)

ELECTRONIC GLOW PLUG SYSTEM DIAGNOSIS (Cont.)
(ALL MODELS)

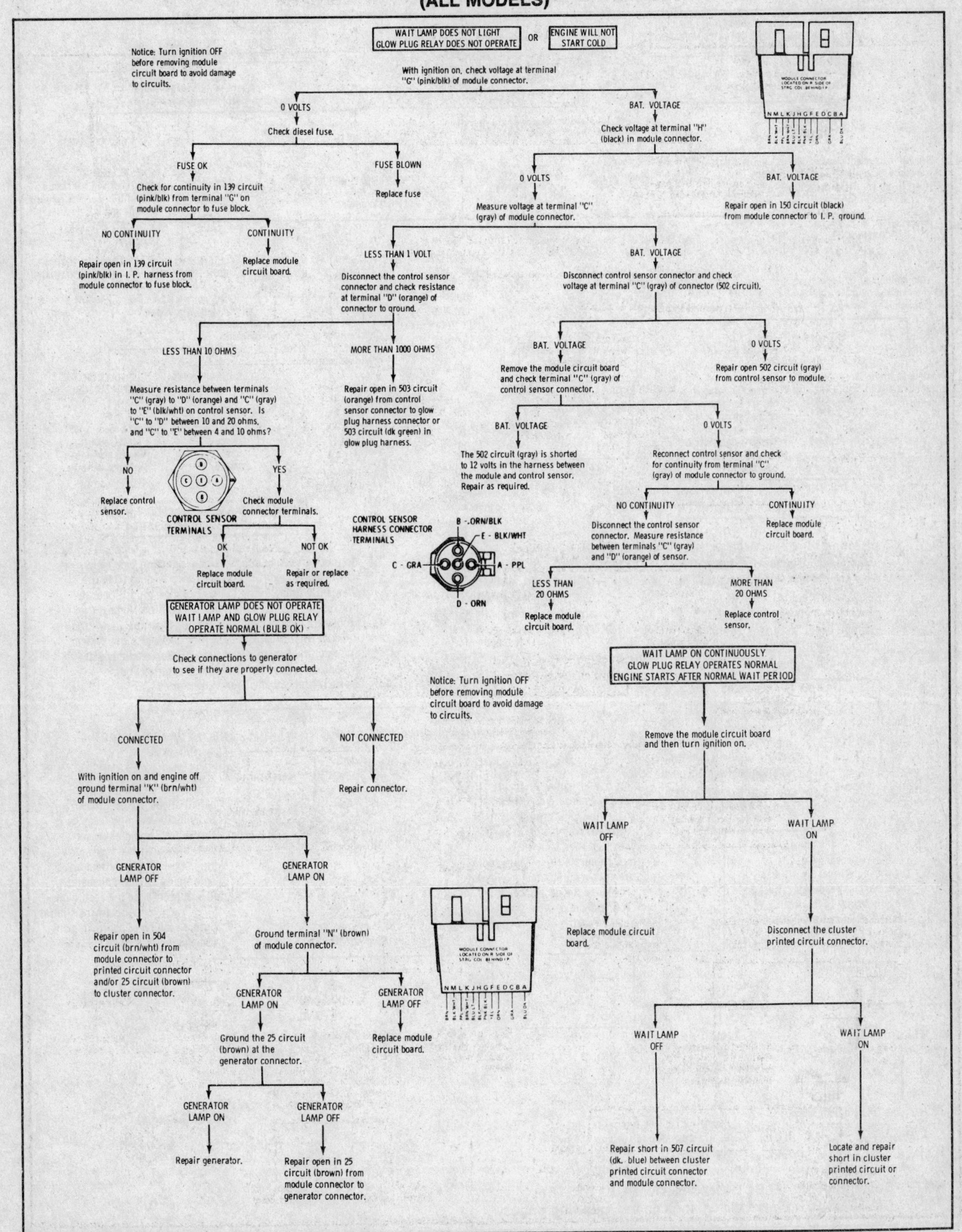

GENERAL MOTORS DIESEL — V6 & V8 (Cont.)

ELECTRONIC GLOW PLUG SYSTEM DIAGNOSIS (Cont.)
(ALL MODELS)

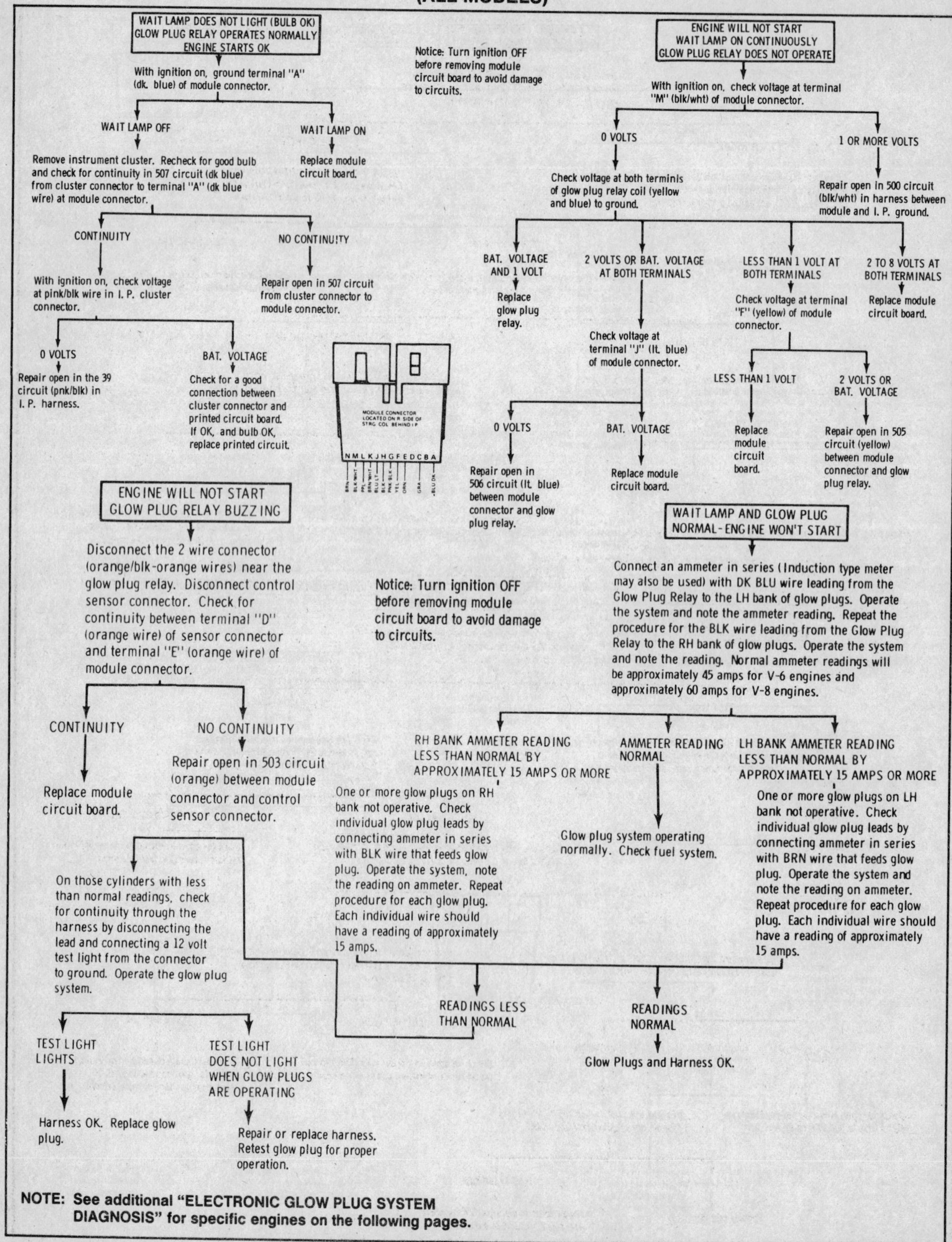

GENERAL MOTORS DIESEL — V6 & V8 (Cont.)

ELECTRONIC GLOW PLUG SYSTEM DIAGNOSIS (Cont.)
(V6 MODELS ONLY)

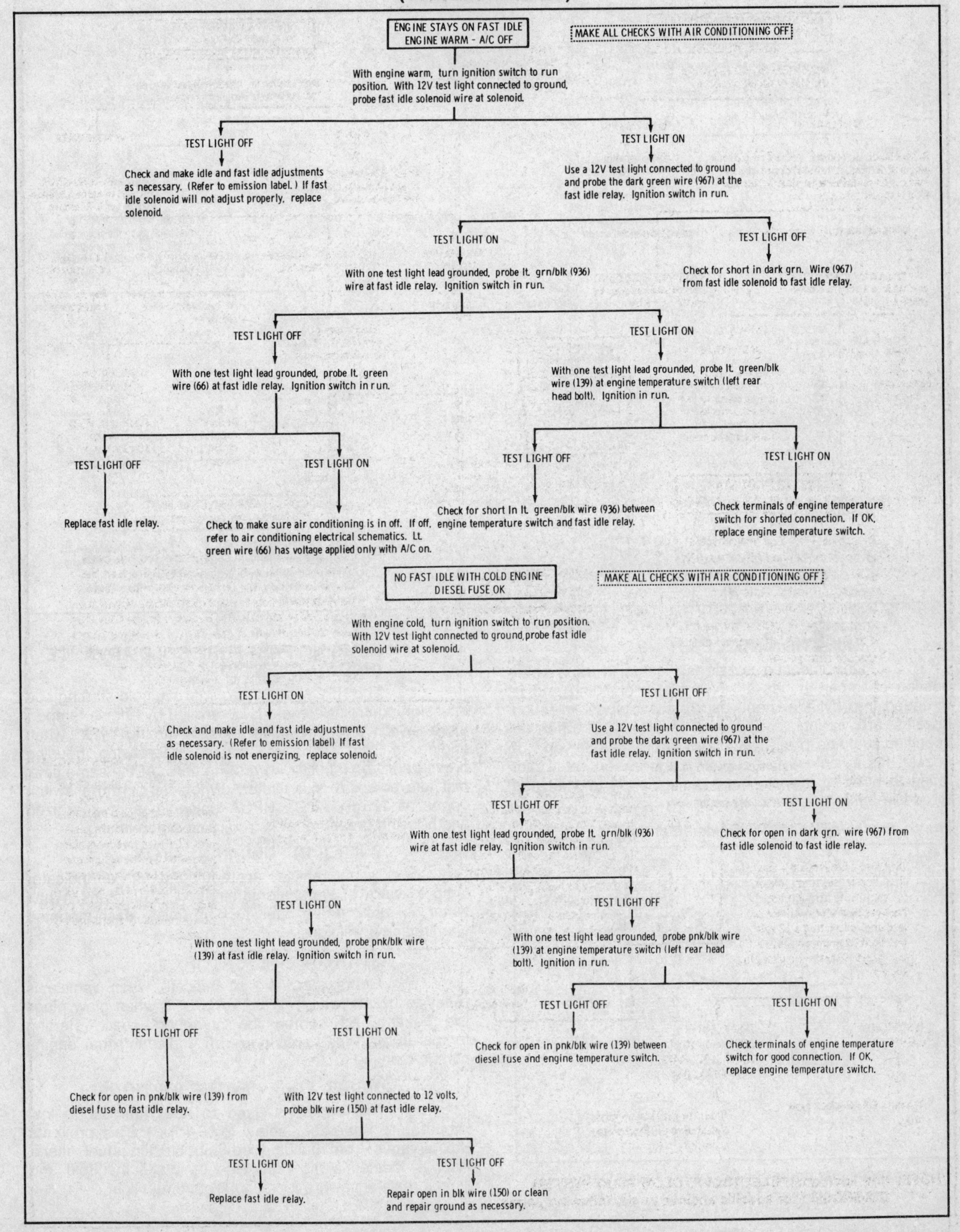

1983 Fuel Injection

GENERAL MOTORS DIESEL — V6 & V8 (Cont.)

ELECTRONIC GLOW PLUG SYSTEM DIAGNOSIS (Cont.)

(V6 MODELS ONLY)

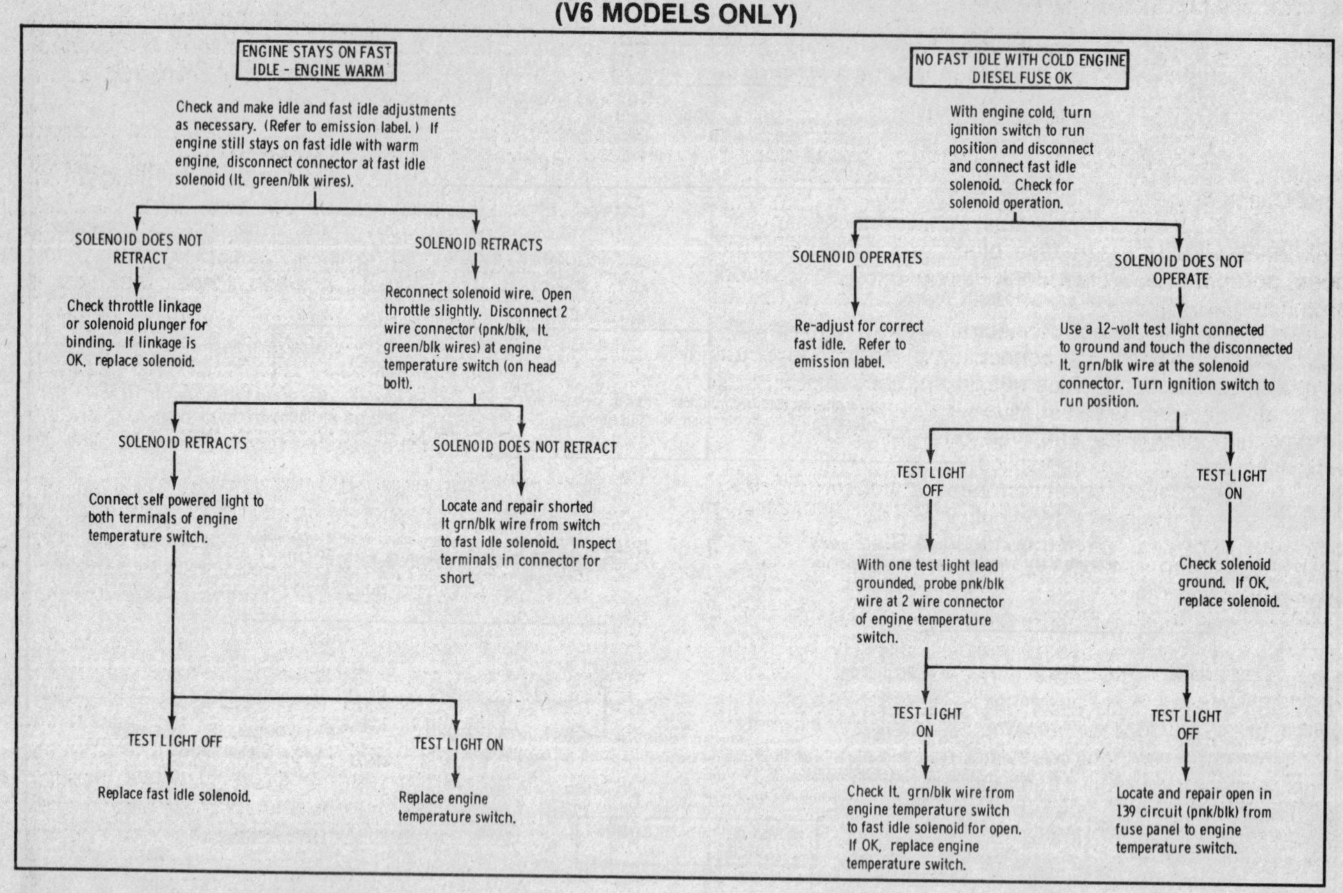

INJECTION NOZZLES

One injection nozzle is located in each combustion chamber. It has a single fuel inlet fitting and is threaded into cylinder head as are glow plugs. Injection nozzles are spring loaded and calibrated to open at specified fuel line pressure. Combustion chamber end of nozzle has a replaceable copper compression seal. Inlet fitting in body of injector must be tightened to specified torque when installed or checked. *See Fig. 5.*

Fig. 5: Diesel Injection Nozzle Identification

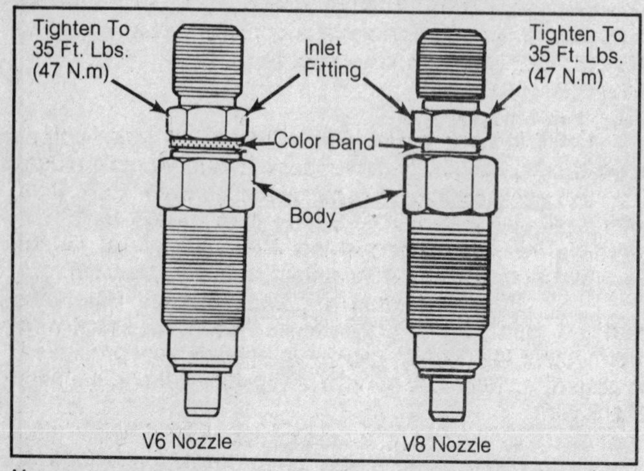

Note presence and color of color band, if equipped.

HOUSING PRESSURE COLD ADVANCE (HPCA) SOLENOID

The HPCA is used to improve cold starting and emission control. Solenoid is controlled by engine temperature switch and advances injection timing by 3° when engine is cold. It does this by decreasing housing pressure from 10 psi (.7 kg/cm²) to zero. At the same time, fast idle solenoid is activated. When temperature switch opens at 125°F (52°C), HPCA solenoid is de-energized and housing pressure rises, retarding pump timing.

WATER IN FUEL INDICATOR

Diesel vehicles are equipped with an indicator lamp to warn of water contamination in fuel tank. When water in tank nears fuel pick-up inlet, dash-mounted warning lamp will light.

STARTING INDICATOR

Lights are used to indicate when vehicle is ready to be started. A "Wait" lamp is lit when glow plugs are heating. As combustion chambers reach starting temperature, "Wait" lamp goes off, indicating that engine can be cranked to start.

DIESEL FUEL HEATER (OPTIONAL)

This option is used to heat fuel during low temperature operation, below 20°F (-7°C). This prevents wax crystals from building up and blocking fuel filters. Filter is located along right side of intake manifold and uses a resistance wire spiralled around fuel line.

THERMAL GLOW PLUG SYSTEM DIAGNOSIS

NOTE: **If a problem occurs when engine is cold, then engine must be cold when trouble shooting.**

No Wait Lamp (Cold Engine)

1) With engine off and ignition switch in "RUN" position, check if charge light is on. If not, check gauges fuse. Check for click at glow plug relay.

2) If relay operates, check for break in Pink/Black wire between fuse block and splice. If relay does not operate, check Pink wires between ignition switch and fuse block.

3) Disconnect connector of wait lamp control relay. Using a jumper wire, connect Blue wire at connector to ground. If wait lamp does not go on, check for burned out bulb. Check for break in Blue wire between wait lamp control relay connector and wait lamp and in Pink/Black wire between wait lamp and splice.

4) Check connection at ground. Connect 1 end of test lamp to Red wire terminal of glow plug relay and other end to ground. Then touch lead to Black wire at wait lamp control relay connector. If light comes on, replace wait lamp control relay.

Wait Lamp Pulses Slowly On and Off

1) With wait lamp pulsing, connect test lamp between White and Yellow wires at wait lamp control relay. If test lamp is on when wait lamp is off and off when wait lamp is on, replace wait lamp control relay.

2) If test lamp does not come on, connect test lamp between ground and Orange wire at thermal controller. With wait lamp pulsing, check if test lamp pulses on and off with wait lamp. If test lamp still does not come on, touch to front Red wire and rear Blue and Black wire posts of glow plug relay.

3) Check for break in Red wire between batteries and glow plug relay. Also check for break in Black, Blue, Green or Orange wires between relay and thermal controller or for fault in relay.

4) If test lamp pulses with wait lamp when connected to Orange wire at thermal controller, connect test lamp between Black wire at controller and ground. If test lamp again pulses, repair Black wire between controller and ground. If not, replace controller.

Wait Lamp Stays On More Than 10 Seconds

1) Disconnect connector at diode module. Connect 1 end of test lamp to ground and other end to Red (front) post of glow plug relay. Touch test lamp lead to rear post (Blue and Black wires) of glow plug relay. Test lamp should come on if relay operates.

2) If relay operates, disconnect connector at wait lamp control relay. Wait lamp should go out. Connect test lamp between White and Yellow wires at connector.

3) If test lamp comes on, replace wait lamp control relay. If test lamp does not come on, turn off power and check for 30 ohms resistance at pins 4 and 5 of thermal controller. Replace controller if resistance is high. Check continuity of Black, Dark Green, Dark Blue, Orange/Black (Orange), Pink/Black, Brown, White, Yellow and Black wires.

4) If relay does not operate, check diesel or ECM fuse and ground. Disconnect connector at thermal controller. Connect test lamp between pins 3 and 6 at harness connector.

5) If test lamp comes on with ignition on, check continuity between pins 3 and 6. Replace controller if no continuity. If test lamp does not come on, check glow plug relay coil resistance. Replace if resistance is high. Check continuity of Pink, Pink/Black, Yellow and Black wires.

Engine Does Not Start When Cold (Wait Lamp OK) (Celebrity, Century, Cierra, & 6000 Only)

1) Check that cranking speed is 100 RPM or more. If less, check battery voltage with voltmeter (12.4 volts with ignition off). Using test lamp, check for voltage at Pink wire lead at fuel solenoid of fuel injection pump with ignition switch in "RUN" position. Repair Pink wire if no voltage.

2) If test lamp comes on, turn ignition off. Using self-powered test lamp, check for continuity through fuel solenoid to ground. If no continuity, replace fuel solenoid. With ignition switch in "RUN" position and engine off, listen for glow plug relay operation. It should click on and off.

3) If relay operates, turn ignition switch off. Disconnect all glow plug harness connectors at glow plugs. Connect self-powered test lamp between rear post (Blue and Black wires) of glow plug relay and ground. At each glow plug, touch harness connector to glow plug spade terminal.

4) If test lamp comes on, glow plug and harness lead are good. Disconnect harness connector after testing each glow plug. After testing all glow plugs, reconnect all connectors to glow plugs.

5) If test lamp does not come on, touch harness connector to ground. If lamp comes on, replace glow plug. If lamp does not come on, replace wire to glow plug. If all glow plugs are open-circuited, also replace thermal controller.

6) If relay does not operate and wait lamp went on, then off, disconnect connector at thermal controller. With ignition switch in "RUN" position, connect 1 end of test lamp to ground. Check for voltage on Brown wire. If test lamp comes on, check if coolant temperature switch is closed. If so and engine is cold, replace switch.

7) Check for voltage on Orange/Black wire. If lamp comes on, check for shorted contacts in glow plug relay. If contacts are shorted, replace relay, all glow plugs and thermal controller.

8) Connect 1 end of test lamp to positive battery cable and touch Yellow wire between controller and glow plug relay. If lamp comes on, replace thermal controller. If lamp does not come on, repair Yellow wire.

Engine Does Not Start When Cold (Wait Lamp OK) (All Other Models)

1) Disconnect Dark Blue wire from output terminal of glow plug relay to test left bank of glow plugs. Connect ammeter (60 amp minimum) between Dark Blue wire and output terminal. Set ignition switch to "RUN" position. Note ammeter reading. Normal readings for V6 engines should be about 45 amps (V8 about 60 amps).

2) Turn ignition off. Connect Dark Blue wire and test right bank of glow plugs. Disconnect Black wire from output terminal on glow plug relay. Follow procedure in step **1)** to test right bank. Turn ignition off and connect Black wire.

3) If current readings are normal, glow plug system is good. Using a test lamp, check for voltage at

Pink wire of fuel solenoid in fuel injection pump with ignition in "RUN" position. If no voltage, repair Pink wire.

4) If test lamp comes on, turn ignition off. Using a self-powered test lamp, check for continuity through fuel solenoid to ground. If no continuity exists, replace fuel solenoid. If continuity exists, check fuel system.

5) If current readings are 15 amps or lower, 1 or more glow plugs are not working. Disconnect individual glow plug leads on side of engine with low current reading. Connect ammeter between electrical lead and glow plug.

6) Turn ignition switch to "RUN" position. Note ammeter reading at glow plug. Current reading at each plug should be about 15 amps. Repeat test at each glow plug. Turn ignition switch off.

7) At each glow plug with low current reading, connect a test lamp between electrical connector and ground. Turn ignition switch to "RUN" position. If test lamp comes on, harness is good. Replace glow plug.

8) If test lamp does not come on, repair or replace harness. After repairing harness, repeat current test to test each glow plug.

Engine Runs Rough When Cold

1) With engine off, turn ignition switch to "RUN" position. Disconnect connector at engine temperature switch. Touch jumper wire to 2 terminals on connector. Check that fast idle solenoid extends. If not, check throttle linkage or solenoid plunger for binding. If no binding exists, replace solenoid.

2) If fast idle solenoid extends, attach tachometer and start engine. With jumper wire still connected, remove connector at cold advance solenoid of fuel injection pump. Engine speed should change 30 RPM when connector is removed. Check solenoid and fuel pump if no change.

Fig. 6: Glow Plug System Wiring Diagram (Electronic Type — V6)

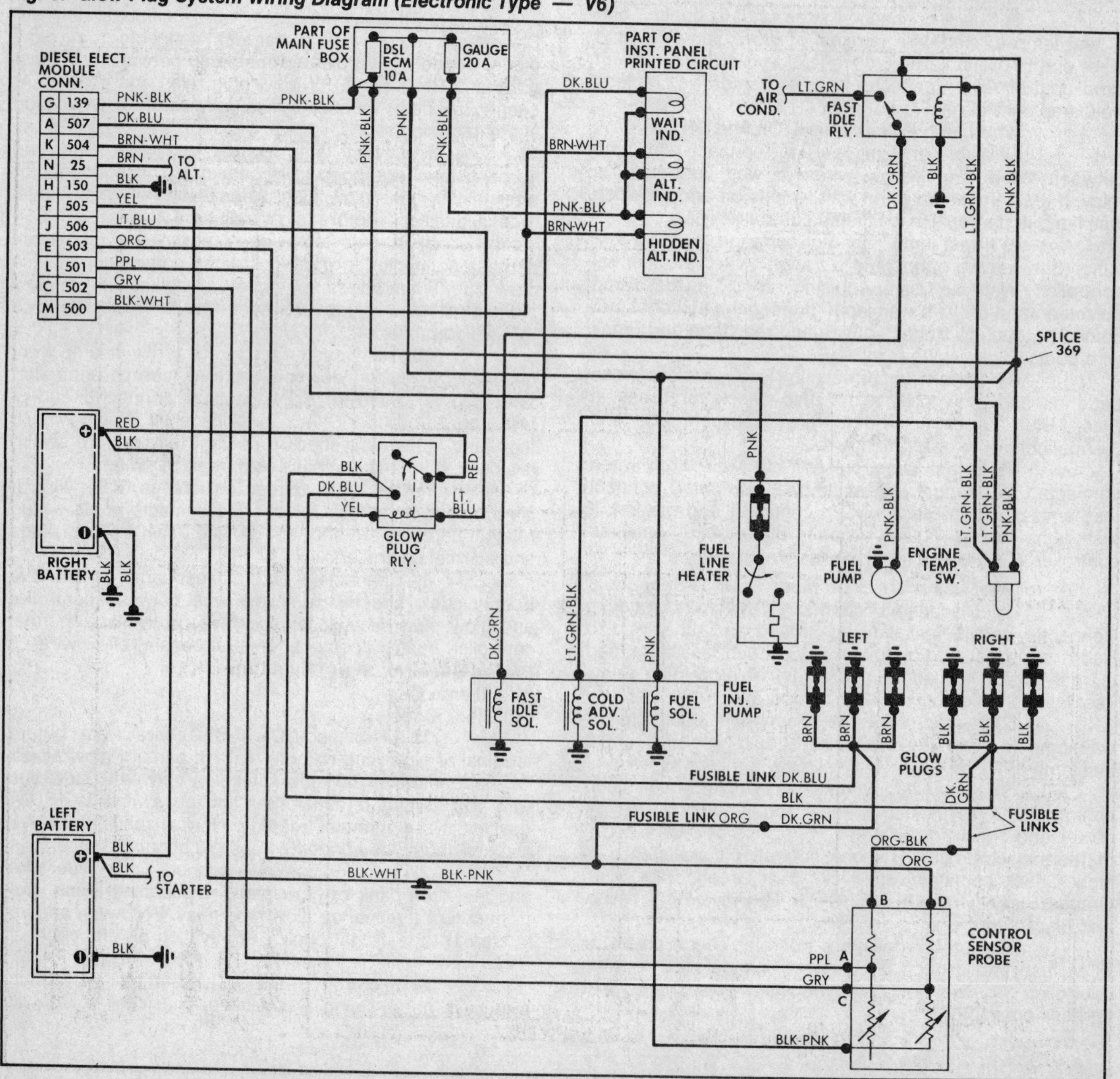

1983 Fuel Injection

GENERAL MOTORS DIESEL — V6 & V8 (Cont.)

3) Turn engine off. Using self-powered test lamp, check that engine temperature switch has continuity below 120°F (49°C) and no continuity above 120°F (49°C). Replace switch if bad.

4) Connect 1 end of test lamp to ground. With engine off and ignition switch in "RUN" position, touch other end of test lamp to Green wire pin at diode module. If lamp comes on and engine is cold, replace coolant temperature switch.

5) Turn ignition switch off. Disconnect all glow plug harness connectors at glow plugs. Connect self-powered test lamp between rear post (Blue and Black wires) of glow plug relay and ground. At each glow plug, touch harness connector to glow plug spade terminal.

6) If test lamp comes on, glow plug and harness lead are good. Disconnect harness connector after testing each glow plug. After testing all glow plugs, reconnect all connectors to glow plugs.

7) If test lamp does not come on, touch harness connector to ground. If lamp comes on, replace glow plug. If lamp does not come on, replace wire to glow plug. Check fuel system for proper fuel delivery.

No Fast Idle When Cold

1) With engine off, turn ignition switch to "RUN" position. Disconnect connector at engine temperature switch. Connect jumper wire to both terminals on harness connector. Disconnect connector at fast idle solenoid and then reconnect it, checking solenoid operation.

2) If solenoid operates, readjust for current fast idle operation. *Refer to Emission Control Tune-Up Decal for specifications and adjustment procedures.*

3) If solenoid does not operate on Celebrity, Century, Cierra, and 6000 models, connect 1 end of test

Fig. 7: Glow Plug System Wiring Diagram (Thermal Type — V6)

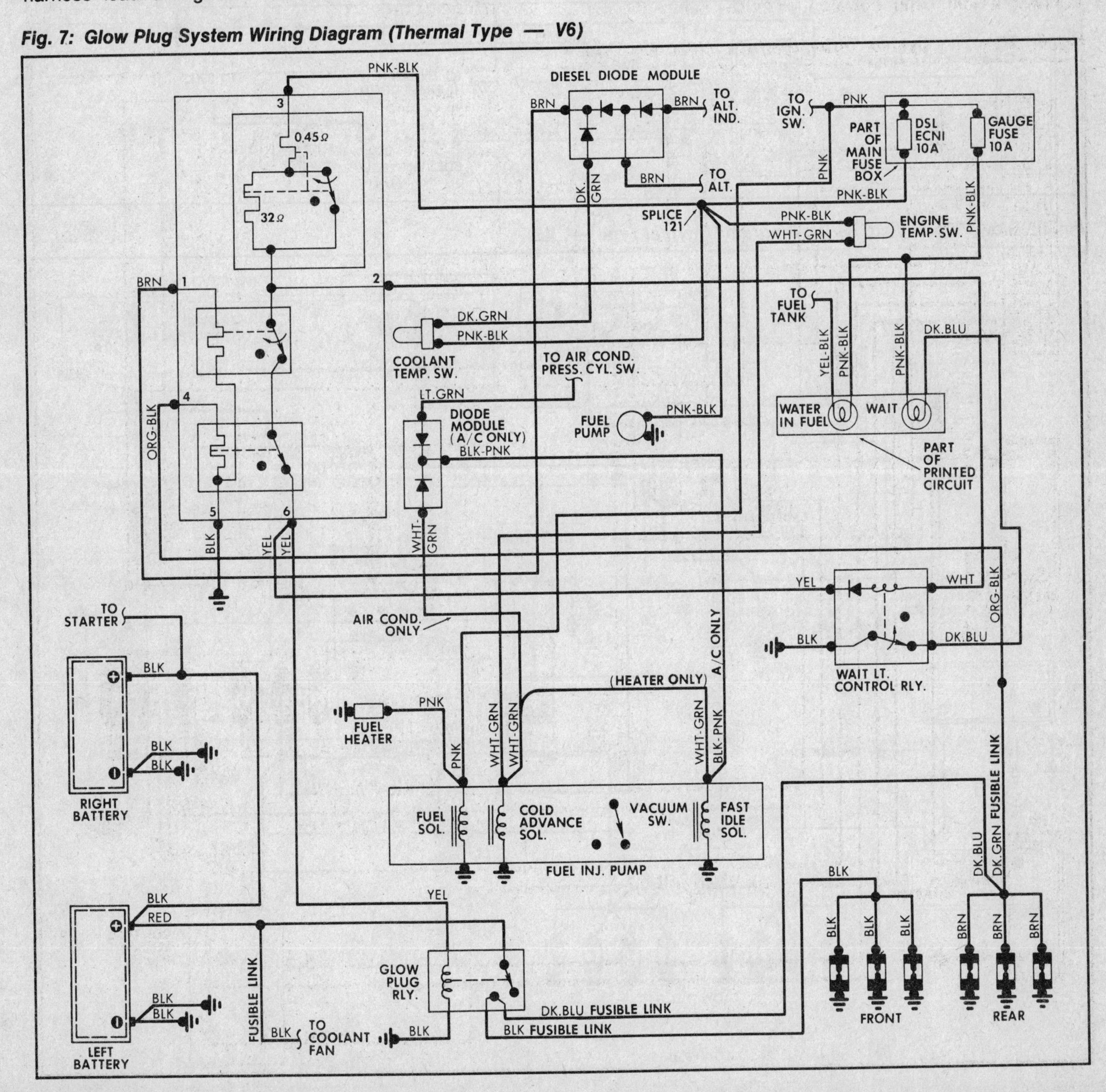

1983 Fuel Injection

GENERAL MOTORS DIESEL — V6 & V8 (Cont.)

Fig. 8: Glow Plug System Wiring Diagram (Electronic Type — V8)

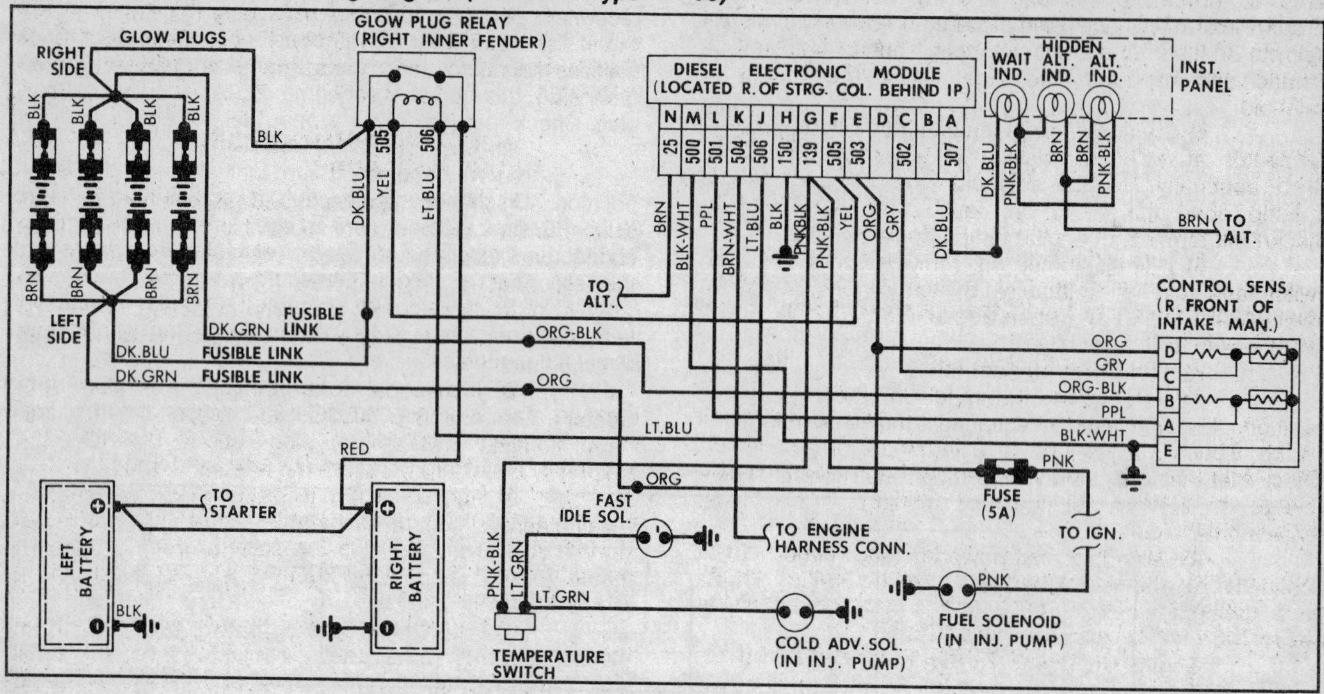

Fig. 9: Glow Plug System Wiring Diagram (Thermal Type — V8)

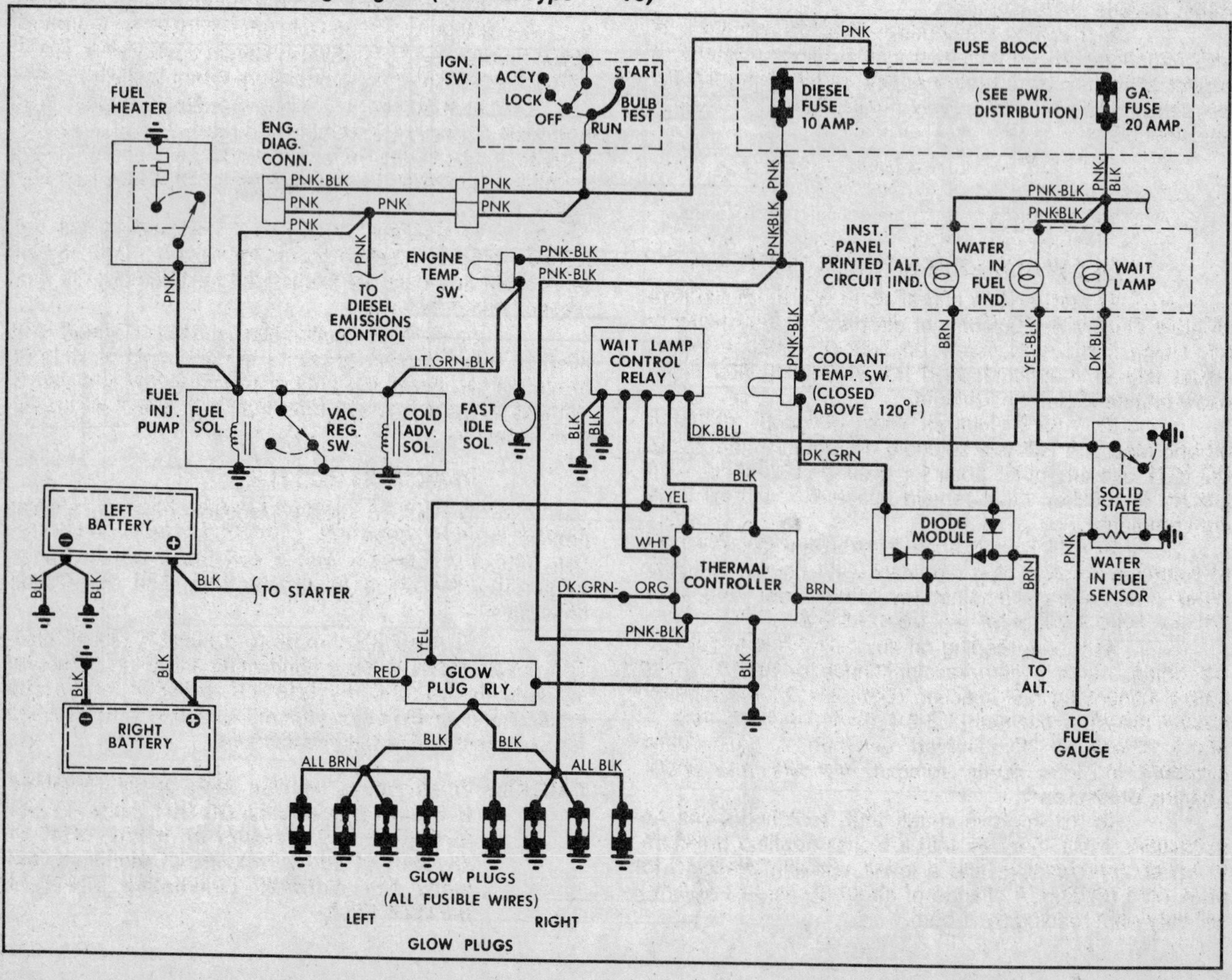

1983 Fuel Injection

GENERAL MOTORS DIESEL — V6 & V8 (Cont.)

lamp to ground and other end to White/Green lead (Black/Pink on A/C equipped models). If solenoid does not operate on all other models, connect 1 end of test lamp to ground and other end to Light Green/Black lead at solenoid.

4) On all models, if lamp comes on, disconnect connector at solenoid. Using self-powered test lamp, check continuity. Replace solenoid if no continuity exists. If lamp does not come on, touch test lamp lead to Black/Pink terminal of engine temperature switch.

5) If lamp comes on, remove connector from switch and test for continuity. Switch should be closed below 120°F (49°C) and open above 125°F (52°C). If not, replace switch.

Engine Stays on Fast Idle

1) With engine off, turn ignition switch to "RUN" position. Disconnect connector at engine temperature switch. Touch jumper wire to 2 terminals on connector. Check that fast idle solenoid extends. If not, check throttle linkage or solenoid plunger for binding. If no binds, replace solenoid.

2) Using a self-powered test lamp, check continuity of engine temperature switch. Switch should have continuity below 120°F (49°C) and no continuity above 120°F (49°C). Replace switch if bad.

Engine Continues To Run With Ignition Off

1) With ignition switch off and engine still running, disconnect connector at diode module. If engine stops, replace diode module.

2) If engine continues to run, disconnect Pink wire connector at fuel solenoid in fuel injection pump. If engine continues to run, stop engine by crimping flexible fuel return line near fuel supply pump. Repair or replace fuel solenoid.

TESTING

GLOW PLUG RESISTANCE TEST

1) Start engine and allow to warm up. Remove all glow plug wires. Disconnect alternator 2-lead connector. Using idle speed screw on side of injection pump, adjust idle to roughest speed not exceeding 900 RPM. Allow engine to run for 1 minute.

2) Attach jumper wire between voltmeter ground lead and fast idle solenoid on fuel injection pump. DO NOT use any other point for ground connection. This ground connection must remain connected until all tests are completed.

3) Check resistance by touching positive lead of voltmeter to glow plug terminals (with engine running). Write down values obtained in firing order sequence (V6 — 1-6-5-4-3-2 or V8 — 1-8-4-3-6-5-7-2).

4) If ohm reading on any cylinder is about 1.2-1.3 ohms, make a compression check on that cylinder before continuing fuel injection diagnosis. Most cylinders should measure between 1.8-3.4 ohms. If more than .3 ohms difference is observed between 2 consecutive cylinders in firing order, remove injectors and check opening pressure.

5) To improve rough idle, switch nozzles as necessary. Install nozzles with a higher opening pressure to lower ohm reading, and a lower opening pressure to raise ohm reading. A change of about 30 psi (2.1 kg/cm²) will vary ohm reading by .1 ohm.

6) Repeat procedure to confirm idle improvement. Be sure to check glow plug resistance at the same idle speed both times. If no improvement is observed, injection line replacement or injection pump calibration may be necessary.

INJECTION PUMP HOUSING FUEL PRESSURE

1) Engine must be at normal operating temperature. Remove air crossover assembly and install screen covers over openings in intake manifold. Remove pressure tap plug or torque screw from injector pump. To remove torque screw, add a second nut. Back screw out with both nuts attached to prevent tampering with torque screw adjustment.

2) Place seal from pressure tap plug onto pressure tap adapter J-29382 and screw adapter into pump housing in place of plug. Screw pressure tap adapter J-28526 into pressure tap adapter J-29382.

3) Connect a low pressure gauge to adapter. Install magnetic pick-up tachometer. Start engine and run at 1000 RPM with transmission selector in "P". Pressure should be 8-12 psi (.56-.84 kg/cm²), with no more than 2 psi (.14 kg/cm²) fluctuation.

4) If pressure is zero, remove connector from housing pressure cold advance terminal. If pressure is still zero, remove injection pump cover and inspect solenoid operation. Free up solenoid if binding.

5) If pressure became normal when solenoid lead was disconnected, check operation of temperature switch on rear head bolt. Switch should open above 125°F (52°C), then close when temperature drops to 95°F (35°C).

6) If pressure is still low, replace or clean fuel return line connector assembly and return line. If pressure is too high, check fuel return system for restrictions. If fuel return line connector assembly is replaced, check injection timing.

7) Recheck pressure. If pressure is still not correct, remove injection pump for repair. Pump is not serviceable and must be exchanged for another unit. *See Injection Pump Removal.*

8) Remove tachometer, pressure gauge and adapter. Install a NEW pressure tap plug seal on plug or torque screw. Install tap plug or torque screw into pump. Remove screened covers from manifold. Install air crossover assembly.

INJECTION NOZZLE

1) Remove injection nozzles. *Refer to removal procedure under REMOVAL & INSTALLATION.* Clean carbon from tip of nozzle with a soft brass brush. Check torque of inlet fitting to nozzle body and correct as necessary.

2) Assemble nozzle to a suitable diesel injection nozzle tester using a connecting line (high pressure) 12" long by 1/4" O.D. by 1/16" I.D. between nozzle and tester. Refer to test equipment manufacturer's instructions for exact tester operating instructions.

CAUTION: When testing nozzles, keep spray contained to avoid serious injury. DO NOT allow injector to release line pressure on hands, arms or any part of body. Pressure of atomized test spray has sufficient penetrating power to puncture flesh.

3) Build nozzle pressure slow enough to determine exact minimum opening pressure of nozzle. Minimum opening pressure for new nozzles on V6 models is 1000 psi (70 kg/cm²) without color band or with Green color band; 800 psi (56 kg/cm²) on models with Red color band.

4) Minimum opening pressure for new nozzles on V8 models is 1225 psi (86 kg/cm²) without color band or with White collar band. Opening pressure is about 200 psi (14 kg/cm²) less for all used nozzles.

5) When nozzle releases pressure, note spray pattern and compare with examples shown in *Fig. 10*. If incorrect, or if a liquid stream, replace nozzle.

6) To test nozzle seat for leakage, decrease pressure to at least 290 psi BELOW actual opening pressure. Dry nozzle tip with compressed air, then increase pressure to 150 psi (10 kg/cm²) BELOW actual opening pressure. Maintain pressure for 5 seconds and compare fuel leakage to examples shown in *Fig. 11*.

7) Replace defective nozzles, then reinstall all nozzles. Install carefully and tighten.

Fig. 10: Injector Nozzle Spray Patterns

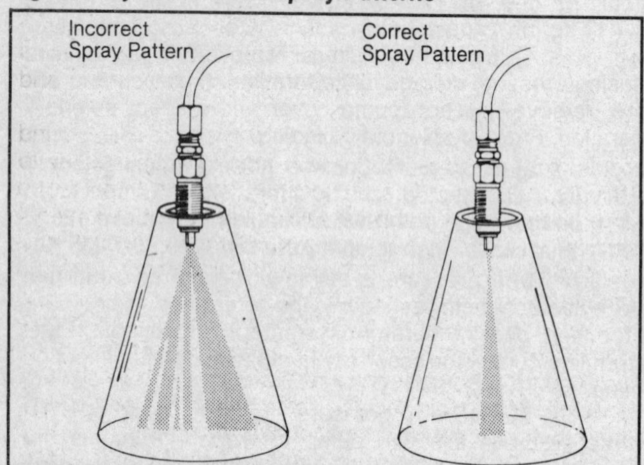

Keep spray contained to prevent injury to any body part.

Fig. 11: Injection Nozzle Seat Tightness Check

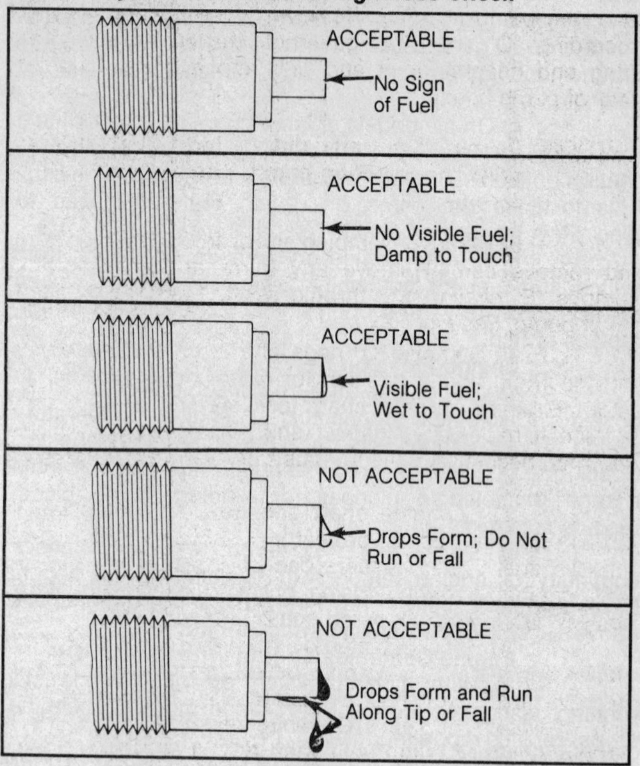

REMOVAL & INSTALLATION

NOTE: Manufacturer does not recommend disassembly of pump. However, pump cover, guide stud, and throttle shaft seals may be replaced to eliminate leaks. For all other problems, pump must be removed and taken to an authorized repair station.

INJECTION PUMP SEAL REPLACEMENT

CAV Type

1) Remove air cleaner and crossover. Install screens over air intakes. Clean injection pump cover and upper pump area. Place rags in engine valley to catch fuel. Remove fuel return pipe and control cover screws, discarding washers and gasket.

2) Remove fast idle solenoid. Scribe a line on vacuum regulator valve and pump body so valve can be reinstalled without resetting. Remove vacuum regulator valve. Disconnect throttle cable, T.V./detent cable and throttle return springs.

3) Install tool (J-29601) over throttle shaft with slots of tool engaging vacuum return valve drive lock pin. Put spring clip of tool over throttle shaft light load advance cam and tighten wing nut. Without loosening wing nut, pull tool off shaft. This provides a reference for proper alignment during reassembly.

Fig. 12: CAV Injection Pump Throttle Shaft & Seals

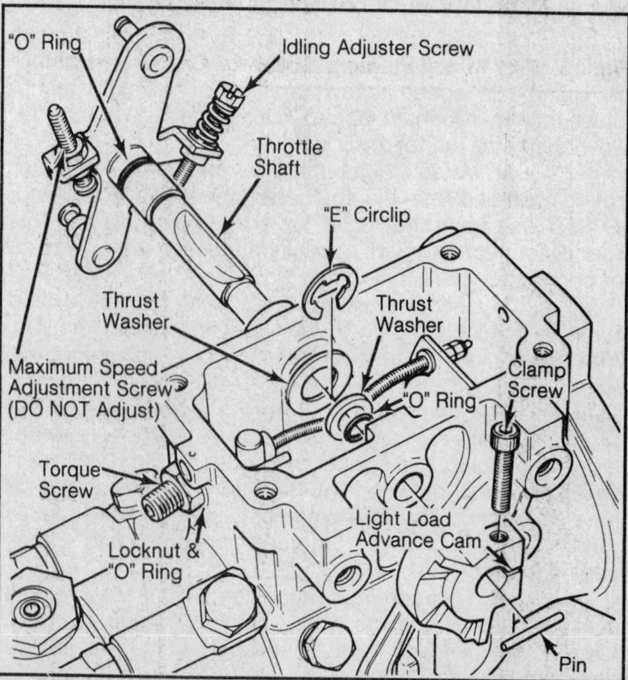

Do not allow dirt or foreign objects to fall into pump.

1983 Fuel Injection

GENERAL MOTORS DIESEL — V6 & V8 (Cont.)

4) Drive roll pin (locking pin) from throttle shaft and from pump housing. Remove governor support rod, discarding "O" ring. Tilt governor carrier assembly by lifting end nearest drive end of pump and ease carrier clear of pump housing.

CAUTION: Do not allow any dirt or foreign objects to drop into injection pump. Engine damage will result.

5) Remove clamping screw from light load cam and remove cam. Remove any burrs on end of shaft. Remove "E" circlip from throttle shaft. Pull throttle shaft out of pump. *See Fig. 12.*

6) Remove "O" rings and thrust washers from throttle shaft, noting position for reassembly. Discard "O" rings. Examine throttle shaft for wear or damage and replace if necessary. Inspect shaft bushings. If replacement is necessary, pump must be sent to authorized repair dealer.

7) Lubricate shaft and new "O" rings. Install larger "O" ring using protector (J-33097). Slide shaft through until thrust washers can be installed on shaft in their original positions. Using protector (J-33098), install smaller "O" ring over tapered end of protector.

8) Insert protector, tapered end first, into sleeve and slide "O" ring onto outside diameter of sleeve. Remove "cap" portion of protector. Slide sleeve with "O" ring over end of shaft. Continue sliding shaft towards opposite side of pump until shaft end is supported. Push "O" ring into shaft groove. Keep shaft horizontal and withdraw shaft enough to remove protector.

9) Slide shaft fully into housing. Place light load advance cam on shaft and insert clamping screw, but do not tighten. Install new "E" circlip into shaft recess. If new throttle shaft assembly has been installed, check shaft end play and adjust with selective thrust washers, if necessary. End play should be .006-.012" (.15-.30 mm).

10) Install new pin on shaft end. Realign advance cam in original position so tool (J-29601) can be reinstalled over throttle shaft. Place pin in slots and spring clip over advance cam. Tighten cam screw and remove tool.

11) Rotate throttle lever forward toward drive (idling) end of pump. *See Fig. 13.* Tilt governor carrier assembly to place idle spring with leaf spring on governor control arm. Lower carrier into housing and engage lug on underside of throttle block with notch in throttle shaft. Lubricate governor support rod and new "O" ring. Install "O" ring on support rod using tool (J-33096).

12) Insert plain end of governor support rod through rear of governor housing and into carrier assembly sleeve. Fully install rod into housing and install new locking pin. Install new gasket and governor control cover. Torque cover screws to 25 INCH lbs. (2.8 N.m).

13) Install fuel return lines and throttle return springs. Connect throttle and T.V./detent cables. Install vacuum regulator valve, aligning marks made during removal. Install fast idle solenoid. Start engine and check for leaks. Remove intake manifold screened covers. Install air crossover and air cleaner.

Fig. 13: CAV Injection Pump Governor Carrier Assembly

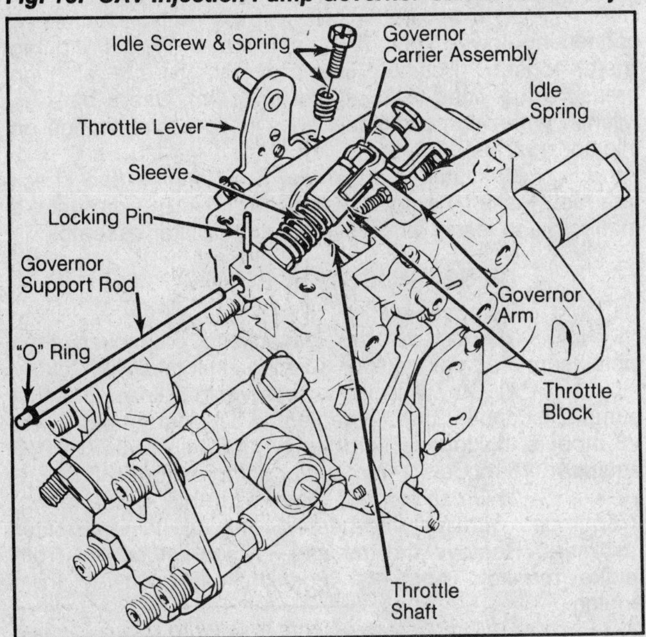

Roosa-Master Type

1) Disconnect ground cables from both batteries, then remove air cleaner and crossover. Install screens over air intakes. Disconnect fuel return line and wiring from injection pump.

2) Clean injection pump cover and area around throttle rod and guide stud. Place rags in engine valley to catch fuel. Scribe a line on vacuum regulator valve and pump body so valve can be reinstalled without resetting. Remove vacuum regulator valve. Remove throttle and T.V./detent cable (V6), throttle rod (V8) and return springs. Remove throttle cable bracket (V8).

3) Install tool (J-29601) over throttle shaft with slots of tool engaging pin. Put spring clip of tool over throttle shaft advance cam and tighten wing nut. Without loosening wing nut, pull tool off shaft. This provides a reference for proper alignment during reassembly.

4) Drive pin from throttle shaft. Loosen clamp screw and remove advance cam and fiber washer. Remove any burrs that may have been caused by pin removal. Remove injection pump cover and remove screws from cover.

CAUTION: Do not allow any dirt or foreign objects to drop into injection pump. Engine damage will result.

5) Note position of metering valve spring over top of guide stud. This position must be exactly duplicated during reassembly. Remove guide stud and washer, noting position for reassembly. Rotate min-max governor assembly up and remove from throttle shaft.

6) Remove throttle shaft and inspect. It may be necessary to loosen and rotate pump slightly to remove throttle shaft. If damaged or worn, replace throttle shaft. Inspect shaft bushings. If replacement is necessary, pump must be sent to authorized repair dealer.

7) Remove throttle shaft seals. Do not cut off, as a nick on shaft will cause leakage. Coat new seals lightly with grease and install on shaft.

8) Slide shaft into pump until min-max governor will slip onto throttle shaft. Rotate governor downward, hold in position, and slide throttle shaft and governor into place.

GENERAL MOTORS DIESEL — V6 & V8 (Cont.)

Fig. 14: Roosa-Master Injection Pump With Advance Cam Tool Installed

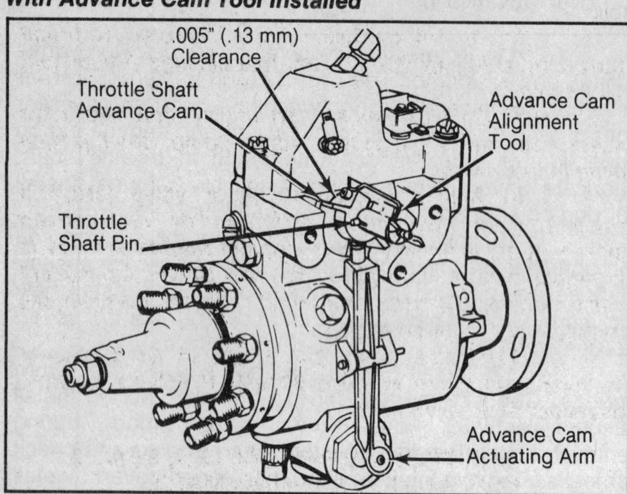

Fig. 15: Roosa-Master Injection Pump With Cover Removed

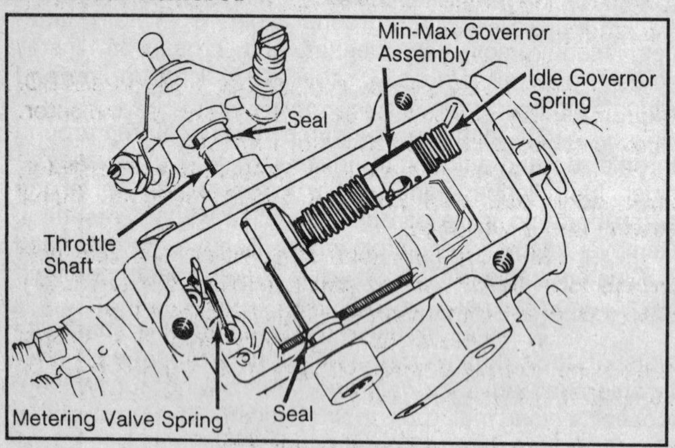

9) Install new fiber washer, throttle shaft advance cam (do not tighten screw) and new throttle shaft drive pin. Realign advance cam in original position with tool (J-29601). Place a .005" (.13 mm) feeler gauge between fiber washer and cam. Tighten cam screw and apply locking compound.

10) Reinstall guide stud with new washer. Ensure that metering valve spring extension rides on top of guide stud. Tighten guide stud to 85 INCH lbs. (10 N.m). Overtightening of guide stud will strip aluminum threads in housing.

11) Hold throttle in idle position and install new pump cover seal. Do not insert screws in cover; position cover slightly forward and above pump. Carefully move cover rearward and downward into position, taking care not to damage seal.

12) Insert screws, using flat and lock washers with flat washers against pump cover. Tighten screws to 33 INCH lbs. (4 N.m). Install vacuum regulator valve, aligning marks made during removal.

13) Connect battery ground cables, turn ignition switch to "RUN" position, and touch pink solenoid wire to solenoid terminal. A clicking sound should be heard as solenoid operates. If not, remove cover and check for solenoid operation.

CAUTION: If clicking sound is not heard as solenoid wire is connected, DO NOT start engine. Throttle may be stuck in wide-open position.

14) If solenoid clicks, connect all wires to pump housing. Reconnect throttle cable and T.V./detent cable (V6), throttle cable bracket and throttle rod (V8) and throttle return springs.

15) Adjust pump timing and throttle linkage. Install fuel return line and check that all fuel lines are tight. Start engine and check for leaks. Allow engine to idle for several minutes to purge air bubbles and smooth out idle. It may be necessary to stop engine for several minutes to allow air to rise and be purged.

16) Adjust vacuum regulator valve. Remove intake manifold screens. Reinstall air crossover and air cleaner.

AIR CROSSOVER

Removal

Remove air cleaner, then remove filters and pipes from air crossover. Remove bolts and washers and lift crossover from manifold. Place screened covers over intake manifold openings.

Installation

Reverse removal procedure. Torque air crossover bolts to 24 ft. lbs. (33 N.m) on V6 models or 22 ft. lbs. (30 N.m) on V8 models. Be sure to install new gaskets between crossover and intake manifold.

INJECTION PUMP FUEL LINES

Removal

1) Remove air cleaner and crossover, then install screened covers over openings in intake manifold. It is not necessary to remove pump to replace a line(s). Remove injection pump line clamps. It is not necessary to use a back-up wrench when removing lines from pump.

2) Remove injection pump lines and cap open lines, nozzles and pump fittings. Using a back-up wrench on upper injector nozzle hex, disconnect injection pump lines at nozzle inlet fittings.

Installation

1) If several lines are to be replaced, start by connecting lower lines first. Install new injection pump line(s) loosely. Position line properly. Torque all high pressure fuel lines to 25 ft. lbs. (34 N.m). Use a back-up wrench when tightening fuel lines to fuel inlet fittings on injector nozzles.

2) Install line clamps. Start engine and check for fuel leaks. Remove screened covers from intake manifold and install air crossover and air filter assembly.

DIESEL INJECTION PUMP

Removal

1) Remove air cleaner and crossover, then install screened covers over openings in intake manifold.

2) On V6 models, remove fuel lines and fuel pump. Disconnect throttle cable and T.V./detent cable. On V8 models, disconnect throttle rod and bellcrank. On A/C equipped V8 models, remove rear compressor brace.

3) On all models, remove throttle return spring. If equipped with fuel line heater, remove line and heater fasteners. Remove throttle and T.V./detent cables from intake manifold brackets. Position cables away from engine.

GENERAL MOTORS DIESEL — V6 & V8 (Cont.)

4) On V8 models, remove crankcase depression regulator valve. Disconnect fuel line at fuel filter. On all models, remove fuel filter (with bracket on V8 models). Disconnect fuel return line at fuel pump.

5) Remove fuel line clamps. Disconnect lines at injection pump and cap all openings. Carefully position fuel lines out of way to gain clearance to remove pump.

6) Using special wrench (J-26987 or equivalent), remove 2 bolts (V6) or 3 nuts (V8) securing injection pump. Remove pump and discard "O" ring between pump and adapter.

Installation

1) Position cylinder No. 1 at TDC by lining up crankshaft pulley mark with indicator. Line up offset tang on pump driveshaft with pump driven gear. *See Fig. 16.* Install new pump-to-adapter "O" ring. Install pump and fully seat by hand.

Fig. 16: Pump Driven Gear Offset at TDC (Shown with Intake Manifold Removed)

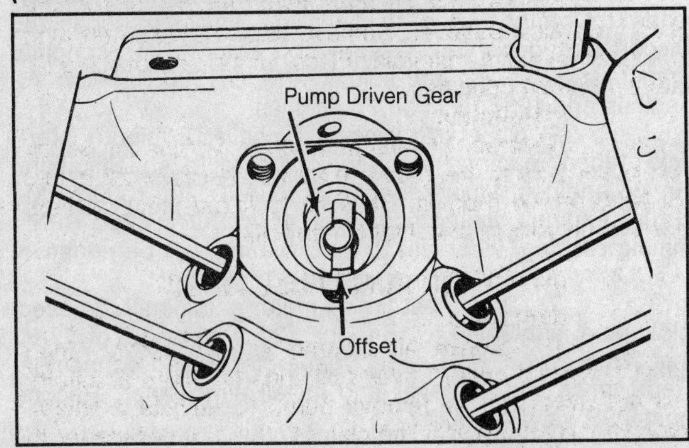

2) If new adapter (V8) or intermediate adapter (V6) is installed, set injection pump at center of slots in pump mounting flange. If original adapter (intermediate adapter) is retained, align pump timing with mark on adapter. *See Fig. 17.*

Fig. 17: Aligning Timing Marks on Pump & Adapter

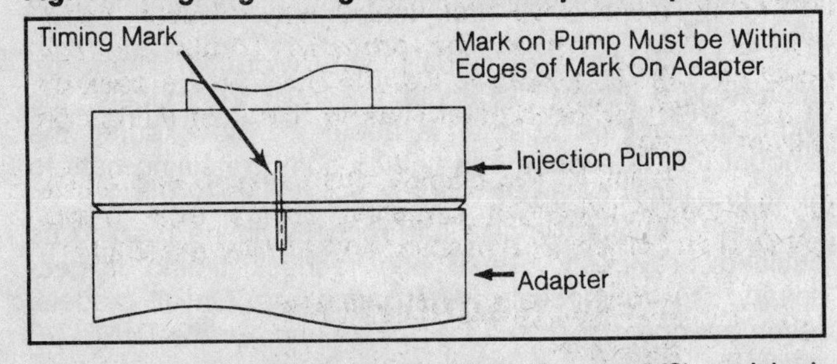

3) Install 2 bolts (V6) or 3 nuts (V8) and lock washers securing pump and torque to 38 ft. lbs. (51 N.m) on V6 or 18 ft. lbs. (24 N.m) on V8.

4) Remove caps from all openings. Connect pump lines at nozzles and tighten to 25 ft. lbs. (34 N.m) with 2 wrenches. Install line clamps. Connect fuel return line to injection pump. Install fuel filter (with bracket on V8 models). If equipped with fuel line heater, install clamps. On V8 models, install crankshaft depression regulator valve. If equipped with A/C, install rear compressor brace.

5) On all models, install throttle and T.V./detent cables into intake manifold brackets. On V6 models, connect throttle and T.V./detent cables to pump throttle lever. Connect throttle return spring and adjust T.V./detent cable.

6) On V8 models, connect throttle rod and return spring. Adjust throttle rod. *See Linkage Adjustment in this article.*

7) On all models, start engine and check for leaks. Check and, if necessary, adjust pump. *See Injection Timing in this article.*

8) Adjust vacuum regulator valve ONLY if valve's original position is disturbed or replacement injection pump is installed. *See Vacuum Regulator Valve in this article.* Adjust idle speed. *See Idle Speed Adjustment in this article.* Remove screened covers from intake manifolds. Install air crossover.

11) Install tubes and hoses in air crossover and ventilation filters in valve covers. Install air cleaner. Reconnect EGR valve hose.

INJECTION PUMP ADAPTER, SEAL & NEW ADAPTER TIMING MARK

Removal

Remove air cleaner, air crossover, injection pump and lines. Remove injection pump adapter. Remove seal from pump adapter.

Installation

1) Rotate engine to place No. 1 piston at TDC. Align mark on balancer with ZERO mark on indicator. Index is offset to the right with No. 1 at TDC.

2) Apply chassis lube to seal area on adapter, taper edge and seal area on intake manifold. Install adapter and leave loose.

3) Thoroughly lube seal, inside and out, with chassis lube. Install seal on seal installation tool (J-28425). Push seal onto pump adapter using installation tool.

4) Remove tool. Observe seal for proper positioning. Torque adapter bolts to 35 ft. lbs. (47 N.m) on V6 or 25 ft. lbs. (34 N.m) on V8.

Fig. 18: Installation of New Adapter Seal

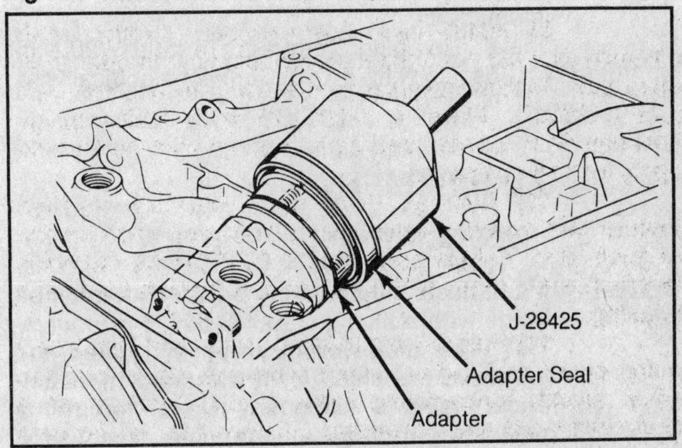

INJECTION NOZZLES

NOTE: **When working on right (rear) bank of a transverse-mounted V6 engine, intermediate steering shaft must be disconnected from rack and pinion stub shaft.**

Removal

1) On transverse-mounted V6 engines, rotate intermediate steering shaft so steering gear stub shaft clamp bolt is accessible. Remove clamp bolt. Disconnect intermediate shaft from stub shaft. Remove engine support strut.

2) Place floor jack under front crossmember of engine cradle. Raise jack until car just begins to raise. Remove front 2 body mount bolts with lower cushions and retainers. Remove cushions from bolts.

3) Thread body mount bolts with retainers at least 3 turns into "cage" nuts so bolts restrain cradle movement. Slowly release jack until crossmember contacts body mount bolt retainers. Correct any interference with hoses, lines, cables and pipes as jack is being lowered. Do not lower cradle without restraining cradle to prevent damage to underhood items.

4) On all models, remove fuel lines from injection pump-to-nozzle on bank of engine where nozzle is to be serviced. DO NOT bend lines out of way to remove nozzle. Cap open fittings and nozzles. Remove nozzle, using wrench on largest hex of injector nozzle. Make sure copper compression seal is removed with nozzle. Protect tip of nozzle from damage and/or dirt.

Installation

1) Lubricate threads of V6 nozzles before installation. Use new copper compression seal and install nozzle. Tighten to 25 ft. lbs. (34 N.m).

2) Install fuel lines to fuel inlet fittings and using a back-up wrench on the upper hex of injector, tighten lines to 25 ft. lbs. (34 N.m).

3) On transverse V6 engines, reverse steps **1)** through **3)** to connect steering. On all models, start engine and check for leaks.

GLOW PLUGS

Removal

1) Glow plugs are mounted near each injector nozzle in the cylinder heads. They are threaded and have an electrical wire plugged into the top end.

2) Remove electrical wire from glow plug and remove plug with deep socket. Be sure to engage socket on largest diameter hex surfaces.

Installation

Install glow plug. Torque to 15 ft. lbs. (20 N.m) on V6 or 12 ft. lbs. (16 N.m) on V8. Connect electrical wire.

ADJUSTMENT

INJECTION TIMING

NOTE: **1983 Diesel model timing adjustment must be made with a timing meter (J-33075 or equivalent). This meter picks up engine speed and crankshaft position from the crankshaft balancer using a luminosity signal through a glow plug probe to determine combustion timing. Engine malfunctions should be corrected before a timing adjustment is made. Timing mark alignment may be used in emergency situations, but for optimum engine operation the timing meter should be used as soon as possible.**

NOTE: **Failure to have engine fully warmed up will result in incorrect timing reading and adjustments.**

Checking

1) Place transmission selector in "P", apply parking brake and block drive wheels. Start engine and run at idle until fully warmed up. Shut off engine.

2) Remove air cleaner assembly and plug air crossover using cover (J-26996-1 or equivalent). Disconnect EGR valve hose. Clean engine probe holder (RPM counter) and crankshaft balancer rim.

3) Clean lens on both ends of glow plug probe and lens in photo-electric pick-up. Using a dulled toothpick, scrape carbon from combustion chamber side of glow plug probe. Retarded readings will result if probe is not clean.

4) Install RPM probe into crankshaft RMP counter (probe holder). Remove glow plug from cylinder No. 1 on V6 models or No. 3 on V8 models. Install glow plug probe into glow plug opening and tighten to 8 ft. lbs. (11 N.m).

5) Set timing meter offset selector to "A" (20) on V6 models or "B" (99.5) on V8 models. Connect meter leads to battery (Red to positive, Black to negative). Disconnect generator 2-lead connector. Start engine (transmission in "P") and adjust RPM to 1300 RPM on V6 engines and 1250 RPM on V8 engines.

6) Observe timing readings at 2 minute intervals. When readings stabilize, compare to specification. On V6 engines, timing should be 6° ATDC @ 1300 RPM. On V8 engines, timing should be 4° ATDC @ 1250 RPM. Timing reading, when set to specification, will be negative (ATDC).

7) Disconnect timing meter and install removed glow plug, tightening to 15 ft. lbs. (20 N.m) on V6 or 12 ft. lbs. (16 N.m) on V8. Connect generator 2-lead connector. Remove crossover cover and install air cleaner. Reconnect EGR valve hose.

Adjusting

1) Shut off engine. Note position of marks on pump flange and pump intermediate adapter (V6) or pump adapter (V8). Loosen bolts or nuts holding pump to adapter until pump can be rotated.

2) Place an offset open end wrench (1" on V6, 3/4" on V8) on boss at front of injection pump. Rotate pump to left to advance or to right to retard timing as necessary.

3) On V6 models, the width of mark on intermediate adapter is about 2/3°. On V8 models, the width of mark on adapter is about 1°. Move pump the amount that is needed and tighten pump retaining nuts to 35 ft. lbs. (48 N.m) on V6 or 18 ft. lbs. (24 N.m) on V8.

4) Start engine and recheck timing reading as outlined previously. Reset and recheck timing if necessary. On V8 models, adjust pump rod. On all models, reset fast and curb idle speeds. *See appropriate TUNE -UP article.*

NOTE: **Sooty or dirty probes will result in retarded readings. The luminosity probe will soot up very fast when used in cold engine. Wild needle fluctuations on timing meter indicate a cylinder not firing properly. Correct this condition prior to timing adjustment.**

LINKAGE ADJUSTMENT

NOTE: **V6 linkage is cable operated and no adjustment is necessary.**

GENERAL MOTORS DIESEL — V6 & V8 (Cont.)

Throttle Rod Adjustment (V8 Only)

1) With engine off, check pump timing. If equipped with cruise control, remove clip from cruise control throttle rod and disconnect rod from throttle lever.

2) Disconnect transmission T.V. or detent cable from throttle assembly. Loosen lock nut on pump rod and shorten by several turns. Rotate bellcrank lever to full throttle position and hold.

3) Lengthen rod until injection pump lever just contacts full throttle stop. Release bellcrank assembly and tighten pump rod lock nut.

Fig. 19: Disassembled View of V8 Throttle Linkage

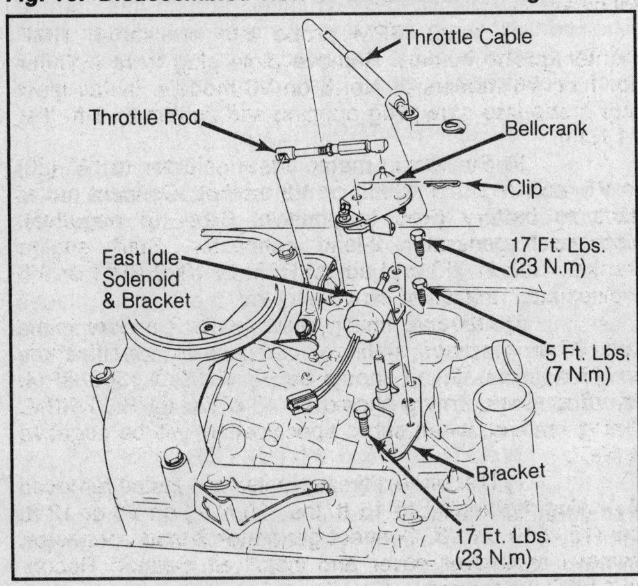

Fig. 20: Transmission T.V. or Detent Cable Adjustment

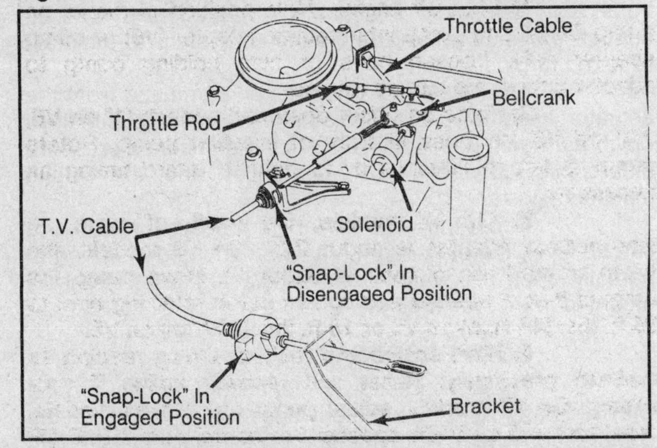

4) Reconnect transmission T.V. or detent cable. Depress and hold metal lock tab on upper end of cable. Move slider away from lever assembly until it stops against metal fitting. Release metal tab.

5) Install cruise control servo rod (if equipped). Rotate bellcrank lever assembly to full throttle stop and release lever assembly. Adjust vacuum regulator valve. *See Vacuum Regulator Valve in this article.* Adjust idle speed. *See appropriate TUNE -UP article.*

VACUUM REGULATOR VALVE

1) Remove air crossover and install screen covers over openings. On V6 models, disconnect throttle and T.V./detent cables from pump throttle lever. On V8 models, disconnect throttle rod from pump.

Fig. 21: Vacuum Regulator Valve Adjustment

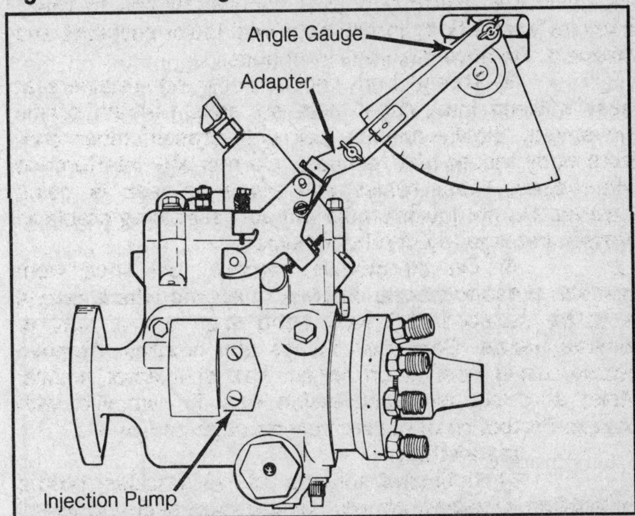

2) Loosen vacuum regulator valve-to-pump bolts. Install carburetor angle gauge to injection pump throttle lever. Rotate throttle lever to wide-open throttle position and set angle gauge to zero degrees, then center bubble.

3) Set angle gauge to 49° (V6) or 58° (V8). Rotate throttle lever until bubble is centered. Attach vacuum pump to port "A" of vacuum regulator valve and vacuum gauge to port "B". *See Fig. 22.*

4) Apply 18-24 in. Hg vacuum to port "A", then rotate vacuum valve clockwise to obtain 10.6 in. Hg. Tighten bolts and remove vacuum gauge, pump and angle gauge.

5) Connect throttle and T.V./detent cables (V6) or throttle rod to pump lever (V8). Remove screen covers on intake manifold. Install air crossover.

Fig. 22: Vacuum Regulator Valve Port Locations

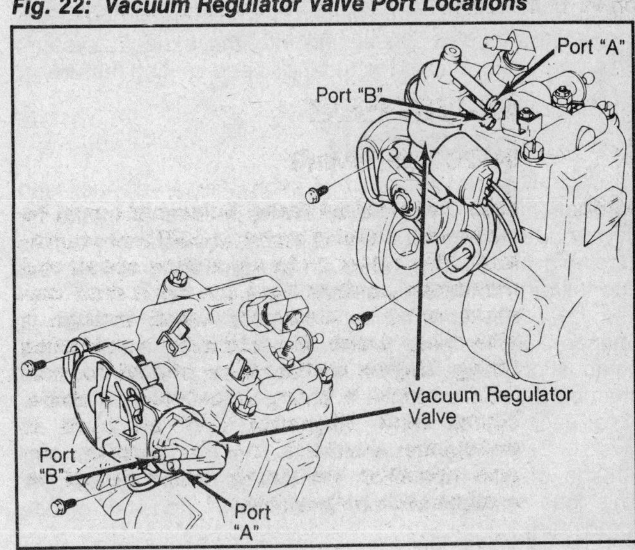

1983 Turbocharging Systems

FORD MOTOR CO.

Capri, Cougar, Mustang, Thunderbird Models with 2.3L 4-Cyl.

DESCRIPTION

The turbocharging system is mounted on the right side of the engine. The system includes an air vane meter, turbine/compressor assembly, plenum chamber, air throttle body assembly and a wastegate.

The turbine is spun by exhaust gas which causes the compressor to draw air. Air from the compressor is blown through air throttle body assembly and into the intake manifold.

Fig. 1: 2.3L Turbocharged Engine Component Location

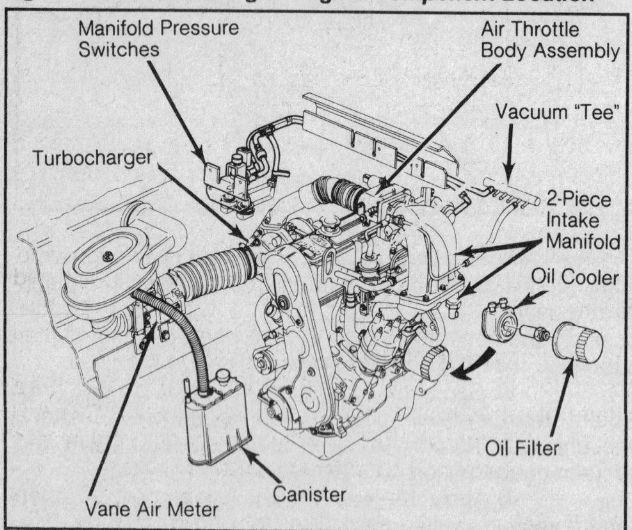

Maximum manifold pressure (boost) is controlled by an exhaust by-pass valve called a wastegate. Operation of the wastegate is controlled by a spring loaded diaphragm called an actuator.

The actuator senses intake manifold pressure to determine how much exhaust gas should be routed to the turbine wheel. Any excess exhaust gas by-passes around the turbine wheel and into the exhaust system. This process provides the turbine speed limiting feature.

OPERATION

Air is drawn in through the air cleaner and vane air meter. The vane air meter measures intake air flow and temperature. The compressor wheel compresses incoming air, directs it through the plenum chamber and into the air throttle body assembly.

As engine load increases and throttle is opened, an increased amount of air flows into the combustion chamber. Fuel is injected into the combustion chamber by an electronically operated fuel injection nozzle (1 for each cylinder).

As the air/fuel mixture is burned, a greater volume of hot exhaust gas enters the exhaust system. This gas is directed into the turbine housing of the turbocharger.

The energy created by moving exhaust gas is used to increase the speed of the turbine wheel. The turbine wheel is connected, with a shaft, to the compressor wheel. As the compressor wheel turns faster, it compresses incoming air and forces a denser air/fuel charge into the combustion chambers. Greater horsepower and torque output is the result.

PLENUM & AIR THROTTLE BODY

The plenum directs compressed air from the compressor housing into the air throttle body assembly. The air throttle body assembly controls the amount of air entering the intake manifold. A single butterfly valve, connected to conventional throttle linkage, provides the necessary air flow for all engine operating conditions.

An air by-pass channel, around the throttle plate, controls both cold and warm engine idle air flow. The by-pass channel is regulated by an air by-pass valve which is controlled by the EEC-IV computer.

TURBINE ASSEMBLY

The turbine assembly is mounted on the right side of the engine with the compressor. It is connected to the compressor with a shaft. When the turbine wheel turns, so must the compressor wheel.

Hot exhaust gas is fed into the turbine through the exhaust manifold. Gases hitting the turbine blades cause the blades to spin. The more exhaust entering the turbine, the faster it will spin. This will then turn the compressor faster. With this process, the turbocharger can produce more power as demand increases.

WASTEGATE & ACTUATOR

When manifold pressure (boost) reaches a predetermined level, there must be some method of controlling or limiting boost past that point. The wastegate performs this function.

Exhaust gas enters the turbine continuously. Once engine demand has been satisfied and the proper boost level has been attained, the wastegate by-passes enough exhaust gas into the exhaust system to maintain required turbine speed.

The wastegate operates on command from the actuator assembly. The actuator is a pressure sensitive diaphragm unit. It is installed so that it can sense pressure differences between the compressor and the intake manifold.

Once the differential in pressure reaches a certain level, the diaphragm reacts on an integral spring to partially open the wastegate. The wastegate is integrally mounted in the outlet elbow.

COMPRESSOR

The compressor is connected to the turbine with a shaft. As the turbine wheel turns, so must the compressor wheel. No exhaust gas is actually passed into the compressor. The spinning compressor forces more air into the intake manifold than would normally be drawn in under atmospheric pressure.

With higher intake manifold pressure and denser air/fuel charge available, more air is forced into the combustion chambers on the piston intake stroke. A denser mixture results in greater horsepower and torque output from the engine. As the compressor spins faster, a greater amount of air is compressed into the intake manifold.

FORD MOTOR CO. (Cont.)

Fig. 2: Exploded View of Turbocharger Assembly

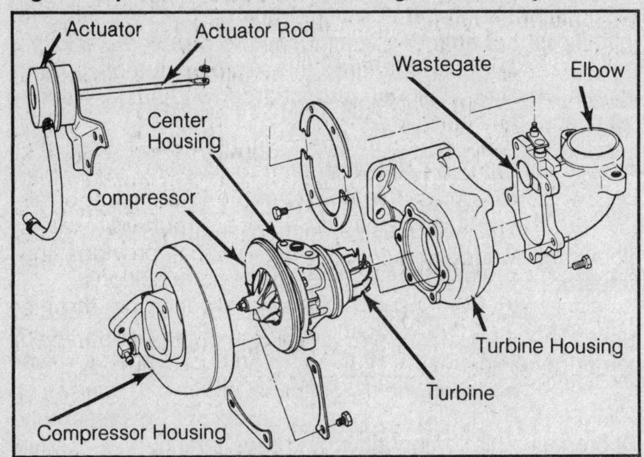

OIL SUPPLY

The rotating assembly, consisting of the turbine wheel, connecting shaft and compressor wheel, can reach speeds of 120,000 RPM. A sufficient supply of clean oil is absolutely necessary for proper operation of the rotating assembly.

An oil feed pipe runs from a "T" fitting on the left side of the engine block to the turbocharger. Engine oil enters the turbocharger center housing rotating assembly through an inlet fitting. Oil drains from the turbocharger through a hole in the bottom of the center housing and is returned to the engine through an oil return line. Any interruption or contamination of the oil will result in major turbocharger damage. *See Fig. 3.*

Fig. 3: Cutaway View of Turbocharger Showing Lubrication System

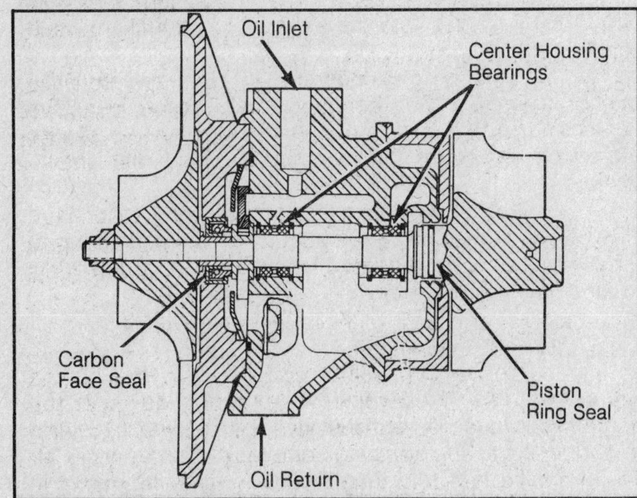

Whenever engine oil and filter are changed on a turbocharged engine, the oiling system must be primed with oil prior to starting engine.

This can be done by first disconnecting the electrical connector from the ignition module on the distributor. *See Fig. 4*. Crank the engine several times (not longer than 30 seconds at a time) and observe when the engine oil light goes out. Reconnect the electrical connector to the ignition module and start the engine.

Fig. 4: Disconnecting Ignition Module Connector from Distributor

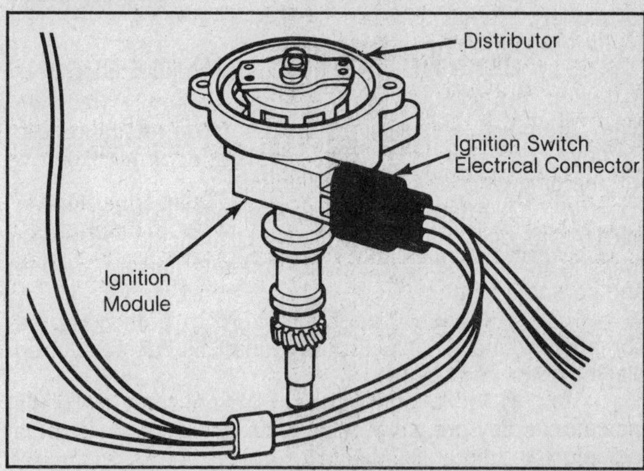

This connector must be disconnected and engine cranked to prime lubrication system after engine oil or filter change.

Whenever the oiling system has been contaminated in any way, change the oil and filter and flush the turbocharger assembly with clean oil. Any time the center housing rotating assembly is replaced, oil and filter should be changed.

BOOST PRESSURE INDICATORS

Two manifold pressure switches activate a Green or Red indicator lamp mounted on the instrument panel. During normal turbocharger operation, .75-11.5 psi (.05-.81 kg/cm²), the Green indicator lamp will glow.

When boost pressure exceeds 11.5 psi (.81 kg/cm²), the pressure switch will turn out the Green lamp and light the Red lamp. In addition to lighting the Red lamp, the switch will also sound a warning buzzer.

Fig. 5: Boost Pressure Indicator System

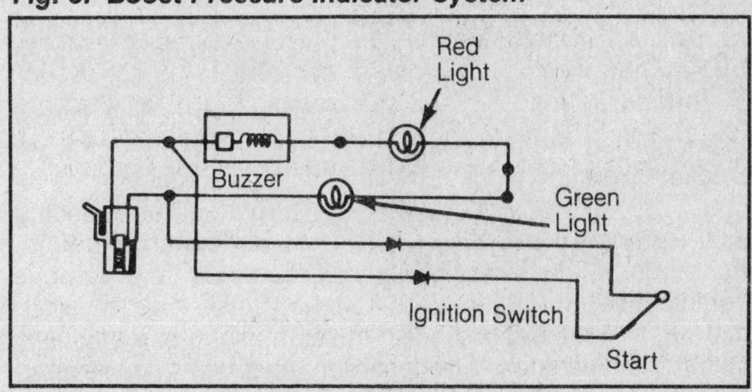

TESTING

BEARING AXIAL CLEARANCE CHECK

1) Remove turbocharger assembly from engine. Remove 5 bolts attaching turbine outlet elbow to center housing. Remove outlet elbow.

2) Attach a dial indicator to center housing so that indicator plunger contacts shaft. Manually push turbine wheel as far away from plunger as possible.

3) While holding turbine wheel away from plunger, set dial indicator to zero. Manually push turbine wheel assembly toward plunger as far as possible.

1983 Turbocharging Systems

FORD MOTOR CO. (Cont.)

4) If bearing axial clearance is less than .001" (.025 mm) or greater than .003" (.076 mm), replace turbocharger assembly.

BEARING RADIAL CLEARANCE CHECK

1) Remove turbocharger assembly from engine. Remove wastegate actuator rod retaining clip. Remove actuator rod from wastegate arm. Remove turbine oil inlet line from center housing.

2) Attach dial indicator plunger adapter (T79L-4201-A) to dial indicator. Attach dial indicator to center housing so that plunger adapter extends through oil inlet and contacts shaft.

3) Manually apply pressure to both compressor and turbine wheels to move shaft as far away from dial indicator as possible.

4) While holding pressure on shaft, zero dial indicator. Apply pressure in opposite direction (toward dial indicator) and note dial indicator reading.

5) If bearing radial clearance is less than .003" (.076 mm) or greater than .006" (.152 mm), replace turbocharger assembly.

REMOVAL & INSTALLATION

TURBOCHARGER ASSEMBLY

Removal

1) Disconnect negative battery cable from battery. Remove 2 bolts retaining throttle body discharge tube to turbocharger. Loosen upper clamp on inlet hose.

2) Disconnect all vacuum hoses that may interfere with turbocharger removal. Disconnect PCV tube from turbocharger air inlet elbow. Remove throttle body discharge tube and hose as an assembly.

3) Disconnect ground wire from air inlet elbow. Remove turbocharger oil supply line. Disconnect oxygen sensor connector at turbocharger.

4) Raise vehicle on hoist. Remove 2 bolts that attach exhaust pipe to turbocharger. Disconnect exhaust pipe from turbocharger.

5) Remove 2 bolts from oil return line below turbocharger. Remove bolt attaching lower turbocharger bracket to engine block. Lower vehicle from hoist.

6) Remove lower front turbocharger retaining bolt. Remove 3 remaining nuts from turbocharger retaining studs. Slide turbocharger off of studs and remove from vehicle.

Installation

Reinstall turbocharger assembly in reverse order of removal procedure. Be sure to install with new gaskets. Tighten all bolts to proper torque.

WASTEGATE ACTUATOR

Removal

1) Disconnect hoses from actuator diaphragm. Remove turbocharger from engine. Remove clip that attaches actuator rod to wastegate arm.

2) Remove 2 bolts that attach actuator diaphragm assembly to compressor housing. Remove actuator assembly.

Installation

1) Install 2 bolts that attach actuator diaphragm assembly to compressor housing. Tighten bolts.

2) With wastegate in fully closed position, unscrew actuator rod end until it fits over wastegate arm. Install clip that attaches actuator rod to wastegate arm.

3) Apply Loctite to threads on actuator rod and tighten lock nut. Reinstall turbocharger on engine. Reconnect vacuum hose to diaphragm.

OUTLET ELBOW

Removal

1) Disconnect turbocharger downpipe at outlet elbow and wastegate assembly. Remove clip that attaches actuator rod to wastegate arm.

2) Remove 5 bolts attaching outlet elbow to center housing assembly. Remove outlet elbow from center housing.

Installation

Reinstall in reverse order of disassembly. Tighten all outlet elbow attaching bolts evenly.

TIGHTENING SPECIFICATIONS

Application	INCH Lbs. (N.m)
Air Inlet Tube Bolts	180-264 (20-30)
Exhaust Pipe-to-Turbocharger Bolts	300-420 (34-47)
Turbocharger-to-Exhaust Manifold Bolts	44-89 (5-10)
Outlet Elbow-to-Center Housing	168-180 (19-20)

1983 Turbocharging Systems

GENERAL MOTORS

VEHICLE APPLICATION

GENERAL MOTORS

Application	VIN Code
3.8L V-6 4-Bbl. Turbo	8

DESCRIPTION

The turbocharging system is mounted on top of engine. It includes a turbine/compressor assembly, plenum chamber, wastegate, and carburetor. Turbine is spun by exhaust gas and causes compressor to draw air. Air is drawn through carburetor and plenum chamber, into compressor, then forced into intake manifold.

A slightly modified 4-barrel carburetor provides air and fuel to compressor assembly. Maximum manifold pressure (boost) is controlled by an exhaust bypass valve called a wastegate. This valve, sensing pressure differences through a diaphragm type actuator, determines how much exhaust should be routed to turbine. Any excess exhaust gas is bypassed into exhaust system.

OPERATION

Air is drawn in through air cleaner and carburetor assembly. Carburetor mixes an appropriate amount of fuel with incoming air and passes it into compressor assembly. As engine load increases and throttle is opened, more air/fuel mixture flows into combustion chambers. As this mixture is burned, a greater volume of hot exhaust gas enters exhaust system. This gas is directed into turbocharger turbine housing.

Some energy contained in exhaust gas is used to increase speed of turbine wheel. The turbine wheel is connected by a shaft to compressor wheel. As compressor wheel spins faster, it compresses incoming carburetor air/fuel mixture and forces a denser charge into combustion chambers. Higher power output is the result.

CARBURETOR & PLENUM

Carburetor is a standard 4-barrel unit with some minor modifications to throttle linkage, enrichment system and choke system. Carburetor is mounted on a plenum that leads directly to compressor intake.

Fig. 1: Diagram Showing Air Flow Pattern For Turbocharged V6 Engine

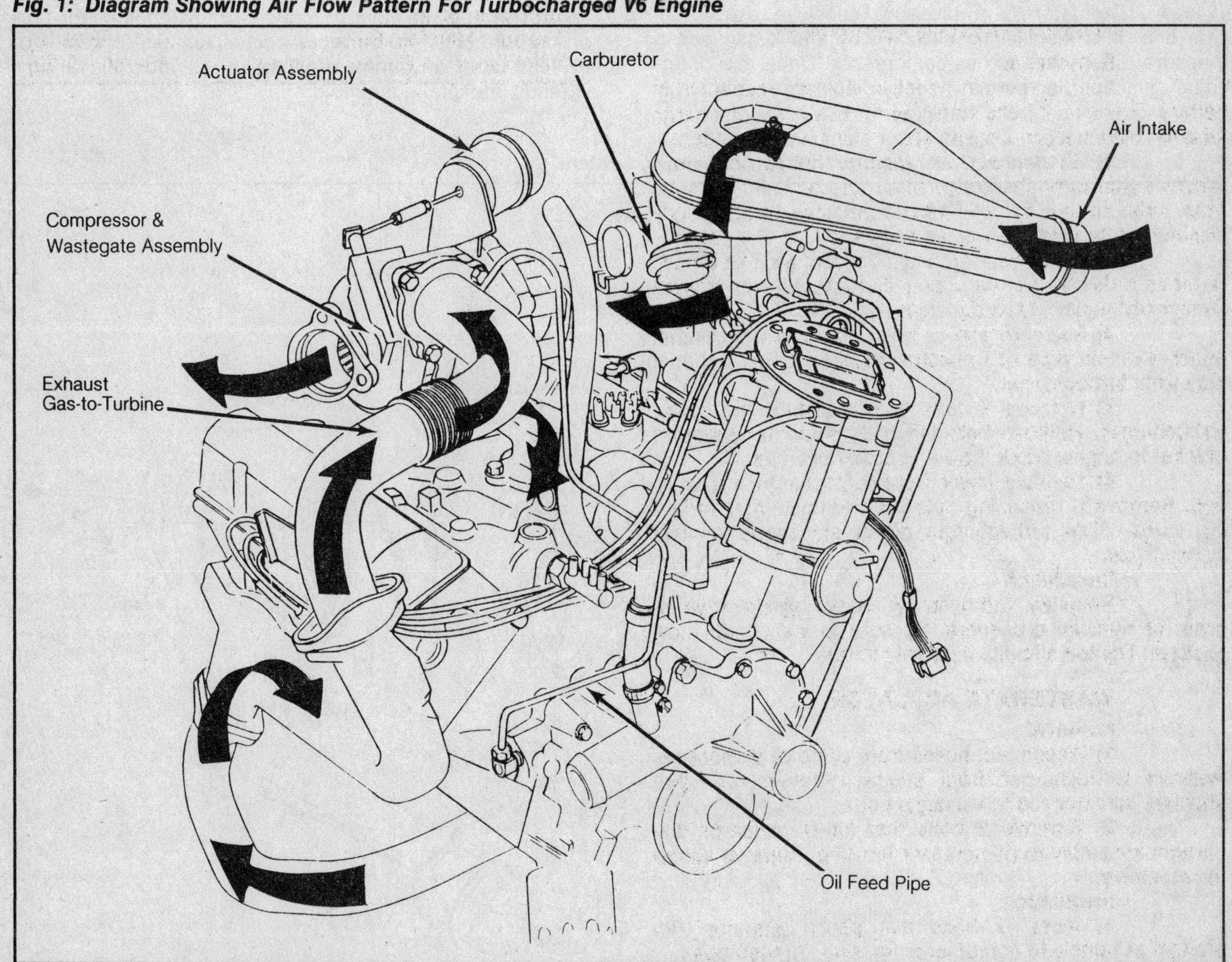

GENERAL MOTORS (Cont.)

An electric Early Fuel Evaporation (EFE) heater is used on all Turbo engines. A ceramic heating grid is built into carburetor spacer and minimizes fuel puddling during cold operation.

TURBINE ASSEMBLY

Turbine is mounted on top of intake manifold with compressor. It is connected to compressor by a shaft. When turbine wheel turns, compressor wheel must turn. Hot exhaust gas is fed into turbine through a pipe. Gas hitting the turbine blades causes blades to spin. The more exhaust gas piped to turbine, the faster it will spin, in turn spinning compressor faster. Thus, the turbocharger assembly can produce more power as demand increases.

WASTEGATE & ACTUATOR

When manifold pressure (boost) reaches a certain predetermined level, there must be some method of controlling or limiting boost past that point. The wastegate performs this function. Exhaust gas is piped into turbine continuously. Once engine demand is satisfied and the proper boost level is attained, the wastegate, acting on command from actuator assembly, bypasses enough exhaust gas into exhaust system to maintain required turbine speed.

Actuator is a pressure sensitive diaphragm type unit. It is installed in such a way that it can sense pressure differential across compressor. Once this differential reaches a certain level, diaphragm reacts in conjunction with an integral spring, to partially open wastegate. The wastegate is mounted to turbine assembly.

COMPRESSOR

Compressor is connected to turbine by a shaft. As turbine wheel turns, so does compressor wheel. No exhaust gas is actually passed into compressor. Carburetor directs air/fuel mixture into compressor. The spinning compressor forces more air/fuel mixture into intake manifold than would normally be drawn in under atmospheric pressure.

With a higher intake manifold pressure and denser charge available, more mixture is drawn into combustion chamber on piston intake stroke. A denser mixture results in more power output from engine. The faster the compressor spins, more air/fuel mixture is compressed into manifold. Thus, engine demand can be satisfied. *See Fig. 2.*

POWER ENRICHMENT VACUUM REGULATOR (PEVR)

Due to change in engine vacuum caused by turbocharger operation, a vacuum regulator is used to control vacuum signals. PEVR is used to direct a controlled vacuum flow to power piston enrichment port on carburetor. Vacuum input port is located in center of PEVR; output on perimeter of valve. Manifold signal port extends into intake manifold.

Fig. 2: Exploded View of General Motors V6 Turbocharging System

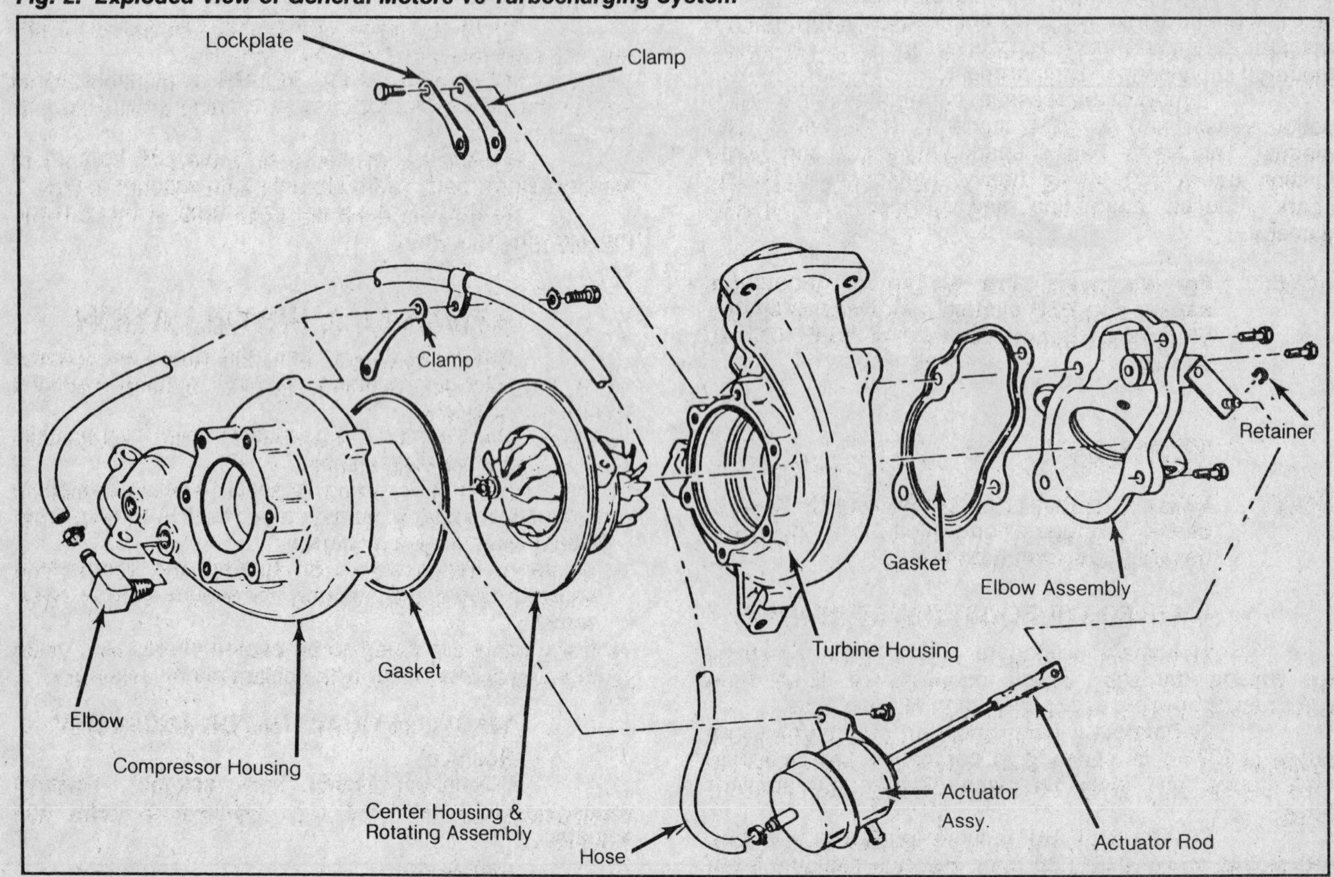

GENERAL MOTORS (Cont.)

OIL SUPPLY

Rotating assembly, consisting of turbine wheel, connecting shaft and compressor wheel, can reach speeds of 140,000 RPM. A sufficient supply of clean engine oil is absolutely necessary to proper operation of assembly. Engine oil is fed directly to center housing rotating assembly. Any interruption or contamination of oil will result in major turbocharger damage. An oil feed pipe runs from a fitting on engine block to turbocharger.

Whenever oil and filter are changed on a turbocharged engine, oil system must be primed with oil prior to starting. This can be done (after oil and filter are correctly installed) by disconnecting Pink wire (ignition switch) at H.E.I. distributor, cranking engine several times (not longer than 30 seconds at a time), and observing when oil light goes out. Reconnect Pink wire and start engine.

Whenever oiling system has been contaminated in any way, change oil and filter and flush turbocharger assembly with clean oil. Any time center housing rotating assembly is replaced, in part or in whole, oil and filter should be changed.

IGNITION SYSTEM

Turbocharged engines use a modified H.E.I. system called Electronic Spark Control (ESC). This system is used to control engine detonation by automatically retarding timing during periods when detonation occurs. The 4 major components of system are intake manifold, detonation sensor, controller and H.E.I. distributor.

The sensor is mounted at rear of intake manifold. It can be recognized by large diameter (1.12") hex shape and single electrical connection on top. Sensor detects detonation and reports it to ESC controller, mounted in passenger compartment.

Controller processes information from detonation sensor and sends a signal to special 5-pin HEI module. The signal delays spark timing and can retard ignition up to 22° during heavy detonation. Retarding spark reduces detonation and possibility of engine damage.

NOTE: **For diagnosis and testing of detonation sensor and ESC system, see General Motors Electronic Spark Control in ELECTRICAL Section.**

TESTING

NOTE: **Either road test or shop test may be used to check wastegate operation. It is not necessary to perform both tests.**

WASTEGATE/BOOST PRESSURE TEST

1) Inspect wastegate and actuator assembly for linkage damage. Check condition of hose from compressor housing to actuator, then remove hose.

2) Connect a hand operated vacuum/pressure pump (J-23738) in series with compound vacuum/pressure gauge, and install in place of plenum-to-actuator hose.

3) With 3 in. Hg vacuum applied to actuator, rod should move .015" (.38 mm). Replace actuator if not operating properly. Check new unit and crimp threads on rod to maintain proper calibration.

4) Remove test equipment. Reconnect plenum-to-actuator hose.

BOOST PRESSURE ROAD TEST

1) Install compound vacuum/pressure gauge between compressor and boost gauge or vacuum switches. Use tubing to place gauge in passenger compartment.

CAUTION: **Be sure that gauge and tubing are in good condition to prevent leakage of air/fuel mixture into vehicle while testing.**

2) Perform a wide-open throttle acceleration test from 0-50 MPH. Boost pressure should reach 8-9 psi (.56-.63 kg/cm²). If not, replace actuator and retest.

POWER ENRICHMENT VACUUM REGULATOR (PEVR) TEST

1) Inspect valve and hoses for wear or damage. Replace as needed.

2) Tee one hose from manometer (J-23951) between Yellow striped hose and input port. Connect other manometer hose to output port of PEVR.

3) Start engine and run at idle speed. There should be no more than 14" H_2O difference. If there is, replace PEVR.

4) If PEVR passes this test but is still suspected to be faulty, remove PEVR from manifold and plug manifold opening.

5) Connect input and output hoses back to PEVR. Tee compound gauge (J-28474) into output hose from PEVR.

6) Start engine and run at idle speed. Compound gauge reading should be 7-9 in. Hg.

7) Apply 3 psi (.21 kg/cm²) to manifold signal port of the PEVR. Output vacuum reading should be 1.4-2.6 in. Hg.

8) Apply a minimum of 5 psi (.35 kg/cm²) to manifold signal port. There should be no vacuum output.

9) If PEVR does not pass both of these tests, replace with new unit.

REMOVAL & INSTALLATION

Before beginning any unit repair procedures on a turbocharging system, several general cautions should be considered.

- Clean area around turbocharger with non-caustic solution before disassembly.
- Use extreme care during removal to avoid damaging turbine blades. Any damage may result in turbocharger failure when engine is started.
- Scribe reference marks on turbine and compressor housing before disassembly to ensure correct reassembly.
- If any joints are found to be coated with sealer, clean thoroughly and recoat with sealant during assembly.

WASTEGATE/ACTUATOR ASSEMBLY

Removal

Disconnect hoses from actuator. Remove wastegate-to-actuator rod clip. Remove 2 bolts and actuator.

Installation

To install, reverse removal procedure.

GENERAL MOTORS (Cont.)

ELBOW ASSEMBLY & CENTER ASSEMBLY

Removal

1) Disconnect turbocharger exhaust outlet pipe from elbow assembly. Raise vehicle. Disconnect outlet pipe from catalytic converter. Lower vehicle. Disconnect inlet pipe from right exhaust manifold and turbine housing.

2) Remove 2 bolts securing turbine housing to intake manifold bracket. Disconnect turbocharger oil feed pipe from center housing. Remove oil drain hose from pipe.

3) Remove clip securing wastegate linkage to actuator rod. Remove 6 bolts holding backplate to compressor housing and 6 bolts holding turbine housing to center assembly.

Installation

To install, reverse removal procedure.

TURBOCHARGER & ACTUATOR ASSEMBLY

Removal

1) Disconnect exhaust inlet and outlet pipes at turbocharger. Disconnect oil feed line from center housing, then remove linkage from carburetor.

2) Disconnect linkage bracket from plenum and remove 2 bolts securing plenum to side bracket. Disconnect fuel line and all necessary hoses. Drain cooling system and disconnect hoses from front and rear of plenum.

3) Remove power brake vacuum line, then disconnect plenum front bracket from intake manifold. Remove 2 bolts securing housing to manifold. Disconnect EGR manifold from intake manifold and plenum, then remove AIR by-pass hose from pipe.

4) Remove 3 bolts attaching compressor housing to intake manifold. Remove turbocharger and actuator, still attached to carburetor and plenum. Remove 6 bolts and turbocharger assembly. Remove oil drain from center housing.

Installation

To install, reverse removal procedure.

INTERNAL INSPECTION

TURBOCHARGER

1) Remove exhaust outlet pipe from elbow assembly on turbocharger.

2) Using a mirror, observe movement of wastegate while operating actuator linkage manually.

3) If wastegate fails to open or close, replace elbow assembly.

4) Remove turbocharger assembly from engine. Do not separate center housing rotating assembly from turbine housing.

5) Inspect for loose backplate-to-center housing rotating assembly bolts. Tighten if needed.

6) Gently spin compressor wheel. Replace if binding.

7) Remove oil drain from center housing. Check housing for sludging in oil drain area. If slightly dirty, clean. If heavily sludged or caked, replace center housing rotating assembly.

8) Inspect compressor wheel for signs of oil leakage. If present, replace center housing rotating assembly (CHRA).

9) Inspect compressor wheel for damage or caking. Replace as necessary.

NOTE: **If CHRA is being replaced, lubricate with clean engine oil.**

10) Inspect compressor housing (on engine) and turbine housing for gouges, nicks or distortion. Replace either housing if damaged.

11) If CHRA is not being replaced, remove turbine housing from CHRA and check bearing clearances as described in the following procedures. If clearances are correct, install oil drain and turbocharger assembly.

NOTE: **Before connecting exhaust pipe to turbocharger assembly, gently spin turbine wheel to be sure it is not binding or scraping housing.**

BEARING CLEARANCES

Journal Bearing Radial Clearance

1) Attach dial indicator with 2" long, 1" offset extension rod contacting shaft of turbine. Insert shaft through oil outlet port. *See Fig. 3.*

Fig. 3: Dial Indicator Installation for Measuring Journal Bearing Radial Clearance

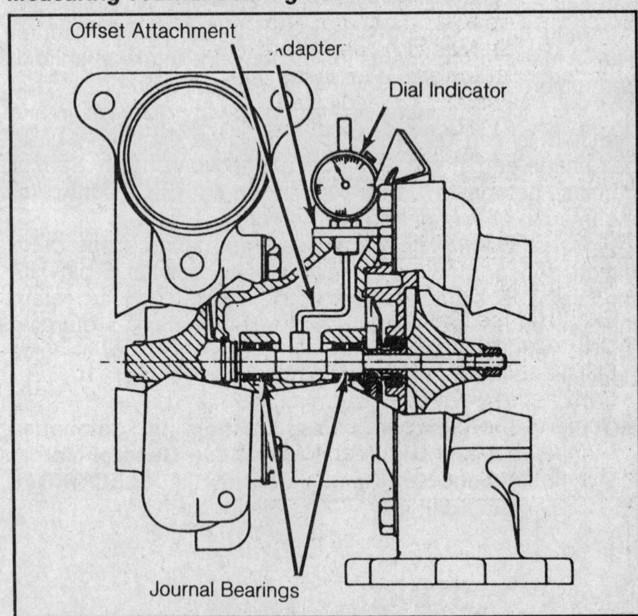

2) Apply finger pressure to both turbine and compressor wheels to move shaft AWAY from dial indicator plunger. Set indicator to ZERO.

3) Move shaft TOWARD dial indicator, rotating slightly to ensure it moves as far as possible. Record maximum reading. Move shaft away from indicator and check to be sure indicator moves to ZERO.

4) Repeat procedure to ensure clearance has been measured accurately. If not within .003-.006", replace center housing rotating assembly (CHRA) and inspect turbine and compressor housings.

CAUTION: **If turbocharger is operated with improper radial bearing clearance, severe damage may occur to housing.**

GENERAL MOTORS (Cont.)

Fig. 4: Dial Indicator Installation for Measuring Thrust Bearing Axial Clearance

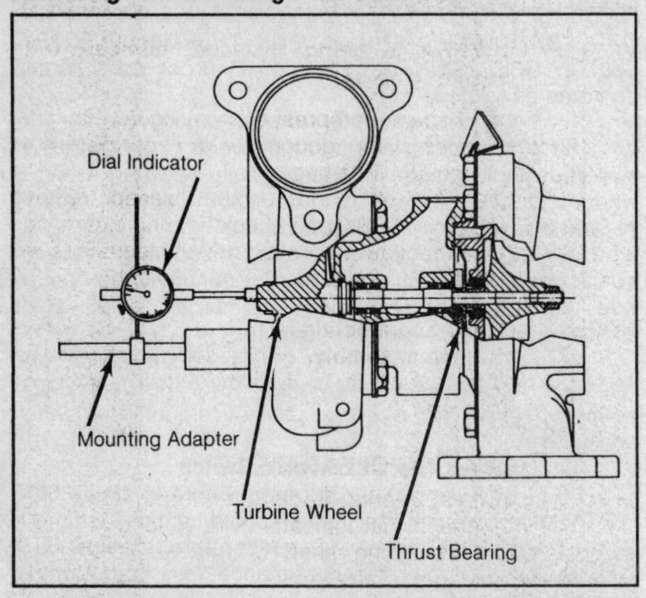

Thrust Bearing Axial Clearance

1) Mount dial indicator on turbine end of housing so tip rests on end of turbine wheel. *See Fig. 4.*

2) Manually apply pressure to turbine shaft and move it toward and away from indicator plunger. Record maximum travel indicated.

3) Repeat procedure after rotating turbine several times. If clearance is not within .001-.003", replace CHRA and inspect housings.

TIGHTENING SPECIFICATIONS

Application	Ft. Lbs. (N.m)
Exhaust Pipe Fittings	15 (20)
CHRA-to-Housings	15 (20)
EGR Manifold-to-Intake Manifold	15 (20)
Carburetor-to-Plenum	21 (28)
Compressor-to-Plenum	21 (28)
Compressor-to-Intake Manifold	35 (48)
Detonation Sensor	14 (19)

Latest Changes & Corrections

FOR 1983 AND PREVIOUS MODELS

AMERICAN MOTORS

1 *ALL 1982 AMC 4-CYL. MODELS: REVISED ENGINE IDENTIFICATION CODE* — Identification code is a 3 character code. All 1982 4-cyl. engine codes begin with the letter "X" and end with a code number/letter combination. Identification code is located at front, top left-hand corner of engine block.

2 *ALL 1982 6-CYL. MODELS WITH FUEL FEEDBACK SYSTEM BUILT AFTER FEBRUARY 1982: SERVICE PROCEDURES FOR COOLANT TEMPERATURE AND INTAKE MANIFOLD HEATER CONTROL SWITCHES* — When servicing dual function coolant temperature/intake manifold control switch, replace existing switch with new version consisting of 2 switches and a harness adapter. *See EFE Switches and Adapter table.* To install new EFE control switches and wire harness proceed as follows:

1) Drain about 3 quarts of coolant from radiator. Disconnect heated air tube and air duct from air cleaner. Remove air cleaner. Disconnect coolant temperature/intake manifold heater (EFE) control switch wire harness from engine compartment wire harness. Remove switch and harness from intake manifold.

2) Apply sealer to threads of EFE control switch (3242321). Install switch in place of original combination switch. Tighten switch to 20 ft. lbs. (27 N.m).

3) Remove and discard pipe plug at forward end of intake manifold. Apply sealer to threads of replacement coolant temperature switch (3242318) and install switch in place of pipe plug. Tighten switch to 20 ft. lbs. (27 N.m).

4) Connect wire harness adapter (8130477) to 2 new switches and to engine compartment wire harness. Secure harness adapter away from engine or linkage components.

5) Install air cleaner and connect heater air tube and air duct to air cleaner. Refill radiator with drained coolant.

Coolant Temperature and Intake Manifold Heater Switch

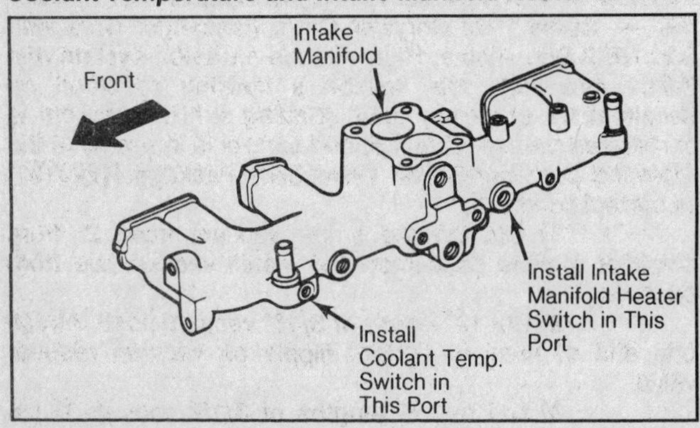

EFE SWITCHES & ADAPTER

Part Description	Part Number
Coolant Temp. Switch	3242318
Intake Man. Heater Switch	3242321
Wire Harness Adapter	8130477

3 *ALL AMC MODELS EQUIPPED WITH CEC FUEL FEEDBACK SYSTEM: REVISED PROCEDURES FOR "CHECK COOLANT SWITCH" AND "CHECK THERMAL ELECTRIC SWITCH OPERATION"* — Revision in procedures should be noted as follows:

Check Coolant Switch Operation

1) Test for continuity between pins A and B of switch using ohmmeter. If no continuity between A and B when coolant temperature is above 160°F (71°C), replace coolant temperature switch and retest.

2) If continuity exists, disconnect vacuum switch assembly connector. Test continuity from Yellow wire terminal of vacuum switch connector to pin B of coolant temperature switch connector.

3) If no continuity, repair open circuit and retest. If continuity exists, repair wire between MCU connector pin 6 and pin A of coolant temperature switch and retest.

Check Thermal Electric Switch

1) If air cleaner air temperature is above 65°F (18°C), infinite or high resistance should be indicated.

2) If air cleaner air temperature is below 65°F (18°C), closed circuit or low resistance (less than 2 ohms) is indicated.

CHRYSLER CORP.

4 *1983 CORDOBA, DIPLOMAT, GRAN FURY, MIRADA AND NEW YORKER WITH 3.7L ENGINE: OFF IDLE HESITATION* — Some 1983 Cordoba, Diplomat, Gran Fury, Mirada and New Yorker models with 3.7L engines may experience an off idle hesitation. A new driveability package (4293788) is now available to correct this condition. Use the following procedure to install this package:

1) Cut out a 4" section from the EGR vacuum hose 12" from the EGR valve end of hose.

2) Cut two 1 1/2" sections of 3/16" vacuum hose (3780507) and install on new vacuum delay valve.

3) Install new hose connectors in the ends of the delay valve/hose assembly.

4) Install the delay valve assembly in place of the vacuum hose section removed from the EGR valve vacuum hose in step **1)**. Ensure that Orange end of delay valve is installed toward the EGR valve.

5 *1983 ARIES, E CLASS, HORIZON, LEBARON, NEW YORKER, OMNI, RELIANT, 400 & 600 WITH 2.2L ENGINE: ROUGH IDLE & SURGE* — Some 1983 Aries, E Class, Horizon, LeBaron, New Yorker, Omni, Reliant, 400 and 600 models with 2.2L engine may develop driveability problems including rough and poor idle, poor performance, engine surge and poor fuel economy. This condition may be caused by a cracked vacuum hose from the flow control valve to the intake manifold. A new design flow control valve assembly (4213590) is now available to correct this condition. Use the following procedure to install assembly:

1) If flow control valve hose is cracked, remove air cleaner crossover and air inlet box assembly.

2) Locate flow control valve (Black and White) assembly on left side of carburetor between intake

FOR 1983 AND PREVIOUS MODELS (Cont.)

manifold vacuum fitting and carburetor main body nipple under air horn.

3) Remove and discard complete original flow control valve and hose assembly.

4) Install new flow control valve assembly with White end of valve toward intake manifold fitting and hose labeled "CARB" on carburetor fitting.

Flow Control Valve Assembly Installation

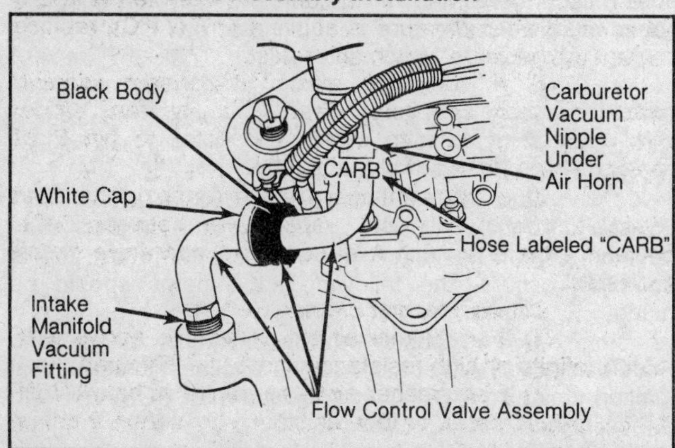

6 *1981 CHRYSLER CORP. VEHICLES WITH 2.2L ENGINES: BLUE SMOKE & DETONATION DURING WIDE OPEN THROTTLE OPERATION* — Some 1981 Chrysler Corp. vehicles with 2.2L engines may have a problem in which vehicle exhausts excessive amounts of blue smoke and experiences detonation during wide open throttle operation. This can be caused by baffle in vent module being installed upside down. This condition can be repaired using following procedure:

1) Remove vent module from rear of valve cover. Check position of vent module. Large open end of baffle should be pointing upward when it is in its installed position on valve cover.

2) Reinstall vent module on valve cover, making sure that baffle is intact and does not rotate in vent module during installation. Road test vehicle to confirm that problems have been corrected.

7 *1982 1/2-83 CHRYSLER FRONT WHEEL DRIVE MODELS EQUIPPED WITH 2.6L ENGINE AND 180°F (82°C) THERMOSTAT: COLD FAST IDLE ADJUSTMENT* — Some 1982 1/2-83 Chrysler Front Wheel Drive models equipped with 2.6L engine and 180°F (82°C) thermostat may exhibit excessive fast idle or very slow idle RPM after cold engine start-up. This cold fast idle adjustment procedure applies only to vehicles with the following engine part numbers (last 3 digits):

Federal: 535, 538, 540, 543
California: 536, 537, 541

These part numbers are found on the top left side of the engine cam cover.

1) Start engine and idle until it reaches normal operating temperature. Operating temperature is reached when radiator fan starts to operate with A/C off.

2) Install tachometer. Allow cooling fan to turn off. Do not allow fan to run during adjustment.

3) Disconnect vacuum advance hose at distributor diaphragm and plug hose. Open throttle and install adjustment tool (Miller C-4812) on choke cam follower pin.

4) Release throttle lever. Check engine RPM. Fast idle speed should be 900-1000 RPM. To adjust idle speed, turn screw at underside of primary throttle lever.

5) Remove adjuster tool from throttle lever and reconnect distributor vacuum advance hose at diaphragm.

Cold (Fast) Idle Adjustment on Chrysler Corp. 2.6L

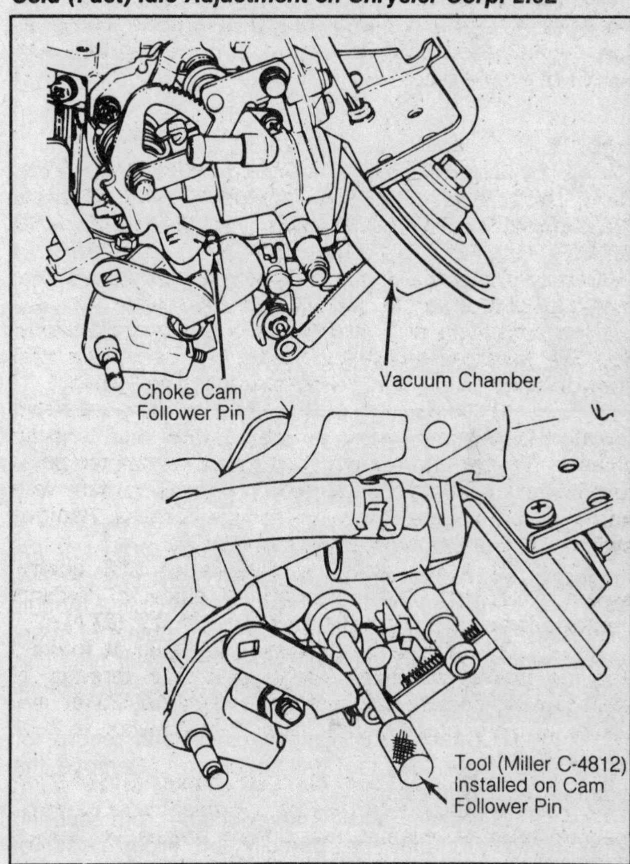

8 *1982 CHRYSLER CORP. PASSENGER CARS WITH 5.2L V8 2-BBL. ENGINE, HIGH ALTITUDE EMISSION SYSTEM & 2.94:1 AXLE RATIO: DECELERATION BUCKING* — Some 1982 Chrysler Corp. Passenger Cars with 5.2L V8 2-Bbl. engine, High Altitude emission system and 2.94:1 axle ratio may exhibit a bucking condition on deceleration, especially after cresting a hill. Symptom is sometimes more severe if speed control is in use. Use the following procedures and Driveability Package (4293791) to correct condition:

1) Cut Orange stripe vacuum hose 2" from amplifier molded connector and install vacuum tee from package.

2) Cut 12" length of 3/16" vacuum hose. Attach one end of hose to bottom nipple on vacuum reducer valve.

3) Cut two 8" lengths of 3/16" vacuum hose. Install on remaining nipples of vacuum reducer valve. On loose end of 3/16" vacuum hose just installed, place large ends of vacuum hose connectors from package.

4) Cut Yellow stripe venturi signal hose midway between carburetor and vacuum amplifier and insert vacuum reducer valve assembly.

5) Position vacuum reducer assembly to right of carburetor. Install ESA/EFA module from package.

Latest Changes & Corrections

FOR 1983 AND PREVIOUS MODELS (Cont.)

6) Start engine and warm to normal operating temperature. Adjust ignition timing and curb idle speed as necessary.

Driveability Package For Deceleration Bucking on 5.2L

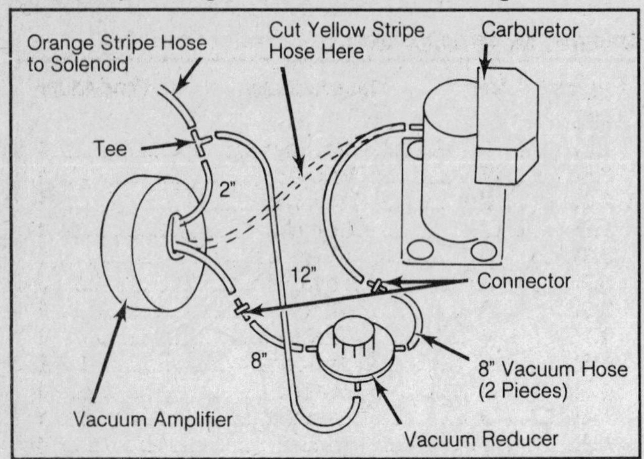

FORD MOTOR CO.

9 *1983 ESCORT, EXP, LN7 & LYNX WITH 1.6L EFI ENGINES: SPARK KNOCK DURING HOT ENGINE OPERATION* — Some 1983 Escort, EXP, LN7 and Lynx models with 1.6L EFI engines may experience a problem of spark knock during hard acceleration when engine is hot. This condition can be corrected by installing a 3° retard octane rod (12A335) in the distributor.

1) Check initial ignition timing and record for future reference. Turn the ignition key off. Remove the distributor cap and rotor.

2) Locate and remove octane rod securing screw. Slide octane rod partially off from boss of distributor housing to a point where Hall Effect switch assembly can move freely.

3) Gently lift rod over Hall Effect switch assembly post. Remove octane rod and grommet.

4) Install new 3° retard octane rod with old grommet. Reinstall new octane rod in distributor. Reinstall distributor cap and rotor.

5) Verify that initial ignition timing is retarded 3°.

10 *1983 CAPRI, LTD, MARQUIS, MUSTANG, THUNDERBIRD & COUGAR WITH 3.8L ENGINES: ENGINE STALLS DURING DECELERATION* — Some 1983 Capri, LTD, Marquis, Mustang, Thunderbird and Cougar models with 3.8L engines may develop a problem in which the engine stalls during decelation. This can be correct by replacing the throttle speed positioner (TSP).

Models with Air Conditioning

1) Check part number on TSP. If part number is not E2AE-9E957-AB, replace TSP with TSP having part number E2AZ-9S520-D.

2) Reinstall vacuum line to TSP. Tape existing TSP hot lead to wiring harness as it is not used with replacement TSP.

3) With transmission in "D" and TSP vacuum hose disconnected, set idle speed to 550 RPM. Adjust idle speed using saddle bracket adjusting screw.

Models without Air Conditioning

1) Check part number on TSP. If part number is not E2AE-9S520-BB, replace TSP with TSP having part number E2AZ-9S520-B.

2) With transmission in "D" and vacuum hose connected to TSP, set idle speed to 550 RPM. Adjust idle speed by turning saddle bracket adjusting screw.

3) With transmission in "D" and TSP vacuum hose disconnected, set idle speed to 450 RPM. Adjust idle speed using curb idle speed adjusting screw.

GENERAL MOTORS

11 *1982 CHEVETTE: TIP-IN HESITATION WHEN ENGINE IS HOT* — Some 1982 Chevette models may develop a tip-in hesitation when the engine is hot. If this condition occurs, the following adjustments should be made:

1) On models with manual transmissions and Federal or High Altitude emissions packages, reset initial ignition timing to 8°BTDC and replace the PROM unit with a recalibrated unit (1226080).

2) On models with manual transmissions and California emission packages, reset initial ignition timing to 4°BTDC.

3) On all models with automatic transmissions, reset initial ignition timing to 8°BTDC.

12 *1982 REGAL WITH 3.8L TURBOCHARGED ENGINE: ENGINE SURGES UNDER HEAVY ACCELERATION* — Some 1982 Regal models with 3.8L turbocharged engines may exhibit an engine surge condition while under heavy acceleration at speeds above 45 MPH. This condition may be caused by the transmission converter clutch being engaged during wide open throttle. A new ECM PROM unit (1225906 for Federal models or 1225907 for California models) should be installed to correct this condition.

1) Remove ECM from right kick panel. Remove calibration PROM and install new PROM.

2) After new PROM has been installed, use a felt pen to change the information on the ECM label. On Federal vehicles, cross out "MR" and write in "ARW" and cross out 16017094 and write in 16025254.

3) On California vehicles, cross out "NH" and write in "ARX" and cross out 16017224 and write in 16025264. Reinstall ECM in vehicle.

13 *1982-83 CAPRICE & IMPALA WITH 3.8L (229") ENGINE: IDLE SHAKE* — Some 1982-83 Caprice and Impala models with 3.8L (229") engine may demonstrate an objectionable shake at idle in drive range. This condition is caused by grounded engine mounts. Grounded engine mounts result from improper spacing of frame mount brackets. Use the following repair procedure:

1) Install .24" (6 mm) of shims between the left side engine mount and the engine block.

2) Three 3/8" flat washers (446363) may be used with longer bolts (454913) at each location.

3) If the shake is improved, but not to an acceptable level, the right side mount should be shimmed in the same manner.

14 *1983 GENERAL MOTORS VEHICLES WITH QUADRAJET CARBURETOR USED ON 4.1L V6 (VIN 4) AND DUALJET CARBURETORS USED ON 3.0L V6 (VIN E) and 3.8L V6 (VIN A): REVISED IDLE SPEED CONTROL* — A revised Idle Speed Control (ISC) assembly was introduced on 1983 Quadrajet carburetors used on 4.1L V6 engine (VIN 4), Dualjet carburetors used on the 3.0L V6 engine (VIN E) and 3.8L V6 engine (VIN A). The new ISC assembly is identified by the numeral "II" on the motor housing. This assembly has a silent throttle contact switch that does not click when actuated.

15 *1983 CELEBRITY, CITATION, OMEGA, PHEONIX, SKYLARK & 6000 WITH 2.8L ENGINE: ENGINE ROUGHNESS* — Some Celebrity, Citation, Omega, Pheonix, Skylark and 6000 models with 2.8L engines may exhibit engine roughness. Cause may be stray electronic signals received by the distributor module. These signals produce a false (high RPM) tachometer reference pulse to ECM. Roughness is most evident at idle, but may persist during acceleration and at driving speeds. To repair condition, re-orient distributor module and use repair procedure as follows to re-route lead wires:

1) Disconnect primary coil leads at coil. Disconnect ECM 4-wire connector.

2) Remove ignition wires and coil wire from distributor cap and remove cap.

3) Cut a 9" length of conduit (8919354) and install on distributor primary leads.

4) Cut a 3.3" length of same conduit and install on 4-wire ECM leads at distributor.

5) Crank engine until White timing mark on torsional damper and "O" on timing indicator are in alignment and distributor rotor is in #1 spark position.

6) Remove distributor clamp screw and hold-down clamp. Slowly raise distributor until rotor just stops turning counterclockwise.

7) Rotate distributor base and rotor. Rotate simultaneously in clockwise direction until lead wires are in 7 o'clock position when viewed from rear along engine centerline. Ensure rotation is adequate to clear lead wires from coil bracket hold-down bolt.

8) Reinstall distributor and hold-down clamp and clamp screw. Reinstall distributor cap, ignition and coil wires. If #3 ignition wire is too short, replace with new wire (12036948).

9) Route primary coil lead under right side ignition wires (#1, 3 and 5). Attach to coil.

10) Set ignition timing to specification on emission label. Tighten hold-down clamp screw. Reconnect ECM 4-wire connector.

16 *1981-82 GENERAL MOTORS ENGINES: IGNITION TIMING ADJUSTMENT PROCEDURES* — When setting basic ignition timing, find the applicable engine in the chart and use the applicable procedure number. Refer to the emission control label for specified timing. The procedure numbers are listed below:

Basic Ignition Timing Setting Procedures

1) Disconnect the 4-wire EST connector.

2) Ground the test terminal in the connector under the dash.

3) Disconnect the distributor vacuum advance hose at the distributor.

4) Ground Blue distributor by-pass pigtail.

5) Disconnect the by-pass connector.

6) Disconnect the reference signal connector (connector is Green).

7) Open the "set" timing connector.

8) Set timing at 1100 RPM.

GENERAL MOTORS ENGINES

Engine	VIN	Manufacturer	Procedure
1981			
1.6L	9	Chevrolet	1
2.5L	5	Pontiac	1
2.8L	X	Chevrolet	1
2.8L	Z	Chevrolet	1
3.8L	A	Buick	1
3.8L	K	Chevrolet	3
3.8L	3	Buick	1
4.1L	4	Buick	1
4.3L	F	Oldsmobile	1 & 8
4.3L	S	Pontiac	4
4.4L	J	Chevrolet	1
4.9L	T	Pontiac	4
4.9L	W	Pontiac	4
5.0L	H	Chevrolet	1
5.0L	Y	Oldsmobile	1 & 8
5.7L	L	Chevrolet	1
5.7L	6	Chevrolet	1
6.0L	9	Cadillac	7
1982			
1.6L	C	Chevrolet	3
1.8L	G	Chevrolet	
1.8L	0	Pontiac	2
2.5L	R	Pontiac	2
2.5L	2	Pontiac	2
2.8L	X	Chevrolet	1
2.8L	Z	Chevrolet	1
2.8L	1	Chevrolet	1
3.0L	E	Buick	1
3.8L	A	Buick	1
3.8L	K	Chevrolet	2
3.8L	3	Buick	1
4.1L	4	Buick	1
4.1L	8	Cadillac	6
4.3L	8	Oldsmobile	2 & 8
4.4L	J	Chevrolet	1
5.0L	H	Chevrolet	1
5.0L	Y	Oldsmobile	2 & 8
5.0L	7	Chevrolet	5
5.7L	L	Chevrolet	1
5.7L	8	Chevrolet	5
6.0L	9	Cadillac	7